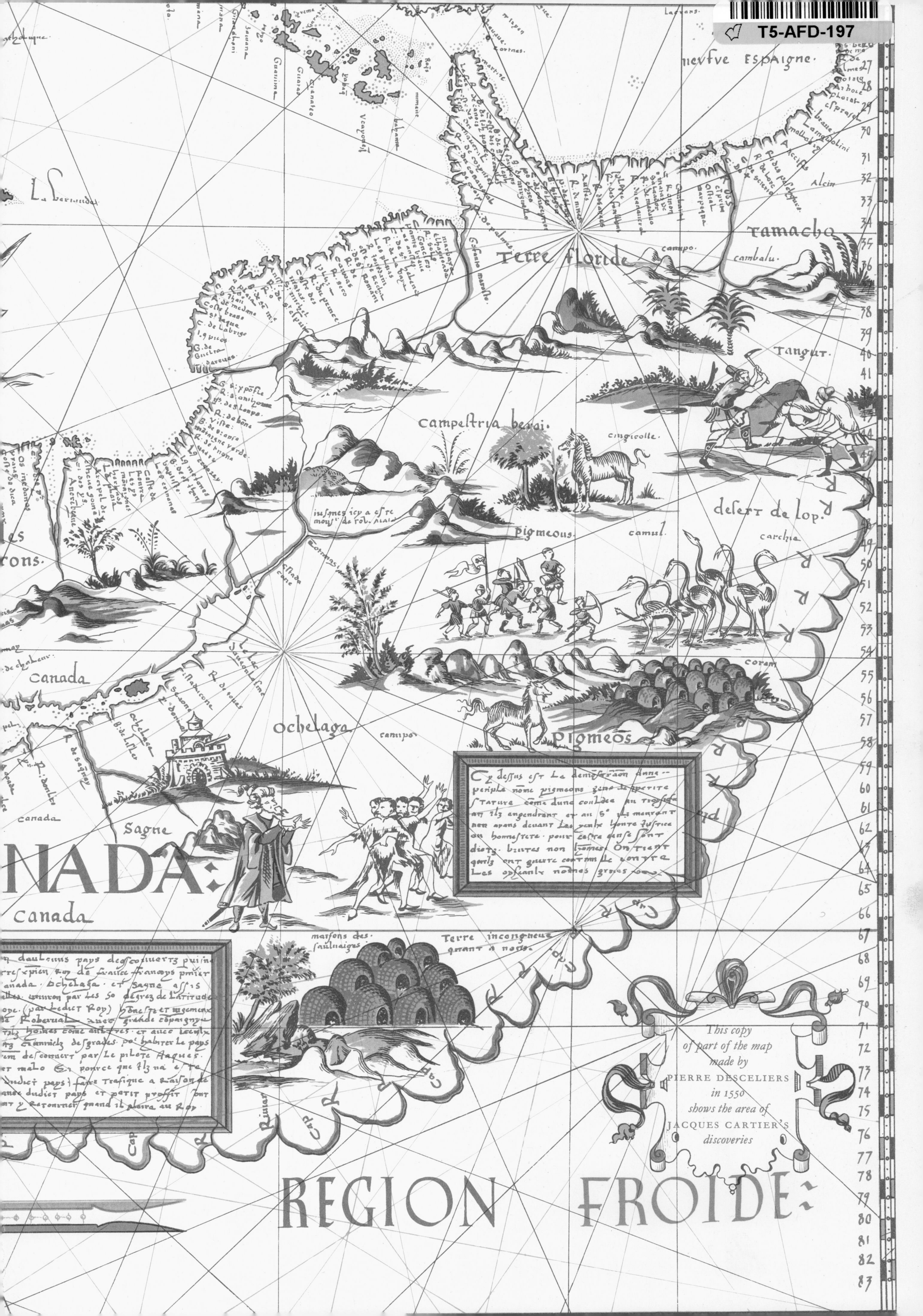

ncvfve ESPAIGNE.

L. Bermudas

Terre floride

ramacha

cambalu.

campo.

Tangut.

campeſtria berai.

cingicolle.

deſert de lop.

pigmeous.

camul.

carchia

Coram

canada

Pigmeos

Ochelaga

canupo

canada

Sagne

NADA:

canada

marſons des ſaulnaiges

Terre incongneue gnant á noſt.

REGION FROIDE:

This copy
of part of the map
made by
PIERRE DESCELIERS
in 1550
shows the area of
JACQUES CARTIER'S
discoveries

THE READER'S DIGEST

GREAT WORLD ATLAS

THE READER'S DIGEST ASSOCIATION

LONDON · NEW YORK · SYDNEY · MONTREAL · CAPE TOWN

THE READER'S DIGEST GREAT WORLD ATLAS

Prepared and Published by The Reader's Digest Association Limited. Planned under the direction of the late

FRANK DEBENHAM

O.B.E., M.A., D.SC. (HON.), EMERITUS PROFESSOR OF GEOGRAPHY, CAMBRIDGE UNIVERSITY

The Reader's Digest expresses its gratitude to the following
who have generously contributed to and advised on the preparation of this Atlas:

Academy of Science of the U.S.S.R.

P. J. Adams, B.SC., PH.D., F.G.S., Institute of Geological Sciences

J. B. Allen, B.SC., PH.D., F.G.S., Institute of Geological Sciences

W. R. Aykroyd, C.B.E., M.D., SC.D.

E. D. Baldock

John Bartholomew & Son Ltd.

Andrew Boyd, M.A.

British and Foreign Bible Society

British Broadcasting Corporation

British Medical Association

Maurice Burton, D.SC.

Wm. Collins, Sons & Co. Ltd.

J. G. Cook, PH.D., F.R.I.C.

Gordon F. Delaney

F. W. Dunning, O.B.E., B.SC., F.G.S., Institute of Geological Sciences

T. P. Eddy, C.B.E., London School of Hygiene and Tropical Medicine

F. V. Emery, B.LITT., M.A., University of Oxford

A. Fleming. M.A., University of Sheffield

Food and Agriculture Organization of the United Nations

General Register Office

Geographical Projects Ltd.

Madeleine Glemser, M.A.

Greater London Council

Michael Hart, M.A.

Cdr. H. R. Hatfield, R.N.

Information Service of India

Institute for Strategic Studies

B. Gyrth Jackson, M.SC., School of Agriculture, University of Cambridge

E. A. Jobbins, B.SC., F.G.S., Institute of Geological Sciences

Michael Kenward, New Scientist

H. C. King, PH.D., M.SC., F.R.A.S., F.B.O.A.

H. A. G. Lewis, Esq., Directorate of Military Survey (War Office and Air Ministry)

Lick Observatory

Longmans, Green & Co. Ltd.

Dr. D. M. Mackay, Senior Lecturer, London School of Hygiene and Tropical Medicine

N. B. Marshall, M.A., D.SC., F.R.S., University of London

R. J. Marston, B.SC., PH.D., F.G.S., Institute of Geological Sciences

Ministry of Agriculture, Fisheries and Food

Ministry of Health

The Rev. Vernon P. Mitchell

Patrick Moore, O.B.E., F.R.A.S., Director, Lunar Section of the British Astronomical Association

Mount Wilson and Palomar Observatories

G. Murdoch, M.A., PH.D.

National Institute of Oceanography

B. M. Nichol, O.B.E., M.B., CH.B., Nutrition Adviser, Government of Nigeria

K. P. Oakley, D.SC., F.B.A., British Museum (Natural History)

Office of the South African High Commissioner

Professor E. G. Parrinder, M.A., PH.D., D.D., D.LITT., University of London

E. Penkala, Esq.

The Polar Institute

The late Rev. B. M. G. Reardon, M.A.

C. S. Roetter, LL.B.

I. Ridpath, Esq.

C. A. Ronan, M.SC., F.R.A.S., Royal Society

Royal Geographical Society

Scientific Liaison Office, Australia, New Zealand, Canada

Scottish Office

Peter Small, Esq.

P. A. Smithson, B.SC., F.R.MET.S., University of Sheffield

Robert Spencer, B.A., British Trust for Ornithology

United Nations, London Information Centre

B. B. Waddy, D.M., London School of Hygiene and Tropical Medicine

G. R. Wadsworth, M.D., London School of Hygiene and Tropical Medicine

The Wellcome Foundation Ltd.

The Wellcome Museum of Medical Science

Bernard Workman, M.A.

World Health Organization

Norman C. Wright, C.B., M.A., PH.D., D.SC., F.R.I.C., F.R.S.E., Deputy-Director-General, Food and Agriculture Organization of the United Nations

Yerkes Observatory

Acknowledgment is also made to the numerous authors
and compilers of technical books and journals to which reference was made
in the preparation of this Atlas

CONTENTS

SECTION ONE

THE FACE OF THE WORLD

page 5

SECTION TWO

THE COUNTRIES OF THE WORLD

page 29

SECTION THREE

THE WORLD AS WE KNOW IT

page 105

SECTION FOUR

INDEX

page 153

From the centre of the Earth

to the outermost limits of space

PARADISE IS SOMEWHERE IN THE FAR EAST. JERUSALEM IS THE CENTRE OF ALL NATIONS AND COUNTRIES, AND THE WORLD ITSELF IS· A FLAT DISK SURROUNDED BY OCEANS OF WATER. So the monks, map-makers of the Middle Ages, saw the world they lived in.

Today, our knowledge of the world has increased through travel and exploration and scientific discovery. This Atlas has drawn on the sum of that knowledge— knowledge that has been accumulated through many life-times of research.

We look at THE FACE OF THE WORLD, starting with a view of our Earth in space. The following maps made from sculptured models show in relief how our world would appear to an observer at a point some hundred miles above the Earth's surface. The peaks of the great mountain ranges show in sharp contrast to the worn surfaces of older rocks and the flat plains formed by the great rivers. The levels of the ocean floor tell the history of submerged lands and of yet unexplored deeps. Here, a new dimension has been added to standard map-making.

Next come THE COUNTRIES OF THE WORLD. Towns and cities, rivers and railways can all be found easily, for the colouring is subdued and the text clear and definitive. Together with the relief maps they complete a picture of the landscape of our Earth and of the places where we live.

The third section portrays THE WORLD AS WE KNOW IT. Incurably inquisitive, man searches continually for knowledge about our world and about other worlds beyond. He now knows that he is only one of many forms of life on the thin crust of a planet revolving round the Sun—a minor star at the edge of the Milky Way. A multi-million starred galaxy, the Milky Way is itself only one among a million other galaxies moving in the black infinity of space where traditional concepts of north and south are meaningless.

It is a vision that dwarfs the globe on which we live and makes man seem very small; but it also gives him a new importance. For on this tiny planet life has been created and developed, and as yet we do not know whether the delicate balance of conditions which has made evolution possible on this planet has ever been repeated on any other.

The marvel of this creation cannot be told by any single map or chart. Each feature in the third section of this Atlas has been devised to illustrate a facet of it—our place in the universe, the mystery of our neighbours in space, the world beneath our feet, the evolution of life, the creatures around us, the growth and disappearance of civilizations, the beliefs of man, and his migrations. Each subject is linked to another: climate to cultivation, cultivation to food, food to health, for none of the world's problems can be seen in isolation. All are related to and interwoven with one another.

This Atlas, in presenting geographically the facts about Earth and life and space, also offers many pointers towards exploration in the future which lies before us.

THE EDITORS

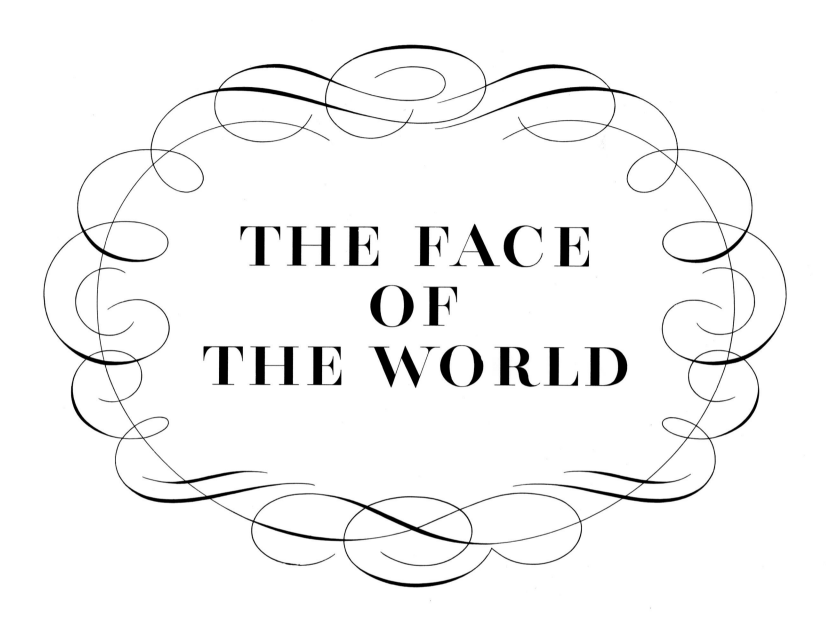

THE FACE OF THE WORLD

CONTENTS

	PAGE		PAGE
AROUND THE WORLD	6	THE BRITISH ISLES	18
SOUTH POLE AND NORTH POLE	8	EURASIA	20
CANADA	10	THE FAR EAST	22
UNITED STATES OF AMERICA AND MEXICO	12	AUSTRALASIA	24
SOUTH AMERICA	14	NORTHERN AFRICA	26
EUROPE	16	SOUTHERN AFRICA	28

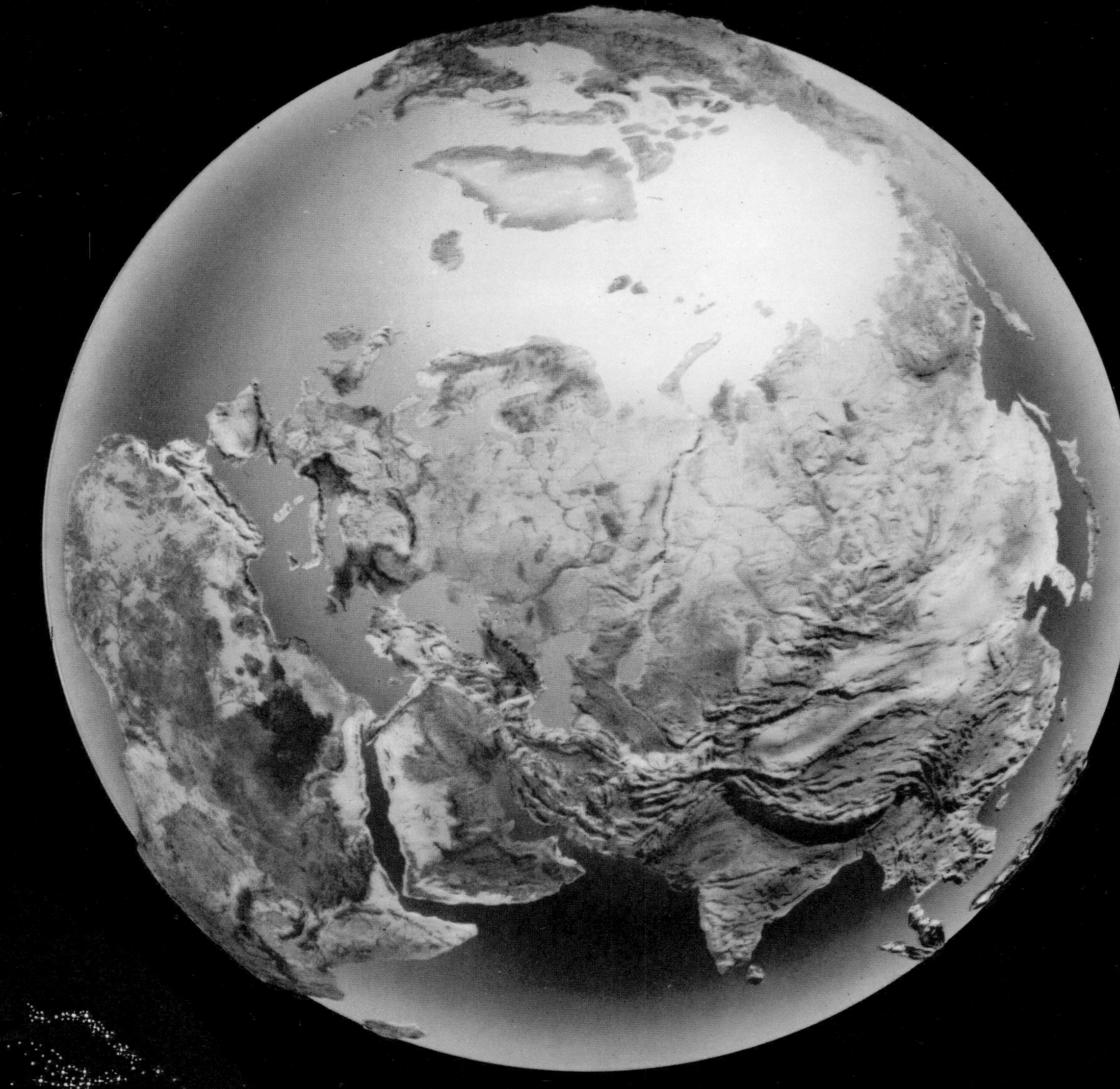

THE MASS OF LAND

In full summer, from a point above central eastern Europe, the whole range of the Earth's surface structure can be seen. To the north a great plain stretches from the North Sea across Europe into Siberia, and finally merges into the close-packed ice-floes of the Arctic. To the south an immense desert barrier sweeps from the shores of the Atlantic in a giant scimitar curve across the north of Africa, Arabia, Turkestan and to the Gobi. Except for the Chinese borderlands, this desert barrier has been dominated for a thousand years by the Muslim religion, so that both Europe and Christianity were shut off from the immemorial East until the Portuguese found a sea-way round Africa—an ocean ring-road round the Middle East. In Asia mountain-fringed plateaux broaden out from Turkey through Iran and Afghanistan to the great Tibetan plateau, which is cut off from India by the still higher wall of the Himalayas. To the south and east of this mountain barrier there live the dense populations of the great river valleys of Asia.

In winter a view from the same point would reveal a dramatically unbroken sheet of snow stretching from the northern plain of Poland to the Pacific, demonstrating how the cold intensifies as the land recedes from the maritime western edges and reaches into the heart of the continent.

AROUND

THE EARTH   FROM SPACE

Hold these pages 18 inches from your eyes and each half-world will be just the size the Earth would look if you were 25,000 miles out in space. But no astronaut will ever see the Earth like this, for we have removed the mantle of swirling cloud that always obscures most of the surface.

WHERE MAN LIGHTS THE NIGHT

At night the populated areas of the world prick out patterns of light, which are clustered thickly where population is densest.

In this picture, centred on London, the lights of western Europe form a bright galaxy with 100 towns each of over 250,000 people. Another 100 towns of similar size glow in eastern Europe and the U.S.S.R., fading out into the depths of Siberia. Across the Atlantic Ocean, in the eastern half of the U.S.A. and Canada, are the lights of another 100 such towns. On the upper right shine the bright clusters of southern and eastern Asia where 1,800 million people live.

Elsewhere are smaller concentrations of light—in California, on the banks of the Nile, round the coasts of the continents—almost everywhere except in the polar seas. Great black patches can be seen where unilluminated night broods over the circle of frozen northlands and over vast deserts and mountain ranges.

A CONTINENT OF ICE

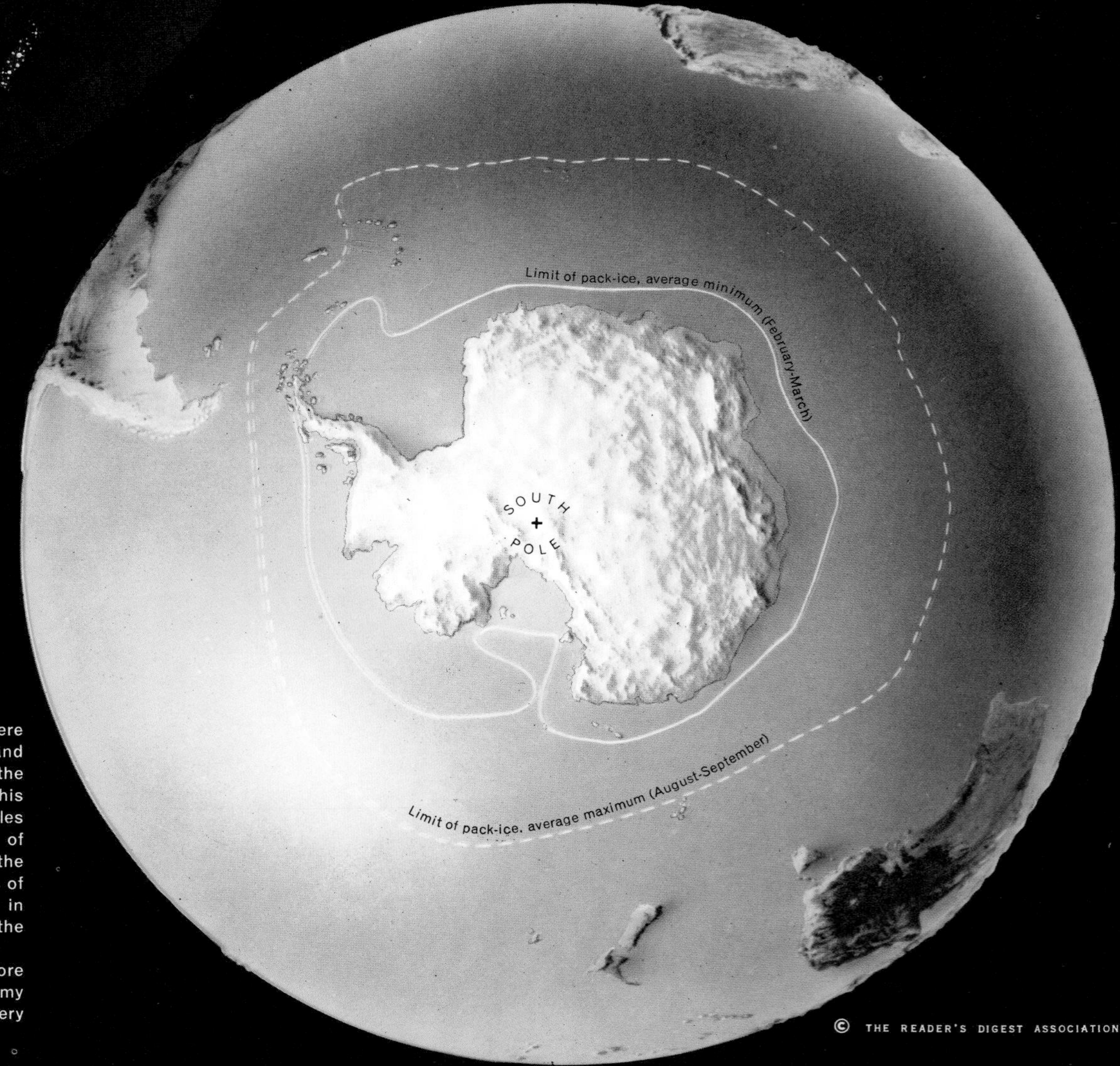

Seen from a point directly over the South Pole, the Southern Hemisphere seems to be dominated by the shining ice cap that covers an island larger than the continent of Europe. In almost every direction the horizon is sea, although the tips of three continents extend into this half-world. Cape Horn, at the tip of South America, is 2,350 miles from the South Pole; Buenos Aires, the most southerly large town of South America, is 3,800 miles from it; the Cape of Good Hope, at the tip of Africa, with the port of Cape Town and the broadening mass of South Africa beyond, lies a similar distance away; Christchurch in New Zealand and Hobart in Tasmania, the largest towns near to the Pole, are 3,200 miles distant from it.

In all the Southern Hemisphere there are only 75 towns with more than 250,000 people and 50 of these are near the Equator. The stormy Southern Ocean is deserted by ships and planes, and pack-ice every winter extends half-way from Antarctica to other lands.

6

THE WATER PLANET

Tahiti is at the centre of this half-world—a half-world that is almost all water. The Pacific, largest of all oceans, shows its vast expanse. To the east and south of Tahiti are thousands of square miles of ocean without a single island or reef. In the western Pacific groups of tiny islands gleam white in the sunlight; far to the north Hawaii stands out as a solitary stepping stone on the 6,200 mile hop from North America to Asia. Solid land masses are far away, only just appearing on the horizon. To the south-west is Australia—with Sydney, a mere 3,801 miles from the island of Tahiti. The vast semicircle of the Americas serrates the opposite skyline; Vancouver is 4,888 miles away, Panama 5,180, Cape Horn 4,950. China and Japan lie out of sight. Tokyo is 5,893 miles from Tahiti.

Compare this hemisphere with the one to its left. There, millions of people live in the heart of Asia, and may be as far as three thousand miles from the open sea. Here, in the water hemisphere, live only a few hundred thousand people, thousands of miles from any sizeable land.

THE WORLD

Without clouds the Earth is shown from different aspects: as a tangle of plains and mountains, as a world of water topped by ice-capped Poles, and rotating into and out of sunlight. The ordinary earthbound man knows the broad truths of geography only from the jigsaw of the details: here the jigsaw has been put together and we see the Earth in the round.

DAWN ADVANCES

"Half-Earth" as seen by an astronaut on May 1st. Dawn is advancing along the Equator westwards at over 1,000 m.p.h. (15° of longitude each hour). In London it is 6 a.m. Greenwich Mean Time, though the clocks say it is 7 a.m. B.S.T. (British Standard Time). The sun rose $1\frac{1}{2}$ hours ago in London, and dawn will reach Labrador and the easternmost tip of Brazil within the hour. In New York, where the clocks say it is 2 a.m. Eastern Summer Time, $4\frac{1}{2}$ hours of night still lie ahead. But it is noon in Calcutta.

Only at the Equinoxes (in March and September) does every place on the Earth have 12 hours of daylight and 12 hours of night: dawn is then at the same sun-time at all places on the same longitude. By June the tilt of the Earth's axis will bring daylight all round the clock to the North Pole; it will be midsummer in the Northern Hemisphere, but night all round the clock at the South Pole and midwinter in the Southern Hemisphere.

NORTH
+
POLE

THE ROOF OF THE WORLD

The North Pole, with its monotonous waste of broken ice, is the hub of this crowded view. The floating ice of the North Pole merges into the surrounding land masses. Round the Arctic lies the expanse of frozen northlands of Russia, Canada and Alaska. To their south a belt of coniferous forest girdles the world from Atlantic Ocean to Pacific and sweeps on again across North America from Pacific to Atlantic. On these forests' southern margins is the northern limit of permanent settlement—and the beginning of a 1,500 mile wide band in which are most of the largest towns of the Northern Hemisphere. Interweaving among these towns is the densest web of communications in the world, with continental highways and railways and air-routes linked by "great circle" routes across the oceans. On the extreme rim of this view there lies the mighty barrier of desert (from Sahara to Gobi) and of Asian mountains that separates temperate from tropical lands in Eurasia and Africa.

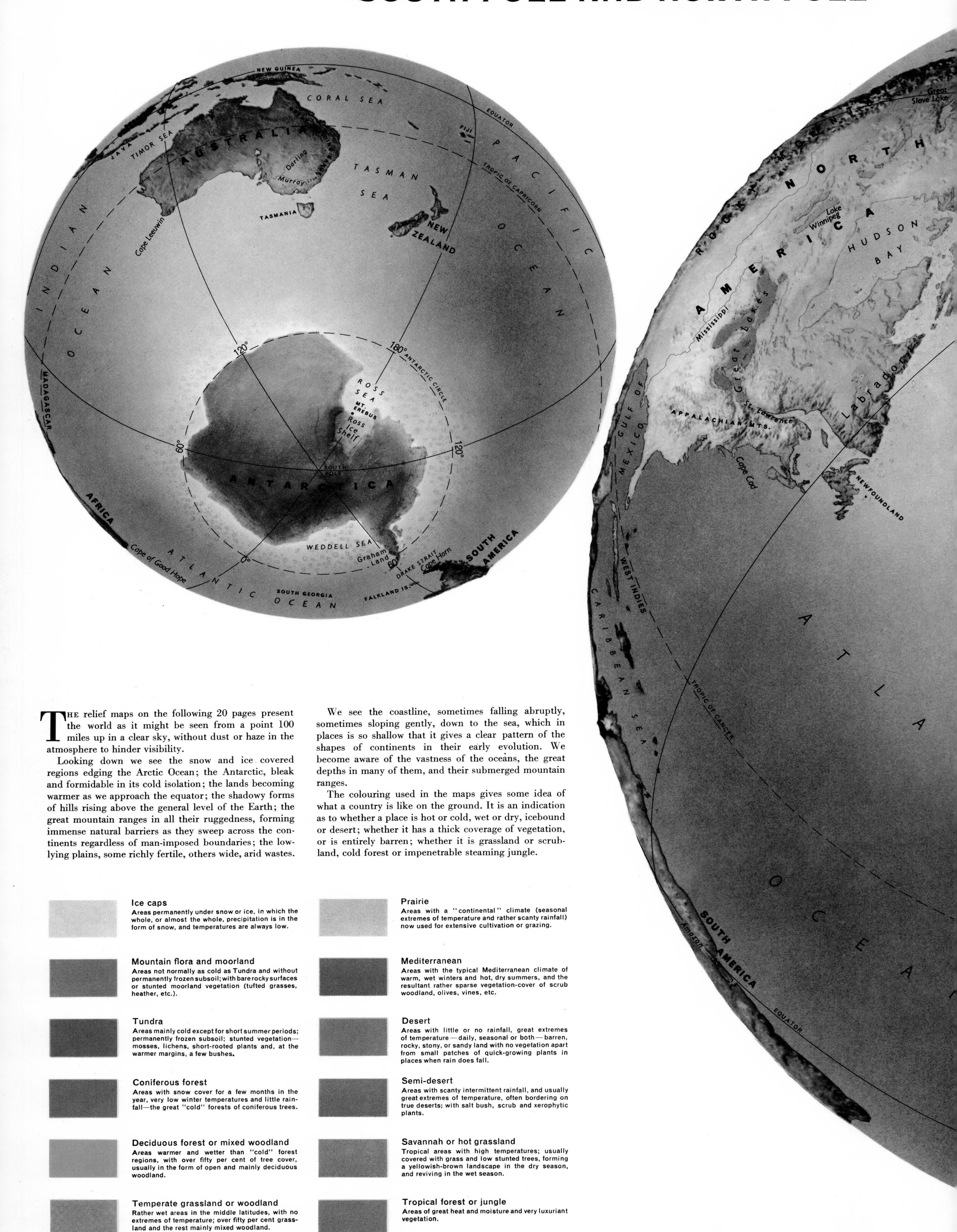

THE relief maps on the following 20 pages present the world as it might be seen from a point 100 miles up in a clear sky, without dust or haze in the atmosphere to hinder visibility.

Looking down we see the snow and ice covered regions edging the Arctic Ocean; the Antarctic, bleak and formidable in its cold isolation; the lands becoming warmer as we approach the equator; the shadowy forms of hills rising above the general level of the Earth; the great mountain ranges in all their ruggedness, forming immense natural barriers as they sweep across the continents regardless of man-imposed boundaries; the low-lying plains, some richly fertile, others wide, arid wastes.

We see the coastline, sometimes falling abruptly, sometimes sloping gently, down to the sea, which in places is so shallow that it gives a clear pattern of the shapes of continents in their early evolution. We become aware of the vastness of the oceans, the great depths in many of them, and their submerged mountain ranges.

The colouring used in the maps gives some idea of what a country is like on the ground. It is an indication as to whether a place is hot or cold, wet or dry, icebound or desert; whether it has a thick coverage of vegetation, or is entirely barren; whether it is grassland or scrub-land, cold forest or impenetrable steaming jungle.

Ice caps
Areas permanently under snow or ice, in which the whole, or almost the whole, precipitation is in the form of snow, and temperatures are always low.

Mountain flora and moorland
Areas not normally as cold as Tundra and without permanently frozen subsoil; with bare rocky surfaces or stunted moorland vegetation (tufted grasses, heather, etc.).

Tundra
Areas mainly cold except for short summer periods; permanently frozen subsoil; stunted vegetation—mosses, lichens, short-rooted plants and, at the warmer margins, a few bushes.

Coniferous forest
Areas with snow cover for a few months in the year, very low winter temperatures and little rain-fall—the great "cold" forests of coniferous trees.

Deciduous forest or mixed woodland
Areas warmer and wetter than "cold" forest regions, with over fifty per cent of tree cover, usually in the form of open and mainly deciduous woodland.

Temperate grassland or woodland
Rather wet areas in the middle latitudes, with no extremes of temperature; over fifty per cent grass-land and the rest mainly mixed woodland.

Prairie
Areas with a "continental" climate (seasonal extremes of temperature and rather scanty rainfall) now used for extensive cultivation or grazing.

Mediterranean
Areas with the typical Mediterranean climate of warm, wet winters and hot, dry summers, and the resultant rather sparse vegetation-cover of scrub woodland, olives, vines, etc.

Desert
Areas with little or no rainfall, great extremes of temperature—daily, seasonal or both—barren, rocky, stony, or sandy land with no vegetation apart from small patches of quick-growing plants in places when rain does fall.

Semi-desert
Areas with scanty intermittent rainfall, and usually great extremes of temperature, often bordering on true deserts; with salt bush, scrub and xerophytic plants.

Savannah or hot grassland
Tropical areas with high temperatures; usually covered with grass and low stunted trees, forming a yellowish-brown landscape in the dry season, and reviving in the wet season.

Tropical forest or jungle
Areas of great heat and moisture and very luxuriant vegetation.

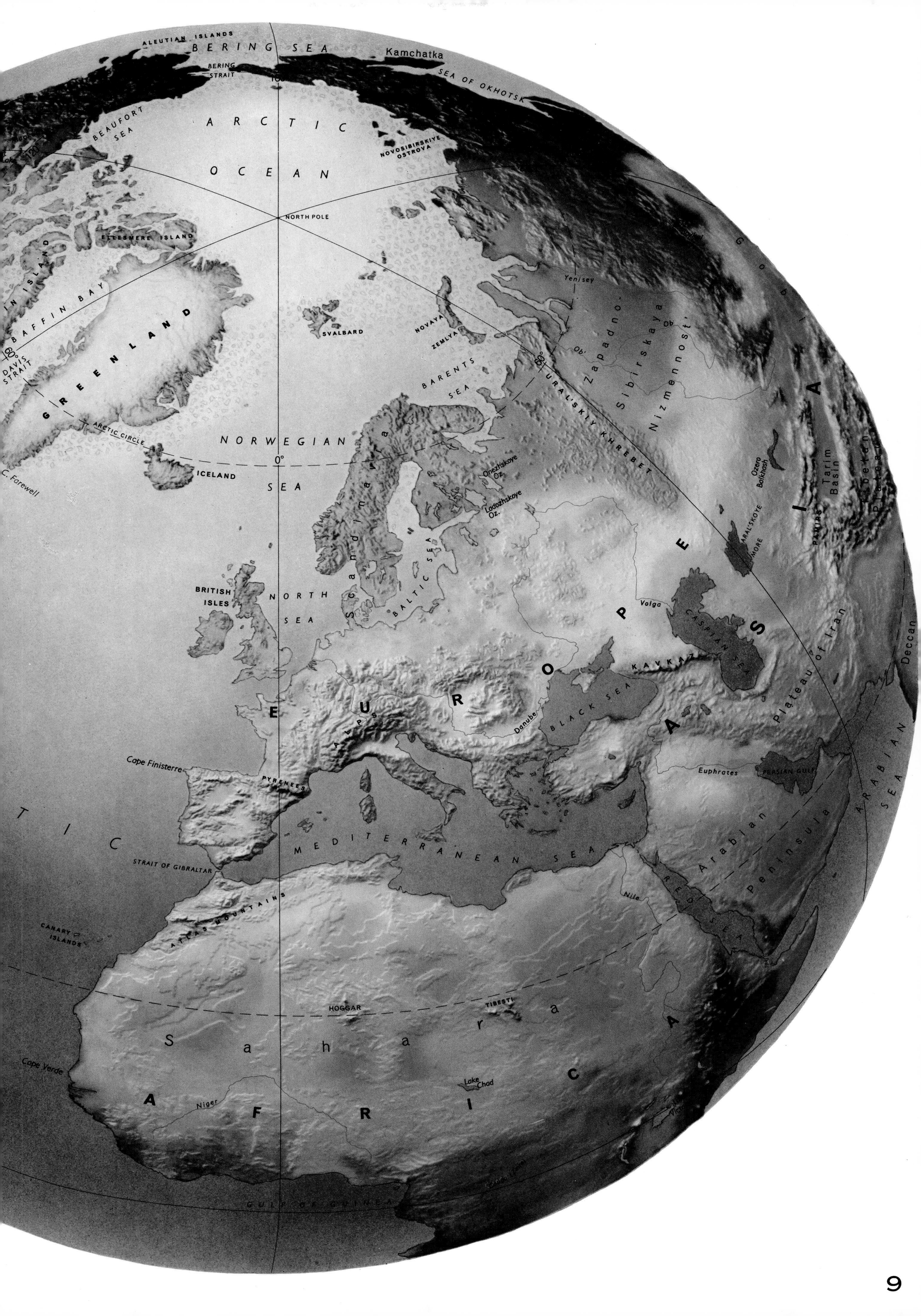

ALEUTIAN ISLANDS

BERING SEA   Kamchatka

BERING
STRAIT   SEA OF OKHOTSK

A R C T I C

BEAUFORT
SEA   NOVOSIBIRSKIYE
                                                       OSTROVA

O C E A N

ELLESMERE ISLAND

BAFFIN BAY   NORTH POLE

GREENLAND   SVALBARD   Yenisey

                                              NOVAYA
                                              ZEMLYA   Ob'

ARCTIC CIRCLE   BARENTS   SEA   Zapadno-   Sibirskaya   Nizmennost'

C. Farewell   ICELAND   URAL'SKIY KHREBET

                 NORWEGIAN   0°   Tarim
                                                                                                                           Basin
                 SEA
                                        Onezhskoye
                                        Oz.   Ozero
                                                                                                            Balkhash
                              Ladozhskoye
                              Oz.   ARAL'SKOYE
                                                                                               MORE
                              BALTIC SEA   Plateau
BRITISH   NORTH   of Iran
ISLES   SEA   Volga   CASPIAN SEA

                                                                                                                         Deccan

                                        E   U   R   O   P   E   S

                                                                     KAVKAZ
                 E
                        A   BLACK SEA
Cape Finisterre   L
                        P   Danube   A
                  S

             PYRENEES   Euphrates   PERSIAN GULF

                                                                                       Plateau of Iran

                                   MEDITERRANEAN   SEA
T I C   STRAIT OF GIBRALTAR   ARABIAN
                                                                        Nile   SEA

                    ATLAS MOUNTAINS   Arabian
                                                                              Peninsula
CANARY
ISLANDS

                                                                              RED SEA

Cape Verde   HOGGAR   TIBESTI

               S   a   h   a   r   a

                                              Lake Chad
         A   F   R   I   C   A
              Niger

                        GULF OF GUINEA

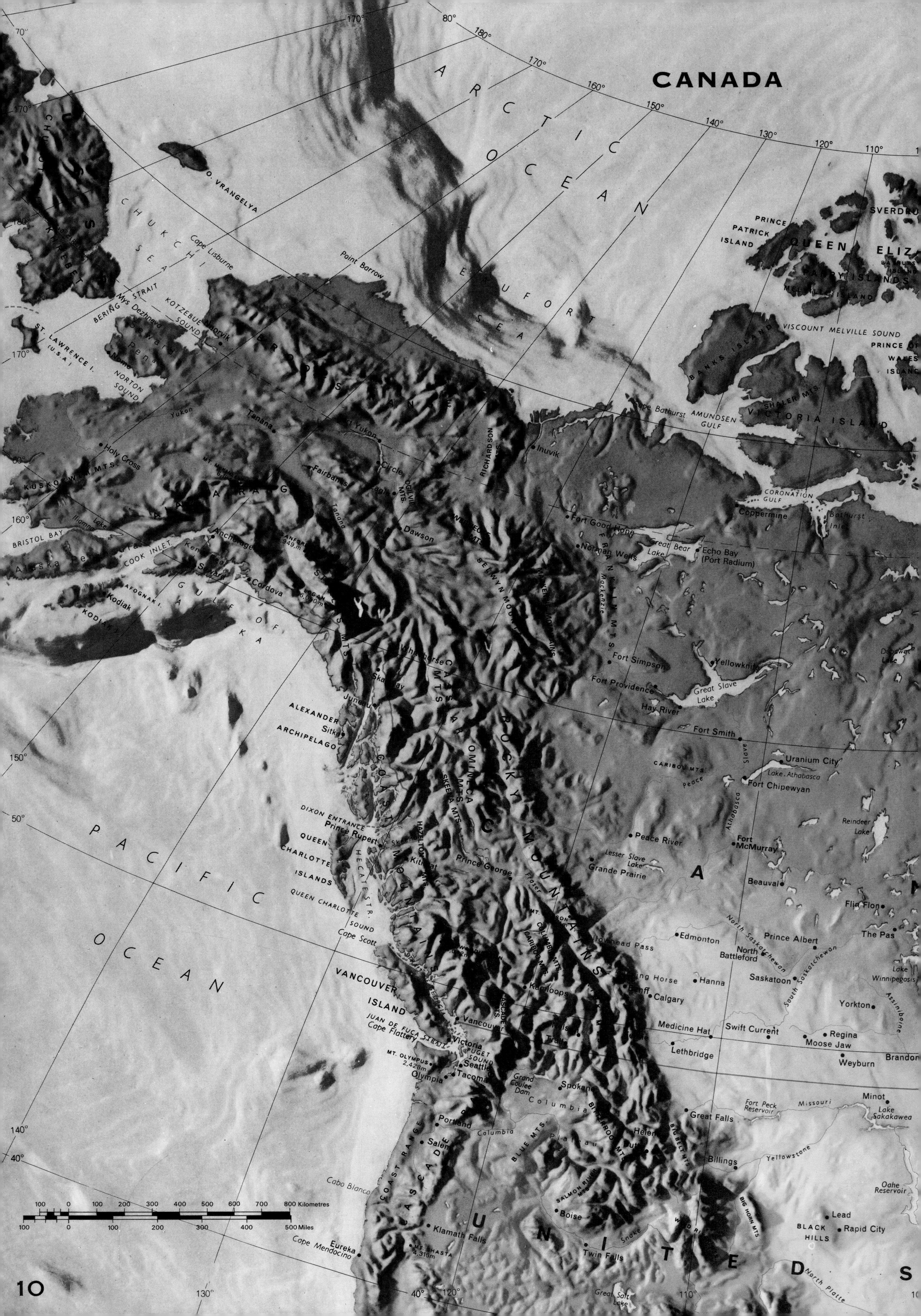

CANADA
ARCTIC OCEAN
PACIFIC OCEAN
O. VRANGELYA
CHUKCHI SEA
Cape Lisburne
Point Barrow
BEAUFORT SEA
BERING STRAIT
Mys Dezhneva
KOTZEBUE SOUND
ST. LAWRENCE I. (U.S.A.)
NORTON SOUND
Nome
Yukon
Tanana
Holy Cross
KUSKOKWIM MTS.
Fairbanks
Circle
OGILVIE MTS.
RICHARDSON MTS.
Inuvik
Dawson
BRISTOL BAY
Iliamna Lake
COOK INLET
Anchorage
Cordova
AFOGNAK I.
Kodiak
GULF OF ALASKA
PRINCE PATRICK ISLAND
QUEEN ELIZ
SVERDRU
VISCOUNT MELVILLE SOUND
BANKS ISLAND
PRINCE OF WALES ISLAND
SHALER MTS.
VICTORIA ISLAND
Cape Bathurst
AMUNDSEN GULF
CORONATION GULF
Coppermine
Bathurst Inlet
Fort Good Hope
Norman Wells
Great Bear Lake
Echo Bay (Port Radium)
SELWYN MTS.
Mackenzie
Fort Simpson
Yellowknife
Fort Providence
Great Slave Lake
Hay River
Fort Smith
Whitehorse
Skagway
Juneau
ALEXANDER ARCHIPELAGO
Sitka
CARIBOU MTS.
Peace
Uranium City
Lake Athabasca
Fort Chipewyan
Slave
Athabasca
DIXON ENTRANCE
Prince Rupert
QUEEN CHARLOTTE ISLANDS
HECATE STR.
QUEEN CHARLOTTE SOUND
Kitimat
SKEENA MTS.
OMINECA MTS.
ROCKY MOUNTAINS
Peace River
Fort McMurray
Reindeer Lake
Lesser Slave Lake
Grande Prairie
Prince George
Fraser
Beauval
Flin Flon
The Pas
Cape Scott
COAST MOUNTAINS
Edmonton
North Saskatchewan
Prince Albert
North Battleford
Saskatoon
South Saskatchewan
Lake Winnipegosis
VANCOUVER ISLAND
CARIBOO MTS.
Kamloops
Banff
Calgary
Hanna
Yorkton
Assiniboine
JUAN DE FUCA STRAIT
Cape Flattery
Vancouver
Victoria
PUGET SOUND
Medicine Hat
Swift Current
Regina
Moose Jaw
Lethbridge
Weyburn
Brandon
MT. OLYMPUS 2,428 m
Seattle
Olympia
Tacoma
Grand Coulee Dam
Spokane
Columbia
Fort Peck Reservoir
Missouri
Minot
Lake Sakakawea
Great Falls
Portland
Salem
BLUE MTS.
BITTERROOT MTS.
BIG BELT MTS.
Billings
Yellowstone
COAST RANGE
CASCADE
Cabo Blanco
SALMON RIVER MTS.
Boise
BIG HORN MTS.
Oahe Reservoir
Lead
Rapid City
BLACK HILLS
Klamath Falls
Eureka
Cape Mendocino
MT. SHASTA 4,316 m
Snake
Twin Falls
UNITED S
North Platte
Great Salt Lake
100 0 100 200 300 400 500 600 700 800 Kilometres
100 0 100 200 300 400 500 Miles

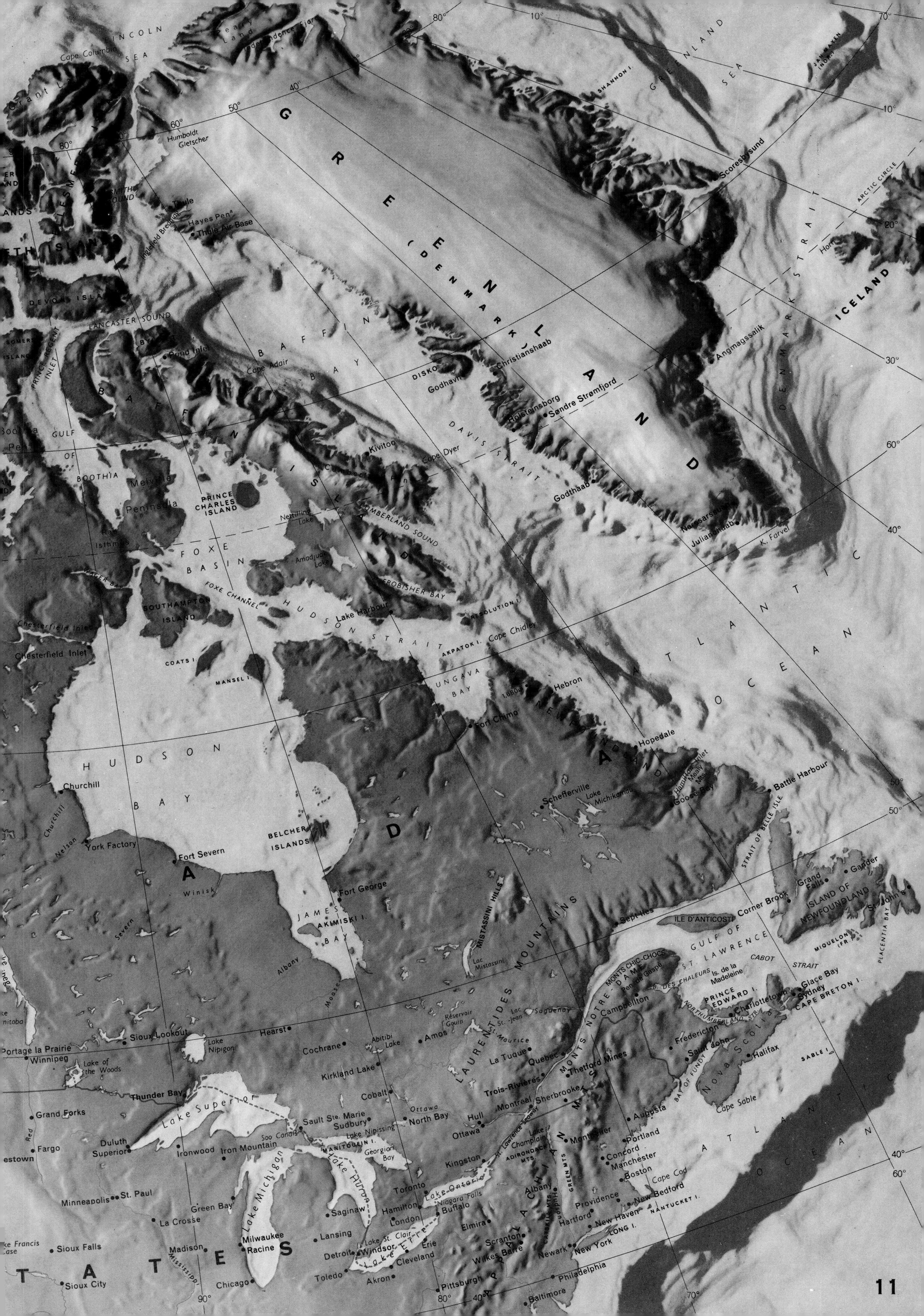

NCOLN
Cape Columbia
SEA
Kearny
Land
Independence Fiord
GRE
80°
Grant Land
80°
Humboldt
Gletscher
Thule
60°
Hayes Pen?
Thule Air Base
Ringefeld Brae
GREENLAND
(DENMARK)
N
L
A
N
D
SHANNON I.
JAN MAYEN
(NOR.)
10°
50°
40°
GREENLAND SEA
Scoresbysund
10°
ARCTIC CIRCLE
DEVOLS ISLAND
20°
LIEMERE
SMITH
SOUND
SH ISLAND
ICELAND
SOMER
ISLAND
LANCASTER SOUND
PRINCE REGENT INLET
Pond Inlet
BAFFIN
BAY
Cape Adair
DISKO
Godhavn
Christianshaab
30°
Angmagssalik
Bootha
Pen
GULF
OF
BOOTHIA
Melville
Peninsula
BAFFIN
Kivitoo
DAVIS STRAIT
Holsteinsborg
Søndre Strømfjord
Cape Dyer
60°
PRINCE
CHARLES
ISLAND
ISLAND
CUMBERLAND SOUND
Godthaab
Narsarssuaq
Julianehaab
K. Farvel
40°
Nettilling
Lake
FOXE
BASIN
Amadjuak
Lake
FROBISHER BAY
FOXE CHANNEL
HUDSON
Lake Harbour
RESOLUTION I.
SOUTHAMPTON
ISLAND
Chesterfield Inlet
Chesterfield Inlet
COATS I.
MANSEL I.
STRAIT
AKPATOK I.
Cape Chidley
UNGAVA
BAY
1,880?
Hebron
ATLANTIC
OCEAN
Fort Chimo
Hopedale
HUDSON
Churchill
Churchill
Nelson
York Factory
Fort Severn
BAY
BELCHER
ISLANDS
A
Scheffervile
Lake
Michikamau
Goose Bay
Battle Harbour
50°
STRAIT OF BELLE ISLE
50°
Winisk
Fort George
D
Grand
Falls
Gander
ISLAND OF
NEWFOUNDLAND
Severn
JAMES
AKIMISKI I.
BAY
Albany
Moose
Fort George
Lac
Mistassini
MISTASSINI HILLS
Sept-Iles
Corner Brook
St. John's
ILE D'ANTICOSTI
GULF OF
ST. LAWRENCE
MIQUELON
(FR.)
PLACENTIA BAY
manitoba
Réservoir
Gouin
Lac
St.-Jean
Saguenay
LAURENTIDES MOUNTAINS
MONTS CHIC-CHOCS
Is. de la
Madeleine
CABOT
STRAIT
Glace Bay
Sydney
CAPE BRETON I.
Portage la Prairie
Winnipeg
Sioux Lookout
Lake
Nipigon
Hearst
Cochrane
Abitibi
Lake
Amos
Maurice
La Tuque
MONTS NOTRE - DAME
B. DES CHALEURS
Pen.de Gaspé
PRINCE
EDWARD I.
NORTHUMBERLAND STR.
Charlottetown
Grand Forks
Thunder Bay
Kirkland Lake
Cobalt
Quebec
Thetford Mines
Campbellton
Fredericton
Saint John
Halifax
Lake Superior
Sault Ste. Marie
Sudbury
Ottawa
North Bay
Trois-Rivières
Sherbrooke
APPALACHIAN
BAY OF FUNDY
NOVA SCOTIA
Red
Duluth
Superior
Ironwood
Iron Mountain
Soo Canals
Lake Nipissing
Hull
Ottawa
Montreal
ST. LAWRENCE
Champlain
Augusta
Portland
Concord
Manchester
Cape Sable
Cape Sable
SABLE I.
40°
estown
Fargo
Minneapolis
St. Paul
MANITOULIN I.
Georgian
Bay
Kingston
ADIRONDACK
MTS.
Montpelier
Boston
GREEN MTS.
ATLANTIC
60°
Lake Michigan
Green Bay
La Crosse
Saginaw
Hamilton
Toronto
Lake Ontario
Niagara Falls
Buffalo
Elmira
Albany
Hartford
Providence
New Bedford
Cape Cod
OCEAN
St. Francis
case
Sioux Falls
Madison
Milwaukee
Racine
Lansing
London
Detroit
Windsor
Lake St. Clair
Lake
Erie
Scranton
Wilkes Barre
New Haven
NANTUCKET I.
LONG I.
New York
Newark
Sioux City
Chicago
Mississippi
Toledo
Akron
Cleveland
Pittsburgh
Philadelphia
Baltimore
90°
80°
40°
70°
11
TATES

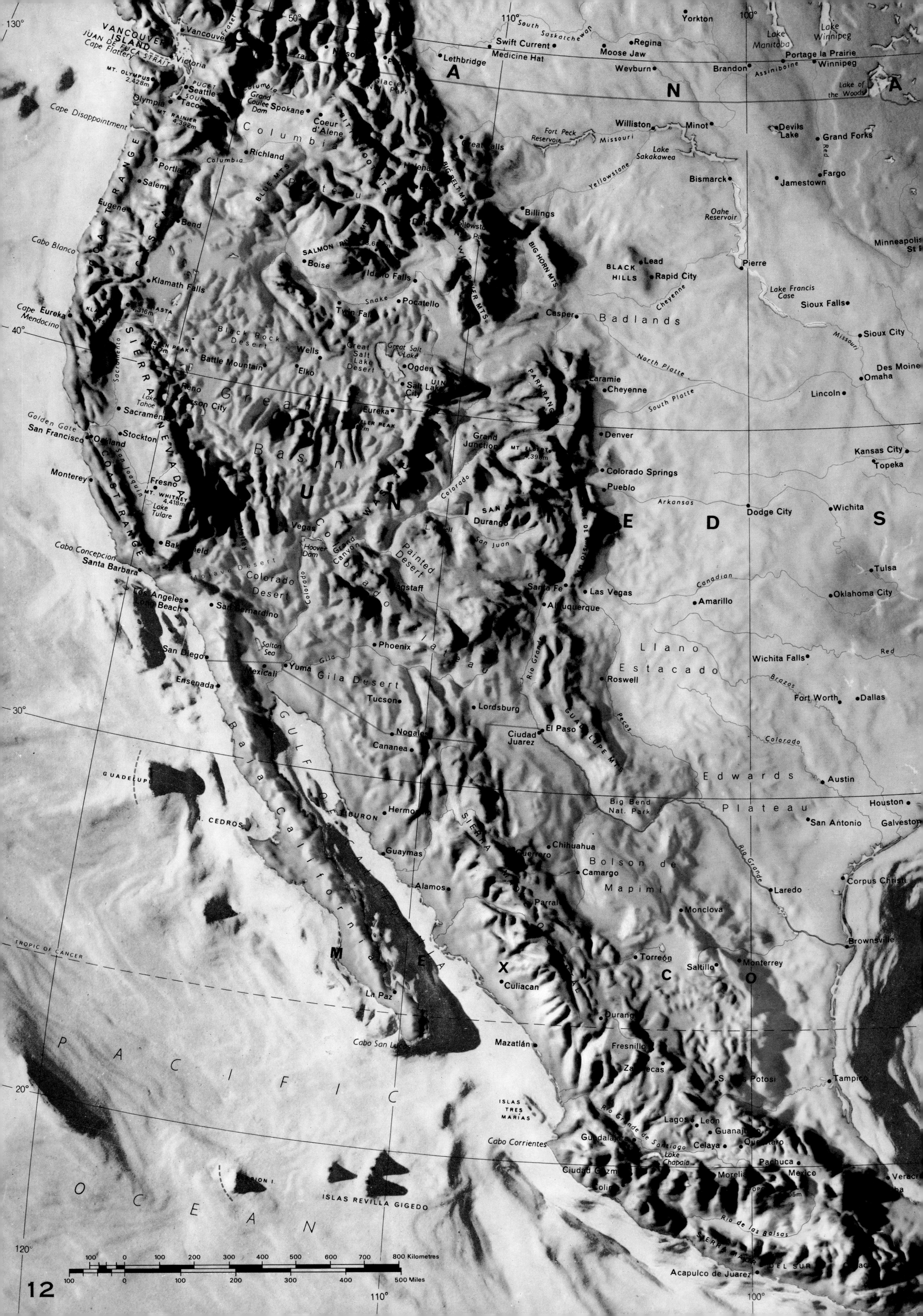

VANCOUVER ISLAND
Vancouver
JUAN DE FUCA STRAIT
Cape Flattery
Victoria
MT. OLYMPUS 2,428m
PUGET SOUND
Seattle
Olympia
MT. RAINIER 4,392m
Grand Coulee Dam
Spokane
Coeur d'Alene
Cape Disappointment
Columbia
Richland
Portland
Salem
Eugene
Bend
BLUE MTS
Cabo Blanco
Klamath Falls
Cape Mendocino
Eureka
Black Rock Desert
Wells
Elko
Battle Mountain
Great Salt Lake Desert
Great Salt Lake
Ogden
Salt Lake City
Reno
Lake Tahoe
Sacramento
Golden Gate
San Francisco
Oakland
Stockton
Monterey
Fresno
MT. WHITNEY 4,418m
Lake Tulare
SIERRA NEVADA
COAST RANGE
Great Basin
Eureka
Cabo Concepcion
Santa Barbara
Los Angeles
Long Beach
San Bernardino
Mojave Desert
Colorado Desert
Hoover Dam
Grand Canyon
Painted Desert
Salton Sea
San Diego
Mexicali
Yuma
Gila
Gila Desert
Ensenada
Phoenix
Tucson
Lordsburg
Nogales
Cananea
Ciudad Juarez
El Paso
GUADALUPE MTS
Baja California
GULF OF CALIFORNIA
GUADELUPE
CEDROS
TIBURON
Hermosillo
Guaymas
Alamos
Chihuahua
Guerrero
Camargo
Bolson de Mapimi
Parral
Culiacan
La Paz
Cabo San Lucas
Mazatlán
TROPIC OF CANCER
Durango
Torreon
Monclova
Saltillo
Monterrey
Fresnillo
Zacatecas
San Luis Potosi
ISLAS TRES MARIAS
Cabo Corrientes
Rio Grande de Santiago
Lagos
León
Guanajuato
Celaya
Querétaro
Guadalajara
Lake Chapala
Pachuca
Ciudad Guzmán
Colima
Morelia
Mexico
Rio de las Balsas
SIERRA MADRE DEL SUR
Acapulco de Juarez
ISLAS REVILLA GIGEDO
PACIFIC OCEAN
MEXICO
UNITED STATES
CANADA
South Saskatchewan
Swift Current
Medicine Hat
Lethbridge
Moose Jaw
Regina
Yorkton
Weyburn
Brandon
Assiniboine
Portage la Prairie
Winnipeg
Lake Manitoba
Lake Winnipeg
Lake of the Woods
Fort Peck Reservoir
Missouri
Williston
Minot
Lake Sakakawea
Devils Lake
Grand Forks
Red
Fargo
Jamestown
Bismarck
Yellowstone
Great Falls
Helena
Billings
BIG HORN MTS
Oahe Reservoir
Pierre
SALMON RIVER MTS
Boise
Idaho Falls
Snake
Pocatello
Twin Falls
BLACK HILLS
Lead
Rapid City
Lake Francis Case
Cheyenne
Sioux Falls
Casper
Badlands
Sioux City
North Platte
Laramie
Cheyenne
South Platte
Omaha
Des Moines
Lincoln
Denver
Grand Junction
Colorado
Colorado Springs
Pueblo
Arkansas
Dodge City
Wichita
Kansas City
Topeka
Durango
San Juan
Tulsa
Oklahoma City
Canadian
Santa Fe
Las Vegas
Albuquerque
Amarillo
Flagstaff
Llano Estacado
Rio Grande
Roswell
Wichita Falls
Red
Brazos
Fort Worth
Dallas
Pecos
Colorado
Edwards Plateau
Austin
Big Bend Nat. Park
Houston
San Antonio
Galveston
Corpus Christi
Laredo
Brownsville
Tampico
Minneapolis
130°
120°
110°
100°
50°
40°
30°
20°
800 Kilometres
500 Miles

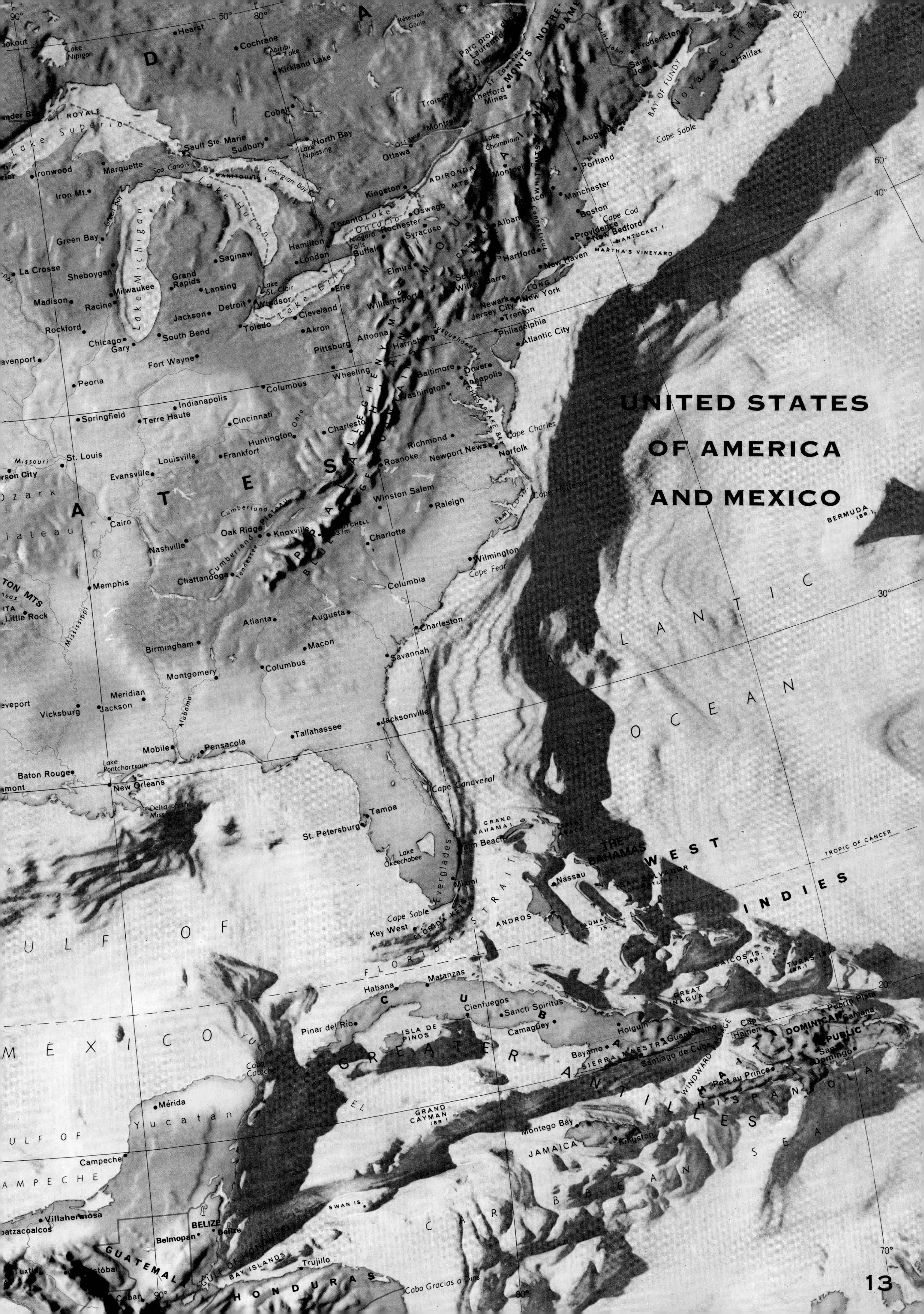

UNITED STATES
OF AMERICA
AND MEXICO

13

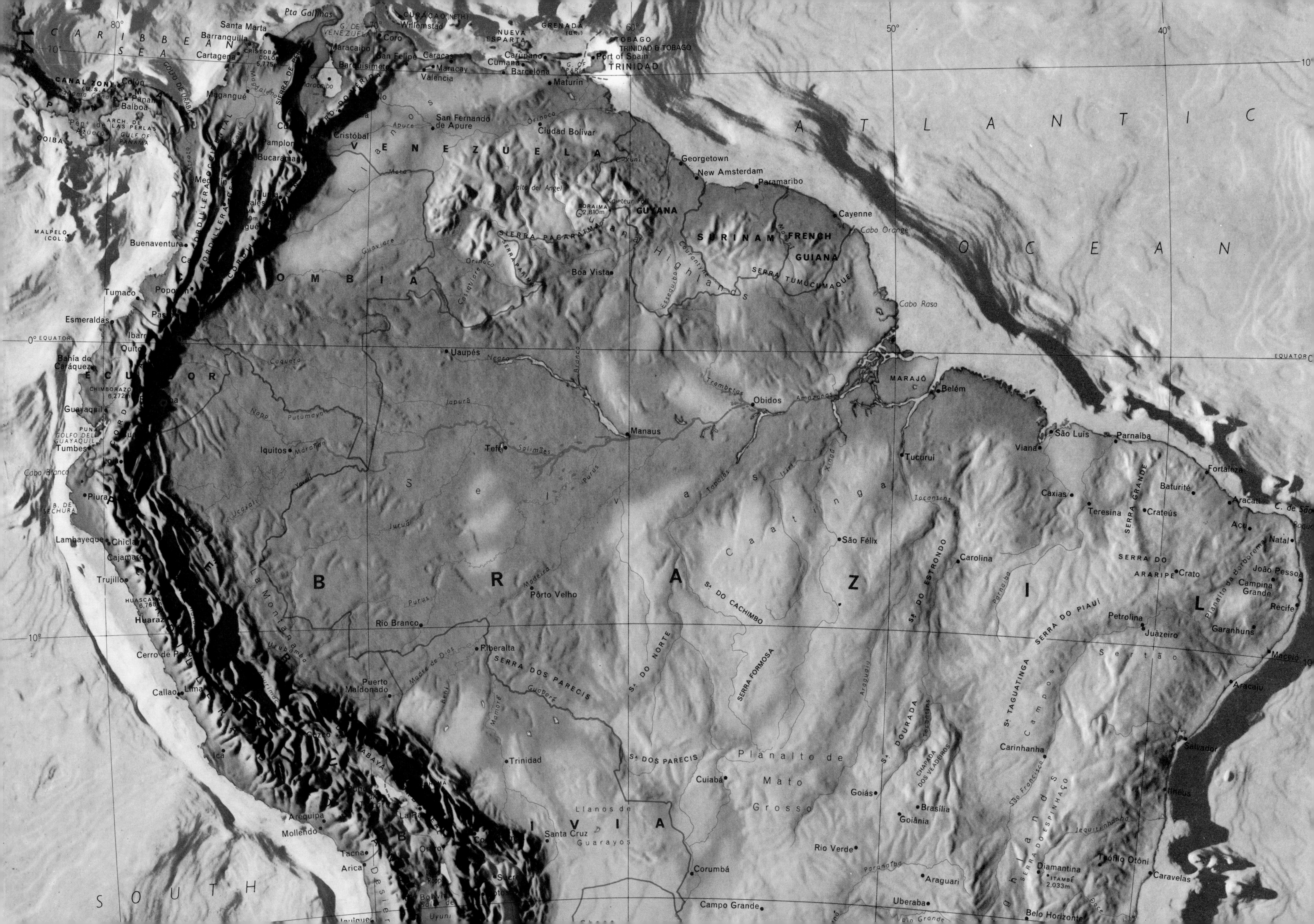
CARIBBEAN SEA
ATLANTIC OCEAN
SOUTH
BRAZIL
VENEZUELA
COLOMBIA
ECUADOR
GUYANA
SURINAM
FRENCH GUIANA
TRINIDAD & TOBAGO
TOBAGO
TRINIDAD
Port of Spain
GRENADA (BR.)
NUEVA ESPARTA
CURAÇAO (NETH.)
Willemstad
Pta Gallinas
Santa Marta
Barranquilla
Cartagena
Magangué
CANAL ZONE
Colón
Panamá
Balboa
ARCH. DE LAS PERLAS
GULF OF PANAMA
COIBA
MALPELO (COL.)
Maracaibo
Coro
San Felipe
Barquisimeto
Caracas
Maracay
Valencia
Carúpano
Cumaná
Barcelona
Maturín
San Fernando de Apure
Ciudad Bolívar
Salto del Angel
Cristóbal
Pamplona
Bucaramanga
Medellín
Buenaventura
Tumaco
Popayán
Esmeraldas
0° EQUATOR
Quito
Bahía de Caráquez
CHIMBORAZO 6,272m
Guayaquil
GOLFO DEL GUAYAQUIL
Tumbes
Cabo Blanco
Piura
B. DE SECHURA
Lambayeque
Cajamarca
Trujillo
HUASCARÁN 6,768m
Huaraz
Cerro de Pasco
Callao
Lima
Ica
Arequipa
Mollendo
Tacna
Arica
Georgetown
New Amsterdam
Paramaribo
Cayenne
Cabo Orange
Cabo Raso
RORAIMA 2,810m
SERRA PACARAIMA
SERRA PARIMA
Boa Vista
SERRA TUMUCUMAQUE
Highlands
Uaupés
Obidos
MARAJÓ
Belém
Manaus
Iquitos
Tefé
Tucuruí
São Luís
Viana
Parnaíba
Fortaleza
Caxias
Teresina
Baturité
Crateús
SERRA GRANDE
Aracati
C. de São Roque
Açu
Natal
SERRA DO ARARIPE
Crato
João Pessoa
Campina Grande
Recife
Garanhuns
Petrolina
Juàzeiro
SERRA DO PIAUÍ
Maceió
Aracaju
Salvador
Ilhéus
Caravelas
Teófilo Otôni
Diamantina
ITAMBÉ 2,033m
Belo Horizonte
S. TAGUATINGA
Carinhanha
SERRA DO ESPINHAÇO
Carolina
S. DO ESTRONDO
São Félix
S. DO CACHIMBO
S. DO NORTE
SERRA FORMOSA
S. DOURADA
CHAPADA DOS VEADEIROS
Brasília
Goiânia
Goiás
Rio Verde
Araguari
Uberaba
Campo Grande
Corumbá
Planalto de Mato Grosso
Cuiabá
S. DOS PARECIS
SERRA DOS PARECIS
Pôrto Velho
Rio Branco
Riberalta
Puerto Maldonado
Trinidad
Llanos de Guarayos
Santa Cruz
BOLIVIA
La Montaña
EQUATOR

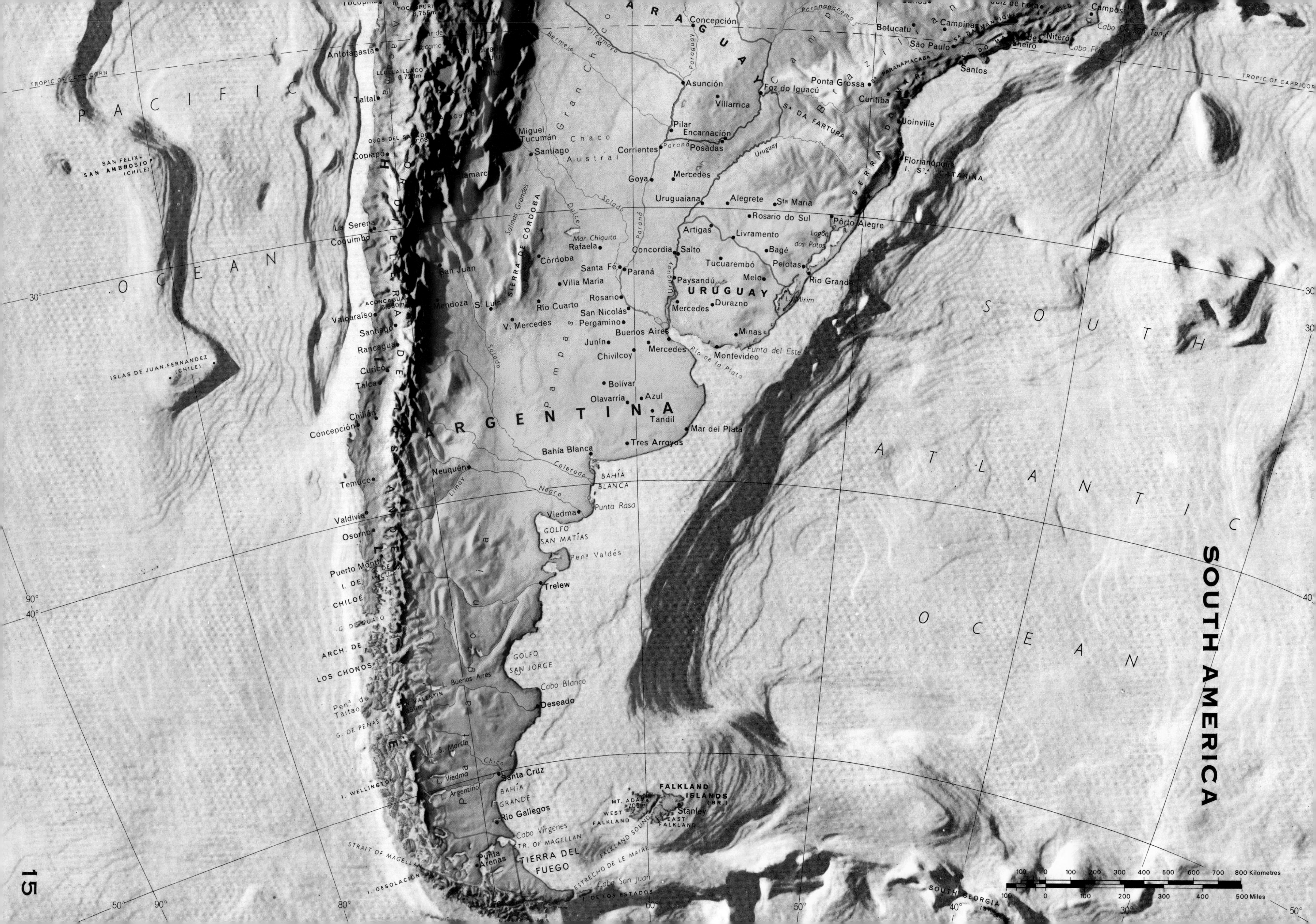

SOUTH AMERICA

800 Kilometres
500 Miles

SOUTH ATLANTIC OCEAN

PACIFIC OCEAN

TROPIC OF CAPRICORN

Cabo de São Tomé
Campos
Cabo Frio
Niterói
Rio de Janeiro
Santos
São Paulo
Campinas
Botucatu
Curitiba
Ponta Grossa
Joinville
Foz do Iguaçú
Villarrica
Florianópolis
I. ST. CATARINA
S. DA FARTURA
Pôrto Alegre
Concepción
Asunción
Encarnación
Posadas
Sta Maria
Rio Grande
Lagôa dos Patos
Pelotas
Bagé
Rosario do Sul
Alegrete
Livramento
Tucuarembó
Artigas
Salto
Paysandú
URUGUAY
Melo
Durazno
Minas
Punta del Este
Montevideo
Rio de la Plata
Mar del Plata
Tres Arroyos
Pilar
Mercedes
Uruguaiana
Concordia
Paraná
Corrientes
Goya
Santa Fé
Rosario
San Nicolás
Pergamino
Buenos Aires
Mercedes
Chivilcoy
Junín
Olavarría
Azul
Tandil
Bolívar
Santiago
Tucumán
Rafaela
Córdoba
Villa María
Río Cuarto
V. Mercedes
San Luis
San Juan
Mendoza
Neuquén
Bahía Blanca
BAHÍA BLANCA
Colorado
Punta Raso
Viedma
Viedma
GOLFO SAN MATÍAS
Peña Valdés
Trelew
GOLFO SAN JORGE
Cabo Blanco
Deseado
Santa Cruz
Río Gallegos
Punta Arenas
TIERRA DEL FUEGO
STRAIT OF MAGELLAN
FALKLAND ISLANDS
Stanley
MT. ADAM
WEST FALKLAND
EAST FALKLAND
SOUTH GEORGIA
Antofagasta
Taltal
Copiapó
La Serena
Coquimbo
Valparaíso
Santiago
Rancagua
Curicó
Talca
Chillán
Concepción
Temuco
Valdivia
Osorno
Puerto Montt
I. DE CHILOÉ
CHILOÉ
ARCH. DE LOS CHONOS
G. DE PENAS
ARGENTINA
CORDILLERA DE LOS ANDES
ISLAS DE JUAN FERNÁNDEZ (CHILE)
SAN FELIX
SAN AMBROSIO (CHILE)
TROPIC OF CAPRICORN

15

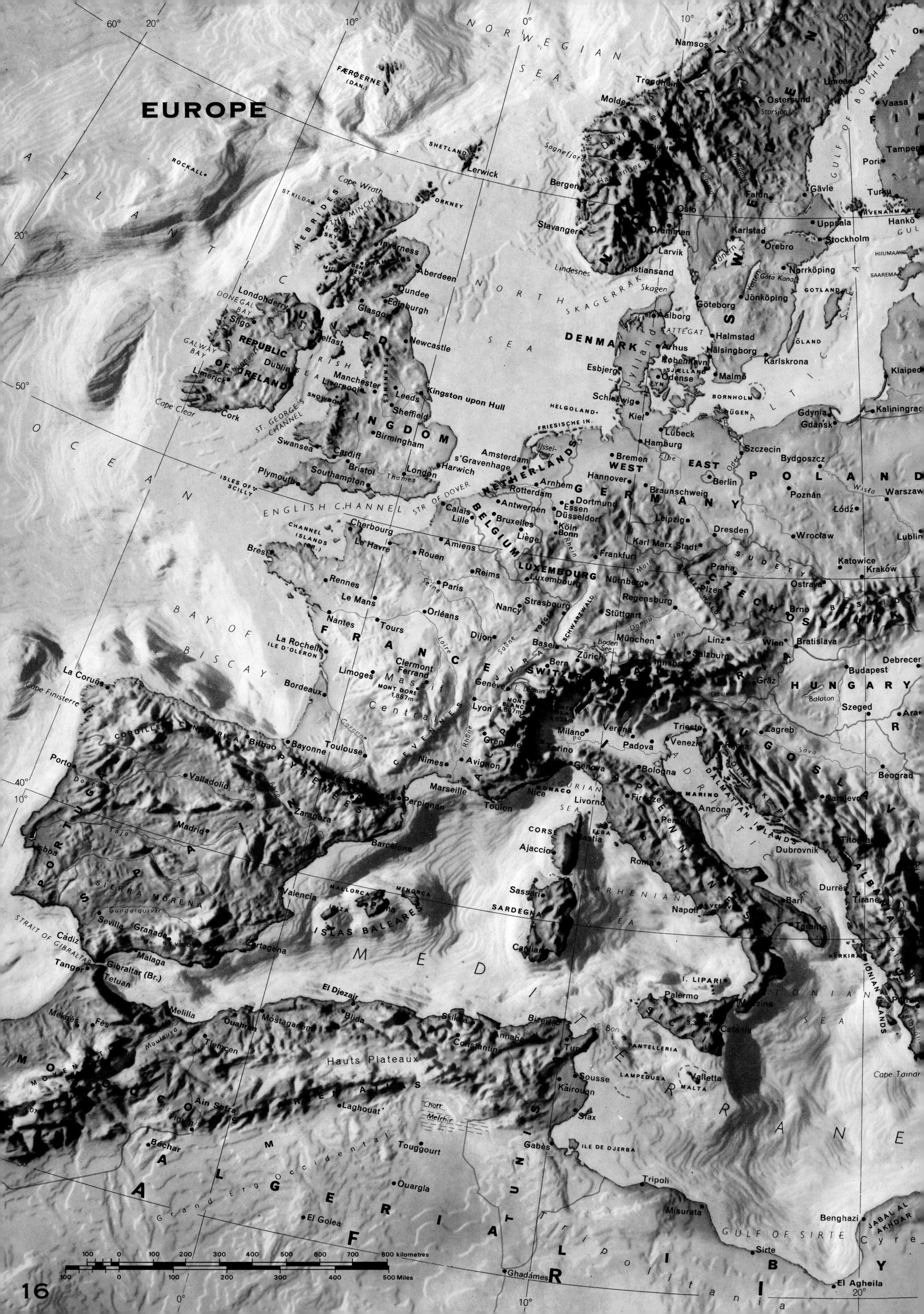

EUROPE

60° 20° 0° 10° 0° 10° 20°

NORWEGIAN SEA

Namsos
Trondheim
Molde

FÆRØERNE
(DAN.)

ATLAN

ROCKALL

Cape Wrath
ST KILDA
SHETLAND
Lerwick
ORKNEY

SKYE
THE MINCH
HEBRIDES
BEN NEVIS
Inverness
Aberdeen
Dundee

Londonderry
DONEGAL BAY
Belfast
Glasgow
Edinburgh
UNITED
Newcastle
Sligo
REPUBLIC
OF IRELAND
Dublin
Manchester
Liverpool
Leeds
Sheffield
Kingston upon Hull

GALWAY BAY
Limerick
IRISH SEA
PENNINES
KINGDOM

Cork
Cape Clear
ST. GEORGE'S CHANNEL
SNOWDON
Birmingham
Swansea
Cardiff
Bristol
London
Thames
Harwich

Plymouth
Southampton
ISLES OF SCILLY

ENGLISH CHANNEL
STR. OF DOVER

CHANNEL ISLANDS (Br.)
Cherbourg
Le Havre
Rouen
Amiens

Brest
Rennes
Le Mans
Paris
Seine

BAY OF BISCAY
Nantes
Tours
Orléans
Dijon

La Rochelle
ILE D'OLÉRON
F R A N C E
Limoges
Clermont Ferrand
MONT DORE 1887m
Massif
Central

La Coruña
Cape Finisterre
Bordeaux

PORTO
CORDILLERA CANTÁBRICA
Bilbao
Bayonne
Toulouse
PYRÉNÉES
CÉVENNES

Porto
DOURO
Valladolid
Zaragoza
S P A I N
Madrid
Tajo

Lisboa
PORTUGAL
SIERRA MORENA
Guadalquivir
Sevilla
Granada
Córdoba
STRAIT OF GIBRALTAR
Cádiz
Málaga
Gibraltar (Br.)
Tánger
Tetuán

Valencia
Cartagena
MALLORCA
MENORCA
IBIZA
ISLAS BALEARES
Barcelona

Bergen
Sognefjord
Stavanger
Lindesnes

NORTH SEA

Oslo
Drammen
Larvik
Kristiansand

SKAGERRAK
Skagen

DENMARK
KATTEGAT
Halmstad
Esbjerg
Århus
København
Schleswig
Odense
Kiel
HELGOLAND
FRIESISCHE IN.
Amsterdam
IJsselmeer
s'Gravenhage
NETHERLANDS
Rotterdam
Arnhem
Antwerpen
BELGIUM
Bruxelles
Liège
Lille
Calais

LUXEMBOURG
Luxembourg
Reims
Nancy
Strasbourg

Basel
SWITZERLAND
Bern
Genève
L. Léman
MONT BLANC 4807m
Lyon
Grenoble
Rhône
Nîmes
Avignon
Marseille
Toulon

Molde
Östersund
Storsjön

Namsos

Umeå
GULF OF BOTHNIA
Vaasa
Pori
Tampere
Turku
HVENANMAA
Hankö
GUL

Falun
Gävle
Uppsala
Stockholm
Örebro
Norrköping
Karlstad
VÄNERN
VÄTTERN
GOTLAND
Göteborg
Jönköping
S
ÖLAND

HELSINGBORG
Malmö
Karlskrona
BORNHOLM
RÜGEN
BALTIC
KLAIPEDA
Gdynia
Gdańsk
Kaliningrad

Lübeck
Hamburg
Bremen
Hannover
WEST
EAST
Berlin
Szczecin
Bydgoszcz
POLAND

Elbe
Braunschweig
GERMANY
Magdeburg
Leipzig
Dresden
Poznań
Warszawa
Wisła
Łódź

Dortmund
Essen
Düsseldorf
Köln
Bonn
Rhein
Frankfurt
Karl Marx Stadt
Wrocław
Lublin

Nürnberg
Regensburg
Stuttgart
SCHWARZWALD
Donau
München
Praha
CZECHOSLOVAKIA
Plzeň
Brno
Ostrava
SUDETY
Katowice
Kraków

Linz
Salzburg
Wien
Bratislava
Graz
Budapest
HUNGARY
Szeged
Debrecen
Arad

Boden See
Zürich
JURA
VOSGES
Inn
A L P S

Milano
Verona
Trieste
Zagreb
Torino
Po
Padova
Venezia
YUGOSLAVIA
Sava
Beograd
Drava
Balaton

Genova
Bologna
Firenze
Ancona
DALMATIAN ISLANDS
Sarajevo

LIGURIAN SEA
Nice
MONACO
Livorno
SAN MARINO
APENNINES
Dubrovnik
DINARSKE PL.
ADRIATIC SEA

CORSE
Ajaccio
Bastia
ELBA
Roma
Pescara
Titograd

Sassari
SARDEGNA
Napoli
VESUVIO
Bari
Taranto
Durrës
Tiranë
ALBANIA
KÉRKIRA

Cagliari

TYRRHENIAN SEA

I. LIPARI
Palermo
Messina
SICILIA
Catania
ETNA

IONIAN ISLANDS

El Djezair
Blida
Skikda
Annaba
Constantine
C. Bon
Bizerta
Tunis
PANTELLERIA
MALTA
Valletta
Cape Tainar
IONIAN SEA

Melilla
Mostaganem
Meknès
Fès
Oran
Tlemcen
HAUTS PLATEAUX
Sousse
Kairouan
Sfax
LAMPEDUSA

M E D I T E R R A N E A N   S E A

MAROC
ATLAS
Ain Sefra
Laghouat
CHOTT MELRHIR
Gabès
ILE DE DJERBA

Béchar
Figuig
A L G E R I A
Grand Erg Occidental
Touggourt
Tripoli
TRIPOLITANIA
Misurata
Benghazi
JABAL AL AKHDAR
Cyrenaica
GULF OF SIRTE

Ouargla
TUNISIA
El Golea
Sirte
Ghadames
El Agheila
L I B Y A

800 kilometres
100 0 100 200 300 400 500 600 700
100 0 100 200 300 400 500 Miles

16

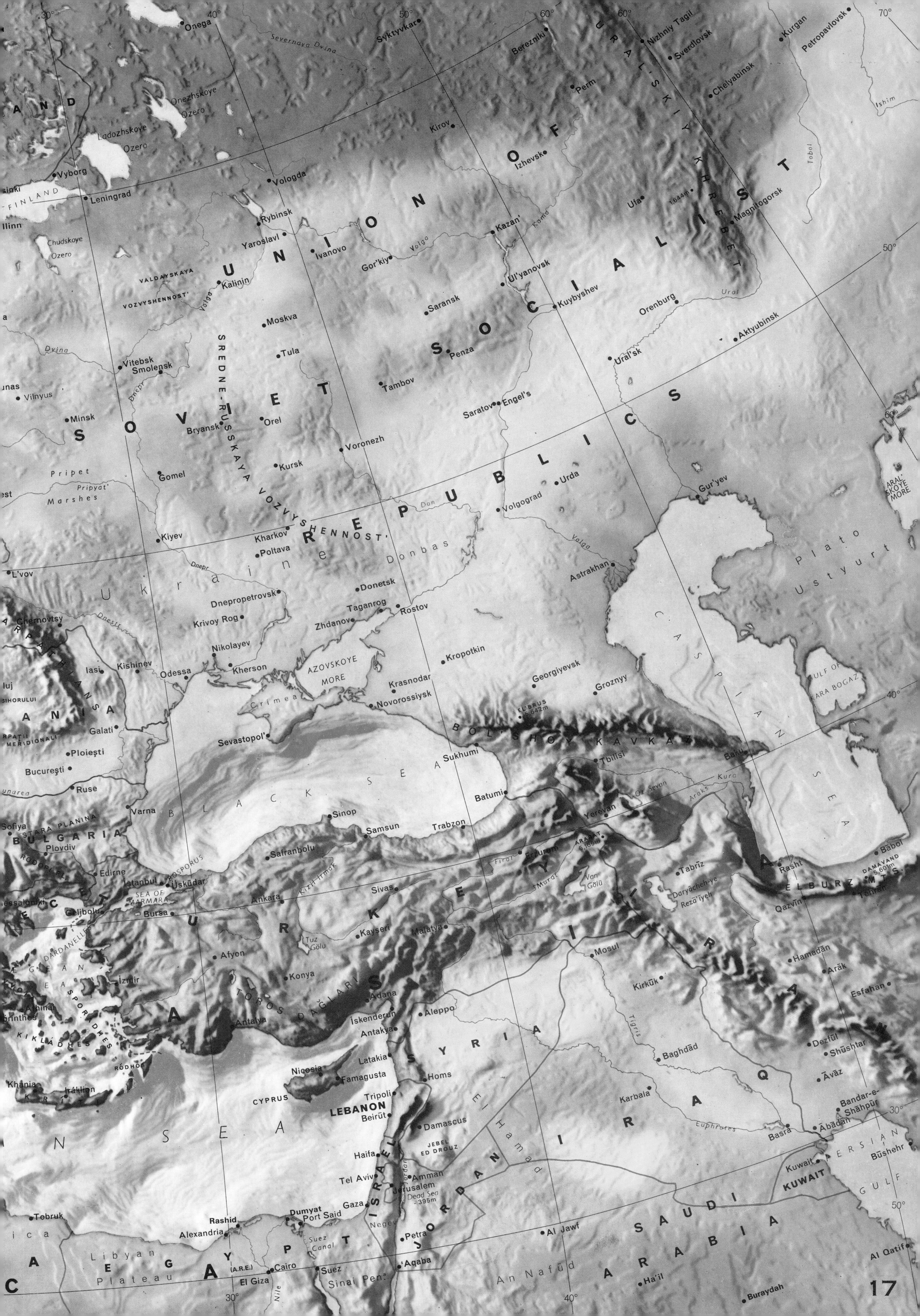

AND

Onega

Severnaya Dvina

Syktyvkar

Berezniki

Nizhniy Tagil

Sverdlovsk

Kurgan

Petropavlovsk

Ishim

Onezhskoye
Ozero

Ladozhskoye
Ozero

Vyborg

sinki

Leningrad

FINLAND

Ilinn

Chudskoye
Ozero

Vologda

Rybinsk

Kirov

Izhevsk

Perm

Ufa

Chelyabinsk

Magnitogorsk

Tobol

UNION OF

SOVIET SOCIALIST

REPUBLICS

Yaroslavl

Kalinin

VALDAYSKAYA
VOZVYSHENNOST'

Ivanovo

Volga

Kazan'

Kama

Ul'yanovsk

Kuybyshev

Orenburg

Ural'sk

Aktyubinsk

Ural

Moskva

Gor'kiy

Saransk

Penza

Vitebsk

Smolensk

Tula

Dvina

SREDNE-RUSSKAYA

Tambov

Saratov

Engel's

Urda

Gur'yev

ARAL'SKOYE MORE

Vilnyus

Minsk

Bryansk

Orel

Dnepr

Voronezh

Kursk

Don

Plato
Ustyurt

unas

Pripet

Pripyat'
Marshes

est

Gomel

Kiyev

Kharkov

Poltava

VOZVYSHENNOST'

SHENNOST'

RE

Donbas

Volgograd

Astrakhan

Volga

CASPIAN

L'vov

Ukraine

Dnepr

Dnestr

Dnepropetrovsk

Donetsk

Chernovtsy

Krivoy Rog

Nikolayev

Taganrog

Zhdanov

Rostov

Kropotkin

Georgiyevsk

Groznyy

CARP

CAR

Iasi

Kishinev

Odessa

Kherson

AZOVSKOYE
MORE

Krasnodar

ELBRUS
5642m

ANI

BIHORULUI

luj

Crimea

Novorossiysk

BOL'SHOY KAVKAZ

SEA

A

RPATII
MERIDIONALI

Galati

Sevastopol'

BLACK SEA

Sukhumi

Tbilisi

Kura

Ozero Sevan

Baku

GULF OF
KARA BOGAZ

Ploiesti

Bucuresti

Ruse

Varna

Batumi

Yerevan

Araks

unarea

Sofiya

STARA PLANINA

BULGARIA

Plovdiv

RODO

Edirne

Sinop

Samsun

Trabzon

Firat

Erzurum

ARARAT
5165m

Van
Gölü

Tabriz

Daryacheh-ye
Reza'iyeh

Rasht

Babol

DAMAVAND
5660m

ELBURZ MTS

essaloniki

Istanbul

Üsküdar

Safranbolu

Kizil Irmak

Sivas

Murat

Qazvin

AEGE

Gallipoli

SEA OF
MARMARA

Bursa

Ankara

TURKEY

Kayseri

Malatya

Mosul

Kirkük

Hamadan

Arak

Esfahan

DARDANELLES

GEAN

SEA

Izmir

SPORADHES

TOROS DAGLARI

Afyon

Konya

Tuz
Gölü

Adana

IRAN

Athina

KIKLADHES

Antalya

Iskenderun

Aleppo

Tigris

Dezful

Shushtar

rinthos

RÓDHOS

Latakia

Antakya

SYRIA

Baghdad

Avaz

Khania

Iráklion

CYPRUS

Nicosia

Famagusta

Homs

Karbala

IRAQ

Bandar-e
Shahpur

KR

LEBANON

Tripoli

Beirût

Damascus

JEBEL
ED DRÜZ

Hama

Euphrates

Basra

Abadan

PERSIAN

Haifa

Tel Aviv

Jerusalem

Dead Sea
-395m

Amman

JORDAN

Kuwait

KUWAIT

Bushehr

GULF

Tobruk

Rashid

Dumyat
Port Said

Gaza

Negev

Petra

ISRAEL

Al Jawf

SAUDI

Al Qatif

ica

Libyan
Plateau

Alexandria

El Giza

Suez
Canal

(A.R.E.)

Cairo

EGYPT

Suez

Nile

Sinai Pen.

'Aqaba

An Nafüd

ARABIA

Ha'il

Buraydah

17

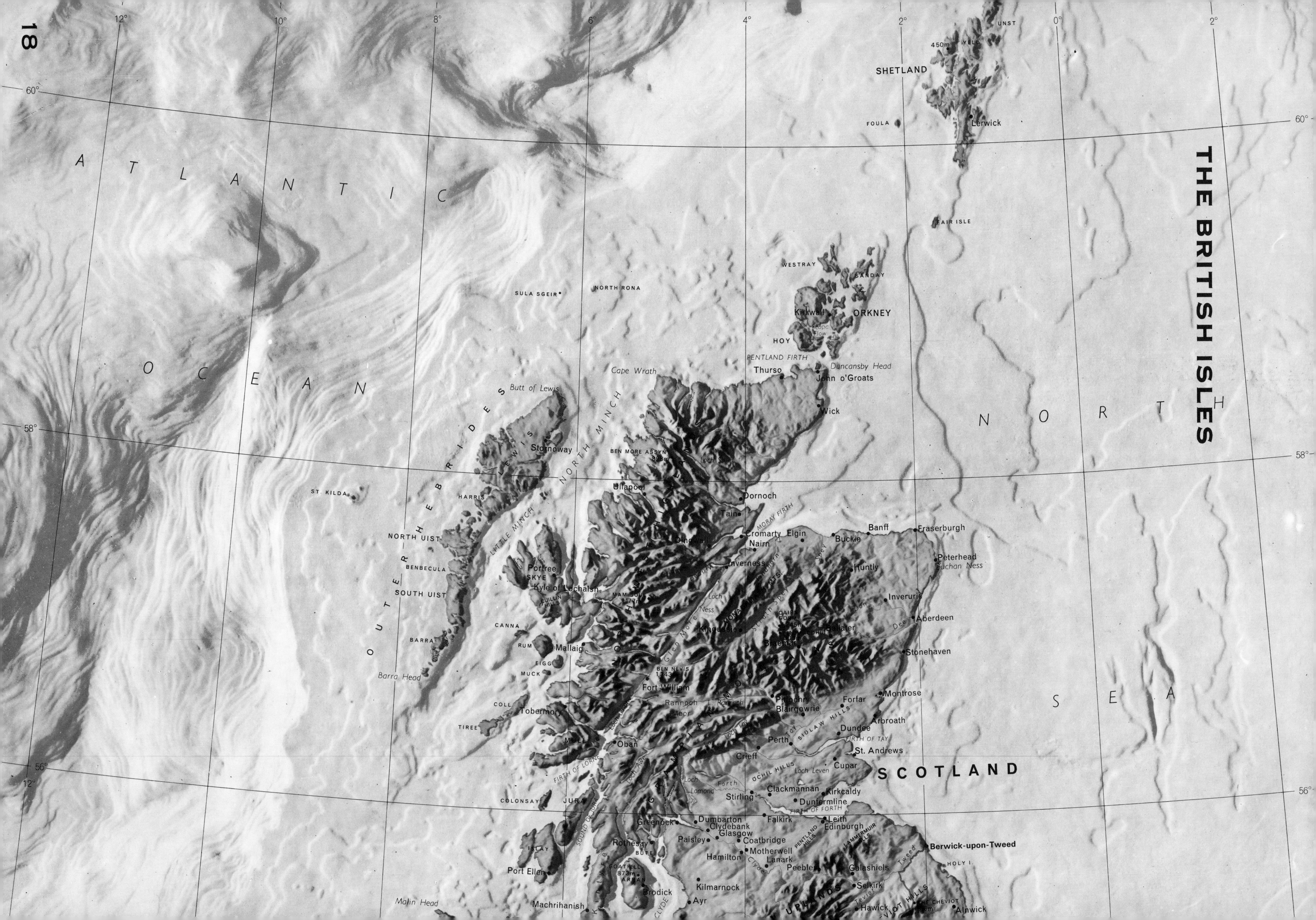

THE BRITISH ISLES

A T L A N T I C   O C E A N

N O R T H   S E A

S C O T L A N D

SHETLAND

UNST
MELLS
450m
Lerwick
FOULA
FAIR ISLE

ORKNEY
SKIDAY
WESTRAY
KIRKWALL
HOY
PENTLAND FIRTH
Duncansby Head
John o'Groats
Thurso
Wick

NORTH RONA

SULA SGEIR

ST KILDA

BUTT of LEWIS
Stornoway
Cape Wrath
BEN MORE ASYNT
3273ft
Ullapool
Dornoch
Cromarty
Nairn
Elgin
Inverness
Loch Ness

HARRIS
NORTH MINCH
LITTLE MINCH
O U T E R   H E B R I D E S
NORTH UIST
BENBECULA
SOUTH UIST
BARRA
Barra Head

Portree
SKYE
MALLAIG
CANNA
RUM
EIGG
MUCK
COLL
TIREE
Kyle of Lochalsh
Mallaig
Fort William
BEN NEVIS
Rannoch
Oban
Tobermory

Fraserburgh
Peterhead
Buchan Ness
Banff
Buckie
Aberdeen
Stonehaven
Huntly
Inverurie
Dee
Montrose
Arbroath
Forfar
Dundee
FIRTH OF TAY
St. Andrews
Cupar
Pitlochry
Blairgowrie
Perth
Crieff
SIDLAW HILLS
Kirkcaldy
Loch Leven
Dunfermline
Clackmannan
FIRTH OF FORTH
Leith
Edinburgh
Stirling
Falkirk
OCHIL HILLS
Dunbarton
Clydebank
Glasgow
Coatbridge
Motherwell
Hamilton
Lanark
Paisley
Greenock
Kilmarnock
Rothesay
BUTE
Brodick
Port Ellen
COLONSAY
JURA
ISLAY
Machrihanish
Malin Head

Berwick-upon-Tweed
HOLY I.
CHEVIOT
Tweed
Gelashiels
Selkirk
Peebles
Hawick
Alnwick
LAMMERMUIR
PENTLAND HILLS
Ayr

SOUND OF JURA
FIRTH OF LORN
SOUND OF MULL

60°   58°   56°

0°   2°   4°   6°   8°   10°   12°

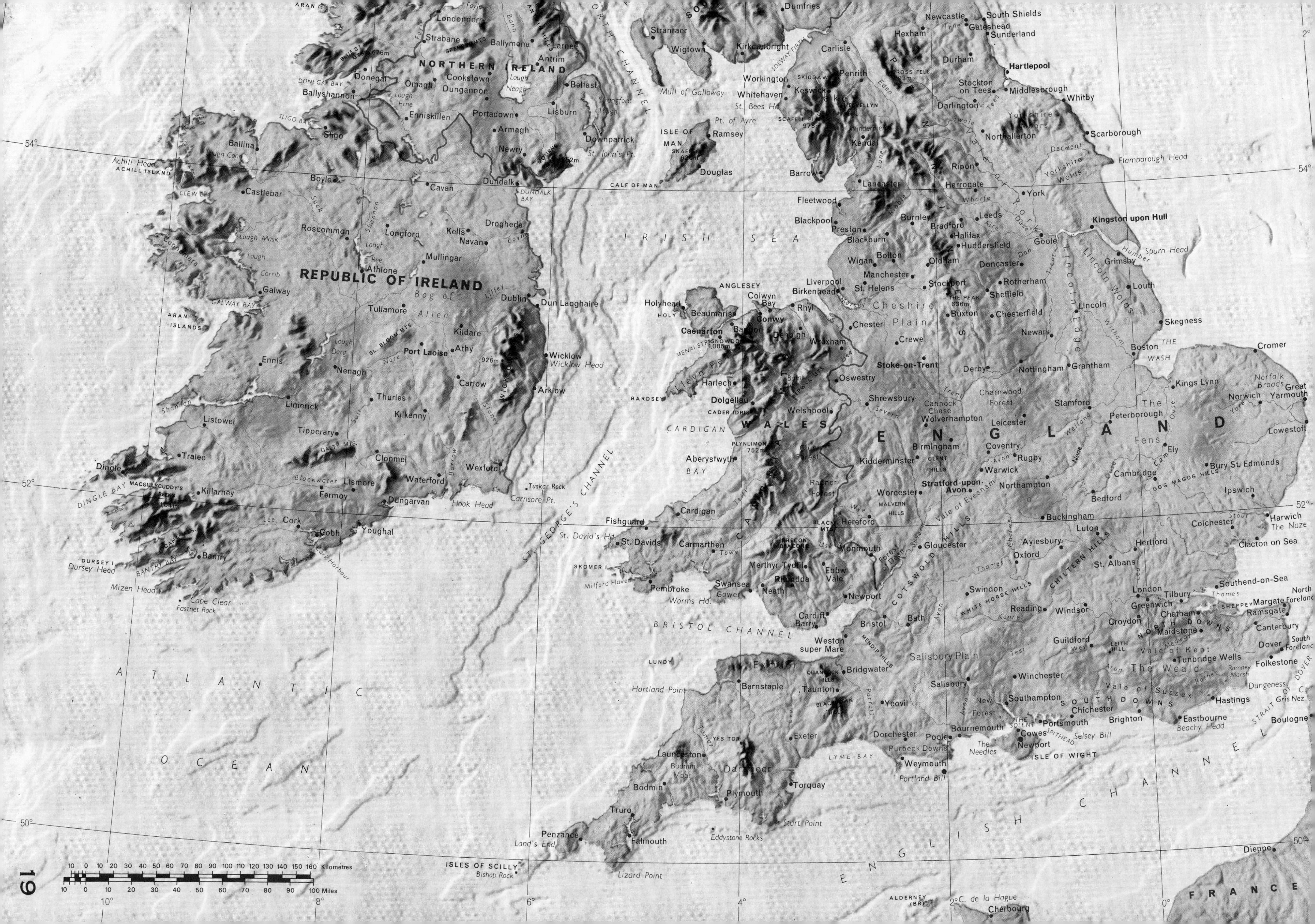
REPUBLIC OF IRELAND
NORTHERN IRELAND
ENGLAND
WALES
FRANCE
ATLANTIC OCEAN
IRISH SEA
NORTH CHANNEL
ST. GEORGE'S CHANNEL
BRISTOL CHANNEL
ENGLISH CHANNEL
STRAIT OF DOVER
CARDIGAN BAY
LYME BAY
THE WASH
Londonderry
Strabane
Ballymena
Larne
Antrim
Donegal
Omagh
Cookstown
Dungannon
Belfast
Ballyshannon
Enniskillen
Portadown
Lisburn
Armagh
Newry
Downpatrick
Sligo
Ballina
Castlebar
Boyle
Cavan
Dundalk
Drogheda
Roscommon
Longford
Kells
Navan
Mullingar
Athlone
Galway
Dublin
Dun Laoghaire
Tullamore
Kildare
Port Laoise
Athy
Wicklow
Wicklow Head
Ennis
Nenagh
Carlow
Arklow
Limerick
Thurles
Kilkenny
Listowel
Tipperary
Clonmel
Tralee
Wexford
Waterford
Dingle
Killarney
Lismore
Fermoy
Dungarvan
Cork
Cobh
Youghal
Bantry
Achill Head
ACHILL ISLAND
DONEGAL BAY
SLIGO BAY
CLEW BAY
GALWAY BAY
ARAN ISLANDS
DINGLE BAY
BANTRY BAY
DURSEY I.
Dursey Head
Mizen Head
Cape Clear
Fastnet Rock
Hook Head
Carnsore Pt.
Tuskar Rock
Bog of Allen
Lough Neagh
Lough Erne
Lough Mask
Lough Corrib
Lough Derg
Shannon
Dumfries
Stranraer
Wigtown
Kirkcudbright
Mull of Galloway
ISLE OF MAN
Ramsey
Douglas
CALF OF MAN
Pt. of Ayre
Carlisle
Workington
Whitehaven
St. Bees Hd.
Keswick
Penrith
Barrow
Kendal
Lancaster
Fleetwood
Blackpool
Preston
Blackburn
Burnley
Wigan
Bolton
Manchester
Oldham
Liverpool
Birkenhead
St. Helens
Stockport
Newcastle
South Shields
Gateshead
Sunderland
Hexham
Durham
Hartlepool
Stockton on Tees
Middlesbrough
Darlington
Whitby
Northallerton
Scarborough
Flamborough Head
Ripon
Harrogate
York
Leeds
Bradford
Halifax
Huddersfield
Goole
Kingston upon Hull
Spurn Head
Grimsby
Doncaster
Rotherham
Sheffield
Lincoln
Louth
Skegness
Boston
Chesterfield
Buxton
Newark
Nottingham
Grantham
Derby
Cheshire Plain
Chester
Crewe
Stoke-on-Trent
ANGLESEY
Holyhead
Beaumaris
Colwyn Bay
Conwy
Rhyl
Caernarton
Bangor
Denbigh
Wrexham
Harlech
Dolgellau
BARDSEY
Oswestry
Shrewsbury
Welshpool
Aberystwyth
PLYNLIMON 752m
Cardigan
Fishguard
St. Davids
St. David's Hd.
Carmarthen
SKOMER I.
Milford Haven
Pembroke
Swansea
Neath
Merthyr Tydfil
Rhondda
Ebbw Vale
Newport
Cardiff
Barry
Worms Hd.
Hereford
Monmouth
Kidderminster
Worcester
Birmingham
Wolverhampton
Coventry
Rugby
Warwick
Stratford-upon-Avon
Leicester
Stamford
Peterborough
Kings Lynn
Norwich
Great Yarmouth
Lowestoft
Cromer
Fens
Ely
Cambridge
Bury St. Edmunds
Ipswich
Bedford
Northampton
Buckingham
Luton
Colchester
Harwich
The Naze
Clacton on Sea
Gloucester
Cotswold Hills
Chiltern Hills
Aylesbury
Oxford
Hertford
St. Albans
Swindon
Reading
Windsor
London
Tilbury
Greenwich
Southend-on-Sea
Chatham
Croydon
Margate
Ramsgate
Canterbury
Dover
Folkestone
Maidstone
Tunbridge Wells
Guildford
North Downs
South Downs
The Weald
Hastings
Eastbourne
Beachy Head
Brighton
Chichester
Portsmouth
Southampton
Winchester
Salisbury Plain
Salisbury
Bath
Bristol
Weston super Mare
Bridgwater
Taunton
Yeovil
Dorchester
Weymouth
Portland Bill
Poole
Bournemouth
Cowes
Newport
ISLE OF WIGHT
The Needles
Selsey Bill
LUNDY
Hartland Point
Barnstaple
Exeter
Torquay
Plymouth
Dartmoor
Launceston
Bodmin Moor
Bodmin
Truro
Falmouth
Penzance
Land's End
Lizard Point
Start Point
Eddystone Rocks
ISLES OF SCILLY
Bishop Rock
ALDERNEY
C. de la Hague
Cherbourg
Dieppe
Boulogne
Gris Nez
Dungeness
Kilometres
Miles

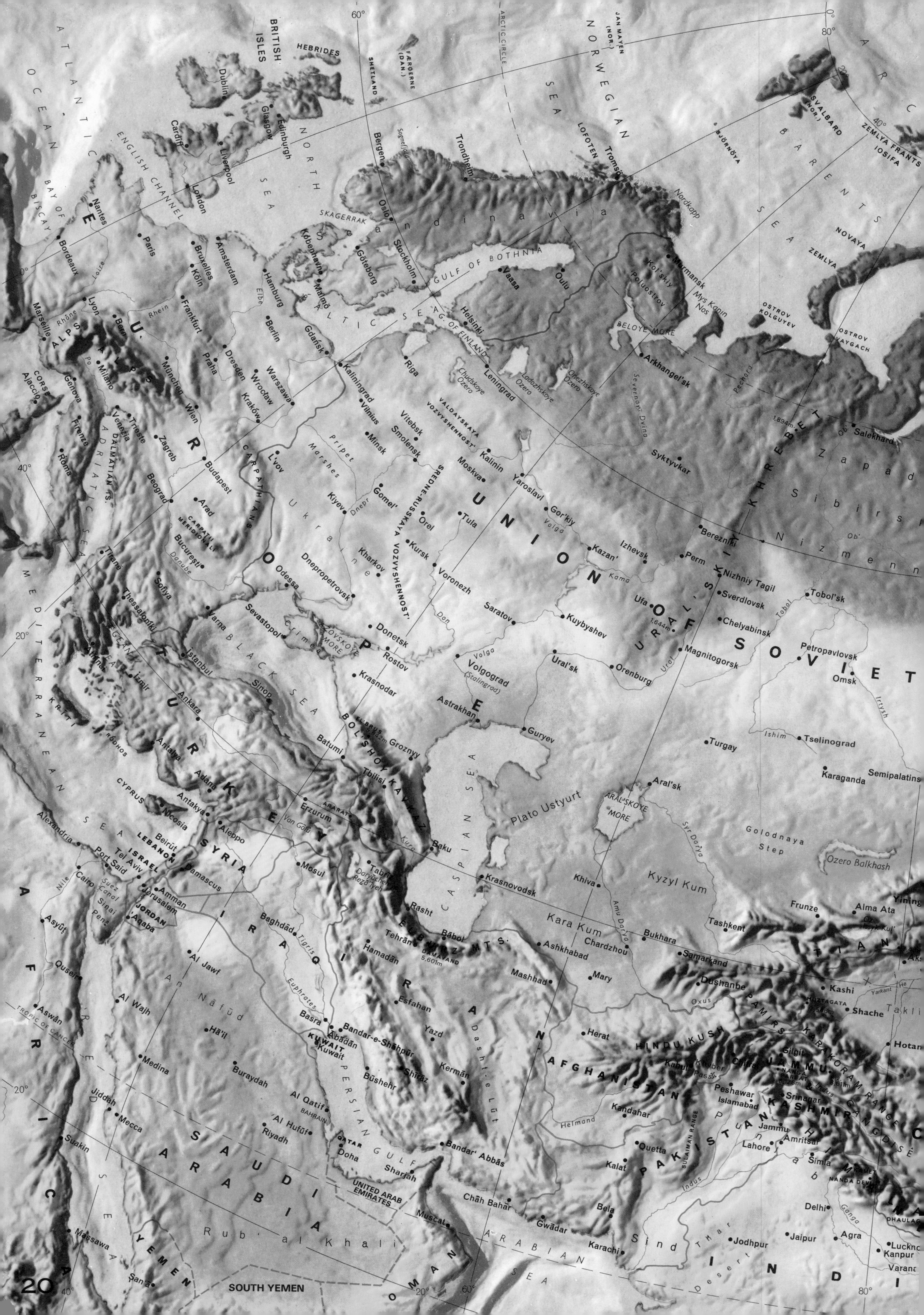

BRITISH ISLES
HEBRIDES
FÆRØERNE (DAN.)
SHETLAND
JAN MAYEN (NOR.)
ARCTIC CIRCLE
NORWEGIAN SEA
ATLANTIC OCEAN
Dublin
Glasgow
Edinburgh
Cardiff
Liverpool
London
ENGLISH CHANNEL
NORTH SEA
BAY OF BISCAY
Nantes
Bordeaux
Paris
Loire
Bergen
Trondheim
LOFOTEN
Tromsø
BJØRNØYA
SVALBARD (NOR.)
ZEMLYA FRANTSA IOSIFA
BARENTS SEA
Nordkapp
NOVAYA ZEMLYA
SKAGERRAK
Oslo
Stockholm
Göteborg
København
Malmö
Bruxelles
Amsterdam
Köln
Hamburg
Elbe
Rhein
Frankfurt
Berlin
GULF OF BOTHNIA
Vaasa
Oulu
Murmansk
Kol'skiy Poluostrov
Mys Kanin Nos
OSTROV KOLGUYEV
OSTROV VAYGACH
BELOYE MORE
BALTIC SEA
GULF OF FINLAND
Helsinki
Leningrad
Gdańsk
Lyon
Rhône
Marseille
Bern
ALPS
Po
Milano
Genova
CORSE
Ajaccio
München
Praha
Dresden
Wrocław
Warszawa
Kraków
Wien
Kaliningrad
Vilnius
Riga
Chudskoye Ozero
Ladozhskoye Ozero
Onezhskoye Ozero
Severnaya Dvina
Arkhangel'sk
Pechora
Venezia
Trieste
Firenze
Roma
ADRIATIC SEA
DALMATIAN IS.
Zagreb
Budapest
CARPATHIANS
L'vov
Pripet Marshes
Minsk
Vitebsk
Smolensk
VALDAYSKAYA VOZVYSHENNOST'
Kalinin
Moskva
Yaroslavl
Syktyvkar
Salekhard
Ob'
Zapadno Sibirskaya Nizmennost'
Beograd
Arad
CARPAŢII MERIDIONALI
Bucureşti
Danube
Kiyev
Dnepr
Gomel'
Orel
Tula
SREDNE-RUSSKAYA VOZVYSHENNOST'
Ukraine
Kursk
Kharkov
Gor'kiy
Volga
Kazan'
Izhevsk
Perm
Berezniki
Kama
Nizhniy Tagil
Sverdlovsk
Ufa
Chelyabinsk
Tobol'sk
Tobol
URAL'SKIY KHREBET
Tirane
Sofiya
Thessaloníki
Odessa
Dnepropetrovsk
Voronezh
Saratov
Kuybyshev
Magnitogorsk
Petropavlovsk
Omsk
Irtysh
UNION OF SOVIET
Varna
BLACK SEA
Sevastopol
Crimea
AZOVSKOYE MORE
Donetsk
Rostov
Don
Volgograd (Stalingrad)
Ural'sk
Orenburg
Ural
İstanbul
AEGEAN SEA
Athínai
İzmir
Ankara
Sinop
Krasnodar
Astrakhan
Guryev
Turgay
Ishim
Tselinograd
KRITI
RÓDHOS
Antalya
TURKEY
Adana
ELBRUS
Batumi
Groznyy
BOL'SHOY KAVKAZ
Tbilisi
CASPIAN SEA
Aral'sk
ARAL'SKOYE MORE
Plato Ustyurt
Karaganda
Semipalatinsk
MEDITERRANEAN SEA
CYPRUS
Nicosia
Antakya
Aleppo
Erzurum
ARARAT
Van Gölü
Kura
Baku
Syr Dar'ya
Golodnaya Step
Ozero Balkhash
Alexandria
Beirūt
LEBANON
ISRAEL
Tel Aviv
Port Said
SYRIA
Damascus
Mosul
Tabrīz
Daryācheh-ye Rezā'iyeh
Krasnovodsk
Khiva
Kyzyl Kum
Cairo
Nile
Suez Canal
Sinai Pen.
Amman
Jerusalem
JORDAN
'Aqaba
Rasht
Kara Kum
Amu Dar'ya
Tashkent
Frunze
Alma Ata
Yining
Asyūt
Baghdād
Tigris
IRAQ
Tehrān
Bābol
ELBURZ MTS.
DAMAVAND 5,601m
Ashkhabad
Chardzhou
Bukhara
Samarkand
Quseir
Al Jawf
Hamadān
Mashhad
Mary
Dushanbe
Kashi
TIAN SHAN
Aswān
TROPIC OF CANCER
Al Wajh
An Nafūd
Euphrates
Esfahan
IRAN
Oxus
PAMIRS
MUSTAGATA
Shache
Yarkant He
Ha'il
Basra
Bandar-e-Shahpūr
Abādān
KUWAIT
Kuwait
Yazd
Herat
HINDU KUSH
KARAKORAM RANGE
Hotan
Medina
Buraydah
PERSIAN GULF
Būshehr
Shīrāz
Kermān
Dasht-e Lūt
AFGHANISTAN
Kabul
Khyber Pass
Gilgit
JAMMU
Peshawar
Islamabad
Srinagar
KASHMIR
Jiddah
Mecca
Al Qatif
BAHRAIN
Al Hufūf
Riyadh
Helmand
Kandahar
SULAIMAN RANGE
Jammu
Amritsar
Lahore
Simla
Suakin
RED SEA
SAUDI ARABIA
QATAR
Doha
Sharjah
Bandar' Abbās
Quetta
PAKISTAN
Kalat
Indus
Punjab
NANDA DEVI
UNITED ARAB EMIRATES
Chāh Bahār
Bela
Delhi
Ganga
Agra
Lucknow
Kanpur
DHAULAGIRI
Rub' al Khali
Muscat
Gwādar
Karachi
Sind
Thar Desert
Jodhpur
Jaipur
Varanasi
Massawa
YEMEN
Şan'ā
SOUTH YEMEN
OMAN
ARABIAN SEA
INDIA
AFRICA
EUROPE

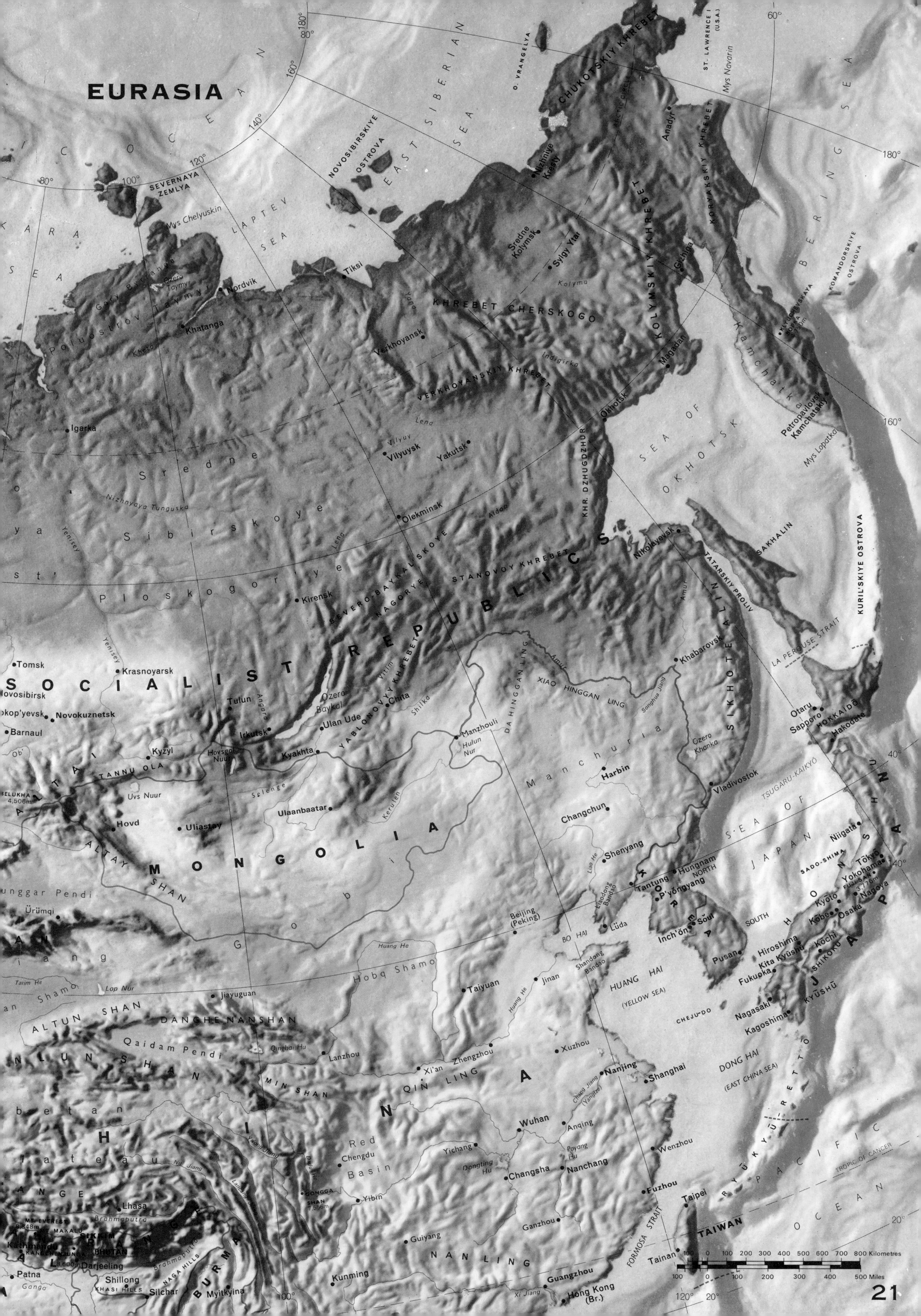

EURASIA

KARA SEA

SEVERNAYA ZEMLYA

Gory Byrranga
Ozero Taymyr
Poluostrov Taymyr
Mys Chelyuskin

LAPTEV SEA

EAST SIBERIAN SEA

NOVOSIBIRSKIYE OSTROVA

O. VRANGELYA

CHUKOTSKIY KHREBET

Mys Navarin

ST. LAWRENCE I. (U.S.A.)

BERING SEA

Igarka

Tiksi

Nordvik

Khatanga

Kheta

Verkhoyansk

Vilyuy

Vilyuysk

Yakutsk

Srednekolymsk

Sylgy Ytar

Kolyma

Indigirka

Nizhneye Kresty

Anadyr

KORYAKSKIY KHREBET

KOLYMSKIY KHREBET

KHREBET CHERSKOGO

VERKHOYANSKIY KHREBET

Lena

Olekminsk

Aldan

Okhotsk

KHR. DZHUGDZHUR

Kamchatka

Petropavlovsk-Kamchatskiy

Mys Lopatka

KOMANDORSKIYE OSTROVA

SEA OF OKHOTSK

Tomsk

Krasnoyarsk

Novosibirsk

Prokop'yevsk

Novokuznetsk

Barnaul

Ob'

BELUKHA 4,506m

ALTAY

TANNU OLA

Kyzyl

Uvs Nuur

Hovd

Yenisey

Tulun

Angara

Ozero Baykal

Ulan Ude

Irkutsk

Kyakhta

Selenge

Hovsgol Nuur

Uliastay

Ulaanbaatar

Nizhnyaya Tunguska

Srednesibirskoye Ploskogor'ye

Kirensk

SEVERO-BAYKAL'SKOYE NAGORYE

Chita

Shilka

YABLONOVYY KHREBET

Vitim

STANOVOY KHREBET

SOCIALIST REPUBLICS

Manzhouli

Hulun Nur

Kerulen

MONGOLIA

Gobi

DA HINGGAN LING

XIAO HINGGAN LING

Amur

Songhua Jiang

Harbin

Manchuria

Changchun

Shenyang

Liao He

Khabarovsk

Ozero Khanka

Vladivostok

Nikolayevsk

SAKHALIN

TATARSKIY PROLIV

SIKHOTE ALIN

Amur

KURIL'SKIYE OSTROVA

LA PEROUSE STRAIT

Otaru

Sapporo

Hakodate

HOKKAIDO

TSUGARU-KAIKYO

SEA OF JAPAN

Niigata

SADO-SHIMA

HONSHU

Tokyo

Yokohama

Fuji-san 3,776m

Nagoya

Kyoto

Kobe

Osaka

Hangzhou

Uliastay

Beijing (Peking)

Huang He

Hobq Shamo

Lüda

BO HAI

Tianjin

P'yongyang

Hungnam

NORTH KOREA

Tantung

Liaodong Bandao

Inch'on

Seoul

SOUTH KOREA

Pusan

CHEJU-DO

Fukuoka

Kita Kyushu

Nagasaki

Kagoshima

KYUSHU

SHIKOKU

Kochi

Hiroshima

JAPAN

Ürümqi

Dzungar Pendi

Taklimakan Shamo

Tarim He

Lop Nur

Jiayuguan

ALTUN SHAN

DANGHE NANSHAN

Qaidam Pendi

KUNLUN SHAN

Qinghai Hu

Lanzhou

MIN SHAN

Huang He

Taiyuan

Jinan

Shandong Bandao

HUANG HAI (YELLOW SEA)

Xi'an

Zhengzhou

Xuzhou

QIN LING

CHINA

Nanjing

Shanghai

DONG HAI (EAST CHINA SEA)

RYUKYU RETTO

Tibetan Plateau

Red Basin

Chengdu

Yibin

GONGGA SHAN 7,556m

Wuhan

Chang Jiang (Yangtze)

Anqing

Yichang

Dongting Hu

Changsha

Poyang Hu

Nanchang

Wenzhou

Fuzhou

Taipei

Fuzhou

TROPIC OF CANCER

PACIFIC OCEAN

Mt. Everest 8,848m

MAKALU

Kanchenjunga

Lhasa

Brahmaputra

HIMALAYA RANGE

SIKKIM

BHUTAN

Darjeeling

Patna

Ganga

Shillong

NAGA HILLS

KHASI HILLS

Silchar

BURMA

Myitkyina

Guiyang

Kunming

NANLING

Guangzhou

Ganzhou

Hong Kong (Br.)

Xi Jiang

Nu Jiang

Lancang Jiang

Salween

FORMOSA STRAIT

Tainan

TAIWAN

0 100 200 300 400 500 600 700 800 Kilometres

0 100 200 300 400 500 Miles

120°

20°

21

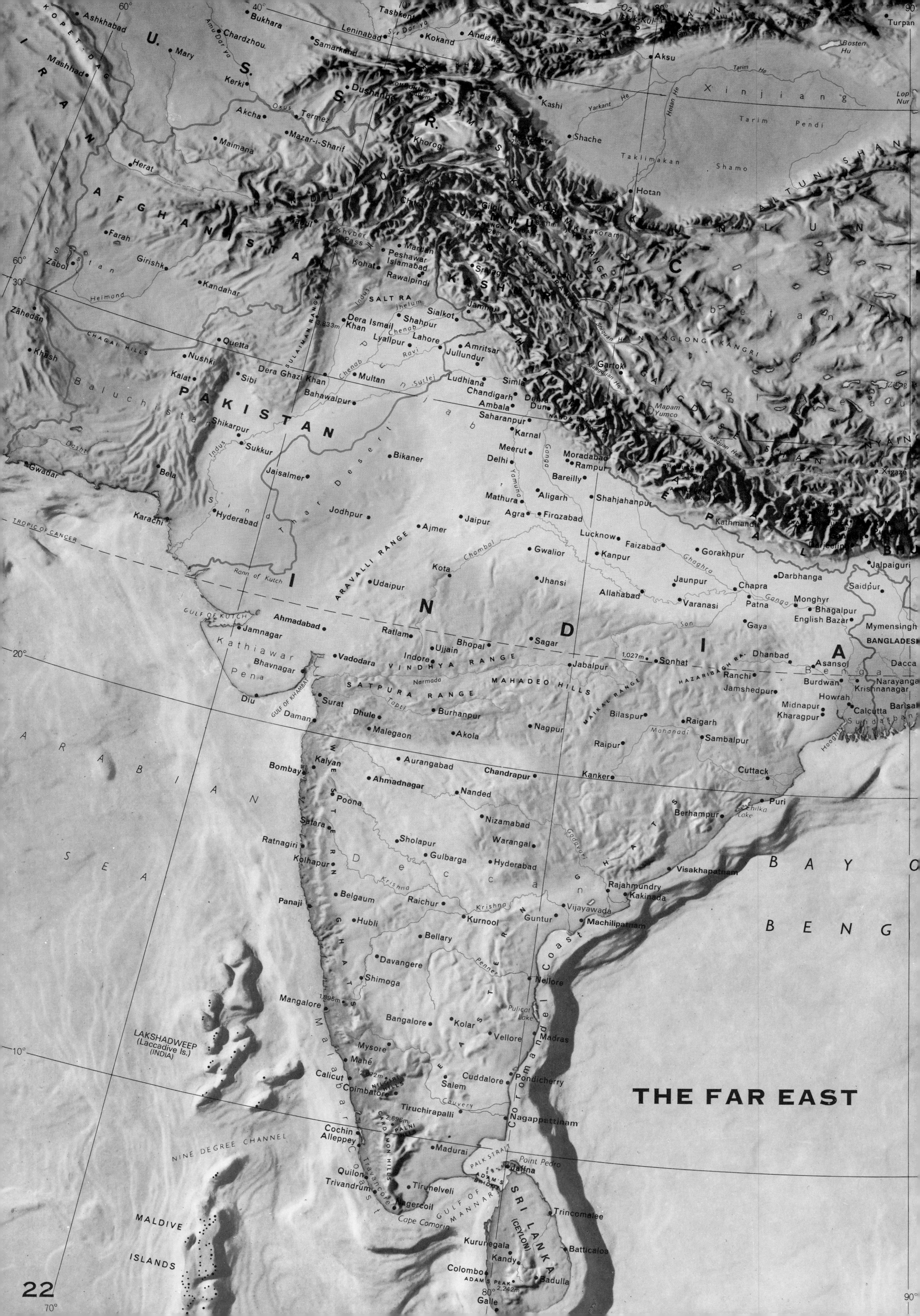
THE FAR EAST
U. S. S. R.
IRAN
AFGHANISTAN
PAKISTAN
INDIA
NEPAL
SRI LANKA
(CEYLON)
BANGLADESH
Xinjiang
Tarim Pendi
Taklimakan
Shamo
ALTUN SHAN
KUNLUN
HINDU KUSH
KASHMIR
KOPET-DAG
Ashkhabad
Mashhad
Mary
Bukhara
Chardzhou
Kerki
Samarkand
Tashkent
Leninabad
Kokand
Andizhan
Aksu
Turpan
Bosten Hu
Lop Nur
Tarim He
Kashi
Yarkant He
Hotan He
Shache
Hotan
Dushanbe
Termez
Akcha
Oxus
Mazar-i-Sharif
Maimana
Khorog
Herat
Farah
Zabol
Girishk
Kandahar
Helmond
Zahedan
Khash
CHAGAI HILLS
Quetta
Nushki
Kalat
Sibi
Baluchistan
Dasht
Gwadar
Bela
Karachi
Hyderabad
Sind
Shikarpur
Sukkur
Indus
Kabul
Khyber Pass
Chitral
Gilgit
Mardan
Peshawar
Islamabad
Kohat
Rawalpindi
SALT RA.
Jhelum
SULAIMAN RANGE
3,333m
Dera Ismail Khan
Shahpur
Chenab
Lyallpur
Lahore
Sialkot
Jammu
Srinagar
Karakoram
KARAKORAM RANGE
Amritsar
Jullundur
Ravi
Sutlej
Dera Ghazi Khan
Multan
Bahawalpur
Ludhiana
Simla
Chandigarh
Ambala
Dehra Dun
Saharanpur
Karnal
Meerut
Delhi
Moradabad
Rampur
Bareilly
Ganga
Yamuna
Mathura
Aligarh
Agra
Firozabad
Shahjahanpur
Bikaner
Jaisalmer
Thar Desert
Jodhpur
Jaipur
Ajmer
ARAVALLI RANGE
Rann of Kutch
GULF OF KUTCH
Udaipur
Kota
Chambal
Gwalior
Jhansi
Lucknow
Faizabad
Gorakhpur
Kanpur
Ghaghra
Kathmandu
Darjeeling
Jalpaiguri
Darbhanga
Saidpur
Jaunpur
Allahabad
Varanasi
Chapra
Patna
Monghyr
Bhagalpur
English Bazar
Mymensingh
Gaya
Son
Gartok
NYAINQENTANGLHA
GANGDISE SHAN
Mapam Yumco
Xigaze
TROPIC OF CANCER
Ahmadabad
Jamnagar
Kathiawar Pen.
Bhavnagar
Diu
GULF OF KHAMBAT
Vadodara
Ratlam
Ujjain
Indore
Bhopal
Sagar
VINDHYA RANGE
1,027m
Sonhat
Jabalpur
HAZARIBAGH RA.
Dhanbad
Asansol
Bengal
Dacca
Narayanganj
Burdwan
Krishnanagar
Howrah
Calcutta
Barisal
Sundarbans
Hooghly
Ranchi
Jamshedpur
Midnapur
Kharagpur
SATPURA RANGE
MAHADEO HILLS
MAIKAL RANGE
Narmada
Tapti
Surat
Daman
Dhule
Burhanpur
Malegaon
Akola
Nagpur
Bilaspur
Raigarh
Sambalpur
Mahanadi
Raipur
Bombay
Kalyan
Aurangabad
Chandrapur
Kanker
Cuttack
Puri
Chilka Lake
Berhampur
Ahmadnagar
Nanded
Poona
Nizamabad
Satara
Ratnagiri
Kolhapur
Sholapur
Gulbarga
Warangal
Hyderabad
Godavari
Deccan
EASTERN GHATS
WESTERN GHATS
Visakhapatnam
Rajahmundry
Kakinada
Krishna
Belgaum
Raichur
Panaji
Vijayawada
Guntur
Machilipatnam
Kurnool
Hubli
Bellary
Davangere
Penner
Shimoga
Nellore
1,895m
Mangalore
Bangalore
Kolar
Pulicat Lake
Vellore
Madras
Mysore
Mahé
Calicut
Coimbatore
NILGIRI HILLS
Salem
Cuddalore
Pondicherry
Cauvery
Tiruchirapalli
Nagappettinam
Malabar Coast
Coromandel Coast
Cochin
Alleppey
2,695m
PALNI
CARDAMON HILLS
Madurai
PALK STRAIT
Point Pedro
Jaffna
Quilon
Trivandrum
Travancore Coast
Tirunelveli
ADAM'S BRIDGE
Nagercoil
Cape Comorin
GULF OF MANNAR
Trincomalee
Kurunegala
Batticaloa
Kandy
Colombo
ADAM'S PEAK
2,242m
Badulla
Galle
ARABIAN SEA
LAKSHADWEEP
(Laccadive Is.)
(INDIA)
NINE DEGREE CHANNEL
MALDIVE ISLANDS
BAY OF BENGAL
60°
40°
80°
90°
30°
20°
10°
70°

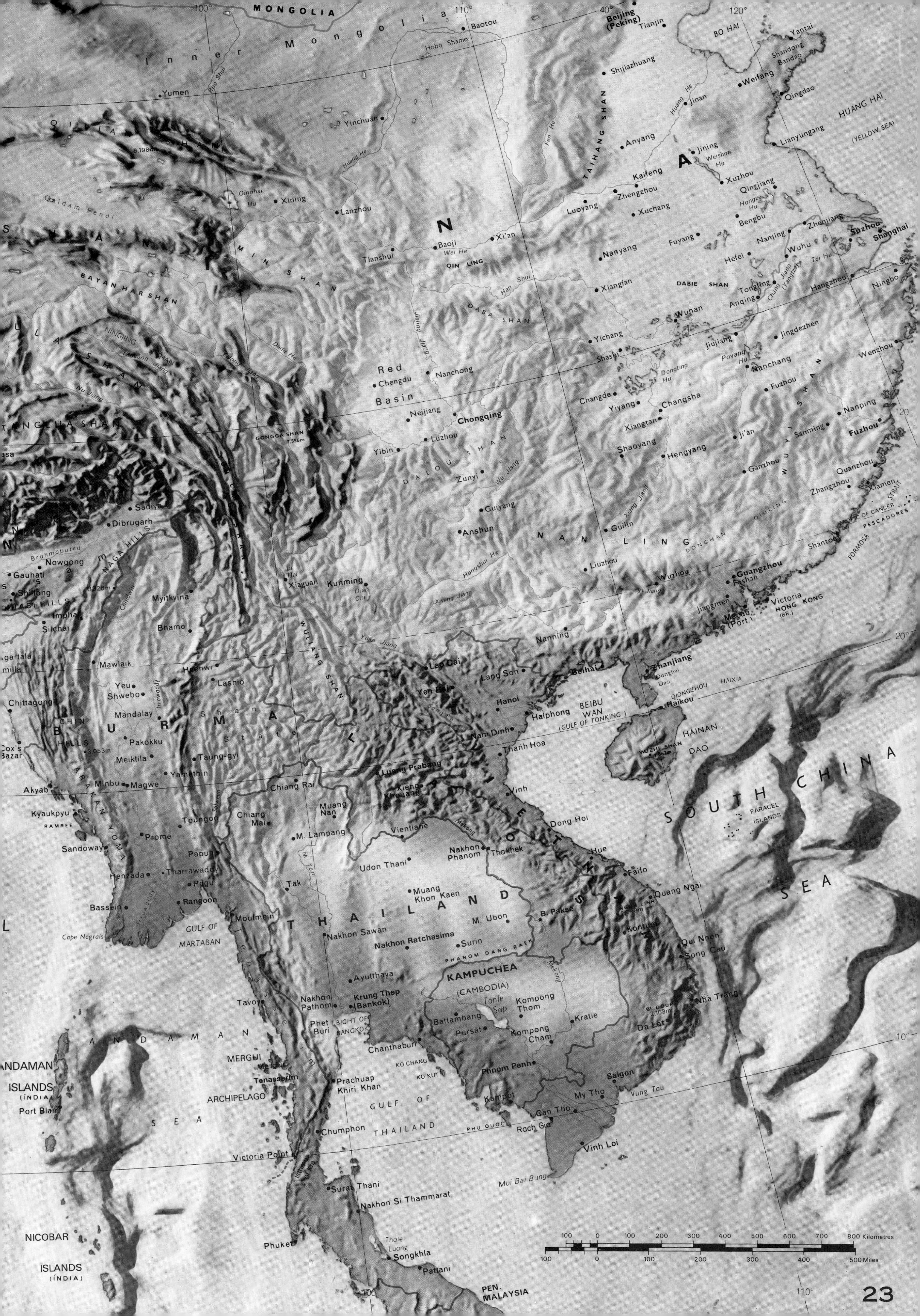

MONGOLIA

Inner Mongolia

100°   110°   40° Beijing
                                                              (Peking)   Tianjin   120°
                                                                                      BO HAI   Yantai
• Yumen   Hobq Shamo   Baotou   Shijiazhuang   Shandong
                                                                                                   Bandao
         Rjao Shui   Huang He • Jinan   Weifang
              • Yinchuan   Anyang   Jining   Qingdao
  8,198m   Huang He   Weishan   Lianyungang   HUANG HAI
                                                N   Kaifeng Zhengzhou   Hu   Xuzhou   Qingjiang   (YELLOW SEA)
     • Xining   Lanzhou   Zhengzhou   Hongze
                                                      Luoyang   Xuchang   Hu   Bengbu
                                                                       Nanyang   Fuyang   Nanjing   Zhenjiang
  Qinghai   • Baoji • Xi'an   Hefei   Wuhu Tai Hu Suzhou Shanghai
  Hu   • Tianshui Wei He   Xiangfan   DABIE SHAN   Tongling Jiang (Yangtze) Hangzhou
Caidam Pendi   QIN LING   Wuhan Anqing   Ningbo
                                                              DABA SHAN   Yichang   Jiujiang   Jingdezhen
BAYAN HAR SHAN   Dongting   Poyang Nanchang
                                        Red   Changde   Hu   Hu   Fuzhou   Wenzhou
NINGJING SHAN   Basin   Nanchong   Yiyang Changsha
                                  • Chengdu   Xiangtan   Ji'an   Nanping
           GONGGA SHAN   Neijiang   Chongqing   Shaoyang Hengyang   Sanming Fuzhou
           7,556m   Ganzhou
                      Yibin • Luzhou   DALOU SHAN   Wu Jiang   Zhangzhou Quanzhou
                                        Zunyi   Xiang Jiang   Xiamen
                                                                                                    TROPIC OF CANCER
                               • Guiyang   N A N   L I N G   DONGNAN   Shantou   PESCADORES
TANGLHA SHAN   QIUTING SHAN FORMOSA STRAIT
                         • Anshun   Hongshui He   Guilin
• Sadiya   Liuzhou   Wuzhou Guangzhou
• Dibrugarh   NAGA HILLS   Xi Jiang Wuzhou Foshan   Victoria HONG KONG
Nowgong   Hai   Jiangmen Macao (BR.)
Gauhati 3,826m Myitkyina   • Xiaguan Kunming Dian   (Port.)
Shillong   Chi   20°
KHASI HILLS   Yuan Jiang   Nanning
Silchar • Bhamo   WULIANG SHAN   Beihai Zhanjiang
Imphal   Lao Cai   Donghai
                                              Yen Bai   Lang Son   Beihai Dao Haikou
gartala   • Mawlaik   Hsenwi   Hanoi   QIONGZHOU HAIXIA
milla   Yeu   • Lashio   Haiphong   BEIBU   WUZHI SHAN HAINAN
Chittagong Shwebo   Nam Dinh   WAN (GULF OF   DAO
          Mandalay Taung-gyi   Thanh Hoa TONKING)
CHIN BURMA   SOUTH CHINA
HILLS   Pakokku   State   Vinh   PARACEL
Cox's 3,053m Meiktila   Xieng   Luang Prabang   ISLANDS
Bazar   Minbu Magwe Yamethin   Khouang   Dong Hoi
Akyab   Chiang Rai   Hue
ARAKAN YOMA   Chiang   M. Nan   Faifo
RAMREE   Prome   Mai   Vientiane   Thakhek   Quang Ngai   SEA
Kyaukpyu   Papun   M. Lampang   Nakhon   Konium
Sandoway   Henzada Tharrawaddy   Phanom Thakhek
        Pegu   Tak   Muang   Qui Nhon
Bassein   Rangoon   Khon Kaen   M. Ubon   Song Cau
Cape Negrais GULF OF   T H A I L A N D   Nakhon Sawan   Nha Trang
         MARTABAN   Nakhon Ratchasima Surin   B. Pakse
                                        PHANOM DANG RAEK   Da Lat   2,163m
                              Ayutthaya   KAMPUCHEA   Nha Trang
ANDAMAN   Tavoy   Nakhon   Krung Thep   (CAMBODIA)   Tonle   Kompong
ISLANDS   Pathom   (Bankok)   Sap   Thom
(INDIA)   MERGUI   Phet   BIGHT OF   Battambang   Kratie
Port Blair   Buri   BANGKOK   Chanthaburi   Pursat Kompong   Saigon
                                                         Cham
      ARCHIPELAGO Prachuap   KO CHANG   Phnom Penh   My Tho
            Tenasserim Khiri Khan   Vung Tau
                                   KO KUT   GULF OF   Kampot   Can Tho
NICOBAR   Chumphon   THAILAND PHU QUOC   Rach Gia
                                                         Vinh Loi
ISLANDS   Victoria Point   Mui Bai Bung
(INDIA)
         Surat Thani
         Nakhon Si Thammarat
Phuket   Thale
         Luang Songkhla
                Pattani
PEN.
MALAYSIA   100°   110°

100 0 100 200 300 400 500 600 700 800 Kilometres
100 0   100   200   300   400 500 Miles

23

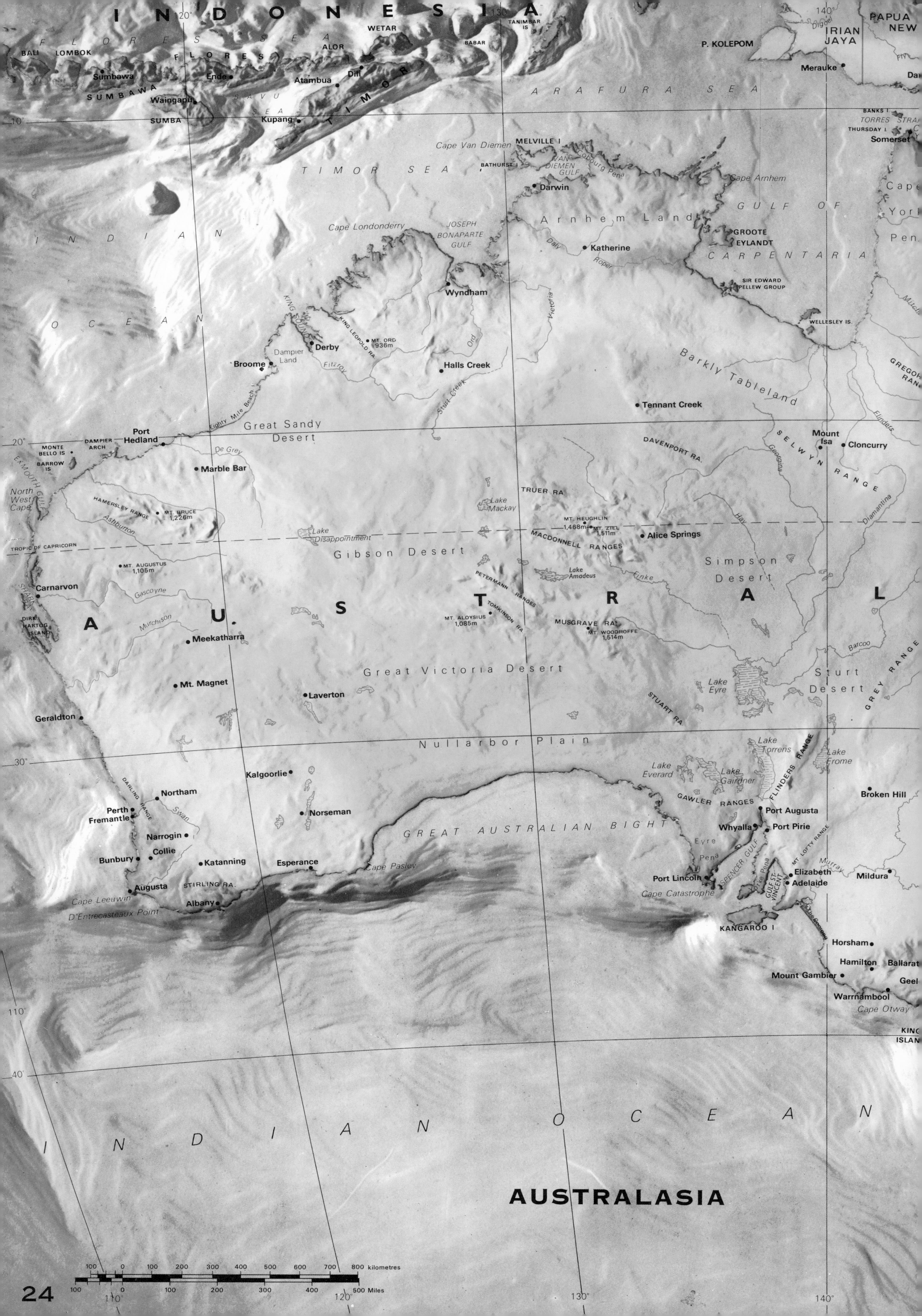

INDONESIA

FLORES SEA

BALI LOMBOK FLORES ALOR WETAR BABAR TANIMBAR IS. P. KOLEPOM IRIAN JAYA PAPUA NEW

Sumbawa Ende Atambua Dili Merauke Dar

SUMBAWA Waingapu SUMBA Kupang TIMOR

JAVA SEA

ARAFURA SEA

BANKS I.
TORRES STRA
THURSDAY I.
Somerset

TIMOR SEA

Cape Van Diemen MELVILLE I.
BATHURST I. VAN
DIEMEN
GULF Coburg Pena. Cape Arnhem
GULF OF
Darwin Arnhem Land Cape Yor
GROOTE
Cape Londonderry JOSEPH
BONAPARTE
GULF Katherine EYLANDT Pen
Daly Roper CARPENTARIA SIR EDWARD
PELLEW GROUP

INDIAN

Wyndham Victoria Ord WELLESLEY IS.

KING SOUND MT. ORD
936m Stuart Creek Barkly Tableland GREGOR
RAN.
Derby KING LEOPOLD RA.
OCEAN Dampier Halls Creek
Land Fitzroy
Broome Tennant Creek

Eighty Mile Beach Great Sandy DAVENPORT RA. SELWYN RANGE Mount
Desert Isa Cloncurry
Port De Grey Georgina Flinders
Hedland
MONTE DAMPIER
BELLO IS. ARCH. Marble Bar
BARROW
IS. TRUER RA.
North HAMERSLEY RANGE Lake Diamantina
West MT. BRUCE Mackay MT. HEUGHLIN
Cape Ashburton 1,226m Lake 1,468m MT. ZIEL Alice Springs
TROPIC OF CAPRICORN Disappointment 1,511m
MACDONNELL RANGES Simpson
MT. AUGUSTUS Gibson Desert Desert
Carnarvon 1,105m Lake
Gascoyne A U S T Amadeus Finke R A L
DIRK Murchison PETERMANN RANGES Barcoo
HARTOG Meekatharra TOMKINSON RA. MUSGRAVE RA. Sturt
ISLAND MT. ALOYSIUS MT. WOODROFFE Lake
A 1,085m 1,514m Eyre Desert GREY RANGE
Mt. Magnet Great Victoria Desert
Laverton
Geraldton STUART RA.
Nullarbor Plain Lake
Torrens FLINDERS RANGE Lake
Lake Frome
Kalgoorlie Everard Lake Broken Hill
Northam Gairdner GAWLER RANGES Port Augusta
Perth Swan Norseman Whyalla Port Pirie
Fremantle DARLING RANGE GREAT AUSTRALIAN BIGHT Eyre MT. LOFTY RANGE
Narrogin Pena. Murray
Bunbury Collie Cape Pasley SPENCER GULF Elizabeth Mildura
Augusta Katanning Esperance Adelaide
STIRLING RA. Port Lincoln
Cape Leeuwin Albany Cape Catastrophe GULF ST. VINCENT
D'Entrecasteaux Point KANGAROO I.
Horsham
Hamilton Ballarat
Mount Gambier Geel
Warrnambool
Cape Otway
KING
ISLAN

INDIAN OCEAN

AUSTRALASIA

100 0 100 200 300 400 500 600 700 800 kilometres

100 0 100 200 300 400 500 Miles

24

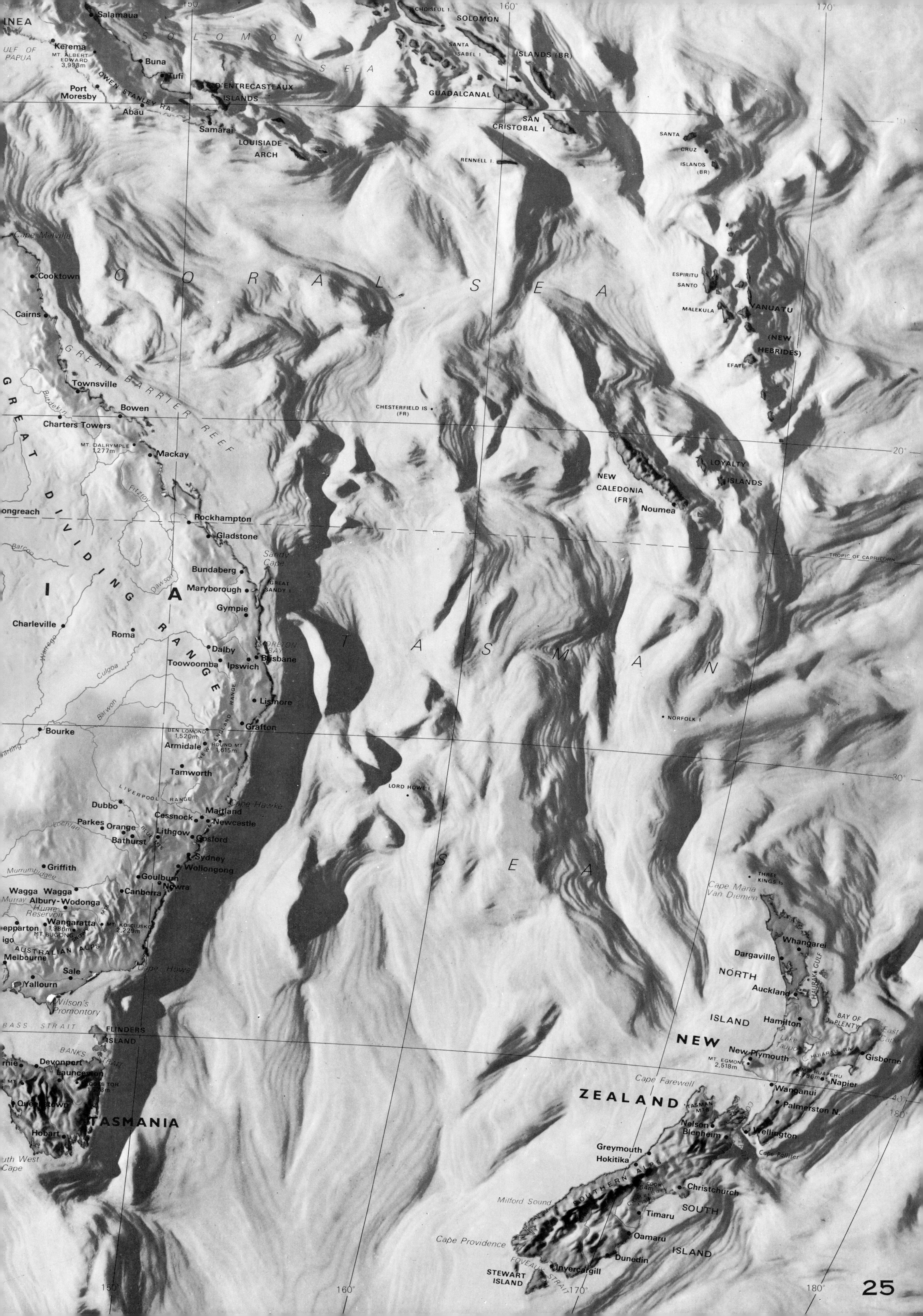

SOLOMON
SOLOMON ISLANDS (BR)
SEA
CHOISEUL I
SANTA ISABEL I
GUADALCANAL
SAN CRISTOBAL I
RENNELL I
Salamaua
Kerema
MT. ALBERT EDWARD 3,993m
Buna
Tufi
Port Moresby
OWEN STANLEY RA.
Abau
D'ENTRECASTEAUX ISLANDS
Samarai
LOUISIADE ARCH
SANTA CRUZ ISLANDS (BR)
ESPIRITU SANTO
MALEKULA
VANUATU (NEW HEBRIDES)
EFATE
C O R A L S E A
Cape Melville
Cooktown
Cairns
GREAT BARRIER REEF
Townsville
Bowen
Charters Towers
MT. DALRYMPLE 1,277m
Mackay
CHESTERFIELD IS (FR)
NEW CALEDONIA (FR)
Noumea
LOYALTY ISLANDS
GREAT DIVIDING RANGE
Rockhampton
Gladstone
Sandy Cape
Bundaberg
Maryborough
GREAT SANDY I
Gympie
Charleville
Roma
Dalby
Toowoomba
Ipswich
Brisbane
MORETON BAY
Lismore
Grafton
Bourke
BEN LOMOND 1,520m
Armidale
ROUND MT 1,615m
NEW ENGLAND RANGE
Tamworth
LIVERPOOL RANGE
Cape Hawke
Dubbo
Maitland
Cessnock
Newcastle
Parkes
Orange
Bathurst
Lithgow
Gosford
Sydney
Wollongong
Griffith
Goulburn
Nowra
Wagga Wagga
Canberra
Albury-Wodonga
Hume Reservoir
Wangaratta
MT. KOSCIUSKO 2,229m
AUSTRALIAN ALPS
Melbourne
Sale
Yallourn
Cape Howe
Wilson's Promontory
BASS STRAIT
FLINDERS ISLAND
BANKS STRAIT
Devonport
Launceston
Queenstown
TASMANIA
Hobart
South West Cape
T A S M A N S E A
NORFOLK I
LORD HOWE I
TROPIC OF CAPRICORN
THREE KINGS Is
Cape Maria Van Diemen
Whangarei
Dargaville
NORTH ISLAND
HAURAKI GULF
Auckland
BAY OF PLENTY
Hamilton
Lake Taupo
NEW ZEALAND
New Plymouth
MT. EGMONT 2,518m
Gisborne
Napier
Wanganui
Palmerston N.
Cape Farewell
Nelson
Blenheim
Wellington
Cape Palliser
Greymouth
Hokitika
SOUTHERN ALPS
Christchurch
Milford Sound
Timaru
SOUTH ISLAND
Oamaru
Dunedin
Cape Providence
FOVEAUX STRAIT
Invercargill
STEWART ISLAND
150°
160°
170°
180°
20°
30°
40°

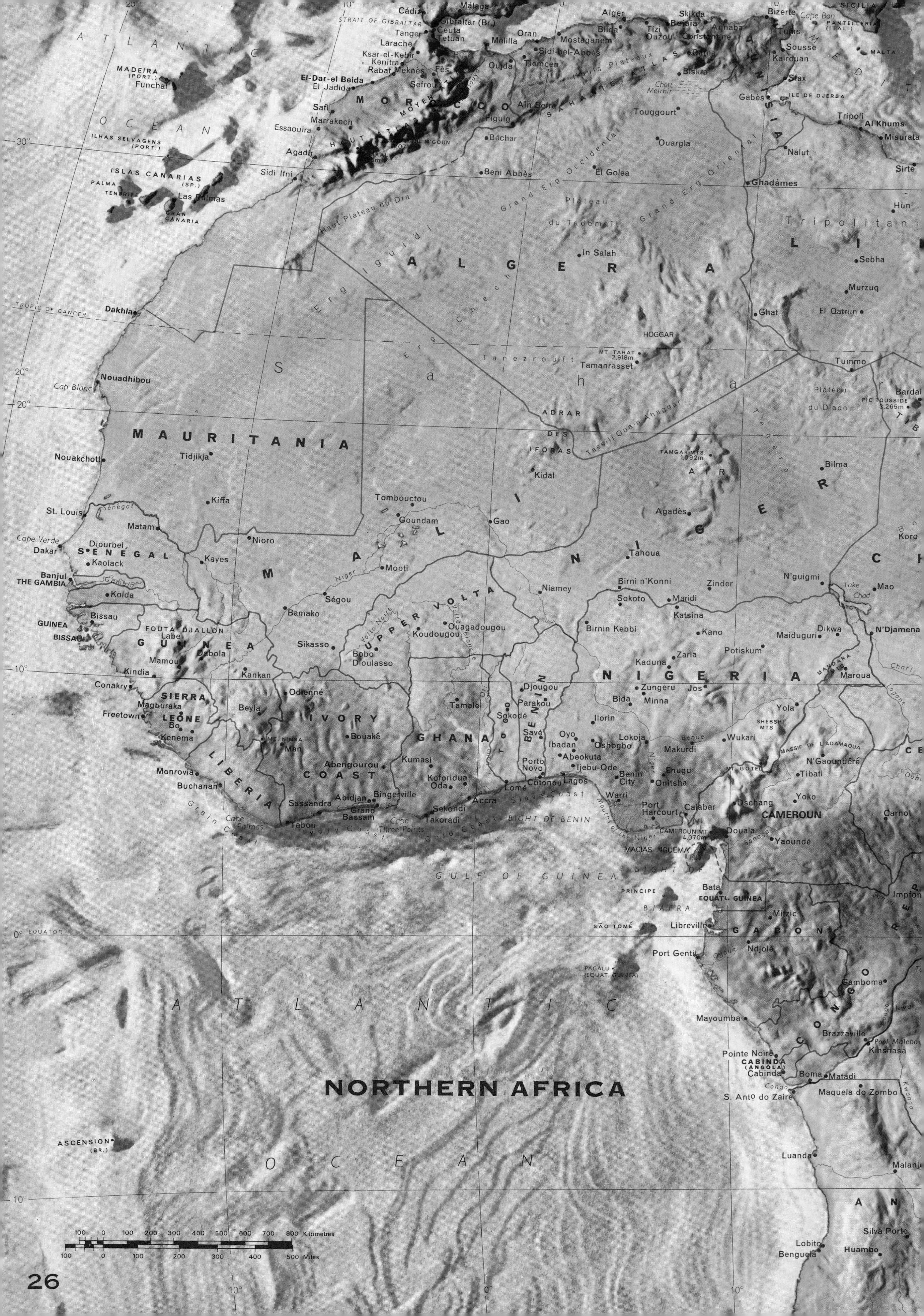
NORTHERN AFRICA
ATLANTIC OCEAN
MAURITANIA
ALGERIA
MALI
NIGER
NIGERIA
SENEGAL
GUINEA
SIERRA LEONE
LIBERIA
IVORY COAST
GHANA
UPPER VOLTA
TOGO
BENIN
CAMEROUN
GABON
CONGO
GULF OF GUINEA
Kilometres
Miles

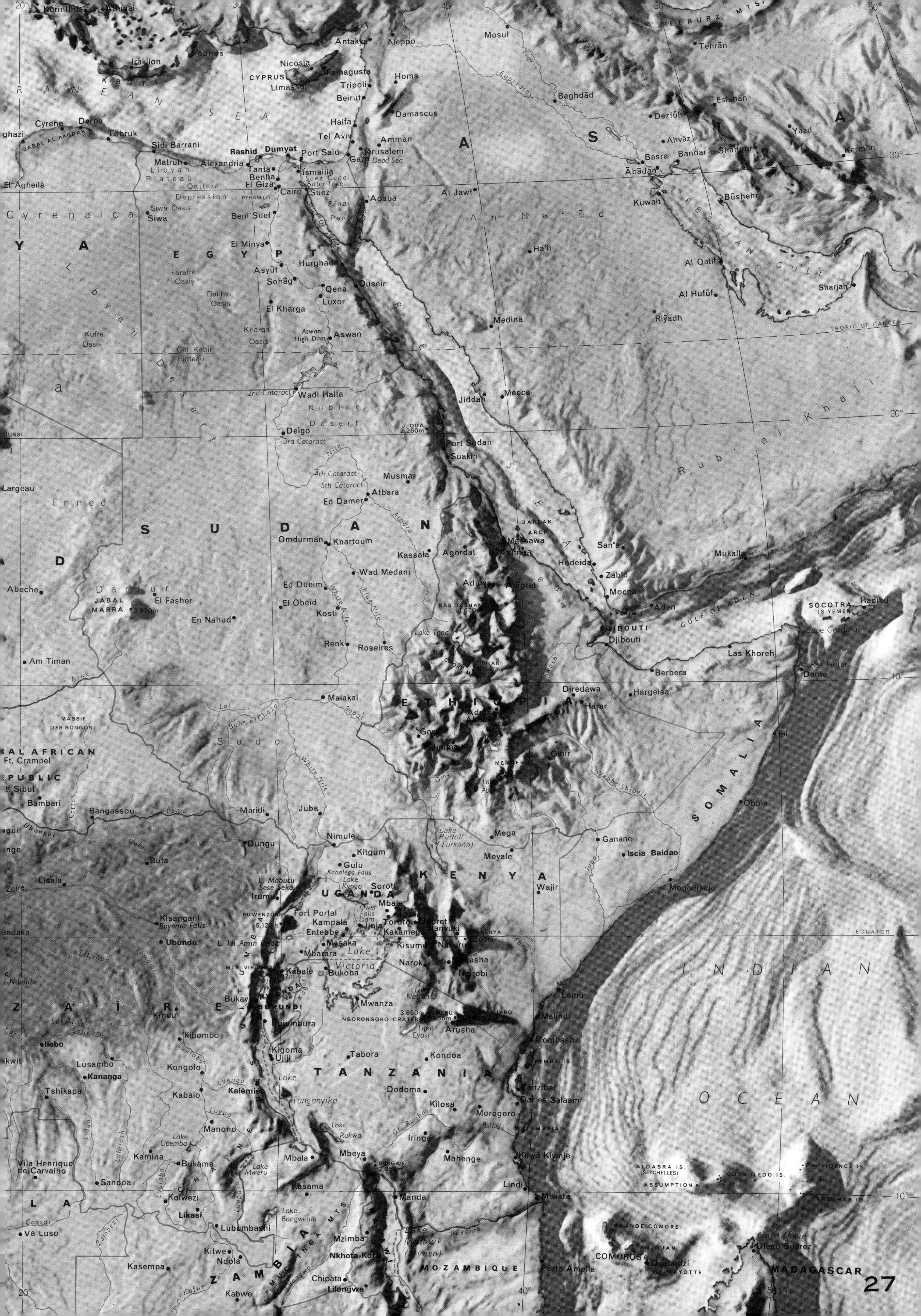

Korinthos
Athinai
Iráklion
Rodhos
Kriti
Nicosia
Famagusta
CYPRUS
Limassol
Antakya
Aleppo
Mosul
ELBURZ MTS.
Tehrān
Homs
Tripoli
Beirūt
Damascus
Tigris
Euphrates
Baghdād
Esfahān
Dezfūl
Yazd
Ahvāz
Kermān
Cyrene
Derna
Tobruk
JABAL AL AKHDAR
Sidi Barrani
Haifa
Tel Aviv
Amman
Jerusalem
Dead Sea
Rashid
Dumyat
Port Said
Gaza
Alexandria
Matruh
Libyan Plateau
Tanta
Benha
El Giza
Ismailia
Suez Canal
Bitter Lake
Cairo
Suez
Qattara Depression
PYRAMIDS
El Agheila
Basra
Bandar-e-Shahpur
Ābādān
Kuwait
Būshehr
Al Jawf
'Aqaba
Sinai
Siwa Oasis
Siwa
Beni Suef
Cyrenaica
An Nafūd
PERSIAN GULF
El Minya
EGYPT
Hurghada
Ha'il
Al Qatīf
Asyût
Sohâg
Farafra Oasis
Qena
Quseir
Luxor
Dakhla Oasis
El Kharga
Al Hufūf
Sharjah
Riyadh
Kufra Oasis
Libyan Desert
Kharga Oasis
Aswan High Dam
Aswan
Medina
TROPIC OF CANCER
Gilf Kebir Plateau
2nd Cataract
Wadi Halfa
Nubian Desert
Jiddah
Mecca
Rub' al Khali
Delgo
3rd Cataract
J. ODA 2,260m
Port Sudan
Suakin
Nile
4th Cataract
5th Cataract
Musmar
Atbara
Ed Damer
Largeau
Ennedi
SUDAN
Atbara
DAHLAK ARCH.
Omdurman
Khartoum
Massawa
Asmara
San'a
Kassala
Agordat
Hodeida
Zabid
Mukalla
Wad Medani
Abeche
Darfur
Ed Dueim
Aduwa
Adigrat
Mocha
JABAL MARRA 3,070m
El Fasher
El Obeid
White Nile
Blue Nile
RAS DASHAN 4,620m
Aden
PERIM I.
GULF OF ADEN
SOCOTRA (S. YEMEN)
Hadibu
En Nahud
Kosti
Lake Tana
DJIBOUTI
Djibouti
Cape Gardafui
Renk
Roseires
Las Khoreh
Am Timan
Berbera
Ras Hafun
Dante
Aouk
Diredawa
Harar
Hargeisa
Malakal
Lol
Bahr el Ghazal
Sobat
ETHIOPIA
MASSIF DES BONGOS
Addis Ababa
Sudd
Gore
Jimma
Ginir
Eil
CENTRAL AFRICAN REPUBLIC
Ft. Crampel
Ft. Sibut
Bambari
White Nile
Omo
Webbe Shibeli
SOMALIA
Obbia
Bangassou
Bomu
Maridi
Juba
Ubangui
Uele
Dungu
Nimule
Lake Rudolf (Turkana)
Mega
Ganane
Kitgum
Moyale
Iscia Baidao
Buta
Gulu
Kabalega Falls
Lake Kyoga
KENYA
Juba
Lisala
L. Mobutu Sese Seko
Soroti
Wajir
Mogadiscio
Zaire
Irumu
UGANDA
Mbale
RUWENZORI 5,120m
Fort Portal
Owen Falls Dam
Kampala
Jinja
Tororo
Eldoret
Kisangani
Boyoma Falls
Entebbe
Kakamega
Nanyuki
Ubundu
L. Idi Amin Dada
Masaka
Kisumu
Nakuru
EQUATOR
Tshuapa
Lomami
Mbarara
Lake Victoria
Narok
Naivasha
Nairobi
INDIAN
MTS. VIRUNGA
Kabale
Bukoba
Lamu
Bukavu
RWANDA
BURUNDI
Kindu
Mwanza
ZAÏRE
Malindi
Bujumbura
NGORONGORO CRATER
Lake Eyasi
Arusha
Ilebo
Kibombo
Mombasa
Lukenie
Sankuru
Kigoma
Ujiji
PEMBA IS.
Kasai
Tabora
Kondoa
Lusambo
Kananga
Kongolo
TANZANIA
Tshikapa
Kalémie
Lake Tanganyika
Dodoma
Zanzibar
Kabalo
Dar es Salaam
OCEAN
Kilosa
Lukuga
Manono
Morogoro
Lake Rukwa
Rufiji
Lake Upemba
MAFIA I.
Iringa
Kamina
Mbeya
Kilwa Kivinje
Mbala
Mahenge
Vila Henrique de Carvalho
Bukama
Lake Mweru
ALDABRA IS. (SEYCHELLES)
COSMOLEDO IS.
PROVIDENCE IS.
ASSUMPTION
Sandoa
RUNGWE 2,959m
Kasama
Lindi
Kolwezi
Likasi
Mtwara
FARQUHAR IS.
Luapula
Manda
Lake Bangweulu
Cassai
Va Luso
Lubumbashi
GRANDE COMORE
Cap d'Ambre
Diego Suarez
Zambezi
Mzimba
Lake Malawi (Nyasa)
Ruvuma
ANJOUAN
Kitwe
Ndola
Nkhota-Kota
MOZAMBIQUE
Porto Amelia
COMOROS
Dzaoudzi
Kasempa
ZAMBIA
MUCHINGA MTS.
MAYOTTE
MADAGASCAR
Chipata
Kabwe
Lilongwe
Kafue

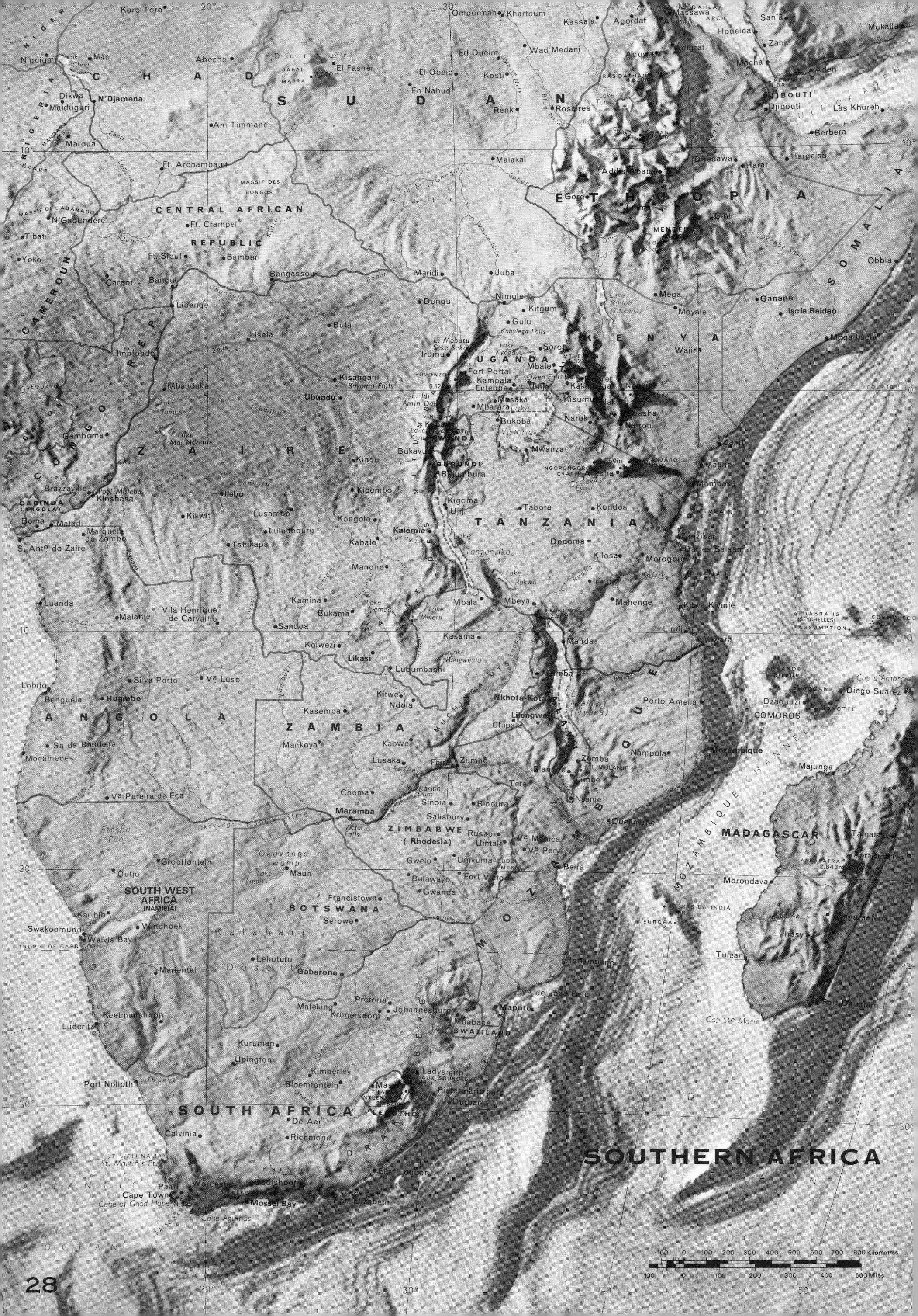
SOUTHERN AFRICA
CHAD
SUDAN
ETHIOPIA
SOMALIA
DJIBOUTI
GULF OF ADEN
CENTRAL AFRICAN REPUBLIC
CAMEROUN
NIGERIA
CONGO REP.
GABON
ZAIRE
UGANDA
KENYA
RWANDA
BURUNDI
TANZANIA
ANGOLA
ZAMBIA
MALAWI
MOZAMBIQUE
ZIMBABWE (Rhodesia)
BOTSWANA
SOUTH WEST AFRICA (NAMIBIA)
SOUTH AFRICA
SWAZILAND
LESOTHO
MADAGASCAR
COMOROS
MOZAMBIQUE CHANNEL
INDIAN OCEAN
ATLANTIC OCEAN
TROPIC OF CAPRICORN
EQUATOR
Koro Toro
N'guigmi
Mao
Lake Chad
Abeche
Darfur
Jebel Marra 3,070m
El Fasher
Dikwa
N'Djamena
Maiduguri
Maroua
Am Timmane
Chari
Ft. Archambault
Massif des Bongos
Massif de l'Adamaoua
N'Gaoundéré
Ft. Crampel
Tibati
Yoko
Ft. Sibut
Bambari
Carnot
Bangui
Bangassou
Libenge
Ubangui
Uele
Bomu
Lisala
Impfondo
Zaire
Buta
Mbandaka
Kisangani
Boyoma Falls
Ubundu
Lake Tumba
Lake Mai-Ndombe
Tshuapa
Gamboma
Kwa
Kasai
Lukenie
Sankuru
Brazzaville
Pool Malebo
Kinshasa
Cabinda (Angola)
Boma
Matadi
Marquela do Zombo
S. Antº do Zaire
Ilebo
Kikwit
Kwilu
Lusambo
Luluabourg
Tshikapa
Kindu
Kibombo
Kongolo
Kabalo
Kalémié
Manono
Kamina
Bukama
Lake Upemba
Lake Mweru
Luanda
Cuanza
Malanje
Vila Henrique de Carvalho
Sandoa
Kolwezi
Likasi
Lubumbashi
Lobito
Benguela
Huambo
Silva Porto
Vª Luso
Kasempa
Kitwe
Ndola
Mankoya
Kabwe
Lusaka
Kafue
Feira
Zumbo
Chipata
Lilongwe
Nkhota Kota
Lake Malawi (Nyasa)
Muchinga Mts
Luangwa
Sa da Bandeira
Moçâmedes
Va Pereira de Eça
Cunene
Cubango
Cuito
Okovango
Caprivi Strip
Etosha Pan
Grootfontein
Outjo
Okavango Swamp
Lake Ngami
Maun
Karibib
Swakopmund
Windhoek
Walvis Bay
Kalahari Desert
Lehututu
Mariental
Gabarone
Keetmanshoop
Luderitz
Serowe
Francistown
Limpopo
Choma
Maramba
Victoria Falls
Kariba Dam
Sinoia
Bindura
Salisbury
Rusapi
Umtali
Va Manica
Va Pery
Gwelo
Umvuma
Fort Victoria
Bulawayo
Gwanda
Beira
Save
Tete
Zambezi
Blantyre
Limbe
Zomba
Mt Mulanje
Nsanje
Quelimane
Nampula
Mozambique
Porto Amelia
Ruvuma
Mtwara
Lindi
Kilwa Kivinje
Mahenge
Iringa
Mbeya
Mbala
Kasama
Lake Bangweulu
Lake Rukwa
Rungwe 2,959m
Manda
Lake Tanganyika
Kigoma
Ujiji
Bujumbura
Bukavu
Lake Kivu
Tabora
Dodoma
Kondoa
Kilosa
Morogoro
Dar es Salaam
Zanzibar
Pemba I.
Mafia I.
Rufiji
Gt. Ruaha
Mwanza
Bukoba
Lake Victoria
Masaka
Mbarara
Entebbe
Kampala
Jinja
Fort Portal
Ruwenzori 5,120m
L. Idi Amin Dada
L. Mobutu Sese Seko
Irumu
Gulu
Kabalega Falls
Lake Kyoga
Kitgum
Soroti
Mbale
Mt Elgon
Tororo
Kisumu
Kakamega
Nakuru
Naivasha
Nairobi
Narok
Ngorongoro Crater
Arusha
Kilimanjaro
Lake Eyasi
Lake Natron
Tana
Lamu
Malindi
Mombasa
Wajir
Lake Rudolf (Turkana)
Mega
Moyale
Juba
Ganane
Iscia Baidao
Mogadiscio
Obbia
Nimule
Dungu
Maridi
Juba
Malakal
Sobat
Bahr el Ghazal
Sudd
White Nile
Blue Nile
Renk
Roseires
Kosti
El Obeid
En Nahud
Ed Dueim
Wad Medani
Omdurman
Khartoum
Kassala
Agordat
Massawa
Asmara
Dahlak Arch
Adigrat
Aduwa
Ras Dashan
Lake Tana
Gore
Jimma
Addis Ababa
Diredawa
Harar
Hargeisa
Berbera
Las Khoreh
Djibouti
Aden
Mocha
Zabid
Hodeida
San'a
Mukalla
Ginir
Webbe Shibeli
Omo
Lake Abaya
Aldabra Is (Seychelles)
Assumption
Cosmoledo Is
Grande Comore
Anjouan
Dzaoudzi
Île Mayotte
Cap d'Ambre
Diego Suarez
Majunga
Tamatave
Antananarivo
Ankaratra 2,643m
Morondava
Fianarantsoa
Ihosy
Tulear
Fort Dauphin
Cap Ste Marie
Europa (Fr.)
Bassas da India
Inhambane
Va de João Belo
Maputo
Mbabane
Pretoria
Johannesburg
Krugersdorp
Mafeking
Kuruman
Upington
Kimberley
Bloemfontein
Vaal
Orange
Ladysmith
Pietermaritzburg
Durban
Drakensberg
Maseru
Thabana Ntlenyana 3,482m
Mont aux Sources
De Aar
Richmond
Calvinia
Port Nolloth
St Helena Bay
St. Martin's Pt.
Gt Karroo
East London
Port Elizabeth
Algoa Bay
Worcester
Oudtshoorn
Paarl
Cape Town
Table Mt 1,087m
Cape of Good Hope
False Bay
Mossel Bay
Cape Agulhas
100 0 100 200 300 400 500 600 700 800 Kilometres
100 0 100 200 300 400 500 Miles

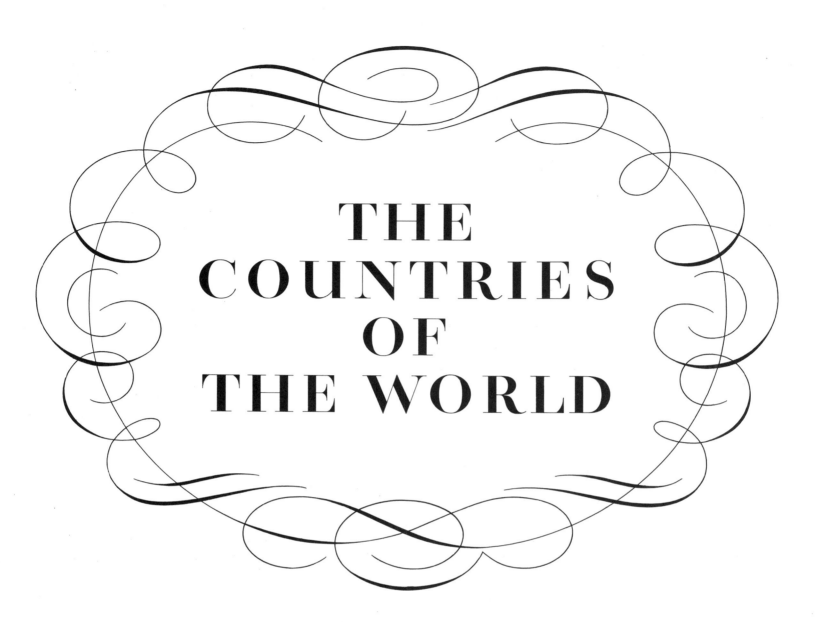

SECTION TWO

CONTENTS

NORTH AMERICA	PAGE
CANADA	30
ATLANTIC PROVINCES	32
ONTARIO AND QUEBEC WITH INSETS OF OTTAWA, TORONTO, QUEBEC AND MONTREAL	34
THE PRAIRIES	36
WEST AND NORTH-WEST CANADA WITH INSET OF VANCOUVER	38
GREAT LAKES	40
UNITED STATES OF AMERICA WITH INSETS OF HAWAII, ALASKA, SAN FRANCISCO AND NEW YORK	42
MIDDLE ATLANTIC STATES	44
SOUTHERN STATES	45
NORTH CENTRAL STATES	46
PACIFIC COAST	47
MIDDLE WEST STATES	48
MEXICO WITH GUATEMALA, HONDURAS, BRITISH HONDURAS, EL SALVADOR	50
THE CARIBBEAN WEST INDIES AND THE PANAMA CANAL	51

SOUTH AMERICA	
SOUTH AMERICA (NORTH) BRAZIL, BOLIVIA, PERU, ECUADOR, COLOMBIA, VENEZUELA, GUYANA, SURINAM, FRENCH GUIANA	52
SOUTH AMERICA (SOUTH) ARGENTINA, CHILE, PARAGUAY, URUGUAY	54
THE ARCTIC	41
THE ANTARCTIC	104
EURASIA	58

EUROPE	PAGE
EUROPE	60
THE BRITISH ISLES	62
THE LOW COUNTRIES BELGIUM, NETHERLANDS, LUXEMBOURG	64
SWITZERLAND	65
SCANDINAVIA AND THE BALTIC NORWAY, SWEDEN, DENMARK, FINLAND, WITH ICELAND AND THE FAROES	66
CENTRAL EUROPE GERMANY, POLAND, CZECHOSLOVAKIA, AUSTRIA	68
IBERIAN PENINSULA SPAIN, PORTUGAL	70
FRANCE AND NORTHERN ALGERIA	72
ITALY	74
THE BALKANS HUNGARY, ROMANIA, YUGOSLAVIA, BULGARIA, GREECE	76
EUROPEAN RUSSIA	80
THE VOLGA BASIN	81

ASIA	
U.S.S.R.	78
THE FAR EAST CHINA, MONGOLIA, KOREA, JAPAN, PHILIPPINES, INDONESIA, MALAYSIA, SINGAPORE, BURMA AND THAILAND	82
EAST CHINA	84
JAPAN	86
SOUTH-EAST ASIA THAILAND, WEST MALAYSIA, SINGAPORE, BURMA, VIETNAM, LAOS, KHMER REPUBLIC	87
INDIA, PAKISTAN, CEYLON, BURMA WITH BANGLADESH, NEPAL, BHUTAN, TIBET, AFGHANISTAN AND SOUTH-WEST CHINA	88
PUNJAB AND KASHMIR	90
PLAIN OF THE GANGES	91
THE MIDDLE EAST AND AFGHANISTAN TURKEY, IRAQ, IRAN, SAUDI ARABIA, KUWAIT, QATAR, UNITED ARAB EMIRATES, OMAN, SOUTHERN YEMEN, YEMEN	92
THE LEVANT AND JORDAN SYRIA, LEBANON, ISRAEL, CYPRUS	94

AFRICA	
SOUTHERN AFRICA REPUBLIC OF SOUTH AFRICA, ZAMBIA, RHODESIA, MALAWI, MOCAMBIQUE, BOTSWANA	95
CENTRAL AND EAST AFRICA ZAIRE, ANGOLA, EQUATORIAL AFRICAN STATES, KENYA, UGANDA, TANZANIA, ETHIOPIA, SOMALI REPUBLIC, WITH MADAGASCAR	96
NORTH AND WEST AFRICA MOROCCO, ALGERIA, TUNISIA, LIBYA, ARAB REPUBLIC OF EGYPT, SUDAN, GHANA, NIGERIA, LIBERIA, SIERRA LEONE	98

AUSTRALASIA	
NEW ZEALAND	55
AUSTRALIA	56
INDIAN OCEAN	100
ATLANTIC OCEAN	101
PACIFIC OCEAN WITH INSETS OF WESTERN SAMOA, TAHITI AND FIJI ISLANDS	102

CANADA

AREA: 9,976,185 sq. km. (3,851,809 sq. miles)
POP: 24,880,700 CAP: Ottawa CURR: 100 cents=1 dollar

HEIGHTS
IN METRES

3600
3000
1800
900
450
180

SEA LEVEL

900

DEPTHS
IN METRES

BEAUFORT SEA

PACIFIC OCEAN

Gulf of Alaska

ALASKA

YUKON TERRITORY

NORTHWEST TERRITORIES

BRITISH COLUMBIA

ALBERTA

SASKATCHEWAN

MANITOBA

WASHINGTON

OREGON

IDAHO

MONTANA

WYOMING

NORTH DAKOTA

SOUTH DAKOTA

MINNESOTA

UNITED STATES

ROCKY MOUNTAINS

MACKENZIE MOUNTAINS

Brooks Range

Vancouver Island

Queen Charlotte Islands

Alexander Archipelago

Victoria Island

Banks Island

30

CHAMBERLIN TRIMETRIC PROJECTION

SCALE: 1:12,500,000   (1 CM = 125 KM)

MAIN HIGHWAYS
RAILWAYS
CANALS
OIL PIPE LINES

Longitude West 100° of Greenwich

8950

Canada, second largest country after Russia, 5,157 km. at its widest and bordering the United States for 6,378 km., comprises a massive central upland or Shield, surrounded by inner flanking lowlands and outer marginal mountains. The Shield covers nearly half the country and is increasingly a source of mineral wealth.

SCALE
KM — MILES

KM	MILES
100	100
200	200
300	300
400	400
500	500
600	600
700	700
800	800
900	900
1000	1000
1100	1100
1200	1200
1300	1300
1400	1400
1500	1500
1600	1600
1700	1700
1800	1800
1900	1900
2000	2000
2100	
2200	
2300	
2400	
2500	
2600	
2700	
2800	
2900	
3000	
3100	
3200	

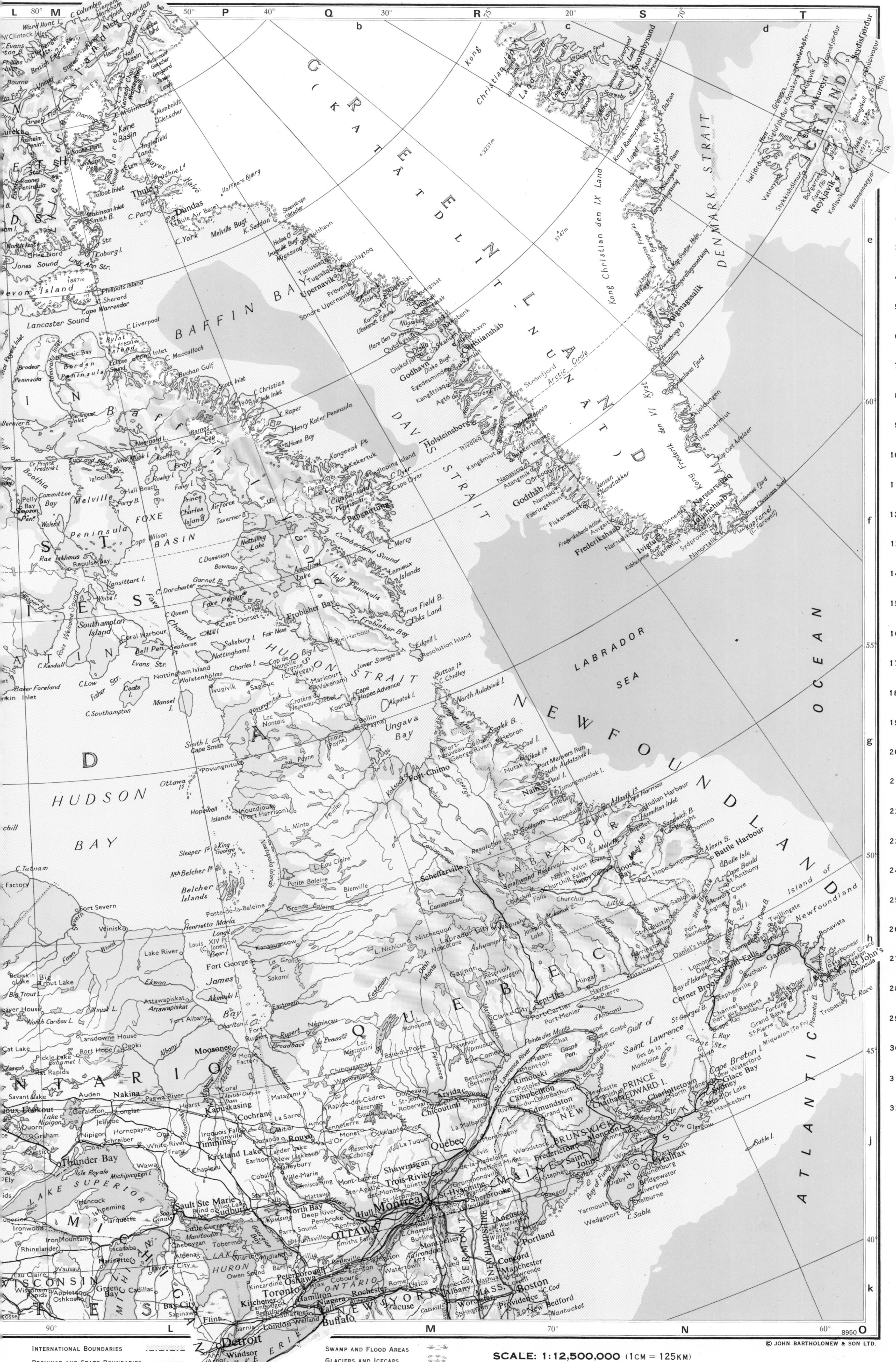

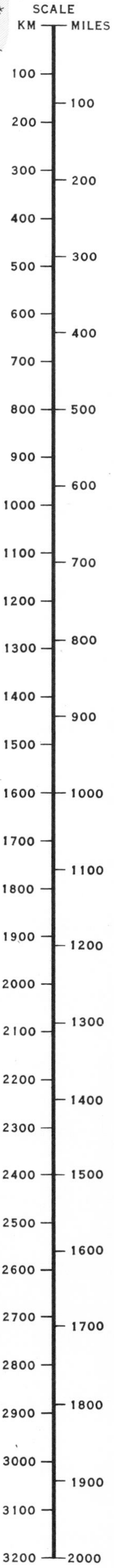

INTERNATIONAL BOUNDARIES
PROVINCE AND STATE BOUNDARIES
SWAMP AND FLOOD AREAS
GLACIERS AND ICECAPS

SCALE: 1:12,500,000 (1CM = 125KM)

Rimming the Atlantic is a succession of
mountain arcs with highlands and lowlands

HEIGHTS
IN METRES

900

450

180

90

SEA LEVEL

180

900

DEPTHS
IN METRES

32

CONIC PROJECTION

SCALE: 1:3,000,000 (1 CM = 30 KM)

ARTERIAL ROADS
OTHER MAIN ROADS   TRACKS
RAILWAYS
MAIN CIVIL AIRPORTS

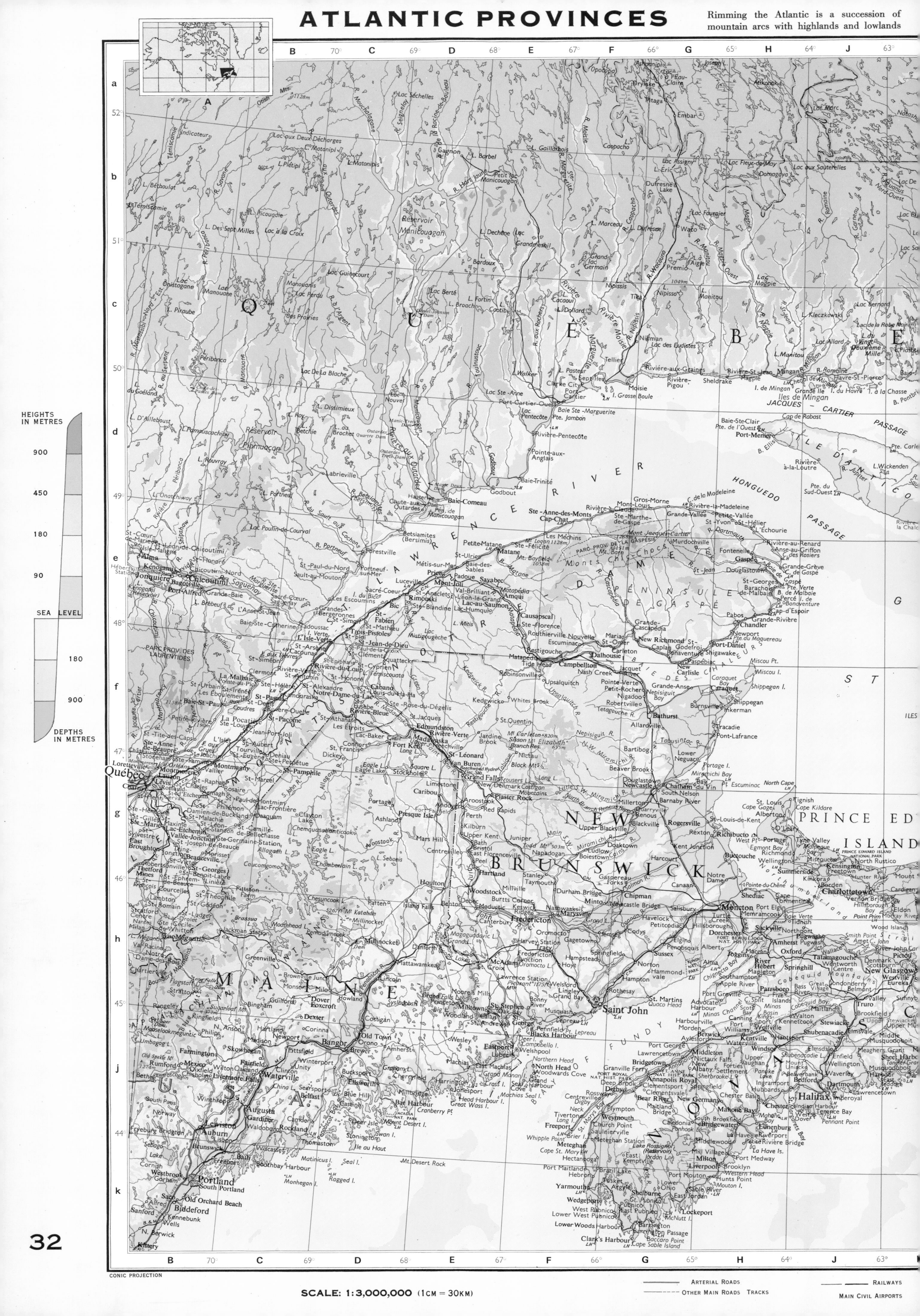

SCALE

KM   MILES

ATLANTIC OCEAN

LABRADOR

NEWFOUNDLAND

GULF OF ST. LAWRENCE

CABOT STRAIT

ÎLES DE LA MADELEINE

CAPE BRETON ISLAND

CAPE BRETON HIGHLANDS NATIONAL PARK

SAINT-PIERRE & MIQUELON
(To France)

LONG RANGE MOUNTAINS

Middle Ridge

St. John's

ATLANTIC OCEAN

SABLE ISLAND BANK

33

INTERNATIONAL BOUNDARIES

PROVINCIAL BOUNDARIES

SWAMP AND FLOOD AREAS

SCALE: 1:3,000,000 (1CM = 30KM)

© JOHN BARTHOLOMEW & SON LTD.

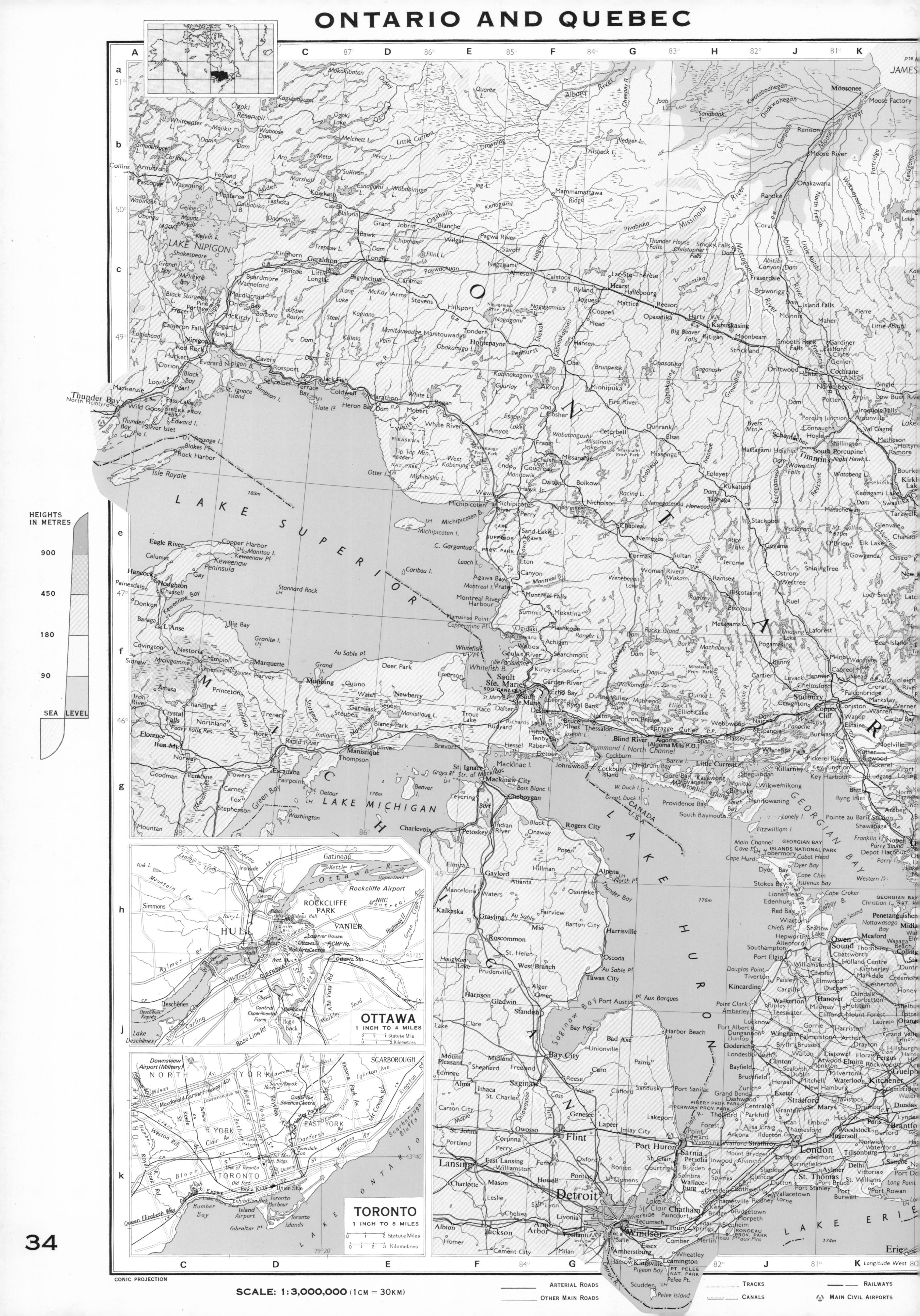

ONTARIO AND QUEBEC
HEIGHTS IN METRES
900
450
180
90
SEA LEVEL
LAKE SUPERIOR
LAKE MICHIGAN
LAKE HURON
LAKE ERIE
GEORGIAN BAY
LAKE NIPIGON
ONTARIO
MICHIGAN
OTTAWA
1 INCH TO 4 MILES
Statute Mile
Kilometres
TORONTO
1 INCH TO 5 MILES
Statute Miles
Kilometres
HULL
ROCKCLIFFE PARK
VANIER
NORTH YORK
SCARBOROUGH
EAST YORK
YORK
ETOBICOKE
LAKE ONTARIO
Thunder Bay
Sault Ste. Marie
Sudbury
Timmins
Kapuskasing
Cochrane
Moosonee
Detroit
Windsor
London
Flint
Lansing
Saginaw
Bay City
Sarnia
Port Huron
Kitchener
Guelph
Brantford
Owen Sound
Isle Royale
Manitoulin Island
Longitude West
CONIC PROJECTION
SCALE: 1:3,000,000 (1CM = 30KM)
ARTERIAL ROADS
OTHER MAIN ROADS
TRACKS
CANALS
RAILWAYS
MAIN CIVIL AIRPORTS

The Great Lakes-St. Lawrence lowlands form the economic heartland of Canada. This region, its economy pulsing along the great axis of the St. Lawrence River and the lakes, is one of the smallest geographic units in the country but contains 60 per cent of the population. It is probably the most productive area in Canada.

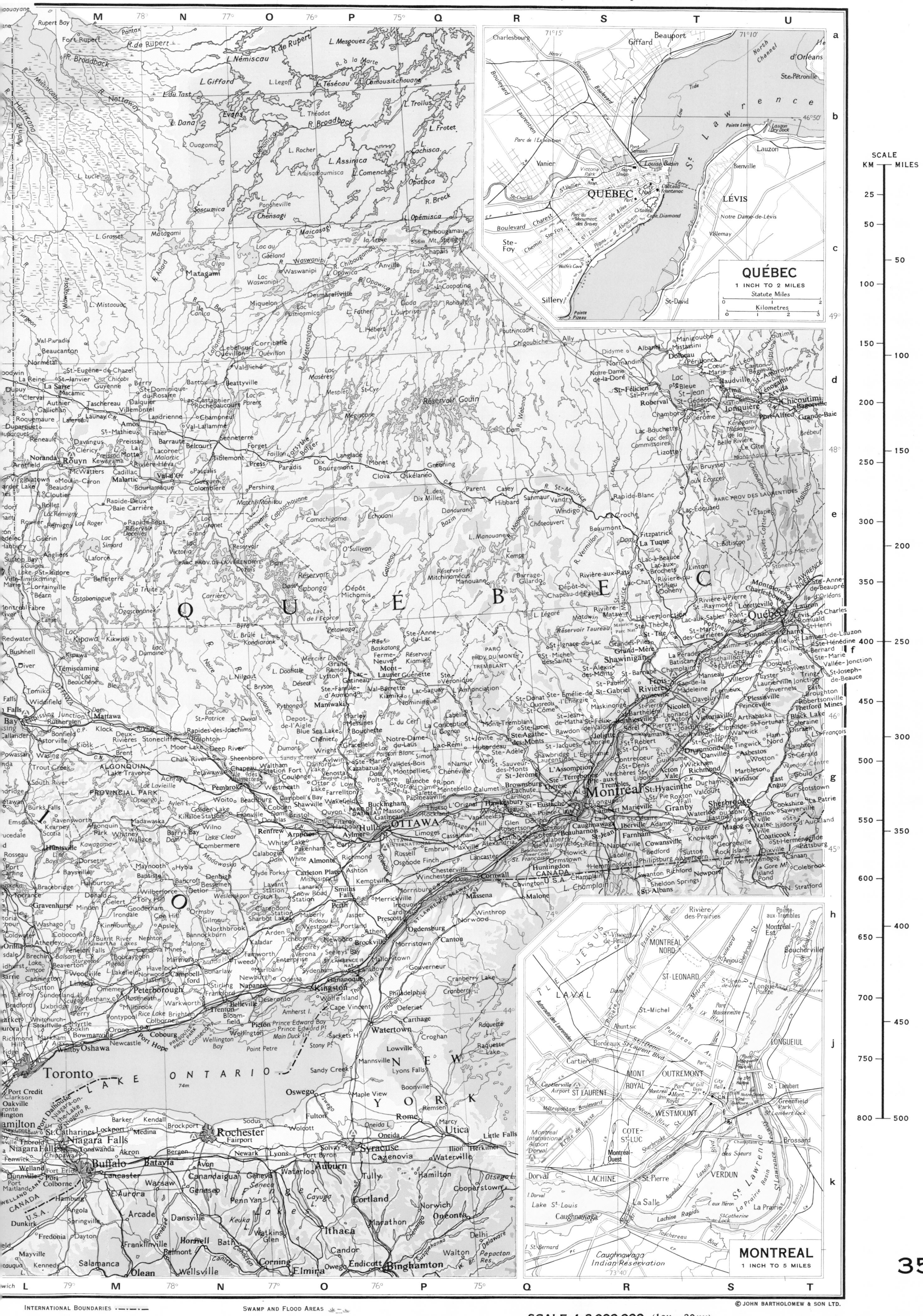

QUÉBEC
1 INCH TO 2 MILES
Statute Miles
Kilometres

MONTREAL
1 INCH TO 5 MILES

INTERNATIONAL BOUNDARIES
PROVINCIAL BOUNDARIES
SWAMP AND FLOOD AREAS

SCALE: 1:3,000,000 (1CM = 30KM)

SCALE
KM — MILES

35

Canada's prairies, taking in large areas of three provinces, were formed by deposits from the Pre-Cambrian Shield and from marginal mountains (the Rockies) laid down

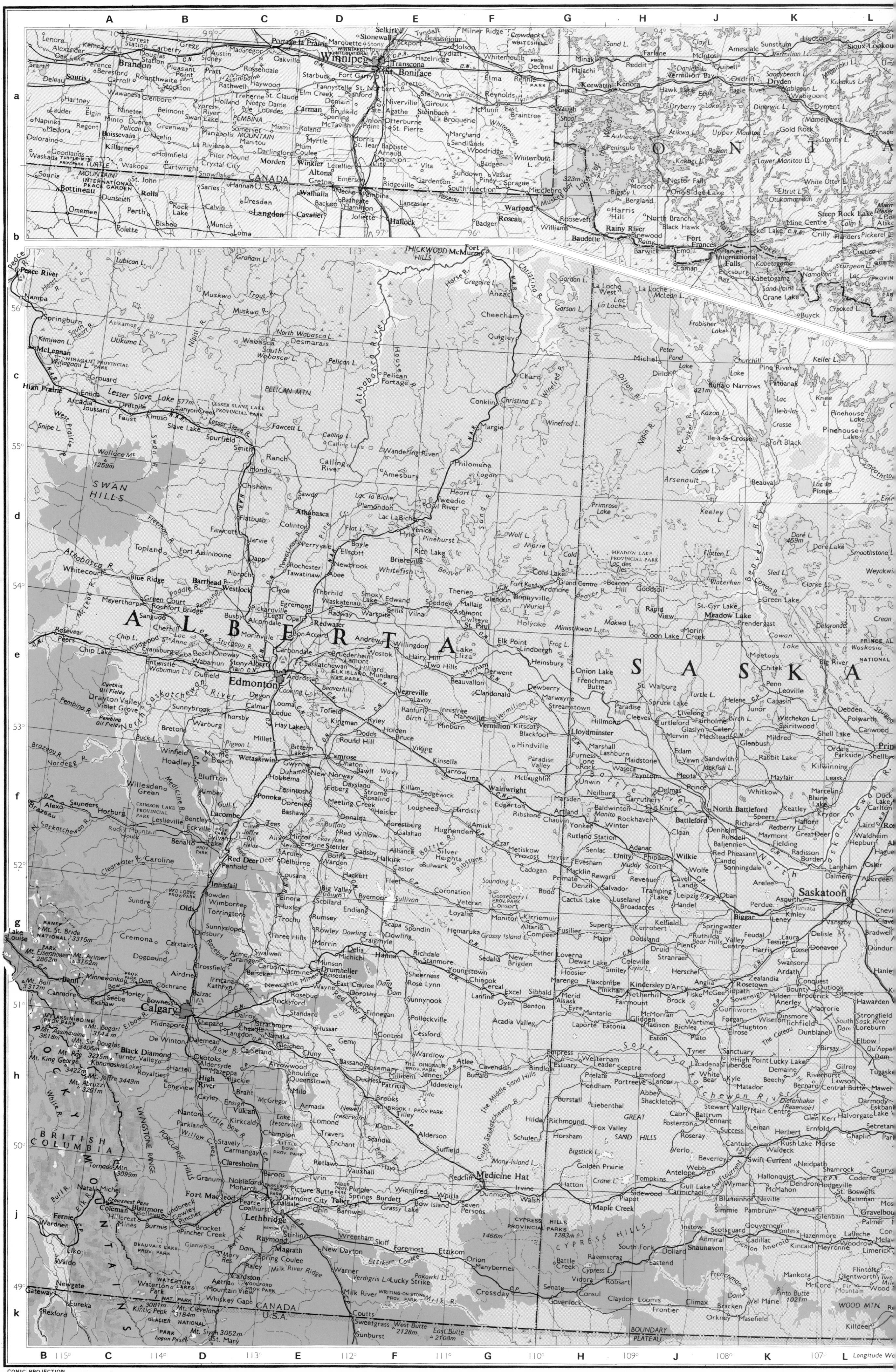

HEIGHTS IN METRES

2700
1800
900
450
180
SEA LEVEL

ALBERTA

BRITISH COLUMBIA

SASKA...

ONTA...

CANADA
U.S.A.

36

CONIC PROJECTION

SCALE: 1:3,000,000 (1CM = 30KM)

ARTERIAL ROADS — TRACKS — RAILWAYS
OTHER MAIN ROADS — CANALS — MAIN CIVIL AIRPORTS

in shallow seas. Their sweeping expanses, relative flatness and rich fertility have made them the bread-basket of the country since the turn of the century. Since the Second World War they have also become a major source of oil and gas.

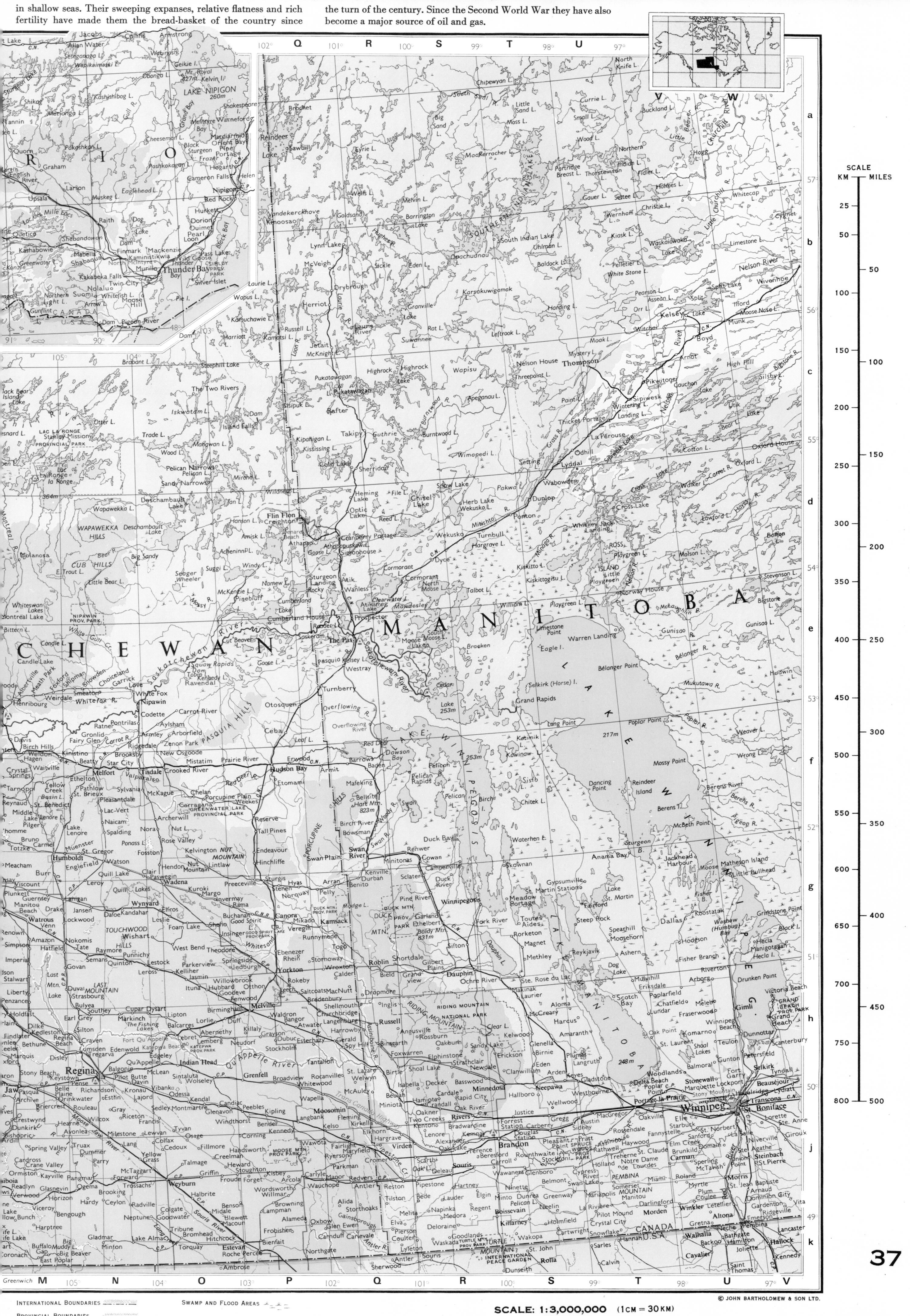

SCALE: 1:3,000,000 (1 CM = 30 KM)

INTERNATIONAL BOUNDARIES
PROVINCIAL BOUNDARIES
SWAMP AND FLOOD AREAS

SCALE
KM   MILES

37

HEIGHTS IN METRES

3600
2700
1800
900
540
180

SEA LEVEL

180
1800

DEPTHS IN METRES

38

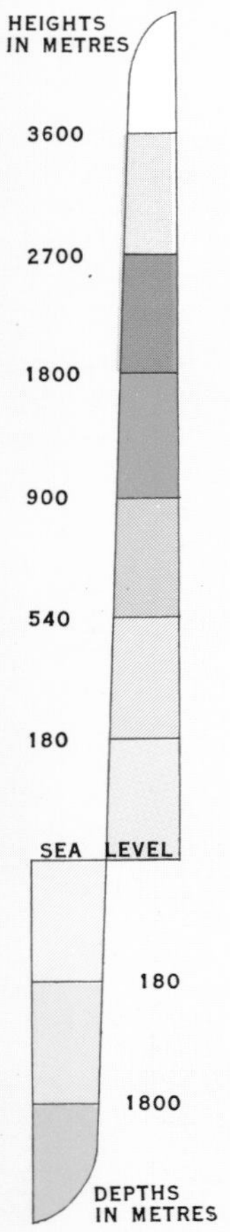

CONIC PROJECTION

SCALE: 1:6,000,000 (1CM = 60KM)

ARTERIAL ROADS — RAILWAYS — CANALS

OTHER MAIN ROADS TRACKS — MAIN CIVIL AIRPORTS — OIL PIPE LINES

DISTRICT OF KEEWATIN

DISTRICT OF MACKENZIE

NORTH-WEST TERRITORIES

VICTORIA ISLAND

Banks I.

BEAUFORT SEA

Amundsen Gulf

Coronation Gulf

GREAT BEAR LAKE

GREAT SLAVE LAKE

MACKENZIE MOUNTAINS

YUKON TERRITORY

ALASKA

Mackenzie River

Yellowknife

Fort Smith

Fort Resolution

Fort Providence

Fort Simpson

Fort Norman

Fort Good Hope

Norman Wells

Coppermine

Port Radium

Echo Bay

Aklavik

Fort McPherson

Dawson

Whitehorse

Uranium City

WOOD BUFFALO NATIONAL PARK

Prince Albert Sound

Dolphin and Union Strait

Melville Hills

Richardson Mountains

Ogilvie Mts.

Brooks Range

Davidson Mountains

Logan Mountains

Backbone Ranges

Selwyn Mts.

Pelly Mountains

Cassiar Mts.

Skagway

Haines

The Canadian Cordillera, second important source of Canadian mineral wealth, 800 km. wide and 2,250 km. long, is the greatest sweep of mountains in the country. It comprises the Rocky Mountains, the interior basins and plateaux, the Coast Range and the outer system of islands along the British Columbia coast.

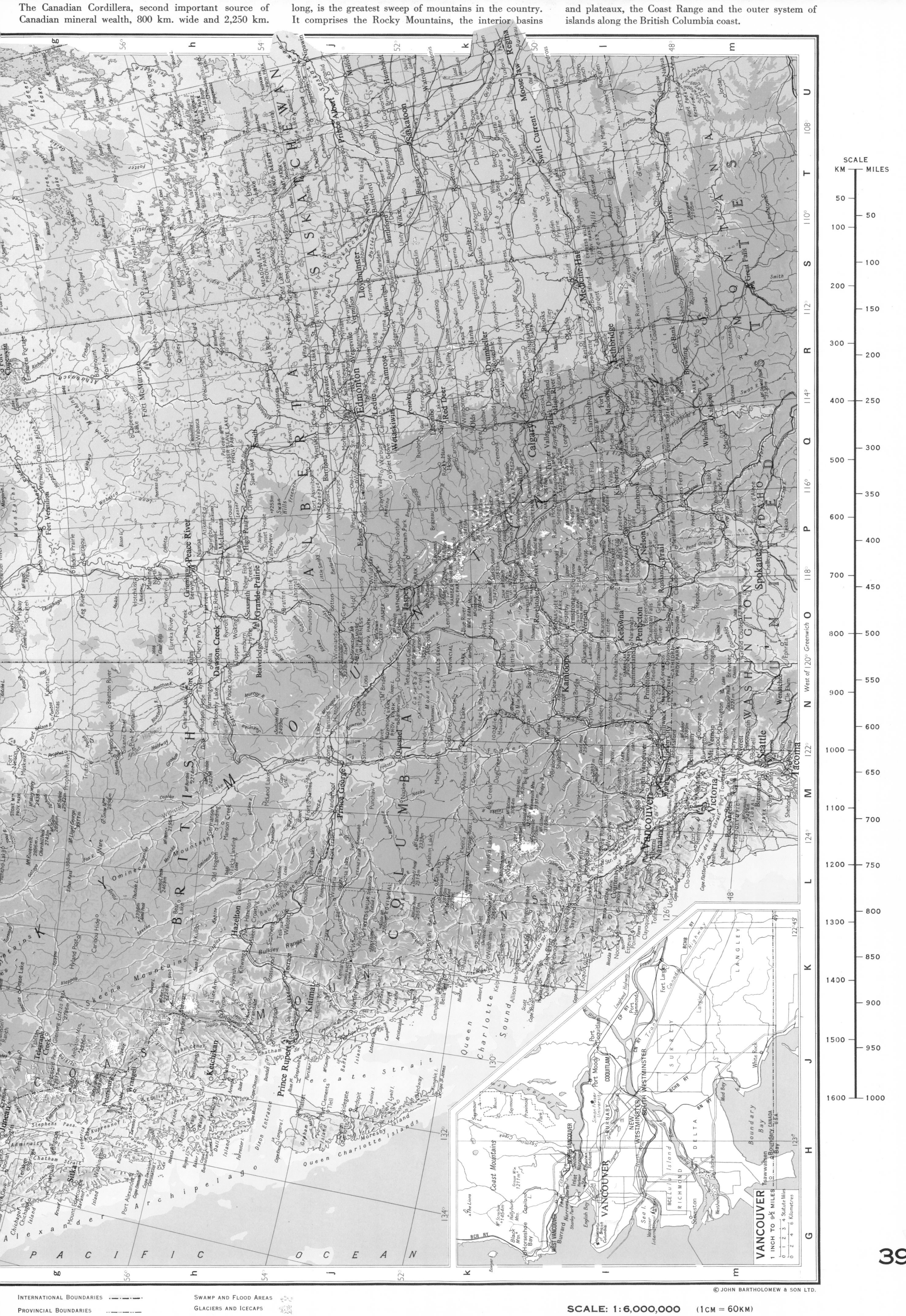

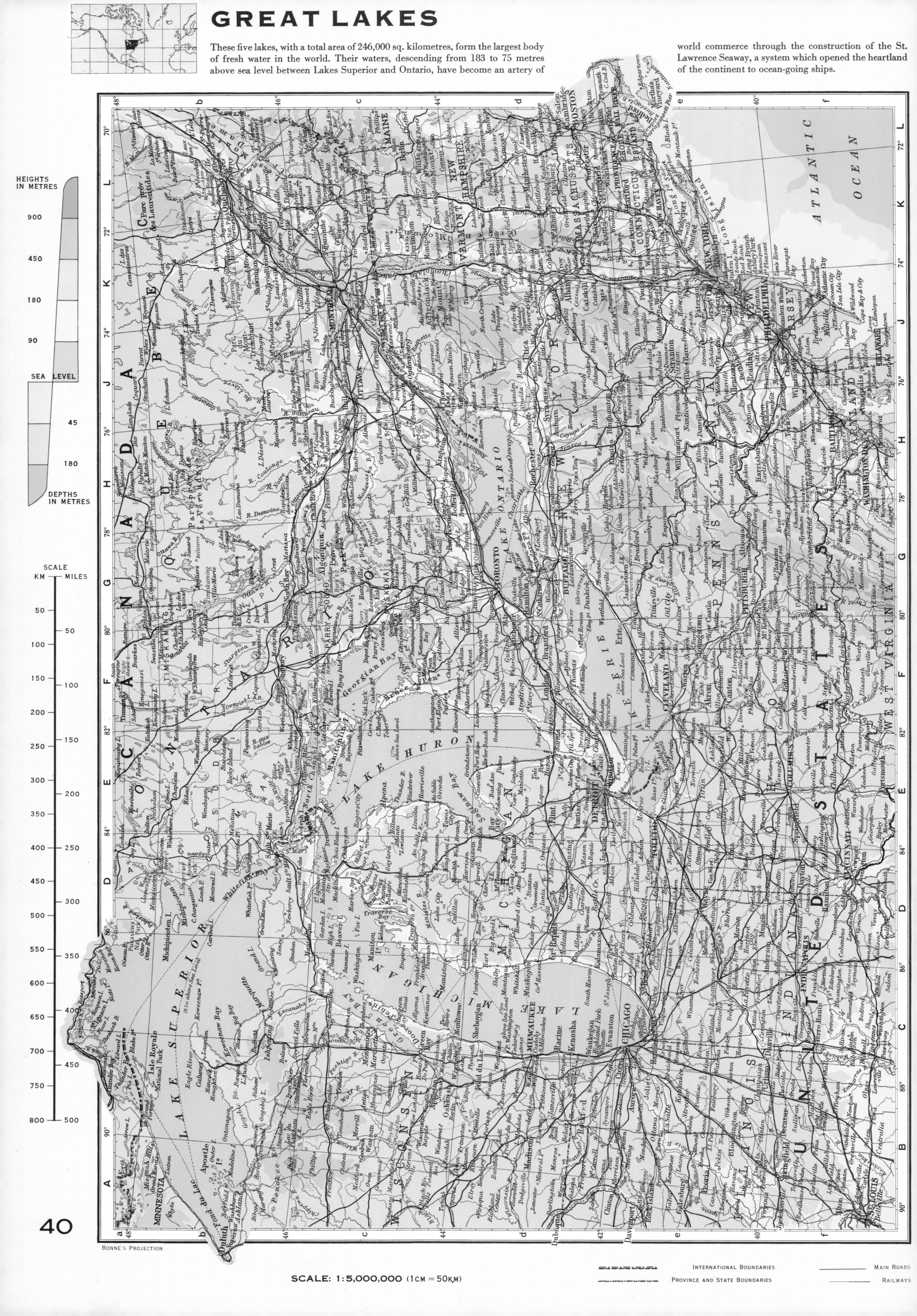

GREAT LAKES

These five lakes, with a total area of 246,000 sq. kilometres, form the largest body of fresh water in the world. Their waters, descending from 183 to 75 metres above sea level between Lakes Superior and Ontario, have become an artery of world commerce through the construction of the St. Lawrence Seaway, a system which opened the heartland of the continent to ocean-going ships.

HEIGHTS IN METRES

900
450
180
90
SEA LEVEL
45
180

DEPTHS IN METRES

SCALE
KM — MILES

50 — 50
100
150 — 100
200
250 — 150
300
350 — 200
400
450 — 250
500
550 — 350
600
650 — 400
700
750 — 450
800 — 500

40

BONNE'S PROJECTION

SCALE: 1:5,000,000 (1 cm = 50 km)

INTERNATIONAL BOUNDARIES

PROVINCE AND STATE BOUNDARIES

MAIN ROADS

RAILWAYS

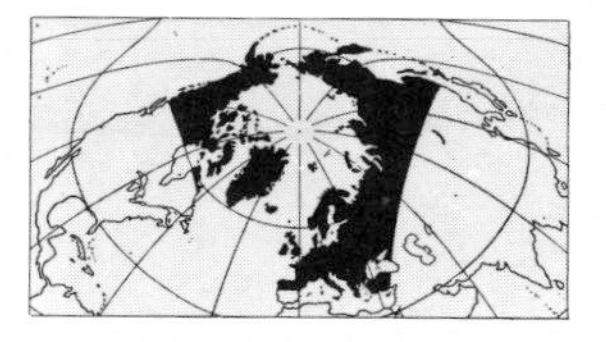

The Asian and North American continents almost meet at the narrow and shallow Bering Strait, only 72 kilometres across. Between them lies the Arctic Ocean, nearly enclosed and always covered with drifting ice. Another outstanding feature of this map is the high plateau of Greenland, covered with ice up to 3,400 metres thick, yet reaching down to the same latitude as Oslo and Leningrad.

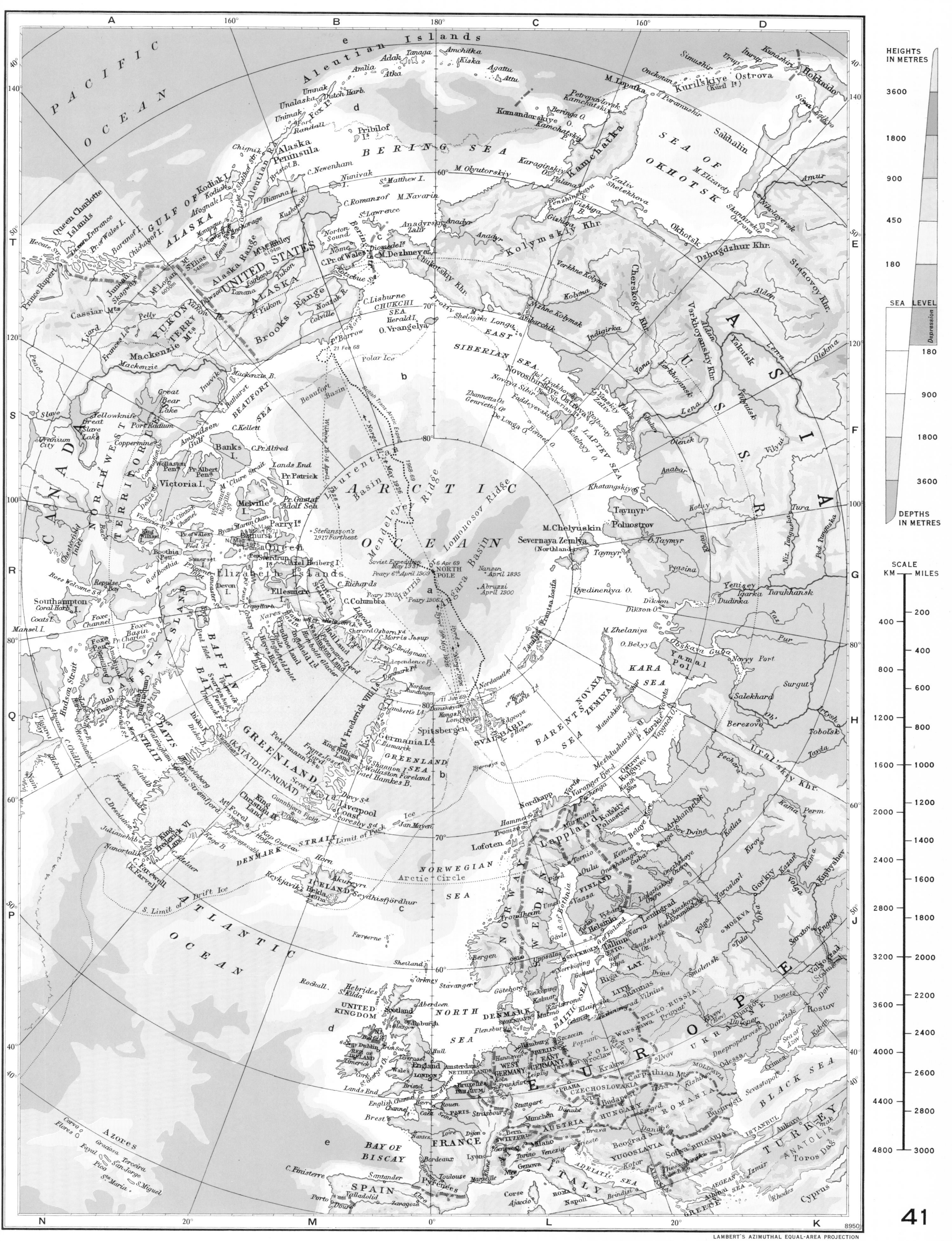

HEIGHTS IN METRES
3600
1800
900
450
180
SEA LEVEL
180
900
1800
3600
DEPTHS IN METRES

SCALE
KM — MILES

41

LAMBERT'S AZIMUTHAL EQUAL-AREA PROJECTION

8950

AREA: 9,363,169 sq. km. (3,615,123 sq. m.)
POP: 216,817,000 CAP: Washington, D.C.
CURRENCY: 100 cents = 1 dollar
The United States can be divided into six

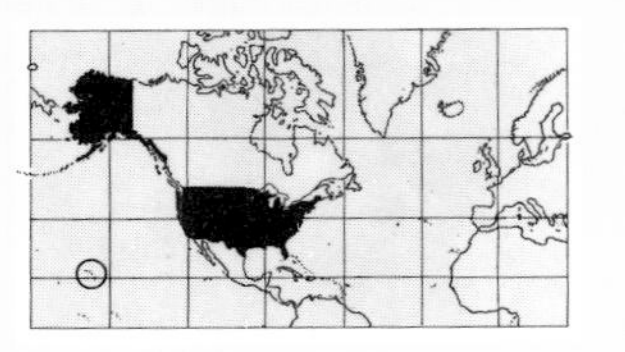

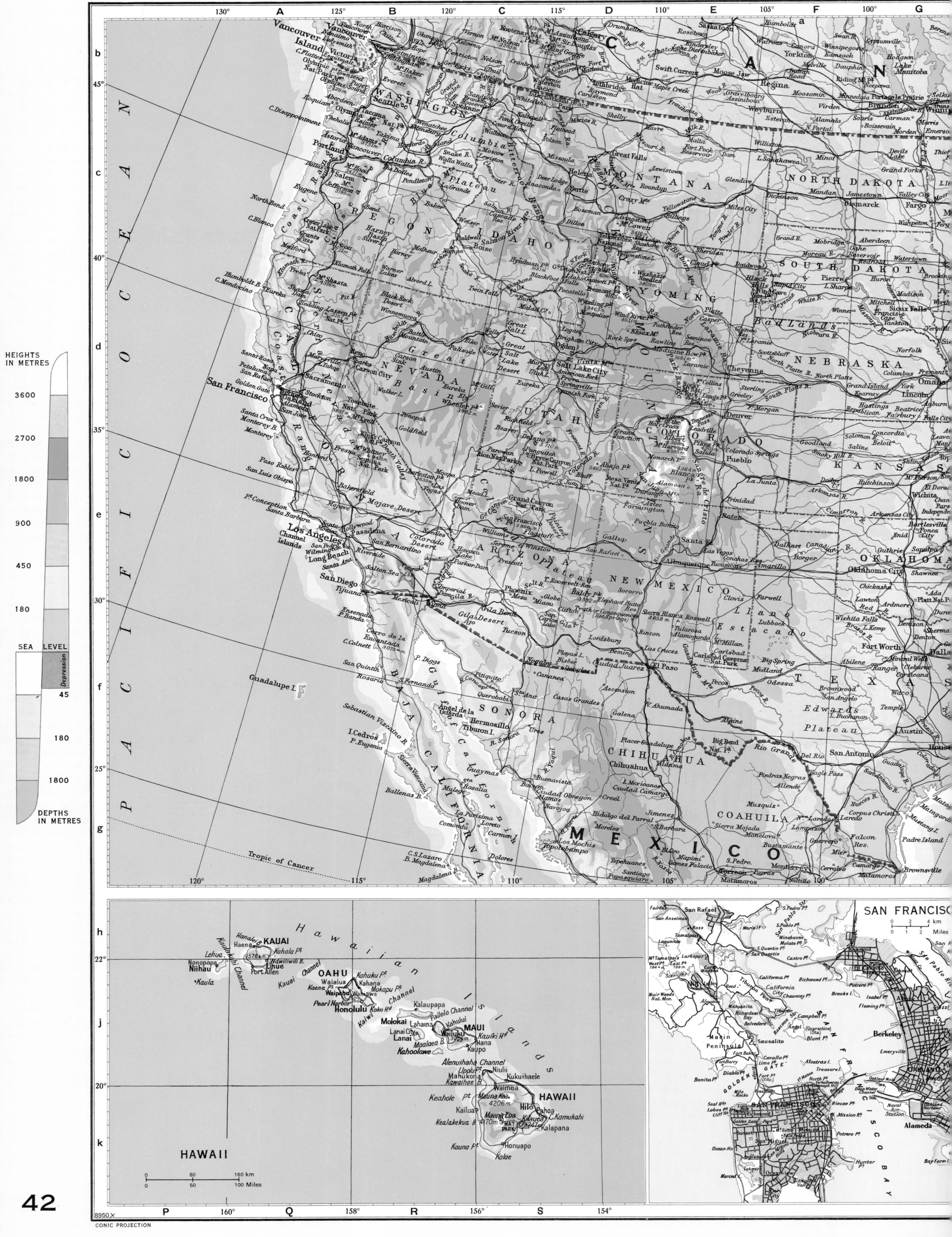

HEIGHTS
IN METRES

3600
2700
1800
900
450
180

SEA LEVEL

Depression
45

180
1800

DEPTHS
IN METRES

PACIFIC OCEAN

HAWAII

SAN FRANCISCO

42

8950 X

CONIC PROJECTION

SCALE: 1:12,500,000   (1CM = 125KM)

MAIN ROADS
RAILWAYS

north–south sections. Reading the map from east to west, these are—a broad plain edging the Atlantic; the Appalachian Mountains; the Mississippi Basin; the Great Plains; the Rocky Mountains, and beyond, and along the Pacific coast, more mountains interspersed with fertile valleys. The State of Alaska, in the extreme north-west, is separated from the main body of the land by Western Canada. The northern part of the State lies within the Arctic Circle, and to the west it is separated from the U.S.S.R. by the Bering Strait. Hawaii consists of 20 islands (eight inhabited) in the North Pacific some 3,200 kilometres from San Francisco.

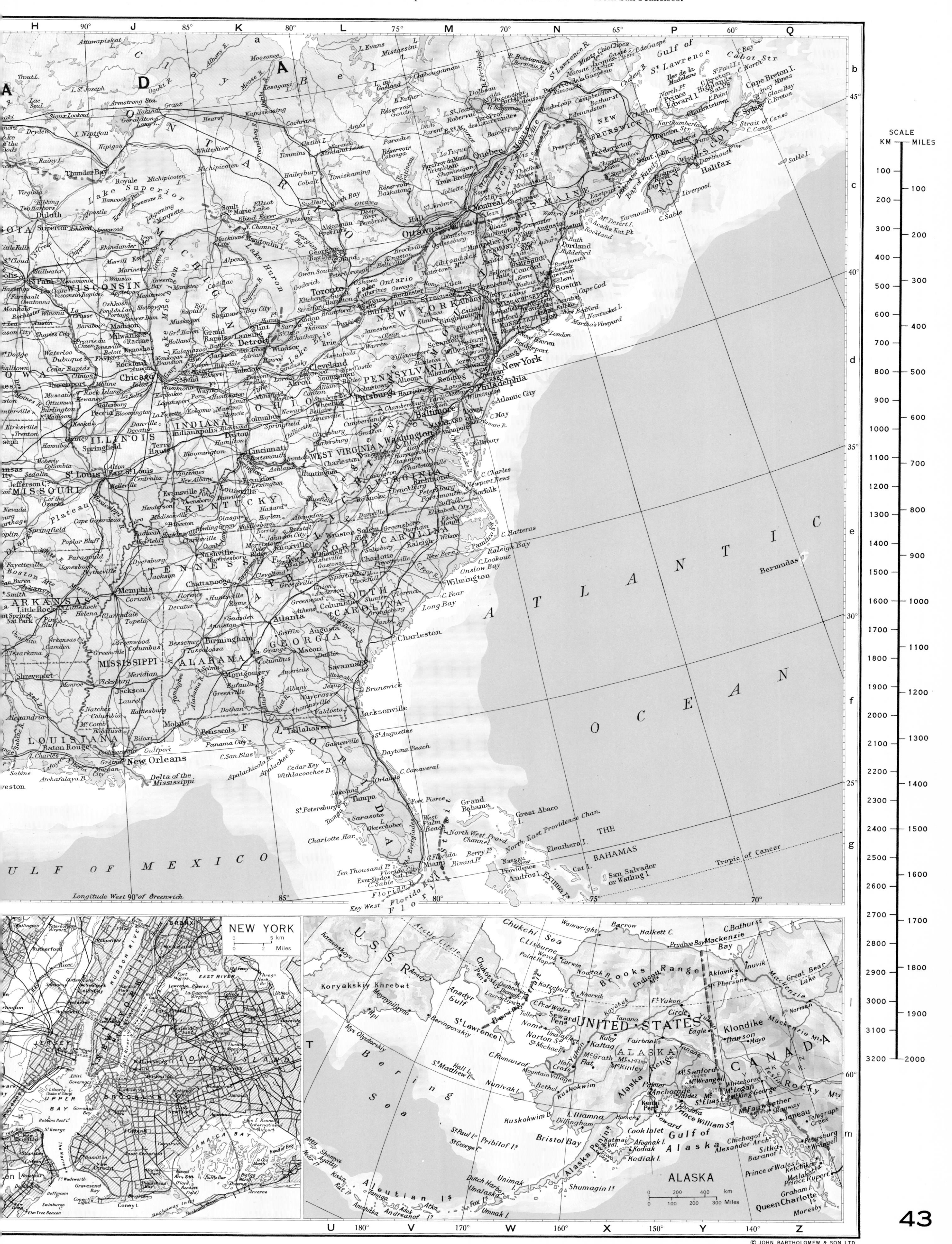

INTERNATIONAL BOUNDARIES
STATE BOUNDARIES

SCALE: 1:12,500,000 (1CM = 125KM)

43

MIDDLE ATLANTIC STATES

The Atlantic seaboard in this north-east area of the United States is flanked by lowlands. The broken coastline is deeply penetrated by Chesa-peake, Delaware and Narragansett Bays. To the west and north of the lowlands lie the Appalachian, Catskill and Adirondack Mountains, while to the north-west is the Allegheny. Plateau. To the south is Washington, in the District of Columbia, the seat of the U.S. Federal Government.

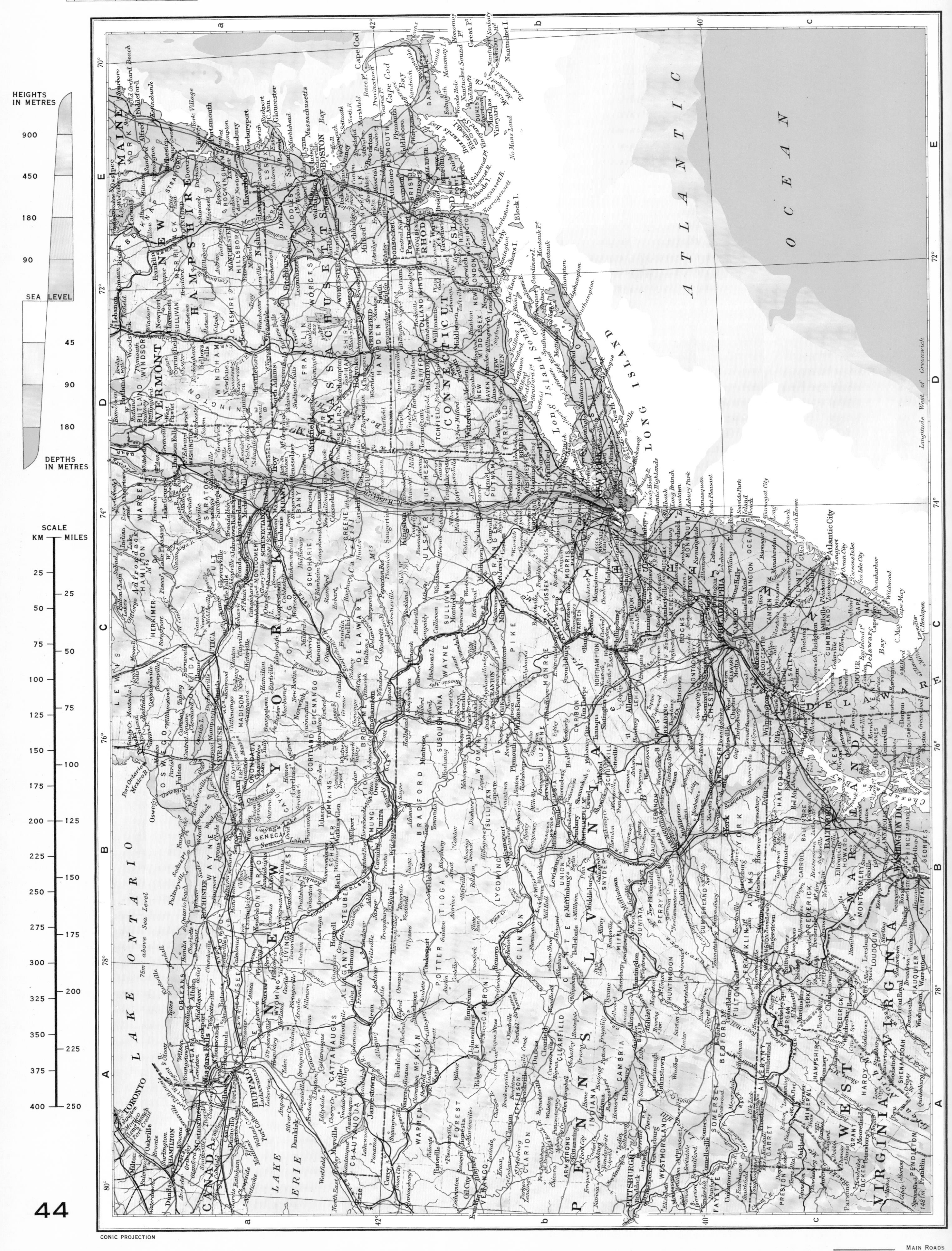

HEIGHTS IN METRES

900
450
180
90

SEA LEVEL

45
90
180

DEPTHS IN METRES

SCALE

KM	MILES
25	25
50	
75	50
100	
125	75
150	100
175	
200	125
225	150
250	
275	175
300	
325	200
350	225
375	
400	250

CONIC PROJECTION

SCALE: 1:2,500,000 (1CM = 25KM)

Main Roads

Railways

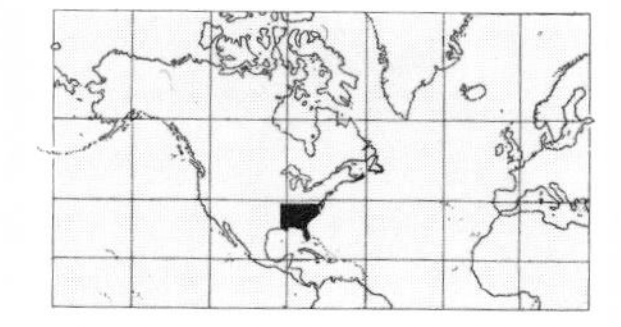

The South, the area east of the Mississippi and south of the Ohio rivers, is sunnier and wetter than the rest of the United States. The Mississippi meanders across a wide flood-plain and through its growing delta in the Gulf of Mexico. The fertile Ohio-Mississippi lowlands and the rich plains of the Atlantic and Gulf coasts enclose the southern ranges of the Appalachian Mountains and the prairie plateaux and hills to their west.

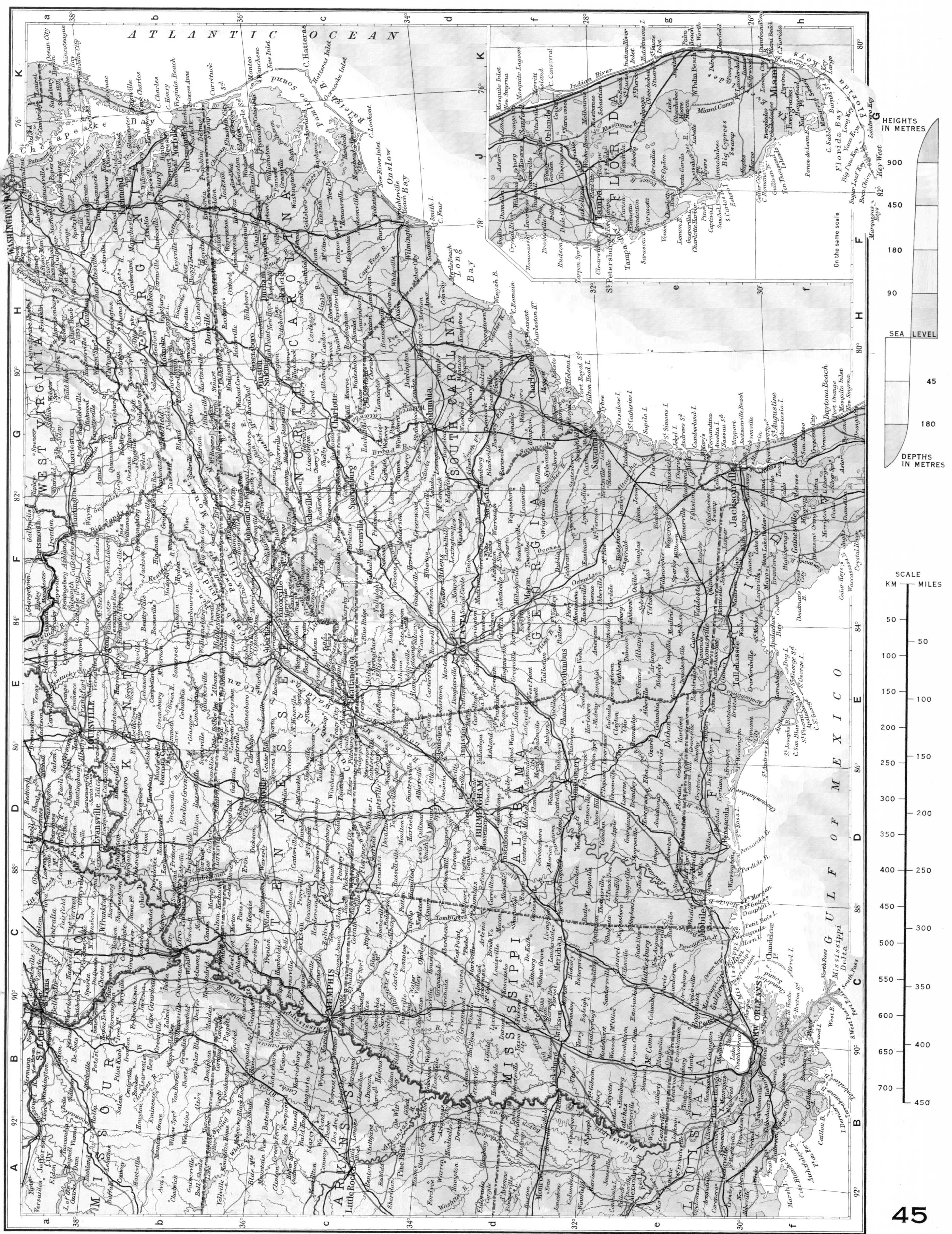

HEIGHTS IN METRES

900
450
180
90
SEA LEVEL
45
180

DEPTHS IN METRES

SCALE
KM — MILES

50
50
100
150
100
200
150
250
300
200
350
400
250
450
500
300
550
600
350
650
700
450

45

BONNE'S PROJECTION

INTERNATIONAL BOUNDARIES
STATE BOUNDARIES
MAIN ROADS
RAILWAYS

SCALE: 1:5,000,000 (1CM = 50KM)

NORTH CENTRAL STATES

Reading from west to east, the four regions shown on this map are: the beautiful Rocky Mountains; the gently rolling grasslands of the Great Plains, which are broken by isolated hilly outcrops and great eastward-flowing rivers like the Missouri and Platte; the wetter, more populous Prairies, which in southern Minnesota and Iowa are some of the richest in the United States; and the glacial lakes and hills of the north-east.

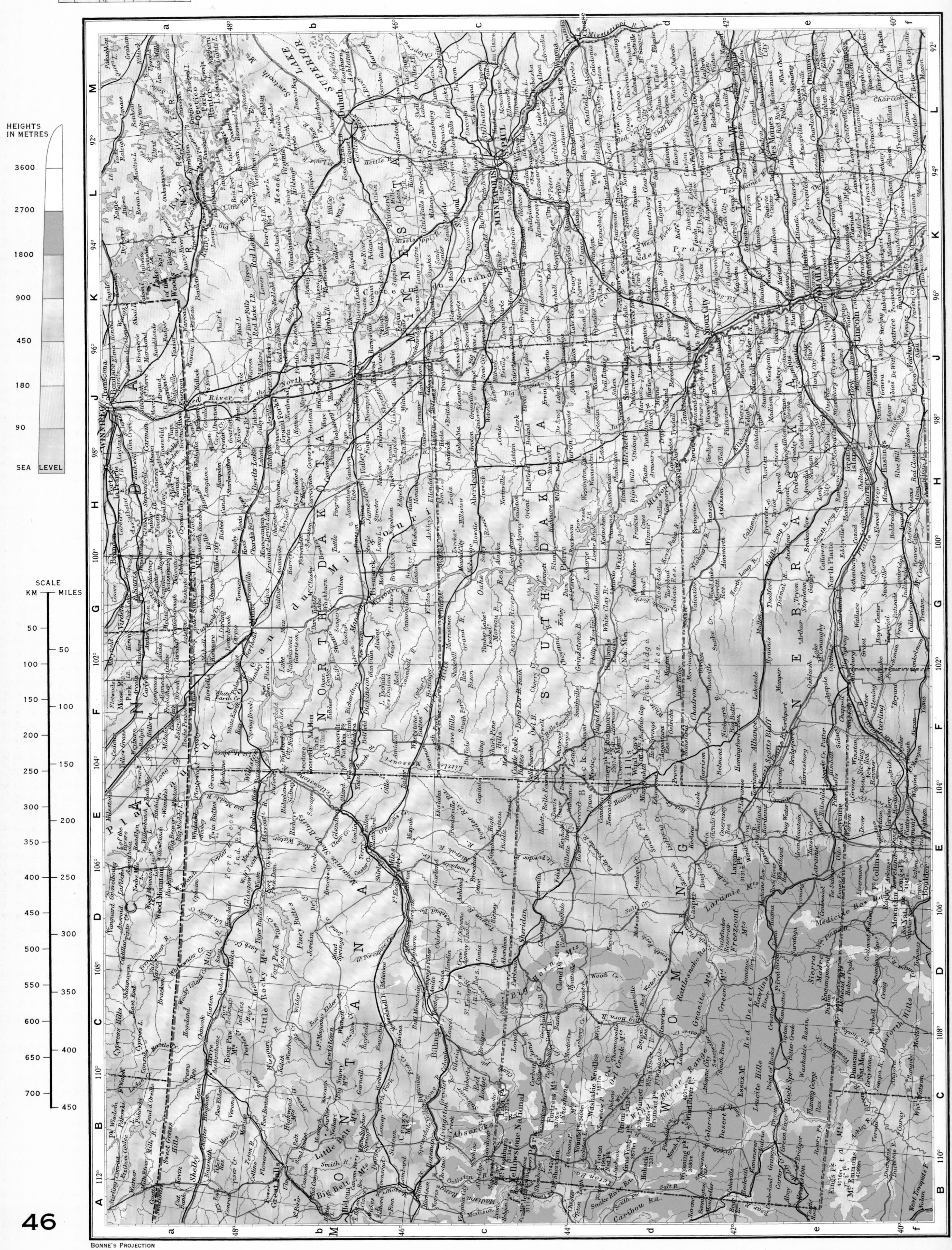

HEIGHTS IN METRES

3600
2700
1800
900
450
180
90
SEA LEVEL

SCALE
KM   MILES

46

BONNE'S PROJECTION

SCALE: 1:5,000,000 (1CM = 50KM)

MAIN ROADS
RAILWAYS
INTERNATIONAL BOUNDARIES
STATE BOUNDARIES

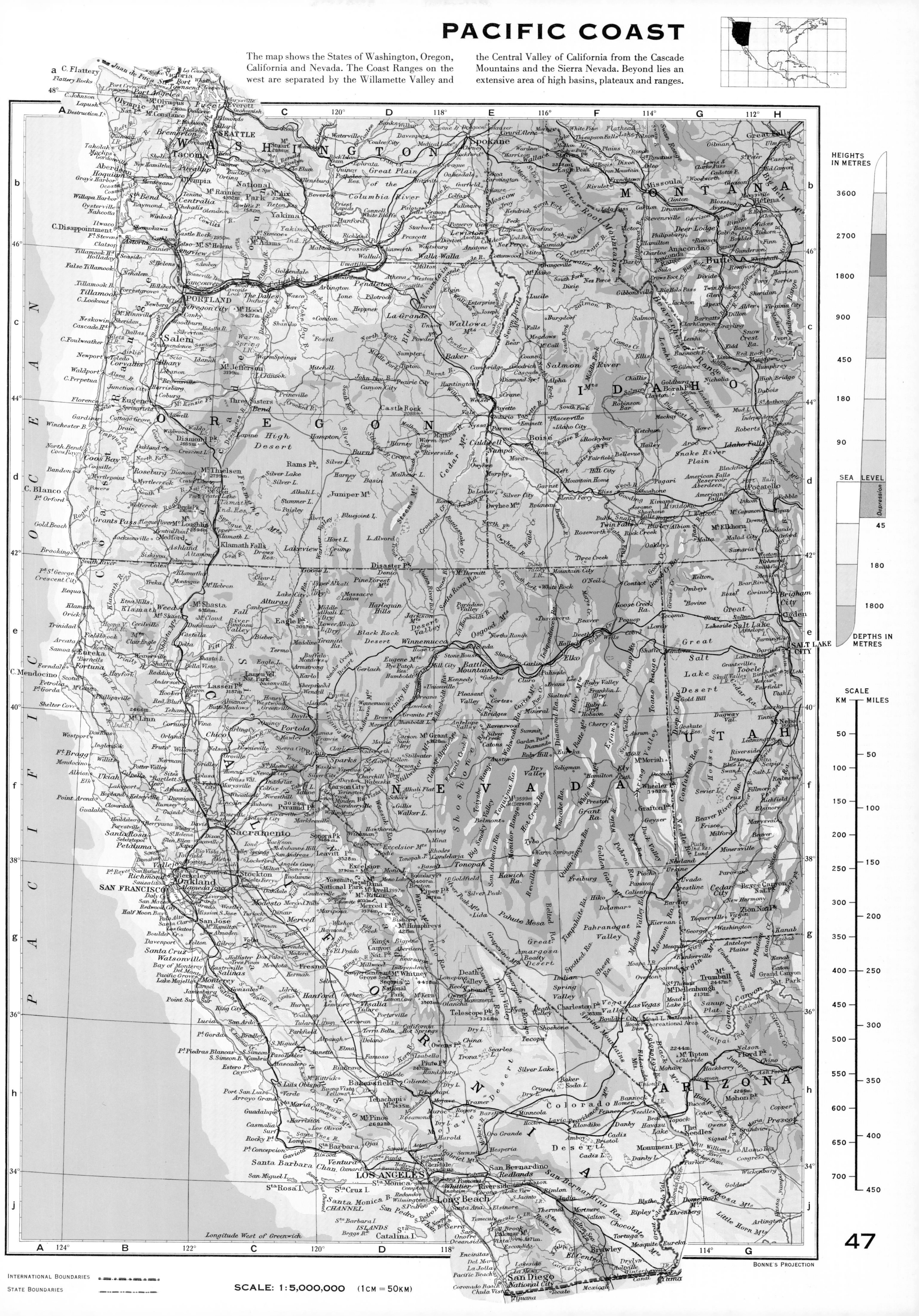

PACIFIC COAST

The map shows the States of Washington, Oregon, California and Nevada. The Coast Ranges on the west are separated by the Willamette Valley and the Central Valley of California from the Cascade Mountains and the Sierra Nevada. Beyond lies an extensive area of high basins, plateaus and ranges.

SCALE: 1:5,000,000 (1CM = 50KM)

47

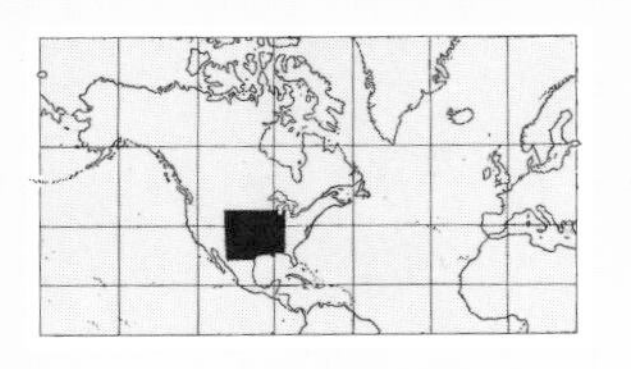

MIDDLE WEST STATES

The United States is divided into contrasting eastern and western halves by the 100° W meridian running down the centre of this map. The east is wetter and agriculturally richer than the west, and

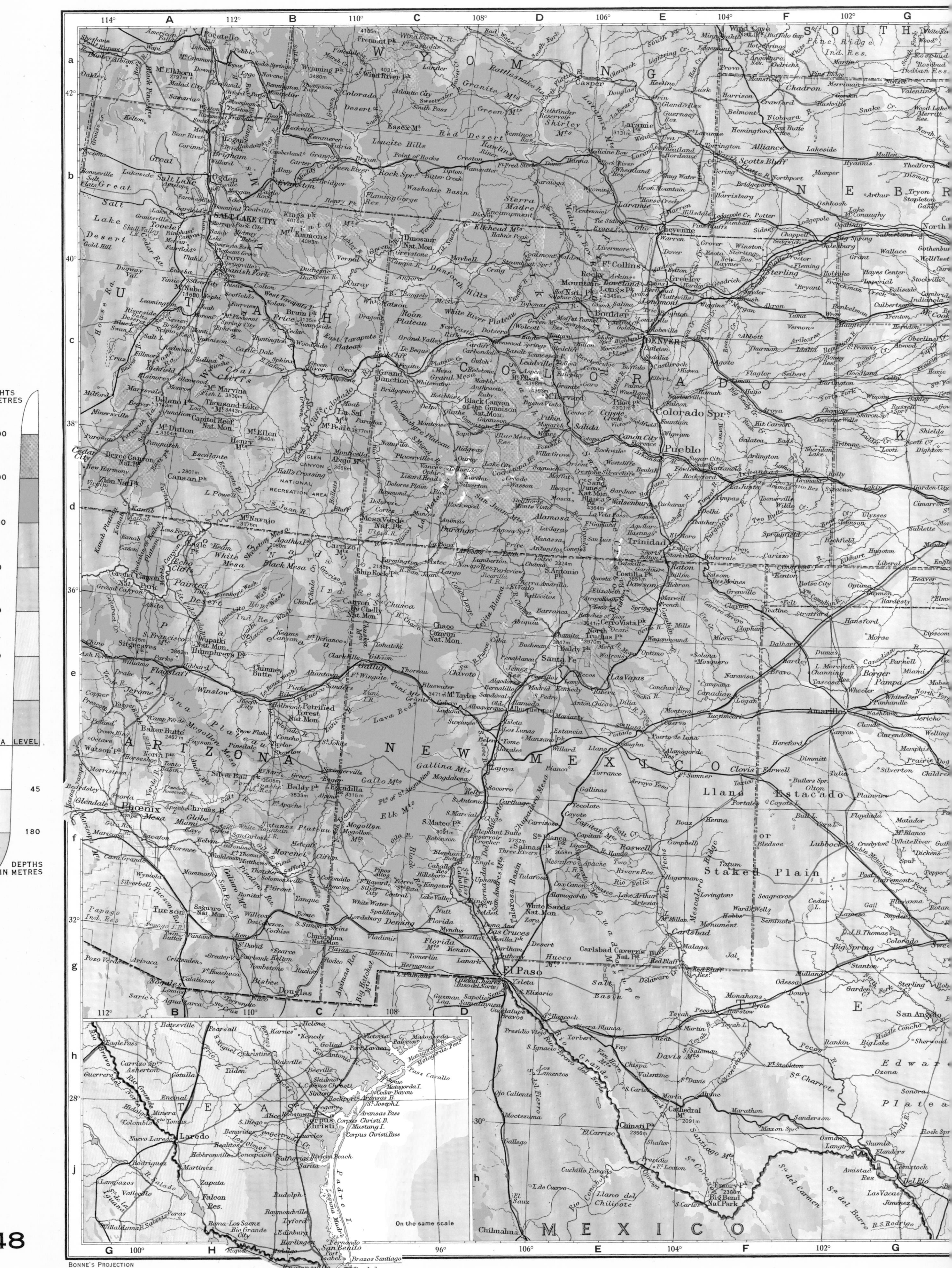

HEIGHTS IN METRES

3600
2700
1800
900
450
180
90

SEA LEVEL

45
180

DEPTHS IN METRES

48

BONNE'S PROJECTION

SCALE: 1:5,000,000 (1CM = 50KM)

Main Roads

Railways

more densely populated. Roughly, the meridian divides the Great Plains to the west from the Prairies to the east. The Plains' short grasslands become drier southwards to Texas, where the Edwards Plateau is semi-desert. West of the Plains rise the snow-capped peaks of the Rocky Mountains, and beyond are the arid high plateaus and flat-topped hills of Arizona and Utah, which are scored by the deeply entrenched Colorado River and its tributaries. Eastwards from 100° W, the fertile long-grass Prairies reach Lake Michigan, the Mississippi lowlands and the rich plains by the Gulf of Mexico. In Arkansas, they are broken by the wooded ranges of the Ozark Mountains.

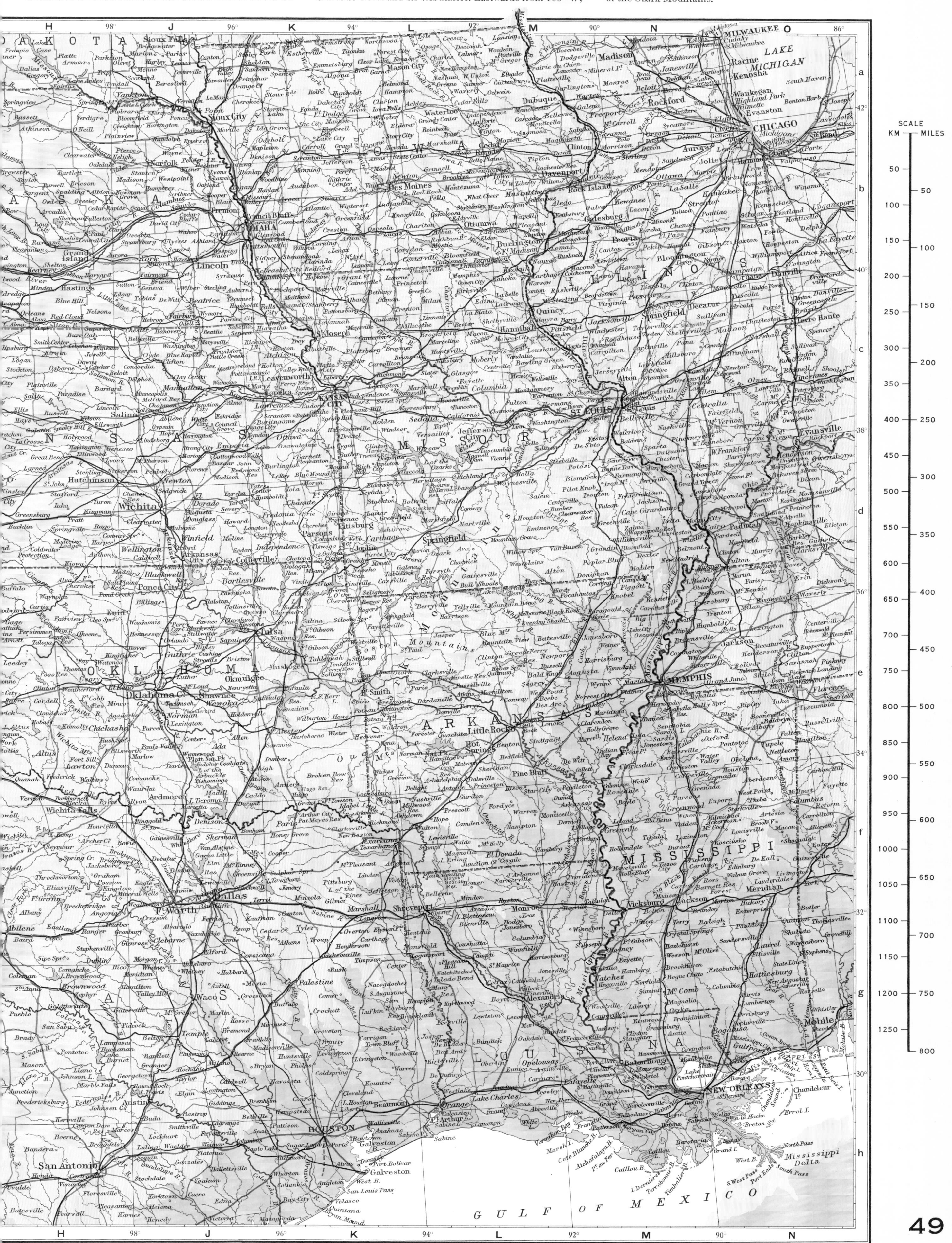

INTERNATIONAL BOUNDARIES
STATE BOUNDARIES

SCALE 1:5,000,000 (1CM = 50KM)

© JOHN BARTHOLOMEW & SON LTD.

SCALE
KM   MILES

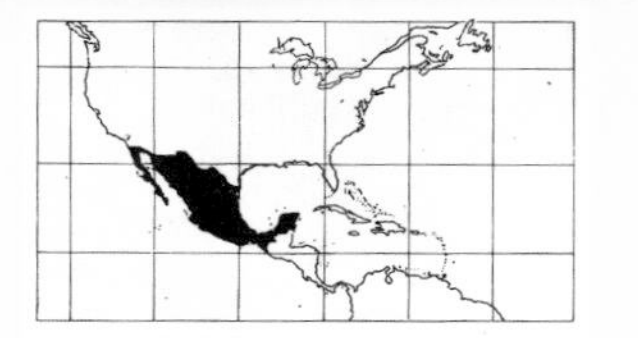

MEXICO GUATEMALA, HONDURAS, BELIZE, EL SALVADOR

MEXICO AREA: *1,972,363 sq. km. (761,530 sq. miles)*
POPULATION: *62,330,000* CAPITAL: *Mexico City*
GUATEMALA AREA: *108,889 sq. km. (42,042 sq. miles)*
POPULATION: *6,300,000* CAPITAL: *Guatemala City*

HONDURAS AREA: *112,087 sq. km. (43,277 sq. miles)*
POPULATION: *3,040,000* CAPITAL: *Tegucigalpa*
BELIZE AREA: *22,966 sq. km. (8,867 sq. miles)*
POPULATION: *150,000* CAPITAL: *Belmopan*

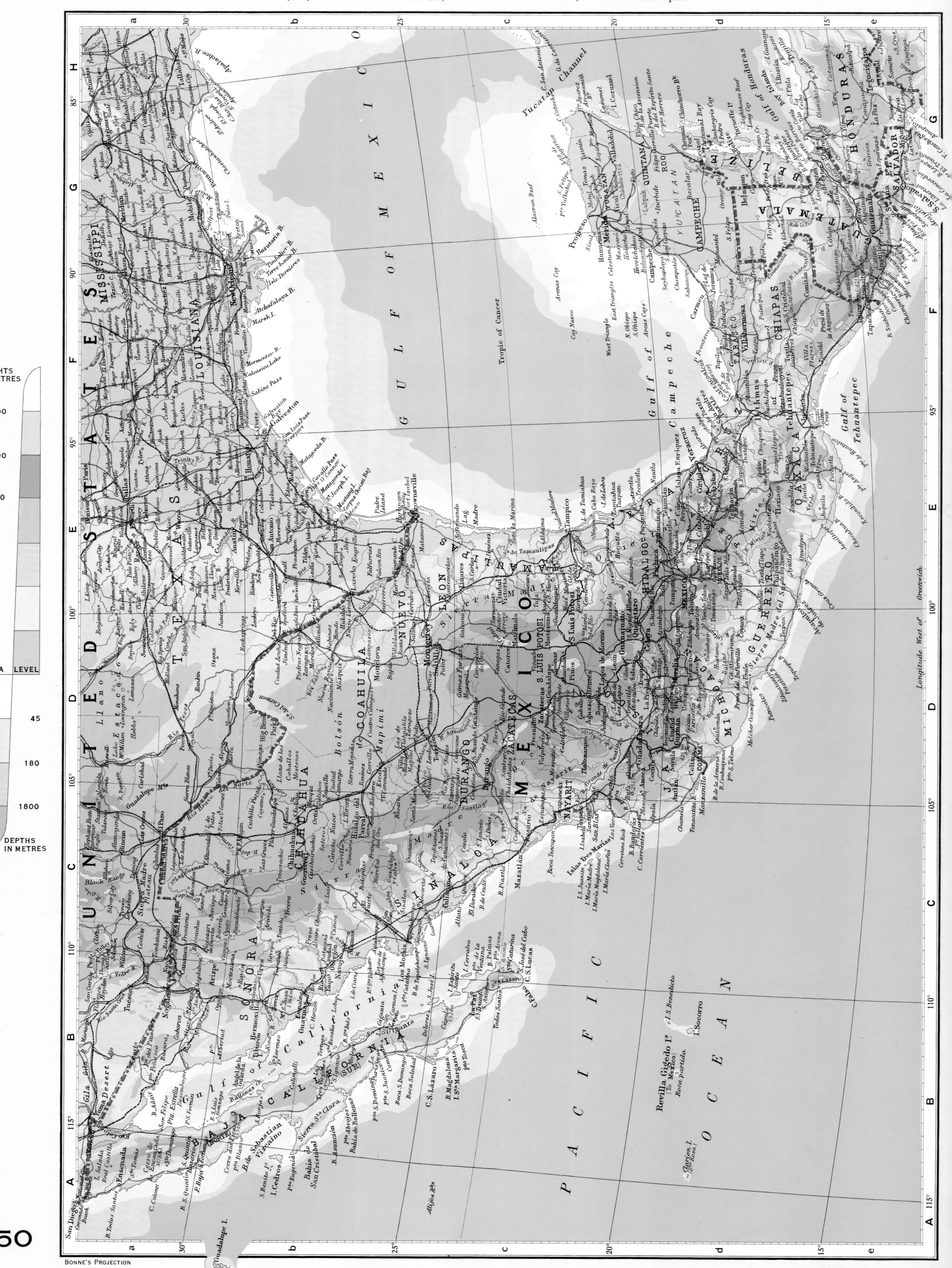

HEIGHTS IN METRES

3600
2700
1800
900
450
180

SEA LEVEL

45
180
1800

DEPTHS IN METRES

50

BONNE'S PROJECTION

SCALE: 1:10,000,000 (1CM = 100KM)

INTERNATIONAL BOUNDARIES
STATE BOUNDARIES

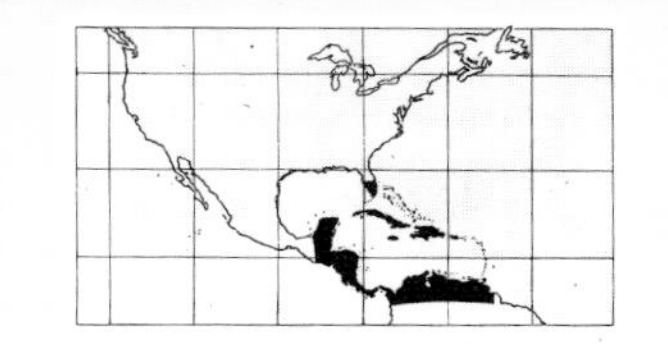

NICARAGUA AREA: *148,000 sq. km. (57,143 sq. miles)*
POPULATION: *2,253,000* CAPITAL: *Managua*
PANAMA AREA: *75,649 sq. km. (29,208 sq. miles)*
POPULATION: *1,670,000* CAPITAL: *Panama City*

CUBA AREA: *114,525 sq. km. (44,218 sq. miles)*
POPULATION: *9,090,000* CAPITAL: *Havana*
JAMAICA AREA: *10,992 sq. km. (4,244 sq. miles)*
POPULATION: *2,030,000* CAPITAL: *Kingston*

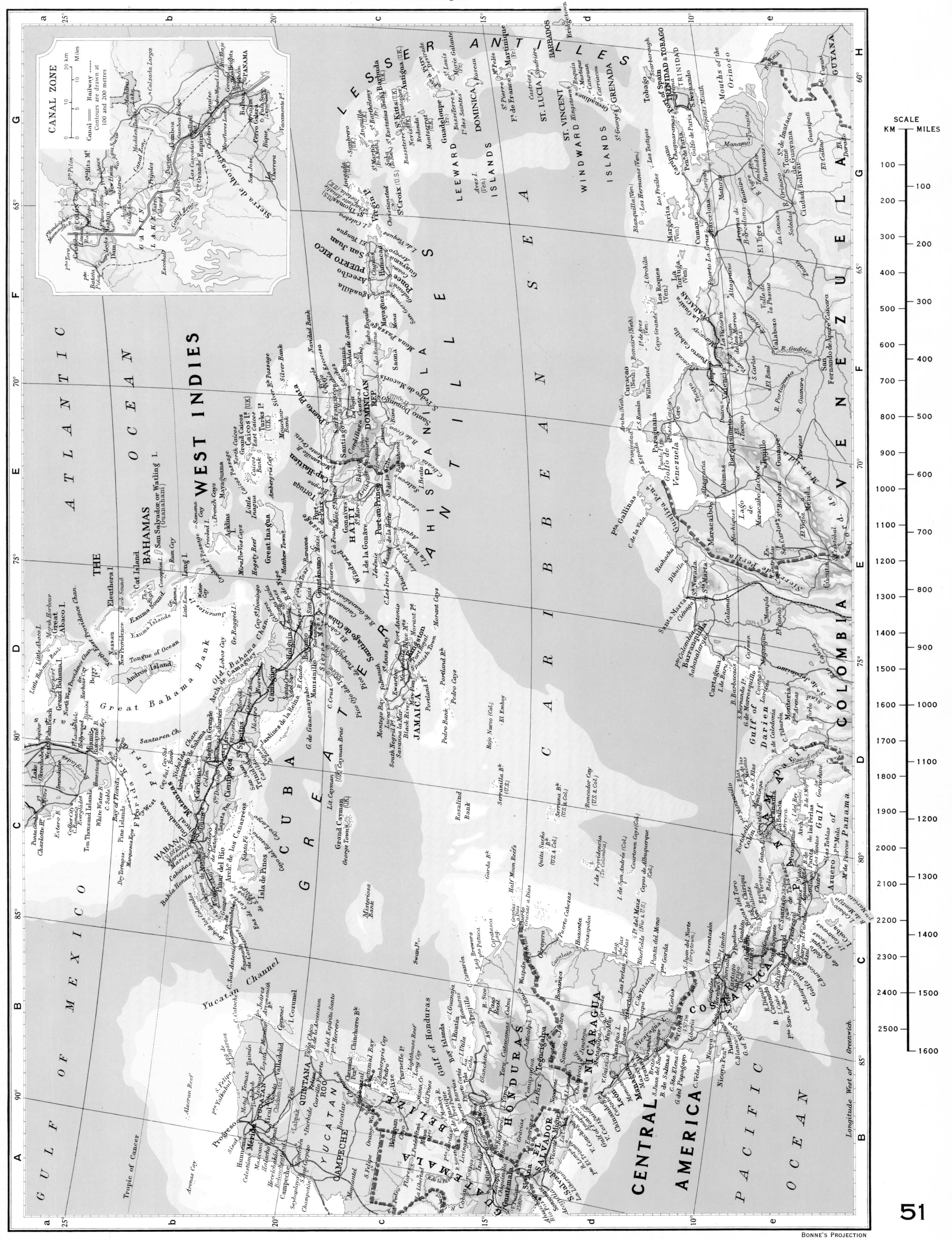

SCALE
KM — MILES

SCALE: 1:10,000,000 (1CM = 100KM)

MAIN ROADS
RAILWAYS

BONNE'S PROJECTION

51

BRAZIL AREA: 8,512,001 sq. km. (3,286,487 sq. miles)
POPULATION: 110,124,000 CAPITAL: Brasilia
BOLIVIA AREA: 1,098,580 sq. km. (424,163 sq. miles)
POPULATION: 5,630,000 CAPITAL: La Paz

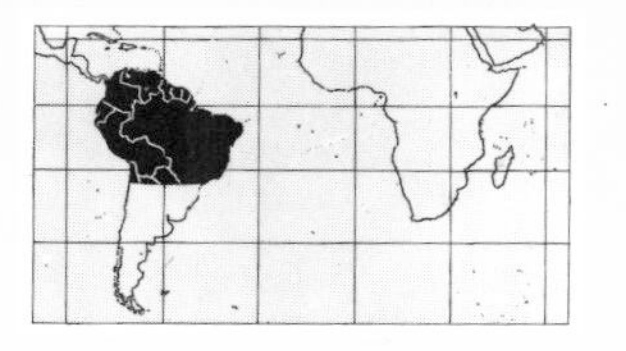

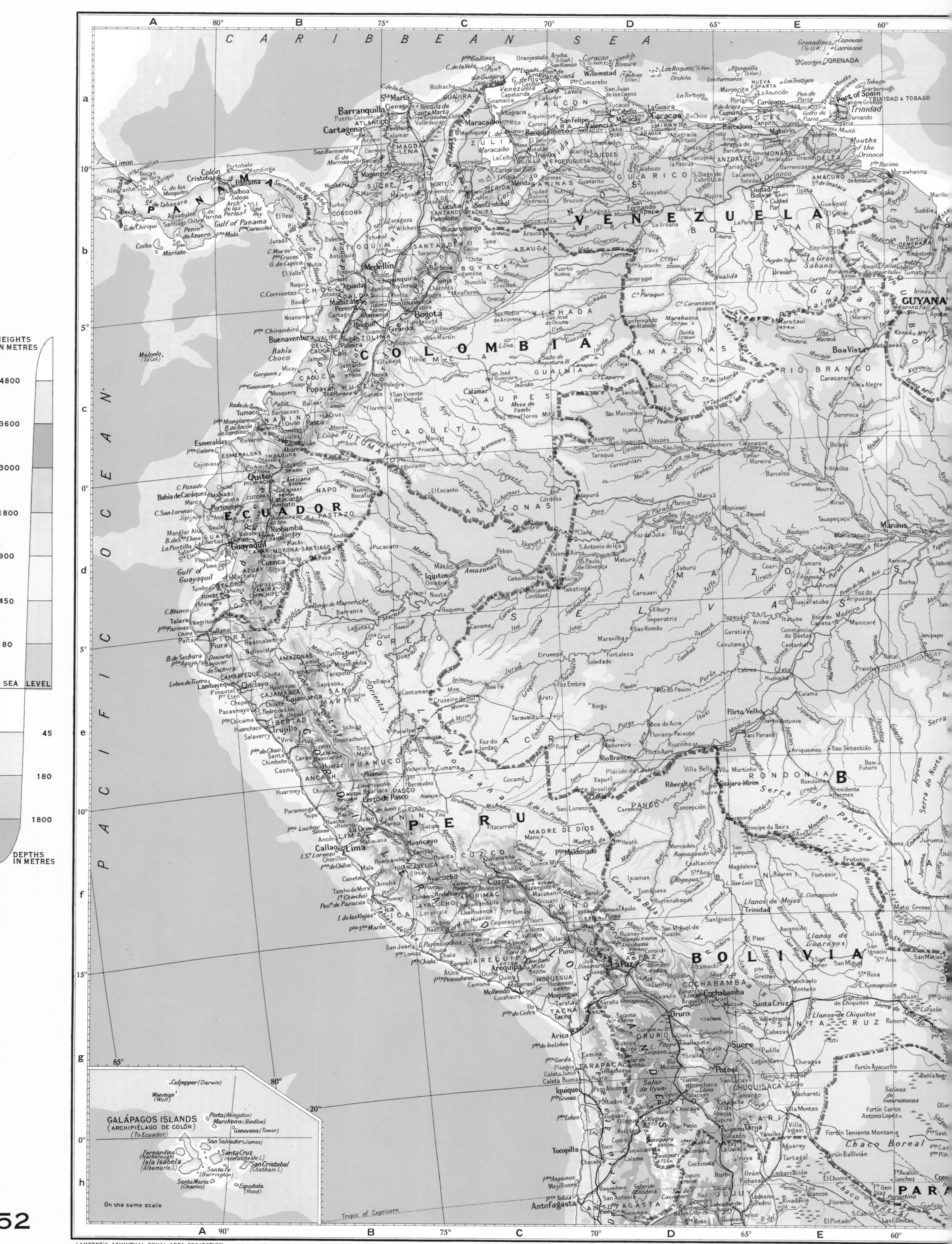

52

LAMBERT'S AZIMUTHAL EQUAL-AREA PROJECTION

SCALE: 1:12,500,000 (1CM = 125KM)

MAIN ROADS
RAILWAYS

PERU AREA: 1,285,220 sq. km. (496,224 sq. miles) POP: 13,568,000 CAP: Lima
ECUADOR AREA: 455,452 sq. km. (175,850 sq. miles) POP: 6,522,000 CAP: Quito
COLOMBIA AREA: 1,138,911 sq. km. (439,734 sq. miles) POP: 25,168,000 CAP: Bogotá
VENEZUELA AREA: 912,050 sq. km. (352,143 sq. miles) POP: 10,750,000 CAP: Caracas
GUYANA AREA: 214,970 sq. km. (83,000 sq. miles) POP: 800,000 CAP: Georgetown
SURINAM AREA: 163,265 sq. km. (63,037 sq. miles) POP: 414,000 CAP: Paramaribo
FRENCH GUIANA AREA: 91,000 sq. km. (35,135 sq. miles) POPULATION: 49,200 CAPITAL: Cayenne

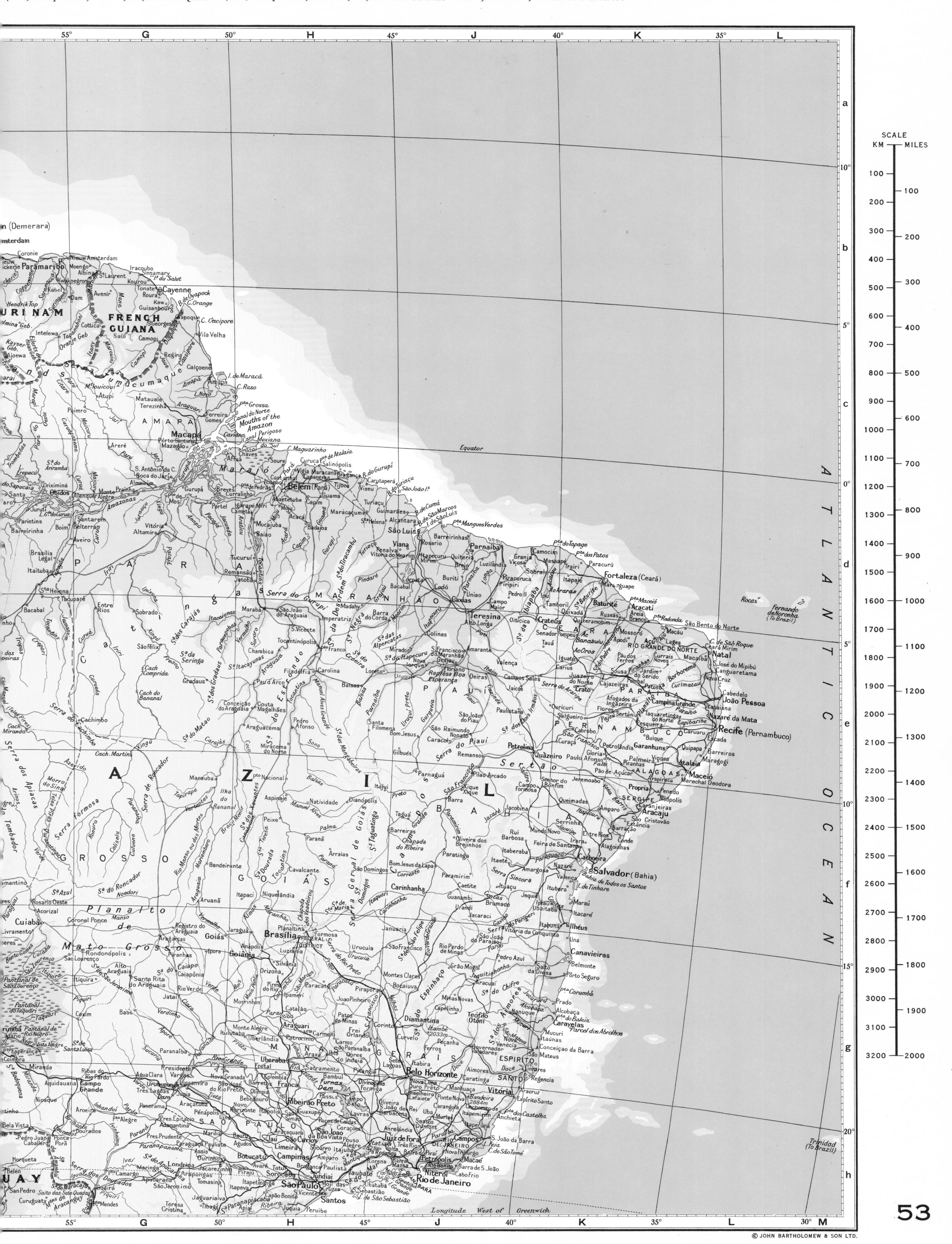

53

© JOHN BARTHOLOMEW & SON LTD.

SCALE: 1:12,500,000 (1CM = 125KM)

SOUTH AMERICA-SOUTH

ARGENTINA, CHILE, PARAGUAY, URUGUAY

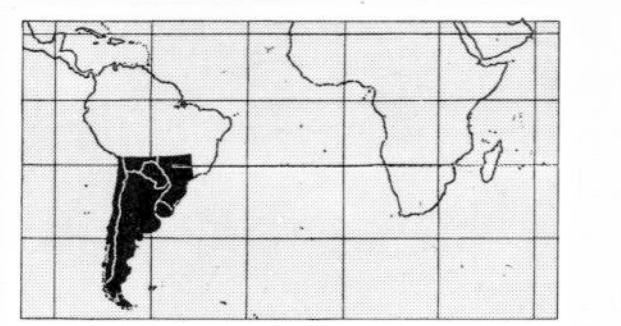

ARGENTINA AREA: *2,777,815 sq. km.*
(1,072,515 sq. miles) POP: *20,900,000*
CAPITAL: *Buenos Aires*

CHILE AREA: *741,767 sq. km.*
(286,397 sq. miles) POP: *10,405,000*
CAPITAL: *Santiago*

PARAGUAY AREA: *406,752 sq. km.*
(157,047 sq. miles) POP: *2,750,000*
CAPITAL: *Asunción*

URUGUAY AREA: *186,925 sq. km.*
(72,172 sq. miles) POP: *2,763,960*
CAPITAL: *Montevideo*

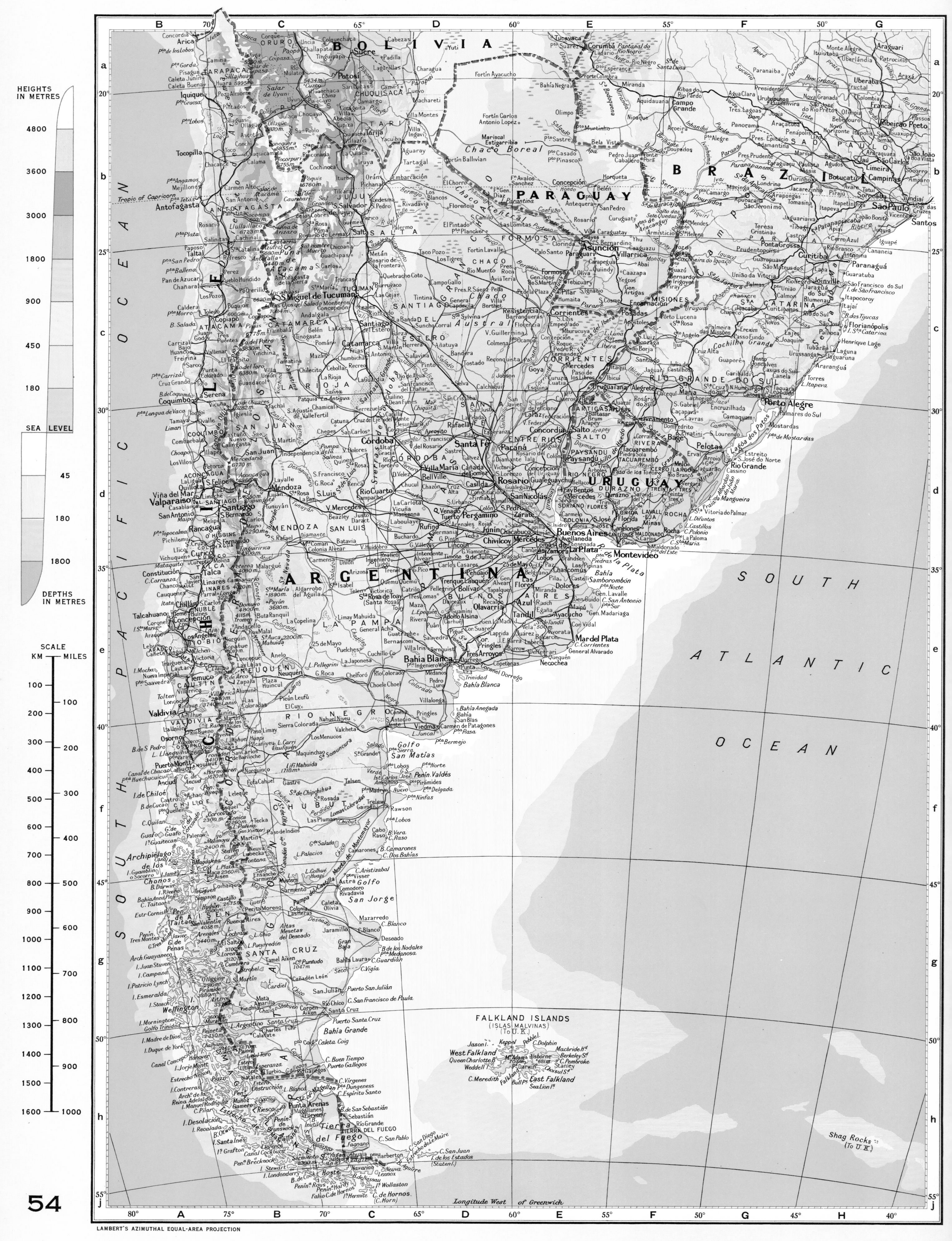

HEIGHTS IN METRES

4800
3600
3000
1800
900
450
180

SEA LEVEL

45
180
1800

DEPTHS IN METRES

SCALE

KM	MILES
100	100
200	
300	200
400	
500	300
600	400
700	
800	500
900	
1000	600
1100	700
1200	
1300	800
1400	900
1500	
1600	1000

54

LAMBERT'S AZIMUTHAL EQUAL-AREA PROJECTION

SCALE: 1:12,500,000 (1CM = 125KM)

━ ━ ━ INTERNATIONAL BOUNDARIES ————— MAIN ROADS

————— PROVINCIAL BOUNDARIES ————— RAILWAYS

NEW ZEALAND

AREA: *268,704 sq. km. (103,747 sq. miles)* POP: *3,129,380* CAPITAL: *Wellington* CURR: *100 cents =1 dollar.* New Zealand includes North Island and South Island, the much smaller Stewart Island, and a number of minor islands. The main islands are mountainous with rich coastal plains. North Island has volcanic peaks and hot springs. South Island includes the Southern Alps (Mount Cook 3,764 metres) and the Tasman Glacier.

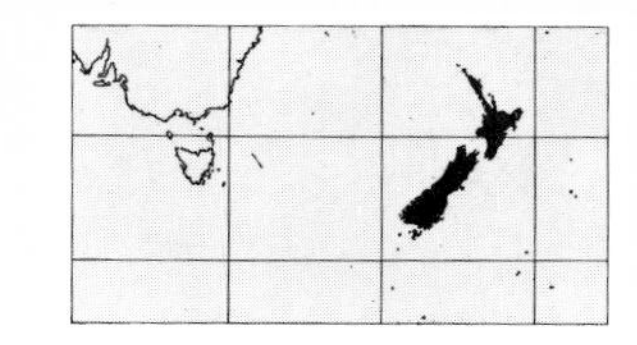

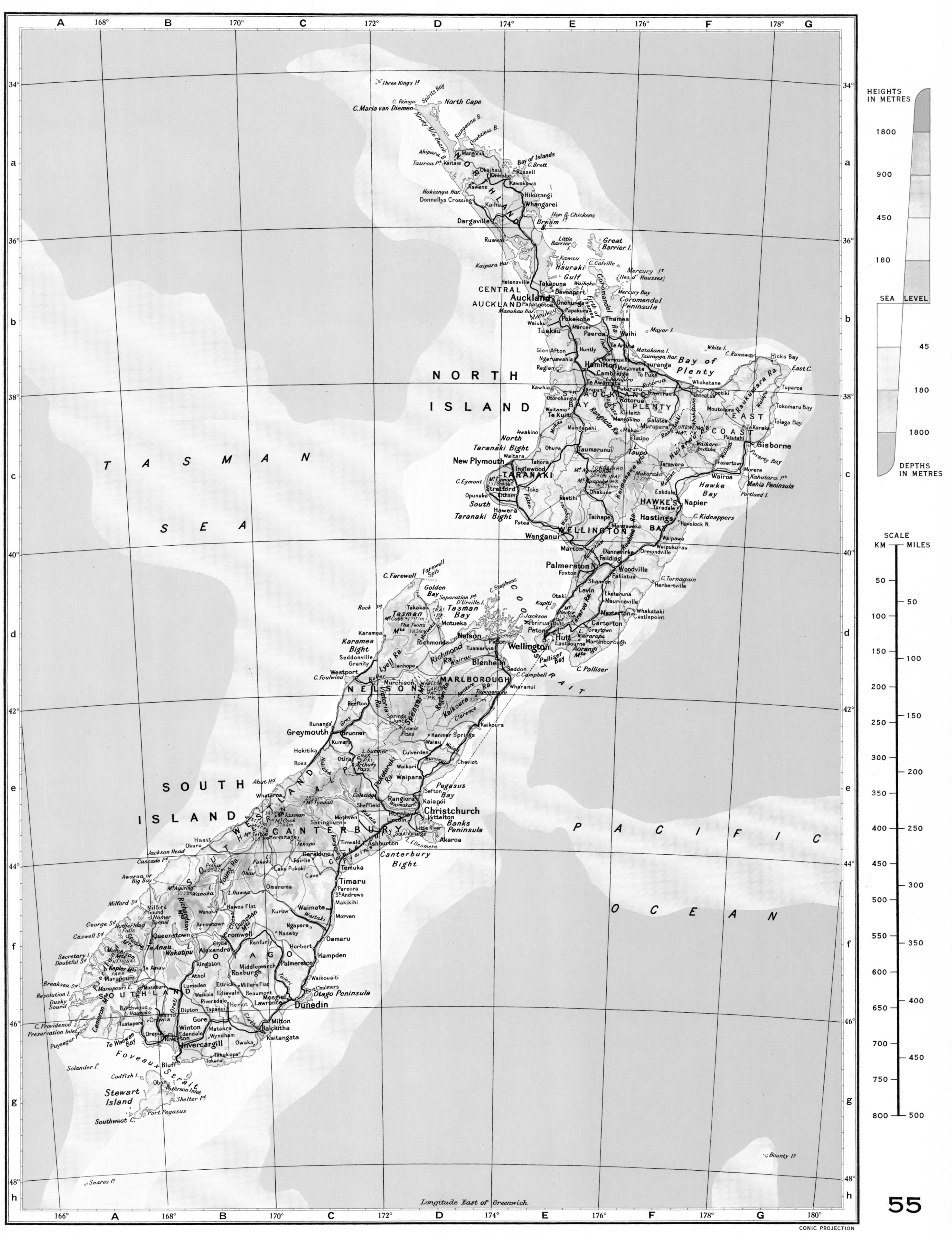

HEIGHTS IN METRES

1800
900
450
180

SEA LEVEL

45
180
1800

DEPTHS IN METRES

SCALE
KM — MILES

55

CONIC PROJECTION

SCALE: 1:5,000,000 (1CM = 50KM)

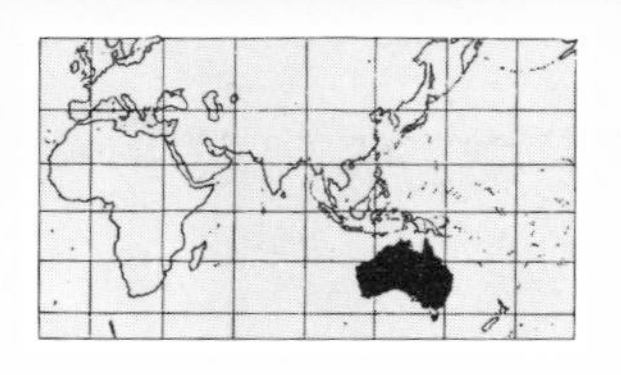

AUSTRALIA

AREA: 7,682,300 sq. km. (2,966,139 sq. miles)
POP: 13,550,000 (excluding full-blooded aborigines).
CAP: *Canberra.* Australia, largest island in the
world, comprises six States and two Territories.

Although two-fifths of Australia lie within the
Tropic of Capricorn, the climate is more temperate
than that of corresponding regions in other parts of
the world. Despite its great deserts, the country has

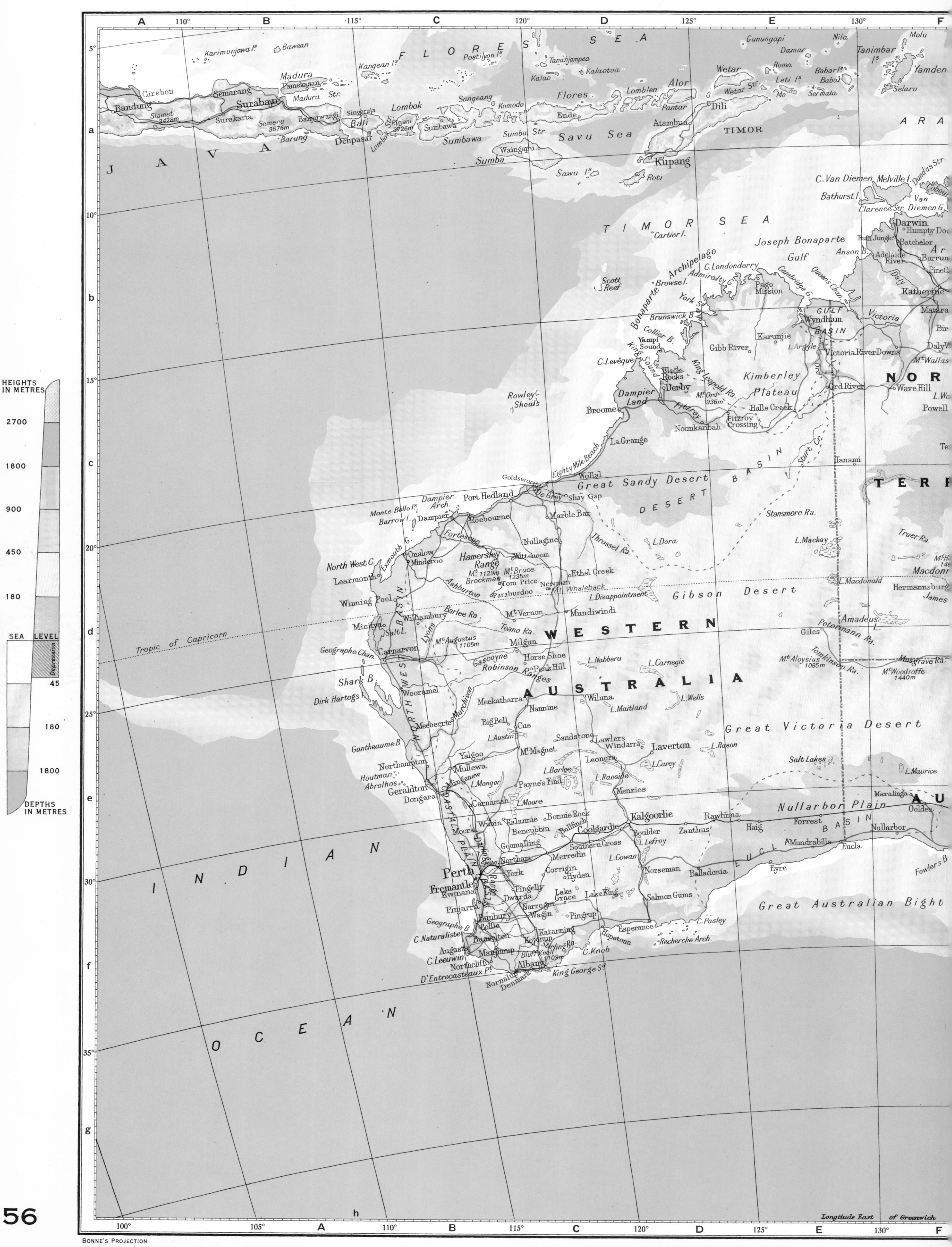

HEIGHTS
IN METRES

2700
1800
900
450
180

SEA LEVEL

Depression
45
180
1800

DEPTHS
IN METRES

BONNE'S PROJECTION

SCALE: 1:12,500,000 (1CM = 125KM)

MAIN ROADS
ARTESIAN BASINS
RAILWAYS

vast acreages of fertile and well-watered land. Reading the map from east to west, one sees a narrow strip of fertile coastland, beyond which mountain ranges reach from Melbourne in the south right up to the Cape York Peninsula. These mountains, the Great Dividing Range, form a natural division between the coastal land and a fertile tableland, which is flanked on the west by an extensive inland plain. North of Spencer Gulf lies the Lake Eyre Basin, an inland drainage basin partly below sea level into which the rivers from the eastern plateau drain. Farther westwards, poorly watered plains give way to enormous deserts. Another strip of watered fertile land lies in the extreme south-west.

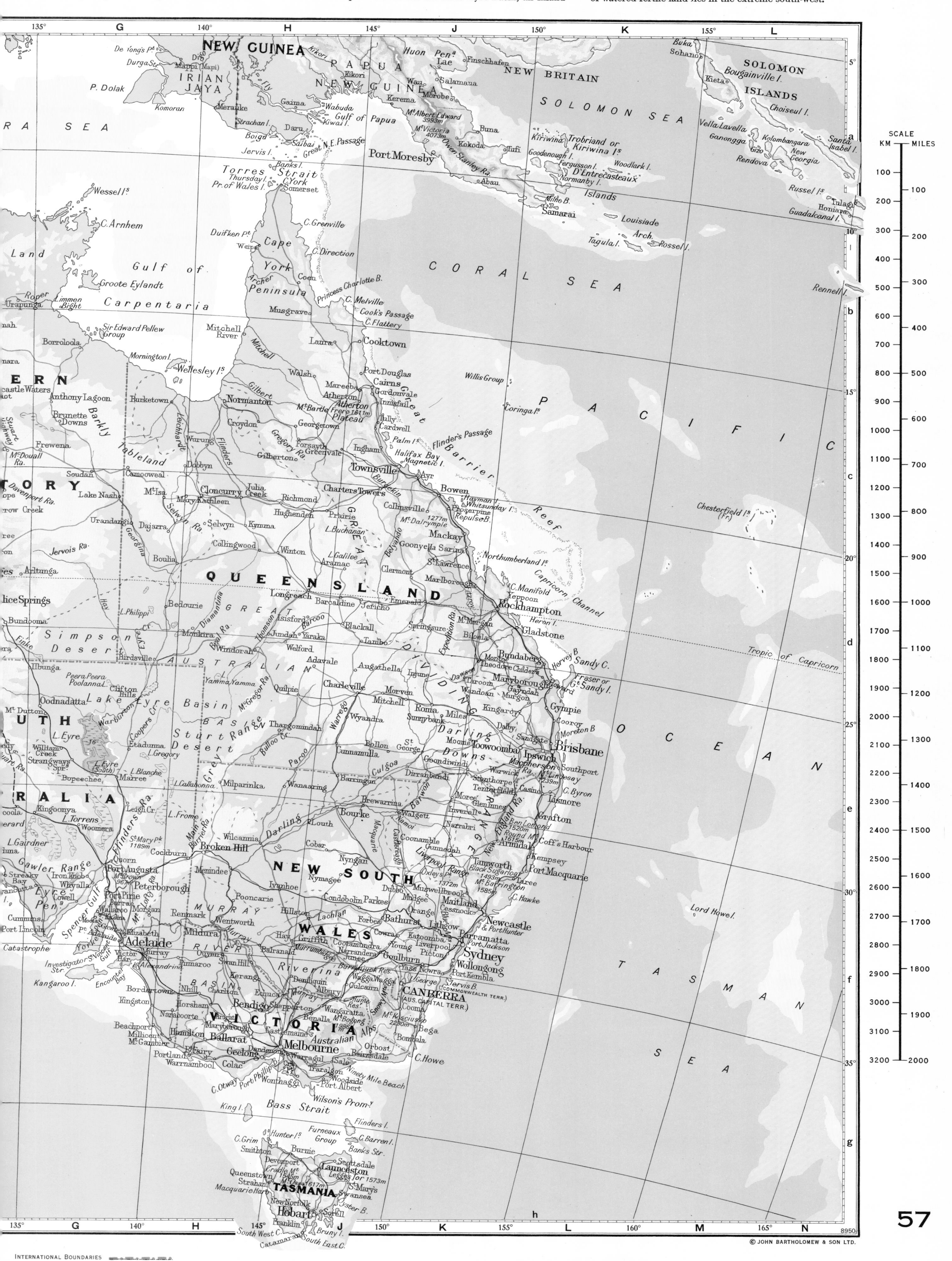

© JOHN BARTHOLOMEW & SON LTD.

INTERNATIONAL BOUNDARIES

STATE BOUNDARIES

SCALE: 1:12,500,000 (1CM = 125KM)

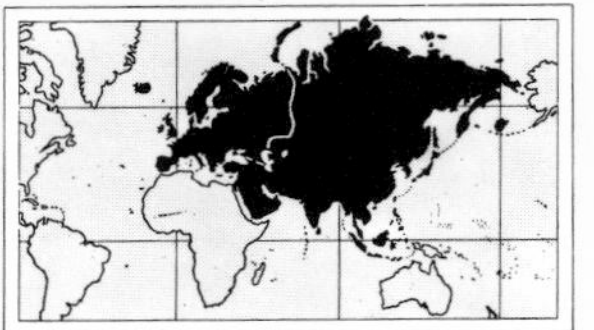

EURASIA

This vast land mass—the largest in the world—covers more than a quarter of the Earth's land surface and is inhabited by over three-quarters of its population. Across the whole area, from the Pyrénées to the backbone of Peninsular Malaysia, runs an almost continuous belt of fold mountains, of which the highest, the Himalayas

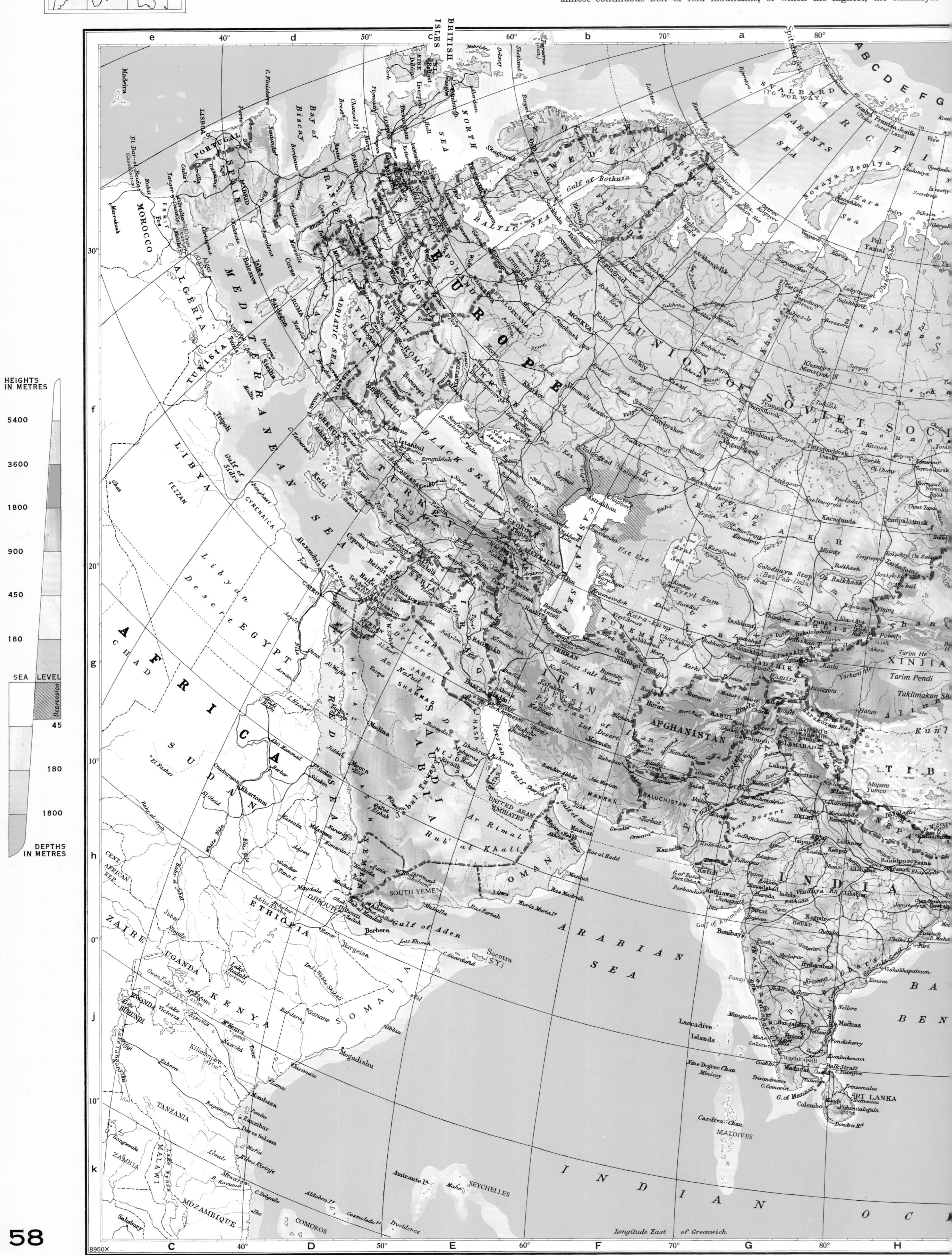

HEIGHTS
IN METRES

5400
3600
1800
900
450
180

SEA LEVEL

Depression

45
180
1800

DEPTHS
IN METRES

58

8950×

LAMBERT'S AZIMUTHAL EQUAL-AREA PROJECTION

SCALE: 1:30,000,000 (1cm = 300km)

INTERNATIONAL BOUNDARIES

STATE BOUNDARIES

(Everest, 8,848 metres), form a central branch. There is also an undersea range fringing the east as a chain of islands from the Aleutians south to the Philippines. Contrasting with the central highlands are the immense low-lying plains of northern Russia, while in between lies a great zone of desert stretching from Mongolia to Arabia. From the frozen tundra of the Arctic to the dense rain forests of Peninsular Malaysia, there is every type of climate and soil, and for climatic reasons the population centres are mainly in the west, south and south-east. In India, for instance, the average population density is almost 80 times greater than it is in Siberia.

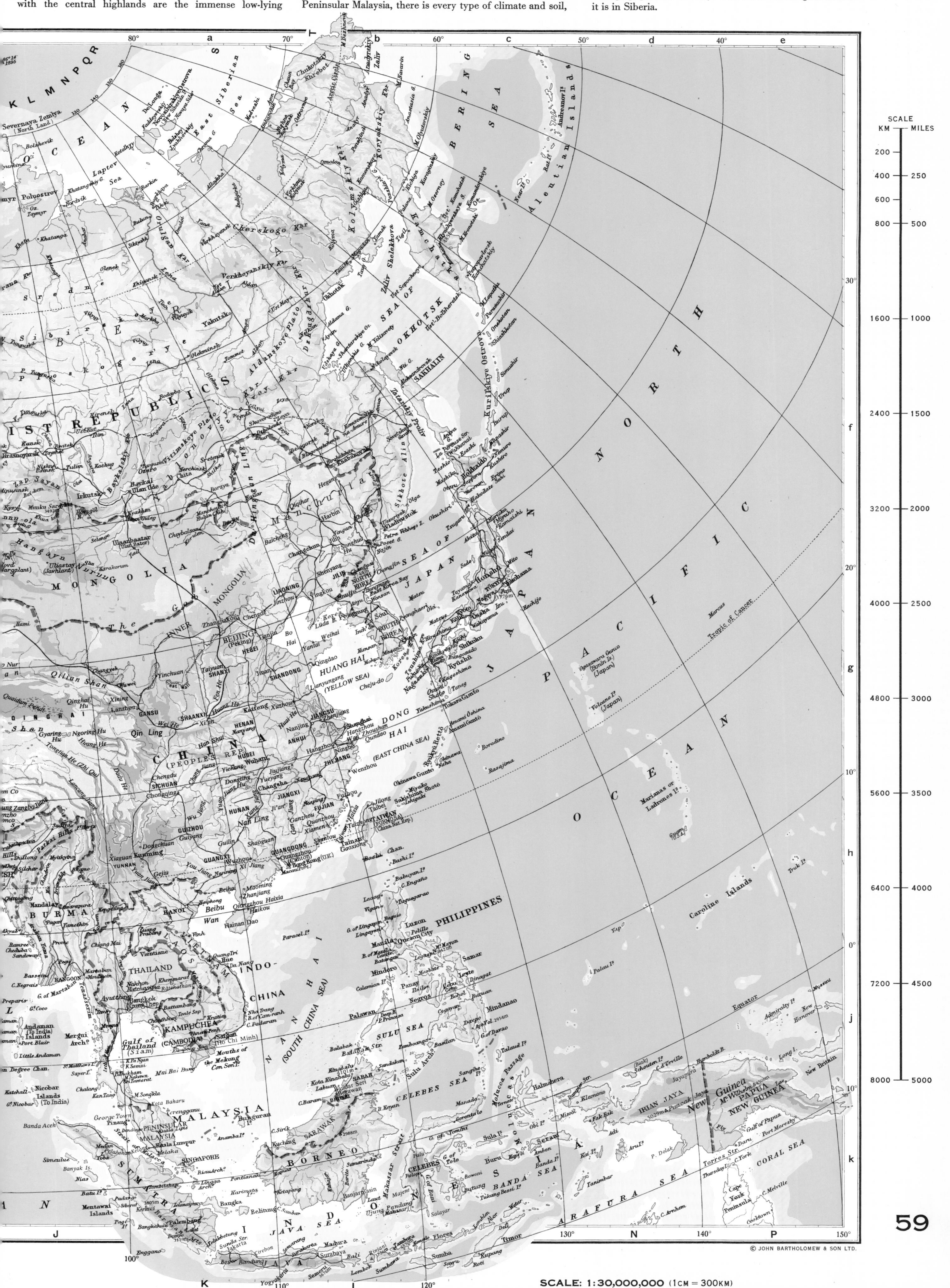

SCALE: 1:30,000,000 (1CM = 300KM)

© JOHN BARTHOLOMEW & SON LTD.

59

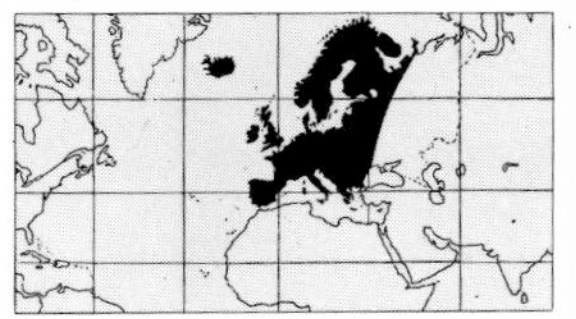

EUROPE

Itself a peninsula of Asia, Europe is made up of smaller peninsulas such as Scandinavia, Iberia, Italy and Greece. Characteristic of these countries are north-south backbones of mountains, some of them offshoots of the great chain of fold mountains that winds across the entire continent from the Pyrénées to the Black Sea.

HEIGHTS
IN METRES

3600
2700
1800
900
450
180

SEA LEVEL

Depression

90
180
450
900
1800
2700

DEPTHS
IN METRES

60

BONNE'S PROJECTION

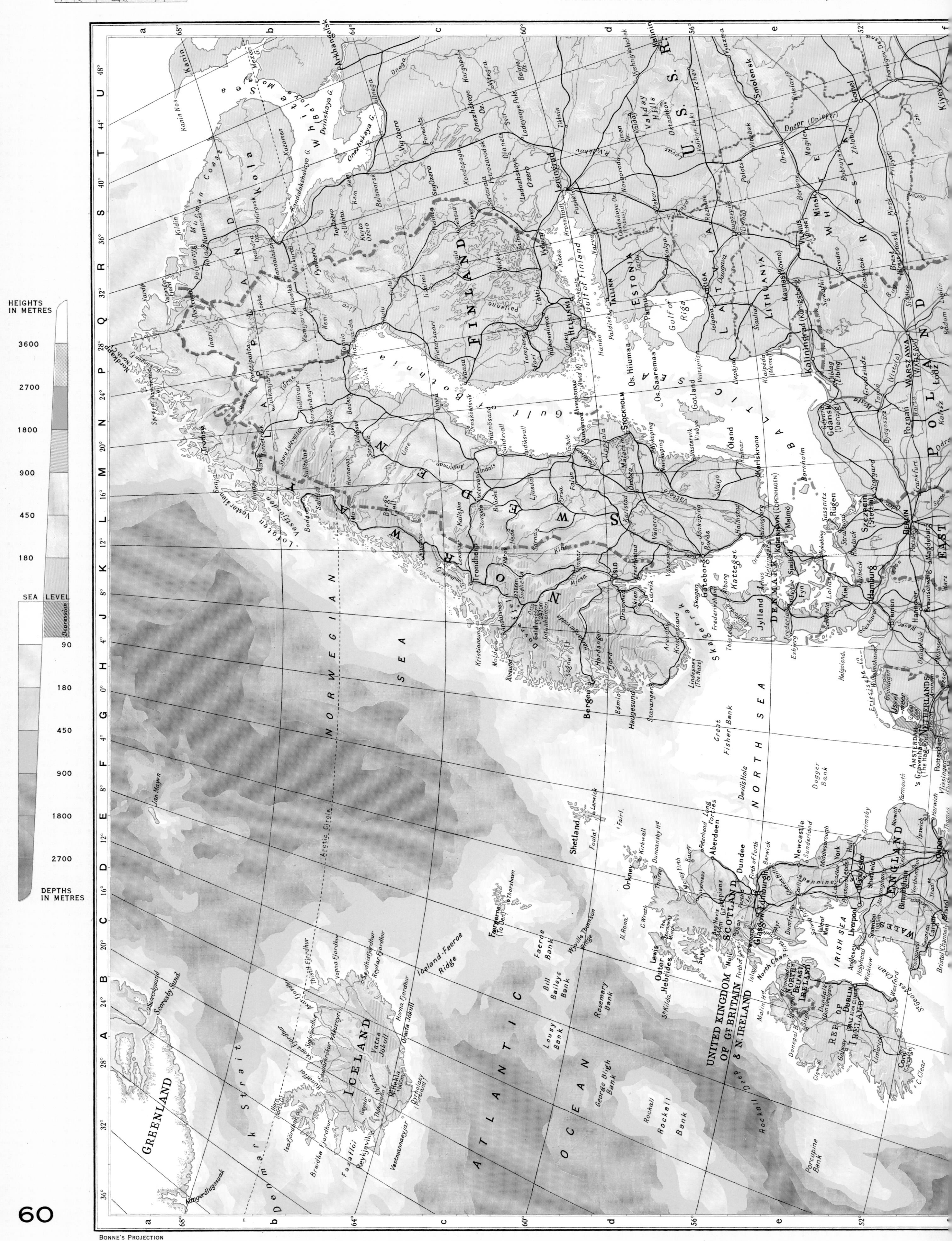

SCALE: 1:10,000,000   (1 CM = 100 KM)

Main Roads
Railways

This east-west axis separates the other two major features of the map: the broad North European Plain stretching from Ireland to Russia, and the two basins of the Mediterranean, each as deep as the mountains are high.

This relatively small continent contains many striking geographical contrasts which are paralleled by the diversity of its peoples and cultures, among them the great Greek and Roman civilizations from which the whole world has

derived so much. The maritime outlook prevalent in the western areas of Europe led to the great explorations that took these people and their cultures to the farthest corners of the Earth.

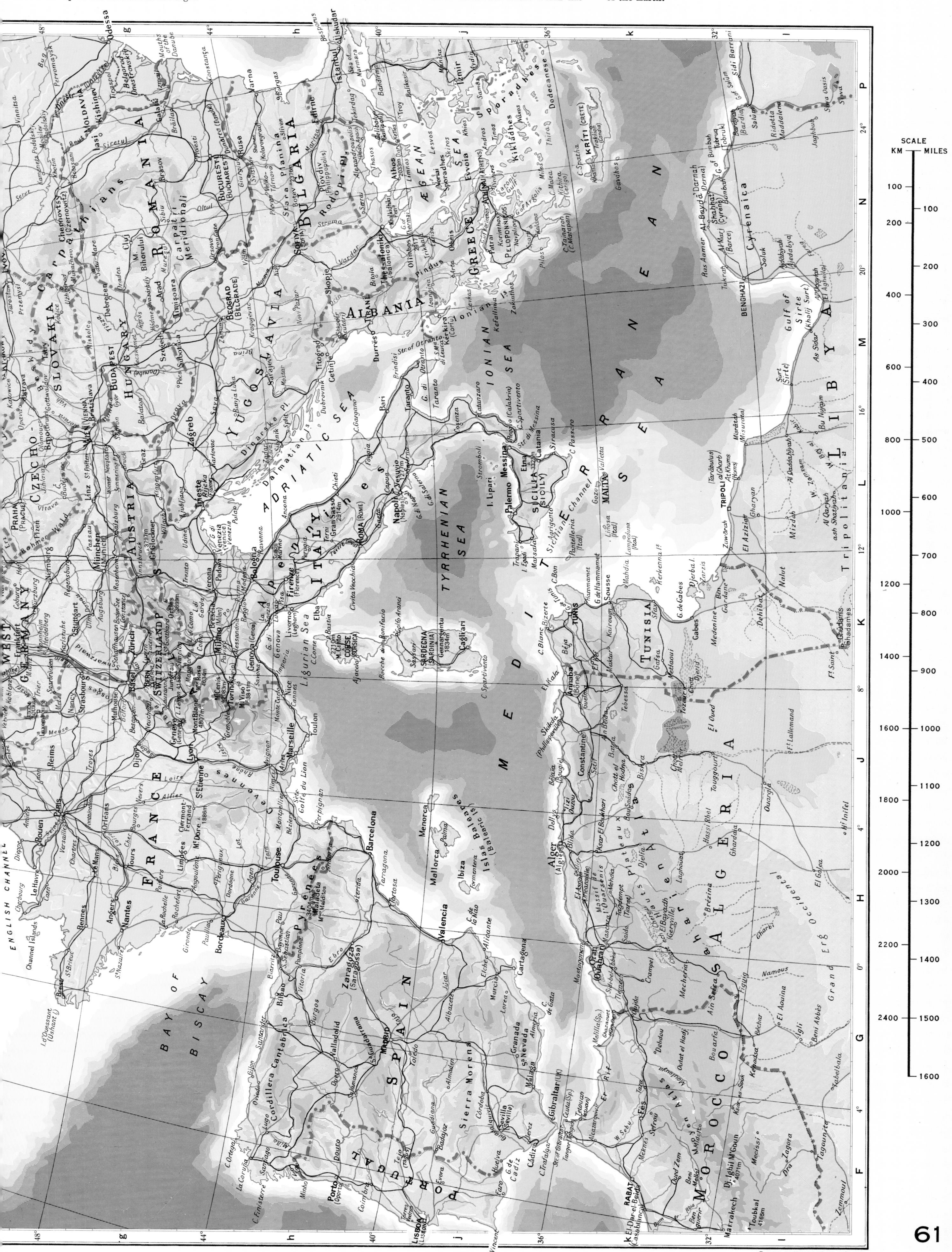

INTERNATIONAL BOUNDARIES
STATE BOUNDARIES

SCALE: 1:10,000,000 (1CM = 100KM)

SCALE
KM — MILES

THE BRITISH ISLES

UNITED KINGDOM (ENGLAND: SCOTLAND: WALES: N. IRELAND)
AREA: 244,019 sq. km. (94,216 sq. miles) POP: 55,970,000
ENGLAND AREA: 130,368 sq. km. (50,335 sq. miles) POP: 46,437,000
WALES AREA: 20,761 sq. km. (8,016 sq. miles) POP: 2,760,000

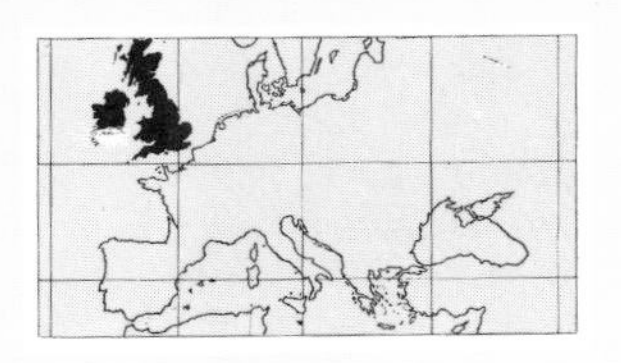

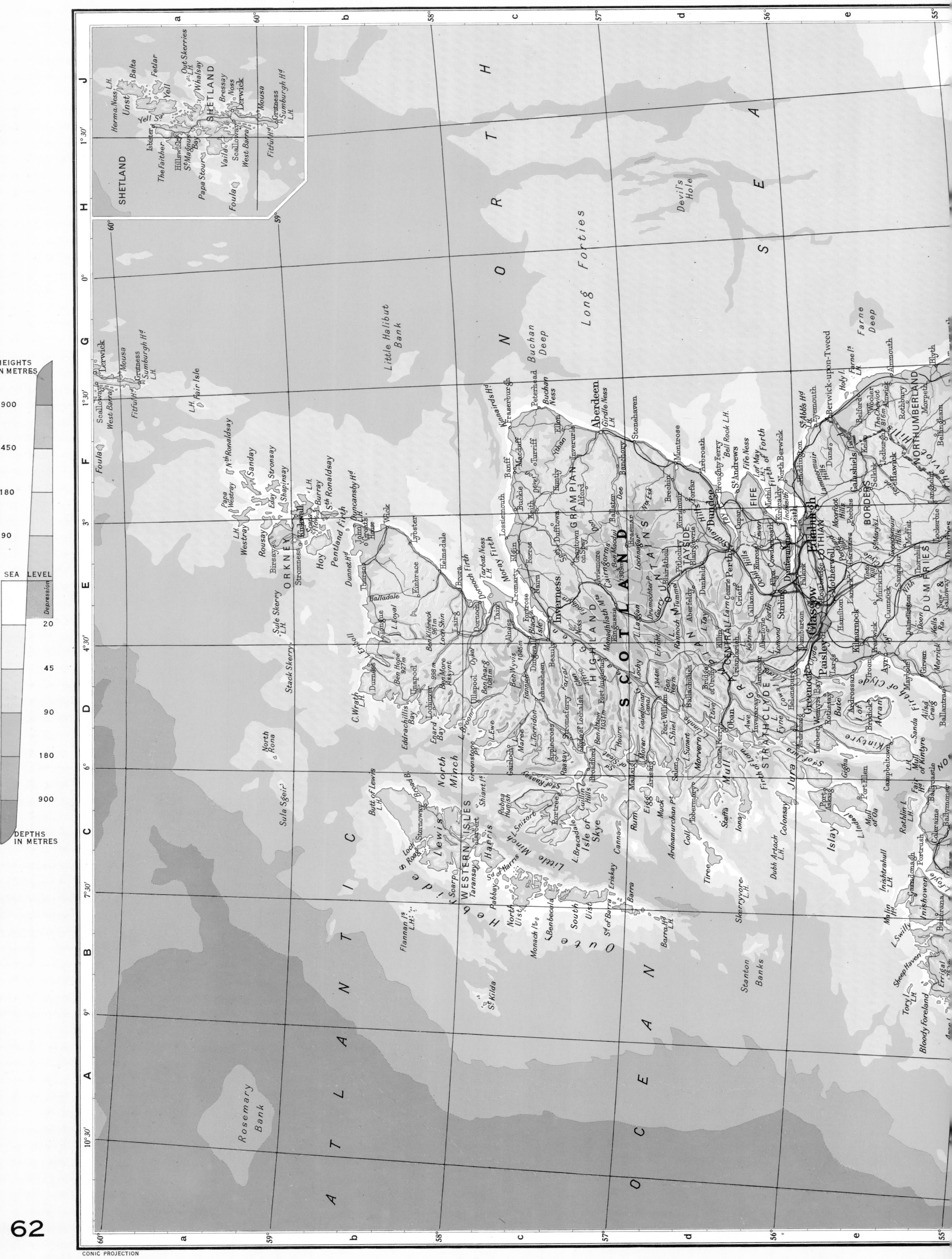

HEIGHTS IN METRES

900
450
180
90

SEA LEVEL

Depression

20
45
90
180
900

DEPTHS IN METRES

SHETLAND

ORKNEY

WESTERN ISLES

SCOTLAND

HIGHLAND

GRAMPIAN

TAYSIDE

CENTRAL

STRATHCLYDE

FIFE

LOTHIAN

BORDERS

DUMFRIES

NORTHUMBERLAND

NORTH SEA

ATLANTIC OCEAN

Long Forties

Devil's Hole

Aberdeen

Inverness

Dundee

Edinburgh

Glasgow

Paisley

Berwick-upon-Tweed

62

CONIC PROJECTION

SCALE: 1:2,500,000 (1CM = 25KM)

MAIN ROADS

RAILWAYS

The British Isles, having regard to their relatively small area, show a structural variety matched by few European countries. A line drawn north-eastwards from the Exe to the Tees roughly separates Great Britain's ancient uplands (stretching from the Scottish Highlands to the moors of Devon and Cornwall) from the more recent rock formations found in the gentler slopes of the Cotswolds and Chilterns, East Anglia and the Weald. Signs of a one-time connection with the Continent are evident in the south, the fens of East Anglia having their counterpart in the low-lying flats of the Netherlands, and the chalk cliffs of Dover and the granitic cliffs of Cornwall in the coast of northern France.

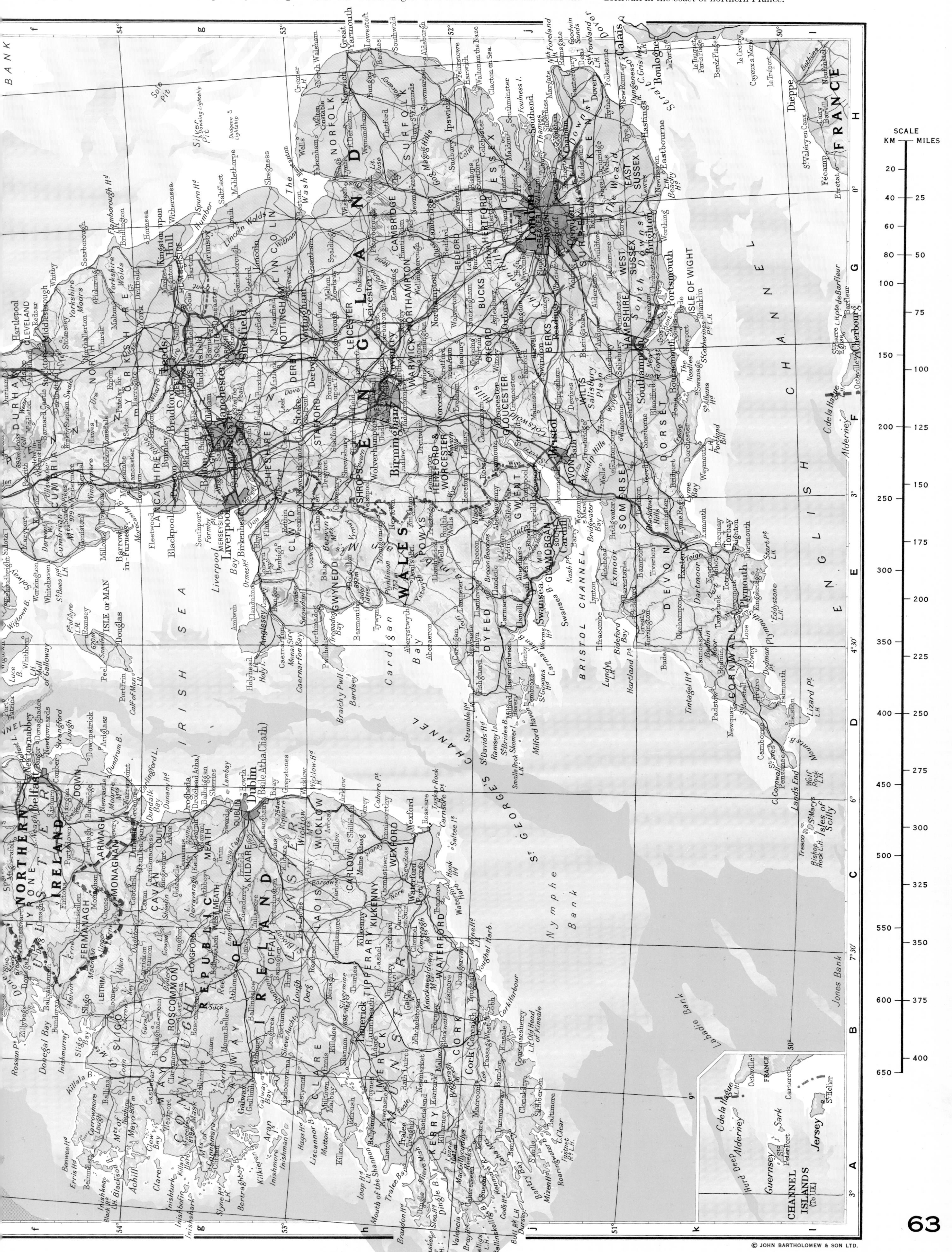

SCALE
KM — MILES

© JOHN BARTHOLOMEW & SON LTD.

SCALE: 1:2,500,000 (1 CM = 25 KM)

IONAL BOUNDARY

NTY/REGION BOUNDARY

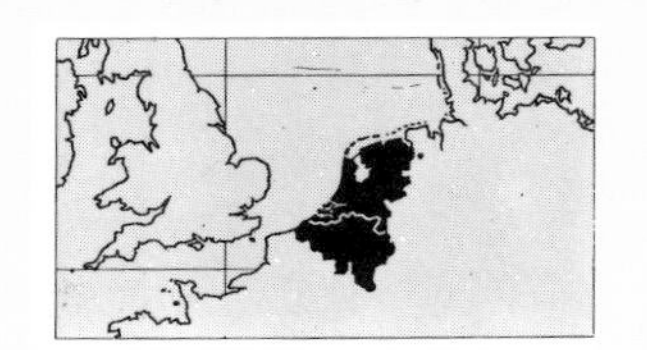

THE LOW COUNTRIES BELGIUM, NETHERLANDS, LUXEMBOURG

BELGIUM AREA: *30,513 sq. km. (11,781 sq. miles)*
POP: *9,790,000* CAPITAL: *Brussels*
CURRENCY: *100 centimes=1 franc*

NETHERLANDS AREA: *36,175 sq. km. (13,967 sq.
miles)* POP: *13,650,000* CAPITAL: *Amsterdam*
(GOVT: *Den Haag*) CURR: *100 cents=1 guilder*

LUXEMBOURG AREA: *2,587 sq. km. (999 sq.
miles)* POP: *360,000* CAPITAL: *Luxembourg*
CURRENCY: *100 centimes=1 franc*

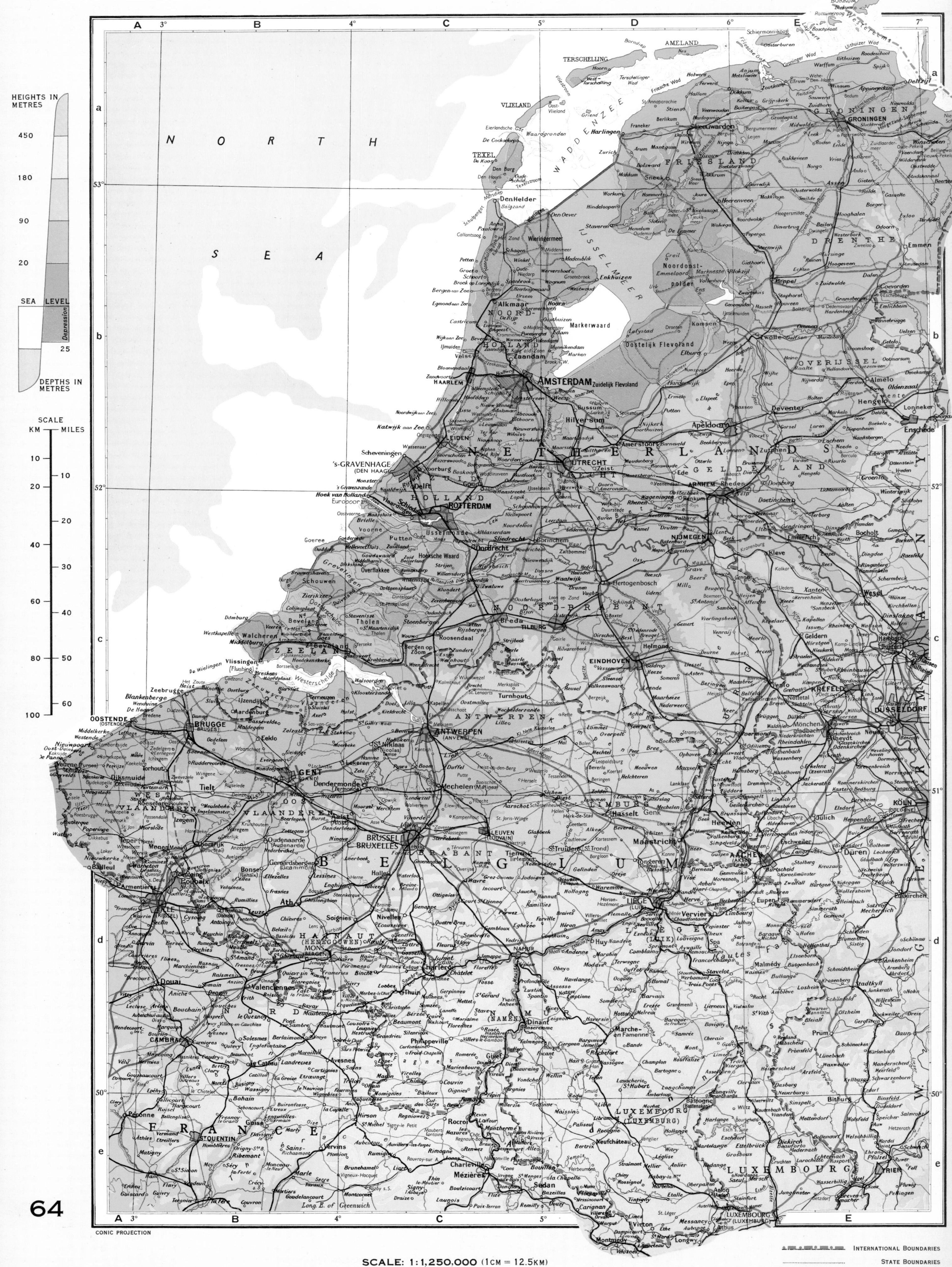

HEIGHTS IN
METRES

450
180
90
20
SEA LEVEL
Depression
25
DEPTHS IN
METRES

SCALE
KM   MILES

64

CONIC PROJECTION

SCALE: 1:1,250,000 (1CM = 12.5KM)

INTERNATIONAL BOUNDARIES

STATE BOUNDARIES

SWITZERLAND

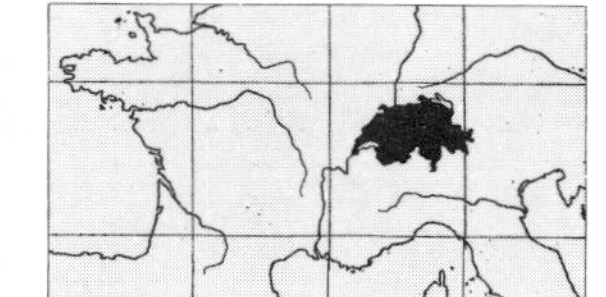

AREA: 41,287 sq. km. (15,941 sq. miles) POP: 6,430,000 CAPITAL: Berne CURR: 100 centimes = 1 franc. The Swiss Alps, rising to 4,634 metres (Monte Rosa), cover more than half of Switzerland, making it the most mountainous country in Europe. The country is divided into three belts, running north-east to south-west, by the broad valley of the Aare and the narrower one of the Upper Rhein and Upper Rhône.

HEIGHTS IN METRES

3600
2700
1800
900
450
180
90

SEA LEVEL

SCALE
KM — MILES

65

MAIN ROADS
RAILWAYS

CONIC PROJECTION

SCALE: 1:1,250,000 (1CM = 12.5KM)

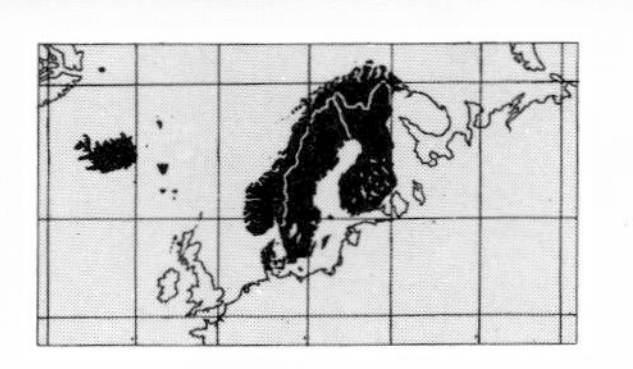

SCANDINAVIA AND BALTIC

NORWAY, SWEDEN, DENMARK, FINLAND, WITH ICELAND

NORWAY AREA: 324,219 sq. km. (125,181 sq. miles)
POP: 4,010,000 CAPITAL: *Oslo* CURRENCY: 100 öre=1 krone
SWEDEN AREA: 449,792 sq. km. (173,665 sq. miles)
POP: 8,200,000 CAPITAL: *Stockholm* CURR: 100 öre=1 kron
From the backbone of mountains shared by Norway and

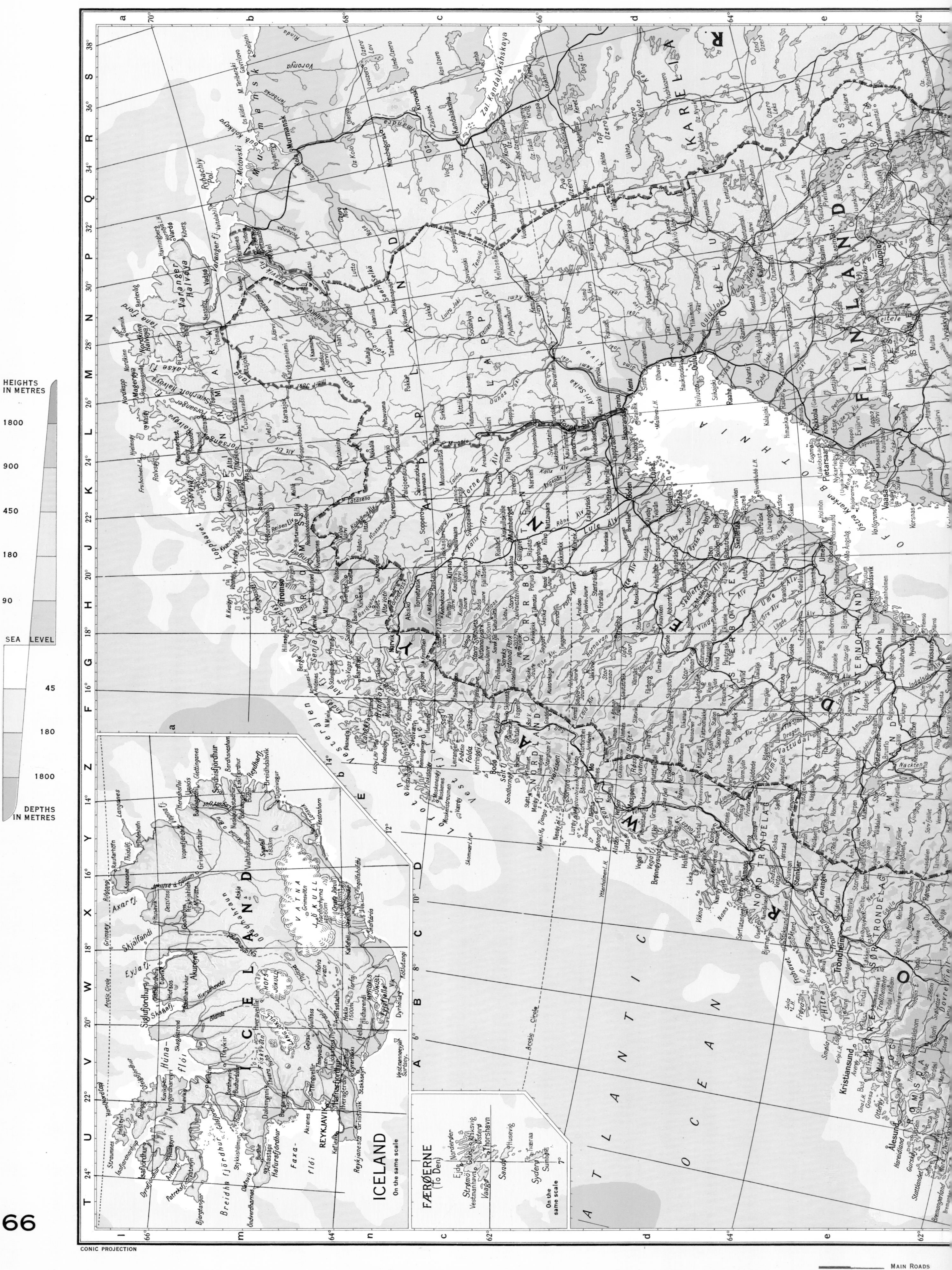

HEIGHTS
IN METRES

1800

900

450

180

90

SEA LEVEL

45

180

1800

DEPTHS
IN METRES

CONIC PROJECTION

66

SCALE: 1: 4,500,000 (1cm = 45km)

MAIN ROADS

RAILWAYS

Sweden come rivers that feed the many lakes on both sides. Norway continues as a high, rugged plateau, falling abruptly to a coastline broken by fjords and islands. Sweden, low-lying in the south, is better suited to cultivation and settlement.

DENMARK AREA: *43,030 sq. km. (16,614 sq. miles)*
POP: *5,050,000* CAP: *Copenhagen* CURR: *100 øre=1 krone*
Smallest and lowest-lying of the Scandinavian countries, Denmark rarely rises more than 150 metres above sea level. Besides the peninsula of Jutland, it comprises the four main islands of Zealand, Fünen, Lolland and Falster.

FINLAND AREA: *360,318 sq. km. (139,119 sq. miles)*
POP: *4,710,000* CAP: *Helsinki* CURR: *100 pennis=1 markka*
ICELAND AREA: *102,828 sq. km. (39,702 sq. miles)*
POP: *220,000* CAP: *Reykjavik* CURR: *100 aurar=1 krona*

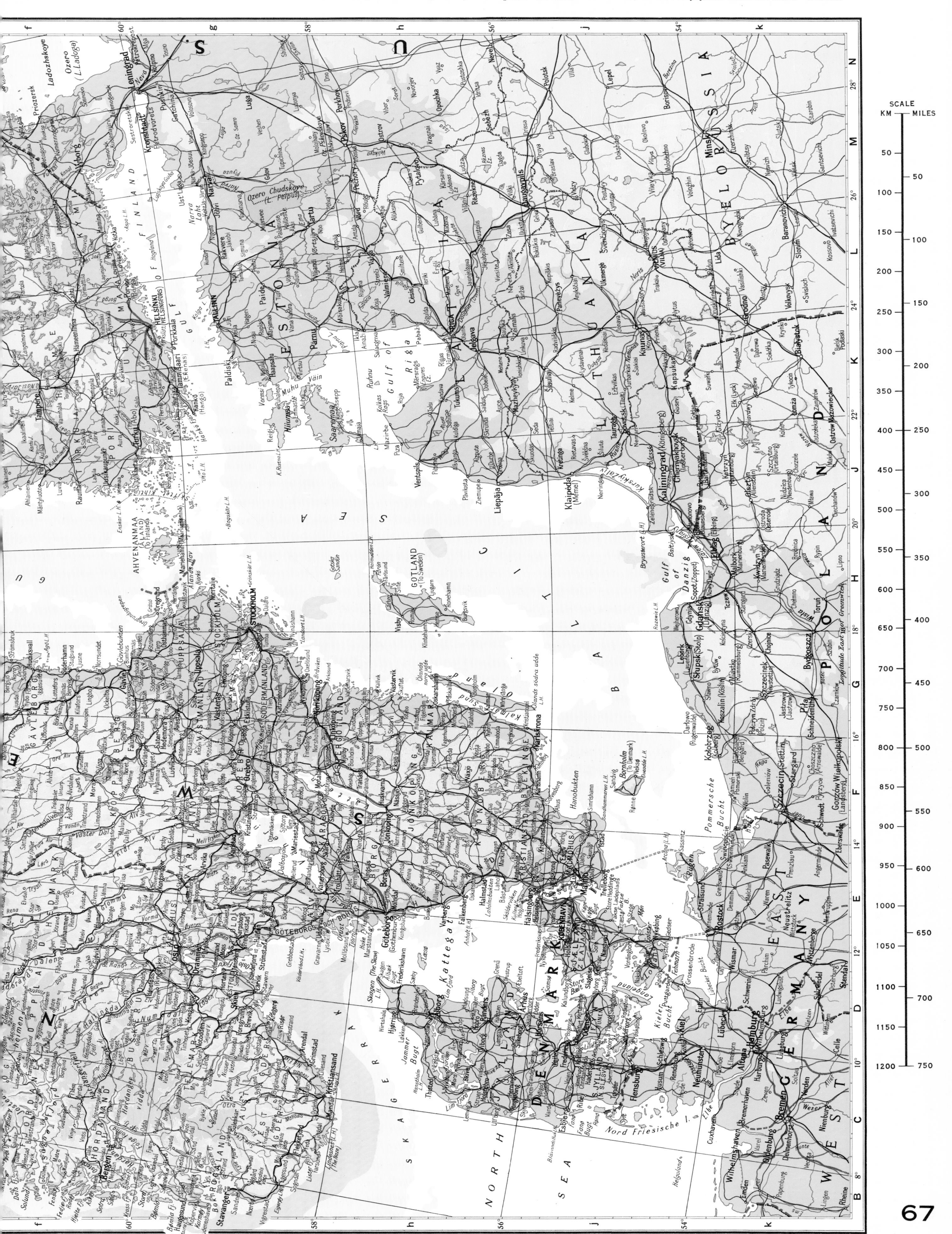

INTERNATIONAL BOUNDARIES
STATE BOUNDARIES

SCALE: 1: 4,500,000 (1CM = 45KM)

SCALE
KM — MILES

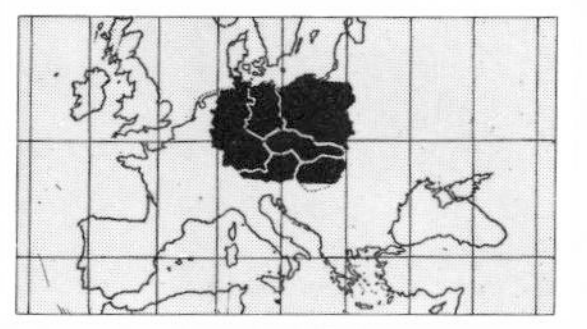

CENTRAL EUROPE

GERMANY, POLAND, CZECHOSLOVAKIA, AUSTRIA

GERMANY (Fed. Republic) AREA: 248,529 sq. km. (95,957 sq. miles)
POP: 61,830,000 CAP: *Bonn* CURR: 100 Pfennige = 1 Deutsche Mark
EAST GERMANY AREA: 107,861 sq. km. (41,645 sq. miles)
POP: 16,850,000 CAP: *East Berlin* CURR: 100 Pfennige = 1 DM Ost
Germany is highest in the south, where the Bavarian Alps form a bound-

HEIGHTS IN
METRES

3600

2700

1800

900

450

180

90

SEA LEVEL

Depression

50

DEPTHS IN
METRES

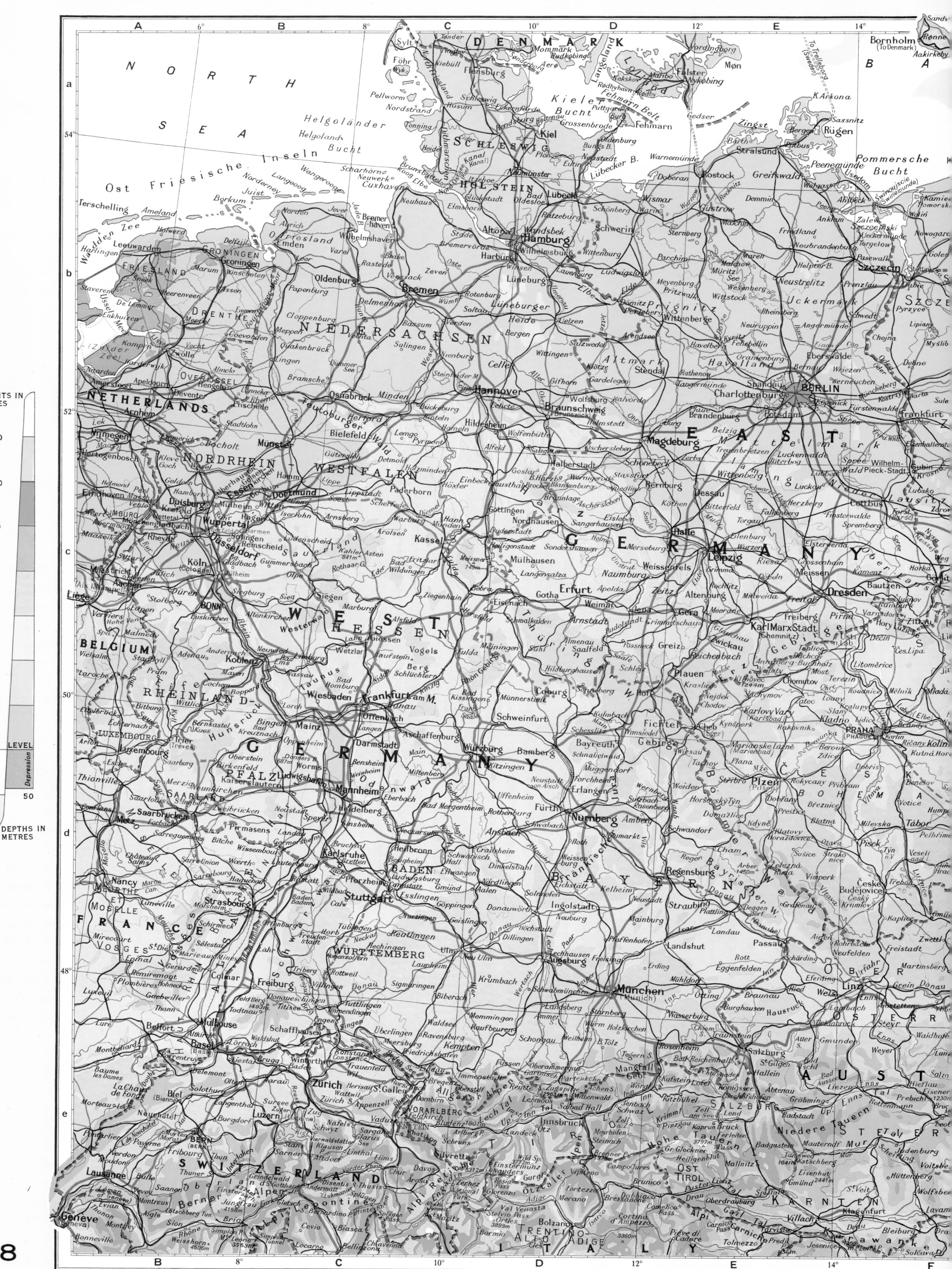

68

SCALE: 1:3,000,000 (1 CM = 30 KM)

MAIN ROADS
RAILWAYS

ary with Austria. Lower mountains in the centre give way
to the North German Plain, now divided between East
and West Germany. Except for the Danube, all important
rivers—the Rhein, Ems, Weser, Elbe and Oder—follow
this northwards slope, flowing into the Baltic or North Sea.

POLAND AREA: *311,701 sq. km. (120,348 sq. miles)*
POP: *34,020,000* CAP: *Warsaw* CURR: *100 groszy=1 zloty*
Except in the south, where it shares the Carpathians with
Czechoslovakia, Poland is a vast plain connecting north
Germany with the Russian steppes.

CZECHOSLOVAKIA AREA: *127,871 sq. km. (49,371 sq. miles)*
POPULATION: *14,760,000* CAPITAL: *Prague*
CURRENCY: *100 haler=1 koruna*
AUSTRIA AREA: *83,849 sq. km. (32,374 sq. miles)*
POP: *7,520,000* CAP: *Vienna* CURR: *100 Groschen=1 Schilling*

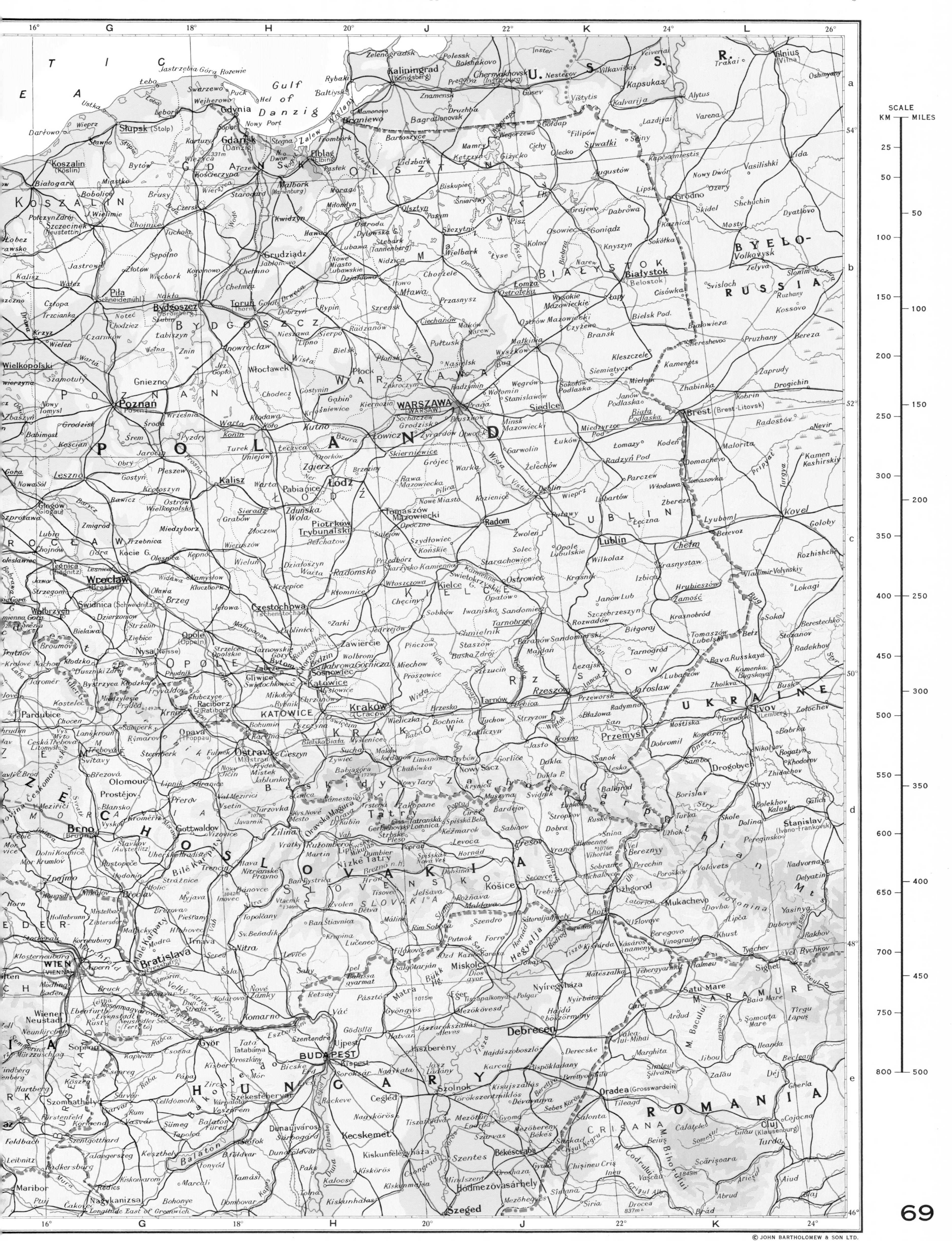

SCALE
KM — MILES

69

© JOHN BARTHOLOMEW & SON LTD.

INTERNATIONAL BOUNDARIES
STATE BOUNDARIES

SCALE: 1:3,000,000 (1CM = 30KM)

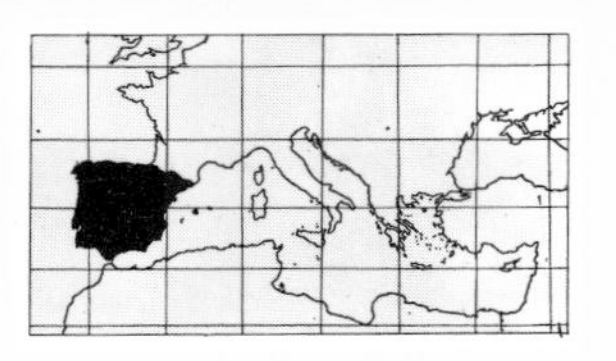

IBERIAN PENINSULA

SPAIN, PORTUGAL

SPAIN AREA: 504,747 sq. km. (194,883 sq. miles) POPULATION: 35,700,000
CAPITAL: *Madrid* CURRENCY: *100 céntimos = 1 peseta*
PORTUGAL AREA: 91,971 sq. km. (35,510 sq. miles) POPULATION: 8,760,000
CAPITAL: *Lisbon* CURRENCY: *100 centavos = 1 escudo*

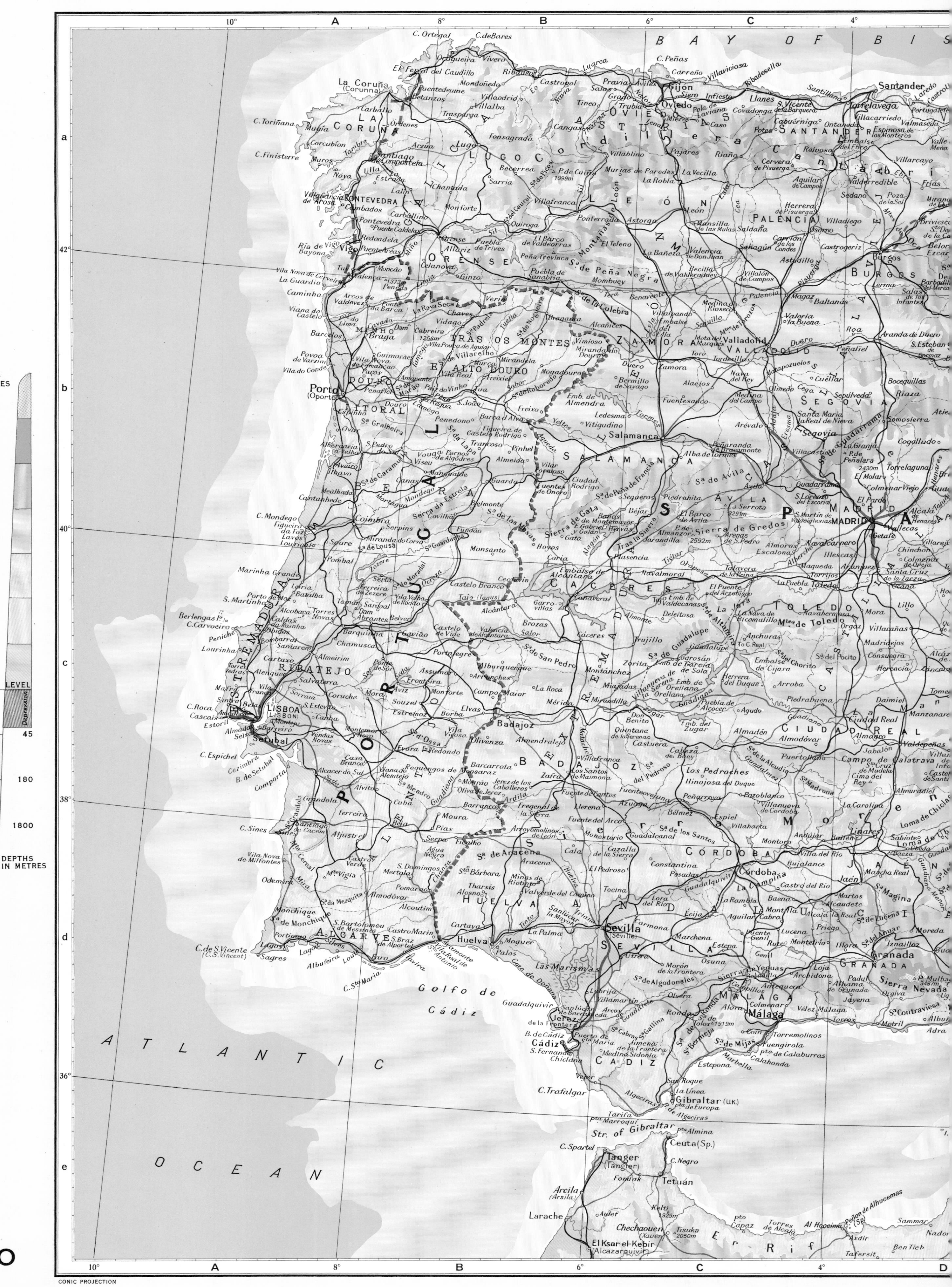

HEIGHTS IN METRES

2700
1800
900
450
180
90

SEA LEVEL

Depression

45
180
1800

DEPTHS IN METRES

70

CONIC PROJECTION

SCALE: 1:3,000,000 (1CM = 30KM)

MAIN ROADS
RAILWAYS

Roughly pentagonal in shape the Iberian peninsula is divided between Spain, Portugal and the small state of Andorra. Seven-eighths of it is bordered by sea, the remainder by the high wall of the Pyrénées, which separates it from France and the land mass of Europe. Southwards, only thirteen and a half kilometres away at its nearest point, lies the continent of Africa. More than half the peninsula is covered by the Meseta, a high central plateau which is surrounded and traversed by mountain ranges. The rivers, notably the Tagus, flow mainly westwards. The four main islands of the Balearic group form a province of Spain; the Canary Islands are another province.

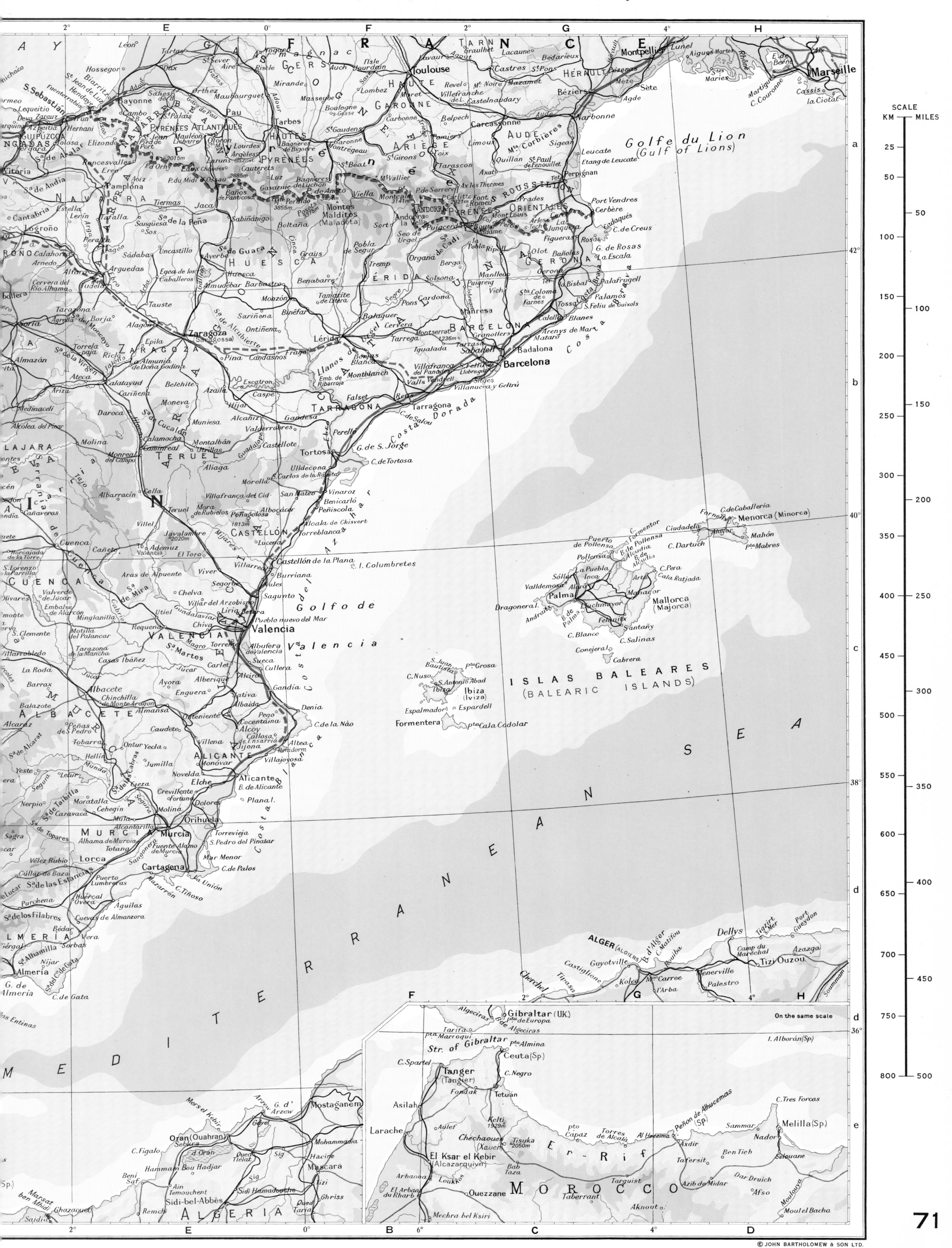

SCALE
KM   MILES

On the same scale

SCALE: 1:3,000,000 (1CM = 30KM)

INTERNATIONAL BOUNDARIES
STATE BOUNDARIES

71

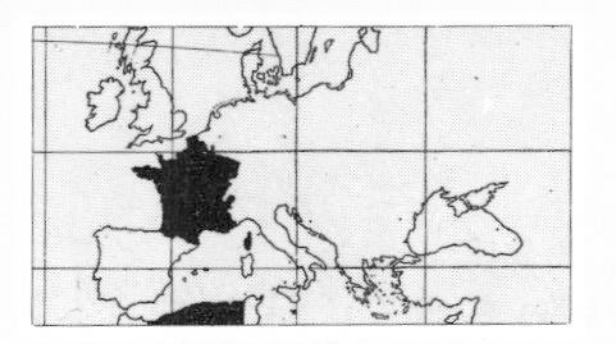

FRANCE
AND NORTHERN ALGERIA

AREA: 549,621 sq. km. (212,209 sq. miles) POP: 53,090,000. CAP: *Paris*
CURRENCY: *100 centimes=1 nouveau franc.* Around France are three seas
into which flow the four great French rivers: the Seine into the English
Channel, the Loire and Garonne into the Atlantic, and the Rhône into

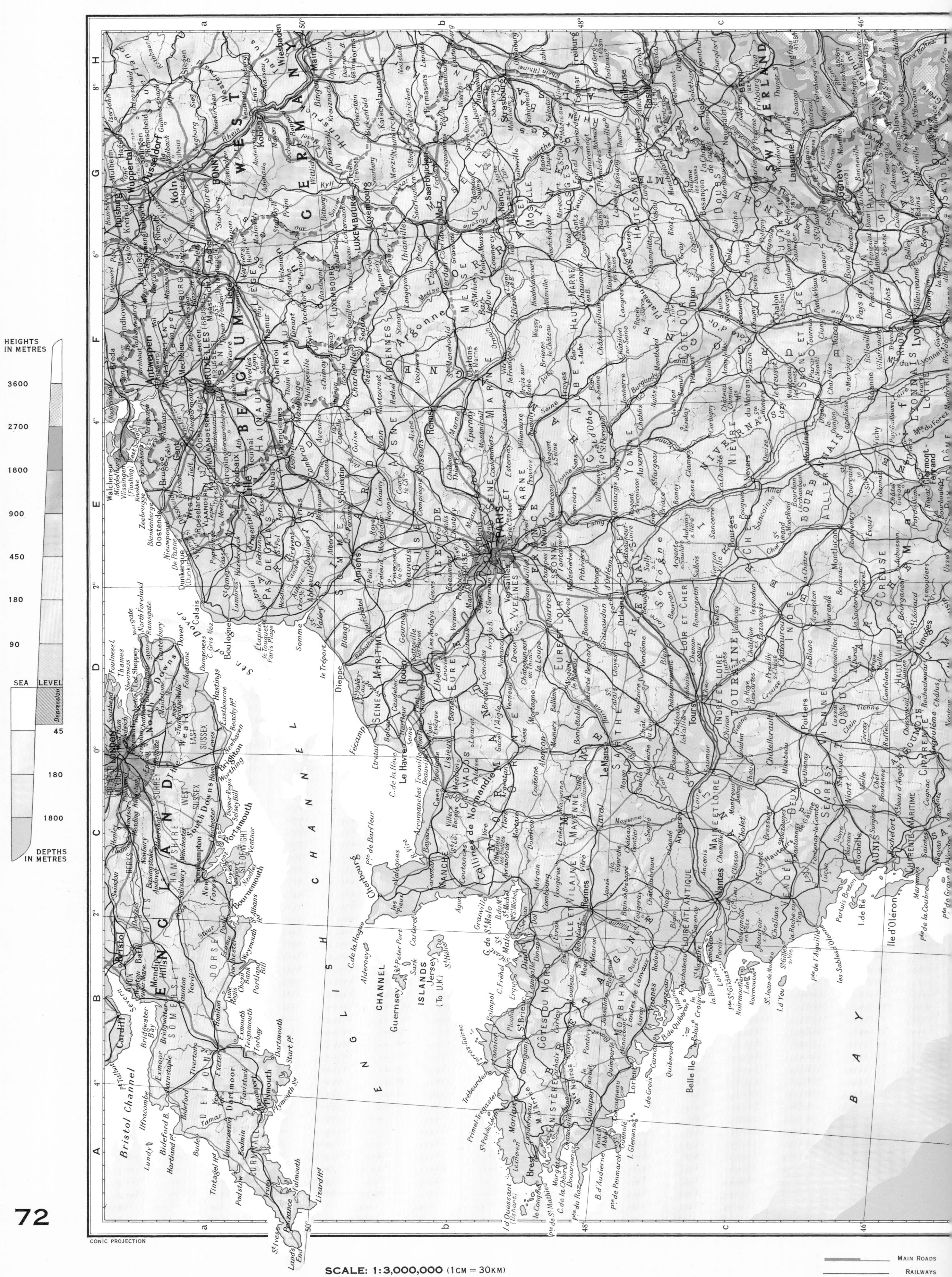

HEIGHTS
IN METRES

3600

2700

1800

900

450

180

90

SEA LEVEL

Depression

45

180

1800

DEPTHS
IN METRES

72

CONIC PROJECTION

SCALE: 1:3,000,000 (1cm = 30km)

MAIN ROADS
RAILWAYS

the Mediterranean. This maritime outlook gives the country its mild and even climate. A line drawn from Sedan, in the north-east, to Bayonne, in the south-west, divides the country roughly into its upland and lowland halves. The north-western half is mainly low-lying and includes the broad plains of Normandy and Brittany. On France's eastern borders rise the high mountains of the Vosges, the Jura and the Alps (Mont Blanc, 4,807 metres, is one of the highest peaks in Europe). Running southwards from the centre is the Massif Central, while the Pyrénées in the south-west form a natural barrier between France and Spain.

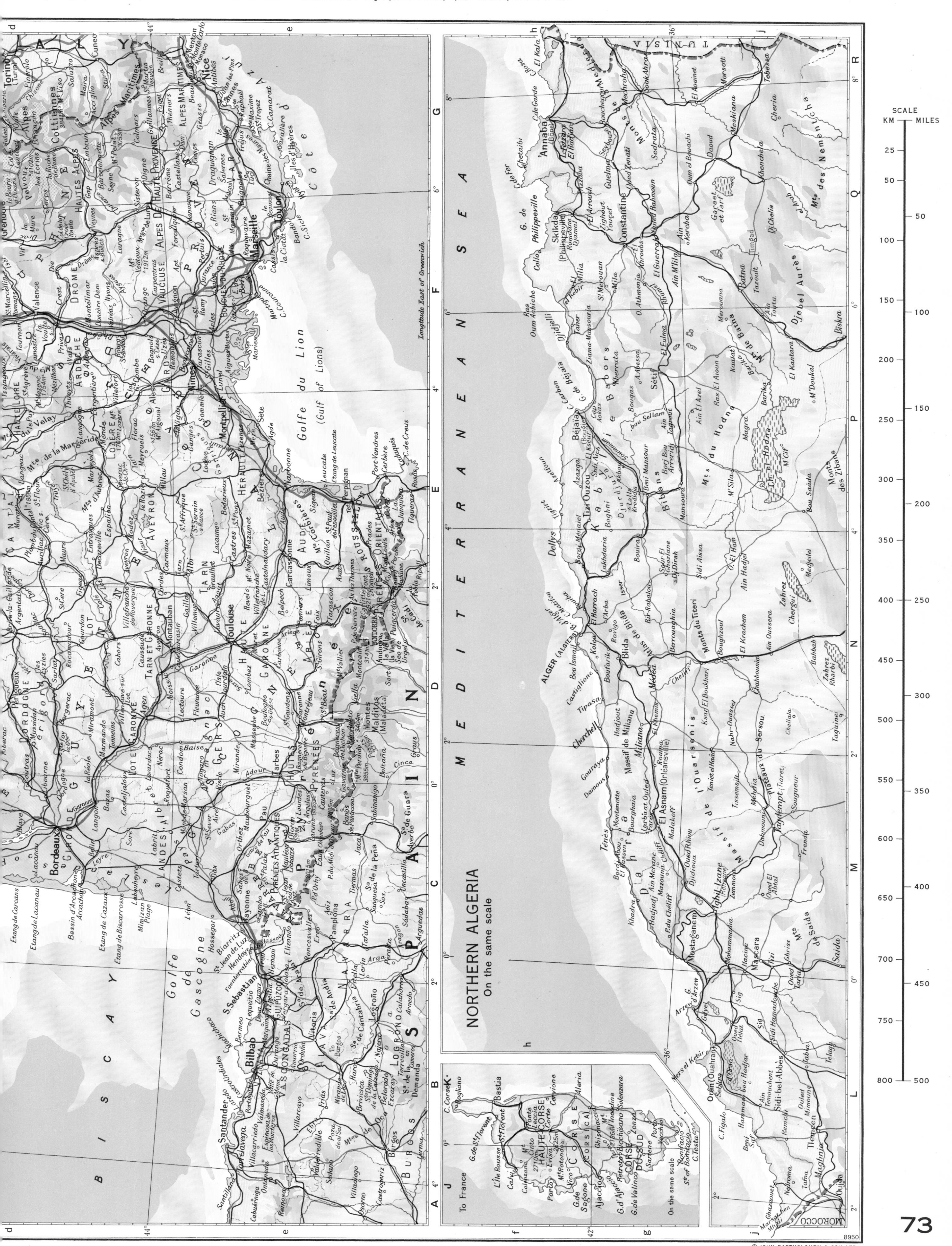

NORTHERN ALGERIA
On the same scale

SCALE
KM — MILES

INTERNATIONAL BOUNDARIES
DEPARTMENT BOUNDARIES

SCALE: 1:3,000,000 (1CM = 30KM)

© JOHN BARTHOLOMEW & SON LTD.

8950

73

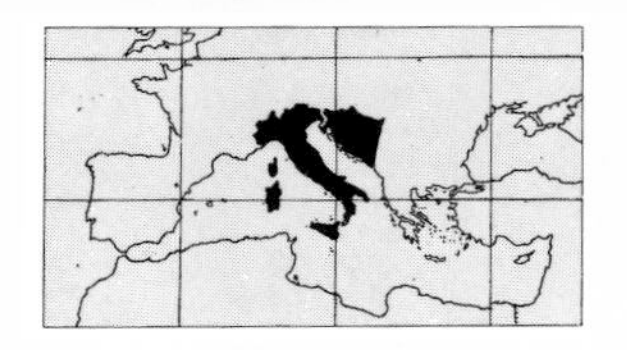

ITALY

AREA: *301,191 sq. km. (116,290 sq. miles)* POP: *56,322,600*
CAPITAL: *Rome* CURRENCY: *Italian lira*

Italy owes its boot-like shape to the Apennines which reach down the whole length of the country, culminating, across the Straits of Messina, in the island of Sicily. To the north the Alps encircle the peninsula like the head of a mushroom, shutting off Italy from the rest of Europe. The strange-shaped Dolomitic Alps (Dolomites) to the east form

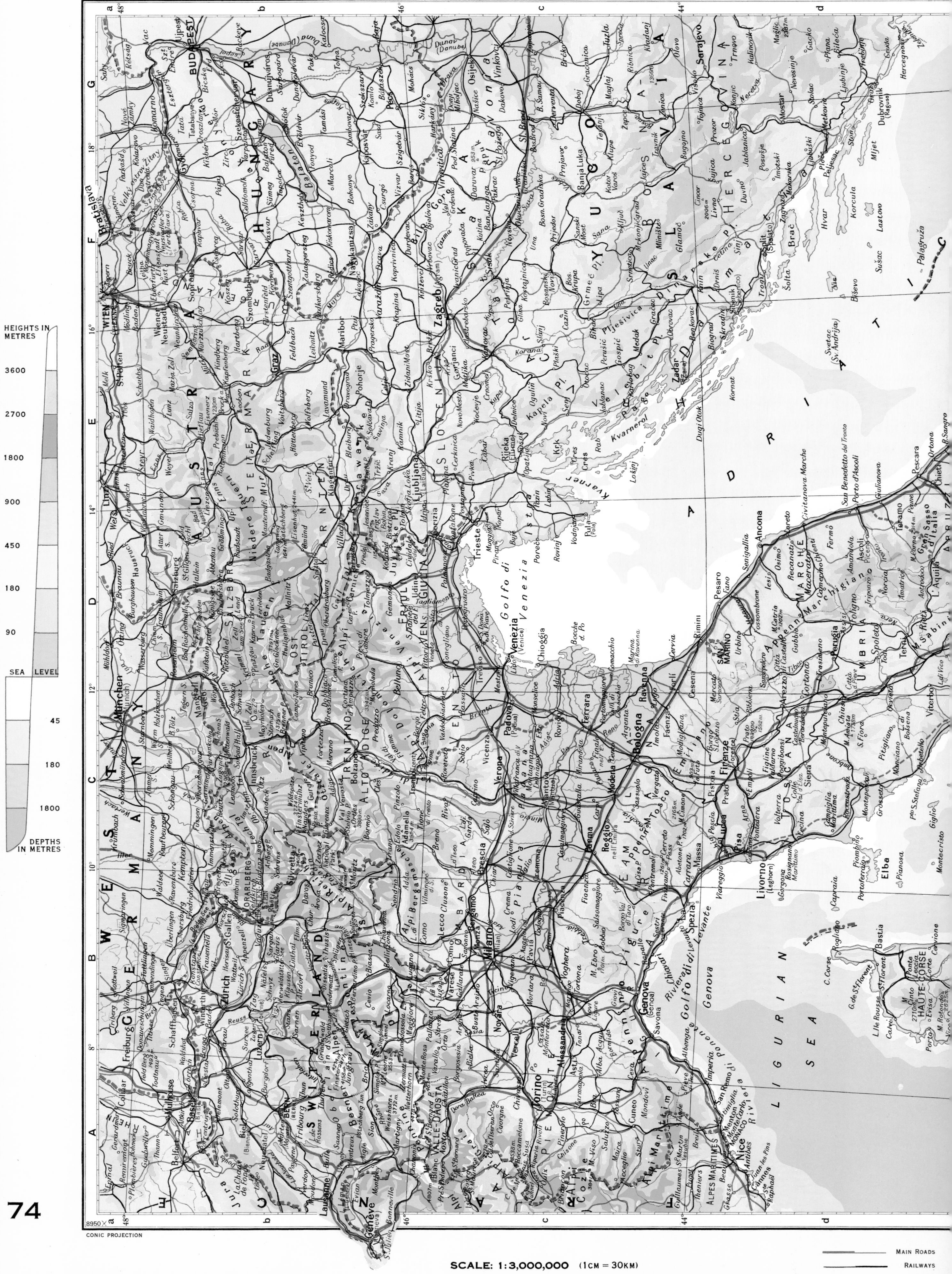

HEIGHTS IN METRES

3600
2700
1800
900
450
180
90
SEA LEVEL
45
180
1800

DEPTHS IN METRES

CONIC PROJECTION

8950×a

SCALE: 1:3,000,000 (1CM = 30KM)

MAIN ROADS
RAILWAYS

an important part of this mountain barrier which makes the country difficult to approach, and the names of the principal passes—the Simplon and St. Gotthard from Switzerland, and the Brenner from Austria—have become household words among travellers all over Europe.

Italy contains two of the most active volcanoes in Europe, notably Etna (the highest, 3,323 metres) in Sicily, and Vesuvius near Naples. Of the rivers, most of which are unnavigable, the longest is the Po (676 kilometres) which waters the fertile plain of Lombardy before entering the Adriatic through its delta between Venice and Ravenna. Other important rivers are the Tiber and the Arno.

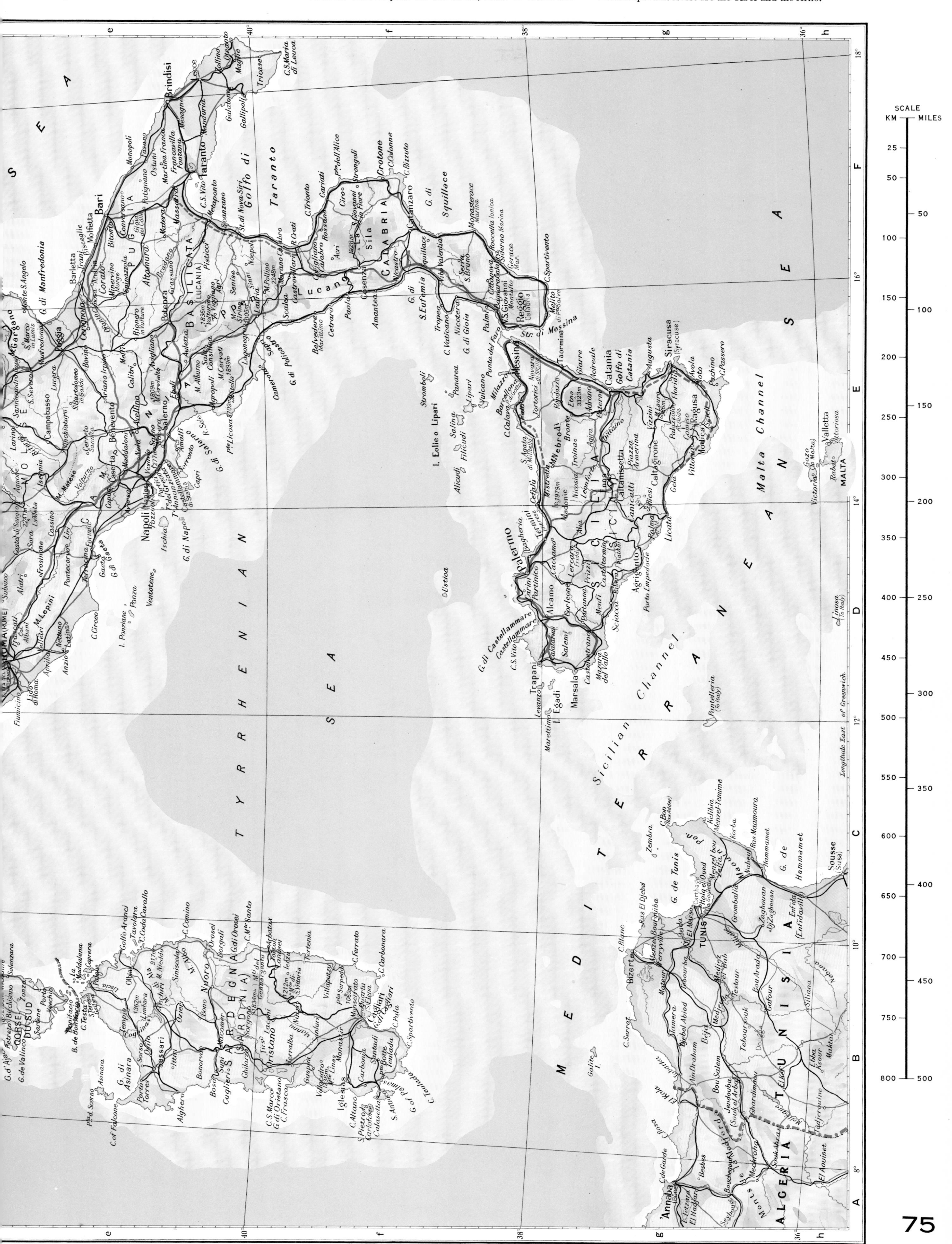

SCALE
KM — MILES

INTERNATIONAL BOUNDARIES
REGIONAL BOUNDARIES

SCALE: 1:3,000,000 (1 CM = 30 KM)

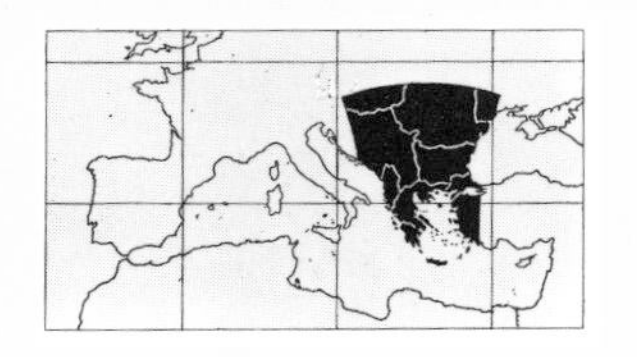

THE BALKANS

HUNGARY, ROMANIA, YUGOSLAVIA, BULGARIA, GREECE

HUNGARY AREA: 93,030 sq. km. (35,919 sq. miles)
POP: 10,670,000 CAP: Budapest CURR: 100 filler = 1 forint
ROMANIA AREA: 237,500 sq. km. (91,699 sq. miles)
POP: 21,180,000 CAP: Bucharest CURR: 100 bani = 1 leu

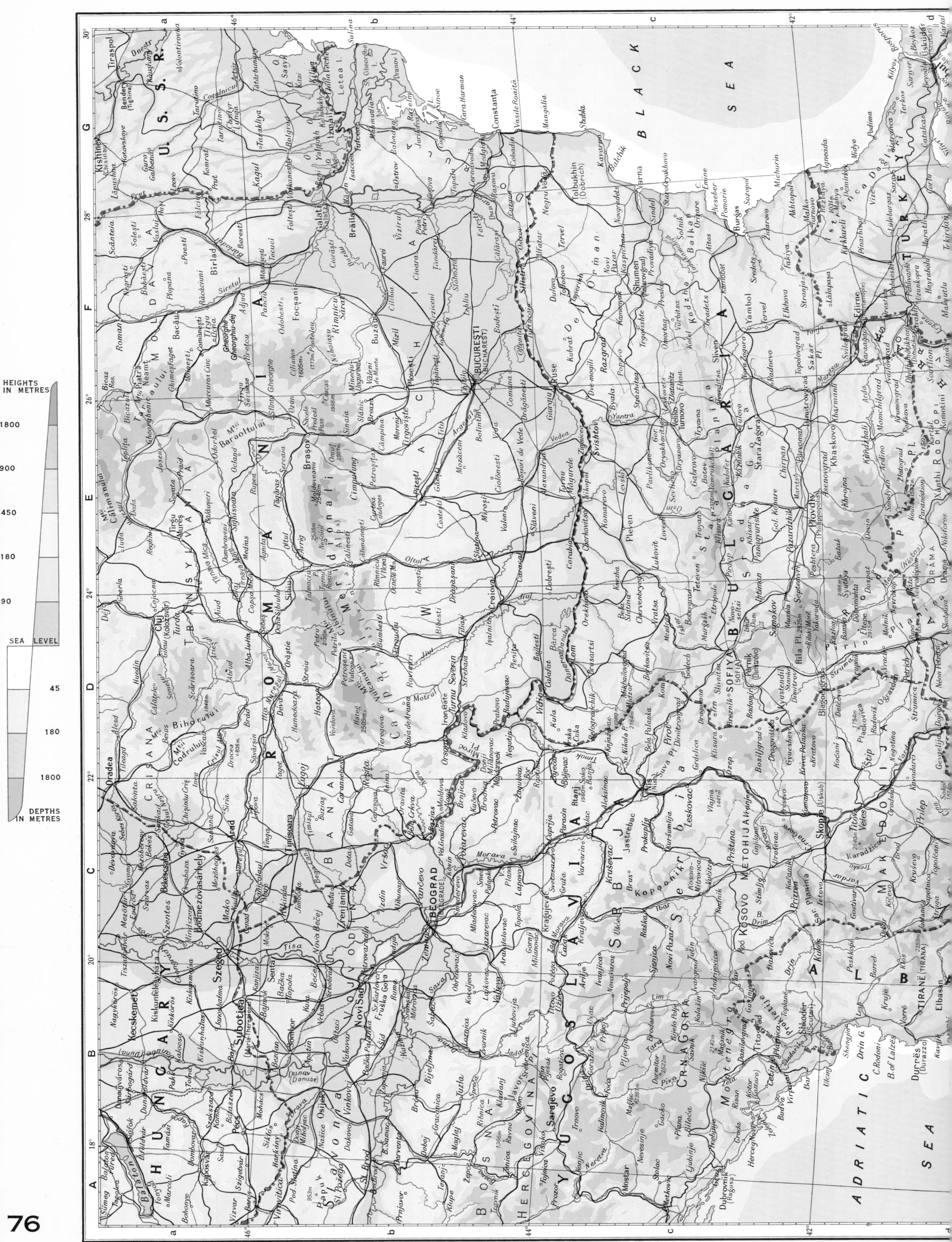

HEIGHTS IN METRES

1800
900
450
180
90
SEA LEVEL
45
180
1800

DEPTHS IN METRES

CONIC PROJECTION

76

SCALE: 1:3,000,000 (1CM = 30KM)

MAIN ROADS
RAILWAYS

YUGOSLAVIA AREA: 255,804 sq. km. (98,725 sq. miles)
POP: 21,330,000 CAP: *Belgrade* CURR: *100 paras=1 dinar*
BULGARIA AREA: 110,912 sq. km. (42,823 sq. miles)
POP: 8,720,000 CAP: *Sofia* CURR: *100 stotinki=1 (new) lev*

GREECE AREA: 131,945 sq. km. (50,944 sq. miles)
POP: 9,200,000 CAP: *Athens* CURR: *100 lepta=1 drachma*
The Balkan peninsula, with its broken coastline and many
offshore islands, is separated from the rest of Europe by

the river Danube (2,848 km. long and western Europe's
longest river) which flows eastwards from Hungary and
through the Iron Gate, a gorge between the Carpathians
and the barren Dinaric Alps in Yugoslavia.

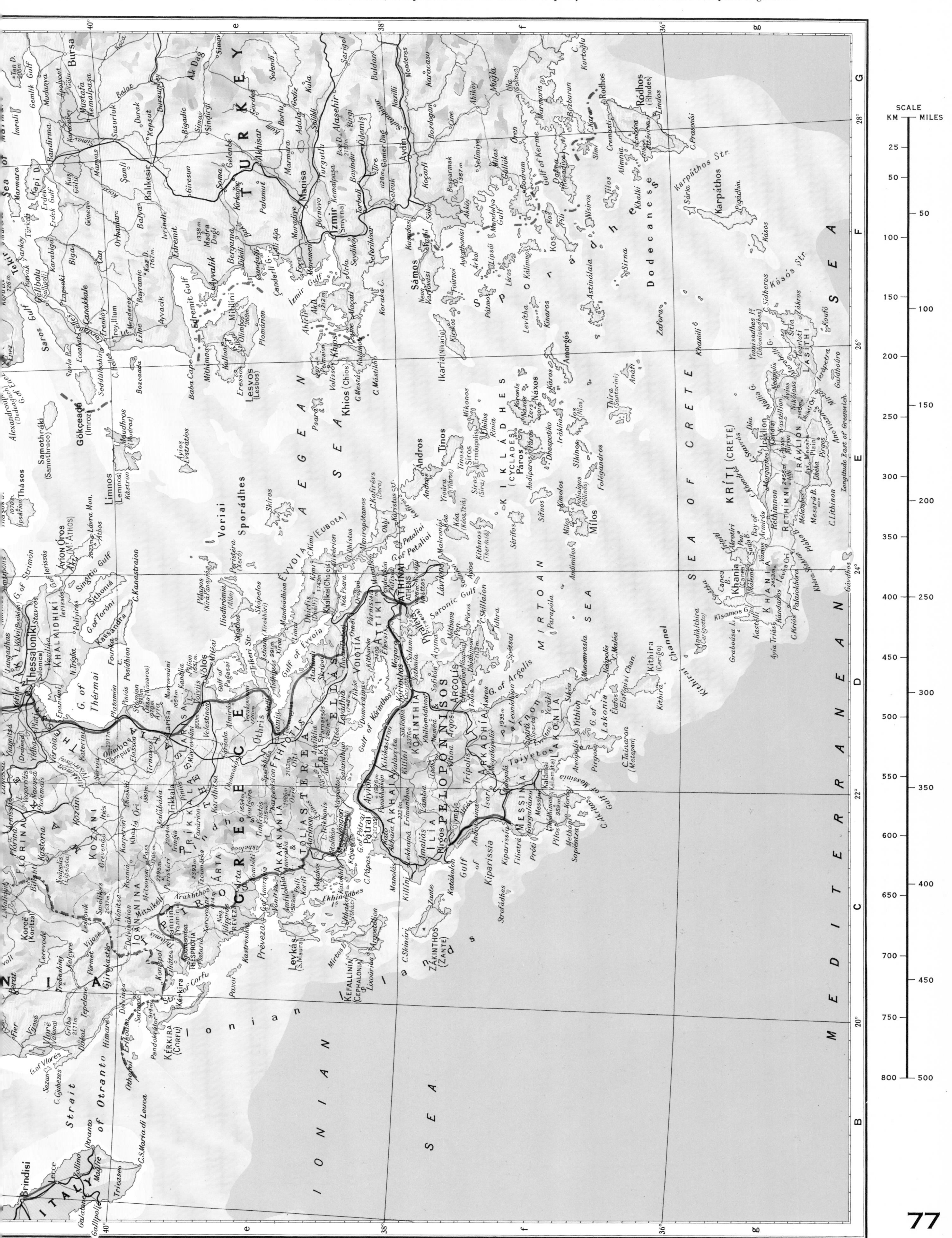

SCALE
KM — MILES

77

INTERNATIONAL BOUNDARIES
PROVINCIAL BOUNDARIES

SCALE: 1:3,000,000 (1CM = 30KM)

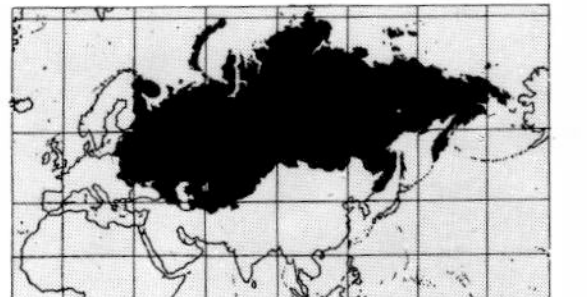

U.S.S.R.

AREA: *22,272,293 sq. km. (8,599,341 sq. miles)* POPULATION: *257,900,000*
CAPITAL: *Moscow* CURRENCY: *100 copecks=1 (new) rouble*
The vast area of the U.S.S.R., straddling all Asia and half of Europe, shares
its immense boundaries with many countries in both continents. It is divided

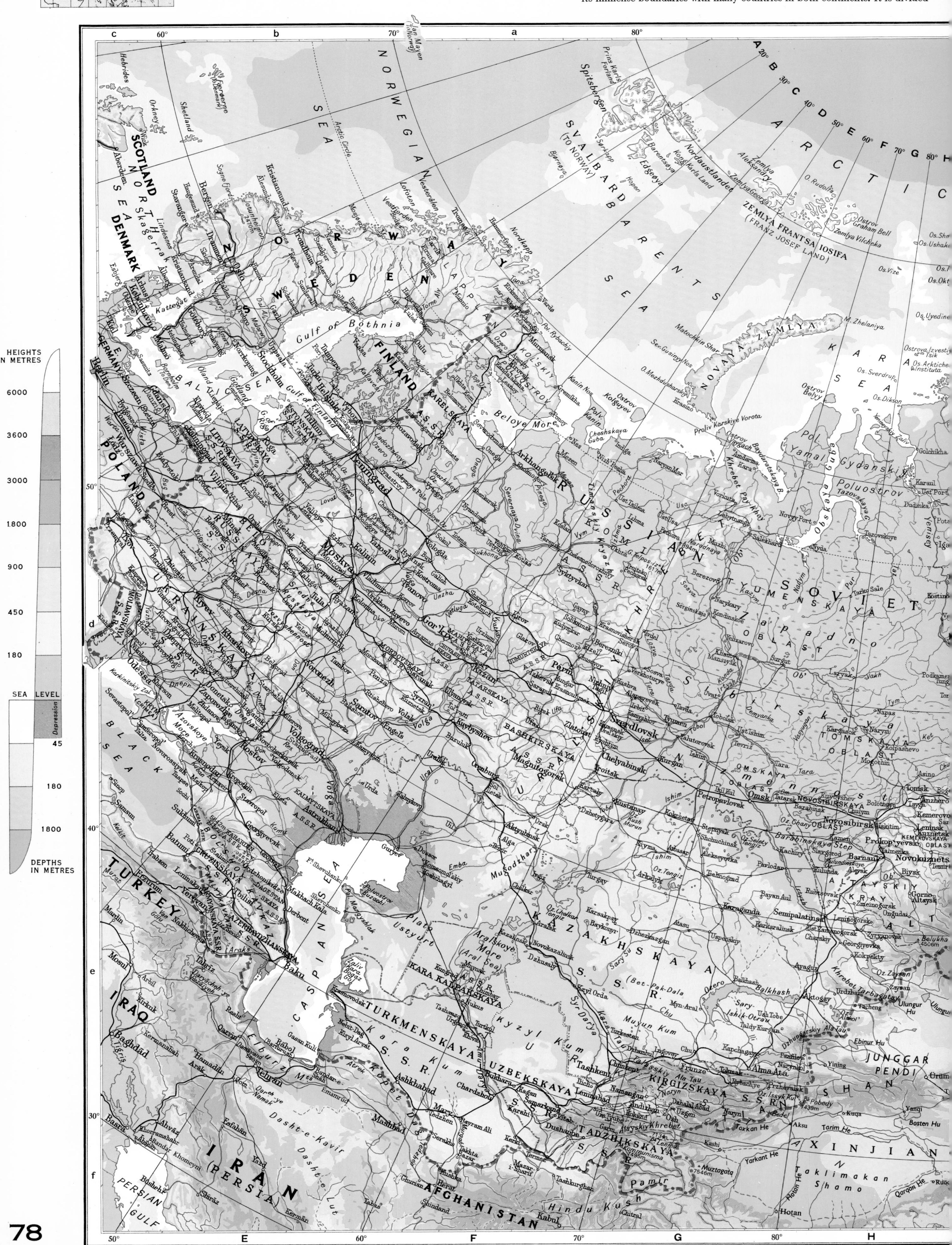

78

CONIC PROJECTION

SCALE: 1:17,500,000   (1cm = 175km)

MAIN ROADS
RAILWAYS

structurally into three regions from west to east: two plains, separated by the Ural'skiy Khrebet (which also form a useful dividing line between Asia and Europe) and a vast region of hazardous country ending in the remote peninsula of Kamchatka. On the north–south axis there are likewise three zones. The frozen tundra of the Arctic merges into forests and fertile plains, which end at the borders of the great desert belt stretching from Mongolia to the Caspian.

In fact, the U.S.S.R. is hemmed in on three fronts by hot or cold deserts or mountains, so that easy access is found only on the western side, through Europe.

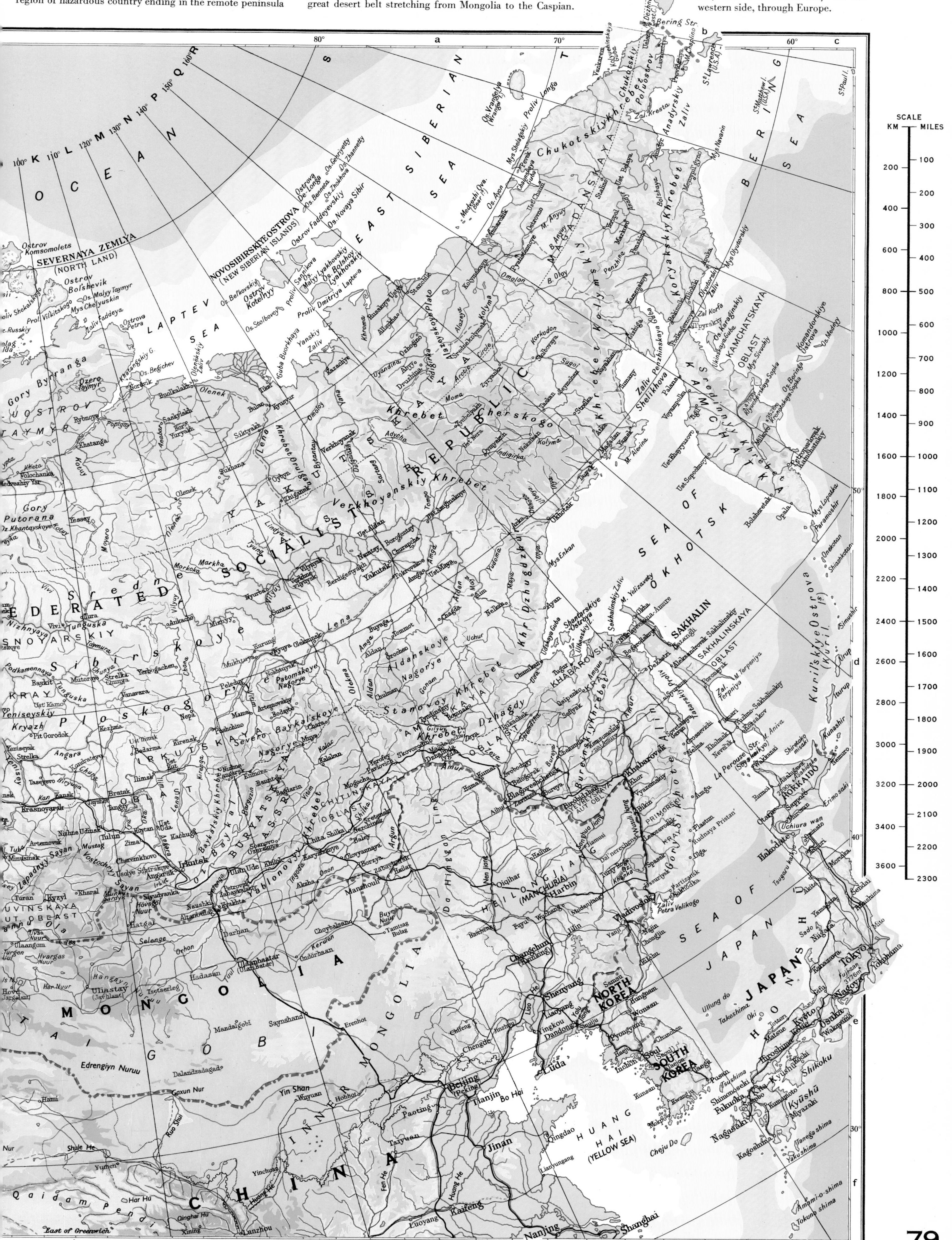

SCALE
KM — MILES

© JOHN BARTHOLOMEW & SON LTD.

INTERNATIONAL BOUNDARIES
STATE BOUNDARIES

SCALE: 1:17,500,000 (1CM = 175KM)

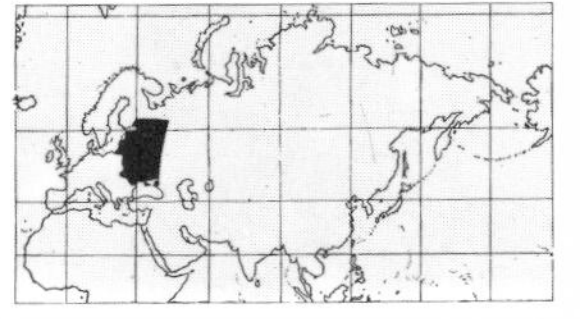

EUROPEAN RUSSIA

The area between the Baltic and the Black Sea is part of the enormous Russian Plain which stretches unbroken to the Central Russian uplands, before continuing eastwards. The comparatively low land in this district is shown up by the meandering rivers and the lakes and marshes of the Pripyat region. To the south, the mild undulations of the Ukrainian steppe interrupt the monotony of the northern plain.

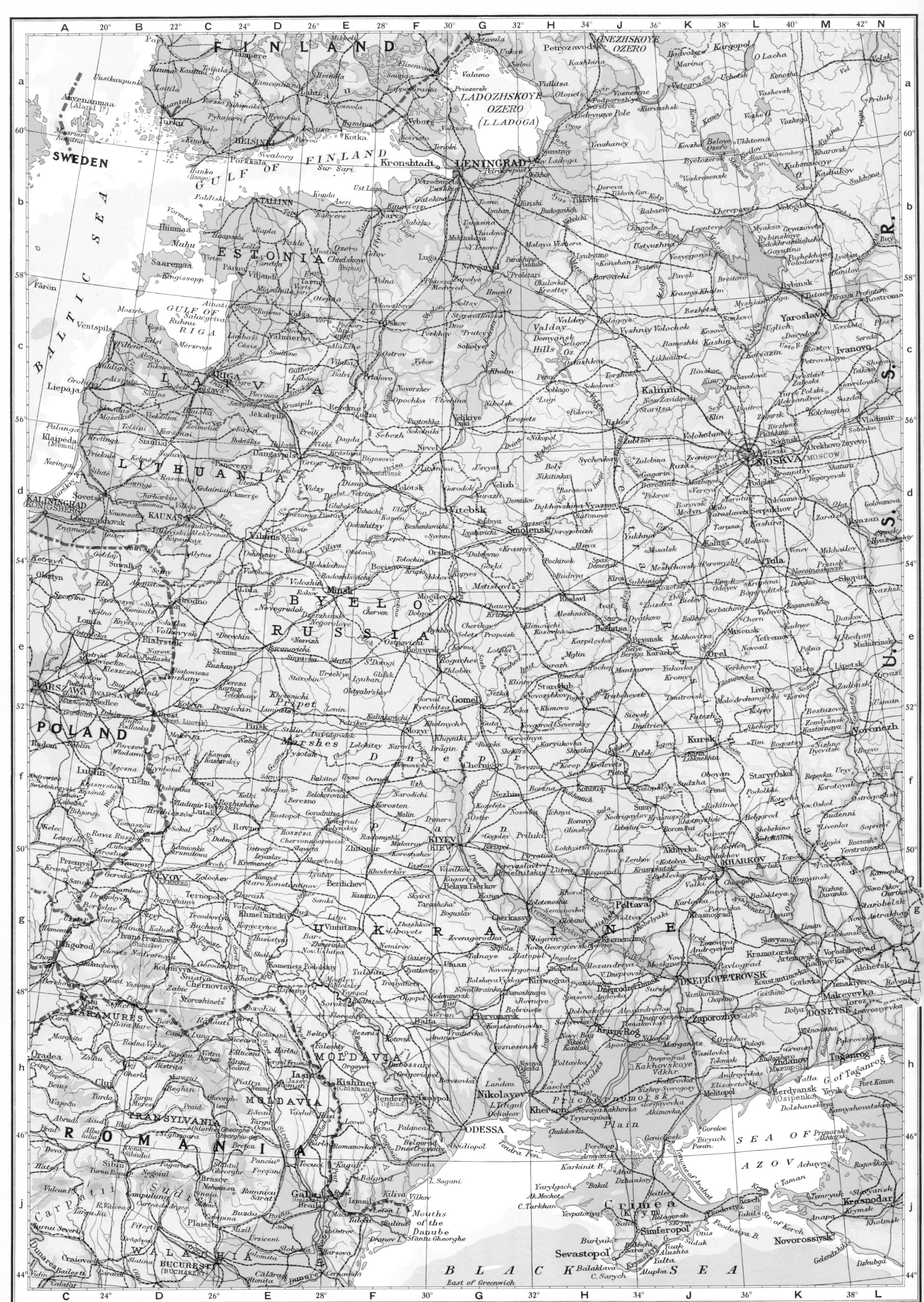

HEIGHTS IN METRES

1800
900
450
180
90
SEA LEVEL
Depression
50
180
DEPTHS IN METRES

80

CONIC PROJECTION

THE VOLGA BASIN

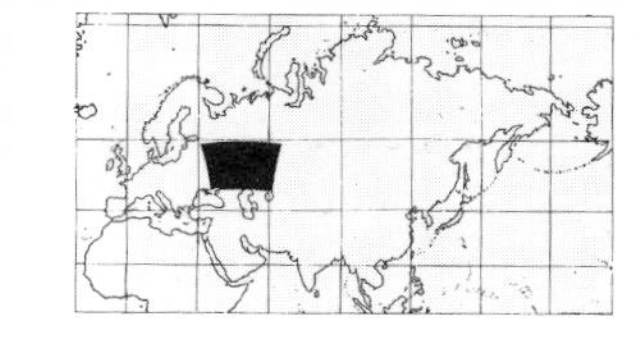

This map shows the highest and the lowest parts of European Russia, from the Urals, up to 1,700 metres high, to the northern end of the Caspian, 15 metres below sea level. The two main rivers are the Don, and the 3,690-kilometres-long Volga which flows through several immense artificial lakes, recently created. The huge, low-lying plain that circles the northern end of the Caspian is the largest area of inland drainage in the world.

SCALE

KM — MILES

CONIC PROJECTION

MAIN ROADS
RAILWAYS

SCALE: 1:6,000,000 (1CM = 60KM)

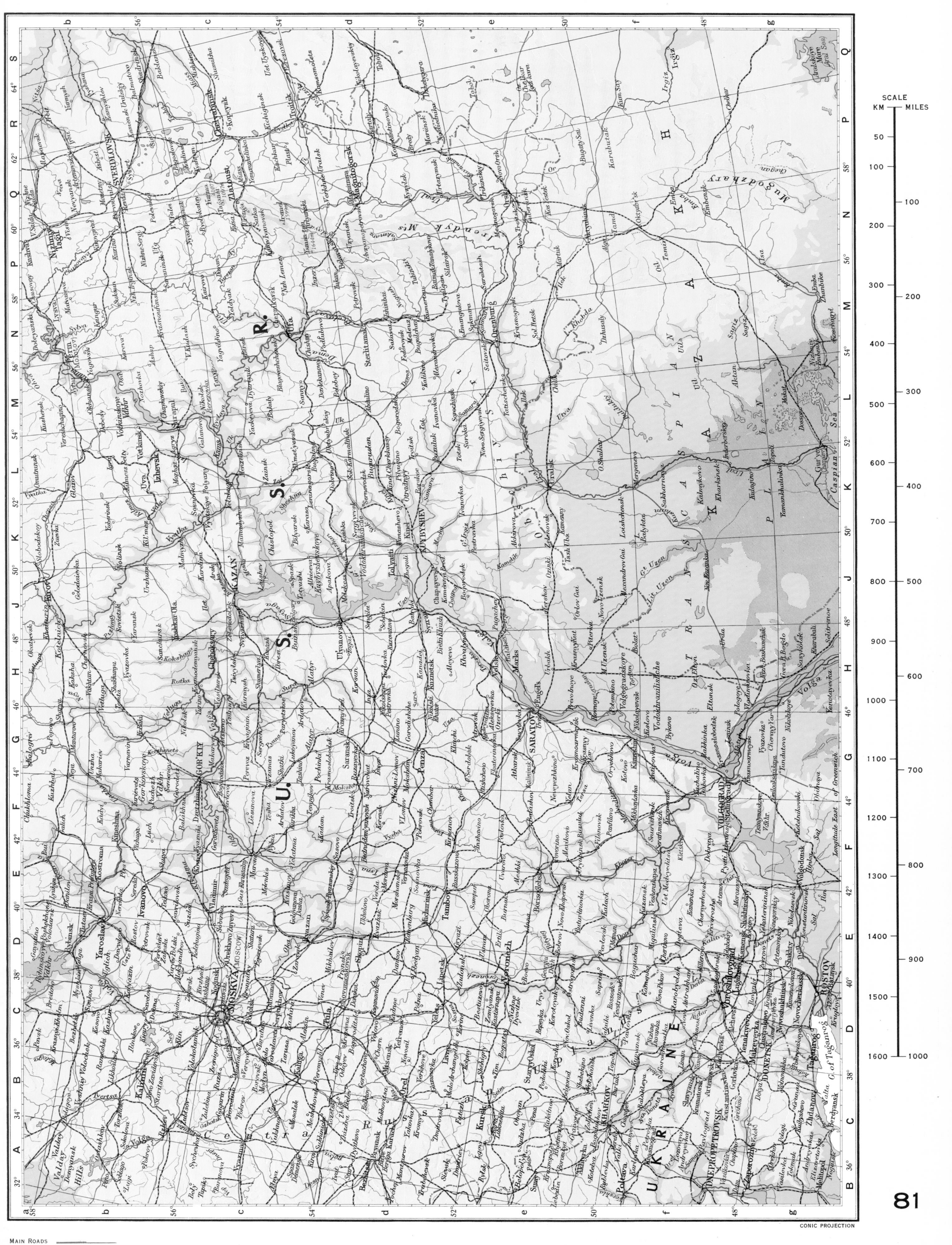

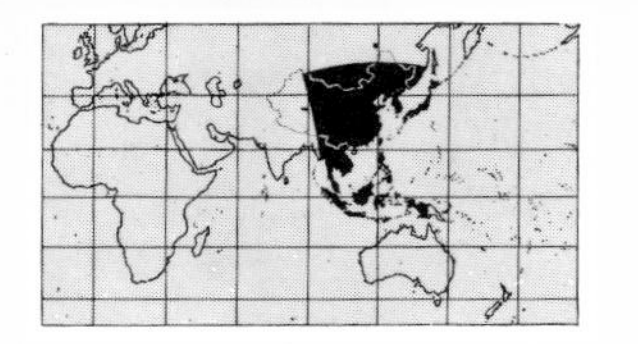

THE FAR EAST

NORTH KOREA, SOUTH KOREA, PHILIPPINES, INDONESIA

NORTH KOREA AREA: 122,313 sq. km. (47,225 sq. miles)
POP: 16,000,000 CAP: *Pyongyang* CURR: 100 jun=1 new won
SOUTH KOREA AREA: 98,425 sq. km. (38,002 sq. miles)
POP: 35,900,000 CAP: *Sŏul* CURR: 10 hwan=1 won

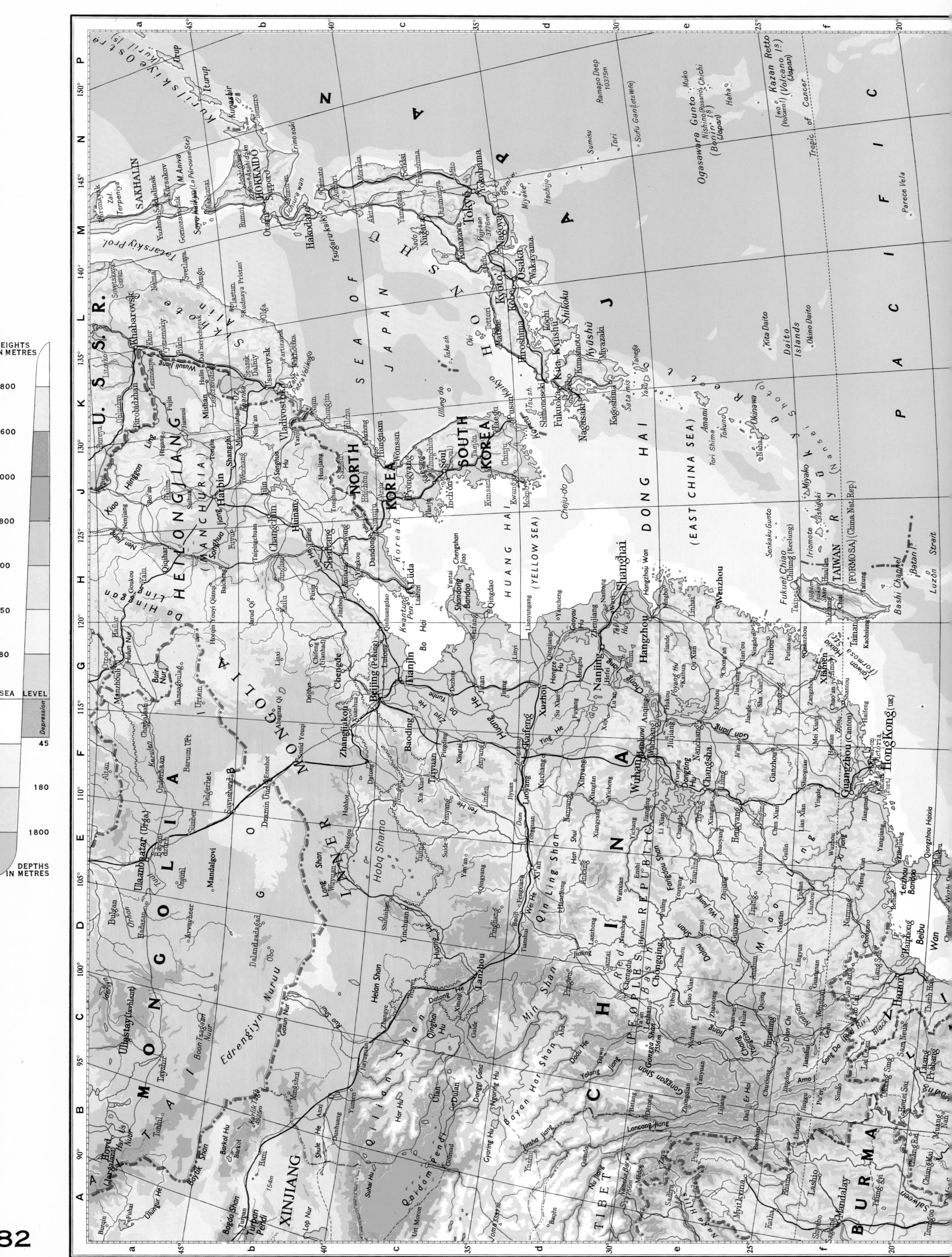

HEIGHTS IN METRES

4800
3600
3000
1800
900
450
180

SEA LEVEL

Depression

45
180
1800

DEPTHS IN METRES

82

BONNE'S PROJECTION

SCALE: 1:15,000,000 (1CM = 150KM)

MAIN ROADS
RAILWAYS

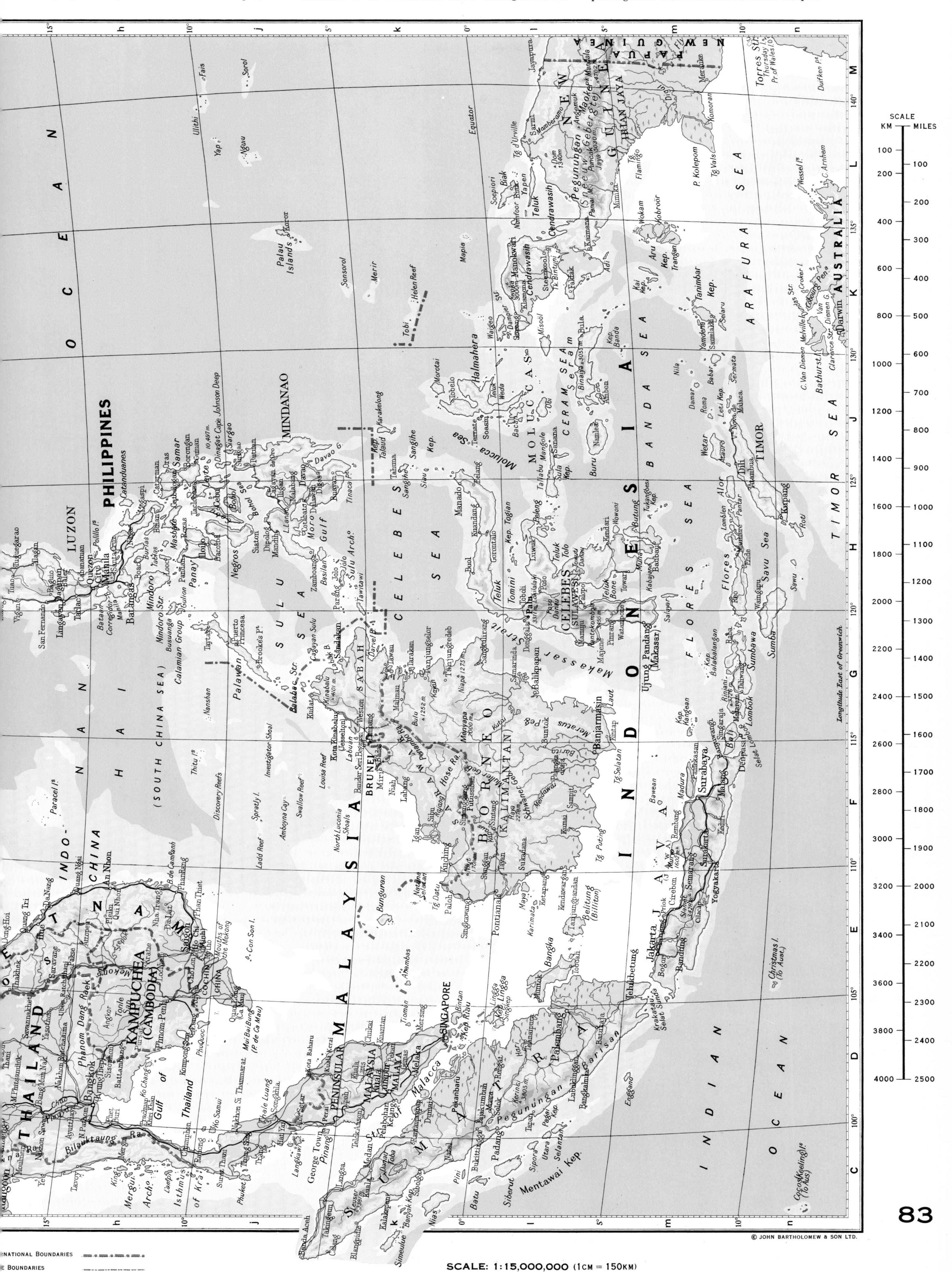

PHILIPPINES AREA: *299,767 sq. km. (115,740 sq. miles)*
POP: *43,940,000* CAP: *Manila* CURR: *100 centavos=1 peso*
INDONESIA AREA: *1,904,344 sq. km. (735,268 sq. miles)*
POP: *133,000,000* CAP: *Jakarta* CURR: *100 sen=1 rupiah*

From the high Tibetan plateau to the deep ocean bed off the Philippines is a drop of over 15,000 metres. The shallow seas of the Indonesian Archipelago and the mainly volcanic formation of the mountainous islands curving round the Malaysian peninsula to New Guinea are a marked contrast to the Himalayan fold mountains. The Philippines, some 7,000 islands, form the apex of a triangle based on Indonesia and pointing north to the mountainous islands of Japan.

SCALE
KM MILES

83

SCALE: 1:15,000,000 (1 CM = 150KM)

NATIONAL BOUNDARIES
E BOUNDARIES

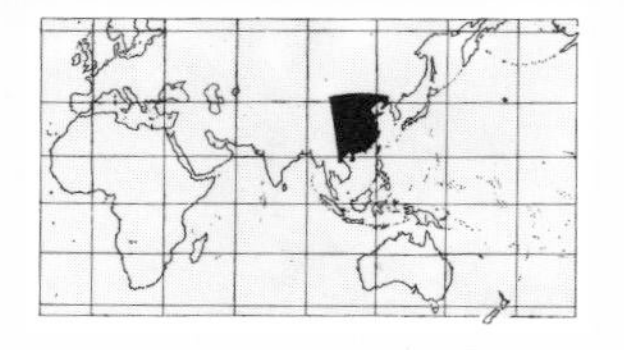

EAST CHINA

CHINA AREA: 9,597,000 sq. km.
(3,705,405 sq. miles) POP: 850,000,000
CAP: Beijing (Peking) CURR: 100 fen=1 yuan
Though half covered by mountains, China has

the largest population of any country in the world, and also the largest area of fertile land. The eastern half of the map shows a semi-circle of low-lying land dotted with lakes, testifying

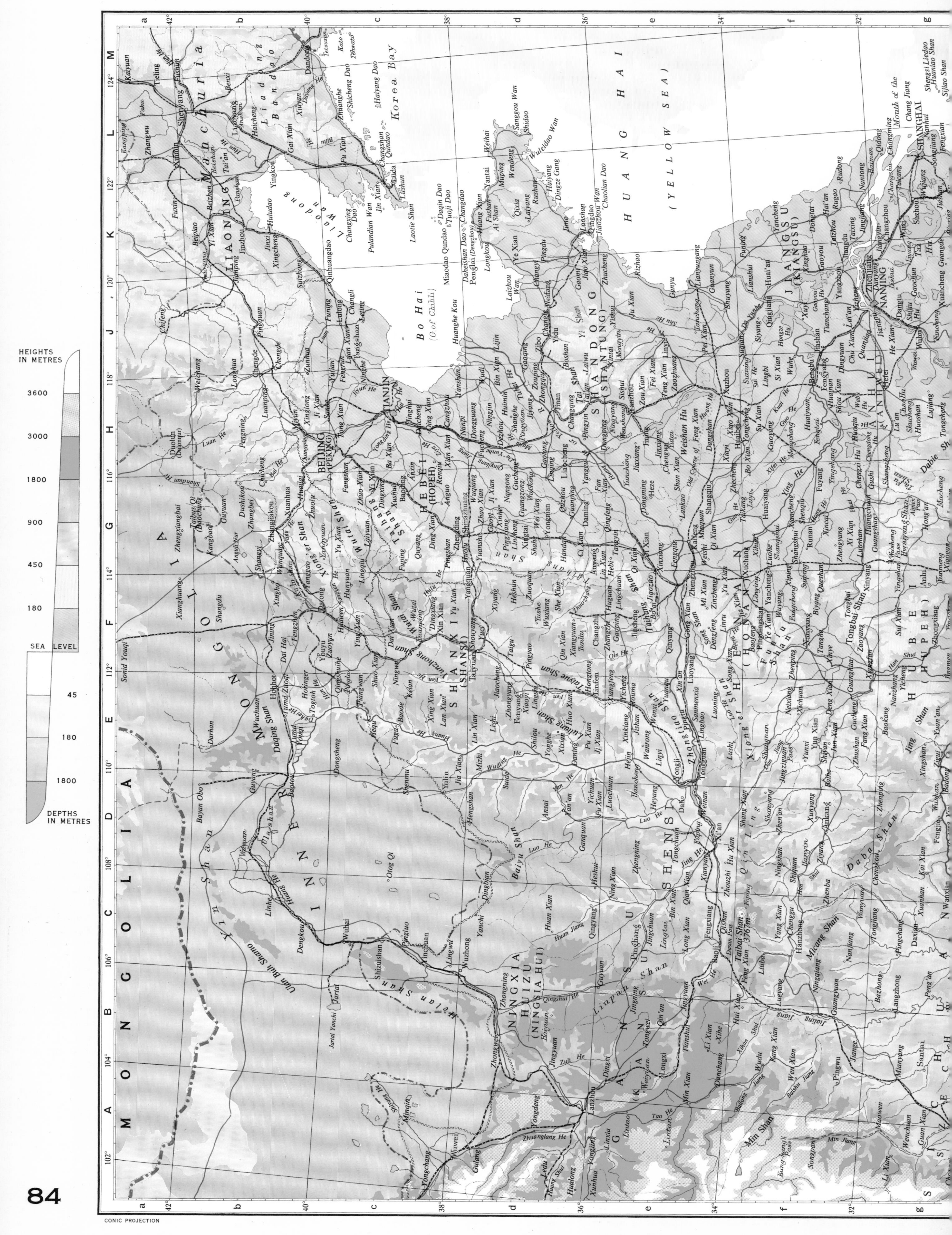

HEIGHTS
IN METRES

3600
3000
1800
900
450
180
SEA LEVEL
45
180
1800

DEPTHS
IN METRES

CONIC PROJECTION

SCALE: 1:6,000,000 (1CM = 60KM)

————————— MAIN ROADS

----------- RAILWAYS

to inadequate river drainage. This area is backed by vast mountain ranges running north-east to Siberia, and cut up by mountainous tracts on a south-east axis reaching down to the coast of Zhejiang. Each of the three main rivers, the Huang He (Yellow River), the Chang Jiang (Yangtze Kiang) and the Xi Jiang, has a broad, well-watered valley, and together contain more than two-thirds of China's inhabitants. Xinjiang, the largest province, is mostly desert. Another desert, the Gobi, which separates northern China from Outer Mongolia, covers nearly one-third of China's total area. China's jagged south-eastern coastline contrasts sharply with the smoother coastline north of Shanghai.

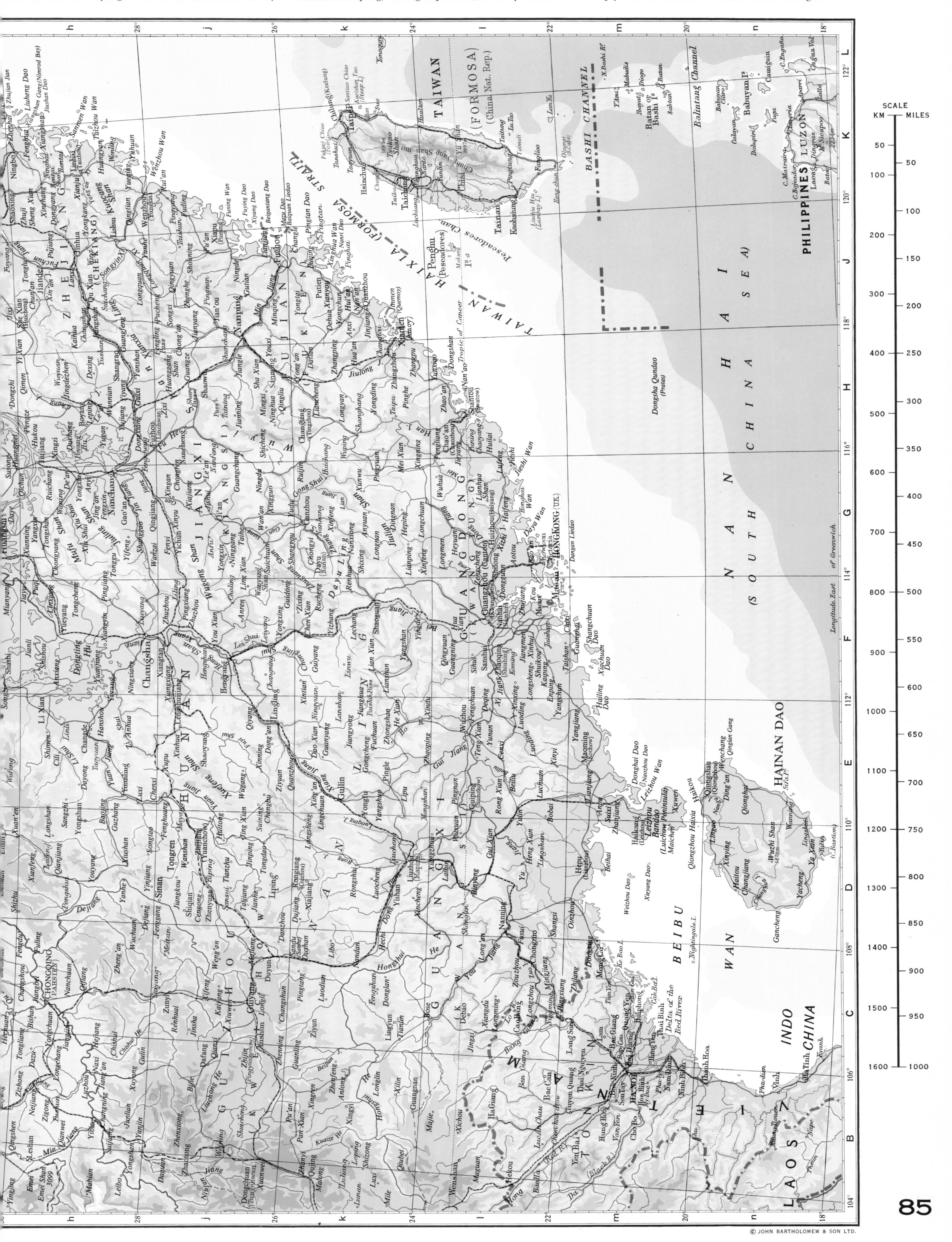

SCALE: 1:6,000,000 (1CM = 60KM)

INTERNATIONAL BOUNDARIES
PROVINCIAL BOUNDARIES

85

JAPAN

AREA: *369,699 sq. km. (142,741 sq. miles)*
POP: *113,086,000* **CAP:** *Tokyo* **CURR:** *100 sen=1 yen*
Japan consists of a group of four large islands

and many smaller ones, stretching from north to south over 1,500 kilometres and separated from China by the shallow Sea of Japan. The

main island is Honshu, which is approximately the same size as Great Britain. Off Japan's east coast the Pacific Ocean is almost at its deepest.

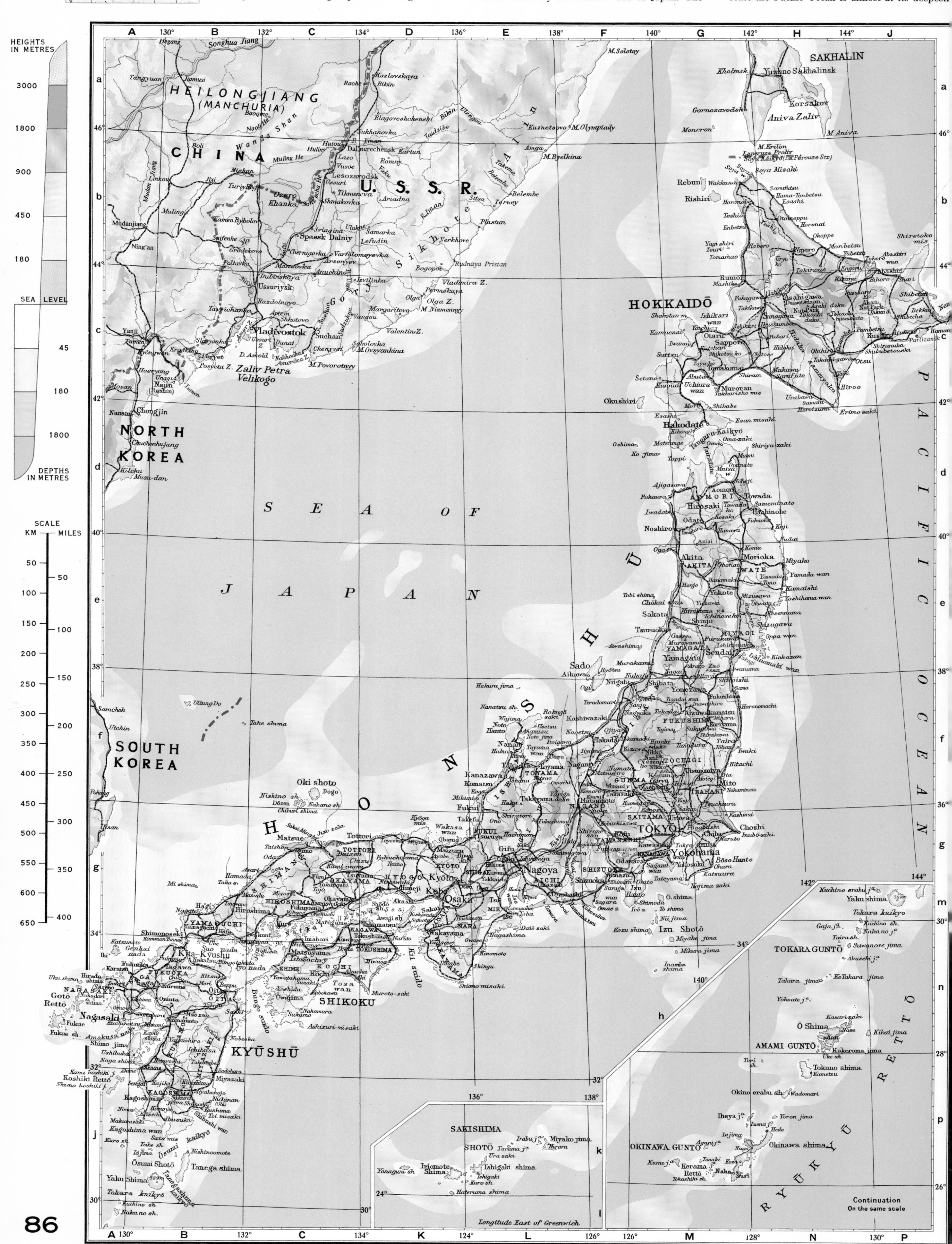

HEIGHTS
IN METRES

3000
1800
900
450
180

SEA LEVEL

45
180
1800

DEPTHS
IN METRES

SCALE
KM — MILES

86

CONIC PROJECTION

SCALE: 1:6,000,000 (1CM = 60KM)

INTERNATIONAL BOUNDARIES
PROVINCIAL BOUNDARIES

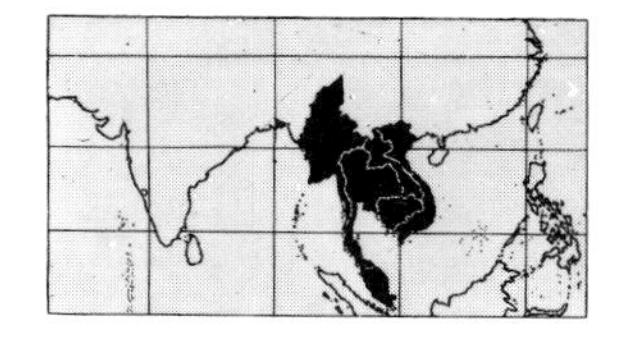
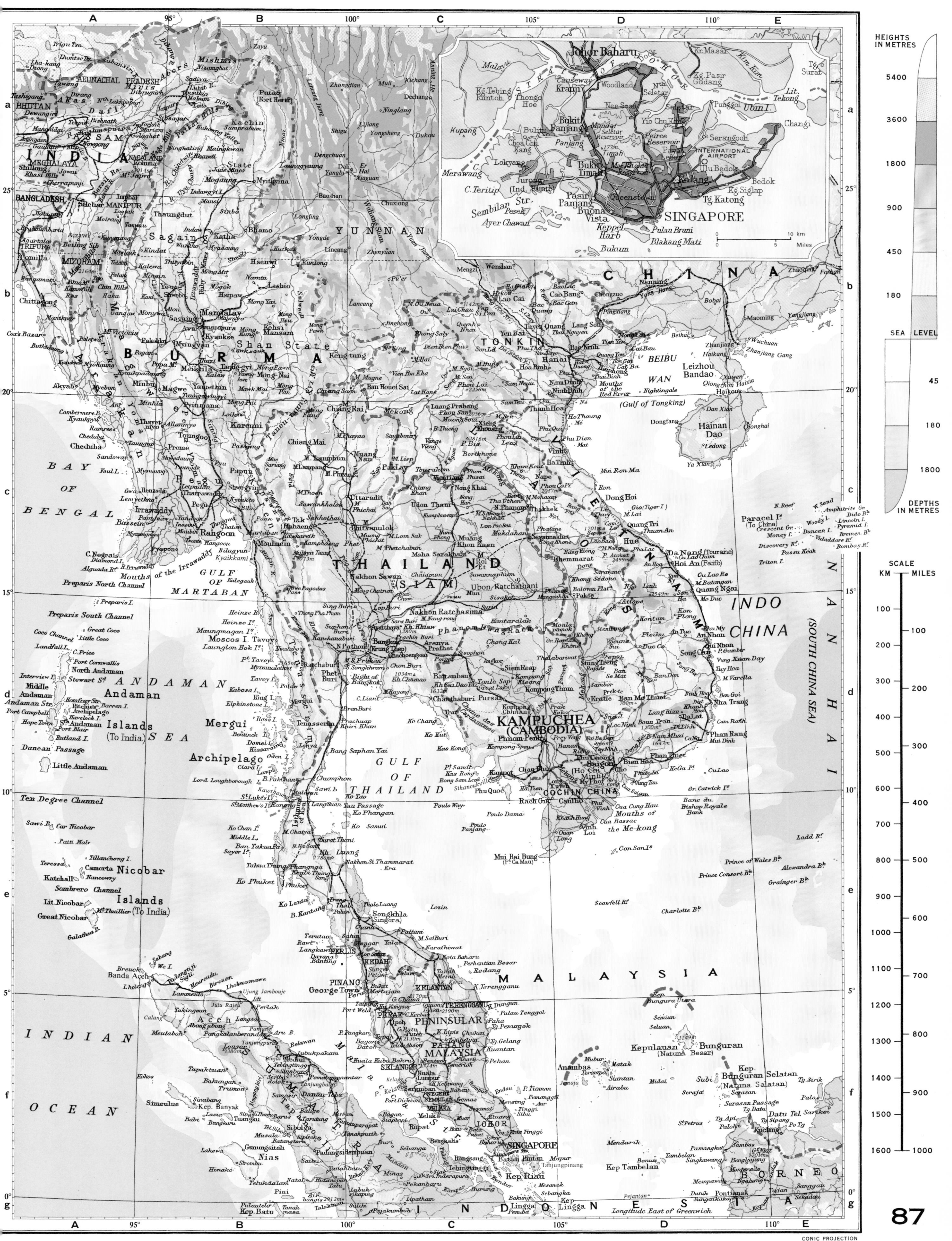

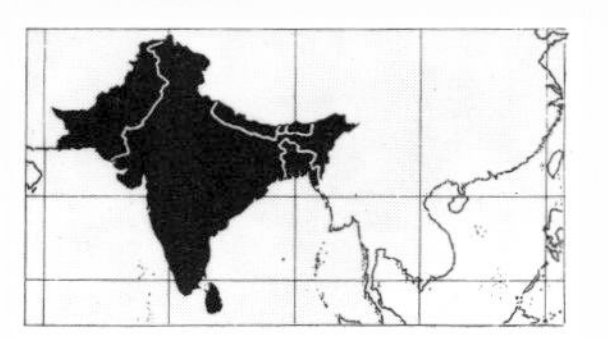

INDIA AND
BANGLADESH, BURMA, PAKISTAN, SRI LANKA

INDIA AREA: 3,287,593 sq. km. (1,269,341 sq. miles) POP: 638,388,000 CAP: *New Delhi*
PAKISTAN AREA: 803,944 sq. km. (310,403 sq. miles) POP: 75,278,000 CAP: *Islamabad*
BANGLADESH AREA: 143,999 sq. km. (55,598 sq. miles) POP: 76,820,000 CAP: *Dacca*

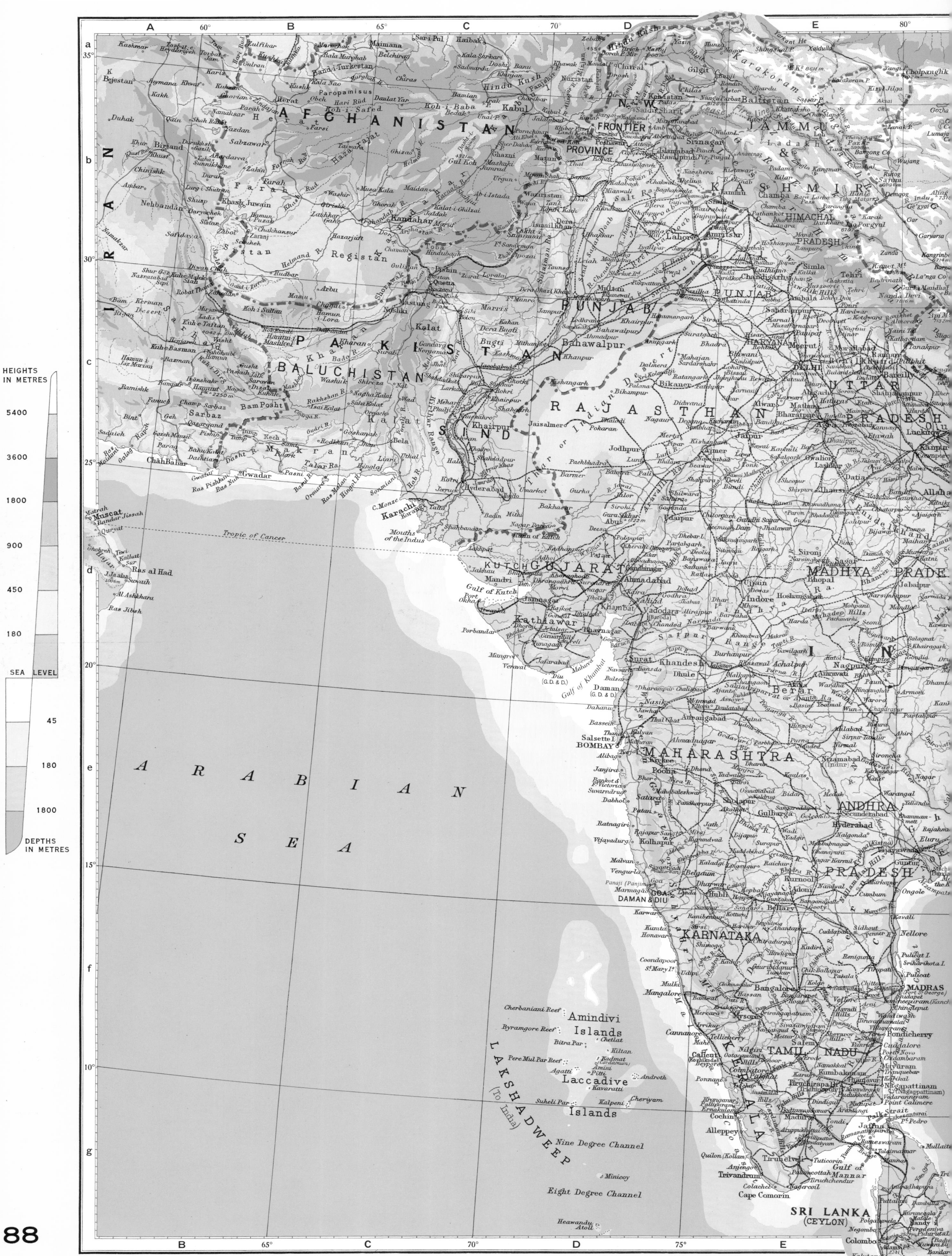

HEIGHTS IN METRES

5400
3600
1800
900
450
180

SEA LEVEL

45
180
1800

DEPTHS IN METRES

88

CONIC PROJECTION

SCALE: 1:10,000,000 (1CM = 100KM)

MAIN ROADS
RAILWAYS

SRI LANKA AREA: 65,610 sq. km. (25,332 sq. miles)
POP: 14,270,000 CAP: Colombo CURR: 100 cents=1 rupee
BURMA AREA: 678,034 sq. km. (261,789 sq. miles)
POP: 31,240,000 CAP: Rangoon CURR: 100 pyas=1 kyat

The Indian peninsula falls into three main regions: the Himalayas, the great plains of the Indus and the Ganges, and the Deccan plateau. The mountains to the north virtually seal off the peninsula from the rest of Asia. Along the coast from the Gulf of Cambay down to Cape Comorin, runs the long mountain range of the Western Ghats. The high mountains of Burma are separated by the valley of the Irrawaddy and Sittang rivers.

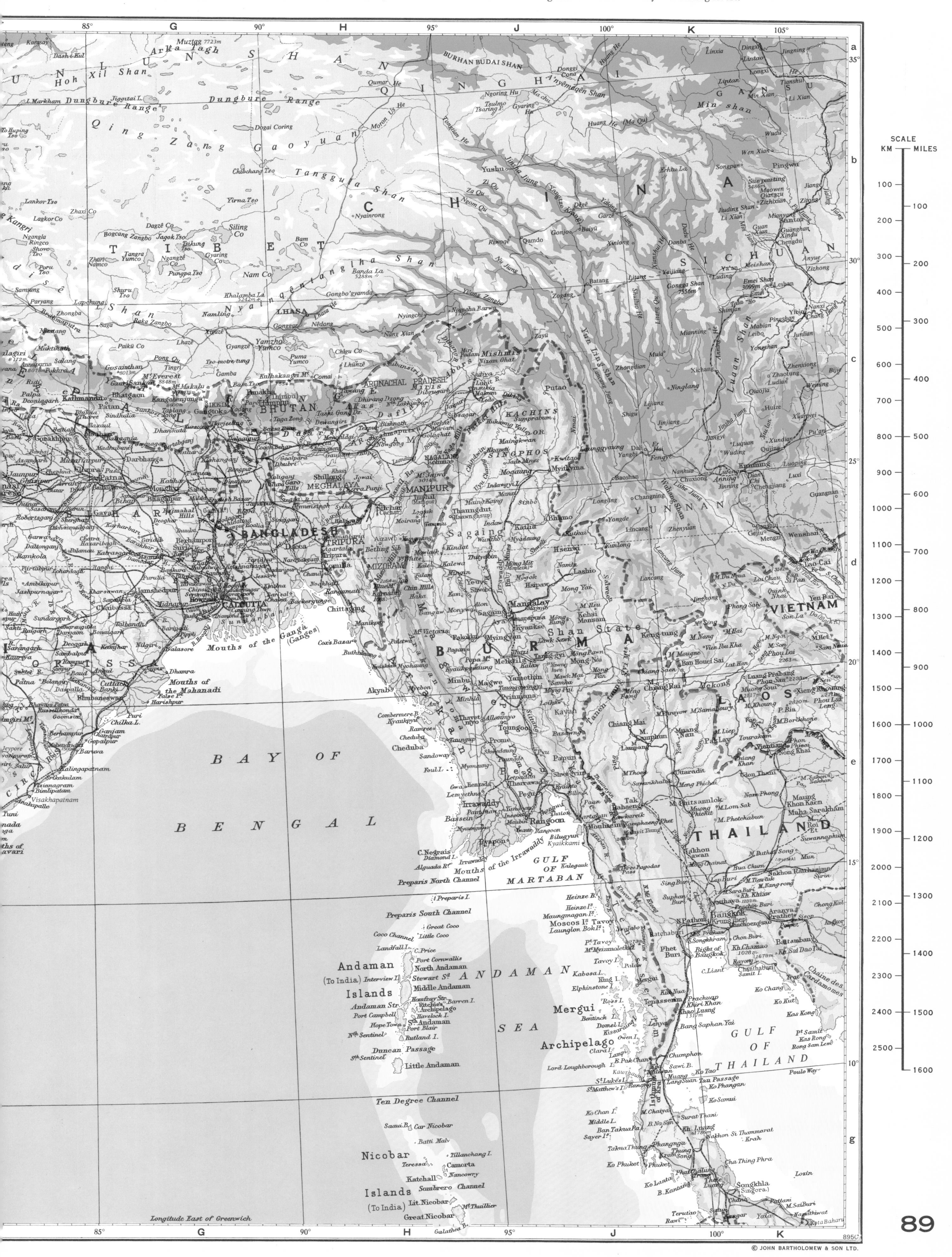

SCALE
KM → MILES

89

© JOHN BARTHOLOMEW & SON LTD.

INTERNATIONAL BOUNDARIES
STATE BOUNDARIES

SCALE: 1:10,000,000 (1CM = 100KM)

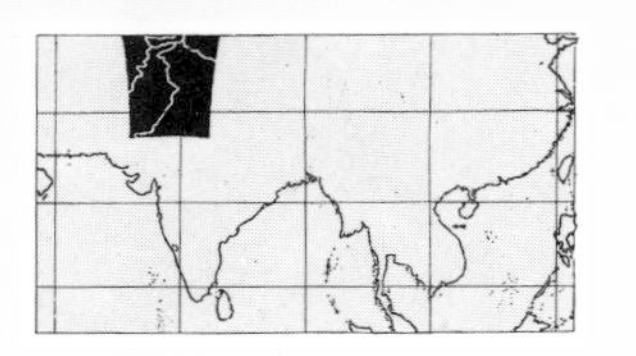

PUNJAB AND KASHMIR

To the north-west of the Indian peninsula a region of contrasts ranges from the arid deserts of the lower Indus plain to the perpetual snows of the high Himalayas in Kashmir, part of the district known as the Roof of the World. The area is intersected by the erratic courses of the Indus and its tributaries, which rise close to the eastward-flowing Brahmaputra River, shown on the opposite map.

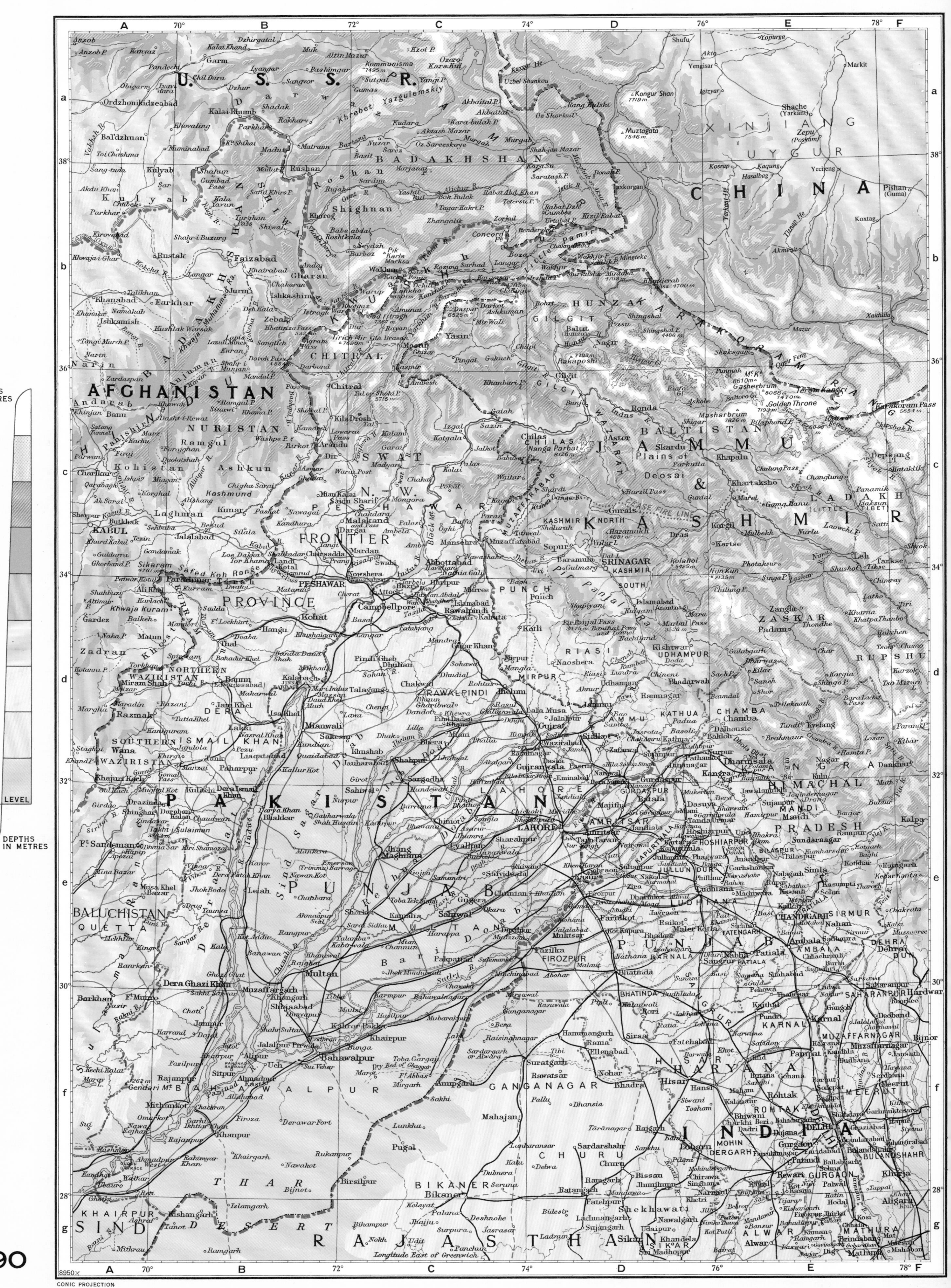

HEIGHTS
IN METRES

5400

4800

3600

3000

1800

900

450

180

SEA LEVEL

DEPTHS
IN METRES

90

CONIC PROJECTION

8950 c

SCALE: 1:4,000,000 (1CM = 40KM)

INTERNATIONAL BOUNDARIES

STATE BOUNDARIES

PLAIN OF THE GANGES

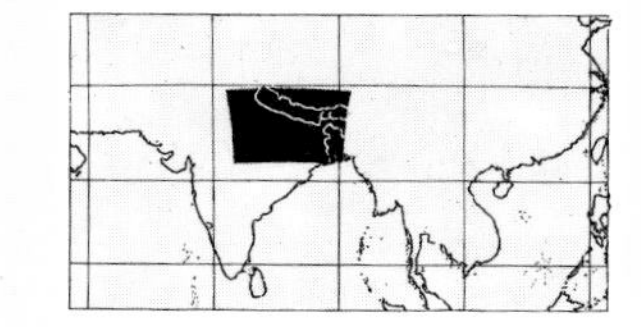

The Ganges valley is one of the most thickly populated regions in the world. The population is entirely dependent on the rivers that flow down from the north-west, across the plain, and through their many deltas into the Bay of Bengal. These rivers bring with them rich alluvial deposits and provide waters for irrigation. The largest river in the plain is revered throughout India as Mother Ganges.

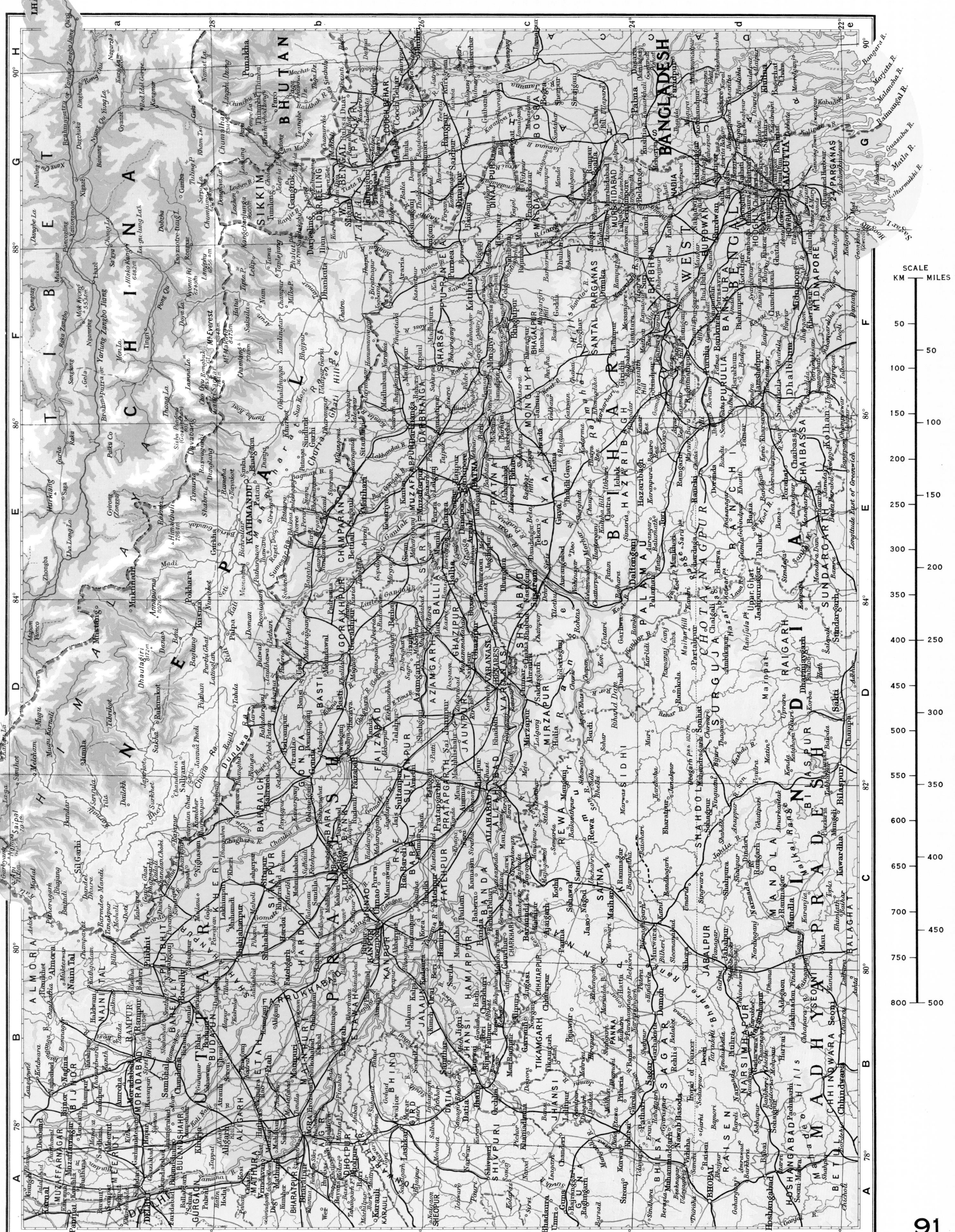

MAIN ROADS _____

RAILWAYS _____

SCALE: 1:4,000,000 (1CM = 40KM)

CONIC PROJECTION

91

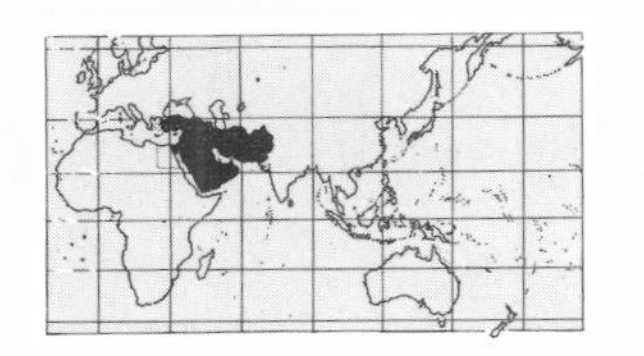

THE MIDDLE EAST
AND AFGHANISTAN

TURKEY AREA: 780,579 sq. km. (301,380 sq. miles) POP: 40,200,000
CAPITAL: *Ankara* CURRENCY: 100 piastres (kurus)=1 lira
IRAQ AREA: 438,446 sq. km. (169,284 sq. miles) POP: 11,500,000
CAPITAL: *Baghdad* CURRENCY: 1,000 fils=1 dinar

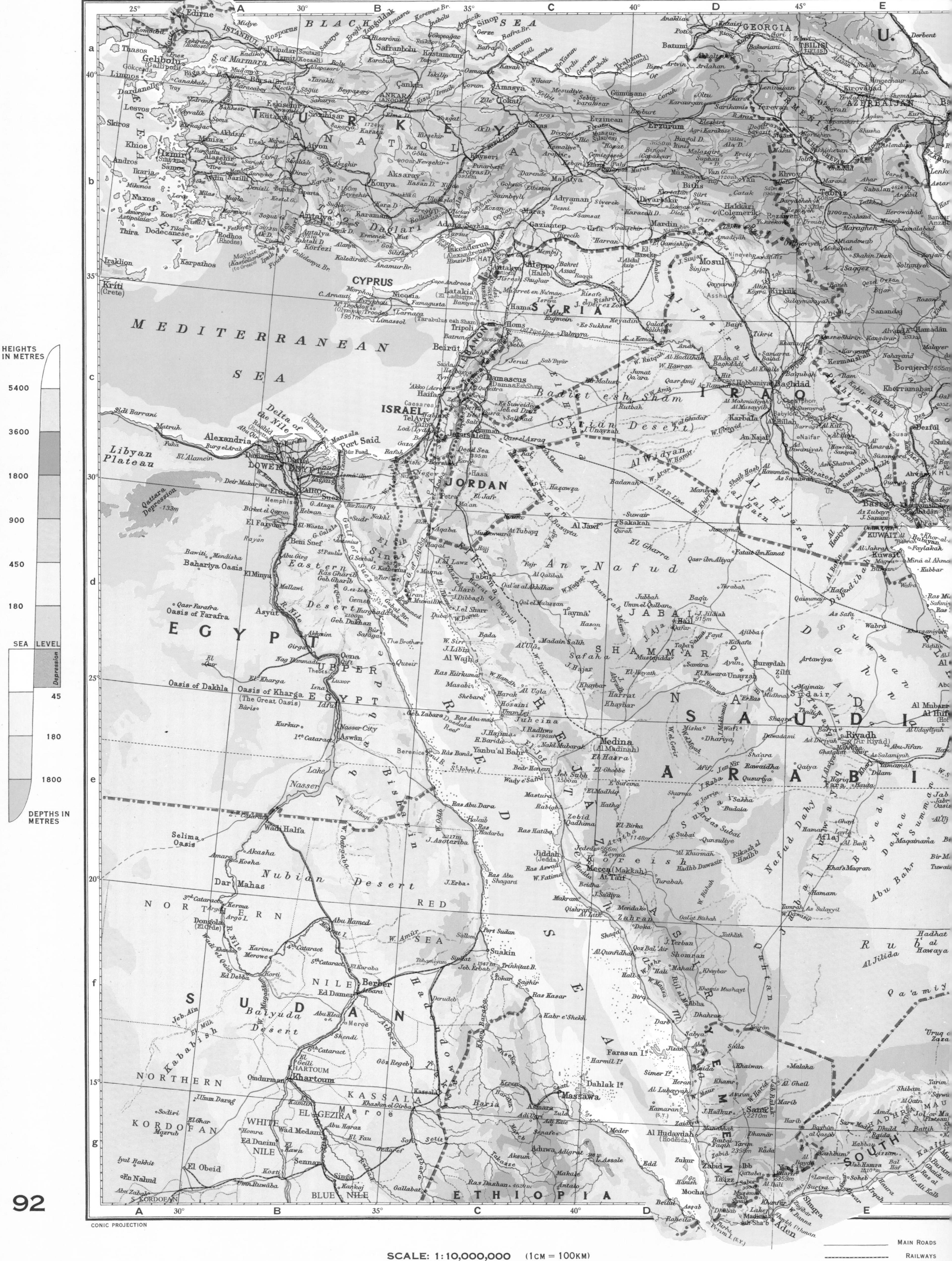

HEIGHTS
IN METRES

5400
3600
1800
900
450
180

SEA LEVEL

Depression

45
180
1800

DEPTHS IN
METRES

92

CONIC PROJECTION

SCALE: 1:10,000,000   (1CM = 100KM)

MAIN ROADS

RAILWAYS

IRAN AREA: 1,648,191 sq. km. (636,367 sq. miles)
POP: 33,592,000 CAPITAL: *Tehran*
AFGHANISTAN AREA: 650,090 sq. km. (251,000 sq. miles)
POP: 19,580,000 CAPITAL: *Kabul*

SAUDI ARABIA AREA: 2,400,930 sq. km. (927,000 sq. miles)
POPULATION: 9,157,000 CAPITALS: *Mecca* and *Riyadh*
CURRENCY: 100 hilallah=1 rial
The map shows the fold mountain belt widening from the

Georgian Caucasus into the broad plateau of Persia, and
narrowing at the heights of the Hindu Kush. The deep rift
of the Jordan and the Dead Sea broadens into the Red Sea,
and continues south as the Great Rift Valley of Africa.

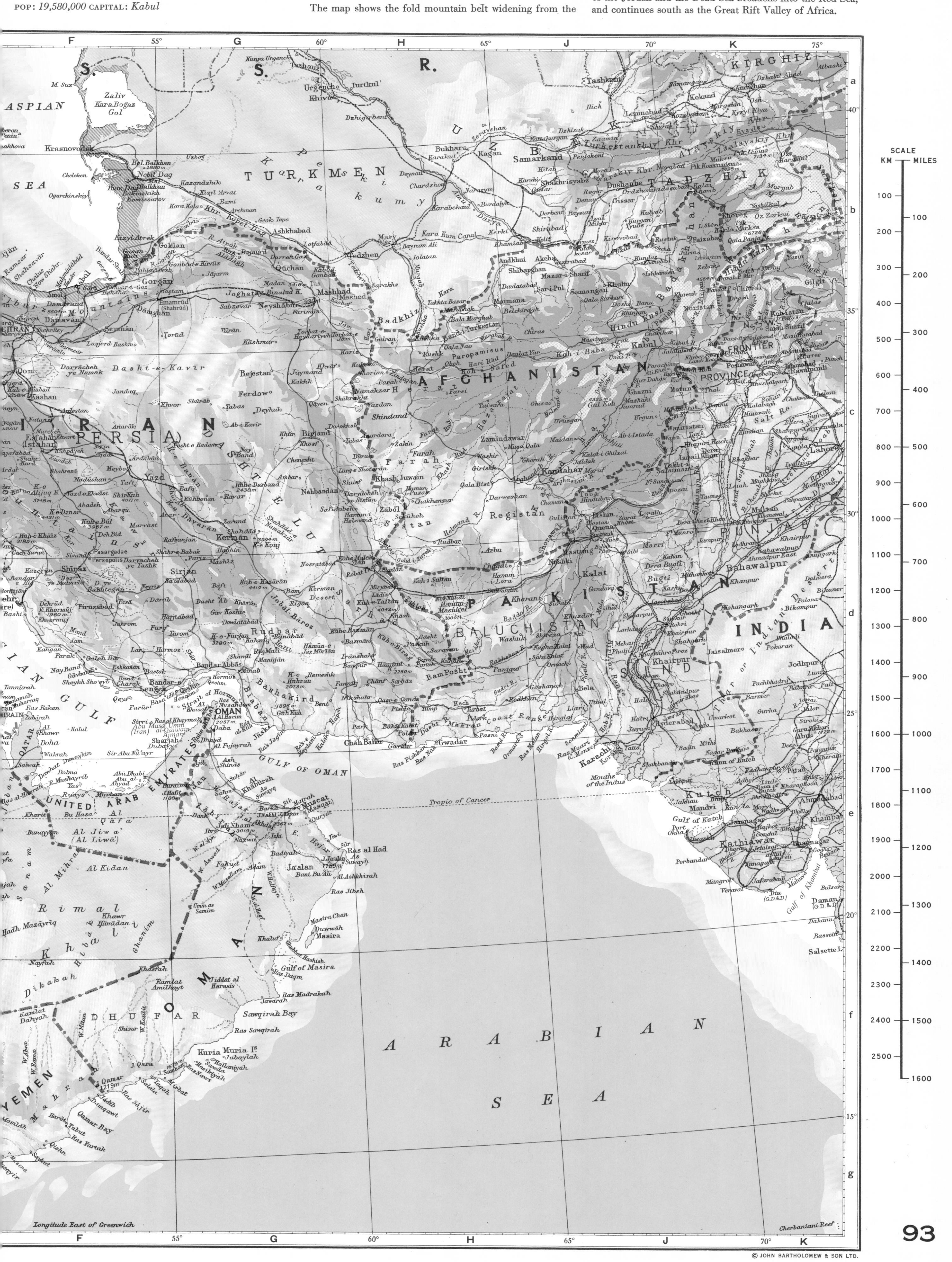

93

INTERNATIONAL BOUNDARIES
STATE BOUNDARIES

SCALE: 1:10,000,000 (1CM = 100KM)

THE LEVANT AND JORDAN

SYRIA AREA: 185,680 sq. km.
(71,691 sq. miles) POP: 8,300,000
CAPITAL: *Damascus*
CURRENCY: *100 piastres = 1 pound*

LEBANON AREA: 10,399 sq. km.
(4,015 sq. miles) POP: 2,870,000
CAPITAL: *Beirut*
CURRENCY: *100 piastres = 1 pound*

ISRAEL AREA: 20,702 sq. km.
(7,992 sq. miles) POP: 3,700,000
CAPITAL: *Jerusalem*
CURRENCY: *100 agorot = 1 pound*

JORDAN AREA: 97,739 sq. km.
(37,737 sq. miles) POP: 2,690,000
CAPITAL: *Amman*
CURRENCY: *1,000 fils = 1 dinar*

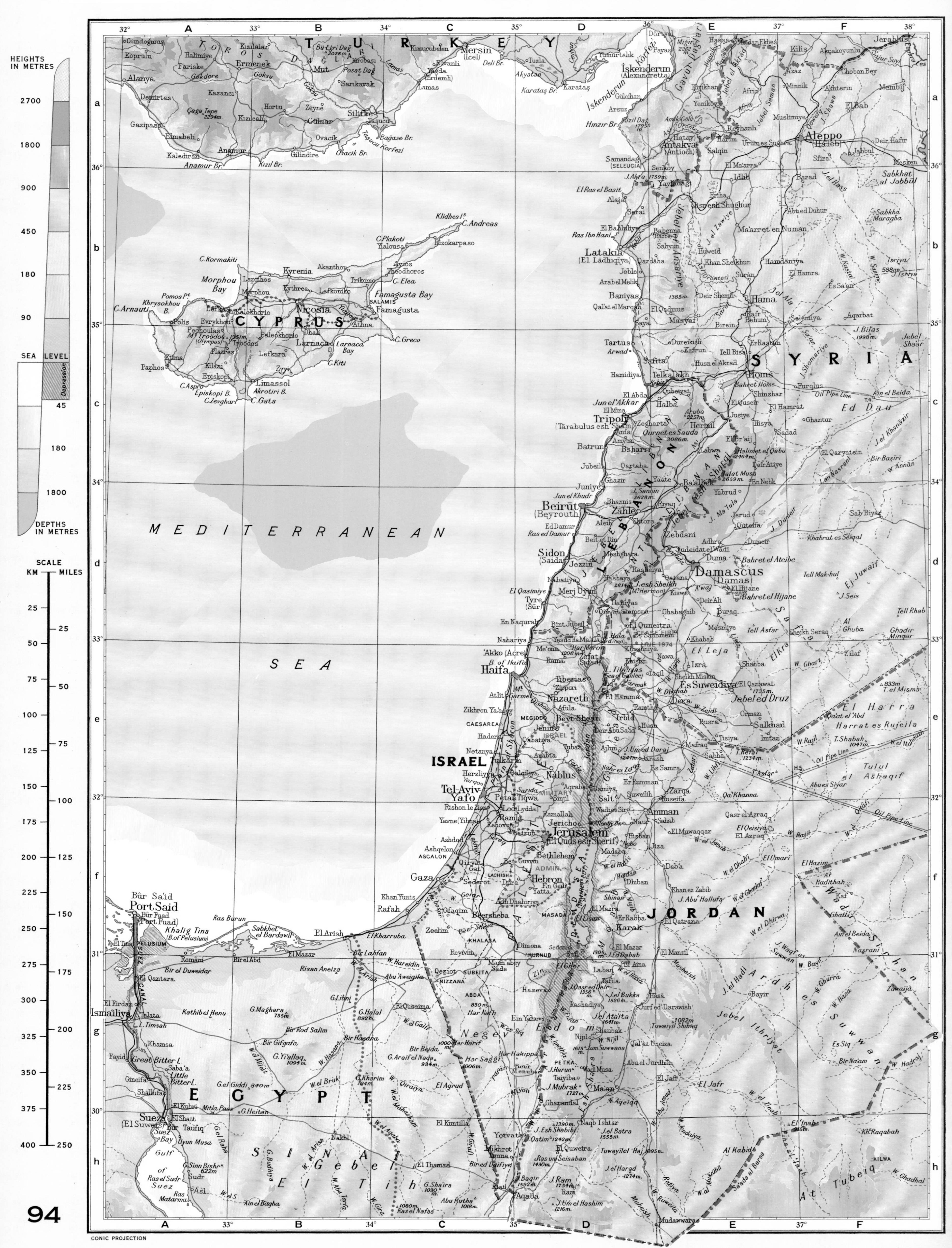

HEIGHTS IN METRES
2700
1800
900
450
180
90
SEA LEVEL
Depression
45
180
1800
DEPTHS IN METRES

SCALE
KM — MILES

94

CONIC PROJECTION

SCALE: 1:2,500,000 (1CM = 25KM)

INTERNATIONAL BOUNDARIES
STATE BOUNDARIES
ARMISTICE LINE

SOUTHERN AFRICA

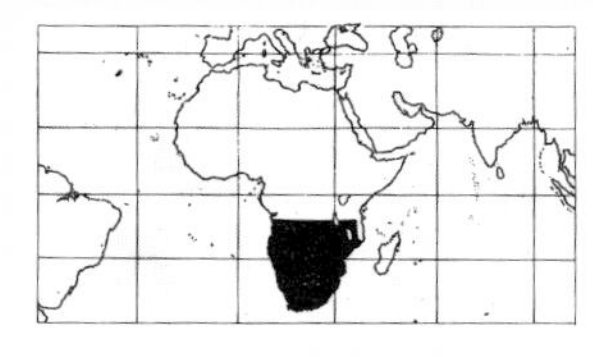

ZAMBIA
AREA: 752,620 sq. km.
(290,587 sq. miles)
POP: 5,138,000
CAP: *Lusaka*

ZIMBABWE
AREA: 390,624 sq. km.
(150,820 sq. miles)
POP: 6,530,000
CAP: *Salisbury*

MALAWI
AREA: 118,039 sq. km.
(45,575 sq. miles)
POP: 5,310,000
CAP: *Lilongwe*

REP. OF S. AFRICA
AREA: 1,221,043 sq. km.
(471,445 sq. miles)
POP: 26,000,000
CAPS: *Pretoria, Cape Town*

BOTSWANA
AREA: 569,800 sq. km.
(220,000 sq. miles)
POP: 680,000
CAP: *Gaborone*

MOZAMBIQUE
AREA: 784,964 sq. km.
(303,075 sq. miles)
POP: 10,000,000
CAP: *Maputo*

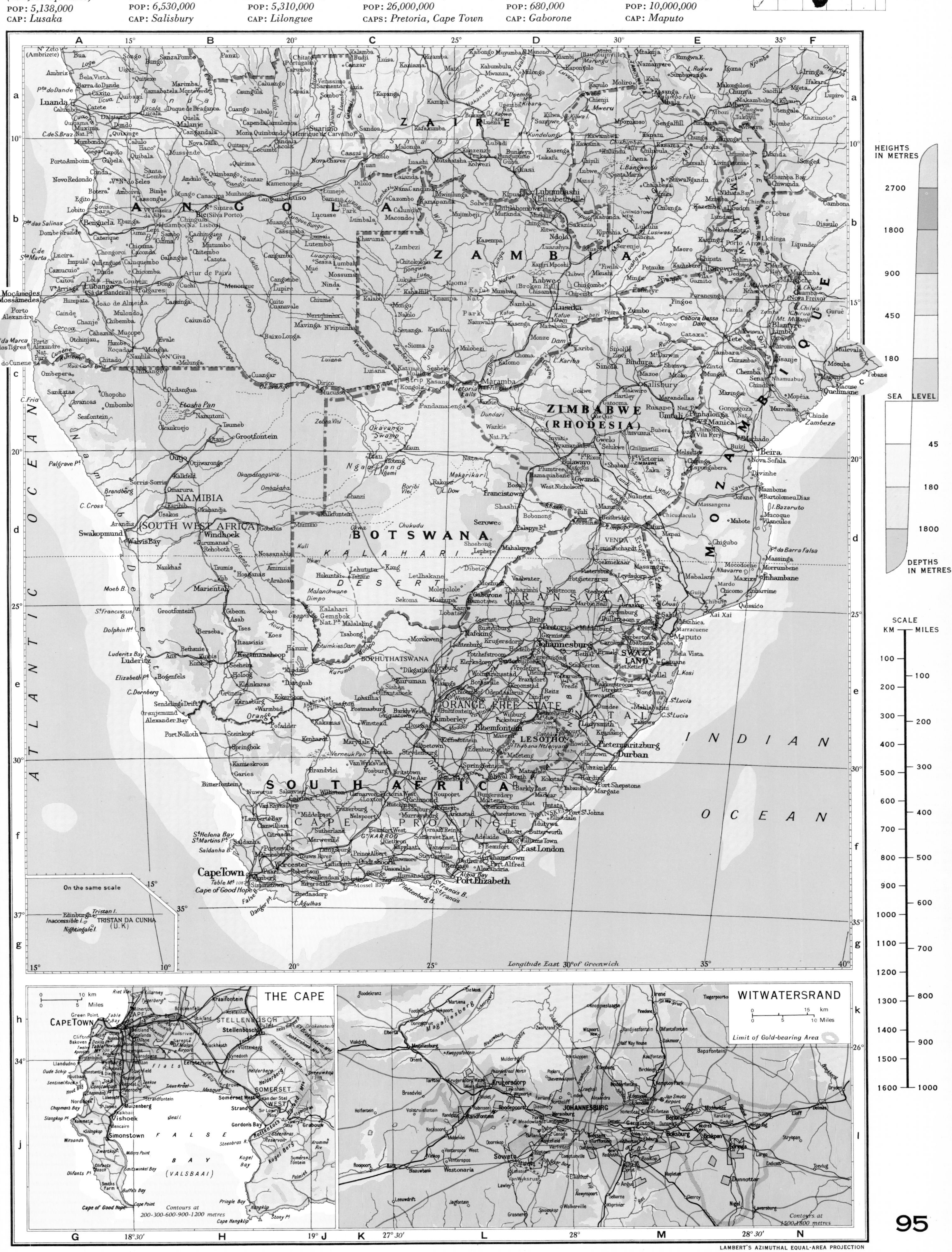

95

LAMBERT'S AZIMUTHAL EQUAL-AREA PROJECTION

MAIN ROADS
RAILWAYS

SCALE: 1:12,500,000 (1CM = 125KM)

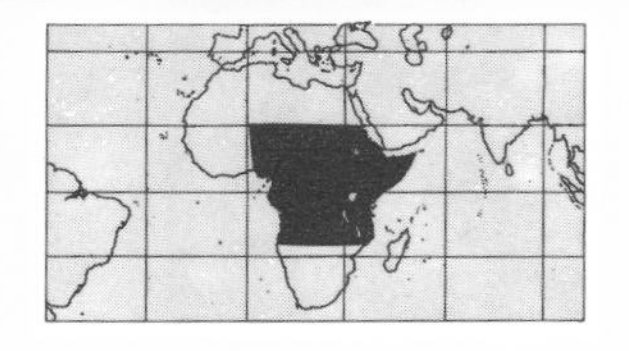

CENTRAL AND EAST AFRICA
ZAIRE, KENYA, UGANDA, TANZANIA, ETHIOPIA, MADAGASCAR

CAMEROUN REPUBLIC
AREA: 475,501 sq. km. (183,591 sq. miles)
POP: 7,500,000 CAP: Yaoundé

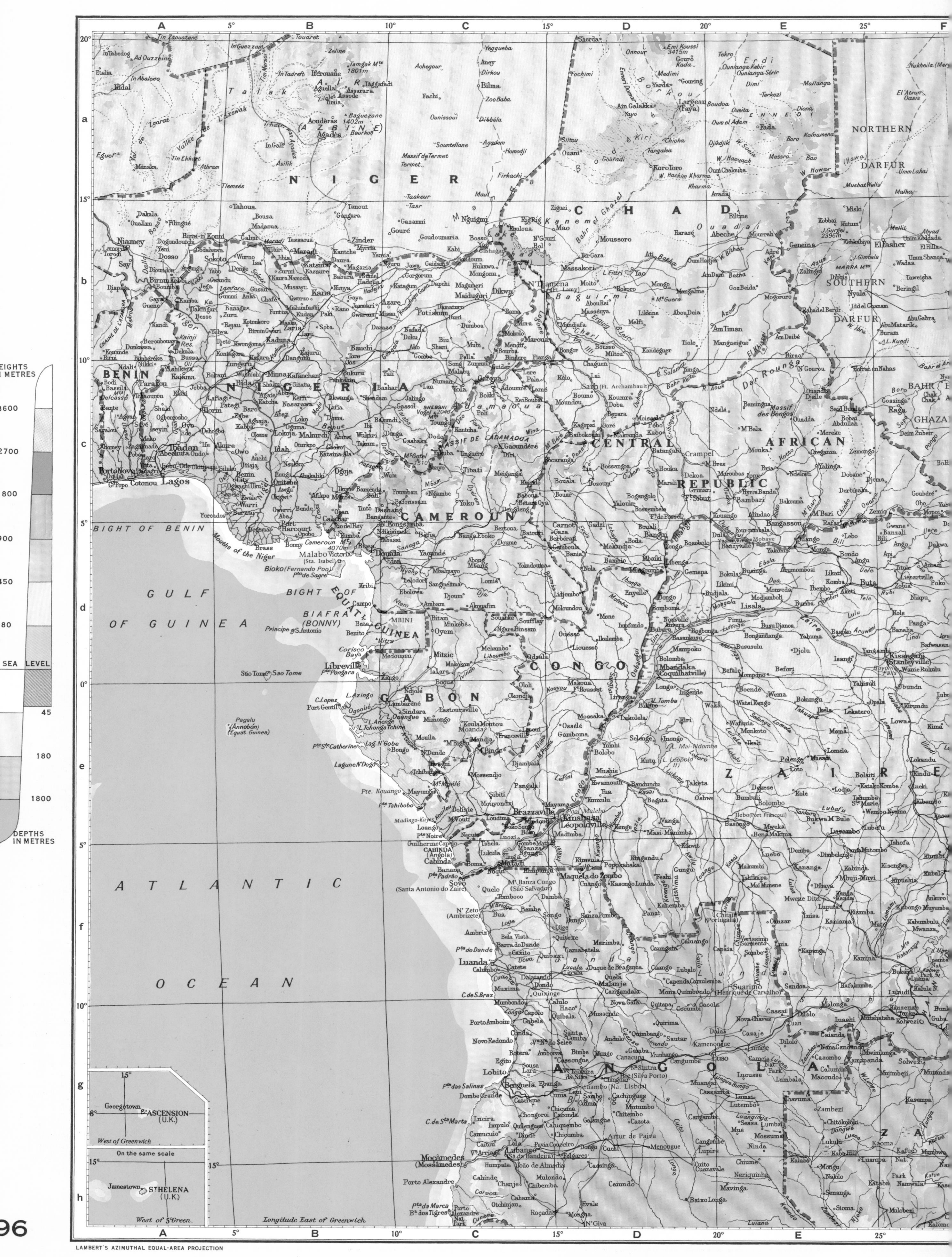

96

LAMBERT'S AZIMUTHAL EQUAL-AREA PROJECTION

SCALE: 1:12,500,000 (1 CM = 125 KM)

MAIN ROADS
RAILWAYS

GOLA AREA: 1,246,700 sq. km. (481,351 miles) POP: 5,800,000 CAP: Luanda

NYA AREA: 582,646 sq. km. (224,960 sq. les) POP: 13,400,000 CAP: Nairobi

REP. OF ZAIRE AREA: 2,344,113 sq. km. (905,063 sq. miles) POP: 25,600,000 CAP: Kinshasa

UGANDA AREA: 236,037 sq. km. (91,134 sq. miles) POP: 11,200,000 CAP: Kampala

TANZANIA AREA: 939,766 sq. km. (362,844 sq. miles) POP: 15,160,000 CAP: Dar es Salaam

ETHIOPIA AREA: 1,221,900 sq. km. (471,776 sq. miles) POP: 27,240,000 CAP: Addis Ababa

SOMALI REP. AREA: 637,541 sq. km. (246,155 sq. miles) POP: 3,170,000 CAP: Mogadiscio

MADAGASCAR AREA: 594,180 sq. km. (229,413 sq. miles) POP: 8,000,000 CAP: Antananarivo

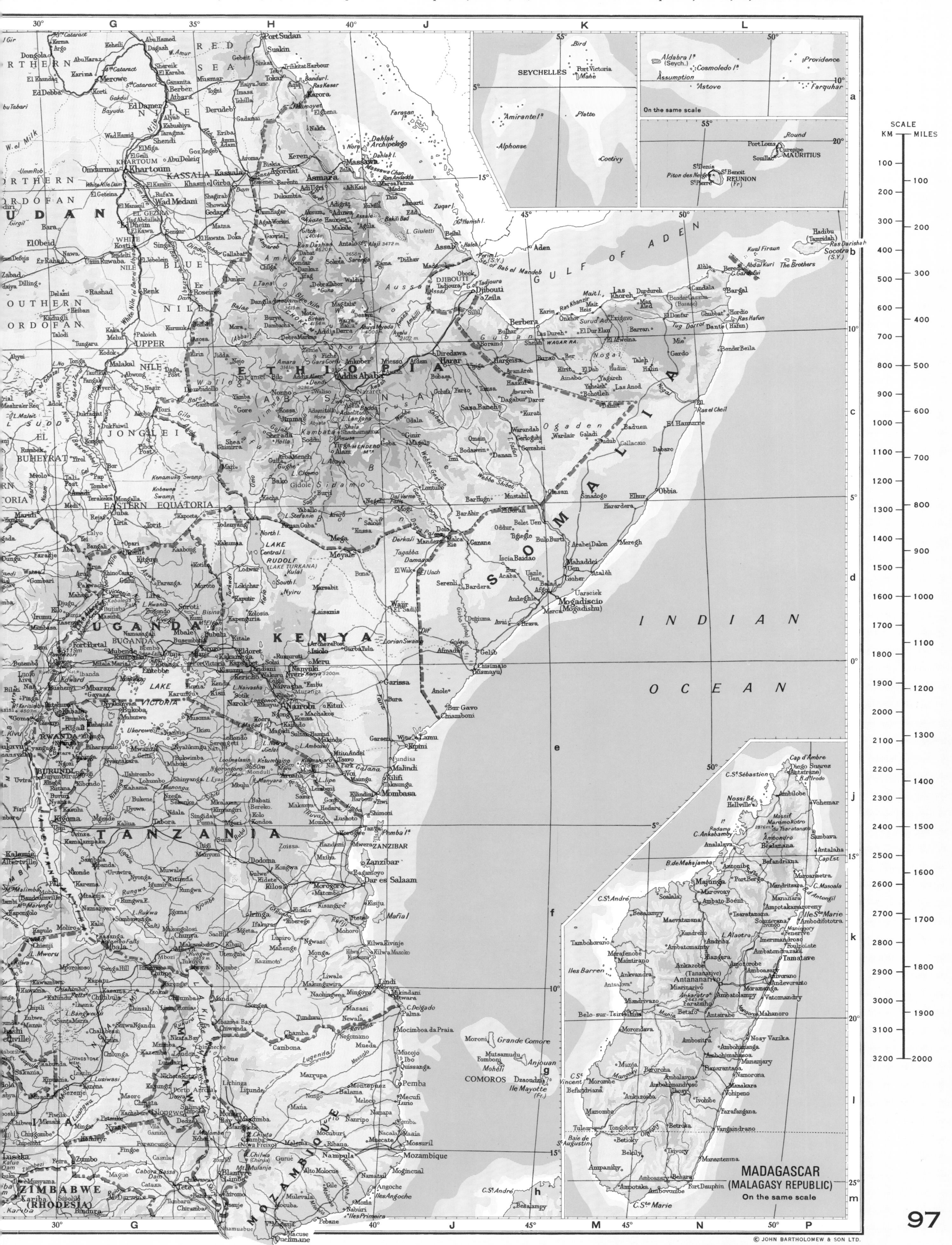

MADAGASCAR
(MALAGASY REPUBLIC)
On the same scale

97

© JOHN BARTHOLOMEW & SON LTD.

SCALE
KM   MILES

INTERNATIONAL BOUNDARIES
STATE BOUNDARIES

SCALE: 1:12,500,000 (1CM = 125KM)

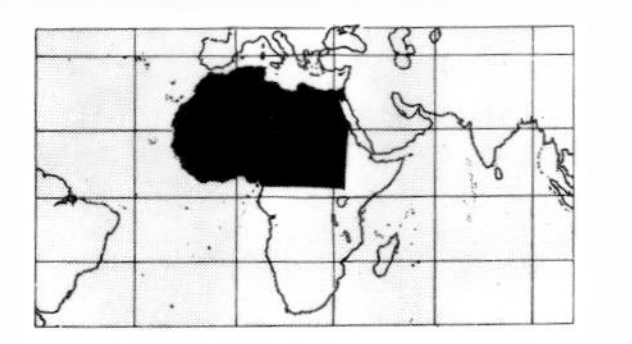

NORTH and WEST AFRICA

MOROCCO, LIBYA, EGYPT, SUDAN, GHANA, NIGERIA

MOROCCO AREA: *659,970 sq. km. (254,815 sq. miles)*
POPULATION: *17,825,000* CAPITAL: *Rabat*
TUNISIA AREA: *164,154 sq. km. (63,380 sq. miles)*
POPULATION: *5,770,000* CAPITAL: *Tunis*

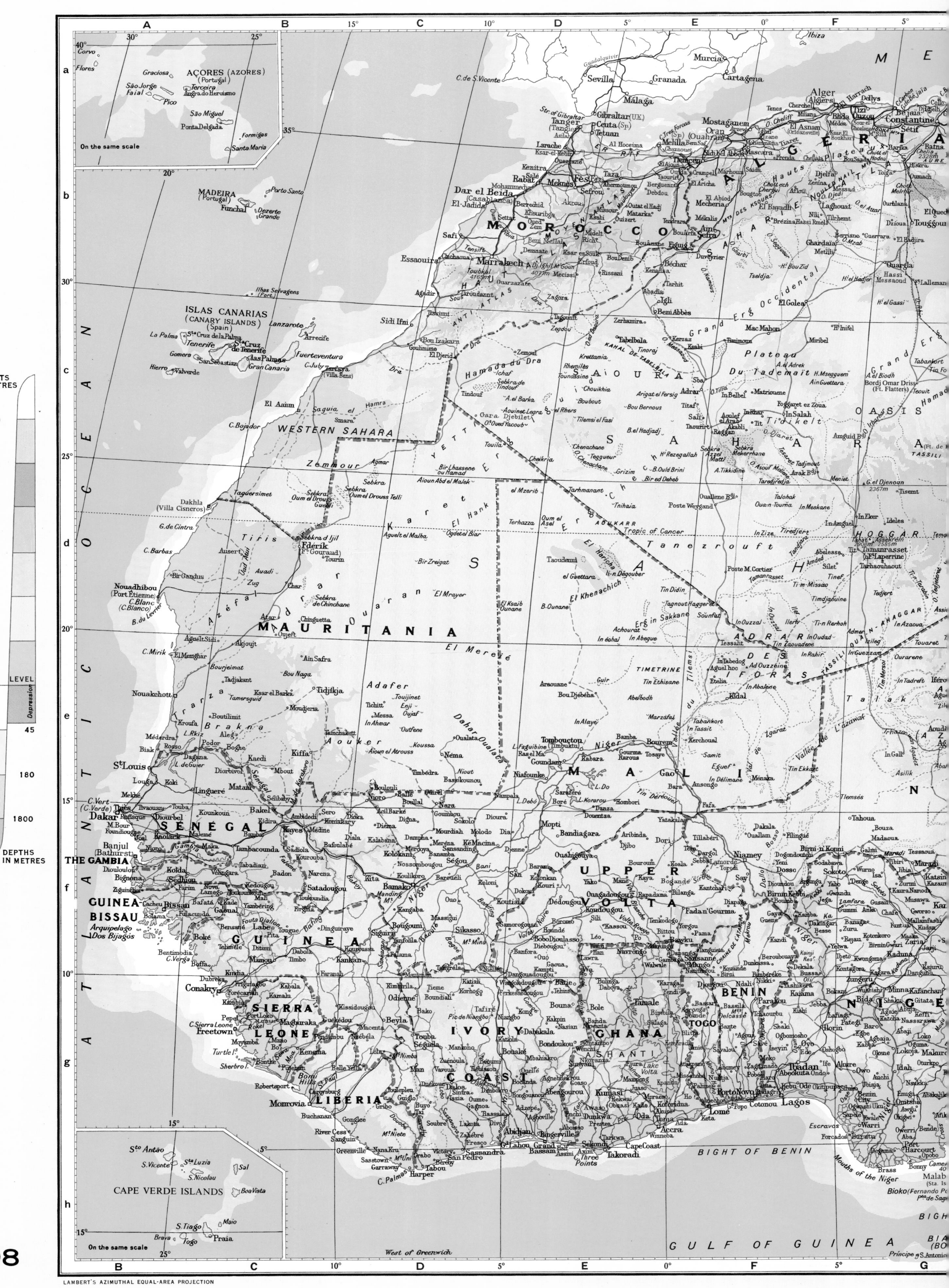

HEIGHTS IN METRES

3600
2700
1800
900
450
180
SEA LEVEL
Depression
45
180
1800
DEPTHS IN METRES

98

LAMBERT'S AZIMUTHAL EQUAL-AREA PROJECTION

SCALE: 1:12,500,000 (1CM = 125KM)

MAIN ROADS
RAILWAYS

LIBYA AREA: *1,759,537 sq. km. (679,358 sq. miles)* POP: *2,630,000* CAP: *Tripoli*
EGYPT AREA: *1,000,253 sq. km. (386,198 sq. miles)* POP: *39,000,000* CAP: *Cairo*

SUDAN AREA: *2,505,802 sq. km. (967,491 sq. miles)* POP: *17,760,000* CAP: *Khartoum*
NIGERIA AREA: *923,770 sq. km. (356,668 sq. miles)* POP: *73,000,000* CAP: *Lagos*

GHANA AREA: *238,306 sq. km. (92,010 sq. miles)* POP: *9,870,000* CAP: *Accra*
LIBERIA AREA: *111,370 sq. km. (43,000 sq. miles)* POP: *1,710,000* CAP: *Monrovia*

SIERRA LEONE AREA: *72,326 sq. km. (27,925 sq. miles)* POP: *3,002,000* CAP: *Freetown*
ALGERIA AREA: *2,381,741 sq. km. (919,591 sq. miles)* POP: *16,780,000* CAP: *Algiers*

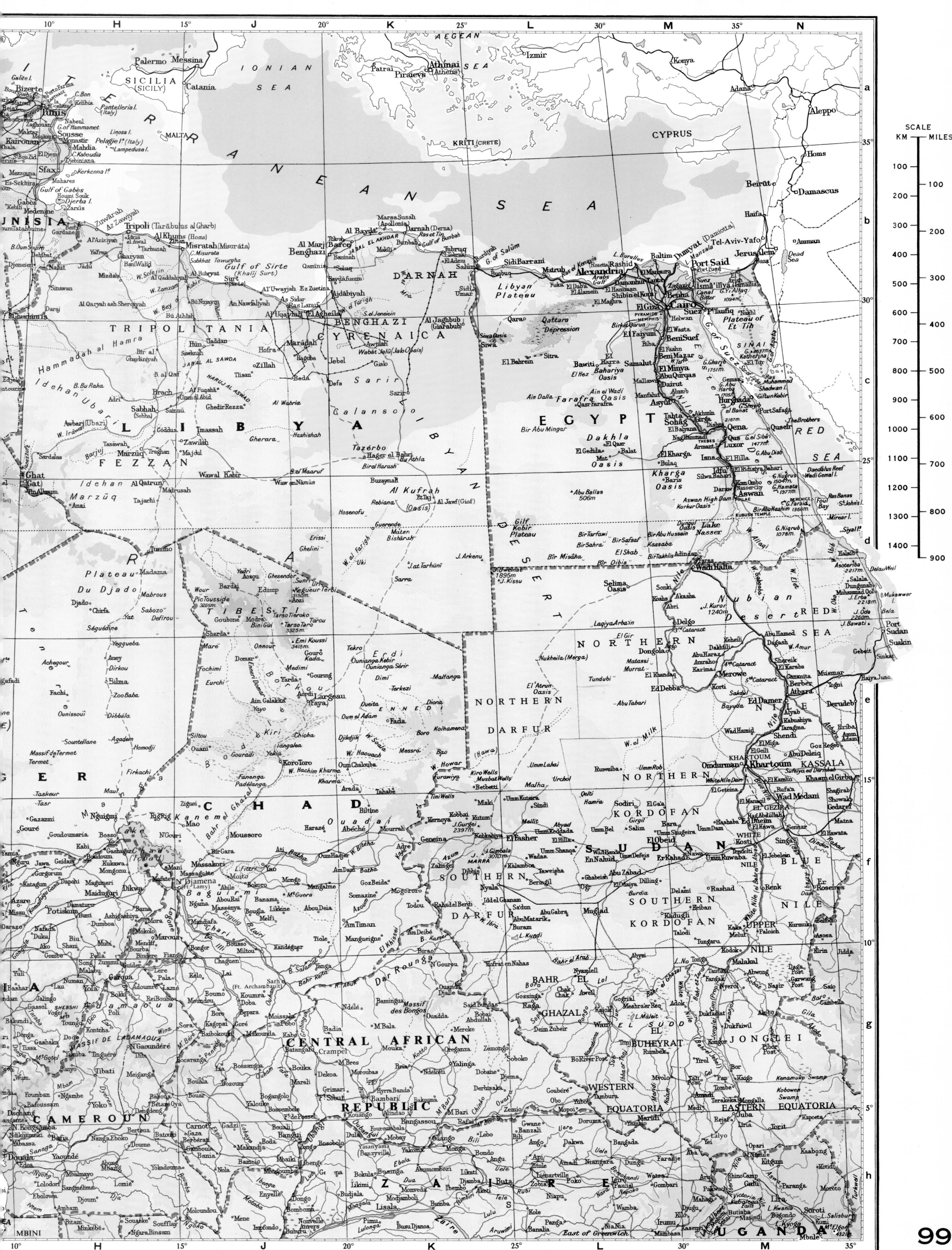

INTERNATIONAL BOUNDARIES
STATE BOUNDARIES

SCALE: 1:12,500,000 (1 CM = 125 KM)

© JOHN BARTHOLOMEW & SON LTD.

99

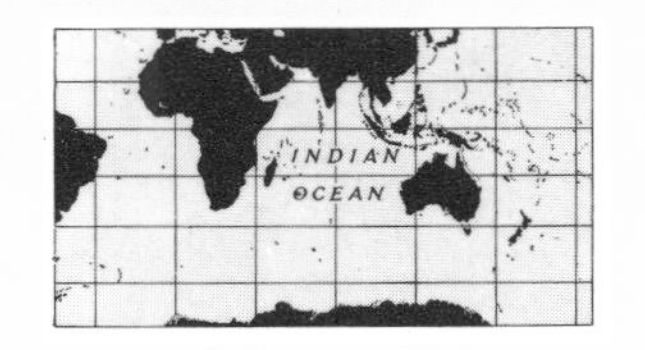

INDIAN OCEAN

With an area of 73,481,000 sq. km. (28,371,000 sq. miles), the Indian Ocean is the world's third largest ocean. It extends from the Indian Cape Comorin down to the Antarctic Continent, and in an east-west direction from Australia to Africa. A remarkable feature of this area is the central ridge of shallower water running down almost to the Antarctic Continent, similar to that in the Atlantic but with no counterpart in the Pacific.

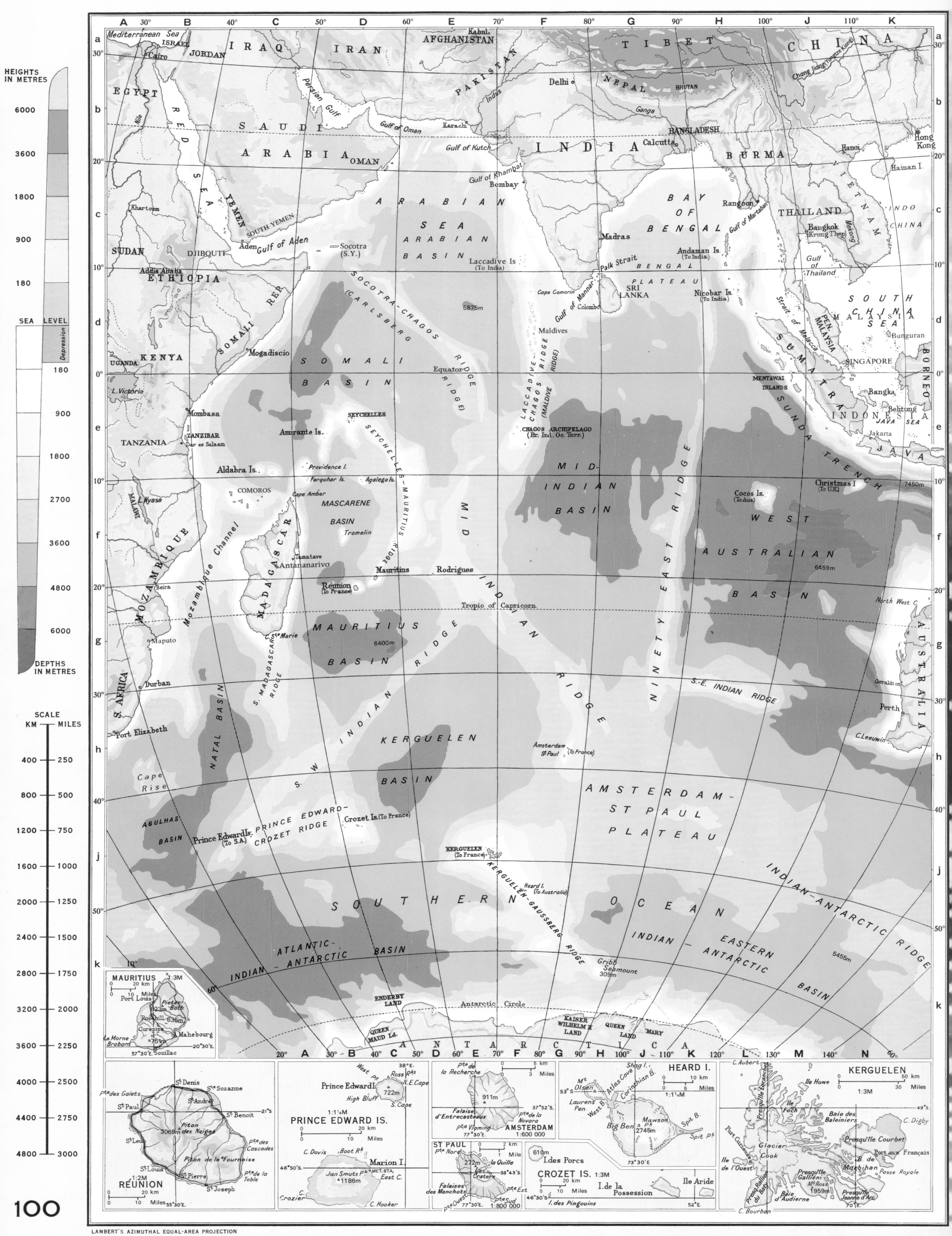

HEIGHTS IN METRES

6000
3600
1800
900
180

SEA LEVEL

Depression

180
900
1800
2700
3600
4800
6000

DEPTHS IN METRES

SCALE
KM — MILES

400 — 250
800 — 500
1200 — 750
1600 — 1000
2000 — 1250
2400 — 1500
2800 — 1750
3200 — 2000
3600 — 2250
4000 — 2500
4400 — 2750
4800 — 3000

LAMBERT'S AZIMUTHAL EQUAL-AREA PROJECTION

SCALE: 1:40,000,000   (1CM = 400KM)

ATLANTIC OCEAN

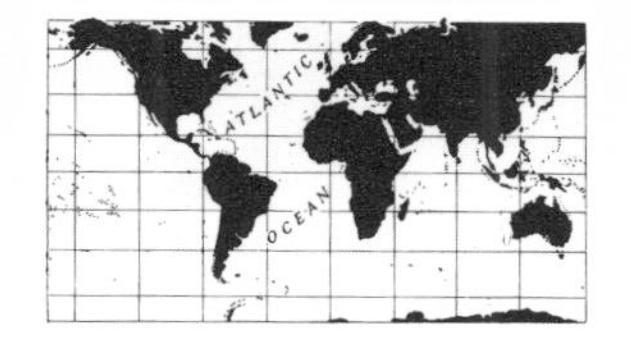

The Atlantic Ocean has an area of 82,217,000 sq. kilometres (31,744,000 sq. miles), and an average depth of 4,230 metres. It has the largest drainage area of all the oceans. Running southwards from Iceland to within a short distance of Antarctica is a well-defined central ridge, the curve of which follows the line of the African coast. Only the surface water on either side of this submarine barrier can cross it.

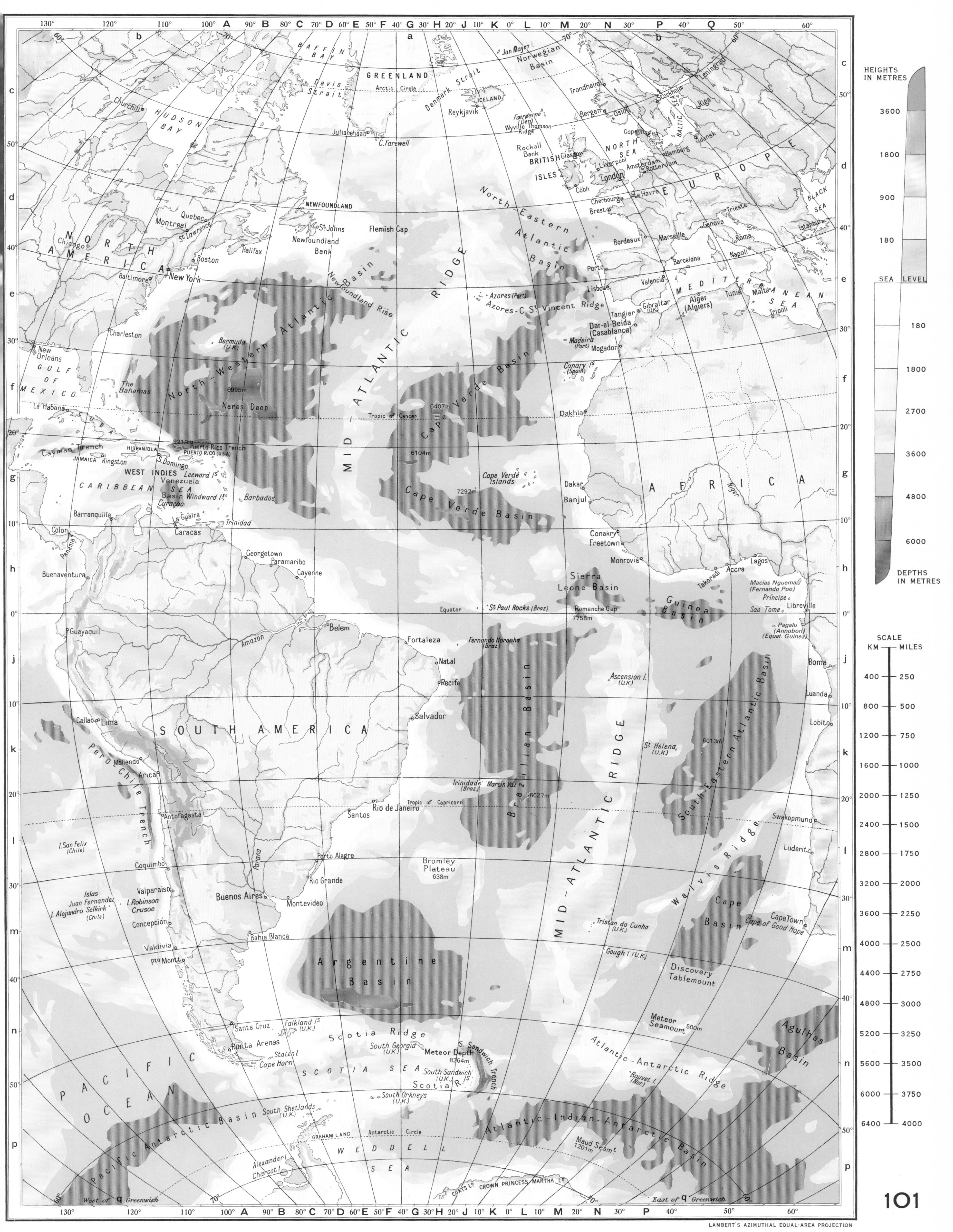

101

LAMBERT'S AZIMUTHAL EQUAL-AREA PROJECTION

SCALE: 1:48,000,000 (1 CM = 480 KM)

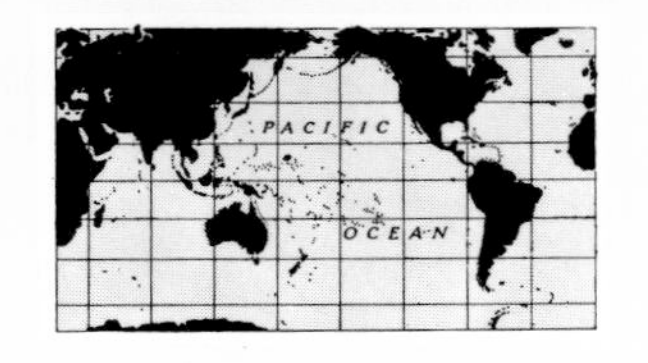

PACIFIC OCEAN

The Pacific, in area some 165,384,000 sq. km. (63,855,000 sq. miles), is the largest of the oceans. It is more than twice the size of the Atlantic, the next largest ocean, and occupies nearly half the Earth's surface. In the north it is almost landlocked, its only outlet to the Arctic Ocean being through the Bering Strait. It stretches 15,216 km. from

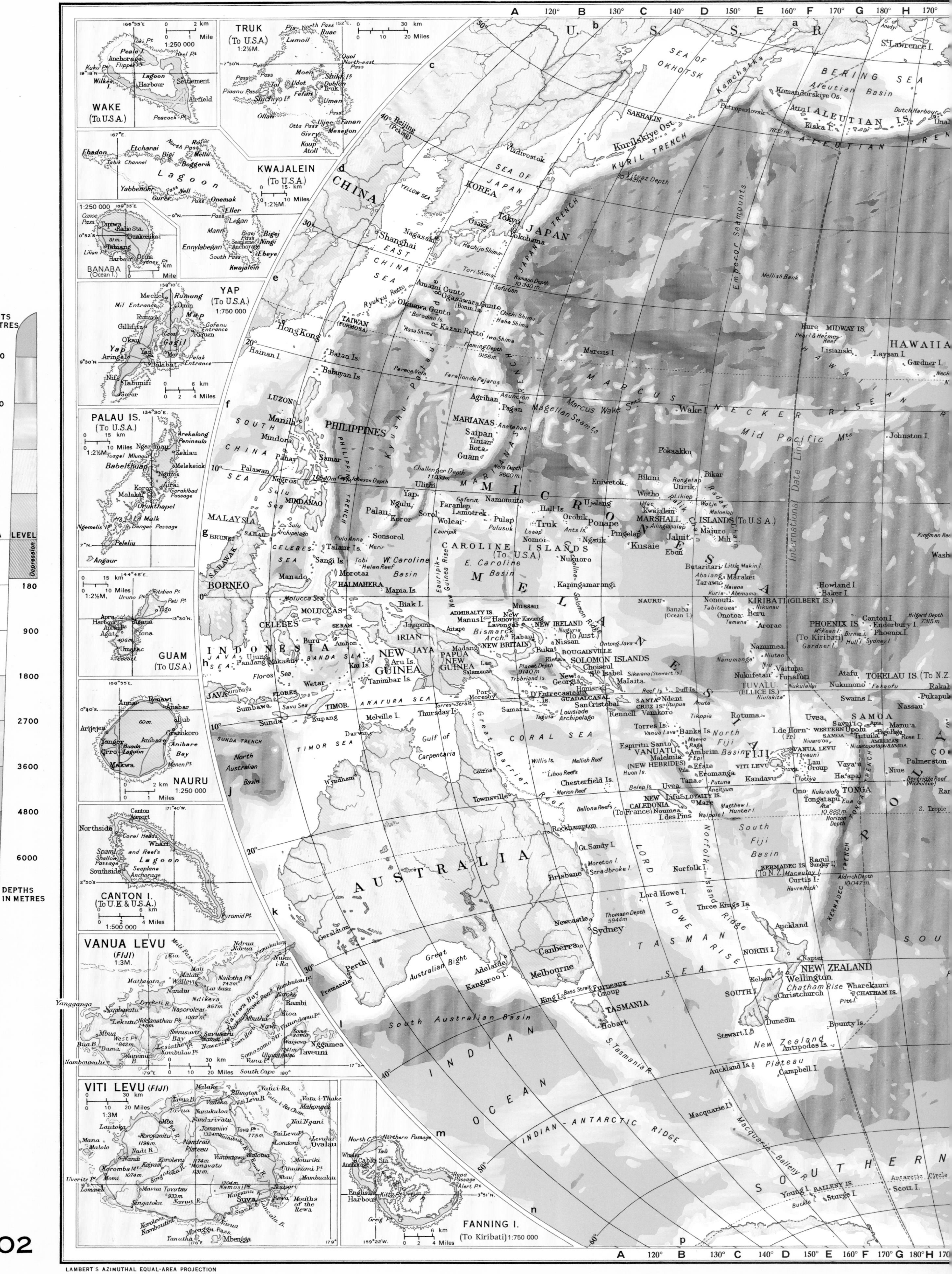

LAMBERT'S AZIMUTHAL EQUAL-AREA PROJECTION

SCALE: 1:45,000,000 (1CM = 450KM)

this strait to the Antarctic and at its broadest is 16,885 kms. across. It has an average depth of about 4,300 metres but in its deepest regions, which are off the Philippine Islands, a depth of 10,912 metres has been recorded. The islands of the Pacific fall into three main groups, Micronesia, Melanesia and Polynesia. Nearly all these islands are either volcanic or have a capping of coral over a submarine volcanic peak. The volcanic islands are very fertile and often mountainous, while the coral islands or atolls are mostly bare, desolate and low-lying. There are active volcanoes in the Solomon Islands, the New Hebrides and the Tonga group and Hawaii.

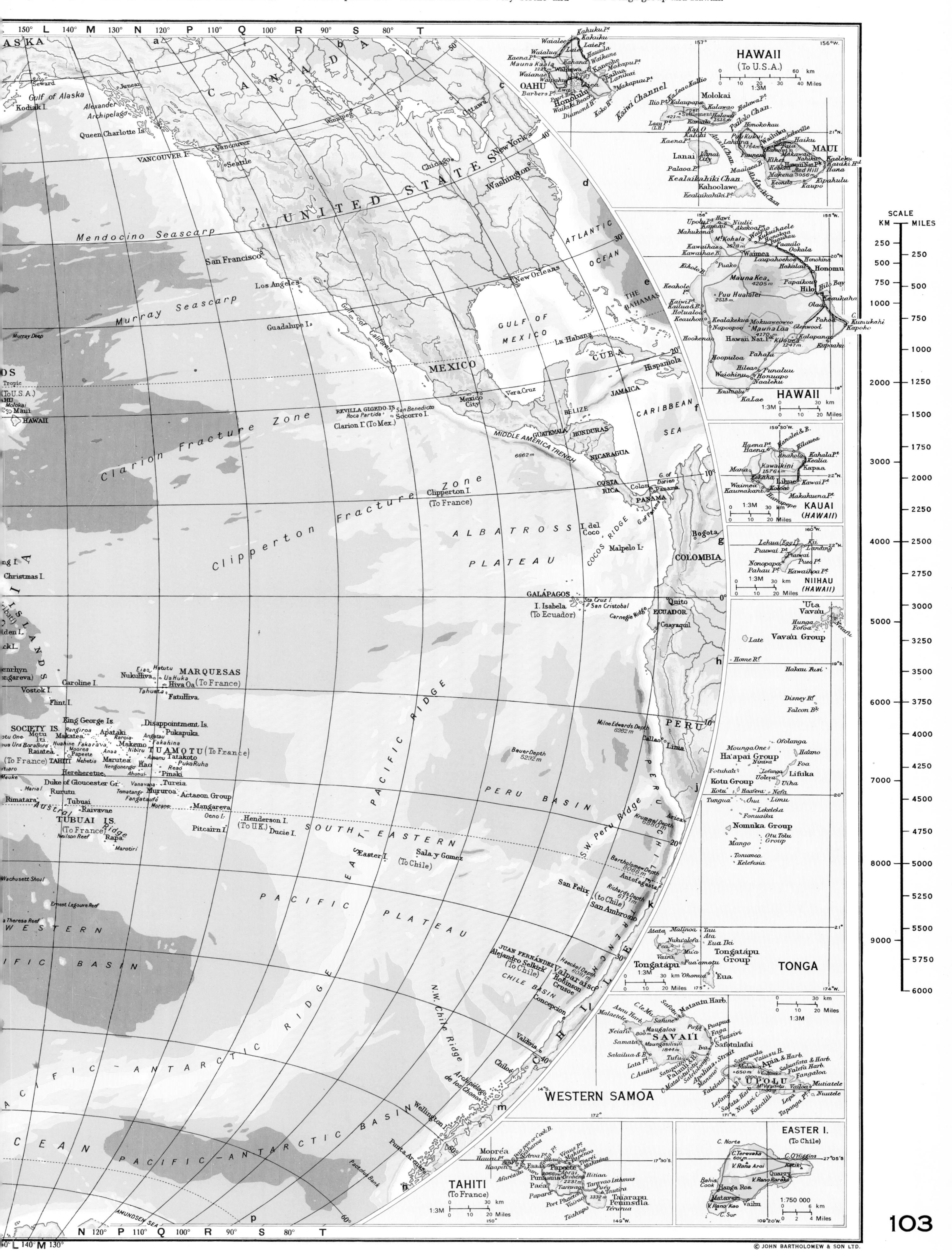

103

© JOHN BARTHOLOMEW & SON LTD.

SCALE: 1:45,000,000 (1CM = 450KM)

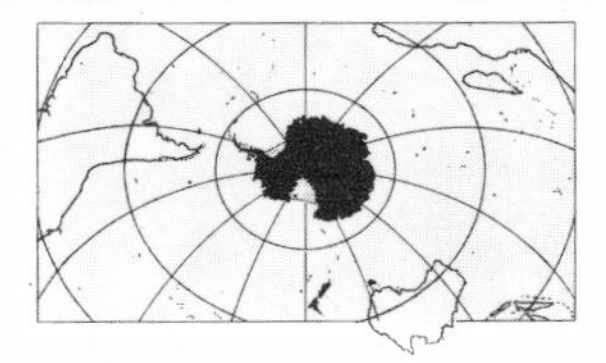

THE ANTARCTIC

The Antarctic comprises those seas and lands round the South Pole which lie within the Antarctic Circle at 66° 33′ S. It has an area of about 11.7 million sq. km. (4.5 million sq. miles). The continent is uniquely isolated, and is covered by an ice cap thousands of metres thick. Much of the rock surface beneath the ice is below sea level. If the ice cap were to melt, the sea level all over the Earth would rise by around 100 metres.

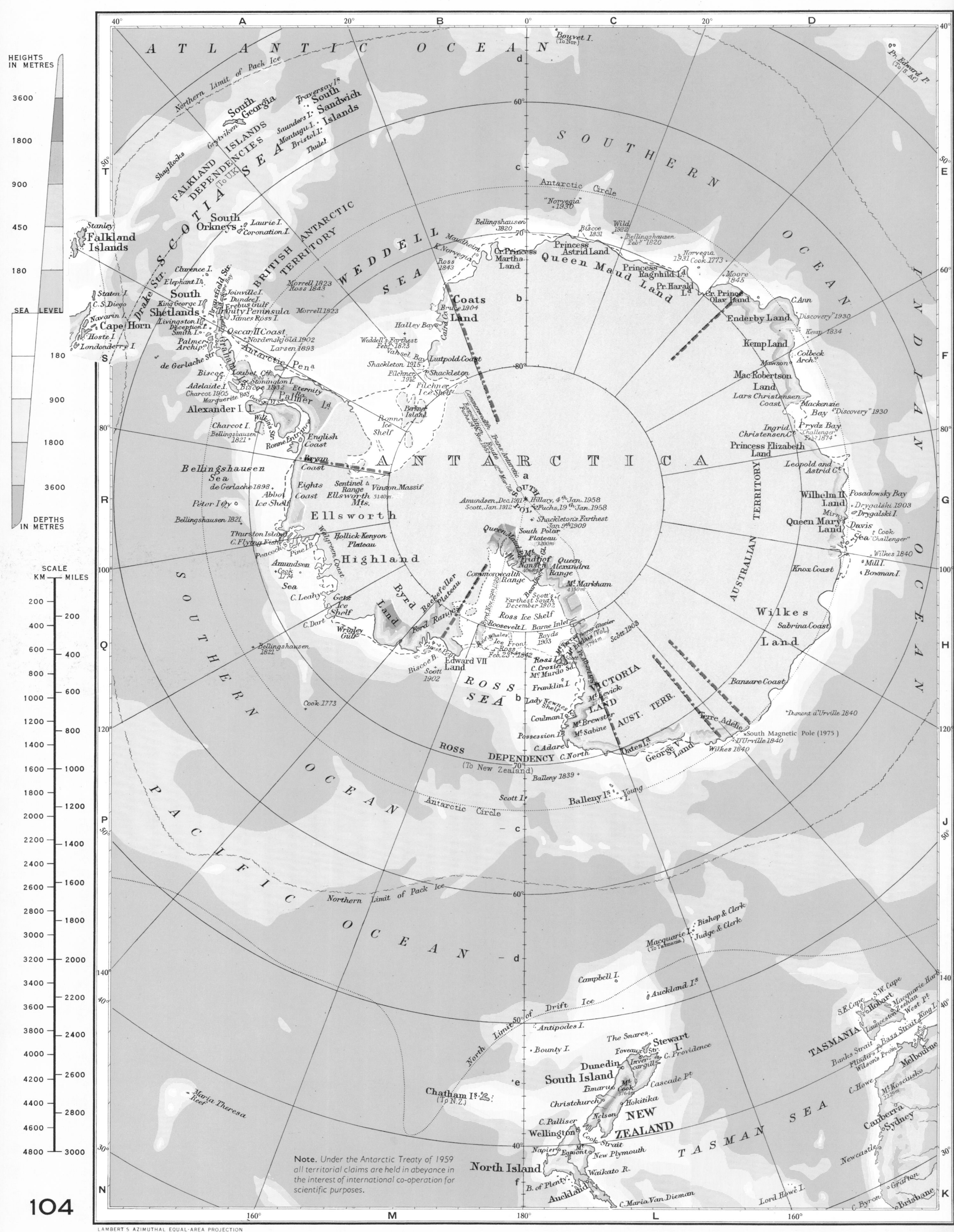

LAMBERT'S AZIMUTHAL EQUAL-AREA PROJECTION

SCALE: 1:30,000,000 (1CM = 300KM)

INTERNATIONAL BOUNDARIES

SECTION THREE

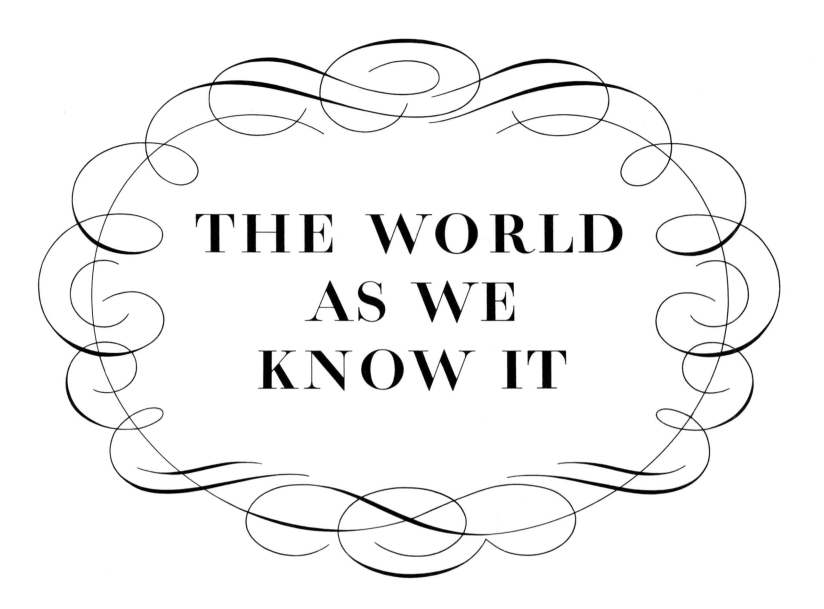

THE WORLD AS WE KNOW IT

CONTENTS

	PAGE		PAGE
OUTER SPACE: THE BOUNDLESS SKY	106	THE EVOLUTION OF MAN	130
THE STARS AROUND US	108	THE GROWTH OF CIVILIZATIONS	132
WHERE EARTH BELONGS: THE SOLAR SYSTEM	110	THE GREAT EXPLORATIONS	134
THE SUN: STAR OF THE SOLAR SYSTEM	112	RELIGIONS OF THE WORLD	136
THE PLANETS OF THE SOLAR SYSTEM	114	PATTERNS OF CLIMATE	138
THE MOON	116	FRONTIERS OF CULTIVATION	140
THE EARTH'S STRUCTURE	118	WHAT THE WORLD IS EATING	142
THE AGES OF THE EARTH	120	WORLD POPULATION	144
THE GREAT OCEANS	122	WORLD HEALTH	146
LIFE IN THE SEA	124	THE EARTH'S TREASURES	148
THE SPREAD OF MAMMALS	126	WORLD ENERGY RESOURCES	150
BIRD MIGRATION	128	FACTS ABOUT THE EARTH	152

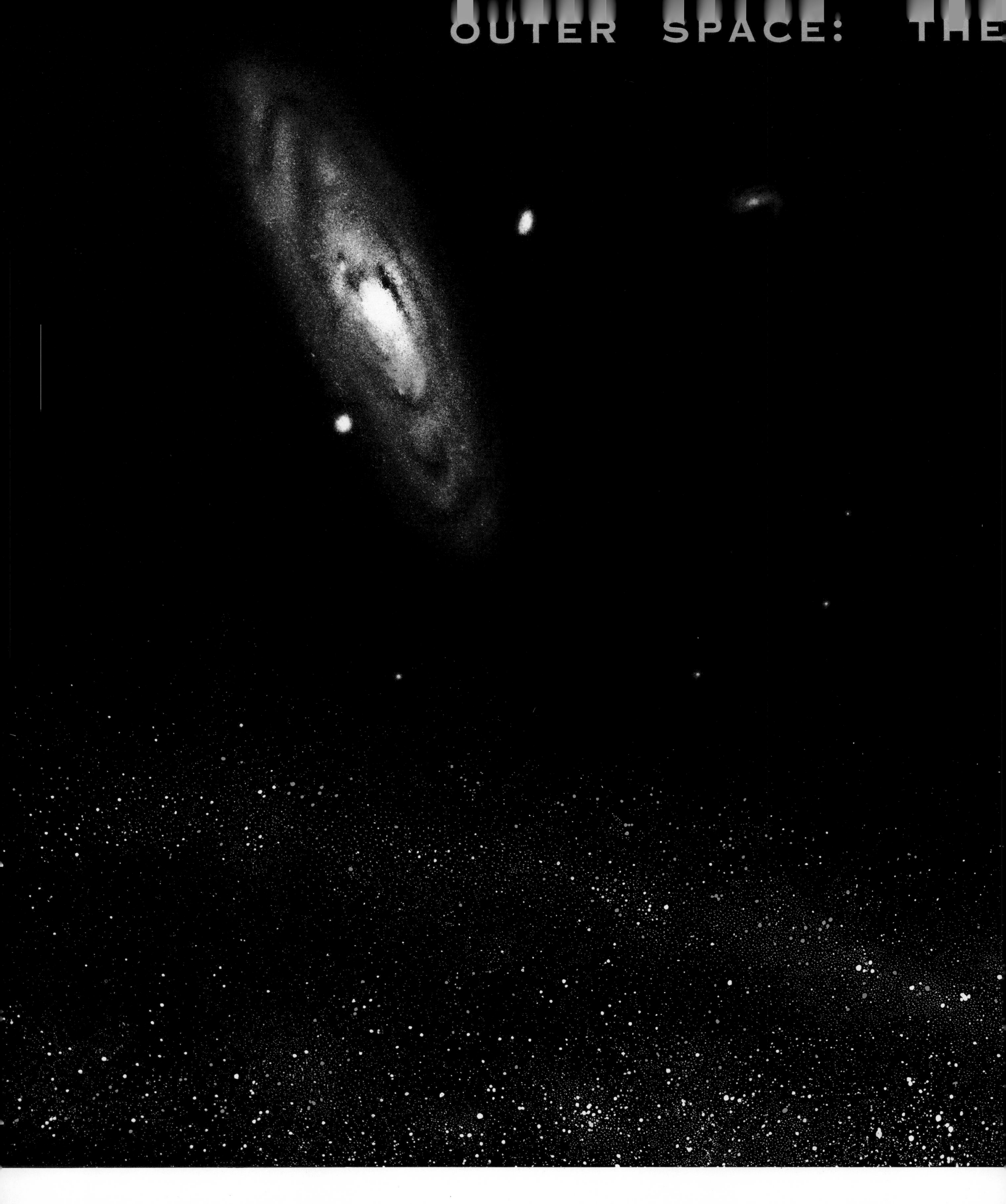

OUR PLACE AMONG THE GALAXIES

*As the stars of the heaven, and as the sand
which is upon the sea shore—*GENESIS 22

FOR centuries man believed the Earth to be the centre of Creation. The true picture is far more awe-inspiring. We live on a small planet revolving round a star of only average size which is itself revolving, with thousands of millions of other stars, in one galaxy among millions in a Universe that may well be boundless.

Scientific observation has as yet revealed no limits to the Universe and has so far probed only a fraction of it. Yet to travel to the frontiers of that observed fraction, even at 186,300 miles per second (the speed of light) would take 6,000 million years, about 20,000 times the total period that human life is estimated to have existed on Earth.

The different bodies and structures in the Universe, all of which appear to be receding from us, range from single galaxies to mammoth clusters containing over 500 galaxies.

Although the cluster of galaxies to which our galaxy belongs is comparatively small (it has only 25 members), our galaxy itself, the Milky Way System, ranks among the larger of the known stellar systems. Counting its almost 100,000 million stars (of which the Sun with its family of planets is one) at the rate of one star a second would take about 2,500 years.

Seen edge-on from outside, the Milky Way System looks like a fairly flat disk with a thick cloud of stars near and round its centre. Seen at right angles, it looks like a giant Catherine wheel in which two main arms spiral out from the centre. The Sun lies in one of these arms. It is so far away from the centre that it needs about 225 million years to complete one orbit round the "hub" of the Catherine wheel. Calculated on the basis of the Sun's estimated age, it can have made only about 30 complete circuits.

The stars forming the Milky Way are not evenly distributed, but thin out from the central plane of the galaxy and from its bulbous centre. The myriads of stars forming the centre are hidden from the Earth by vast formations of cosmic dust and

BOUNDLESS SKY

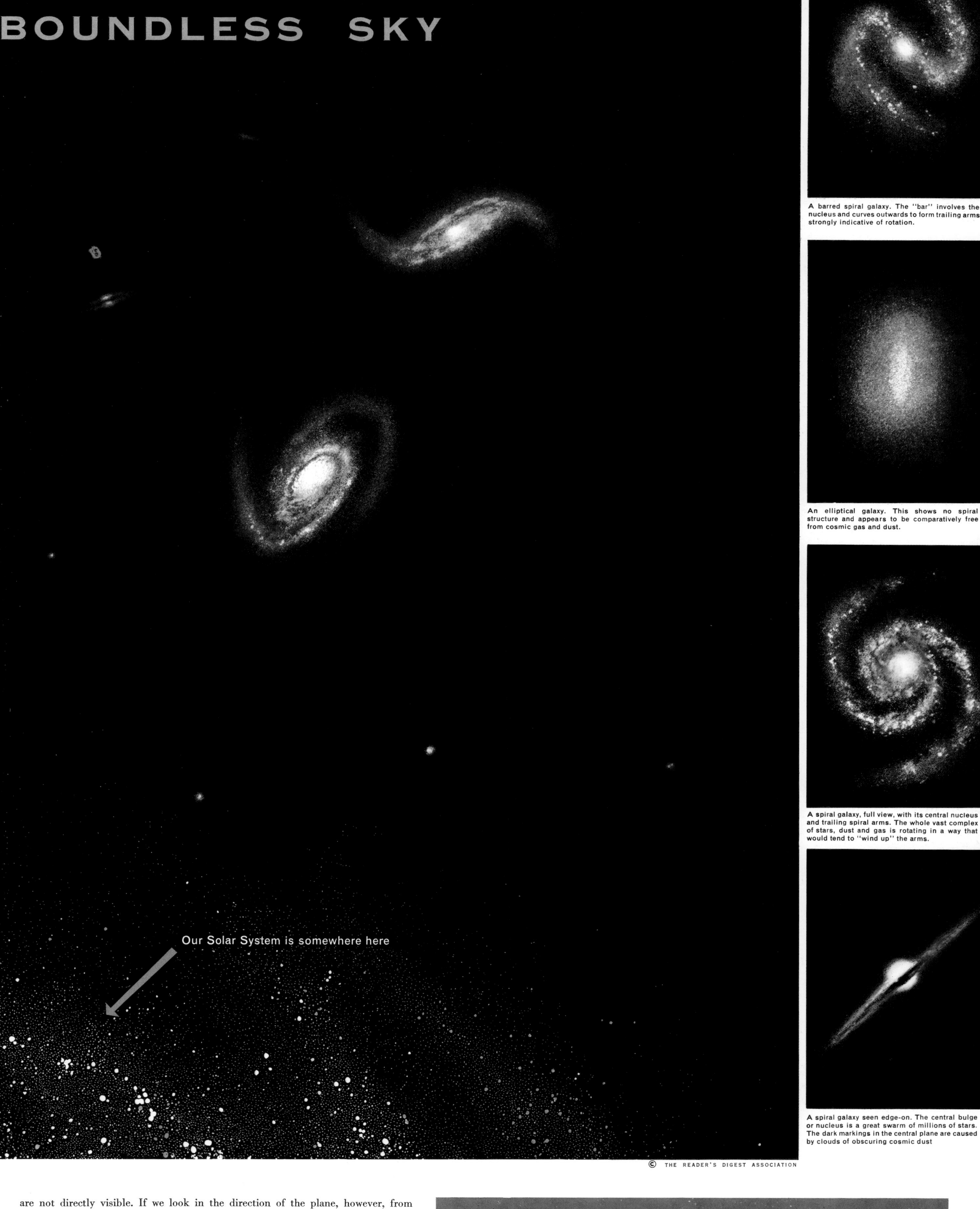

A barred spiral galaxy. The "bar" involves the nucleus and curves outwards to form trailing arms strongly indicative of rotation.

An elliptical galaxy. This shows no spiral structure and appears to be comparatively free from cosmic gas and dust.

A spiral galaxy, full view, with its central nucleus and trailing spiral arms. The whole vast complex of stars, dust and gas is rotating in a way that would tend to "wind up" the arms.

A spiral galaxy seen edge-on. The central bulge or nucleus is a great swarm of millions of stars. The dark markings in the central plane are caused by clouds of obscuring cosmic dust

Our Solar System is somewhere here

Our Solar System

are not directly visible. If we look in the direction of the plane, however, from our position slightly outside it, we see the stars distributed in greater depth and number, so that they appear to merge into a single luminous band. This bright streak in the sky has been known for centuries as the Milky Way, a name now given to the whole of the system.

Surrounding the galaxy and forming part of it are compact swarms of stars known as globular star clusters. Beyond them again lie thousands of millions of other galaxies with a considerable range in size and structure. The nearest comparable in size to our own is the Great Galaxy in Andromeda (centre of left-hand page), just over two million "light-years" away, a distance that light, in travelling at 186,300 miles per second, would take just over two million years to cover.

As man probes deeper into the Universe, the number of galaxies seems to grow as immense as the space through which they hurtle.

The Milky Way, one of the millions of stellar galaxies in the Universe, is so vast that it would take a rocket, hurtling along its diameter at 100,000 miles per hour, 670 million years to make the journey from end to end. Travelling at the same speed across our solar system, from the Sun to its farthest dependent planet, Pluto, a rocket would take only four years and two months.

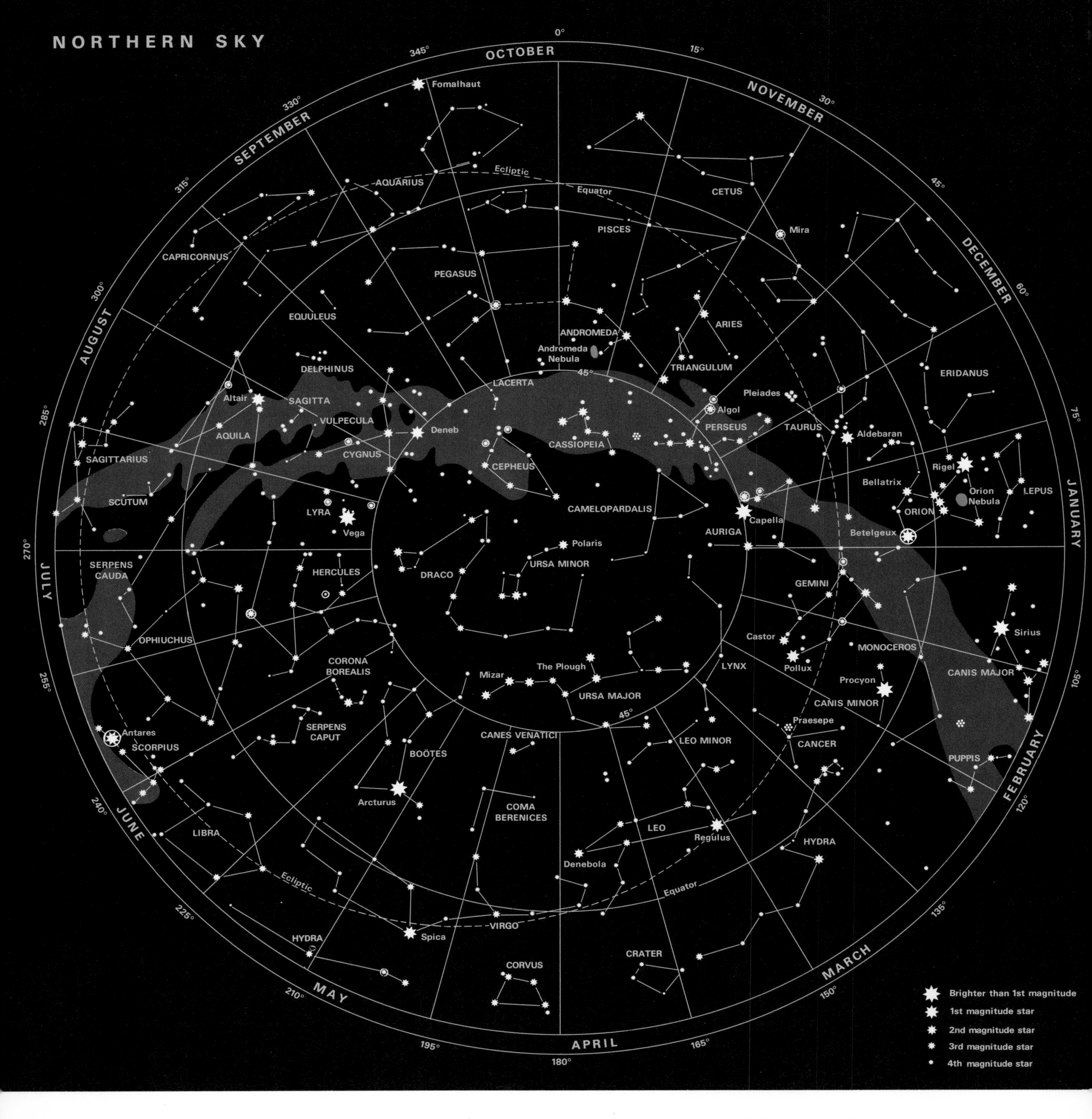

THE STARS AROUND US

For one star differeth from another in glory — 1 CORINTHIANS 15

THERE are countless millions of stars strung out in space but only about 2,000 are visible to the naked eye at any one time from Earth, even on the darkest and clearest night. The stars which we can see arching into the night sky are only our nearest neighbours in space. Most of the 100,000 million or so stars in our Galaxy are concentrated in the hazy band of the Milky Way which is shown spanning the charts above. These charts show the brightest stars in the northern and southern skies and the constellations into which they are grouped.

The main constellations with which we are familiar date back at least to the ancient Greek astronomer Ptolemy who, in AD 150, listed 48 constellations representing mythological beasts and heroes such as Pegasus and Heracles (Hercules). These constellations have been amended and added to until a total of 88 now covers the northern and southern skies. Many of the southern constellations were charted in the 17th and 18th centuries by later astronomers such as Nicolas Louis de Lacaille, and have been given names of relatively modern inventions.

Stars are giant balls of incandescent gas, mostly hydrogen and helium. A star's luminosity is the result of energy released by nuclear reactions within its core. The Sun itself is a star of only average size and brightness. It appears very much brighter than any other star because it is relatively close to Earth at a distance of only 93 million miles, which is 300,000 times closer than the nearest other star.

Apart from the Sun, the next closest star to Earth is Proxima Centauri in the south polar region of the sky, 25 million million miles away. Travelling at a speed of 186,300 miles a second, light takes 4.2 years to cross this distance, so Proxima Centauri is said to be 4.2 light-years away. Despite its proximity this star is invisible without the aid of a telescope or binoculars. With a diameter of about 86,000 miles, it is a cosmic glow-worm known as a red dwarf emitting less than one ten-thousandth the light of the Sun. Proxima is marginally the closest to Earth of a star trio, the two brightest of which appear to the naked eye as one bright star called Alpha Centauri.

The brightest star in the sky, apart from the Sun, is Sirius which is 8.7 light-years away. It emits somewhat more light than the Sun, but its prominence is mostly due to its relative proximity to Earth. Betelgeux, a prominent star in the constellation of Orion, is over 10,000 times brighter than the Sun but it still appears dimmer than Sirius because it is 650 light-years

away. Deneb, the brightest star in the constellation of Cygnus, is 1,500 light-years distant and other prominent stars are even more remote. That these stars are visible at all over such vast distances can only be due to their extreme luminosity, for the Sun would be invisible to the naked eye if it were more than about 55 light-years away.

The ancient Greek astronomer Hipparchus divided stars into six groups according to their brightness. These groups, known as magnitudes, range from first magnitude down to sixth magnitude for the faintest stars visible to the naked eye. A sixth magnitude star is 100 times fainter than one of the first magnitude.

Stars appear white at first glance but they actually vary in colour according to their temperature. They can be blue, white or red hot – the blue ones being the hottest. Betelgeux, Arcturus and Aldebaran, which is the glinting red eye of Taurus the bull, are prominent red stars. The Sun is hotter than these as it is yellow-white. Sirius and Vega are still hotter, appearing white. Rigel, a bright star in the constellation of Orion, is blue hot.

Betelgeux is therefore cooler than the Sun but it emits much more light. The reason is that it is much bigger. Known as a red

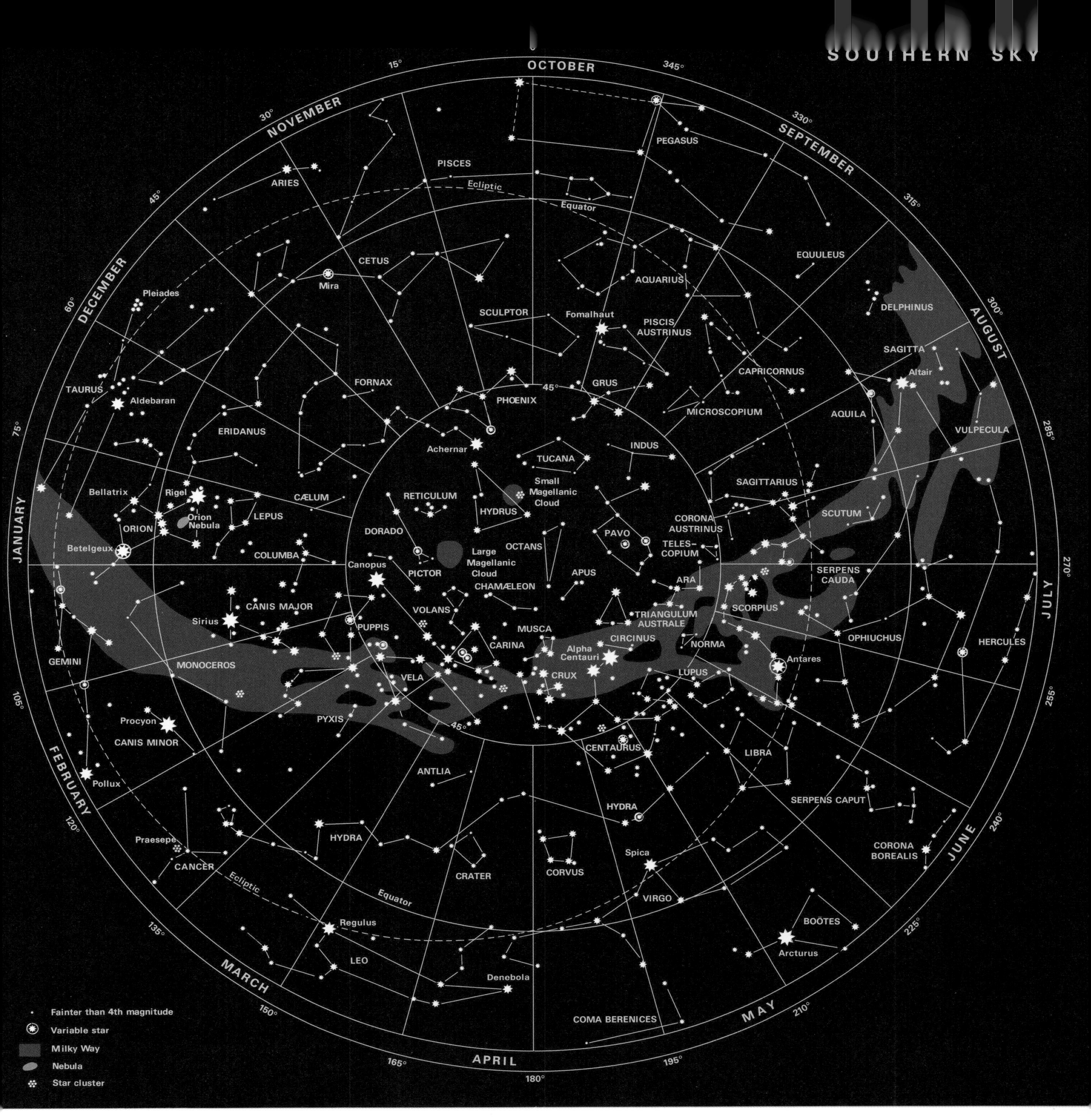

- • Fainter than 4th magnitude
- ⊛ Variable star
- ▬ Milky Way
- ⬭ Nebula
- ⁂ Star cluster

super-giant, Betelgeux is between 300 and 400 times the diameter of the Sun and is one of the largest known stars. In the Sun's position, Betelgeux would engulf the orbits of Earth and Mars.

At the other end of the scale are the dwarf stars which are both smaller and dimmer than the Sun. Barnard's star, which is a red dwarf star believed to have orbiting planets, is the second closest star to the Sun, at a distance of 6 light-years, and lies in the constellation of Ophiuchus. It is invisible to the naked eye.

White dwarfs, which are the remains of dying stars, are even smaller than red dwarfs. Sirius has a white dwarf companion, visible with a telescope, which has the same mass as the Sun, compressed into a ball only 2½ times the diameter of Earth. The matter of which white dwarfs are composed is extremely dense.

Neutron stars are even denser and smaller than white dwarfs. They are the matter left behind after the death of very big stars. The protons and electrons of the atoms of such stars are crushed together by the intense gravitational force and form sub-atomic particles called neutrons. A typical neutron star is only about 10 miles in diameter but it can still contain as much material as the Sun, or more; several thousand million tons of neutron star material could be put into a receptacle no larger than a thimble. If a neutron star's mass is more than about three times that of the Sun, this shrinkage under gravity will continue and the neutron star will collapse even further until it becomes so small and dense that nothing, not even light, can escape from the clutches of its intense gravitational field. Such a phenome-

non is termed a black hole. Astronomers believe they have located a black hole orbiting an ordinary star in the constellation of Cygnus.

Most stars are in groups of two, three or more, like the three-star Alpha Centauri system. Although Castor, in the constellation of Gemini, appears as a single star to the naked eye, it is in reality a system of six stars bound together by gravity. Mizar, the second star in the handle of the Plough, has a fainter companion called Alcor which can just be discerned with keen eyesight.

THE months round the edge of the charts identify which part of the northern sky is visible due south at about 10 p.m. for observers in mid-northern latitudes, and which part of the southern sky is visible due north in mid-southern latitudes. For the northern observer, face south and hold the chart of the northern sky with the relevant month pointing due south. For each hour after 10 p.m., rotate the chart 15° in an anti-clockwise direction and reverse the rotation for each hour before.

For the observer in the south, face north and hold the chart for the southern sky with the current month pointing north. For each hour after 10 p.m., rotate the chart 15° in a clockwise direction or the reverse for each hour before.

The planets are not shown on the charts as their position is constantly changing. But, when visible, they will be found near the line called the ecliptic.

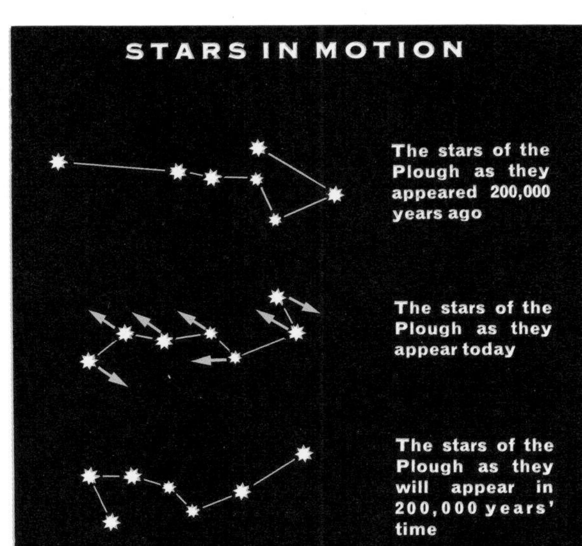

STARS IN MOTION

The stars of the Plough as they appeared 200,000 years ago

The stars of the Plough as they appear today

The stars of the Plough as they will appear in 200,000 years' time

Stars are never stationary although no change is visible to the eye within a human life-span. Accurate star plots measured through a telescope reveal a steady drift called "proper motion." These three diagrams chart the motion of seven of the stars in the constellation of Ursa Major – how they appeared at the dawn of mankind 200,000 years ago, as they now form the familiar shape of the Plough, and as they will look 200,000 years in the future. The proper motion of stars gradually changes the shapes of the constellations which may eventually mean that new characters and objects will have to be found to represent them.

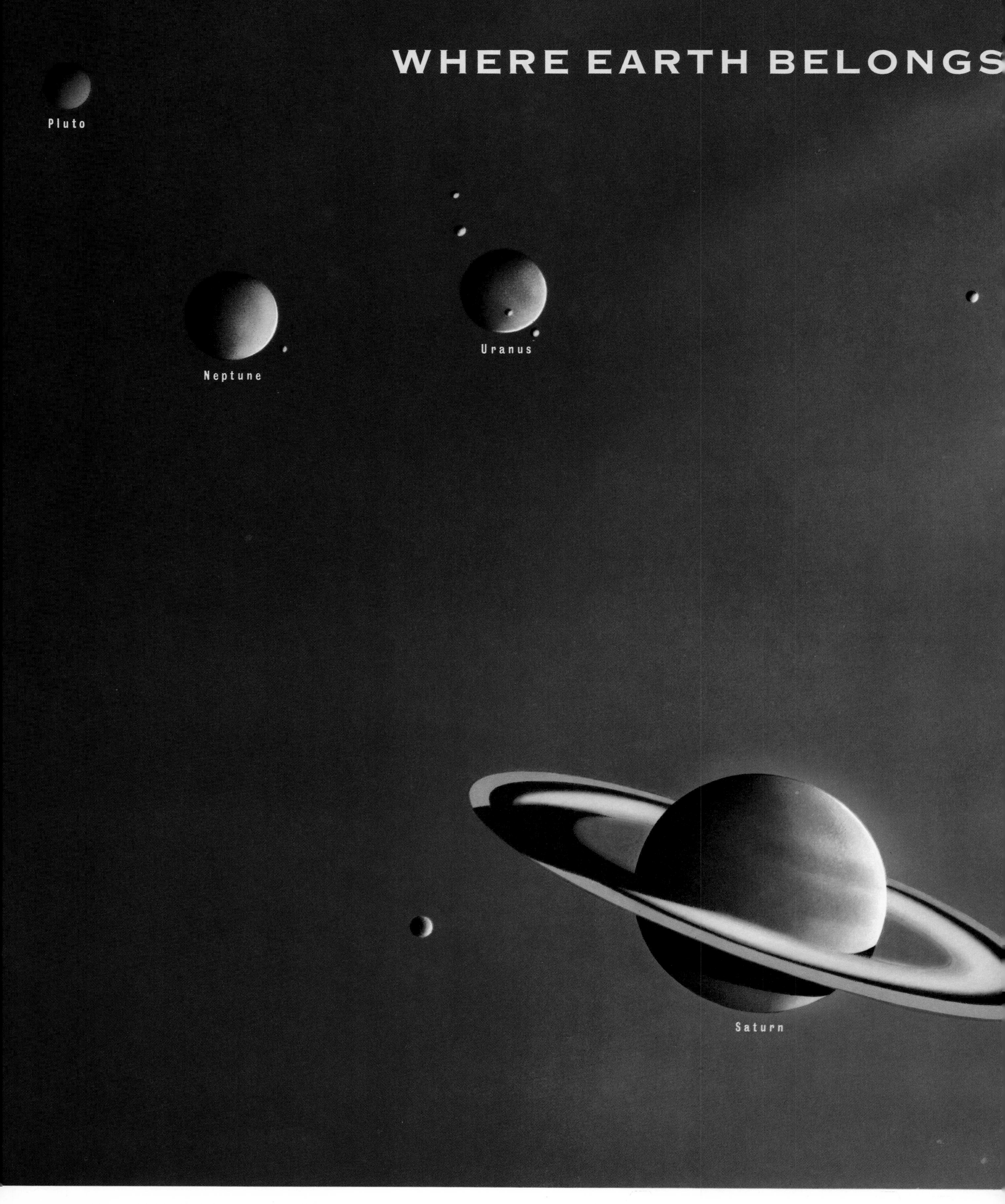

WHERE EARTH BELONGS

Pluto

Neptune

Uranus

Saturn

THE SUN AND ITS PLANETS—AS VIEWED
FROM A POINT IN SPACE

There is one glory of the sun, and another glory of the moon,
and another glory of the stars—1 CORINTHIANS 15

THE Sun dominates and dwarfs its solar family of nine major planets and at least a thousand tiny planets called "asteroids". Jupiter, the Sun's largest dependent planet, is but a speck by comparison with it, and the volume of Jupiter is roughly 1,300 times that of Earth. The Sun contains over 99·87 per cent of the entire mass in our Solar System. Yet, despite their comparative smallness and the enormous distances of empty space that separate them from the Sun and from one another, the Sun keeps its planets under strict control.

Revolving round it continuously in elliptical orbits, these planets are held near the Sun by the pull of gravity, and kept from being drawn into it by the speed with which they move through space. The closer they are to the Sun, the faster they move. Mercury—at an average distance of 36 million miles, the planet nearest to the Sun—averages only 88 days to travel right round it, moving at a speed of nearly 30 miles a second. The Earth, whose average distance from the Sun is 93 million miles, needs exactly one year to complete its orbit, travelling at a speed of 18·5 miles per second, or roughly 66,600 miles per hour. Pluto, the most distant known planet, about 3,666 million miles from the Sun, takes just over 248 years at a speed of a mere three miles a second to make one journey round it.

Moving at different speeds, in separate orbits, and at varying

distances from the Sun, the planets, as viewed from the Earth which is itself moving, *appear* to be changing constantly in size and brightness. Venus, well known as the Morning Star or Evening Star, comes as close to the Earth as about 24·5 million miles, and goes as far away as 160 million miles.

Life as we know it cannot exist on any other planet in our Solar System. Mercury is so close to the Sun that the temperature on its sunlit side is estimated to be of the order of 400°C. Venus, about twice as far from the Sun as Mercury is roughly 25 million miles closer to it than the Earth, and probably has a maximum surface temperature of 440°C. Of the planets farther than Earth from the Sun, Jupiter, Saturn (its semi-transparent rings made up of fine particles, dense enough to throw a shadow over the planet's surface), Uranus,

110

THE SOLAR SYSTEM

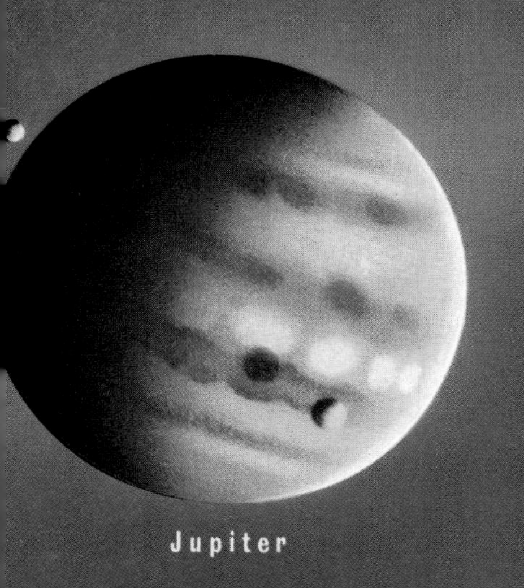
Jupiter

Mars

Earth

Mercury

Venus

SUN

Neptune and Pluto are all too cold, and their atmospheres contain high concentrations of poisonous gases – helium, hydrogen, methane and ammonia. Mars has a very cold climate, and a tenuous atmosphere made up of carbon dioxide.

The Earth is the only member of our Sun's family known to support living creatures. Alone among the planets in the Solar System – though not perhaps among those belonging to the millions of sun-like stars in the Universe – the Earth's composition and distance from the Sun seem to have provided exactly the right conditions in which evolution to an advanced form of life could develop.

The life-giving energy of the Sun, the source of all the heat and light in our Solar System, is generated by nuclear reactions in its interior, which raise the temperature deep inside it to about 15 million degrees Centigrade. So tremendous is the radiation rate of the Sun's energy, that it loses some four million tons in weight every second. Yet, despite this rate of loss, it is estimated that the Sun will survive as a source of energy for at least another 5,000 million years.

DISTANCE OF PLANETS FROM EARTH IN KILOMETRES (MILES)

	MOON		MARS		URANUS	
Max.	407,000	(253,000)	397,500,000 (247,000,000)		3,132,000,000 (1,946,000,000)	
Min.	357,000	(222,000)	55,000,000 (34,000,000)		2,565,000,000 (1,594,000,000)	
	MERCURY		JUPITER		NEPTUNE	
Max.	220,317,000	(136,900,000)	960,700,000 (597,000,000)		4,652,580,000 (2,891,000,000)	
Min.	79,000,000	(49,100,000)	582,600,000 (362,000,000)		4,271,000,000 (2,654,000,000)	
	VENUS		SATURN		PLUTO	
Max.	259,000,000	(160,900,000)	1,646,000,000 (1,023,000,000)		7,251,500,000 (4,506,000,000)	
Min.	39,750,000	(24,700,000)	1,244,000,000 (773,000,000)		4,192,300,000 (2,605,000,000)	

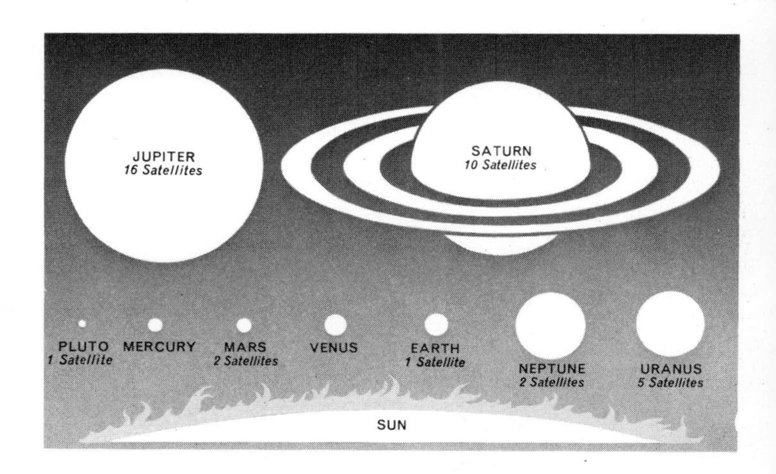

JUPITER
16 Satellites

SATURN
10 Satellites

PLUTO
1 Satellite

MERCURY

MARS
2 Satellites

VENUS

EARTH
1 Satellite

NEPTUNE
2 Satellites

URANUS
5 Satellites

SUN

THE SUN:
STAR OF THE SOLAR SYSTEM

And God made two great lights; the greater light to rule the day—GENESIS I

OUR Sun is a storm-tossed ball of incandescent gas 865,000 miles in diameter, providing the light and heat on which all life on Earth depends. The Sun's apparent magnificence disguises the fact that it is a star like any other. The Sun seems so big and bright compared with other stars simply because it is so much closer. Whereas light takes 8 minutes 20 seconds to cross the 93 million mile gap from Sun to Earth, light from even the nearest star Proxima Centauri, which is 25 million million miles away, takes over four years to reach us. Among stars, the Sun is no colossus; it is classified by astrophysicists as a yellow G-type dwarf. Some stars, such as the red giant Betelgeux in the constellation of Orion the hunter, are so big that they would engulf the Earth if placed where the Sun is. Others, such as the blue giant Rigel, are so hot that they would roast all life on Earth if we orbited them. It is because of the Sun's moderate size and temperature that the life forms on Earth have been able to evolve.

The Sun lies at the hub of a collection of nine planets and numerous lumps of flying debris. All objects held by the Sun's gravitational influence, which extends halfway to Proxima Centauri, are part of the solar system. However, only the frozen balls of gas known as comets are believed to exist in the outer region of the solar system beyond the orbits of Neptune and Pluto.

As the Sun formed from a vast cloud of gas and dust in the Galaxy, 4,700 million years ago (see The Birth of Stars, below), it is believed to have been surrounded by a spinning disk of residual matter. This matter was mainly hydrogen and helium gas, but mixed in was a very small percentage of heavier substances such as atoms of silicon and various metals. As particles collided with each other, larger specks of dust were built up. Over thousands of years these dust specks would have grown into rocky lumps like the meteorites that occasionally fall to Earth from space.

Eventually, bodies big enough to attract each other by gravity would have formed, sweeping up all the particles of rock and metal in the disk around the Sun. These were the infant planets. At the time of their birth, the Sun was only just beginning to shine and the region of the solar system was still relatively dark and cold.

The larger of the young planets drew in gas from the surrounding cloud to form atmospheres. Jupiter and Saturn still retain those primitive atmospheres; in fact, Jupiter is composed almost entirely of hydrogen and helium gas, and so is more like the Sun than the Earth. Jupiter would have evolved into a small star radiating its own light if it had been about ten times bigger.

The smaller planets, such as Mercury, Mars and Earth, did not have a strong enough gravitational pull to retain the light gases from the cloud around the Sun, and these gases drifted away into space. They were replaced around the Earth by heavier gases exhaled from the mouths of volcanoes, as radioactive atoms warmed the Earth's interior. The gases of the Earth's atmosphere and the water of its seas have been released from the planet's interior over the aeons of its existence. But the remnants of the cloud from which the Sun and planets formed 4,700 million years ago can still be seen in the atmospheres of the outer planets like Jupiter and Saturn, and also in the gases of the ghostly comets that swoop on long orbits through the solar system.

THE visible surface of the Sun is a layer of gas about 186 miles deep called the photosphere. It has a temperature of about 6,000°C, but the Sun gets far hotter towards its centre. At the very heart of the Sun, the temperature is estimated to be about 15,000,000°C. Under these conditions, atoms are crushed together in nuclear fusion reactions like those in a hydrogen bomb, releasing the energy that keeps the Sun glowing brightly. However, these reactions occur smoothly in the Sun, so it does not explode like a bomb. The energy released from the core of the Sun takes about 30 million years to reach the surface. For most of this time the energy is being passed from atom to atom in the form of radiation. But, for the last part of the journey, it travels by convection with large masses of gas rising to the surface.

The core of the Sun is a gigantic nuclear cauldron, in which atoms of hydrogen are cooked into atoms of helium. Not all the hydrogen becomes helium; some of it is turned into energy, which appears at the surface of the Sun as light and heat. Every second, 4 million tons of hydrogen are turned into energy, but the supply of hydrogen fuel is so massive that, even at this rate, it will be at least another 5,000 millions years before the Sun begins to burn out.

EVENTUALLY, the Sun will exhaust its supply of hydrogen at the core. As it does so, the central nuclear furnace will move outwards to the layers around the core, in search of new hydrogen fuel. The Sun will start to swell and increase in brightness; it will have become a red giant star. About 6,000 million years from now, the pressure and temperature at the centre of the Sun will become so great that a nuclear chain reaction will start with the helium itself entering into nuclear reactions. This will result in the helium being transformed into carbon, releasing still more energy. In the largest stars—those ten or more times as heavy as the Sun—these nuclear reactions proceed at a runaway rate until the star explodes as a supernova. The nuclear holocaust of a supernova explosion forges the heavy elements of nature and scatters them into space, where they mix with the existing clouds of hydrogen and helium gas, ready to be collected up into the new stars and planetary systems like the solar system.

But this explosive end will not befall the Sun. Its death will be more gentle. The swelling red giant Sun, bloated by the increased output of its raging nuclear fires within, will engulf first Mercury, then Venus, and even the Earth and perhaps Mars. But long before the Earth is swallowed up in the outer layers of the Sun, distended to several hundred times its present size and glowing 10,000 times as brightly as at present, our planet and the life on it will have been roasted to a cinder. Any descendants of ours would have long since fled to another home around a different star.

After engulfing the Earth during the latter stages of its expansion, the Sun will become unstable. Its outer layers will be lost into space like gigantic smoke rings. Over 50,000 years or so the red-hot atmosphere of the super giant Sun will seem to dissolve, leaving the star's small, dense core exposed as a glowing white dwarf. Slowly, over thousands of millions of years, it will cool to an invisible black ball of ash, and any planets that remain in orbit around it will be frozen to the near-absolute cold of space. Several white dwarf stars have been located by astronomers, although they are too faint to be seen by the naked eye. Kuiper's Star is a white dwarf about the size of the planet Mars but its mass is equal to that of the Sun. This star is so dense that a cube of its material 1/10 inch square would weight about half a ton if it were weighed on Earth. White dwarfs produce no energy from nuclear reactions, but simply glow with heat left over from the original star's past.

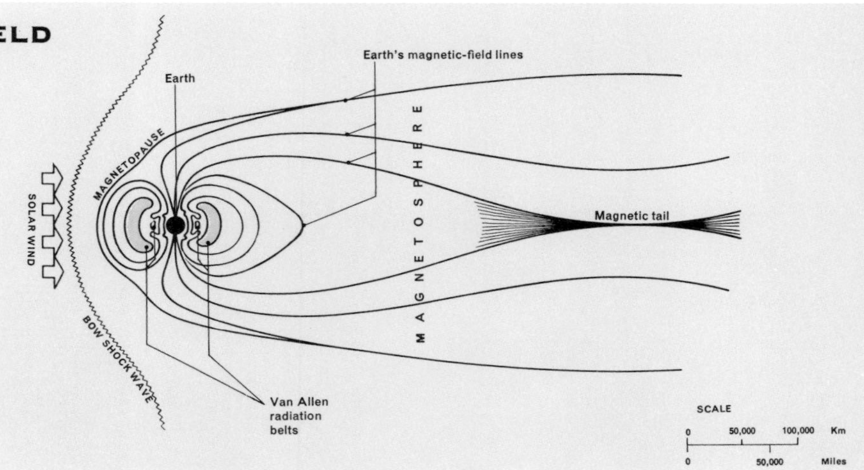

SOLAR WIND SHIELD

Earth orbits inside the thin outer atmosphere of the Sun, sheltered by a magnetic shell known as the magnetosphere. The magnetosphere is distorted by the solar wind – a stream of electrons and protons boiled off the Sun's incandescent surface which flows outwards through the solar system.

The solar wind flattens the sunward side of the magnetosphere, while the other side tails off into space. The boundary between the solar wind and the magnetosphere is termed the magnetopause. Atomic particles from the Sun are trapped in two doughnut-shaped rings inside the magnetosphere, called the Van Allen belts. Occasionally, high-energy solar particles are streamed downward at the poles by Earth's geomagnetic lines of force, causing radio blackouts and the fluorescent displays known as aurorae. Interactions between the solar wind and the Earth's magnetic field are still being studied by means of space satellites.

THE BIRTH OF STARS

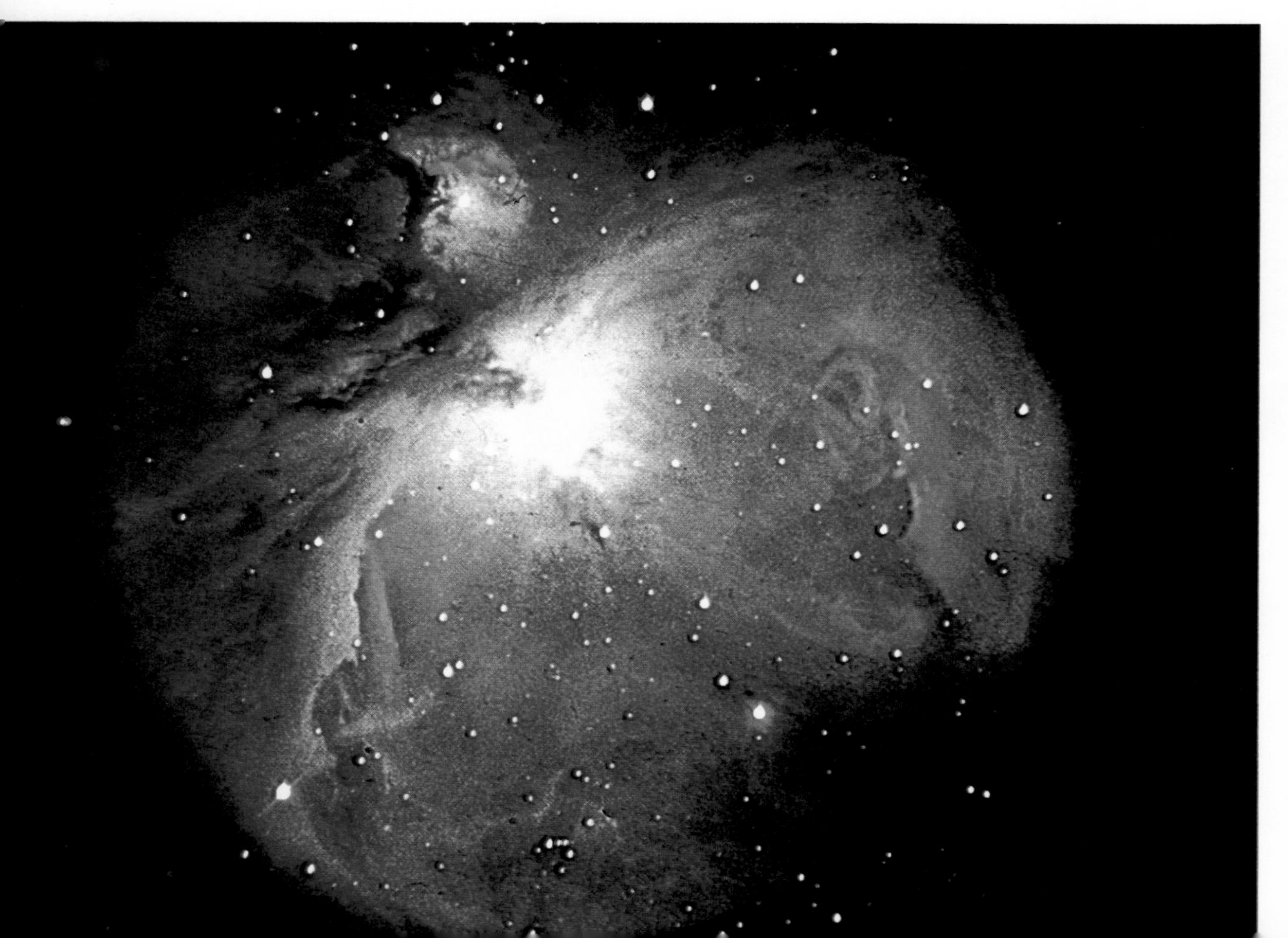

STARS are born from giant clouds of gas and dust lying in the spiral arms of our Galaxy, the Milky Way. One such cloud, the Orion nebula, is shown on the left. This nebula, about 1,500 light years away, contains enough material to make a host of stars and is just visible to the naked eye as a fuzzy patch about the size of the Moon in the constellation of Orion, the hunter. Long-exposure photographs reveal the beautifully coloured wreaths of gas illuminated by the stars that have already formed within the cloud.

Behind the visible cloud, astronomers probing with radio telescopes have detected an even larger dark cloud in which stars are still being born. Such vast fields of thinly spread gas collect under the pull of gravity into small, dense blobs—embryo stars. As gravity pulls them tighter, the star embryos begin to glow of their own accord. They are heated at first by friction as particles of gas and dust rub together; then, after 10 million years for a star the size of the Sun, the temperatures and pressures at the young star's heart become sufficiently extreme to switch on nuclear reactions that power the star for the rest of its life.

Since clouds from which stars form usually contain enough material to make hundreds of stars, the Sun was probably one of a cluster of other young stars at its birth. But due to the lack of gravitational pull, these stars drifted away into the Galaxy. There is a cluster of bright stars called the Pleiades in the constellation of Taurus, which formed within the past 60 million years and where stars have not had time to drift apart.

The life span of a star like the Sun is about 10,000 million years from when the nuclear reactions start until it burns up its energy reserves. The Sun is currently about halfway through its expected life. There are many other glowing gas clouds in space like the Orion nebula, which proves that the birth of stars is a continuing process. As stars grow old and die, new ones are being born elsewhere.

ECLIPSES OF THE SUN AND MOON

Two or three times a year, the Moon in its monthly path around the Earth passes in front of the Sun, blocking off light to give a solar eclipse. About as often, the Moon passes into the shadow cast by the Earth, producing a lunar eclipse. Solar and lunar eclipses do not happen every month, because the Moon's path around the Earth is at an angle to the path of the Earth around the Sun. Only infrequently are the three bodies in line, producing an eclipse.

The motions of celestial bodies are now so well known that astronomers can predict eclipses with confidence centuries ahead. But to early civilizations they were mysterious and frightening events. The ancient Chinese regarded solar eclipses as the attempt of a dragon to eat the Sun. They scared the dragon away by shouting and making a din with musical instruments. A battle between the Medes and Lydians was stopped by a solar eclipse on May 28, 585 BC, the first event in history dated with absolute accuracy. The great monument of Stonehenge on Salisbury Plain is now regarded by many astronomers and historians as an early but remarkably accurate form of eclipse computer, for charting the motions of the Sun and Moon.

A total eclipse of the Sun is only seen from those parts of Earth within the darkest part of the Moon's shadow, the umbra. The umbra traces out a track about 60 miles wide on the Earth as the Moon moves across the Sun, and from any one place on

Earth, a total eclipse is only seen about once every 350 years. A total eclipse can last as long as seven and a half minutes, although two or three minutes is more usual. However, within the lightly shaded penumbra, a partial eclipse is visible over a much greater part of the Earth (see diagram). A total eclipse gives astronomers a valuable opportunity to study the faint outer region of the Sun known as the corona, which is normally swamped by the brilliant light of the photosphere.

The distances between the Sun, Moon and Earth vary slightly so that at times the Moon's umbra does not quite reach the

Earth (see diagram). The Sun is not therefore completely covered, leaving a ring of bright sunshine surrounding the eclipsing Moon. This is termed an annular eclipse, from the Latin *annulus*, meaning a ring. The corona is not visible during annular eclipses, so they are of less interest to astronomers.

Lunar eclipses can be seen over a much wider area, but the whole side of the Moon facing Earth is usually only dimmed as sunlight is refracted on to the lunar surface by the Earth's atmosphere. This situation does not occur during a solar eclipse as the Moon has no atmosphere.

AN ANNULAR ECLIPSE

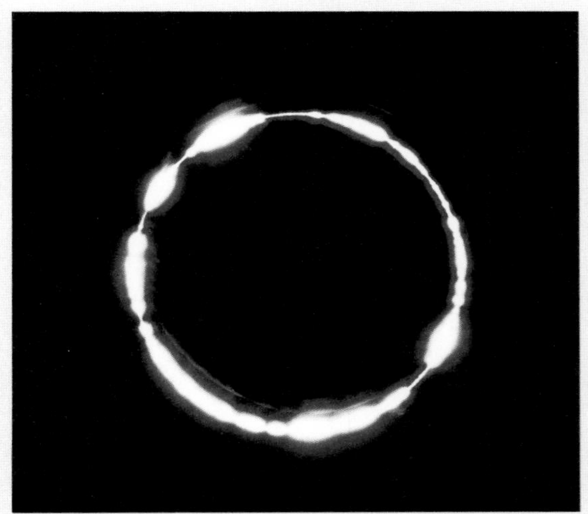

During the annular or ring eclipse of the Sun in May 1966 which was visible from Greece, the apparent diameter of the Moon was only slightly less than the size of the Sun's disk. Sunlight still shone through the lunar valleys but was broken up by the jagged mountains at the Moon's edge, producing this remarkable ring of light called Baily's beads after the English astronomer Francis Baily (1774–1844).

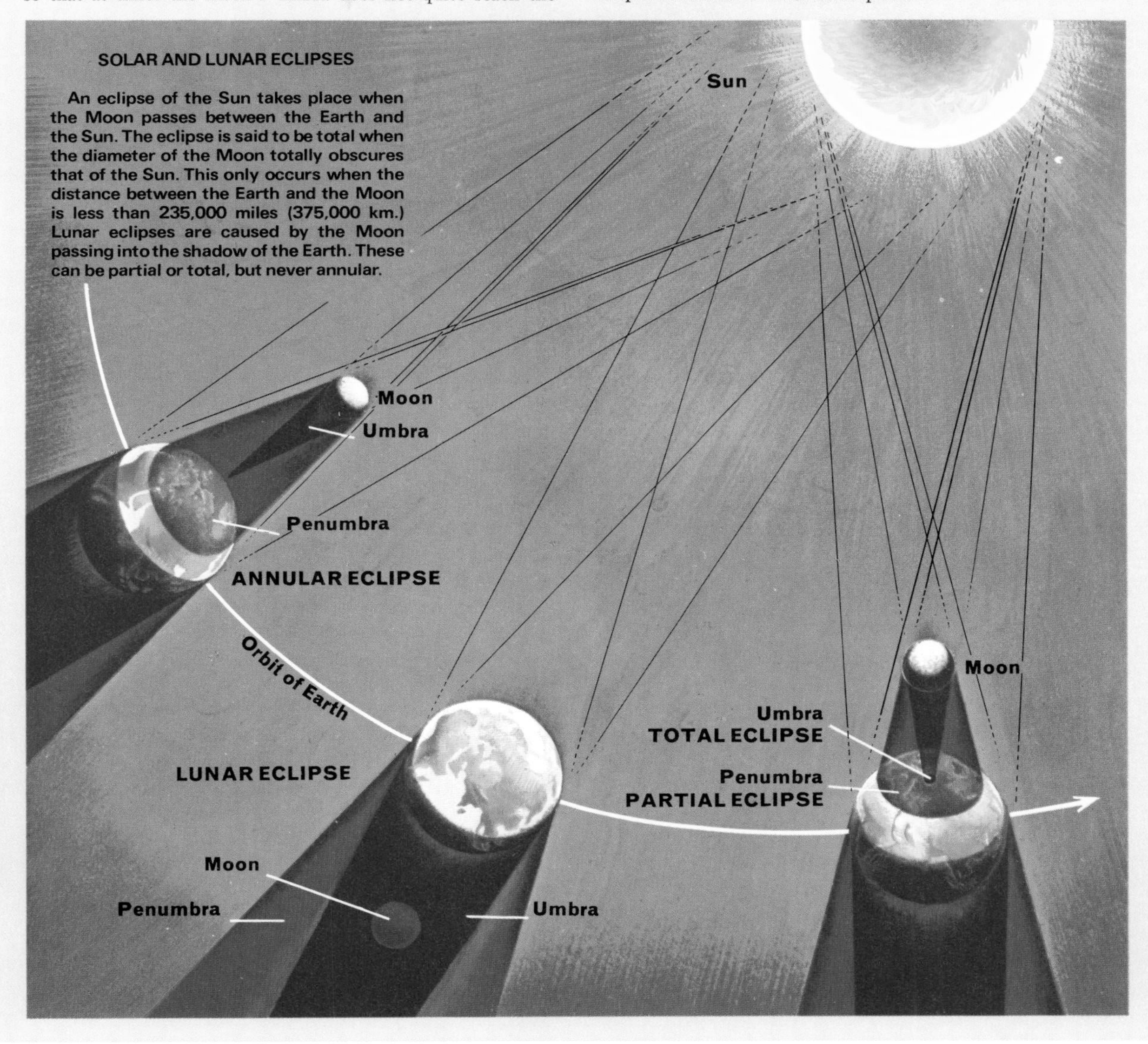

SOLAR AND LUNAR ECLIPSES

An eclipse of the Sun takes place when the Moon passes between the Earth and the Sun. The eclipse is said to be total when the diameter of the Moon totally obscures that of the Sun. This only occurs when the distance between the Earth and the Moon is less than 235,000 miles (375,000 km.) Lunar eclipses are caused by the Moon passing into the shadow of the Earth. These can be partial or total, but never annular.

Sun

Moon
Umbra

Penumbra

ANNULAR ECLIPSE

Orbit of Earth

Moon

Umbra
TOTAL ECLIPSE

Penumbra
PARTIAL ECLIPSE

LUNAR ECLIPSE

Moon

Penumbra

Umbra

SPOTS AND STORMS ON THE SUN

Dark spots that come and go on the Sun's surface are under constant scrutiny by astronomers. Extra-large spots are visible when the Sun is close to the horizon and dimmed by the atmosphere, which is how sunspots were first discovered thousands of years ago. However, it is dangerous to look directly at the Sun with the naked eye at any time. The number of spots usually reaches a maximum about every 11 years, but the period between maximums may vary from 8 to 16 years. The sunspot cycle has even been known to vanish completely, as in the late 17th century when practically no sunspots were seen for a period of 70 years.

Sunspots are areas of gas at a temperature of about 4,500°C which is cooler than the surrounding photosphere (6,000°C). They are associated with strong magnetic fields at the Sun's surface. The Sun's north and south magnetic poles are reversed in each successive sunspot cycle, so astronomers now consider that the true pulse of the Sun's activity is not 11 but 22 years. Occasionally, brilliant eruptions called flares burst out in the magnetic fields around sunspots, firing energetic particles into space which, on entering the Earth's upper atmosphere, cause disturbances such as radio blackouts and the dancing polar lights known as aurorae.

When seen at the Sun's edge, the material shooting out from a flare is termed an eruptive prominence. Other prominences, even larger, form enormous loops along magnetic fields that thread through the Sun's outer atmosphere, the corona. Using special instruments, astronomers can study prominences and the much smaller jagged spikes of gas called spicules which shoot up through the lower part of the Sun's atmosphere, the chromosphere, apparently injecting material from the boiling surface of the photosphere into the corona.

To view these phenomena under the best conditions astronomers flew special solar telescopes in the U.S. Skylab space station orbiting 270 miles above the Earth. Skylab was manned by a series of three crews in 1973 and 1974. On the right are examples of the spectacular photographs obtained, taken at selected wavelengths and artificially colour-coded to reveal extra detail giving the surface of the Sun a granular appearance. Eruptions at the edge of the Sun are shown, flinging hot gas into space. The largest prominence (main picture) extends outwards for 500,000 miles. On this scale, the Earth is about the size of the letter o in this sentence.

But these solar studies are not of purely astronomical significance. The activity on the Sun affects the Earth's atmosphere, our climate, and consequently the success of agriculture in feeding a hungry world.

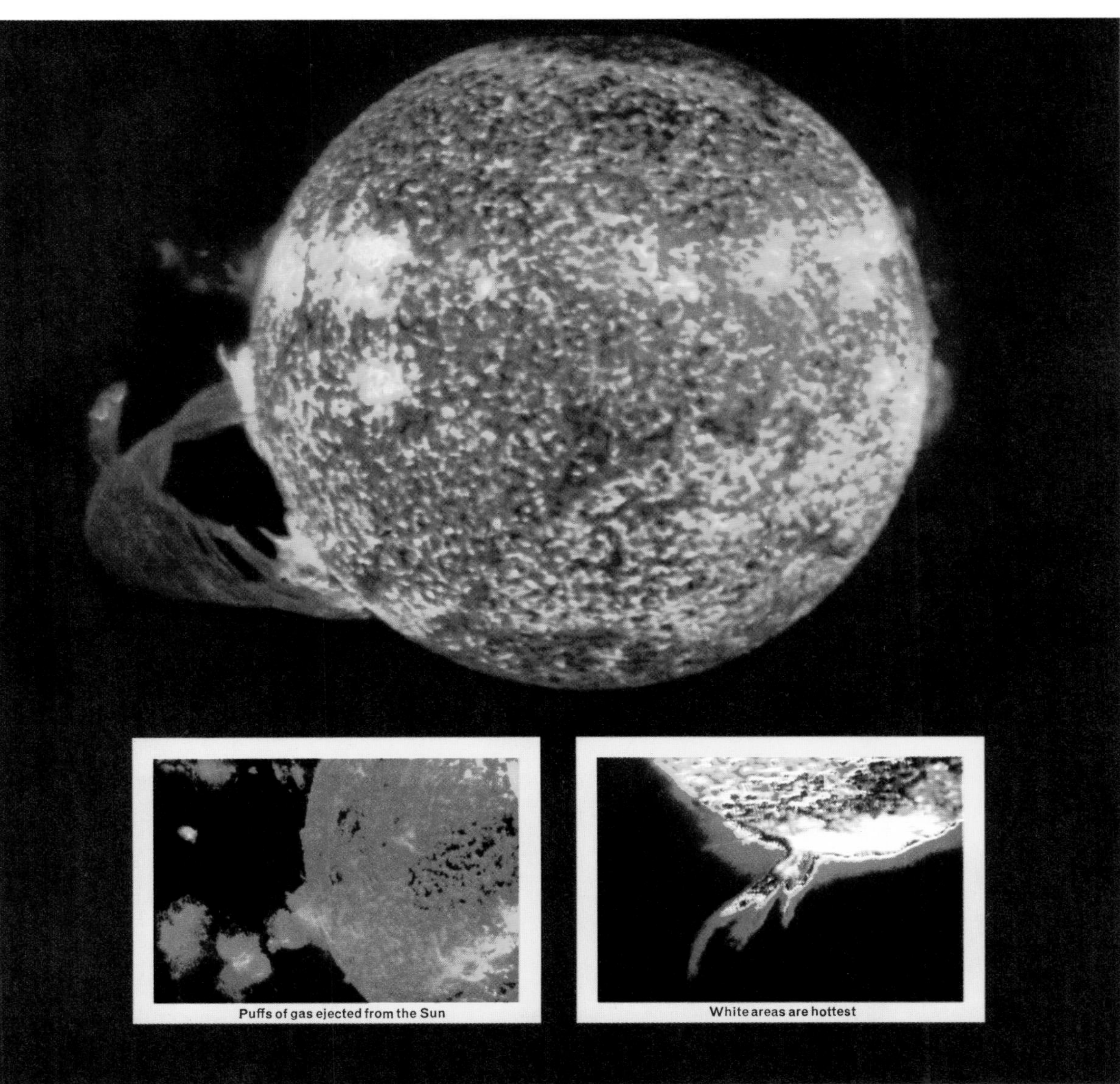

Puffs of gas ejected from the Sun

White areas are hottest

THE PLANETS OF THE SOLAR SYSTEM

By understanding hath he created the heavens—PROVERBS 3

NOBODY knows beyond doubt how the nine planets of the solar system were created, but the most generally accepted theory is that they were formed some 4,600 million years ago from an immense, swirling cloud of gas and dust. This cloud of matter contracted under its own gravitational force and, inevitably, specks of matter collided and coalesced, in a process known as accretion. As the process continued, each of the infant planets captured more and more matter. At the centre of the rotating cloud, with the largest mass of all, was the star we call the Sun, which contains something like 99·9 per cent of all the matter in the solar system. This means that all the matter contained in the Sun's nine attendant planets does not even constitute one per cent.

Some basic facts about the planets and the Sun are summarised in the table below. The average distance from the Sun is given for each planet although their orbits are elliptical and this distance varies between a maximum (apogee) and minimum (perigee). The sidereal revolution period is the time a planet takes to orbit the Sun—its "year". The axial rotation period is the time a planet takes to rotate once on its axis—its "day". For comparison, a planet's "day" and "year" are measured in units of Earth time. The axial inclination is the angle between the rotation axis of a planet and the perpendicular to its plane of orbit. Mass, which is the amount of matter each body contains, is expressed as a multiple of Earth's mass. The escape velocity is the minimum speed an object, such as a rocket, must attain in order to break free from a body's gravitational pull.

THE SOLAR SYSTEM	Mean distance from Sun kilometres (miles)	Equatorial diameter kilometres (miles)	Sidereal revolution period	Axial rotation period	Axial inclination	Mass (Earth=1)	Mean orbital velocity kilometres/sec (miles/sec)	Escape velocity kilometres/sec (miles/sec)	Mean temperature of surface	Known satellites
			Terrestrial time							
SUN	—	1,392,000 (865,000)	—	25 days 1 hr 12 min	—	333,003·0	—	616·4 (383·0)	+5,600°C	—
MERCURY	57,900,000 (36,000,000)	4,880 (3,032)	87·97 days	58 days 15 hr 36 min	0°(?)	0·055	47·9 (29·8)	4·25 (2·64)	+520°C	0
VENUS	108,200,000 (67,200,000)	12,104 (7,521)	224·7 days	243 days	3°	0·815	35·0 (21·7)	10·36 (6·43)	+480°C	0
EARTH	149,600,000 (92,900,000)	12,756 (7,926)	365·26 days	23 hr 56 min 4 sec	23°27′	1·0	29·8 (18·5)	11·18 (6·95)	+22°C	1
MARS	227,900,000 (141,600,000)	6,787 (4,217)	686·98 days	24 hr 37 min 23 sec	23°59′	0·108	24·1 (15·0)	5·02 (3·12)	−23°C	2
JUPITER	778,300,000 (483,600,000)	142,800 (88,700)	4,332·59 days	9 hr 50 min 30 sec	3°05′	317·943	13·1 (8·1)	59·64 (37·06)	−123°C	16
SATURN	1,427,000,000 (886,700,000)	120,000 (75,000)	10,759·22 days	10 hr 14 min	26°44′	95·195	9·6 (6·0)	35·41 (22·0)	−180°C	10 (?)
URANUS	2,869,600,000 (1,783,100,000)	51,800 (32,200)	30,685·4 days	16 hr (?)	82°5′	14·605	6·8 (4·2)	21·41 (13·3)	−218°C	5
NEPTUNE	4,496,600,000 (2,791,100,000)	49,500 (30,800)	60,195 days	18 hr (?)	28°48′	17·232	5·4 (3·4)	23·52 (14·61)	−228°C	2
PLUTO	5,900,000,000 (3,700,000,000)	3,000 (1,800)	90,475 days	6 days 9 hr 18 min	55°	0·002	4·7 (2·9)	1·0 (0·6)	−230°C(?)	1

MERCURY

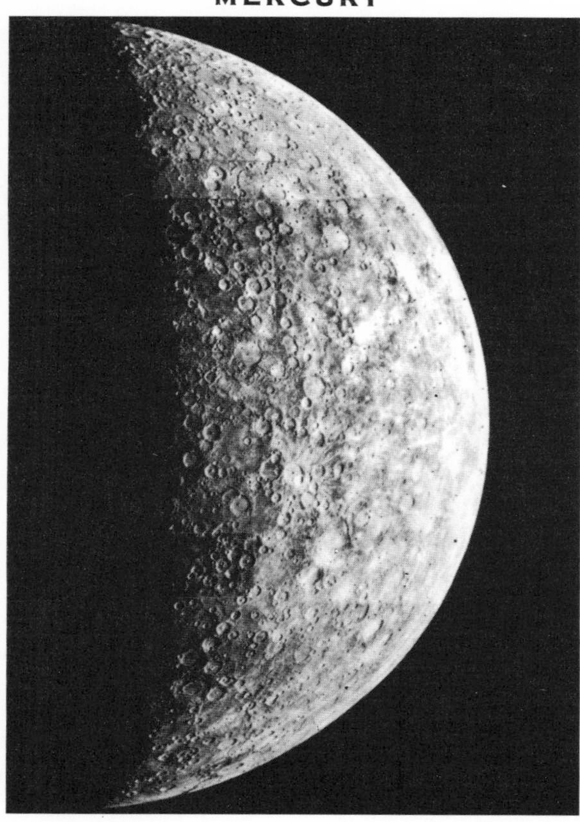

This innermost planet of the solar system is superficially like the Moon in many ways, although the force of gravity at ground level is twice as strong. Its dark rocky surface has plains, craters and ridges like those on the Moon, although they are not so numerous. The planet has no atmosphere and reflects both sunlight and radar pulses like the lunar surface. This latter quality has enabled astronomers to determine many facts about the planet.

Like the other three inner planets of Venus, Earth and Mars, Mercury is composed of heavy elements but with a proportionately larger iron core than Earth—it probably takes up three-quarters of the planet's total diameter of 3,032 miles. Mercury has a magnetic field, but it is only about 1/200th as strong as the Earth's.

It was once thought that the same side of Mercury always faced the Sun and therefore that its rotation was exactly synchronised with its orbit. But, in 1962, American radio astronomers discovered that both sides of the planet radiated heat, which would not have been the case if the same hemisphere had always faced the Sun. In 1965, it was confirmed by the use of radar that the planet rotated on its axis three times every 176 Earth days. This fact was reconfirmed by the American Mariner 10 space probe in 1974. Having established the rotation rate, it was possible to calculate that Mercury only rotates one-and-a-half times on its axis during one complete orbit of the Sun. This means that Mercury's "year" is only made up of one-and-a-half "days".

VENUS

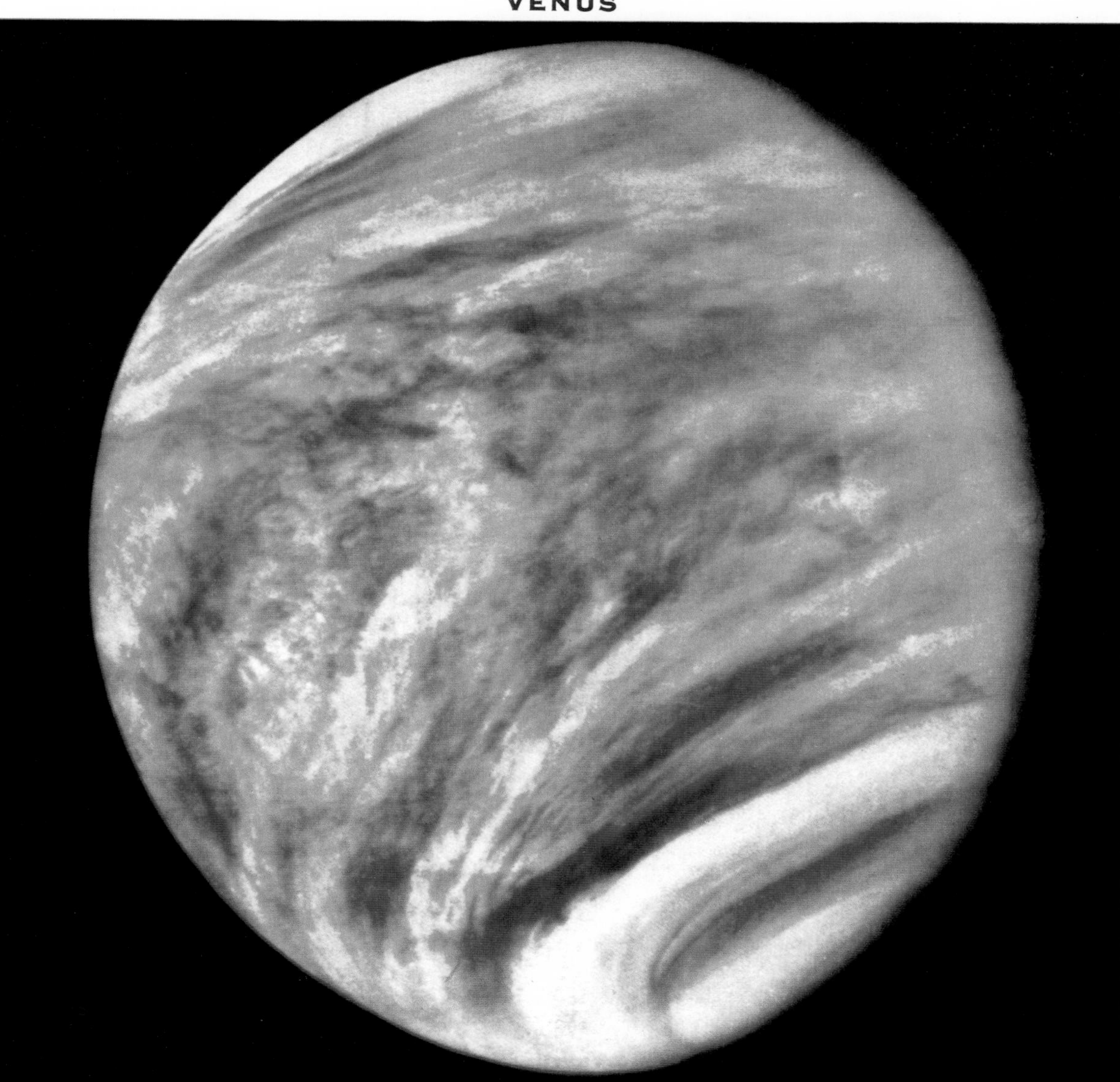

Enveloped in a mass of dense, bright clouds, Venus outshines any other planet or star in the sky apart from the Sun. Early earthbound observation of Venus was limited because the clouds completely obscure the surface, and it was not until the advent of radio-astronomy that precise data could be collected.

Because it is closer to the Sun, Venus should receive about twice as much solar radiation as Earth but this is reduced to about the same level by the clouds, which reflect the radiation back into space. The atmosphere around Venus may once have been as thin as Earth's, but the extra solar radiation it was subjected to would have prevented the water vapour from condensing to form oceans as on Earth, so the vapour remained in the atmosphere, creating a greenhouse effect with the heat from the surface building up below the cloud layer. This accounts for the very high surface temperature of about 500°C. The pressure at ground level on Venus is about 90 times that on Earth, and the main constituent of the atmosphere is carbon dioxide (97 per cent).

In 1974, the Mariner 10 space probe confirmed that astronomers were correct in their prediction that the upper atmosphere of Venus rotates at a greater speed than the planet itself. In fact, the cloud shell rotates in about four Earth days compared with the planet's 243 days, which means that there must be winds of far greater strength than anything experienced on Earth, although it is known that the wind velocity on the surface is much lower. Venus is one of the two planets which rotate in the opposite direction to Earth, so that the sun rises in the west rather than the east. The planet has no magnetic field, which may be due to its very slow rate of rotation.

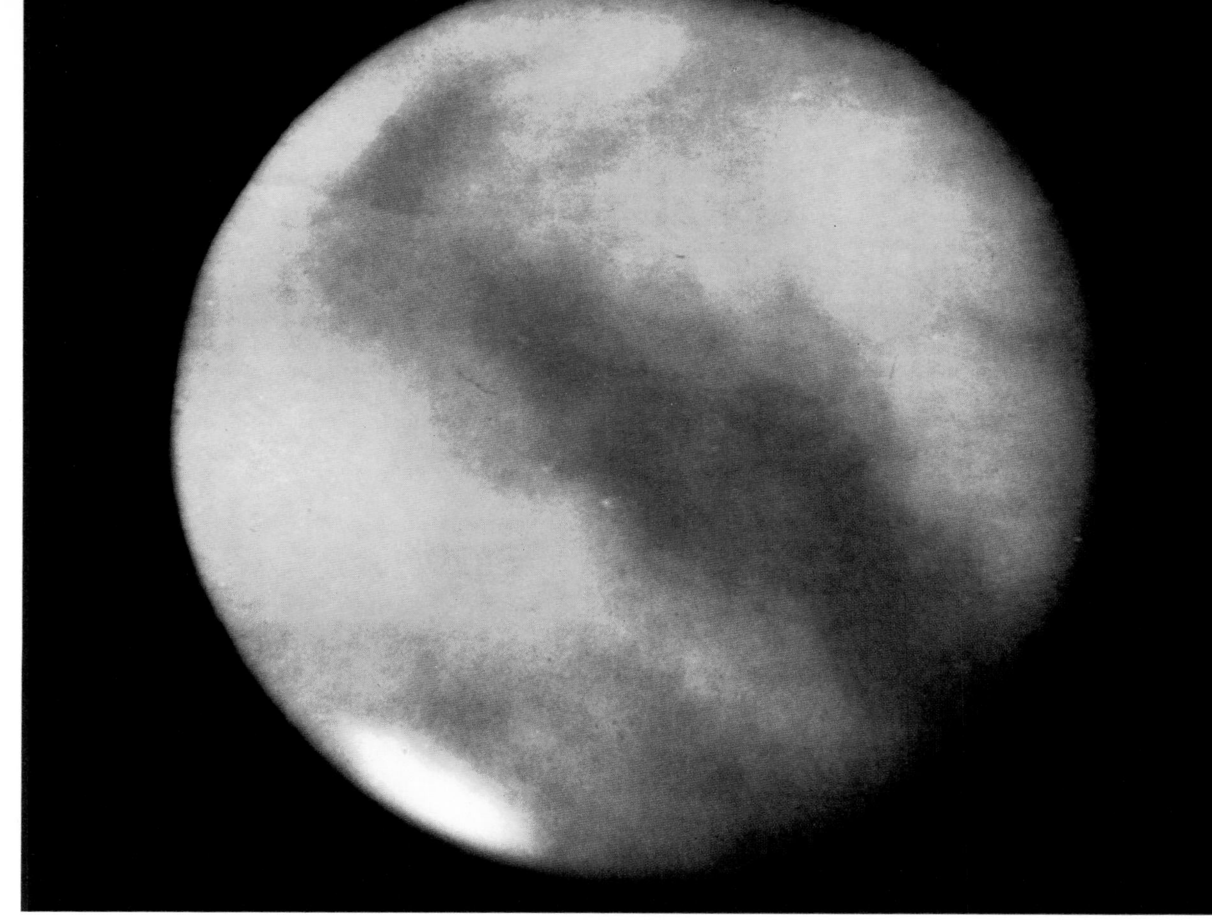

MARS

Mars has long been imagined by man to be the planet most likely to support life forms similar to those on Earth. This was mainly because of the superficial resemblance between the two planets. As Mars and Earth both rotate at about the same speed, the Martian "day" is less than an hour longer than the terrestrial day. There are polar icecaps and equatorial colourations which change seasonally, and clouds are often seen in the planet's atmosphere. Also, astronomers conjectured that long straight lines on the surface might be irrigation canals engineered by some intelligent life form.

Any hopes of a Martian civilization have since disappeared, as it is now known that the "canals" do not exist, there is no vegetation, and the surface is subject to violent dust storms. The pressure at ground level is only about 1/200th of that on Earth. This dead planet, covered with a red dust of iron oxide, has some very spectacular features, including an extinct volcano more than two-and-a-half times the height of Mount Everest and an enormous crevasse with which even the Grand Canyon in Arizona could not compete. Clear pictures of the surface were sent back by the U.S. Viking space probes which landed on Mars in 1976. The Viking 2 discovered that the polar icecaps were frozen water rather than frozen carbon dioxide.

JUPITER

Largest of all the planets, Jupiter exerts its gravitational force throughout the solar system. Its mass is 318 times that of the Earth and nearly two-and-a-half times that of all the other planets put together. Jupiter is composed of liquid hydrogen with possibly a small core of solid hydrogen. The planet radiates about twice as much heat as it receives from the Sun and could have evolved into a star if its mass had been greater. Jupiter's magnetic field, with its complex radiation belts, is much more extensive than the Earth's, and its magnetic pole

is inverted, which means that a compass needle would point to south. The Jovian "day" lasts only about ten hours, but the speed of rotation varies with latitude, which proves that the planet is fluid. In 1979, two Voyager spacecraft transmitted spectacular close-ups of the swirling clouds on Jupiter and showed that one of its moons, Io, had active volcanoes. The 18,000-mile-wide red spot, first seen over 300 years ago, was shown to be a whirlpool in the Jovian clouds. It is believed that the colouration results from red phosphorus.

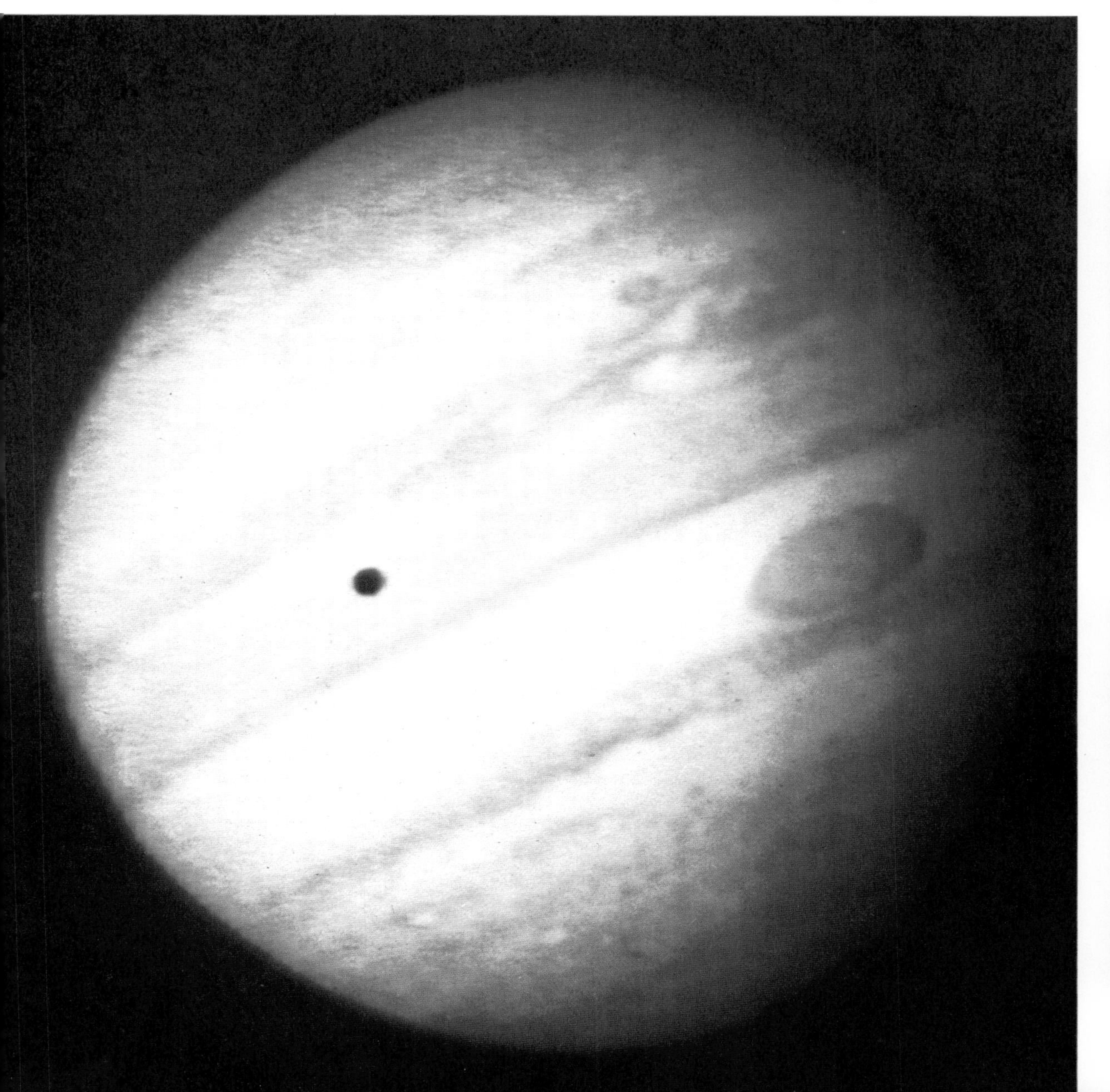

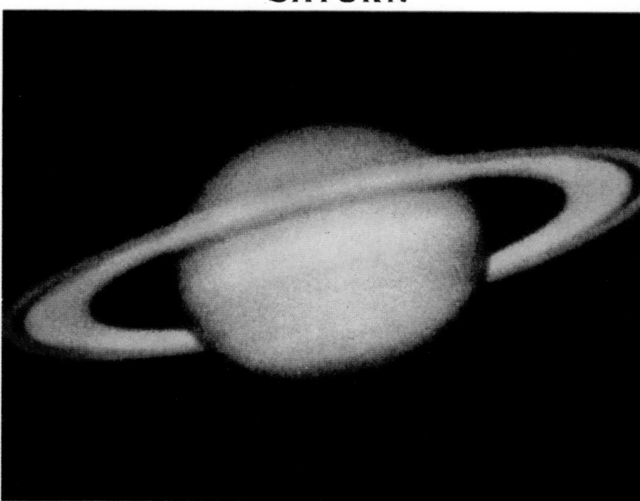

SATURN

Until the discovery of Uranus in 1781, Saturn was believed to be the furthermost planet of the solar system. First reached by space probe in 1979, Saturn, apart from its rings, is like a smaller version of Jupiter. As the planet's rotation rate varies with latitude, Saturn is obviously a fluid world. It is composed mainly of hydrogen with some helium and, although its diameter is only 16 per cent less than that of Jupiter, its mass is one-third of Jupiter's. Titan, the biggest of Saturn's ten moons, is larger than the planet Mercury and is known to have an atmosphere composed mainly of methane.

URANUS

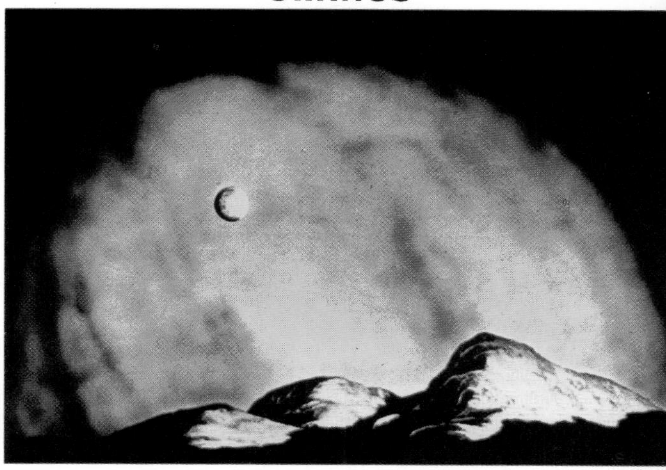

In 1977, American astronomers identified nine faint rings of rocky debris around the planet Uranus. Unlike any of the other planets in the solar system its rotation axis is tilted at an angle of nearly 90° to the perpendicular so that it lies almost in its orbital plane. This results in the planet's north and south poles being presented alternately towards the Sun at the solstices. Its atmosphere could contain large quantities of methane. Uranus, like the planet Venus, rotates in the opposite direction to Earth. The artist's impression shows Uranus rising above the jagged skyline of one of its five satellites.

NEPTUNE

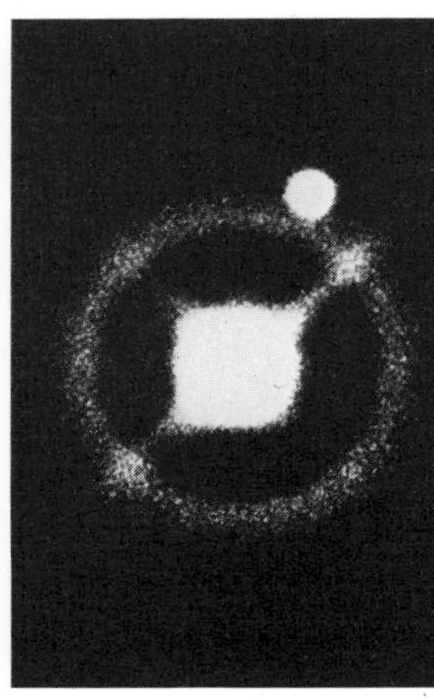

This photograph of the planet Neptune was made with the 120-inch reflecting telescope at the Lick Observatory in California. The planet has two satellites. The larger one, Triton, is visible above the planet and is larger than our Moon. Neptune has an extremely cold surface temperature and, although its "day" is only two-thirds as long as Earth's, its "year" is 165 times longer. The existence of Neptune was confirmed by the German astronomer Johann Gottfried Galle, in 1846.

PLUTO

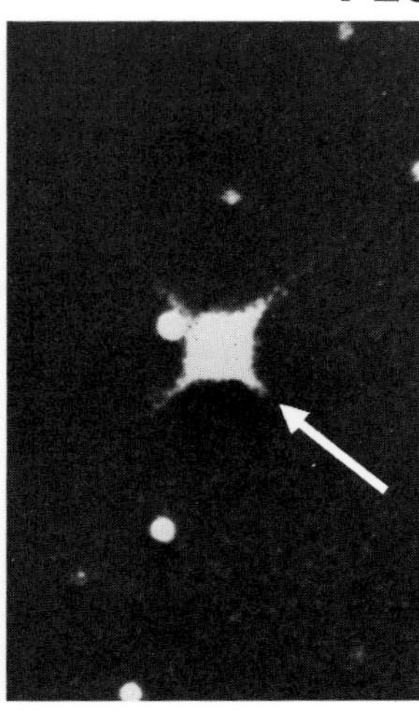

The photograph of Pluto was made with the 200-inch Mount Palomar telescope. Pluto was the outermost planet of the Solar System, but since 1979, the planet's orbit has moved closer to the Sun than Neptune's and will remain so until 1999. Recent measurements have identified Pluto as the smallest planet and the fact that it is much smaller than the other outer planets strengthens the theory that it was once a satellite of Neptune. Pluto was discovered in 1930 and its single moon in 1978. It is probably composed for the most part of frozen gases.

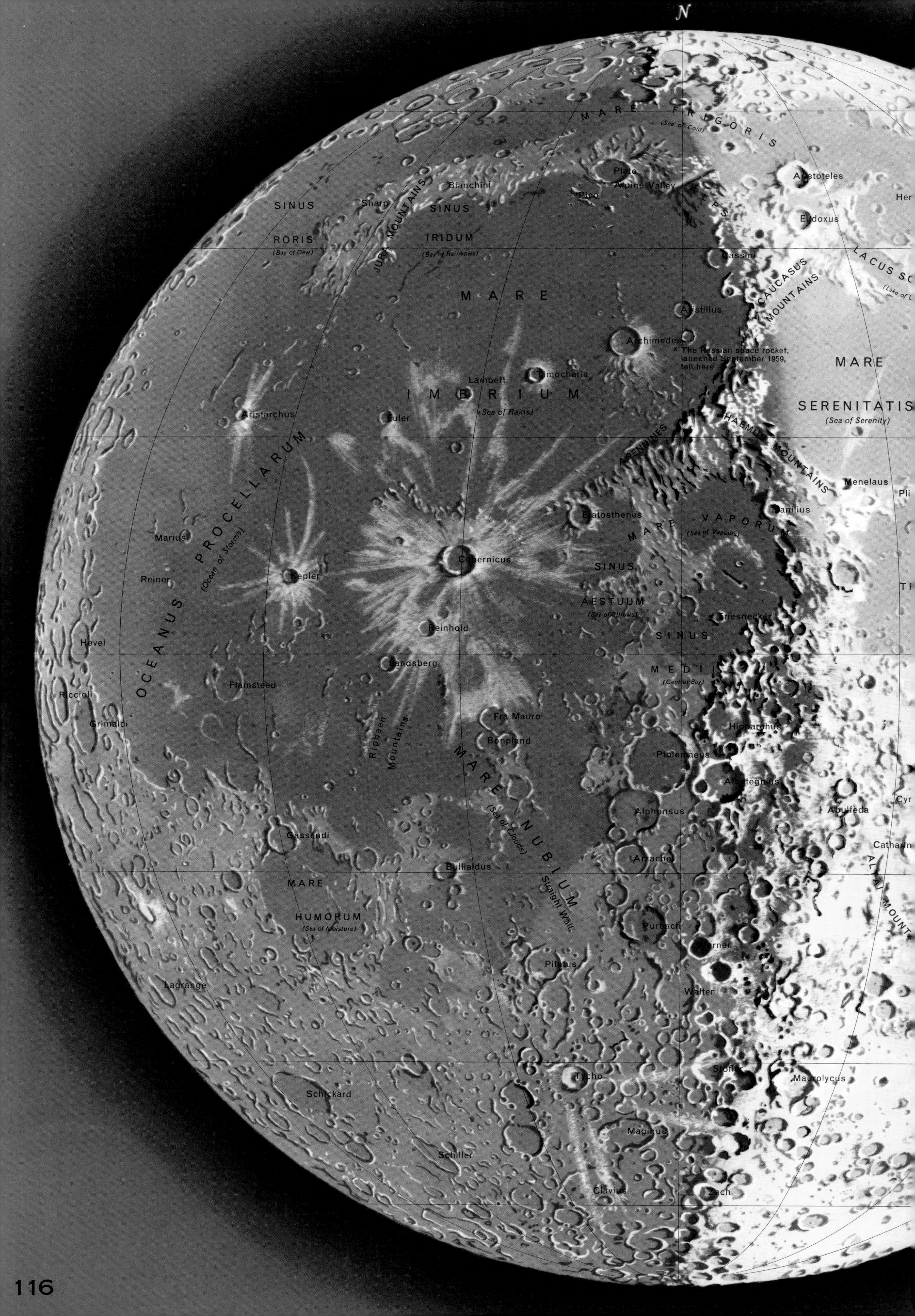
N
MARE FRIGORIS
(Sea of Cold)
Plato
Alpine Valley
Pico
ALPS
Aristoteles
Eudoxus
Her
SINUS
RORIS
(Bay of Dew)
Sharp
Bianchini
JURA MOUNTAINS
SINUS
IRIDUM
(Bay of Rainbows)
Cassini
LACUS SO
CAUCASUS MOUNTAINS
MARE
Aristillus
Archimedes
x The Russian space rocket, launched September 1959, fell here
MARE
SERENITATIS
(Sea of Serenity)
Timocharis
Lambert
IMBRIUM
(Sea of Rains)
Aristarchus
Euler
APENNINES
HAEMUS MOUNTAINS
Menelaus
OCEANUS PROCELLARUM
(Ocean of Storms)
Eratosthenes
Manilius
MARE VAPORUM
(Sea of Vapours)
Marius
Copernicus
Kepler
Reiner
SINUS
AESTUUM
(Bay of Billows)
Triesnecker
Reinhold
SINUS
Hevel
MEDII
(Central Bay)
Landsberg
Flamsteed
Riccioli
Grimaldi
Fra Mauro
Bonpland
Riphaen Mountains
Hipparchus
Ptolemaeus
MARE NUBIUM
(Sea of Clouds)
Albategnius
Alphonsus
Abulfeda
Gassendi
Catharina
Bullialdus
Arzachel
ALTAI MOUNTAINS
MARE
HUMORUM
(Sea of Moisture)
Straight Wall
Purbach
Werner
Pitatus
Lagrange
Walter
Tycho
Stofler
Maurolycus
Schickard
Maginus
Schiller
Clavius
Zach

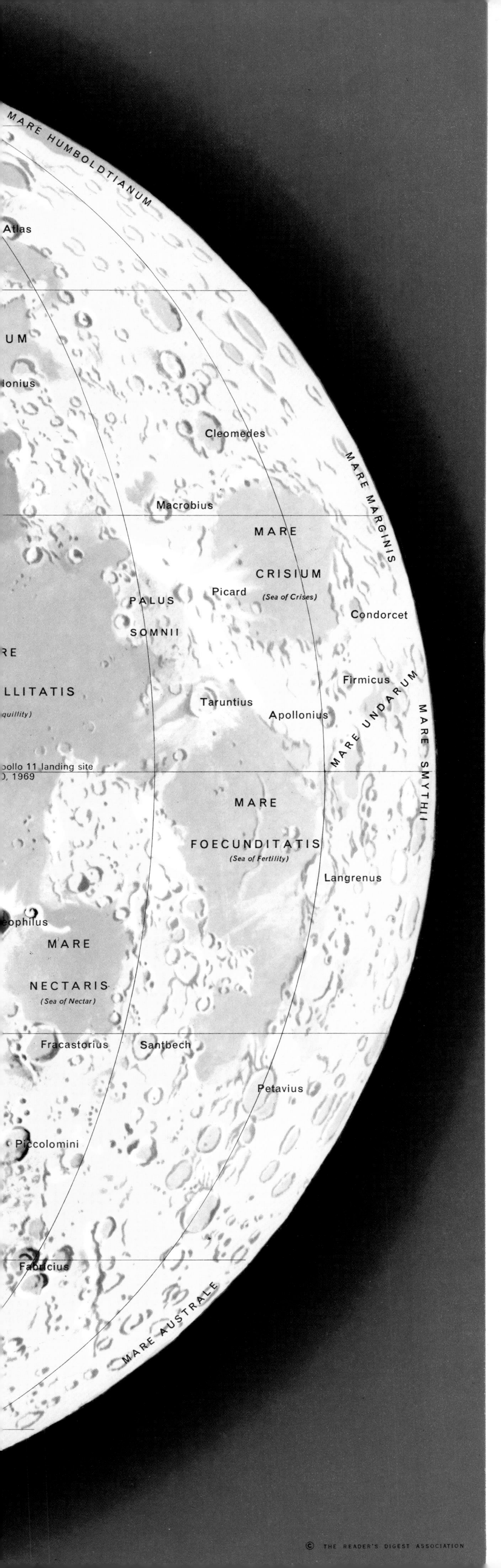

THE MOON

EARTH'S SATELLITE

He appointed the Moon for seasons — PSALM 104

THE Moon is unique in our Solar System. Most of the planets have satellites, but these are very small in relation to their primaries, whereas the Moon has approximately one-quarter the diameter of the Earth. It might even be logical to regard the Earth-Moon system as a double planet.

MOVEMENTS. The Earth and Moon revolve round the "barycentre", or common centre of gravity of the system; but as this point lies within the globe of the Earth, the simple statement that "the Moon goes round the Earth" is good enough for most purposes. The axial rotation period is exactly the same as the orbital period, so that the Moon keeps the same hemisphere turned Earthward. This synchronous rotation is due to tidal effects over the ages.

SURFACE FEATURES. The large map shows the near side of the Moon. All the features shown are visible with good binoculars. The craters are best seen not at full moon, when there are virtually no shadows, but when they are near the "terminator"—that is to say, that region of the Moon over which the Sun is rising or setting. When near the terminator, a peak will cast a long shadow and a crater will have part of its floor in darkness.

The most obvious features are the broad grey plains, mis-called seas; they are still known by romantic names such as the Mare Imbrium (Sea of Showers) and Sinus Iridum (Bay of Rainbows), though in fact the Moon is a waterless world. The main mountain ranges, such as the lunar Apennines, form the boundaries of the major seas.

The Moon's surface is dominated by the craters, ranging in size from huge enclosures well over 150 miles in diameter down to tiny pits. Most are named after past scientists. Two of the finest are Copernicus and Tycho,

which are the centres of bright ray-systems extending far across the Moon; the rays are best seen under high lighting.

The origin of the craters is still a matter for debate. No doubt some are due to volcanic action; others to the impacts of meteorites.

SURFACE CONDITIONS. Because of its low escape velocity, the Moon is without atmosphere or water. Any atmosphere which may have existed in the remote past has long since been lost. This is what makes the Moon so hostile a world. The temperatures are extreme; there is no air to shield the lunar surface during the long lunar day, and nothing to retain warmth during the night. Moreover, the surface rocks are very poor at holding on to heat.

Another effect of this lack of atmosphere is that the Moon is a sterile world. Rock samples brought back from the Apollo and Luna probes confirm that there is no sign of life, either past or present, and it now seems safe to assume that no life has ever developed on the Moon.

In every way the lunar world is inert by everyday standards, though the recording instruments left on the surface by the American astronauts show that slight crustal tremors do occur. It is thought probable that the interior of the globe is hot, although the temperature of the core is almost certainly less than in the case of the Earth.

LUNAR PROBES. The first successful lunar probes were sent up in 1959, by the Russians. During the 1960's there followed the U.S. Rangers, Orbiters and Surveyors, as well as automatic Soviet Lunas. Finally, in July 1969, came the first landing, by Astronauts Armstrong and Aldrin. Five further expeditions were made before the end of the Apollo programme in 1972; it should eventually be possible to set up a full-scale lunar base, perhaps even before the end of the twentieth century.

Average distance from Earth . . 384,365 km. (238,840 miles)	Mass in terms of Earth 1:81
Diameter . . . . 3,476 km. (2,160 miles) (Earth's diameter 12,745 km. (7,920 miles)	Sidereal Period . . . 27·3 days (approx.) (time taken to make one complete circuit of Earth)
Density . . . . 3·3 times that of water (Earth's density 5·5 times that of water)	Synodic Period . . . 29·5 days (approx.) (interval between one new Moon and the next)

THE FAR SIDE OF THE MOON

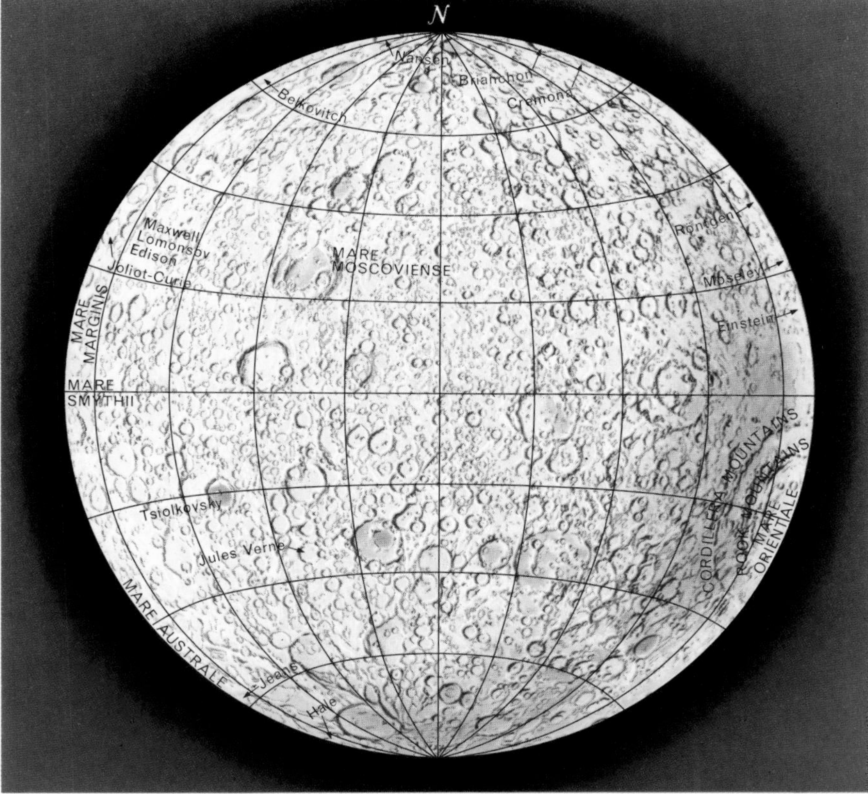

This chart, covering the whole of the Moon's far hemisphere, has been compiled from photographs taken with the U.S. Orbiter vehicles.

Near the edge of the chart appear some features which can be identified on the map of the Earth-turned hemisphere. From Earth we can, for instance, identify the Mare Smythii. Even more interesting is the Mare Orientale (Eastern Sea), which has proved to be a very complex structure

indeed. Note the dark-floored crater Tsiolkovskii, which was identifiable on the first photograph of the Moon's far side sent back by the Russian probe Lunik III in October, 1959.

The mapping of the far side of the Moon is now complete. The names of the features there are under consideration by the International Astronomical Union. The names given in the chart above are those which have already been agreed.

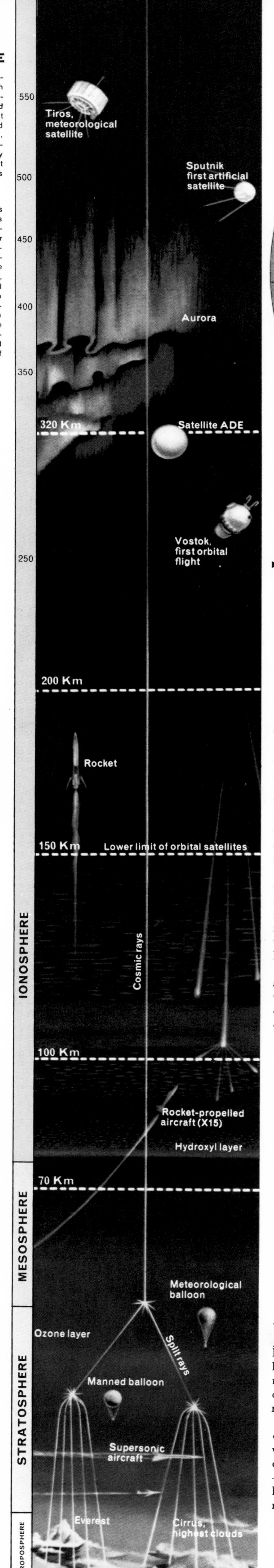

CRUST
Granitic layer (continents)
Basaltic layer (oceans)
Mohorovičić Discontinuity
Pressure at sea level:
1 atmosphere

MANTLE
Compressed iron-magnesium
silicates, probably rigid to a
depth of 450 miles

**POSSIBLE SULPHIDE
AND OXIDE SHELL**

OUTER CORE
Nickel iron, probably molten
Pressure at surface of core:
1.5 million atmospheres

INNER CORE
Nickel iron, probably solid
Pressure at Earth's centre:
about 3.5 million
atmospheres
Temperature: 3–4,000°C.

Diameter of Earth at poles:
7,900 miles
Diameter at Equator:
7,927 miles
Total surface area:
196,950,000 sq. miles
Land area:
57,510,000 sq. miles
Sea area:
139,440,000 sq. miles

© THE READER'S DIGEST ASSOCIATION

THE ATMOSPHERE

The Earth is completely enveloped by stratified gases which form the atmosphere. This element acts as insulation and enables life to exist. Without it, temperatures during day and night would reach extremes. The gaseous layers are interactive and are also affected by solar radiation so they cannot be separated as precisely as the strata of the Earth.

Ionosphere

The air is so rarefied in this region that its composition is less significant than its electrical properties. Intense solar radiation breaks down molecules (mainly oxygen and nitrogen) into atoms. These are stripped of their electrons, producing electrically charged particles called ions which interact with Earth's magnetic field. The aurorae which appear in higher latitudes are the result of collisions between electrically charged solar particles and atoms of the atmospheric gases.

F_2 Layer

At a little above 300 km. (186 miles) this is the most highly ionized level of the ionosphere. Radio waves, which travel in straight lines, can be transmitted round the curvature of the Earth by bouncing them off the ionized layers. This applies only to waves longer than 15 metres; short waves and VHF waves pass through.

F_1 Layer

The lowest level at which satellites can orbit is about 150 km. (93·15 miles). Below this, the air becomes denser and resistance becomes too great for free flight.
The origin of cosmic rays is uncertain, but most come from beyond the solar system. The primary rays are harmful to life but, after colliding with nuclei in the ozone layer, they are split into harmless secondary rays. Meteors usually burn up by the time they reach this level.

E Layer (or Heaviside-Kennelly layer)

This layer is fairly strongly ionized during the day, but unlike the F layers, it dissipates once the Sun has set. In the hydroxyl layer, sunlight breaks down water vapour into hydrogen atoms and molecules of one hydrogen atom plus one oxygen atom—hydroxyl.

D Layer

At this level, ionization is weak and of little use for reflecting radiowaves. The **mesosphere**, where temperature falls with altitude, is an intermediate layer between the stratosphere and the ionosphere.

This layer contains a poisonous oxygen gas called ozone. Temperature rises with altitude, so the stratosphere is termed an inversion layer. This warmer air prevents convection currents rising from the **troposphere** which extends to about 15 km. (9 miles) above the surface. In the troposphere, temperature falls about 6°C for every kilometre in altitude. Climatic conditions affecting the surface occur within this densest layer. At the upper level, convection currents turn over and move horizontally at speeds of several hundred kilometres an hour—the jet streams exploited by supersonic aircraft.

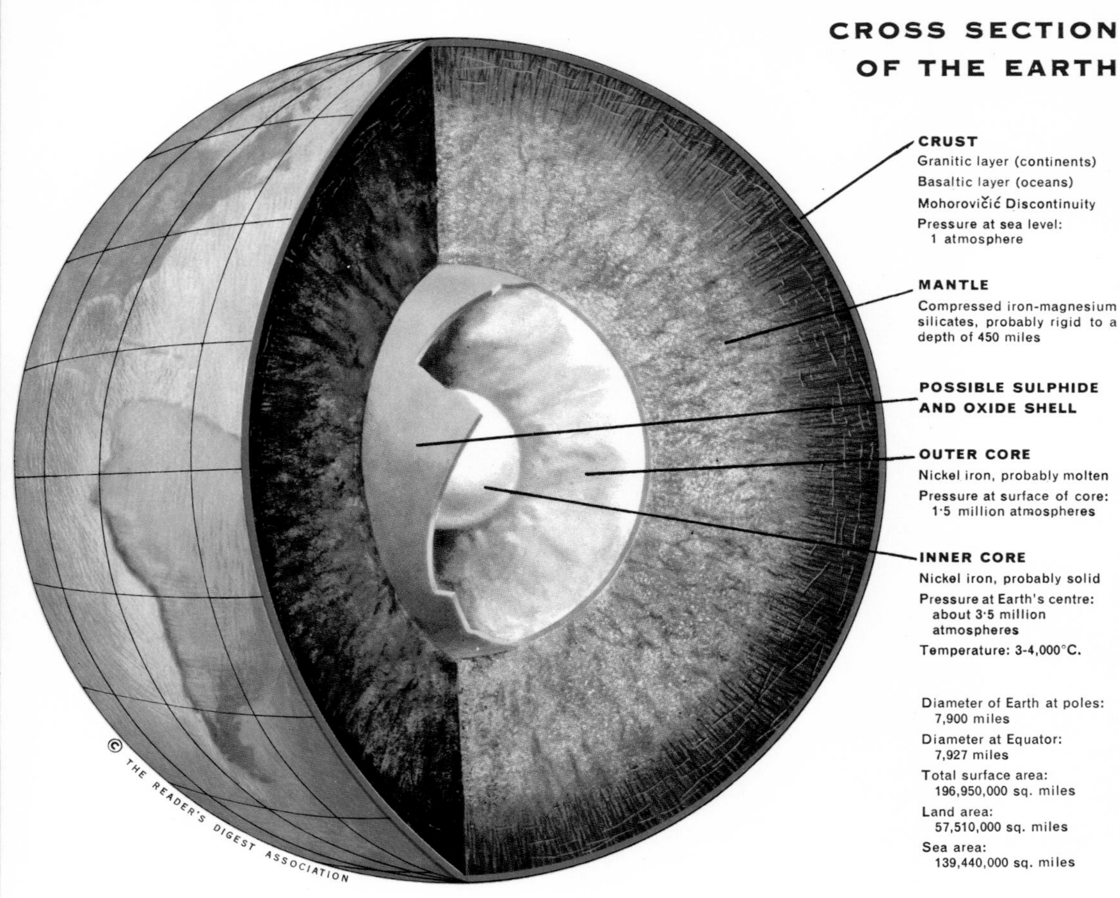

550
Tiros, meteorological satellite
500
Sputnik first artificial satellite
450
400
Aurora
350
320 Km
Satellite ADE
250
Vostok, first orbital flight
200 Km
Rocket
150 Km   Lower limit of orbital satellites
IONOSPHERE
Cosmic rays
100 Km
Rocket-propelled aircraft (X15)
Hydroxyl layer
70 Km
MESOSPHERE
Ozone layer
STRATOSPHERE
Meteorological balloon
Manned balloon
Split rays
Supersonic aircraft
Everest   Cirrus, highest clouds
TROPOSPHERE

THE EARTH'S STRUCTURE

Let the waters under the heaven be gathered together unto one place, and let the dry land appear — GENESIS 1

THE continental parts of the Earth's Crust are composed of many different kinds of rock which, as a whole, have the density and composition of granite. This granite layer is often called "sial" because of the predominance of *si*lica and *al*umina in its composition. The granite layer, or "sial," floats on a denser layer, which has an average density and composition similar to that of the common black volcanic lava known as basalt. This so-called "basaltic" layer (termed "sima" because of its richness in *si*lica and *ma*gnesium) directly underlies the ocean floor, and here forms the thinnest part of the Earth's Crust. In continental areas the granitic and basaltic layers together can reach a thickness of approximately 60 miles. In oceanic areas, the basaltic layer averages a thickness of only about three miles.

Knowledge that the Earth could not consist entirely of these surface rocks came first from the planet's weight, measured by its pull of gravity; for these materials are far too light to account for a total mass of 6,600 million million million tons. The density (weight per unit of volume) of rocks at the Earth's centre may in fact be as high as 16, compared with only 2·7 at the surface.

The best clues to what lies beneath the Earth's exterior are provided by records of earthquake shocks. Shock waves passing through the Earth are found to change their direction and speed at certain levels which are known as discontinuities. The first major discontinuity is at the base

of the basaltic layer where the latter rests on the Mantle. This is named the Mohorovičić Discontinuity (Moho for short) after the Yugoslav scientist who discovered it. At this level a marked change in the velocity of earthquake waves takes place. This could indicate either an actual change in the chemical nature of the rocks or merely a change in their physical state; but precisely which we do not yet know.

The Mantle extends to a depth of 1,800 miles, where a second major discontinuity marks the beginning of the Outer Core. Although nothing is known directly about the rocks of the Earth's interior, it is widely accepted that the material near the inner edge of the Mantle is two to three times as heavy as the surface rocks.

The Outer Core, 1,310 miles thick, is probably formed of heavy metals (iron and nickel) in molten form; but because of the tremendous pressure, this fluid substance would be unlike any fluid we know on the Earth's surface. The next layer, the Inner Core, 850 miles thick, is believed to consist of the same materials as the Outer Core, but forced into a solid state by increased pressure— three million times greater at the centre of the Earth than at the surface. Temperature also increases sharply with descent into the Earth, until it may reach at least 4,000°C.

Some scientists believe that at the centre of the Earth there is a nucleus of high-density atoms, descended from the atoms that were the starting point of our solar system.

ROCKS AND THEIR ORIGINS

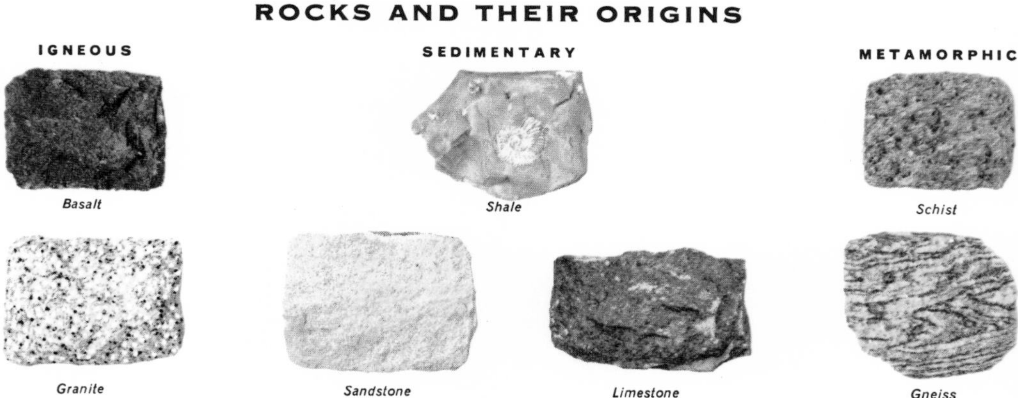

IGNEOUS

Basalt

Granite

SEDIMENTARY

Shale

Sandstone

Limestone

METAMORPHIC

Schist

Gneiss

IGNEOUS rocks are those that solidified directly from molten silicates, which geologists call magma. The Mantle obviously belongs to this category as do also the basaltic layer and much of the granitic layer. Igneous rocks include the fine-grained lavas, which have cooled quickly at the surface, and the coarse grained "plutonic" rocks which have cooled and crystallized slowly at depth.

Sedimentary rocks are formed when igneous rocks are eroded and laid down as sediment under the sea. Shale, which is mud layers compacted under great pressure, composes 80 per cent of these rocks. Others are sandstone —sand cemented into rock-form by other minerals—and limestone and chalk, which are in part the calcareous remains of countless marine creatures. Fossils are often

found in the geologically younger sedimentary rocks.

Sedimentary and igneous rocks of all ages, which have been subjected to the intense pressures and heat in the roots of mountain chains, are now in a "metamorphosed" condition.

Because the older parts of the continents are crisscrossed with old eroded-down mountain chains these "metamorphic" rocks have a wide surface distribution. During metamorphism shales become schists, granite becomes gneiss, limestone becomes marble, and sandstone becomes quartzite. The changes involve re-crystallization, and the growth of new minerals from those composing the original rocks. The older metamorphic rocks are frequently rich in deposits of the base and precious metals.

THE SHIFTING SURFACE OF THE EARTH

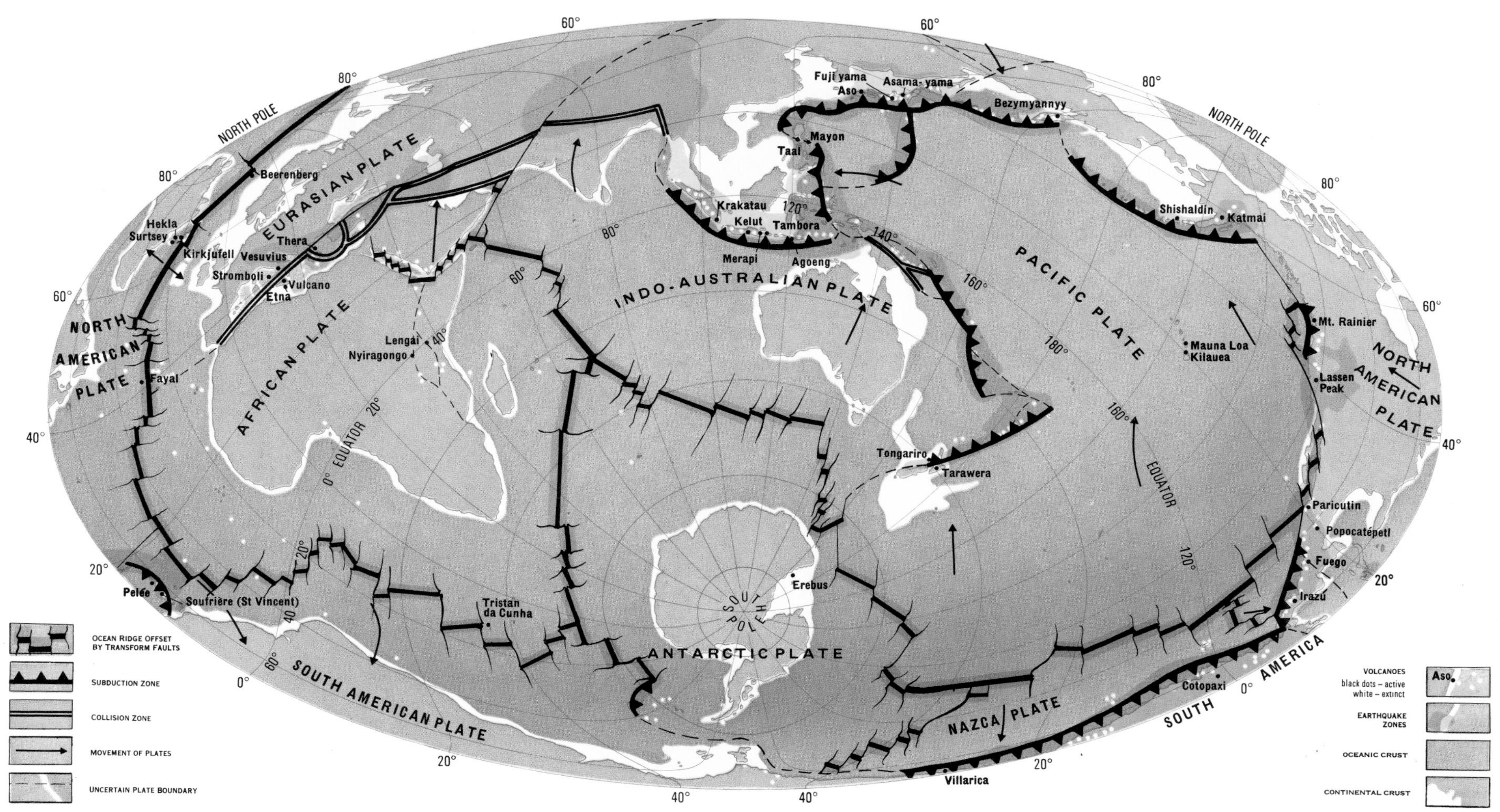

THE apparently solid crust of the Earth is in reality a vast mosaic of rocky plates forever on the move. Each of these plates, 40–60 miles thick, floats on a sea of semi-molten rock and moves at a rate of about half an inch a year. Over millions of years, this movement results in considerable shifting of both continents and oceans. The Sahara once lay at the South Pole and, in 50 million years' time, North and South America will almost certainly have drifted apart.

Most volcanoes and earthquakes occur in narrow bands along the major dislocations in Earth's substructure that mark the edges of the crustal plates. It was in fact the study of earthquakes that led to the identification of the plates and to the discovery of the power that moved them. Oceanic surveys revealed the worldwide system of mid-ocean ridges along which new crust is being continuously formed, and at the same time, seismographic observations showed that many earthquakes had their focal points beneath the ocean trenches. When the movements that produce earthquakes were worked out, it became apparent that a plate generated at a mid-ocean ridge was, thousands of miles away, plunging down an earthquake-ridden subduction zone. In this way the boundaries of the plates were identified. As well as the constructive boundaries along the ridges, and the destructive boundaries of the trenches, 'conservative' boundaries were recognized where one plate grinds jerkily past another. The best known of these is California's San Andreas Fault which was the cause of the earthquake that destroyed San Francisco in 1906.

THE FORCE BENEATH THE EARTH'S CRUST

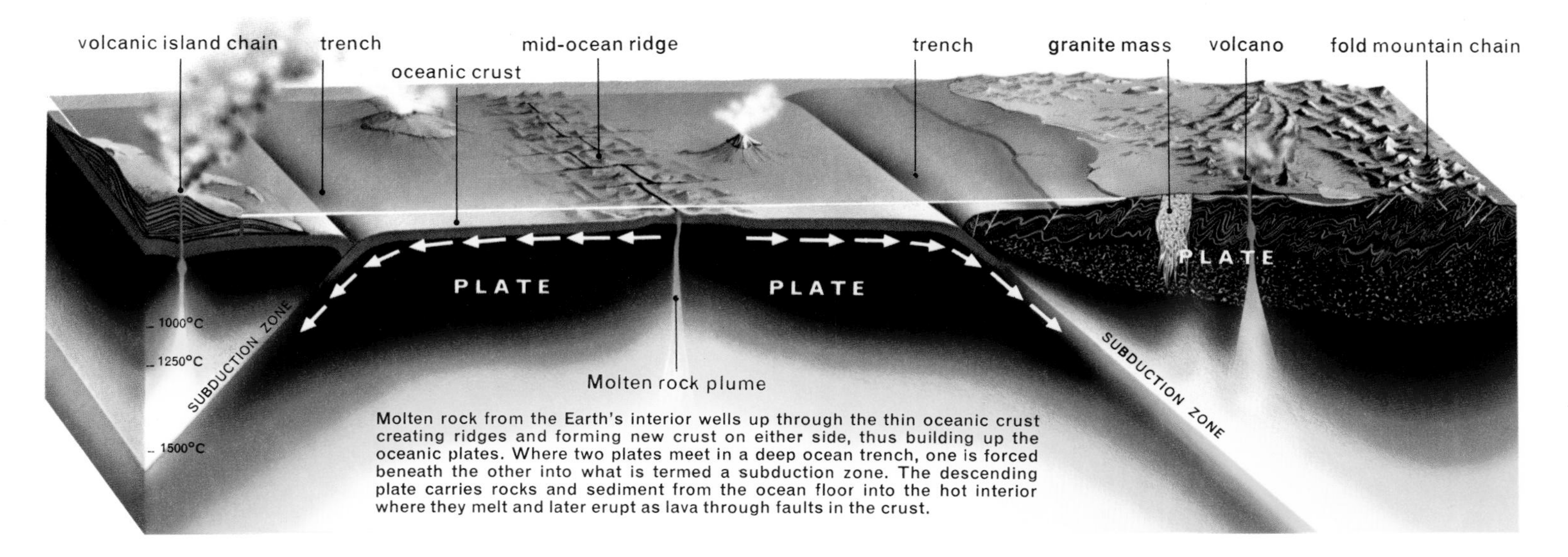

Molten rock from the Earth's interior wells up through the thin oceanic crust creating ridges and forming new crust on either side, thus building up the oceanic plates. Where two plates meet in a deep ocean trench, one is forced beneath the other into what is termed a subduction zone. The descending plate carries rocks and sediment from the ocean floor into the hot interior where they melt and later erupt as lava through faults in the crust.

THE movement of the plates is powered by heat rising from deep below the surface of the Earth. Molten rock wells up through the thin crust of the ocean bed creating ridges as it cools. As molten rock continues to be injected into the ridges, the plates on which the ocean bed rests move aside while thousands of miles away they are forced back into the Earth's interior down the subduction zones that lie beneath the great ocean trenches. The deepest of these trenches, the Marianas Trench, plunges to a depth of more than 6 miles below the surface of the western Pacific. Rocks and sediment from the ocean floor melt in the subduction zones, producing lava which rises to form volcanic island chains in the open sea and volcanoes along the fringes of continents. Sometimes, as the plates move, the oceanic portion of a plate also carrying a continent is forced beneath another land mass. When this occurs, the land masses eventually collide and buckle into mountain ranges, into which molten material from the deeper layers of the continental crust is forced and then cools to form granite.

FOUNDATIONS OF THE CONTINENTS

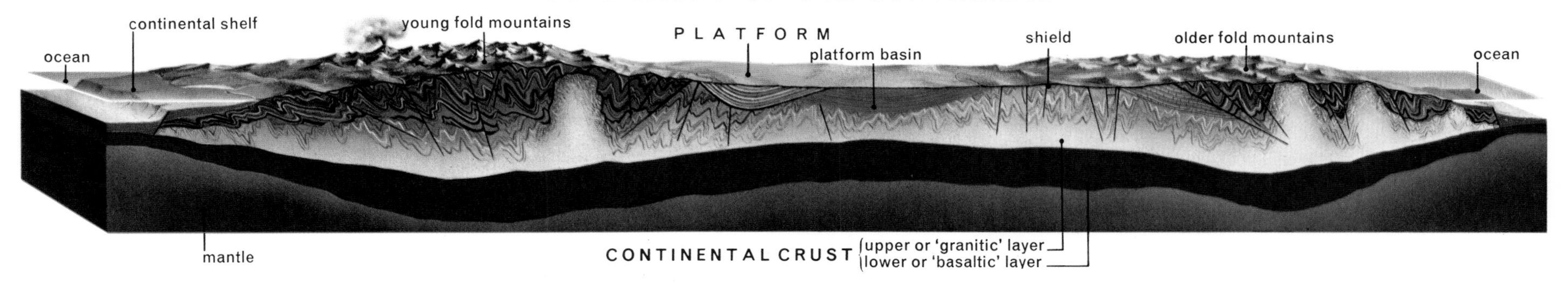

THE upper 'granitic' layer of the continental crust is composed of 92 per cent igneous and metamorphic rock and 8 per cent sedimentary rock. The lower 'basaltic' layer is rather mysterious and could be modified oceanic crust. Low-lying areas like the Prairies, the Russian Steppe and the Australian outback have an ancient igneous-metamorphic foundation which outcrops in *shields* or is covered by flat-lying strata in *platforms*. High mountains like the Alps and the Himalayas are belts of intense folding raised up in the past 25 million years. Lesser ranges like the Scottish Highlands are older, eroded fold mountains deformed 250 to 500 million years ago and uplifted, possibly for the second or third time, in the past 50 million years.

THE AGES OF THE EARTH

And the Earth was waste and void — GENESIS I

THE Earth is more than 4,500 million years old. Its condensation from a cloud of gas, the formation of a rocky crust, of oceans and continents, and the evolution of the life forms we see today are all episodes in the extraordinary story that is historical geology. The story has been pieced together by the geologist using three principles: igneous and metamorphic rocks can be dated by their radioactivity; fossils allow sedimentary rocks to be dated in relative terms, though not in years; and clues in the contents and texture of a rock may mean that conditions in the past can be reconstructed. The 6,000 years that the archaeologist and historian study seem as nothing to the geologist.

The oldest rocks so far discovered are from Greenland and are a staggering 3,800 million years old. Fossilized bacteria in rocks from southern Africa, 3,200 million years old, are the first evidence we have of life on Earth. The evolution of plant cells into seaweeds, and the development of soft-bodied animals during the long ages of the Precambrian period have left little trace in the rocks. Not until animals developed skeletons about 600 million years ago do fossils become at all common. This is the start of Phanerozoic (visible life) time. It is the fossils in Phanerozoic rocks that allow them to be dated and classified in such detail. The earliest vertebrates, primitive fish, did not appear for another 150 million years. Land plants first established themselves about 400 million years ago, and amphibious animals 50 million years after that. Mammals, of which man, through his brain, is the most advanced, date back less than 250 million years; modern man himself has emerged only within the last 40,000 years.

Evolution, the continuous adaptation of animals and plants to new environments, is not a simple straight-line story. There are many side branches to the tree where whole groups of animals have become extinct leaving no descendants. Evolution may be rapid, as when the mammals radiated 60 million years ago, or slow, as in the case of some shellfish which have not changed since the Cambrian period.

Changes in climate and geography, due to the drift and collision of continents resting on the moving plates of the Earth, have had a considerable effect on the course of animal and plant evolution. Phanerozoic time is divided into three great eras on the basis of both evolutionary and geographical changes: the Palaeozoic (ancient life), the Mesozoic (middle life), and the Cainozoic (recent life). Each of these eras is sub-divided into periods, often named after the area where the rocks were first studied.

Thus evidence from rocks and fossils reveals both the evolution of life and the development of continents, oceans, mountains and rivers. From geological research we know that lion, rhinoceros and elephant once roamed over Britain, and that the summit of Mount Everest was formerly beneath the sea.

GEOLOGY OF CANADA

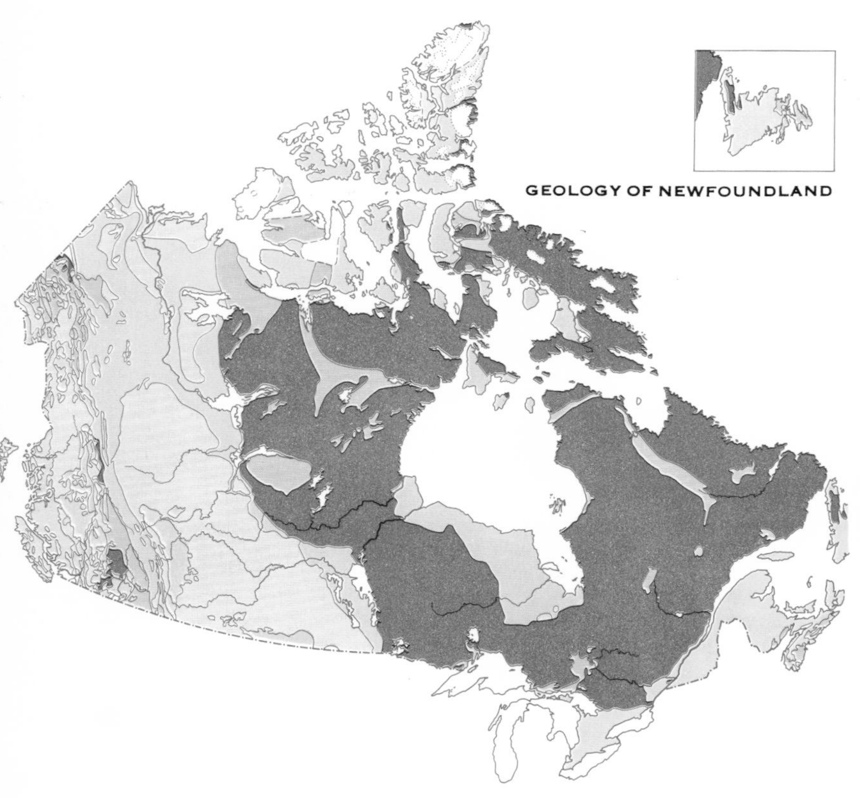

GEOLOGY OF NEWFOUNDLAND

CAINOZOIC FORMATIONS

Mainly sedimentary and volcanic rocks

MESOZOIC FORMATIONS

Mainly sedimentary and volcanic rocks

Granites and other intrusive igneous rocks in western coast ranges

PALAEOZOIC FORMATIONS

Mainly sedimentary and some volcanic rocks (with some intrusive granites, gabbros, etc., in eastern provinces)

PROTEROZOIC AND OLDER FORMATIONS

Mainly sedimentary rocks

Mainly igneous (volcanic and intrusive) and metamorphic rocks (gneisses, schists, etc.)

GEOLOGICAL DIVISIONS	GEOGRAPHICAL CONDITIONS
Holocene — started 10 thousand years ago	The ice continues to retreat, causing the sea level to rise further. Britain, joined to Europe during the glacial period, is cut off from the Continent. Landscape much as we see it today. Climatic conditions gradually become more equable. In North Africa and the Middle East, increasing dryness produces deserts.
Pleistocene — started about 2 million years ago — lasted c 2 million years	Ice-sheets and glaciers cover most of Europe, America, Antarctica and the Himalayas. The ice melts periodically, thus raising the sea level, and the land masses of Europe and North America, which have been pressed down by the enormous weight of the ice, begin to rise. (Scandinavia today continues to rise at a rate of a centimetre a year.) Melting ice forms the Great Lakes of North America, the lakes of Switzerland and Northern Italy, and the lakes of Great Britain. The tremendous weight of retreating glaciers cuts out the fjords of Norway. Landscape begins to take on present-day form and appearance. A period of abnormal and extreme climatic changes.
Pliocene — started about 7 million years ago — lasted c 5 million years	Continents and oceans begin to take on their present form. Land subsidence leads to formation of the North Sea, the Black and Caspian Seas, the Sea of Aral. Formation of mountain ranges continues, though on a reduced scale. Climatic conditions are much like today's, but with a broader temperate zone.
Miocene — started about 26 million years ago — lasted 19 million years	Powerful Earth movements lead to a further retreat of the sea. The Mediterranean becomes virtually a land-locked ocean. The European and Asian land masses are finally joined together. Increased rainfall leads to intense erosion in some parts. Further powerful movements in the Earth's Crust complete formation of the Alps and lead to formation of the Himalayas. Much volcanic activity. Climates tend to become more varied: dry and arid in some regions, cool and wet in others.
Oligocene — started about 38 million years ago — lasted 12 million years	Throughout this period the land mass grows at the expense of the sea. Extensive movements of the Earth's Crust in the Americas and in Europe. The Alps begin to form. Warm, temperate conditions continue, but parts of the land mass experience a cycle of cooler winters.
Eocene and Palaeocene (combined) — started about 65 million years ago — lasted c 27 million years	The subsidence of much of Europe causes the seas to advance once again. Tropical vegetation, like that in present-day Malaya, flourishes in southern England. Mountain ranges which began to form in the Cretaceous period continue to grow. Volcanic activity leads to the formation of the Atlantic and Indian Oceans, and causes vast amounts of lava to be deposited in areas as far apart as the Arctic, Scotland and Ireland, and southern India. Tropical conditions are more widespread than today, but glaciers exist on high mountain ranges in western North America.
Cretaceous chalk — started about 136 million years ago — lasted 71 million years	Pangaea begins to break up. An arm of the sea appears between Africa and North America, and India starts to drift northwards. Chalk is laid down on the sea bed over wide areas of Europe and North America, and can be seen in the white cliffs of Dover and Dorset in southern England. A great river delta covers much of England early in the period, while at the end the Rocky Mountains and the Andes begin to rise. The climate over northern Europe is mild.
Jurassic after Jura mountains in France and Switzerland — started about 193 million years ago — lasted c 57 million years	The seas advance again. Most land areas consist of forests or swampy plains with lakes and meandering rivers. The high mountains, already eroded by the arid climate of the previous period, are reduced to low hills by the wet conditions. Much of Asia and Europe, including the neighbourhood of Britain, is invaded by the sea. A period marked by the formation of limestone, as in the Cotswolds, southern Germany, France and Switzerland. The climate is predominantly mild, becoming sub-tropical in some regions later in the period. There is sufficient rainfall to support luxuriant vegetation.
Triassic after three-fold mountain system in Germany — started about 225 million years ago — lasted c 32 million years	Deserts and shrub-covered mountains make up most of the Earth's land area. What is, today, Britain is covered by warm, salt lakes surrounded by deserts. Formation of marl and sandstone deposits in the warm seas. Hot, dry conditions prevail almost everywhere. Climate becomes wetter towards the end of the period.
Permian After Russian province of Perm — started about 280 million years ago — lasted 55 million years	The three continents of the Palaeozoic era drift together to form a single land mass called Pangaea. Much of Europe, North America and northern Africa constitute part of a vast desert in which evaporating lakes form huge mineral deposits. A mountain chain rises over much of southern Europe, France and south-west England. A great ice-cap covers the Antarctic, Australia, India and southern Africa, contrasting with the hot, dry climate farther north.
Carboniferous the coal age (Upper Pennsylvanian and Lower Mississippian) — started about 345 million years ago — lasted 65 million years	Warm, shallow seas begin to invade the 'Old Red Sandstone Continent'. Great river deltas and, later, vast areas of swampy forest surround the land mass. The typical Carboniferous rocks of northern Europe are limestones laid down in the shallow seas, sandstones formed in the river deltas, and coal formed from vegetation in the swamps. The climate over Europe must have been warm and moist, though by the end of the period it was cold in the south.
Devonian after county of Devon where fossils of this period first found — started about 395 million years ago — lasted 50 million years	A great mountain chain arises, stretching down the line of the present Atlantic Ocean from Greenland and Scandinavia in the north, to Florida and West Africa in the south. The Grampians of Scotland are the eroded remains of part of the chain. This great land mass, known as the 'Old Red Sandstone Continent' from the reddish grits and sands laid down in lakes and deltas around it, is warm and semi-arid. At the same time, deep water covers southern England, France and Germany; the decorative limestones of Devon are of this age.
Silurian after Celtic tribe, the Silures — started about 435 million years ago — lasted c 40 million years	Three great continents are in existence, one comprising Europe and North America, another Asia, and the third Australia, Antarctica, Africa, South America and India. Britain is covered by a warm shallow sea dotted with coral reefs, as are parts of North America. The rocks of Wenlock Edge in Salop and the cliffs that form the Niagara Falls are formed at this time.
Ordovician after Celtic tribe, the Ordovices — started about 500 million years ago — lasted c 65 million years	Water-laid rocks of this period have been found in Scotland, Wales, Bohemia, Australia and the east coast of North America. No rocks laid down on land have been discovered, though they must exist somewhere in the world. Wales and the Lake District are areas of great volcanic activity – Snowdon is carved from volcanic ashes and lavas of this age. Land that is now the Sahara Desert lay over the South Pole, covered by a great ice-cap.
Cambrian after Cambria, Roman name for Wales — started about 570 million years ago — lasted 70 million years	Shallow seas cover much of the continents, including Britain, Scandinavia, Siberia, parts of Australia and much of North America – rocks at the bottom of the Grand Canyon are formed during this period. The position of the continents is not known with any certainty. Shallow seas surround the barren, lifeless land. The period opens with an ice age in Europe and North America.
Precambrian	The molten Earth, formed 4,500 million years ago from a cloud of dust and gas, cools and forms a solidified crust. Unprotected by an atmosphere, great meteorites crash into the surface. High-standing granitic continents slowly form from the basaltic crust. As the surface cools, water vapour condenses to form rivers and seas. The land surface is barren and rocky and the atmosphere noxious. Oxygen is added to the air by the evolving green plants.

CAINOZOIC (MODERN LIFE) · MESOZOIC (MIDDLE LIFE) · PALAEOZOIC (ANCIENT LIFE) · PROTEROZOIC

VEGETATION	LIFE IN THE SEA	LIFE ON LAND	EVOLUTION OF LIFE
...ith the retreat of the ice and ...e arrival of warmer summers, ...rests begin to spread all over ...urope. Tundra vegetation (mossy, ...arshy plains) is replaced by birch ...d pine, followed by hazel and ...en by oak and elder.	Marine life much as it is today.	Man learns to domesticate animals and cultivate plants.	
...ucceeding ice ages cause many ...ants in Europe to perish, leaving ...ly hardier varieties—oak, willow, ...plar, elm, hawthorn. In America ...d Asia, vegetation seeking warmer ...mates encounters no sea or mount- ...n barriers, and more plants survive.	Marine life much as it is today.	Ape-like creatures develop enough intelligence to make stone implements for cutting up animals they have killed, thus marking the transition to primitive man. Probably originating in Africa, primitive man spreads to Asia and Europe. Alternating ice ages and warm periods change the migration habits of other mammals. In one glacial period, reindeer and Arctic fox roam southern England. In the warmer period, hippopotamuses live in the Thames, lions range as far north as Yorkshire. True elephants, horses, oxen first appear.	
...ome plants of this period, such ... the maidenhair tree, die out in ...urope but survive in China and ...orth America.	Giant sharks become extinct, as did creatures that grew to a great size in other periods. Marine life, both plant and animal, becomes much as it is today. There are only marginal developments from this period onwards.	The number of mammal species declines, with the notable exception of the man-like apes, which continue to develop and thrive. These apes come to include not only the forest-dwellers, but the species known as *Australopithecus* which walks upright in open country and may be ancestral to man. Elephants also thrive, and roam as far afield as Suffolk and Norfolk.	
...ild, damp climate in Europe and ...orth America stimulates develop- ...ent of deciduous woods — maple, ...k and poplar. Cedars and sequoias ...e established on higher ground. ...he great plains of North America ...ecome covered with prairie grasses.	Bony fish continue to increase in variety. Sharks, particularly abundant during this period, grow to enormous sizes, measuring over 60 feet in length, and having teeth six inches long.	*Proconsul*, a primitive anthropoid ape living in central Africa, migrates to Asia and Europe. A gibbon-like ape, known as *Pliopithecus*, is common in the forests of southern Europe. Elephants, steadily increasing in size, spread from Africa into Europe, Asia and North America. Long-legged waterbirds, ducks and pelicans live in rivers and lakes. Primitive penguins, some as tall as man, live in Antarctica.	
...a cooler climate affects some ...rts of the world, forests dwindle ...d grasslands spread, leading to an ...crease in grass-eating mammals.	A period in which new species of crabs, mussels and snails evolve.	The ancestors of modern cats, dogs and bears evolve. The number of plant-eating animals increases—small elephants with short trunks, and tusks in both upper and lower jaws, hoofed animals with odd numbers of toes, and giant rhinoceros. A tail-less, primitive ape, possibly related to the ancestors of man, appears.	
...owering plants, including deci- ...ous trees, become dominant. The ...rm climatic zone, which stretches ...ght up to Greenland, allows palms ... grow in the region of Bourne- ...outh, and Malayan-type jungles ... the region of London.	Marine reptiles have become extinct, but two groups of mammals—early whales and sea-cows— begin to adapt themselves to life in the sea. Most species of fish in the ocean take on the shape and forms we know today.	Many varieties of modern mammals come into existence—ancestors of the elephant, the rhinoceros, the horse, the pig, and cattle. Giant reptiles have disappeared, but crocodiles, turtles and land tortoises evolve, as do all groups of insects that we know today. Primitive monkeys and gibbons appear in Burma.	
...mild climate with alternating ...asons—a feature of this period— ...courages the growth of deciduous ...es—fig, magnolia, poplar, plane. ...e parallel evolution of insects and ...ctar-bearing flowers encourages ...e spread of flowering plants.	A period of great evolution of sea urchins and molluscs. At the end of the period, ammonites, belemnites, ichthyosaurs and plesiosaurs all become extinct.	Giant reptiles, dinosaurs and pterosaurs, dominate life on land and in the air. Ichthyosaurs dominate life in the sea. Birds evolve into two types: one with well-developed wings, similar to modern birds, the other a sea-bird, almost wingless but with strongly developed legs for swimming. By the end of the period dinosaurs become extinct. Mammals remain inconspicuous throughout this period, but by its end placental mammals (whose young are nourished directly by the mother's blood until birth) have developed.	
...nifers, cycads, ferns and tree- ...ns continue to flourish. Some ...cads have flower-like cones—the ... step in the evolution of ...wers.	In the seas, the dominant animals are aquatic reptiles like ichthyosaurs. Rapid swimmers, they prey on fish and other marine creatures.	Reptiles increase in size and variety. Many of the dinosaurs, which dominated life on land at this time, were active and agile, and may have been warm-blooded. If so, many of the smaller ones must have been covered with hair or feathers. *Archaeopteryx*, the first bird, is a small feathered dinosaur that took to flight. Giant dinosaurs include *Diplodocus*, which weighed 35 tons and was as long as three London buses. Mammals, also warm-blooded and covered with hair, remained small.	
...id conditions in the Northern ...emisphere discourage the de- ...lopment of plant life at the ...ginning of the period. Later, ...tter conditions stimulate the ...owth of conifers, cycads and ...ns.	The first ichthyosaurs, carnivorous, fish-shaped reptiles, evolve in this period. So do flying fish and the first lobster-like creatures.	Reptiles continue to dominate life on land. The first mammals—warm-blooded creatures—evolve from the reptiles. Dinosaurs, no more than six inches long, are present for the first time. The first flies and termites appear.	
...e southern half of Pangaea is ...vered with forests of the small ...ee called *Glossopteris*. Discovery ...remains of this plant in South ...merica, Africa, India and ...stralia first suggested that the ...ntinents had drifted.	This period marks the end of the dominance by marine creatures, as animal and plant life on land increases.	Reptiles become very abundant on land and consist of two groups, one evolving towards the mammals and the other towards the dinosaurs. *Dimetrodon*, the sail-back, is the best-known animal of this period.	
...ant evergreen trees, reaching ...ights of over 100 feet flourish in ... tropical swamp of the period ...ich knows no seasonal changes ... temperature.	Amphibious creatures continue to develop. Living in swamp-land on the edge of lakes, they are small, salamander-like animals to begin with, but reach sizes of up to 15 feet by the end of the period. Marine life, both plant and animal, abounds in many varieties.	The reptile becomes the first creature to breed on land. Certain species of insects develop wings and giant dragonflies appear. Land snails evolve for the first time.	
...rth begins to look green, as ...nts with roots, stems and leaves ...olve. They range from small, herb- ... growths to trees of 40 feet or ...re in height. By the end of the ...riod, various kinds of ferns, horse- ...s and seed-ferns have evolved.	Rapid evolution of vertebrate animals. Ancestors of all modern fish evolve. Primitive sharks, measuring up to 20 feet, appear. In consequence, this period has become known as the "Age of Fish." By the end of the period, the first amphibious animals have come into existence.	With land plants to feed on, the first invertebrate animals leave the sea and adapt themselves to life on land. They include millepedes, mites, spiders and scorpions.	
...nts first adapt themselves to ...e on land, but are still leafless. ...ossil remains have been found in ...stralia.)	Coral reefs and sea lilies are particularly abundant in Britain, though trilobites and graptolites are becoming less so. Water scorpions, 9 feet long, and small fish evolve in lakes and rivers at the end of the period, and their remains are found both in South Wales and in Scotland.	First plants appear on land.	
...nt life confined to the sea.	New species of mollusc, sea lily, and star fish appear for the first time, as do graptolites, strange animals related to the ancestor of the vertebrates. Scales of the earliest fish have been found in North America.	No life.	
...nt life confined to the sea.	Several animal groups, including sponges, brachiopods, sea snails and trilobites, develop hard skeletons. Soft-bodied animals that have been found fossilized include jellyfish and worms. Seaweeds must have been abundant. The Cambrian is often called the age of trilobites, from the enormous variety of these animals at this period.	No life.	
...aweeds are the only form of ...getation.	Life originates in water soon after the warm seas appear on the land surface about 3,500 million years ago. First bacteria, then green algae, and finally soft-bodied animals appear.	No life.	

EVOLUTION OF LIFE chart labels: Modern Man, Carnivores, Ancestral Man, Horses, Camels, Elephants, Whales, Apes, Bats, Monkeys, Grasses, Birds, Marsupials, Insectivores, Crocodiles, Early Mammals Evolving, Angiosperms, Turtles, Dinosaurs, Dinosaurs, Pterosaurs, Toothed Birds, Ichthyosaurs, Land Reptiles, Cycads, Plesiosaurs, Marine Reptiles, Theriodonts, Conifers, Cotylosaurs, Ammonites, Ferns, Seed Ferns, Crinoids, Labyrinthodonts, Insects, Scale Trees, Blastoids, Sharks, Clams, Cordaites, Brachiopods, Choanichthyes, Starfish, Nautiloids, Corals, Cystoids, Snails, Sponges, Trilobites, Algae

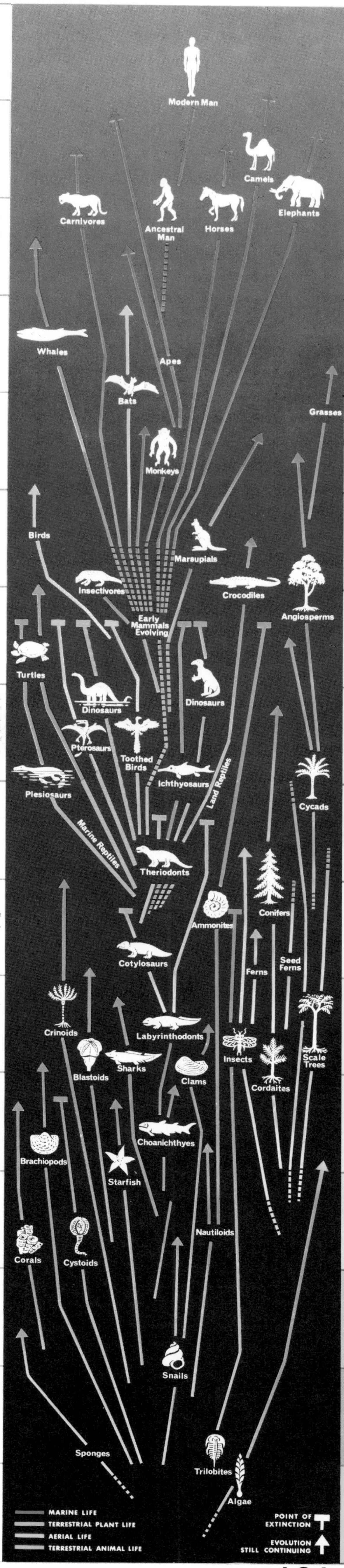

Legend:
MARINE LIFE
TERRESTRIAL PLANT LIFE
AERIAL LIFE
TERRESTRIAL ANIMAL LIFE
POINT OF EXTINCTION
EVOLUTION STILL CONTINUING

THE GREAT OCEANS

Hast thou entered into the spring of the sea? or hast thou walked in the search of the depth? — JOB 38

No other planet in the solar system has any surface water at all as far as we know, whereas the Earth's great oceans and seas cover seven-tenths of the globe. The Pacific Ocean alone covers an area of 63 million square miles. The sea is deeper than the land is high, for the average depth of the sea bed is about 12,000 feet, or 2½ miles, compared with an average height on land of only 2,500 feet.

The oceans are not composed of uniform masses of water, but of a series of layers differing in temperature and salt content, with each level supporting its own form of marine life. Coursing through these layers are currents measuring anything up to 100 miles wide and, in some cases, hundreds of miles long. These ocean currents influence the location of fishing grounds and also have a profound effect on world climate. A change in the temperature of a current by even a few degrees can drastically alter weather conditions far inland. These currents can create strange paradoxes. For instance, the cold current which sweeps up the west coast of southern Africa is teeming with fish, but the land bordering the sea is a dry, almost lifeless desert—the Namib. The temperature of the current, though suitable for the fish, is too cold to allow condensation, so the onshore winds cannot pick up any moisture to provide life-giving rain to the coastal area.

The bed of the sea is not land covered by water; the composition of the Earth's crust beneath the oceans is quite different from that beneath the continents. The ocean floor consists of a thin layer of sediments overlying heavy basaltic rocks. The continents have lighter granitic rock overlying the basaltic layer, so the earth's crust is in fact

THE ATLANTIC OCEAN AND EAST PACIFIC OCEAN

This giant mountain chain in mid-ocean is believed to extend for 40,000 miles. At its crest is found, in many places, a rift valley indicating the tension existing in the oceanic crust. Along this line new oceanic crust is being formed by molten rock welling up from the Earth's interior through fissures in the crust so that the sea floor is continuously spreading away from it. Where a mid-ocean ridge meets a continent, as in the Gulf of Aden, the continent is being split in two and a new ocean is forming.

Winding, steep-sided canyons cut across the edges of many continental slopes. Although some have probably been worn away by underwater currents; others, near the mouths of big rivers, may have been eroded by the rivers when the sea was much shallower.

Unlike oceanic islands, offshore islands such as Britain are still linked beneath the sea to their nearest continents. Dogger Bank, in the North Sea, a plateau only 60 feet below sea level, was dry land in relatively recent times. The relics of forests and Stone-Age animal bones and tools have been found there.

So-called tidal waves are caused by violent earthquakes in the seabed. They travel as fast as 400 miles an hour with intervals of about 90 miles between the waves. In the open sea their crests may rise only one or two feet above the surface, but they can reach a height of 50 feet when nearing a shelving coastline. They cover vast distances: those that hit Japan in 1960 stemmed from earthquakes off the coast of Chile.

The Mid-Atlantic Ridge, part of the mid-ocean ridge system which encircles the globe, is the most extensive range of mountains in the world – 10,000 miles long and 500 miles wide. Its crest lies an average of a mile below the surface.

Ascension, one of the youngest of the large volcanic islands, is scarred with the traces of 40 extinct volcanoes. Few trees can survive on its barren rock; there is a little vegetation, mainly round the island's highest peak, Green Mountain, a huge elliptical crater rising 2,817 feet above sea level.

This mid-ocean canyon is one of the giant ocean river beds scoured in the floor by swift mud-carrying currents. The main branch is 2,000 miles long, two to four miles wide and 150 to 600 feet deep. Scientists suspect that many undersea telephone cable breaks have been caused by these surging masses of water. One such current was estimated to move at 50 miles an hour along a path 100 miles wide. These underwater rivers are believed to overflow their banks and then recede, leaving raised lips of mud like the levees formed along the banks of some land rivers. The largest of these mud banks, forming the shoulders of the Congo submarine canyon, is 600 feet high by 20 miles wide.

thinner below the oceans than the continents. The oceanic crust is continuously being built up along the world-wide system of mid-ocean ridges which are the creative boundaries of the crustal plates. These plates form a vast mosaic continuously shifting over the surface of the globe. This formation of new oceanic crust along the ridges results in the widening of the sea bed in many areas. The Red Sea and the Gulf of California, for example, are gradually getting wider as the sea floor spreads. The age of the ocean floor increases outwards from the ridges, the oldest parts being not more than about 200 million years. At the same time that new ocean crust is forming along the ridges, the older crust is being forced back into the Earth's interior down the deep trenches which are termed subduction zones.

The ocean floor is certainly not flat. There are impressively sculptured features identified by oceanographers using sonar which would dwarf any mountain or canyon that could be found on land.

The Mid-Atlantic Ridge extends from Iceland in a sinuous line all the way down the Atlantic to beyond the southern tip of Africa. There are abyssal plains and plateaux on either side of the ridge with towering isolated peaks and mountain ranges. The highest peaks reach above the surface of the ocean to form islands like the Azores and Cape Verde Islands. The shelves along the edges of some of the continents are submerged land, and offshore islands such as the British Isles are really part of their neighbouring continents. In some areas this shelf is almost completely absent. Along

the Pacific coast of South America, for instance, the coast plunges steeply down into the Peru-Chile Trench. From the depths of this trench to the peaks of the Andes Mountains is a distance of about 8 miles.

The topography of the floor of the Indian Ocean is similar to that of the Atlantic. There are plateaux and ridges running southwards from the Arabian Peninsula and the Bay of Bengal, where there are also vast basins. The Pacific Ocean, on the other hand, is literally peppered with mountains most of which lie beneath the surface. The Pacific is the most active earthquake zone in the world, and near the Mariana Islands a gaping oceanic abyss called the Challenger Deep plummets to a depth of more than 6 miles below the surface of the ocean.

THE WEST PACIFIC OCEAN AND INDIAN OCEAN

The continental slopes mark the edges of the continents. Sloping steeply to the ocean floor, they are the highest and most extensive escarpments known on Earth. Their average height is 12,000 feet, but some plummet in unbroken slopes of 30,000 feet – a thousand feet more than the height of Mount Everest.

The rims of the continental shelves, which are just submerged land, are the true edges of the continents. These shelves vary considerably in width from just a few miles up to 800 miles, as in the Russian Arctic. The gradient of the shelves is gentle and the depth varies between 200 and 1,000 feet.

From the foot of the continental slopes the deep ocean basins reach out across half the surface of our planet. These basins, some two and a half miles down, are, in fact, ribbed with mountain ranges, pitted with deep valleys and floored by abyssal plains.

Most islands which are not part of the continental shelves are of volcanic origin. The volcano of Mauna Kea on the island of Hawaii, if measured from its base on the bed of the Pacific, is the highest mountain on Earth. Although it rises only 13,796 feet above sea level, from base to peak it measures 31,000 feet.

ARCTIC OCEAN

Bering Sea

Sea of Okhotsk

ASIA

Sea of Japan

NORTH PACIFIC OCEAN

Aleutian Trench

HAWAIIAN RIDGE

Hawaii I.

East China Sea

MARCUS-NECKER RISE

Mt Everest

South China Sea

PHILIPPINE TRENCH

SOUTH HONSHU RIDGE

Marianas

Mariana's Trench

Eniwetok

Bay of Bengal

Arabian Sea

Celebes Sea

CAROLINE-SOLOMON RIDGE

SOUTH PACIFIC OCEAN

Banda Sea

Arafura Sea

Coral Sea

Java Sea

Anak Krakatoa

Great Barrier Reef

Java Trench

South-Western Pacific Basin

INDIAN OCEAN

Sunda Strait

NINETY EAST RIDGE

MID-INDIAN RIDGE

AUSTRALIA

Tasman Sea

South Australian Basin

SOUTHERN OCEAN

Part of the volcanic island of Krakatoa completely disappeared in 1883 after a violent eruption which could be heard 3,000 miles away. This eruption caused huge tidal waves, which drowned tens of thousands of people, and even affected the waters of the English Channel. The volcanic dust tinged sunsets the world over for nearly a year. A thousand feet beneath the surface of Sunda Strait was a vast crater, where two-thirds of the island had once stood 1,400 feet above the sea. In 1929, a new island suddenly emerged in the same place, it was named Anak Krakatoa (child of Krakatoa).

At a depth below the surface of nearly 7 miles, Challenger Deep is the greatest known ocean depth in the world. At this level the water is perpetually near-freezing, but forms of marine life are still to be found. On 23rd January 1960, the United States bathyscaphe Trieste touched bottom in Challenger Deep which lies off the southern tip of the Mariana Islands.

Coral is formed of the skeletons of tiny marine animals – yet the coral islands are the largest structures built by any living creature. The Great Barrier Reef of Australia, 1,260 miles long and 500 feet thick, is a vast coral honeycomb where fish, plant and rock forms make the most exotic jungle in the world.

The coral atolls that dot the Pacific are monuments to sunken islands – and to the tiny creatures that build them, keeping pace with each island's descent into the sea bed. When the depth of coral on Eniwetok was measured, it was found that countless generations of coral animals have piled the atoll 4,000 feet thick on the submerged stump of the island.

One of the most intriguing, unsolved mysteries of the sea is the origin of the flat-topped islands beneath the surface of the Pacific. So far about 1,000 have been charted, all over 3,000 feet high. Geologists expect to have found another 10,000 by the time the ocean has been completely surveyed. The islands are encrusted with coral, proving that at one time they must have been at or near the surface, though today many of them are a mile or more beneath it. The coral dates from 100 million years ago, the age of the oldest rocks found in the Pacific. Some scientists believe a violent volcanic upheaval shook the Pacific floor at the time, scattering the sea bed with lava and throwing up the islands which later sank under their own weight. Another theory is that the Moon was torn from the bed of the Pacific, taking with it into space the missing links of rock history.

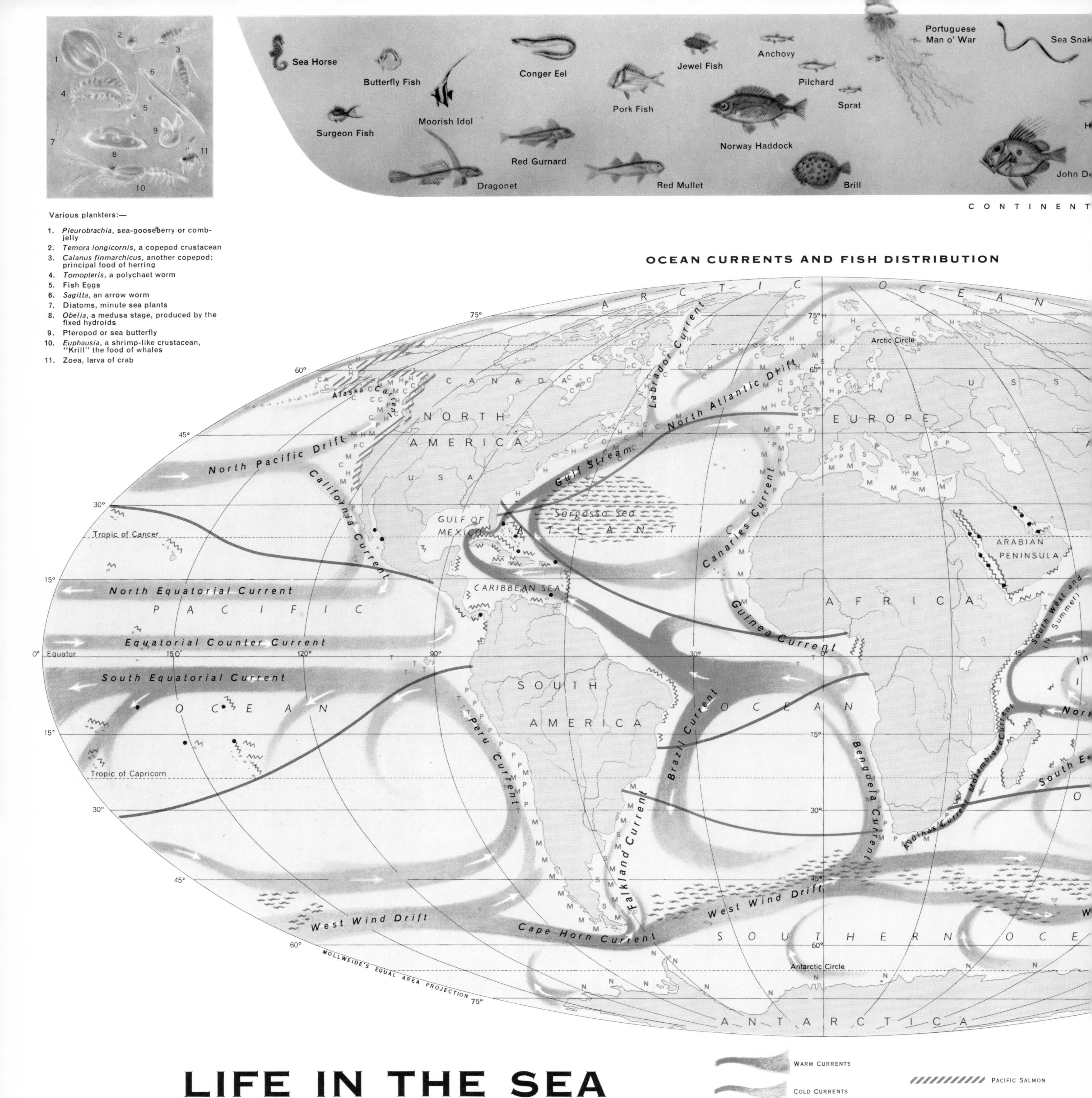

Various plankters:—

1. *Pleurobrachia*, sea-gooseberry or comb-jelly
2. *Temora longicornis*, a copepod crustacean
3. *Calanus finmarchicus*, another copepod; principal food of herring
4. *Tomopteris*, a polychaete worm
5. Fish Eggs
6. *Sagitta*, an arrow worm
7. Diatoms, minute sea plants
8. *Obelia*, a medusa stage, produced by the fixed hydroids
9. Pteropod or sea butterfly
10. *Euphausia*, a shrimp-like crustacean, "Krill" the food of whales
11. *Zoea*, larva of crab

OCEAN CURRENTS AND FISH DISTRIBUTION

Sea Horse
Butterfly Fish
Conger Eel
Moorish Idol
Surgeon Fish
Red Gurnard
Dragonet
Jewel Fish
Pork Fish
Red Mullet
Anchovy
Pilchard
Sprat
Norway Haddock
Brill
Portuguese Man o' War
Sea Snake
John Dory

CONTINENT

WARM CURRENTS
COLD CURRENTS
FLOATING WEED
PACIFIC SALMON
CORAL REEFS
PEARLS

LIFE IN THE SEA

And God said, Let the waters bring forth abundantly the moving creature that hath life—GENESIS 1

THE SEA, where life began, contains representatives of almost all the main groups of animals—including mammals, the order to which man belongs. If it were not for insects, of which close to one million species are known, the species of marine animals, numbering about 160,000, would be twice as many as those on land.

In the sea, as on land, life depends largely on plants, and the plants of the ocean are almost as productive, acre for acre, as the plants on land. The pastures of the sea and the basis of its life cycle are countless myriads of free-floating, microscopic plants known as phytoplankton. These are the food of minute animals called zooplankton. Zooplankton are preyed upon by larger animal species, which themselves provide food for still bigger creatures. So continues a never-ending cycle, for the plants in their turn are nourished by minerals derived in part from the decay of marine organisms.

Life in the sea depends largely on the productivity of microscopic chlorophyll-bearing plants, such as diatoms, various flagellates and blue-green algae. These plants form part of the plankton and flourish where sunlight is strong enough for photosynthesis, which in the open ocean is between the surface and a depth of about 300 feet. Animal plankton is most abundant in this productive zone.

The movement of currents is caused by three main forces: the prevailing wind, the Earth's rotation and differences in the sea's density. Winds drive immense bodies of water before them, forming surface currents. At the same time, the Earth's rotation, which deflects moving things to the right in the Northern Hemisphere and to the left in the Southern Hemisphere, causes these ocean surface currents to move in a clockwise or anticlockwise direction, as shown by the whirls on the map.

Where currents meet or diverge, where cold or salty water sinks below water that is less dense, or where coastal winds blow the surface water seawards, the circulation is such that the surface waters are replaced by deeper, upwelling waters that are rich in nutrient salts. Since this nutrient renewal leads to an overall increase in biological productivity, it is understandable that the world's great fisheries are found in regions where such renewal is most pronounced and persistent.

Beneath the sunlit 300-foot layer, midwater animal life becomes more and more sparse as the depth increases. Quantities of animal life on the bottom also decrease with depth. Many of the midwater animals that live in the twilight zone between 500 and 3,000 feet deep migrate up to the surface waters each day, where their food is most abundant. Luminous crustaceans, squid and fish are among such migrators. Some of the non-migratory fish, such as angler fish and *Gigantura*, are able to swallow prey larger than themselves. Perhaps the most remarkable adaptation to life in the depths is shown by certain kinds of deep-sea angler fish. Their reproduction depends on a chance meeting of the sexes in the sunless depths, after which the female carries the much smaller male permanently with her, and he becomes parasitic on his partner. Representatives of most groups of marine invertebrates live at all levels of the sea floor from coastal to deep-sea reaches of 30,000 feet or more.

For the most part, however, the sea's species have not had to assume such specialized forms to cope with their environment. The oceans are not subject to the harsh seasonal and regional temperature variations experienced on land. Surface-water temperature in any one region seldom varies more than a few degrees, and the invertebrates and nearly all fish, whose bodies consist largely of fluid at the same temperature as their surroundings, do not, therefore, need any particular mechanism for keeping warm or cool. Again, the profusion of wings, limbs and other organs needed on land to overcome the burden of gravity is unnecessary for creatures whose element is the buoyant sea.

In this stable environment some creatures have remained unchanged throughout their entire history. For example, the well-known coelacanth, *Latimeria chalumnae*, one of a group of fish thought to have been extinct for 70 million years, is essentially similar to its fossil relatives. It is the closest relation of the long-extinct fish that was the ancestor of all land animals with a backbone. Though there are few 'living fossils' in the ocean, who can predict that there are none left to discover?

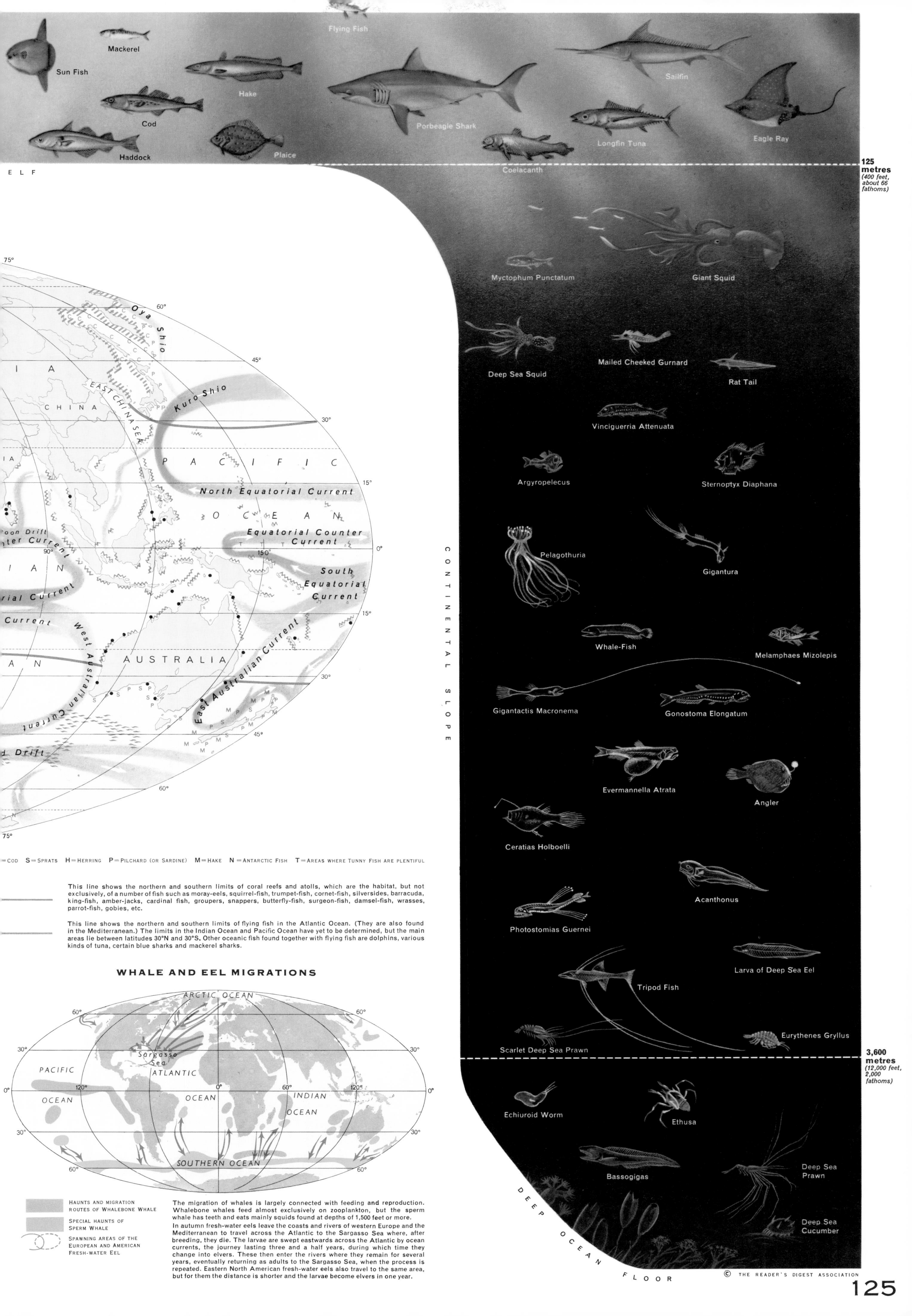

Sun Fish
Mackerel
Flying Fish
Hake
Cod
Plaice
Haddock
Porbeagle Shark
Sailfin
Longfin Tuna
Eagle Ray
Coelacanth

ELF

125 metres (400 feet, about 66 fathoms)

Myctophum Punctatum
Giant Squid
Deep Sea Squid
Mailed Cheeked Gurnard
Rat Tail
Vinciguerria Attenuata
Argyropelecus
Sternoptyx Diaphana
Pelagothuria
Gigantura
Whale-Fish
Melamphaes Mizolepis
Gigantactis Macronema
Gonostoma Elongatum
Evermannella Atrata
Angler
Ceratias Holboelli
Acanthonus
Photostomias Guernei
Larva of Deep Sea Eel
Tripod Fish
Scarlet Deep Sea Prawn
Eurythenes Gryllus
Echiuroid Worm
Ethusa
Bassogigas
Deep Sea Prawn
Deep Sea Cucumber

CONTINENTAL SLOPE

DEEP OCEAN FLOOR

3,600 metres (12,000 feet, 2,000 fathoms)

Oya Shio
EAST CHINA SEA
Kuro Shio
CHINA
PACIFIC OCEAN
North Equatorial Current
Equatorial Counter Current
South Equatorial Current
West Australian Current
AUSTRALIA
East Australian Current
Monsoon Drift
Drift

75° 60° 45° 30° 15° 0° 15° 30° 45° 60° 75°
90° 150°

C = COD   S = SPRATS   H = HERRING   P = PILCHARD (OR SARDINE)   M = HAKE   N = ANTARCTIC FISH   T = AREAS WHERE TUNNY FISH ARE PLENTIFUL

This line shows the northern and southern limits of coral reefs and atolls, which are the habitat, but not exclusively, of a number of fish such as moray-eels, squirrel-fish, trumpet-fish, cornet-fish, silversides, barracuda, king-fish, amber-jacks, cardinal fish, groupers, snappers, butterfly-fish, surgeon-fish, damsel-fish, wrasses, parrot-fish, gobies, etc.

This line shows the northern and southern limits of flying fish in the Atlantic Ocean. (They are also found in the Mediterranean.) The limits in the Indian Ocean and Pacific Ocean have yet to be determined, but the main areas lie between latitudes 30°N and 30°S. Other oceanic fish found together with flying fish are dolphins, various kinds of tuna, certain blue sharks and mackerel sharks.

WHALE AND EEL MIGRATIONS

ARCTIC OCEAN
Sargasso Sea
PACIFIC OCEAN
ATLANTIC OCEAN
INDIAN OCEAN
SOUTHERN OCEAN
60° 30° 0° 30° 60°
120° 0° 60° 120°

HAUNTS AND MIGRATION ROUTES OF WHALEBONE WHALE

SPECIAL HAUNTS OF SPERM WHALE

SPAWNING AREAS OF THE EUROPEAN AND AMERICAN FRESH-WATER EEL

The migration of whales is largely connected with feeding and reproduction. Whalebone whales feed almost exclusively on zooplankton, but the sperm whale has teeth and eats mainly squids found at depths of 1,500 feet or more.
In autumn fresh-water eels leave the coasts and rivers of western Europe and the Mediterranean to travel across the Atlantic to the Sargasso Sea where, after breeding, they die. The larvae are swept eastwards across the Atlantic by ocean currents, the journey lasting three and a half years, during which time they change into elvers. These then enter the rivers where they remain for several years, eventually returning as adults to the Sargasso Sea, when the process is repeated. Eastern North American fresh-water eels also travel to the same area, but for them the distance is shorter and the larvae become elvers in one year.

DISTRIBUTION OF LIVESTOCK

In all the areas of the world colonized by man, the domestication of certain mammals has invariably led to the extinction or near-extinction of the wilder species. The extent of man's advance has depended on the availability of pasture for animals which, through selective breeding, he adapted for his own purposes. Sheep, cattle, pigs, goats and horses (providing food, milk, clothing and transport) are of little interest zoologically but are vastly important economically. In areas with seasonal or scanty rainfall and sparse pasturage, domestic animals may be herded or ranched—a few to the square mile—over wide distances, and may be the primary factor in the regions' economy. In more favoured zones "mixed" farming is usual: animal husbandry and crop cultivation are practised in close conjunction with each other on the same farm unit. In either case wild animals are robbed of the territories best able to support them.

HOME LIVESTOCK	LIVESTOCK BRED IN CONJUNCTION WITH OTHER FARMING PRACTICES	RANCH AND HERD LIVESTOCK

C = CATTLE   S = SHEEP   P = PIGS   FIGURES IN MILLIONS

THE SPREAD OF MAMMALS

Let the Earth bring forth the living creature after its kind — GENESIS 1

FROM the time terrestrial animal life began, some 350 million years ago, the face of the Earth has undergone immense changes, and even in the relatively recent period since mammals evolved from reptiles, more reshaping of land has occurred. It was once possible for species from Southern Asia to spread by age-long migration through Europe and, by means of a land-bridge where the Bering Strait is now, to the Americas. But barriers to migrations, and new avenues for them, have been appearing and disappearing since the time creatures first had need to travel in search of food and warmth.

For the most important animals of the present day—the warm-blooded mammals, of which man himself is one—the Earth has set strict limits. The geological changes that decided the patterns of movement also brought about changes in environment, and these changes, allied to other natural causes, speeded up the evolution of mammals, especially on the African, Euro-Asian and North American continents. One result is that mammals can now be grouped in five main regions, each of which is bounded by natural barriers—mountains, deserts and seas.

The formation of the Sahara Desert created one of the barriers to migration, so that the mammals to the south of the desert, living in tropical or semi-tropical conditions, have evolved in quite a different way from the mammals to the north of it. In Australia, the most primitive species of mammals in the world have

survived, for, with the disappearance of any land connection with Asia some 135 million years ago, they became isolated, and more active and dominating mammals were prevented from reaching the area. The Himalayas, formed about 25 million years ago, stopped any large-scale interchange of species between northern Asia and the Oriental Region; and the Bering Strait, during the recent Pleistocene Period, effectively cut off the Americas from Europe and Asia.

Some mammals learned to hunt in the air, like bats, others to live in trees, like monkeys, some to burrow under the ground, like moles, and still others, such as whales, went back to the sea from which life first came. And all of them developed characteristics according to their surroundings; the whales, for instance, developed layers of blubber under the skin to insulate them from the cold of the oceans, and some of the whales, because of the buoyancy of the water, were able to grow to a huge bulk and so become the largest of all mammals.

A natural spread took some mammals to the cold north, and these became more hairy, like the polar bear and the musk-ox. On the other hand, in the tropics, the elephant and the hippopotamus became almost hairless.

There are nearly 3,700 species of mammals, in bewildering varieties of shape and form. Among them are the primates, headed by man, whose unique specialization is that he can fashion his environment to suit his own needs.

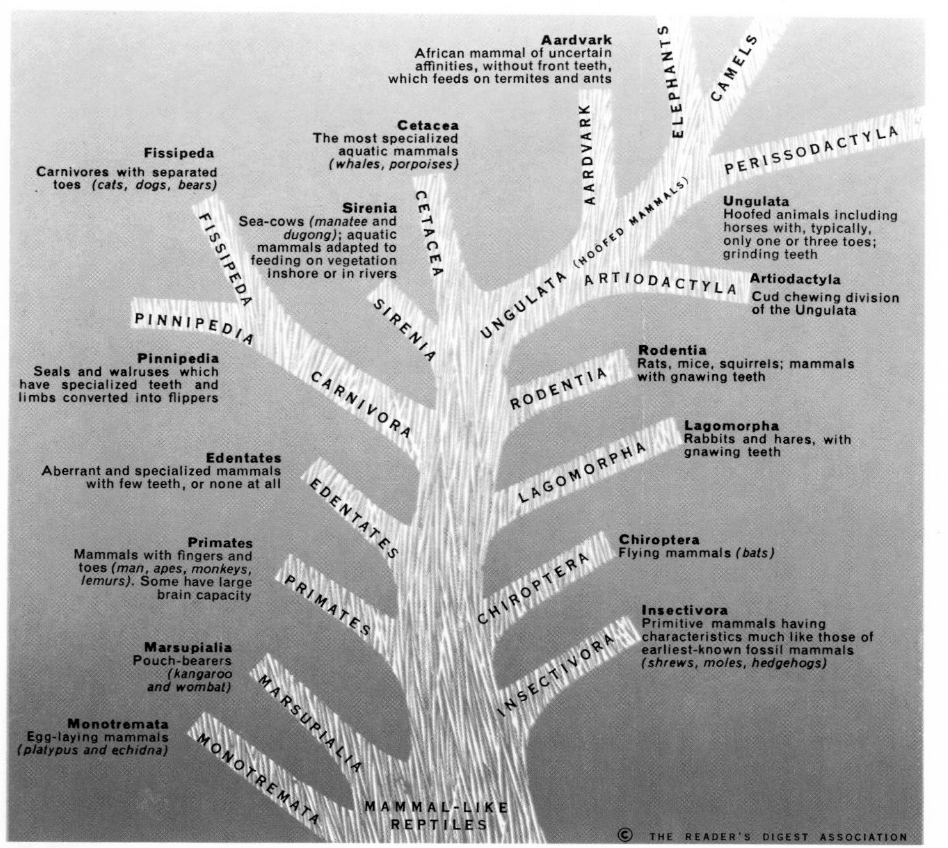

The similarity between the marine animals on either side of the Central American isthmus suggests that here the sea, at one time, was unbroken. Wide rivers across the isthmus now form barriers to the migration of land animals, but the nine-banded armadillo, typical of the South American fauna, has continued to spread northwards, for while swimming it is able to gulp air to inflate its intestines, and thereby gain buoyancy for its heavy body.

The **Neotropical Region** (South America) is characterized by marsupials (opossum and small, shrew-like pouch-bearers) and edentates (mammals with few teeth or none at all, such as sloths, anteaters and armadillos). These were probably the region's only mammals until later Tertiary times when others, notably llamas, jaguars, pumas, some fox-like wolves and a few deer, arrived from the north across the land-bridge of Central America. Peccaries take the place of pigs of other regions, and the monkeys, although similar to those of Africa and Asia, form a distinct sub-order.

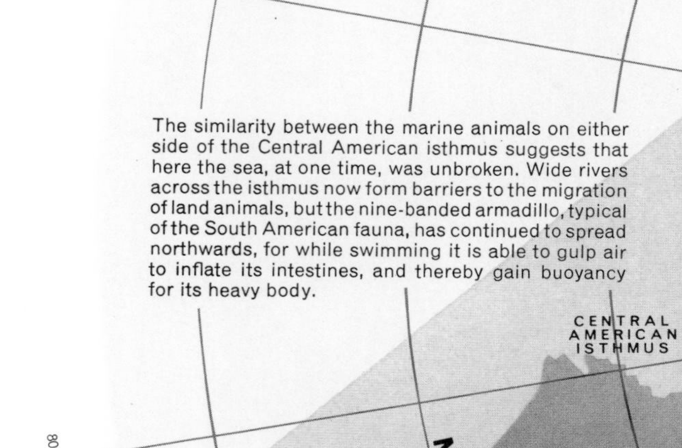

THE MAMMALIAN TREE

As mammals evolve and change their characteristics to suit their environments, their bony structures are the features which modify most slowly. In classifying mammals, therefore, emphasis is always placed on the character of the teeth, skull and skeleton. Where these features have become specialized, the animals are graded according to the degree of their specializations. On this basis man and the other primates appear low down on the genealogical tree, while the camel, elephant and whale are at the top. Man's preeminence in the world is due to his greater brain capacity, his grasping hand and his ability to use speech; but his limbs with their five digits and his face are still anatomically primitive.

126

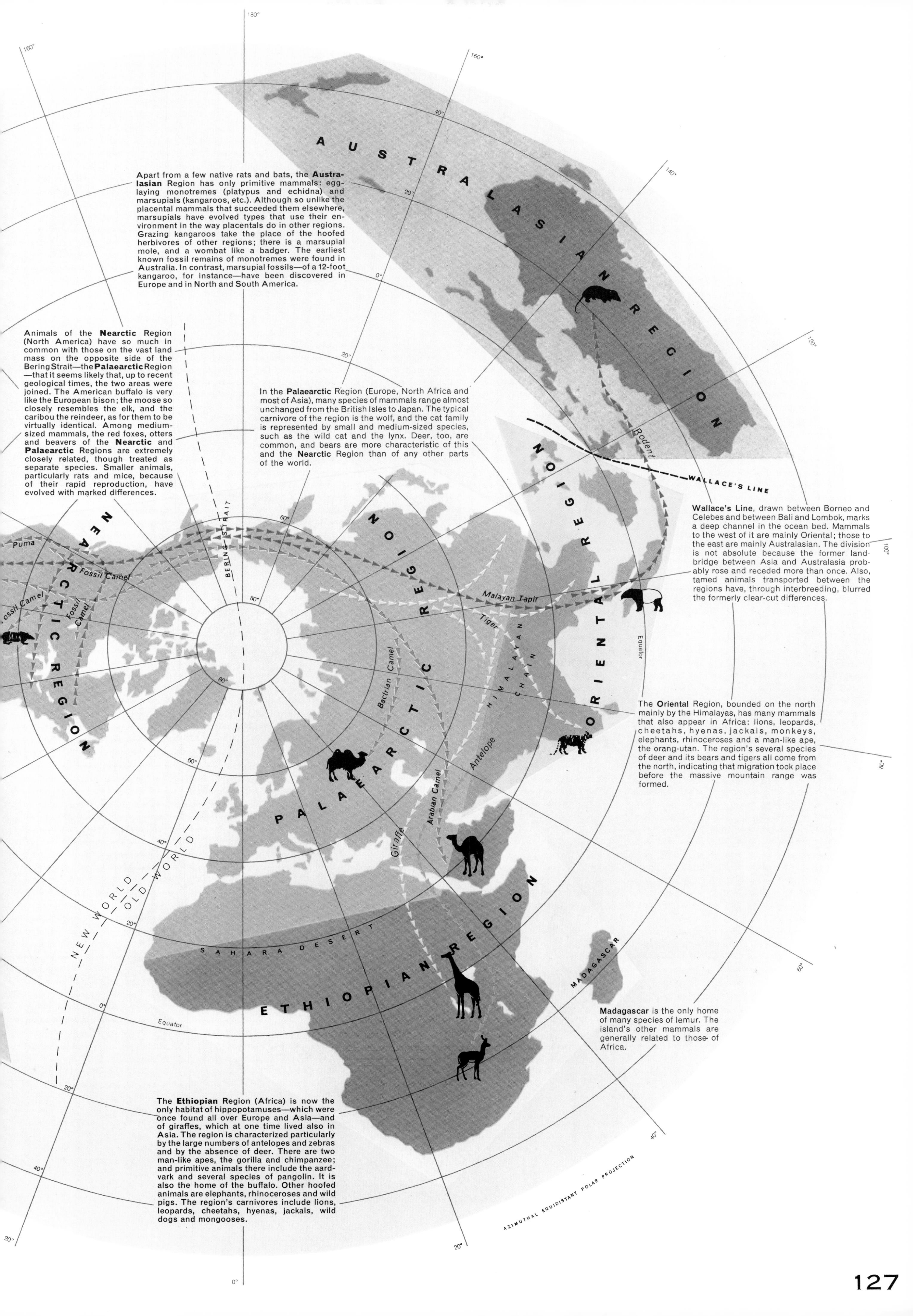

Apart from a few native rats and bats, the **Australasian** Region has only primitive mammals: egg-laying monotremes (platypus and echidna) and marsupials (kangaroos, etc.). Although so unlike the placental mammals that succeeded them elsewhere, marsupials have evolved types that use their environment in the way placentals do in other regions. Grazing kangaroos take the place of the hoofed herbivores of other regions; there is a marsupial mole, and a wombat like a badger. The earliest known fossil remains of monotremes were found in Australia. In contrast, marsupial fossils—of a 12-foot kangaroo, for instance—have been discovered in Europe and in North and South America.

Animals of the **Nearctic** Region (North America) have so much in common with those on the vast land mass on the opposite side of the Bering Strait—the **Palaearctic** Region —that it seems likely that, up to recent geological times, the two areas were joined. The American buffalo is very like the European bison; the moose so closely resembles the elk, and the caribou the reindeer, as for them to be virtually identical. Among medium-sized mammals, the red foxes, otters and beavers of the **Nearctic** and **Palaearctic** Regions are extremely closely related, though treated as separate species. Smaller animals, particularly rats and mice, because of their rapid reproduction, have evolved with marked differences.

In the **Palaearctic** Region (Europe, North Africa and most of Asia), many species of mammals range almost unchanged from the British Isles to Japan. The typical carnivore of the region is the wolf, and the cat family is represented by small and medium-sized species, such as the wild cat and the lynx. Deer, too, are common, and bears are more characteristic of this and the **Nearctic** Region than of any other parts of the world.

Wallace's Line, drawn between Borneo and Celebes and between Bali and Lombok, marks a deep channel in the ocean bed. Mammals to the west of it are mainly Oriental; those to the east are mainly Australasian. The division is not absolute because the former land-bridge between Asia and Australasia probably rose and receded more than once. Also, tamed animals transported between the regions have, through interbreeding, blurred the formerly clear-cut differences.

The **Oriental** Region, bounded on the north mainly by the Himalayas, has many mammals that also appear in Africa: lions, leopards, cheetahs, hyenas, jackals, monkeys, elephants, rhinoceroses and a man-like ape, the orang-utan. The region's several species of deer and its bears and tigers all come from the north, indicating that migration took place before the massive mountain range was formed.

Madagascar is the only home of many species of lemur. The island's other mammals are generally related to those of Africa.

The **Ethiopian** Region (Africa) is now the only habitat of hippopotamuses—which were once found all over Europe and Asia—and of giraffes, which at one time lived also in Asia. The region is characterized particularly by the large numbers of antelopes and zebras and by the absence of deer. There are two man-like apes, the gorilla and chimpanzee; and primitive animals there include the aardvark and several species of pangolin. It is also the home of the buffalo. Other hoofed animals are elephants, rhinoceroses and wild pigs. The region's carnivores include lions, leopards, cheetahs, hyenas, jackals, wild dogs and mongooses.

BIRD MIGRATION

A MYSTERY OF ENDURANCE AND NAVIGATION

And let fowl fly above the earth in the open firmament of heaven — GENESIS 1

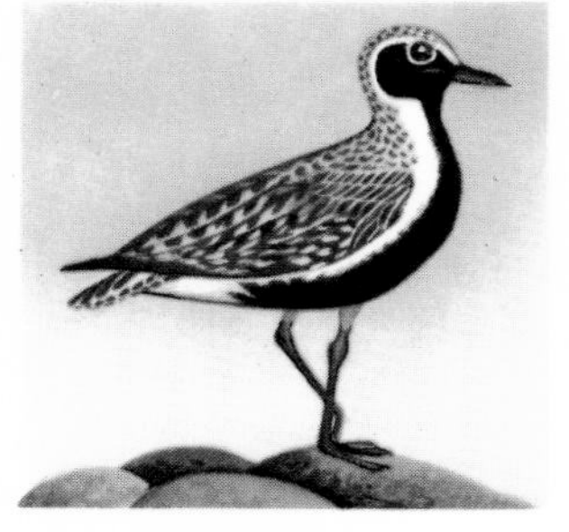

Golden Plover

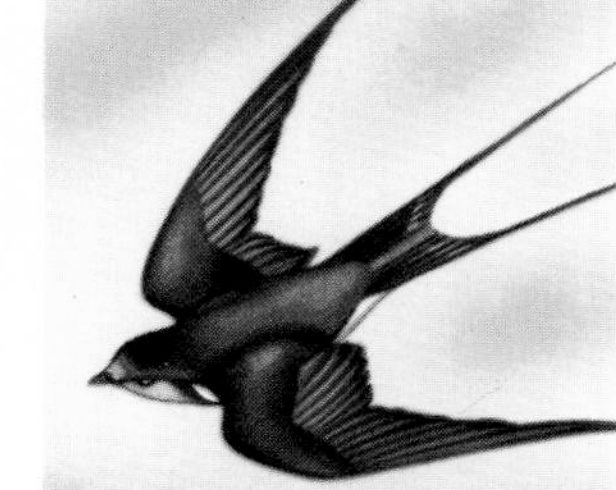

Swallow

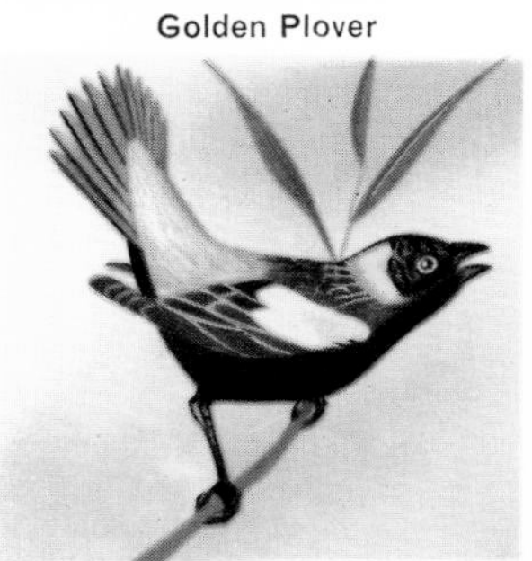

Bobolink

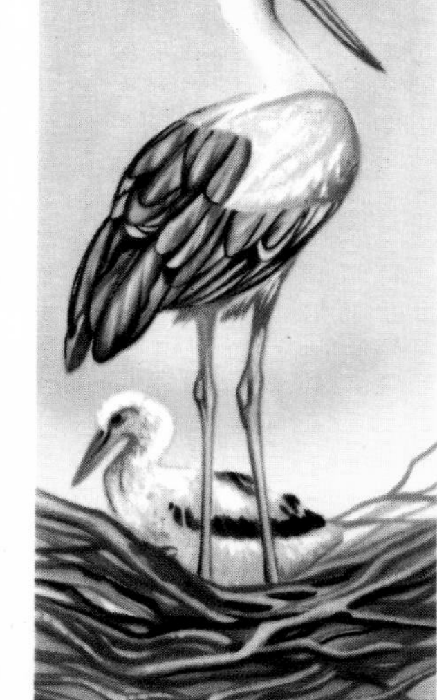

White Stork

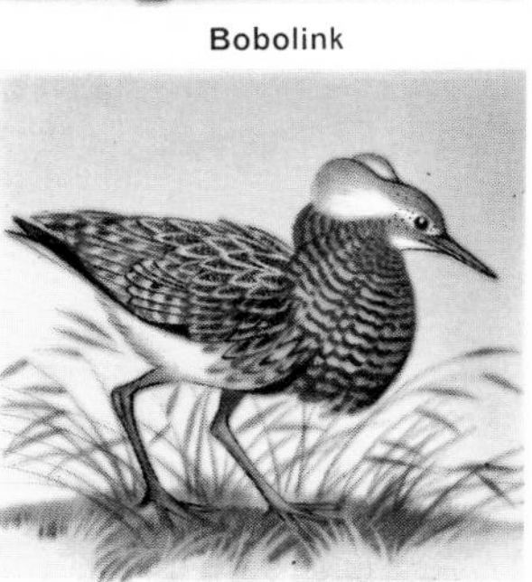

Ruff

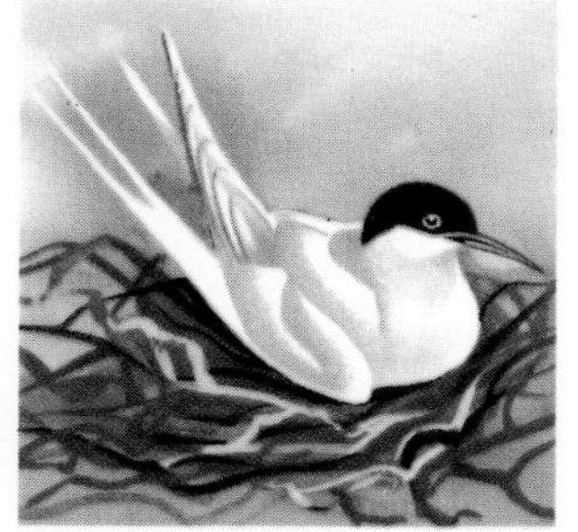

Arctic Tern

Wheatear

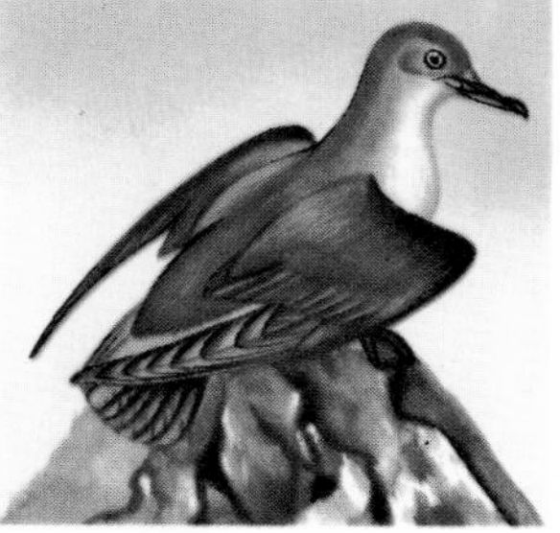

Sooty Shearwater

Arctic Warbler
Willow Warbler

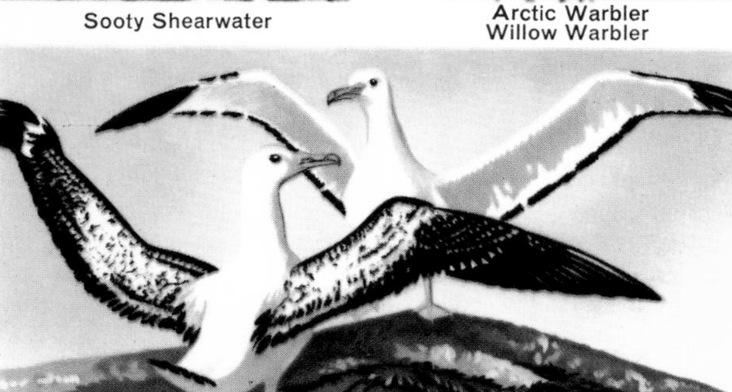

Wandering Albatross

THERE are well over 8,000 known and named species of birds, and a great many of them are migratory. Despite all dangers of storms, droughts, and of man himself, millions of birds undertake twice-yearly journeys that span whole continents and oceans.

In the great northern land masses of the Northern Hemisphere, the arrival of summer produces a superabundance of insect food and long hours of daylight in which to seek it—a critical factor for birds whose young may eat many times their own weight in food during the time they are in the nest. The northern latitudes thus support a huge temporary breeding population of birds which must migrate south for the winter. When breeding is over and the young ones reared, glandular changes within the body, probably triggered by the lengthening nights of approaching winter, stimulate the migratory instinct, but the actual *moment* of departure is influenced by the local weather conditions and the physical readiness of the birds themselves.

Before migrating, birds lay in stores of energy in the form of internal fat deposits. Some species may even double their body weight, and in this way are enabled to stay on the wing for at least 90 hours and perhaps as long as 120. Ornithologists believe that some Wheatears, only a little larger than the House Sparrow, fly direct from Greenland to the north coast of Spain, an over-water flight of nearly 2,000 miles. Others, from Alaska, must first cross the Bering Strait before starting on the immense trans-Asian journey to their ancestral winter quarters in Africa. The Blackpoll Warbler, smaller than the House Sparrow, may fly directly from New England to Venezuela. After such a journey a bird may have halved its starting weight and so must rest while it accumulates fresh stores of fat.

MORE than any species, the Swallow is symbolic of this incredible and complicated migratory instinct. It breeds in Europe, Asia, North Africa and, as the Barn Swallow, in North America, and winters in the Southern Hemisphere. Flying by day, and feeding on the wing, European swallows show a preference for short sea crossings, such as the Strait of Gibraltar, passing south round the edge of the Sahara. In the spring their return journey is more direct: many fly over the Sahara instead of round it, and cross the Mediterranean on a broad front.

Of all migrants, none travels farther than the Arctic Tern. After a short breeding season in the higher latitudes of the Northern Hemisphere (where long hours of summer daylight give ample time for feeding on the abundant supply of fish), some North American Arctic Terns cross the North Atlantic to join up with Arctic Terns from North-West Europe, etc.; others pass down the western Atlantic, and Arctic Terns wearing rings fixed in Russia and Wales have been recovered in Australia. No other bird enjoys as much daylight annually, but finding it involves a journey of about 22,000 miles a year.

Migratory birds often navigate with phenomenal accuracy. The general direction of movements of some of them are indicated by the arrows on the map. The Pacific Golden Plover, which breeds in the extreme west of Alaska and in eastern Siberia, crosses the Pacific to make pinpoint arrivals on such small islands as Hawaii and Tonga. In one experiment, a Manx Shearwater, captured and

ringed in Wales, was flown to Boston, U.S.A., and released. It arrived home 12½ days later, having crossed 3,000 miles of unfamiliar ocean. Manx Shearwaters are great travellers and those from Britain winter off the coasts of Brazil and Argentina; one incredible young bird completed a 5,000-mile journey to Brazil in less than 18 days.

In the Southern Hemisphere, which has much smaller land masses, the long-distance migrants are sea birds; none more so than the members of the Shearwater family. The Great Shearwater, which breeds on the lonely island of Tristan da Cunha, travels north up the western Atlantic to reach the waters off Greenland before turning east to skirt the coast of Europe on the long run south. Its cousin, the Sooty Shearwater (known to sailors as the Mutton Bird), also migrates northwards from its breeding areas in the Falkland Islands and small islands off Cape Horn, Tasmania and New Zealand. One bird, ringed in New Zealand, was recovered in the Sea of Okhotsk, to the north of Japan.

WHILE winter quarters are generally nearer the Equator than summer ones, they are not always directly south. The Willow Warbler is a song bird so small that three barely weigh an ounce. Those that breed in east Siberia undertake the immense journey to East Africa. The Arctic Warbler spends the summer as far west as Northern Norway and winters in south-east Asia and Indonesia—thus crossing at right-angles the path of the Willow Warbler. One species of Shrike nests in central Asia and winters in equatorial Africa—1,200 miles south, but 2,500 miles west.

The instinct to migrate brings together in huge flocks birds that are normally solitary. Even the most hospitable countryside cannot always provide sustenance for more than a few pairs of nesting birds per acre: and yet, with the onset of winter, birds collect in clouds that darken the northern skies. The Bobolink, or Rice Bird, is a solitary inhabitant of North American meadowlands. On the autumn migration flight, Bobolinks gather in immense flocks to devastate the rice fields of the Carolinas.

Size has little to do with the migration instinct. Tiny Humming Birds migrate 500 miles across the Gulf of Mexico. On the other hand, the Wandering Albatross, with a wing span of twelve feet, breeds on islands such as Tristan da Cunha, South Georgia, and Kerguelen, and spends the rest of the year soaring across the southern oceans, far from land. It is thought that these birds may circumnavigate the world several times between their breeding seasons.

The phenomenon of migration was known as long ago as Biblical times. The Book of Jeremiah notes the flight of White Storks, which leave the North European Plain in huge numbers and cross Israel and the Nile Valley. But, despite this long familiarity with migration, there is still much to be learned.

Radar has largely answered the altitude question: most migrations take place below 5,000 feet, but there are records of really small birds travelling as high as 21,000 feet.

Experiments with caged migrants prove that they can use the sun and the stars as aids to navigation. Birds placed in a planetarium, beneath a replica of the night sky, turned at once in the direction of the southern winter quarters to which they were due to fly. Birds, it seems, are equipped with instincts that may match man's most elaborate instruments.

SPECIES	LENGTH CM. (INCHES)	BREEDING AREA	WINTERING AREA	DISTANCE FLOWN KM. (MILES)
Arctic Skua (Parasitic Jaeger)	42 (16½)	Arctic America, Greenland, Arctic Europe, north Siberia	West Africa, Persian Gulf, Arabian Gulf, Australia, New Zealand, South America	6,500-13,000 (4,000-8,000)
Arctic Tern	35-38 (14-15)	North Canada, Greenland, Iceland, north Europe	South and west African coasts, Antarctica	18,000 (11,000)
Arctic Warbler	12 (4¾)	North and north-east Europe, north Siberia	South-east Asia	6,500-13,000 (4,000-8,000)
Blackpoll Warbler	12-14 (5-5½)	Alaska, east to Northern Labrador and New England	Colombia, Venezuela to French Guiana	4,000-8,000 (2,500-5,000)
Black and white Cuckoo	33 (13)	India	East and south-east Africa	5,500-7,000 (3,500-4,500)
Blue-cheeked Bee-eater	28 (11)	North India, west China	East Africa	6,500-9,000 (4,000-5,500)

SPECIES	LENGTH CM. (INCHES)	BREEDING AREA	WINTERING AREA	DISTANCE FLOWN KM. (MILES)
Bobolink	16-20 (6½-8)	South-east Canada, north-east and mid-west U.S.A.	Bolivia, Paraguay, Brazil	8,000 (5,000)
Buff-breasted Sandpiper	19 (7½)	Arctic Canada	Argentina and Uruguay	9,500-13,000 (6,000-8,000)
Willow Warbler	11 (4½)	Eurasia	East Africa	13,000 (8,000)
Great Shearwater	43-46 (17-18)	Tristan da Cunha	North Atlantic	Oceanic wanderer
Long-tailed Cuckoo	42 (16½)	New Zealand	Samoa and Fiji	3,200 (2,000)
Manx Shearwater	35 (14)	British Isles, Brittany Atlantic Islands, Mediterranean	South Atlantic	8,000 (5,000)
Needle-tailed Swift	19 (7½)	East Siberia, Japan	Australia, Tasmania	9,500-13,000 (6,000-8,000)

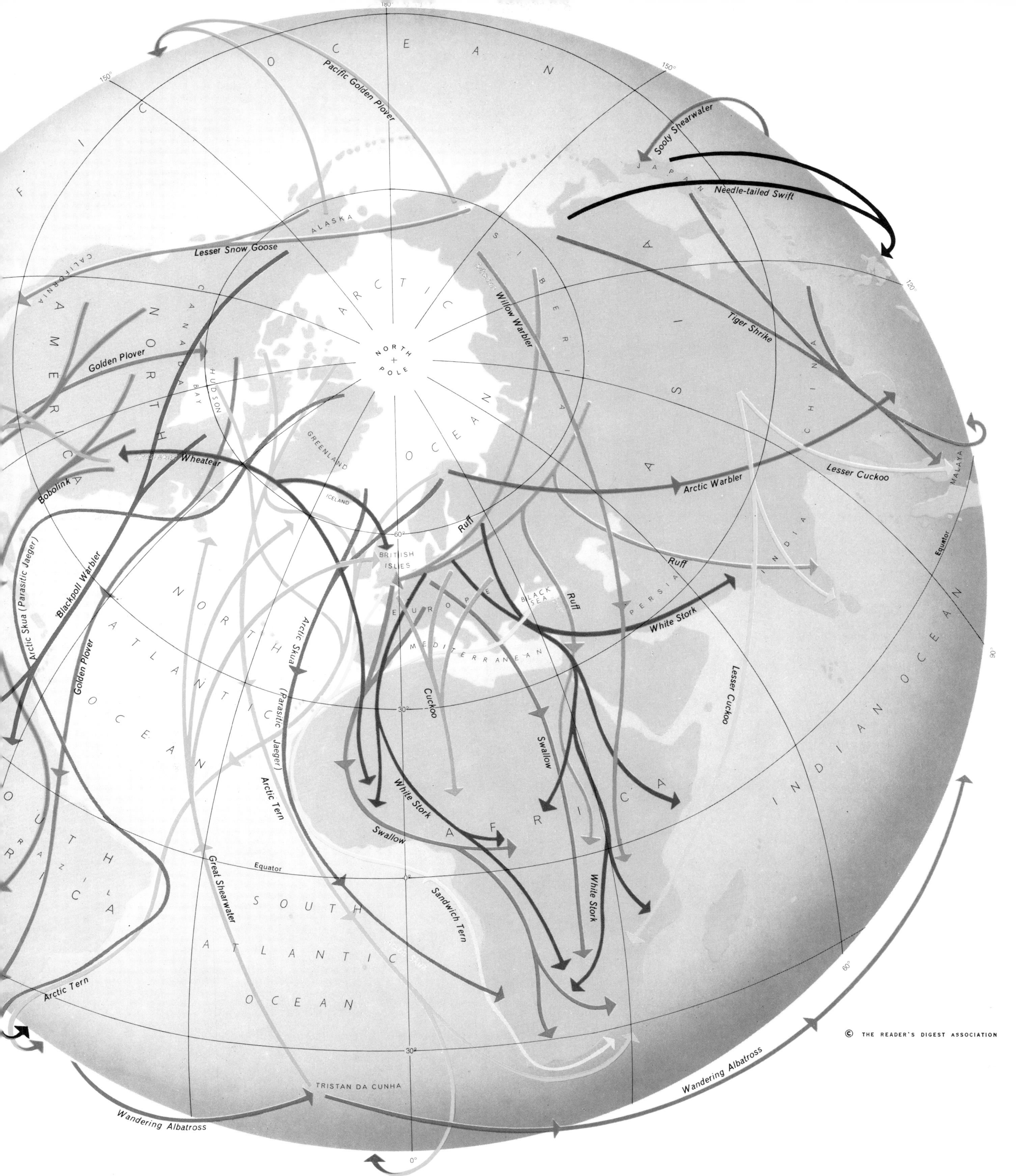

SPECIES	LENGTH CM. (INCHES)	BREEDING AREA	WINTERING AREA	DISTANCE FLOWN KM. (MILES)
Pacific Golden Plover	25-28 (10-11)	West Alaska, north-east Siberia	Hawaii, Tonga, Indonesia, Australia	9,500-13,000 (6,000-8,000)
Pintail (New World)	56 (22)	North-west Alaska east to Hudson Bay, south to Iowa, N. Colorado, S. California	Middle and southern United States to West Indies and Panama, west to Hawaii	1,600-6,500 (1,000-4,000)
Ruff	22-30 (8½-12)	North and west Europe, Siberia	West Europe, Africa, Iraq, Persia, India, Sri Lanka	5,000-9,500 (3,000-6,000)
Sandwich Tern	40 (16)	Shores of North Sea and west Mediterranean, Black Sea	West and South Africa	1,600-8,000 (1,000-5,000)
Scarlet Grosbeak	15 (5½)	North-east Europe	India, south-east Asia	5,000-9,500 (3,000-6,000)
Shining Cuckoo	18 (7¼)	New Zealand	Solomon Islands	2,900 (1,800)

SPECIES	LENGTH CM. (INCHES)	BREEDING AREA	WINTERING AREA	DISTANCE FLOWN KM. (MILES)
Lesser Snow Goose	63-71 (25-28)	Alaska, north-west Canada	Gulf of Mexico, California	3,000-5,000 (2,000-3,000)
Sooty Shearwater	40 (16)	New Zealand, Falkland Is., Cape Horn	North Atlantic, north Pacific	Oceanic wanderer
Summer Tanager	17 (6½)	North America, north to as far as the Great Lakes	Mexico southwards to Peru	1,600-6,500 (1,000-4,000)
Swallow (European)	18-19 (7-7½)	Europe, north to about 68°	Central and South Africa	8,000-11,000 (5,000-7,000)
Tiger Shrike	18 (7)	China, east Siberia, Japan	Malaya, Sumatra	5,000-6,500 (3,000-4,000)
Wandering Albatross	112-135 (44-53)	Tristan da Cunha, Gough Island	Southern oceans, chiefly south of 40° S.	unknown
White Stork	101 (40)	Mid-Europe	Tropical and South Africa	5,000-8,000 (3,000-5,000)

THE EVOLUTION OF MAN

When men began to multiply on the face of the earth —GENESIS 6

MAN is one of the primates, a group that originated about 80 million years ago. This group includes the apes and monkeys as well as less advanced creatures such as the ancestors of today's tree-shrew, lemur and tarsier. Primates have large brains, high intelligence, capable, sensitive hands which can grasp well, and stereoscopic vision; the more advanced members of the group have the ability to stand and walk upright. Primates are sociable animals, quick to imitate and learn from their fellows and they communicate well with one another. They also have the advantage of being highly adaptable and can move into new areas with different climatic and environmental conditions.

Some 20 or 30 million years ago our own ancestors and those of the modern apes – the gorillas, chimpanzees, orang utans and gibbons – took separate evolutionary paths. The apes adapted to a mainly vegetarian life in the tropical forests, while the early hominids, as man's ancestors are called, may have lived in more open country and eaten meat as well as plant foods.

By about 3 million years ago some of these early hominids had learnt to make and use simple stone tools. During the next 2½ million years the forms known as *Homo habilis* and *Homo erectus* developed increasingly skilful hands which enabled them to use more complicated tools. They walked and stood erect and as they learnt to hunt big game they increased in intelligence. Towards the end of this period they had learnt to use fire and they probably developed speech and language. During the last 100,000 years the picture becomes clearer. First Neanderthal man, a sub-species of *Homo sapiens*, appeared; then *Homo sapiens sapiens*—modern man. As more human beings colonised different regions of the world and became physically adapted to fresh climatic conditions, distinctive races gradually evolved until the racial differences that exist today became established.

As the experts are forced to base their opinions about the origins of man on fragmentary fossils found thousands of miles apart, they often differ as to how close any given fossil hominid was to the main evolutionary line. Two or three new finds from the early periods could alter the scheme presented here.

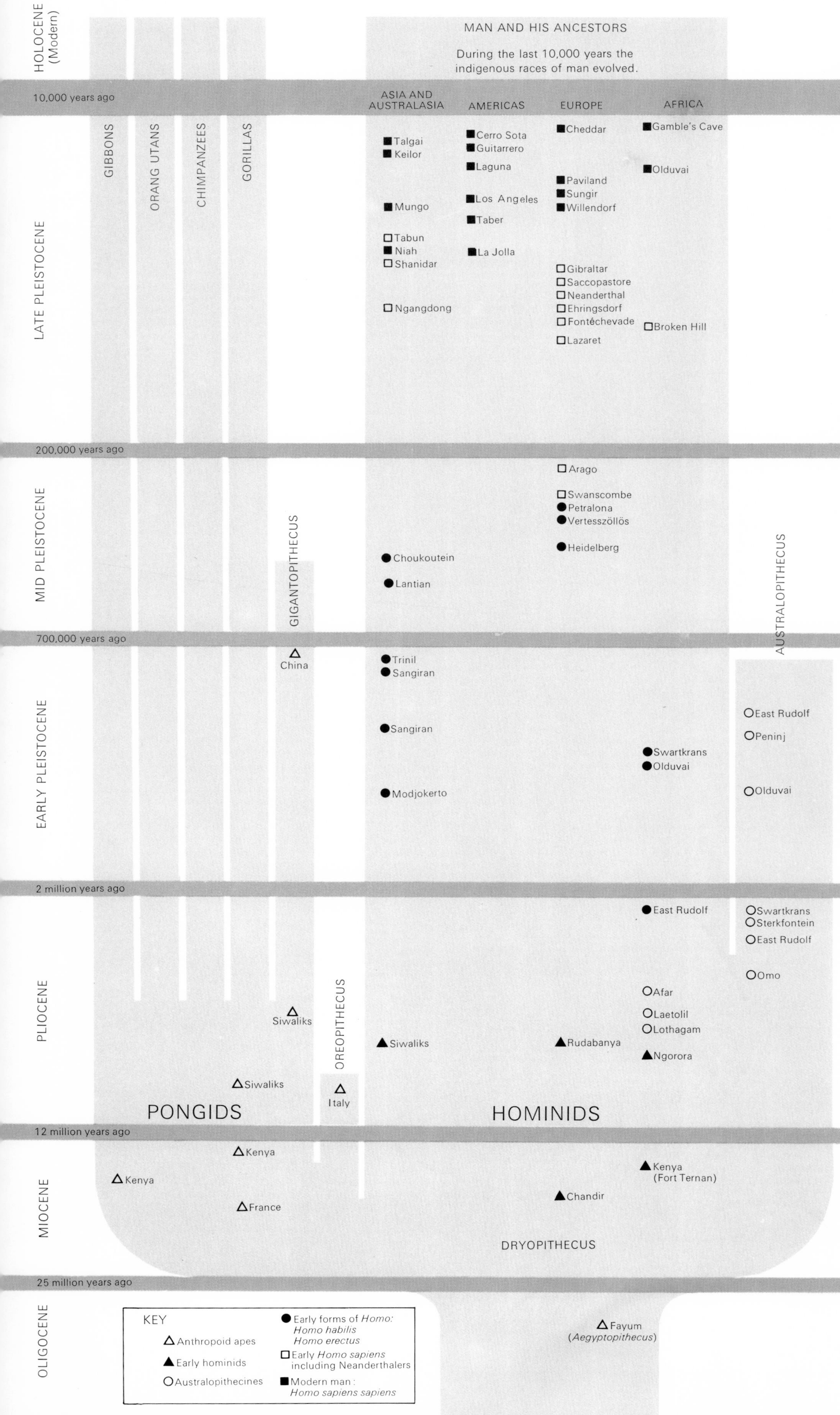

MAN AND HIS ANCESTORS

During the last 10,000 years the indigenous races of man evolved.

There have been no major changes in man's physical form since the end of the last Ice Age, 10,000 years ago. During this period man began to cultivate the land, to domesticate animals and to live a communal life.

Time	PONGIDS				ASIA AND AUSTRALASIA	AMERICAS	EUROPE	AFRICA	AUSTRALOPITHECUS
	GIBBONS	ORANG UTANS	CHIMPANZEES	GORILLAS					

HOLOCENE (Modern)

10,000 years ago

About 70,000 years ago a sub-species of *Homo sapiens* evolved and spread widely through Europe and Asia, only to die out some 30,000 years ago. This was *Homo sapiens neanderthalensis*, Neanderthal man, named after the Neander valley near Dusseldorf, Germany, where his relics were first found. The size of his brain was about the same as that of modern man, he made quite complex flint tools, and his presence in cold northern regions suggests that he may also have made skin clothing. Neanderthal man buried his dead with ceremony, placing food and ornaments in specially dug graves, which indicates the growth of ritual practices and perhaps the development of some early form of religion.

About 35,000 years ago modern man, *Homo sapiens sapiens*, emerged in Europe; his ancestors may have been early Neanderthalers or even earlier forms of man, such as Swanscombe. Modern man had a more varied set of bone and stone tools and he created the world's first known art, the engravings and paintings on the walls of cave shelters in south-west France and Spain, and the 'Venus' figurines found on sites, such as Willendorf, in Eastern Europe.

During the last 30,000 years man has spread across the globe reaching North America from Asia across the land bridge which joined the two continents where the Bering Strait now flows. Man may also have reached Australia at about this time when the continent was still joined to the Asian mainland.

LATE PLEISTOCENE

ASIA AND AUSTRALASIA: ■ Talgai, ■ Keilor, ■ Mungo, □ Tabun, ■ Niah, □ Shanidar, □ Ngangdong

AMERICAS: ■ Cerro Sota, ■ Guitarrero, ■ Laguna, ■ Los Angeles, ■ Taber, ■ La Jolla

EUROPE: □ Cheddar, ■ Paviland, ■ Sungir, ■ Willendorf, □ Gibraltar, □ Saccopastore, □ Neanderthal, □ Ehringsdorf, □ Fontéchevade, □ Lazaret

AFRICA: ■ Gamble's Cave, ■ Olduvai, □ Broken Hill

200,000 years ago

By 500,000 years ago *Homo erectus* had spread through Asia, Africa and Europe. He had learnt how to use fire, he hunted big game, for which cunning and the ability to work in groups would be required, thus exercising and so developing his intelligence. Fine stone hand-axes shaped by these early men have been found in Europe, west Asia and Africa. Then at Swanscombe in England and Steinheim in Germany the bones were discovered of a creature, living about 200,000 years ago, who was even more advanced than *Homo erectus*. The skull, which is very like our own, may indicate that these remains represent an early form of *Homo sapiens* from which our own sub-species, *Homo sapiens sapiens*, later evolved.

MID PLEISTOCENE

GIGANTOPITHECUS

AMERICAS: ● Choukoutein, ● Lantian

EUROPE: □ Arago, □ Swanscombe, ● Petralona, ● Vertesszöllös, ● Heidelberg

700,000 years ago

Australopithecus continued to inhabit Africa, co-existing with more advanced hominids, such as *Homo habilis* ('Handy Man'), until he became extinct about 1¾ million years ago. The remains of *Homo habilis* were found at Olduvai Gorge, East Africa. He walked erect and his brain, though smaller than ours, was bigger than that of an ape; he made simple pebble tools. It is not known today whether *Homo habilis* was no more than an advanced form of *Australopithecus* who also became extinct, or whether he was an early ancestor of man.

The earliest known remains of *Homo erectus* ('Upright Man'), dating back about 1 million years, were found in Java. His brain-size was bigger than that of *Homo habilis*, halfway between that of *Australopithecus* and modern man. He had a receding chin, large teeth and jaws and a low forehead; he was also a tool-maker. It is thought there may be a link in the evolutionary line towards modern man between *Homo erectus* and '1470 Man' who lived 2 million years earlier.

EARLY PLEISTOCENE

△ China

ASIA: ● Trinil, ● Sangiran, ● Sangiran, ● Modjokerto

AFRICA: ● Swartkrans, ● Olduvai, ○ East Rudolf, ○ Peninj, ○ Olduvai

2 million years ago

The best-known fossils from the late Pliocene and early Pleistocene are those of *Australopithecus* ('Southern Ape'). Found at numerous sites in southern and eastern Africa, the remains are 3-5 million years old. Some experts still think that *Australopithecus* was a direct ancestor of man, while others now believe him to represent an extinct side-branch. He was small with a brain no larger than that of a modern ape, but he could stand and walk upright. His teeth were larger than our own and he made simple tools for cutting up the carcasses of baboons and the other animals he hunted.

In 1972 a dramatic new discovery was made on the shore of Lake Rudolf, north Kenya. The skull and leg bones of a creature provisionally named '1470 Man' (from the National Museums of Kenya catalogue number), indicate that another tool-maker, with a larger brain and more human features than *Australopithecus*, lived nearly 3 million years ago. '1470 Man' is probably man's earliest ancestor.

PLIOCENE

OREOPITHECUS

△ Siwaliks, △ Siwaliks, △ Italy

HOMINIDS: ▲ Siwaliks, ▲ Rudabanya, ● East Rudolf, ○ Swartkrans, ○ Sterkfontein, ○ East Rudolf, ○ Omo, ○ Afar, ○ Laetolil, ○ Lothagam, ▲ Ngorora

PONGIDS

12 million years ago

Dryopithecus is the name given to the fossil remains, found in Europe, Asia and Africa, of a number of ape-like creatures who lived about 20 million years ago. One well-known specimen from East Africa, *Proconsul*, may have been the ancestor of the gorilla or the chimpanzee. Another small, tree-dwelling primate, *Kenyapithecus*, dating back 14 million years, could have used, but not made, stone tools. The remains of a similar creature *Ramapithecus*, found in the Siwalik Hills of north-west India, could have been an ancestor of *Australopithecus*.

MIOCENE

△ Kenya, △ Kenya, △ France, ▲ Kenya (Fort Ternan), ▲ Chandir

DRYOPITHECUS

25 million years ago

Primate fossils from this time are rare. The remains of two apes, *Propliopithecus* and *Aegyptopithecus*, were found in the deserts of Egypt. They had small brains and long snouts. Their skulls were like those of monkeys or lemurs, their teeth like those of modern apes. They lived in trees and had tails.

OLIGOCENE

△ Fayum (*Aegyptopithecus*)

KEY

- △ Anthropoid apes
- ▲ Early hominids
- ○ Australopithecines
- ● Early forms of Homo: *Homo habilis*, *Homo erectus*
- □ Early *Homo sapiens* including Neanderthalers
- ■ Modern man: *Homo sapiens sapiens*

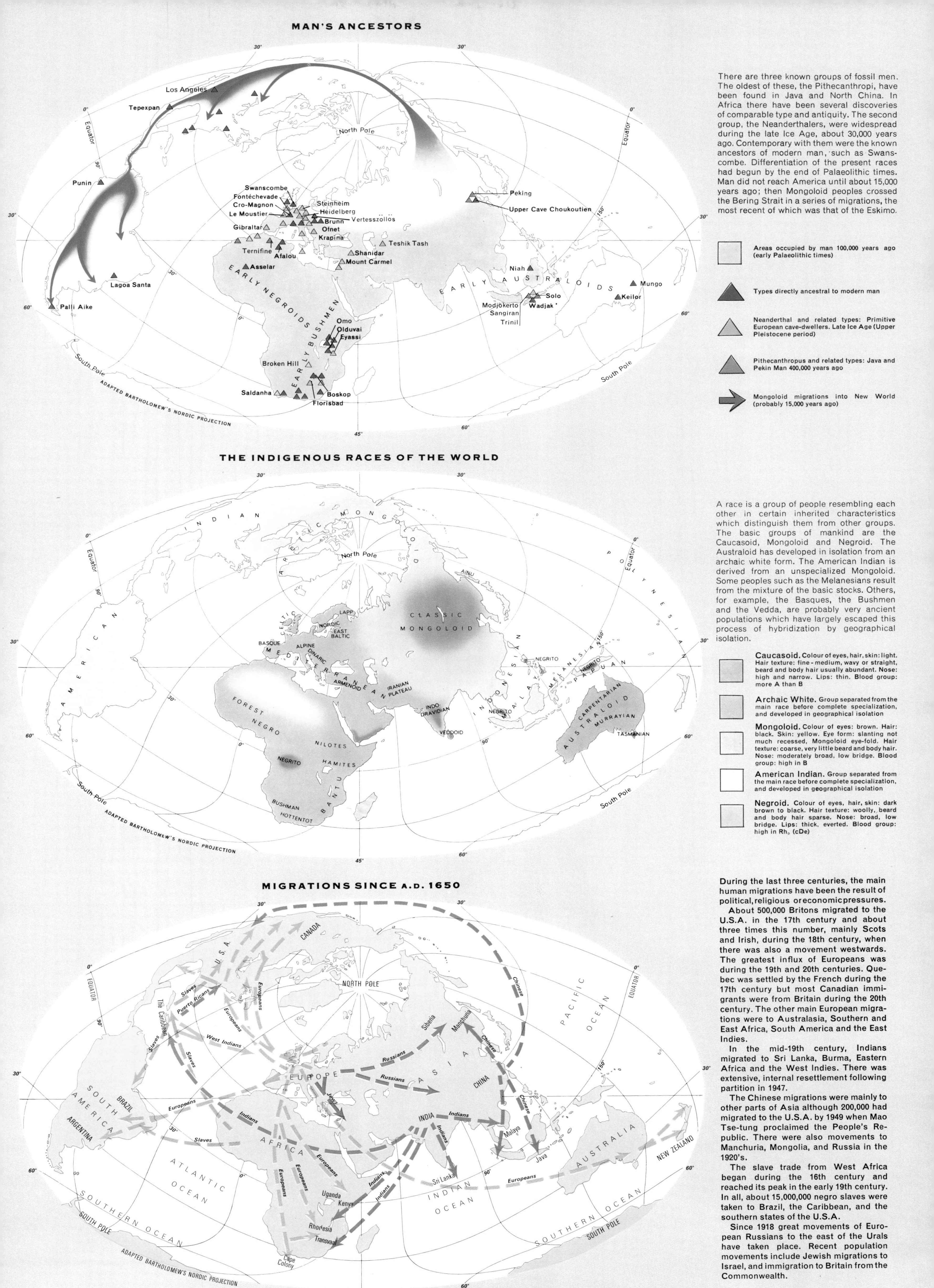

MAN'S ANCESTORS

There are three known groups of fossil men. The oldest of these, the Pithecanthropi, have been found in Java and North China. In Africa there have been several discoveries of comparable type and antiquity. The second group, the Neanderthalers, were widespread during the late Ice Age, about 30,000 years ago. Contemporary with them were the known ancestors of modern man, such as Swanscombe. Differentiation of the present races had begun by the end of Palaeolithic times. Man did not reach America until about 15,000 years ago; then Mongoloid peoples crossed the Bering Strait in a series of migrations, the most recent of which was that of the Eskimo.

Areas occupied by man 100,000 years ago (early Palaeolithic times)

Types directly ancestral to modern man

Neanderthal and related types: Primitive European cave-dwellers. Late Ice Age (Upper Pleistocene period)

Pithecanthropus and related types: Java and Pekin Man 400,000 years ago

Mongoloid migrations into New World (probably 15,000 years ago)

THE INDIGENOUS RACES OF THE WORLD

A race is a group of people resembling each other in certain inherited characteristics which distinguish them from other groups. The basic groups of mankind are the Caucasoid, Mongoloid and Negroid. The Australoid has developed in isolation from an archaic white form. The American Indian is derived from an unspecialized Mongoloid. Some peoples such as the Melanesians result from the mixture of the basic stocks. Others, for example, the Basques, the Bushmen and the Vedda, are probably very ancient populations which have largely escaped this process of hybridization by geographical isolation.

Caucasoid. Colour of eyes, hair, skin: light. Hair texture: fine - medium, wavy or straight, beard and body hair usually abundant. Nose: high and narrow. Lips: thin. Blood group: more A than B.

Archaic White. Group separated from the main race before complete specialization, and developed in geographical isolation

Mongoloid. Colour of eyes: brown. Hair: black. Skin: yellow. Eye form: slanting not much recessed, Mongoloid eye-fold. Hair texture: coarse, very little beard and body hair. Nose: moderately broad, low bridge. Blood group: high in B.

American Indian. Group separated from the main race before complete specialization, and developed in geographical isolation

Negroid. Colour of eyes, hair, skin: dark brown to black. Hair texture: woolly, beard and body hair sparse. Nose: broad, low bridge. Lips: thick, everted. Blood group: high in Rh₀ (cDe)

MIGRATIONS SINCE A.D. 1650

During the last three centuries, the main human migrations have been the result of political, religious or economic pressures.

About 500,000 Britons migrated to the U.S.A. in the 17th century and about three times this number, mainly Scots and Irish, during the 18th century, when there was also a movement westwards. The greatest influx of Europeans was during the 19th and 20th centuries. Quebec was settled by the French during the 17th century but most Canadian immigrants were from Britain during the 20th century. The other main European migrations were to Australasia, Southern and East Africa, South America and the East Indies.

In the mid-19th century, Indians migrated to Sri Lanka, Burma, Eastern Africa and the West Indies. There was extensive, internal resettlement following partition in 1947.

The Chinese migrations were mainly to other parts of Asia although 200,000 had migrated to the U.S.A. by 1949 when Mao Tse-tung proclaimed the People's Republic. There were also movements to Manchuria, Mongolia, and Russia in the 1920's.

The slave trade from West Africa began during the 16th century and reached its peak in the early 19th century. In all, about 15,000,000 negro slaves were taken to Brazil, the Caribbean, and the southern states of the U.S.A.

Since 1918 great movements of European Russians to the east of the Urals have taken place. Recent population movements include Jewish migrations to Israel, and immigration to Britain from the Commonwealth.

131

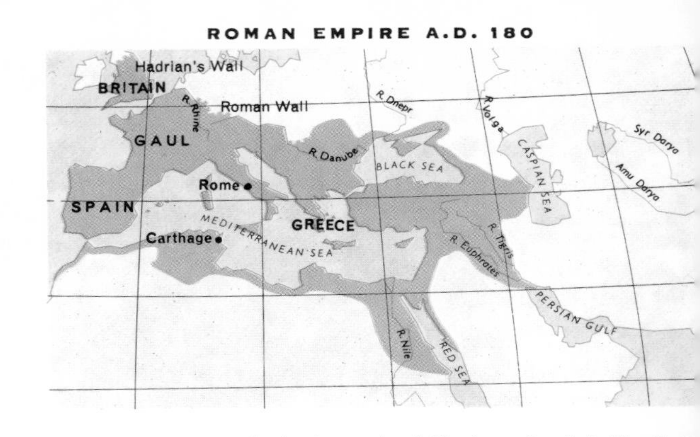

EGYPT AND BABYLONIA 2000-1500 B.C.

HELLENISTIC EMPIRE ABOUT 300 B.C.

ROMAN EMPIRE A.D. 180

THE GROWTH OF CIVILIZATIONS

And from thence did the Lord scatter them abroad upon all the face of the earth—GENESIS II

Almost all the great civilizations originated in river valleys, were nourished by trade, and came to maturity in cities. The conditions of life in the cities provided the intellectual stimulus in which philosophers and scientists could study the meaning of the Universe and the nature of matter; artists and writers could express the ideals and aspirations of their people through the medium of architecture, literature, painting and music.

The course of civilization can be traced in the five main geographical areas shown below. The progress of a civilization is marked by man's increasing control over Nature through applied mathematics and science, the evolution of writing, legal codes, and political and religious organizations. Political development usually began with the formation of city states, some of which expanded into empires or federations, but all have proved to be transient. Religions first exerted local, then national influence; and some spread beyond their countries of origin.

NEAR AND MIDDLE EAST

The union of the peoples of the Upper and Lower Nile some 5,000 years ago heralded the first major civilization in history. During its development, mathematics made possible the building of the Gizeh Pyramids; hieroglyphs were turned into alphabetic writing on stone and papyrus reed; and medicine was born. About 1500 B.C. the Egyptian Empire extended as far as Syria, but slowly declined after its failure to subdue the Hittites and Assyrians. A most vigorous civilization then developed in the fertile valleys of Mesopotamia. Here the Babylonians and Assyrians had adopted the cuneiform writing, the mathematical discoveries and the technical advances of the Sumerians—the first to found city states in the Tigris and Euphrates valleys. The Babylonian and Assyrian Empires spread east and west until they were checked by the rise of the Persians.

The Persian Empire extended from the Indus Valley to the Mediterranean, and embraced Zoroastrianism. Meanwhile the Hebrews, after long migrations and exile in Egypt, settled in the "Promised Land" of Palestine. Their contribution was primarily religious, and paved the way for both Christianity and Islam.

After nearly a thousand years of Greek and Roman domination, another civilization was born in the Near East when, in the 7th century A.D., Arab rule and Islam spread as far as Persia and Spain. The Arabs preserved the knowledge of ancient science, philosophy and geography, translated Ptolemy, Euclid and Aristotle, and introduced into Europe the use of numerals and paper-making. Islam seemed seriously threatened when the Arabs were ousted from Spain and were defeated by the Turks in the Near East. The Turks, in taking over the Arab Empire, became Muslims, and the predominance of Islam continued. After being repelled in Central Europe, the Ottoman Empire began its slow decline. A revival of nationalism among the Arabs led to the foundation of the Arab League.

EUROPE

Western civilization originated in the Aegean, but received its real character from the cultures of Greece, Rome and Jerusalem. The Arabs and the Christian Church developed different aspects of these cultures, and, in their development, carried them farther. The Greeks, entering the Aegean from the north, built city states which, though constantly at odds with one another, shared a common cultural development, used the alphabet brought to them by trading Phoenicians, and provided the starting points for most of our own ideas and ideals.

		BEFORE 2000	2000 1900	1800 1700	1600 1500	1400 1300	1200 1100	1000 900	800 700	600 500	400 300	200 100 B
NEAR & MIDDLE EAST	MESOPOTAMIAN		Sumerian City States		Babylonian Empire			Assyrian Empire			Hellenistic Empires	
	GREEK		First use of irrigation in valleys of Tigris and Euphrates. First extraction of copper and invention of bronze	• Hammurabi, King of Babylon, passes great Code of Law		Military superiority achieved through iron weapons and siege engines. Eastern Mediterranean conquered. Large empire governed from new capital at Nineveh		• Zoroaster, religious prophet—teaches salvation by faith in one god of light who triumphs over evil	• Alexander the Great destroys Pe Empire and enables Greek cul to spread: science and philos flourish; seventy cities found including Alexandria in Egypt centre of arts and sciences un fall of Roman Empire			
	ARAB		First appearance of cuneiform writing		Phoenicians "Missionaries of Civilization"		• Ashurbanipal, Assyrian king, collects library of 20,000 tablets	Persian Empire				
	PHOENICIAN		Maths: invention of sexagesimal system which divides circle into 360 degrees, a degree into 60 minutes, and a minute into 60 seconds	Sailed as far afield as Spain, Britain and West Africa and were masters of Mediterranean trade. Invented 22-consonant alphabet	Carthage founded •		From Indus to Nile		• Euclid, "father of geometry"			
	PERSIAN		Old Kingdom	Middle Kingdom		New Kingdom		Decline of Egypt	• Cyrus, founder of Persian Empire, adopts God of Light as supreme deity: Zoroastrianism becomes state religion	• Archimedes develops joint study of mathematics and physi		
	EGYPTIAN		First use of irrigation in Nile Valley	Great age of architecture and literature. Writing of hieroglyphs on papyrus reed	Science of building continues to develop: Temples at Thebes		Conquered by Assyrians, but architecture, science and medicine continue to flourish				
	TURKISH		First application of maths to large-scale building (Pyramids at Gizeh)	Early Hebrews			Kingdoms of Israel and Judah	Lydians invent coinage	Jews under Foreign Rule		
	HEBREW		First division of time into Solar Years	• Abraham, founder of Jewish Nation	Egyptian captivity. Hittites: Advanced civilization in Anatolia. Efficient system of government and law	• Moses • Exodus from Egypt • Ten Commandments	David and Solomon rule at Jerusalem	Growth of Judaism: Belief in One God, Creator and Judge, and his Elect People • Great Prophets: Isaiah and Jeremiah	• Jerusalem destroyed. Babylonian captivity	Most of Old Testament written	Je Ch bo	
EUROPE	GREEK		Aegean Civilization: includes the Minoan and Mycenæan civilizations		Mycenæan Civilization		Greek City States	Golden Age	Hellenistic Empire		
	WESTERN			Minoan Civilization	Greek-speaking Indo-Europeans invade Greece from North, absorb Minoan culture		Growth of city states—politically divided, culturally united—Sparta, Corinth, Athens, Thebes	Birth of modern philosophy science and literature. Growth of Athenian democracy	Decline of Athens, rise of Macedon, spread of Greek civilization to Near and Middle East In wake of Alexander the Great's armies	• Rome conque Greece	
			Centred on Crete. Prosperity based on Mediterranean trade. Contact with Middle East and Europe. Spread to Mycenæ and Greek States	• Siege of Troy in Asia Minor	• Homer's Iliad and Odyssey composed	• Tragedies of Aeschylus and Sophocles			Rom	
	MINOAN			Palace at Knossos—evidence of high standard of art: sculptures and wall paintings	• Dorians invade Greece and destroy Mycenæ	• First Olympiad	• Pericles • Parthenon built • Thucydides	Caesar conque Gaul an invades Britain		
			Use of hieroglyphic writing	Linear script invented thus speeding the process of writing	Greeks learn alphabet from Phoenicians	• Solon's Laws • Socrates • Pythagoras's Law of Maths • Plato • Alexander the Great • Aristotle				
	ROMAN			Development in copper and bronze working		Invasions of Italy	Roman Republic	Golden Age of literature and architecture		
	BYZANTINE			• Fall of Crete	Greeks found city states in Italy	Etruscans in Rome. Kings expelled and Republic established	Rome conquers Italy and Mediterranean • Punic wars: Rome defeats Carthage	• Cicero • Vi		
					• Founding of Rome	Struggle for political power between Patricians and Plebeians—constitutional experiments			
SOUTHERN ASIA	INDIAN		Indus Valley Civilization	Aryan Invasions		Early Hindu Civilization			Mauryan Dynasty		
	MUSLIM		Dravidians, whose descendants still live in Southern India, establish first city communities in Indus Valley, introduce irrigation schemes, develop pottery and evolve a well ordered system of government	Aryans from north-west conquer original Dravidians, settle and intermarry		Growth of Hindu religion—belief in all pervading World Soul (Brahman): salvation through knowledge: continuous rebirth	• Gautama, originally a Hindu, founds Buddhism—religion of personal salvation through withdrawal, meditation and strict morality. Aim is "Nirvana," a peace beyond this world	All India, except for the far south, is first unified		
	BRITISH		First trade contacts with river civilizations in Mesopotamia		Early Hindus produce a vigorous collection of epic poems and religious hymns: the "Reg-Veda"—a group of early sacrificial hymns	• Ashoka, greatest of Mauryan emperors, establishes Buddhism over most of India, sends missionaries to Syria, Ceylon, Tibet. Reign of peac and reform: education endowe roads and hospitals built			
	INDEPENDENCE				Caste system develops—from Brahmans (priests) to Shudras (labourers)	Upanishads—a collection of Hindu teachings, now in writing	• The Mahabharat great epic poem composed by the Kushans of Afghanistan/Pe		
FAR EAST	CHINESE		Ancient China	Shang Dynasty		Chou Dynasty	Ch'in Dynasty	Ha	
			Origins of Chinese civilization, oldest living civilization in the world, lie in Yellow River valley where so-called Sage Kings are credited with the development of agriculture, medicine, river conservancy	Yellow River civilization expands to territories north and south of Yellow River	Rule of this dynasty extends as far as the Yangtze River. Irrigation works, dams and canals built, but progress is broken by occasional periods of revolt and disunity, and central control is never strong	Loose central control of Chou Dynasty replaced by strong central government	Schools a colleges founded fo education ruling clas	
	MONGOL			Lunar calendar first devised		Golden Age of philosophy: • Lao Tse, legendary founder of Taoism, teaches belief in the harmony and goodness of Nature	• Great Wall of China built to end constant invasions from the north		
				No alphabet, but complicated form of character writing evolved				
	JAPANESE				Silk first manufactured	• Confucius teaches practical lessons of wise and right-eous behaviour in society	Contucianism grow influence and becom State religion	
				Bronze used for making vessels			
THE AMERICAS	PRE-COLUMBIAN		Pre-Columbian Period				
	COLONIAL		Several waves of migration from Asia peopled the American continent over 20,000 years ago.	• First great Indian civilization of Central America, the Olmec. Developed hieroglyphic writing, calendar	Teotihuacán: centre important civilizatio the valley of Mexico Pyramid of the Sun Pyramid of the Moon		
	S. AND CENT. AMERICA			• La Venta, major settlement of Olmec Indians		
	U.S.A.			• Zapotec Indian civilization of S. Mexico. Representation of gods in guise of clay urns. Main builders of mountaintop city of Monte Alban. Lasted till 14th c. A.D.		
	CANADA				

© THE READER'S DIGEST ASSOCI

ARAB EMPIRE A.D. 732

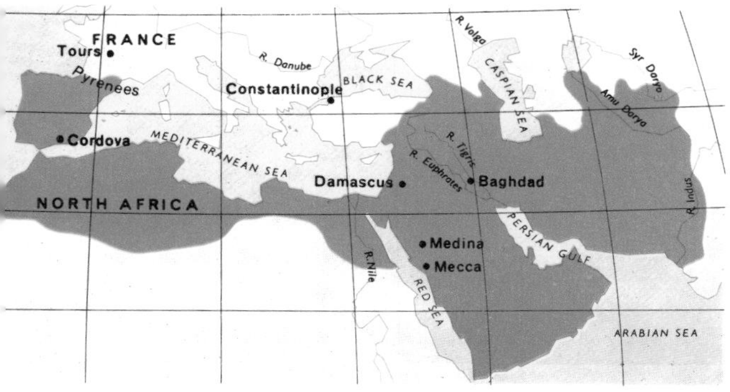

INDIA AND CHINA A.D. 300-900

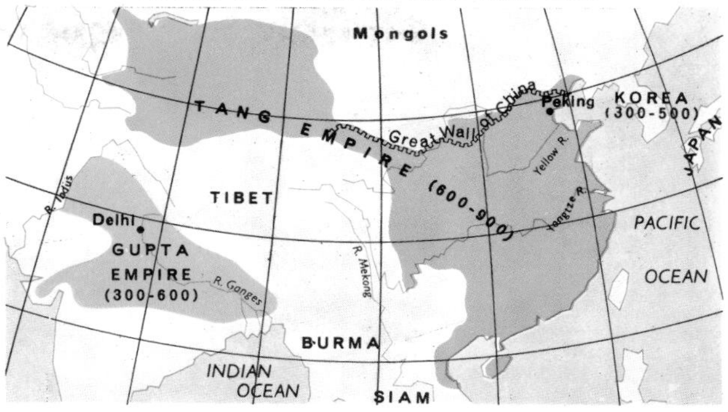

Alexander the Great's victories over the Persian Empire carried Greek culture to the Near and Middle East. But it was spread still farther by the Romans, who conquered Greece and became masters of the Mediterranean and much of Europe. The Romans excelled as administrators. They created an enlightened and impartial system of law, an international language, imposing architecture, and a network of roads. The Roman Empire was divided into East and West in the 4th century A.D., but although the Western Empire disintegrated in the following century, the Eastern or Byzantine Empire, with Constantinople as its capital, resisted the onslaught of the Arabs and the Turks for nearly ten centuries, and spread its religion and culture to Bulgaria and Russia.

Meanwhile Christianity penetrated central Europe, the Church becoming responsible for the preservation of knowledge inherited from the past. The rebirth of classical learning during the Renaissance started a scientific and artistic revolution. Protestantism broke the religious supremacy of the Church of Rome. New lands were discovered, and European ideas spread to many parts of the world. The 19th century saw a great industrial revolution, brought about by the advance of science and technology and an unprecedented growth in population.

S. ASIA—INDIA & PAKISTAN

Indian history is a record of constant invasions from the north-west, which brought contacts with foreign civilizations and an influx of alien races and religions. Until recently, political unity has never lasted long. The formative influences on Indian thought, art and society have been religious. India has produced many outstanding spiritual leaders from Buddha to Gandhi.

The ancient city civilization of the Indus Valley was destroyed by Aryan invaders, who intermingled with the original inhabitants and evolved the Hindu religion. In the 6th century B.C. Buddhism branched off from the main stream of Hinduism but made little impact until the 3rd century B.C., when Asoka, the greatest of the emperors of the Mauryan dynasty, patronized it, encouraged its adoption by the people and sent Buddhist missionaries to Burma and Ceylon. After Asoka's death came a revival of Hinduism in India. Buddhism rapidly lost its hold there, but spread to China, where it was widely accepted.

Hindu culture saw its golden age under the Gupta dynasty in the 4th century A.D., when mathematics, astronomy, scholarship and architecture made great forward strides.

In the 10th century A.D., waves of Muhammadan invaders settled in India, and so initiated the long rivalry between Hindu and Muslim. In the 16th century new invaders, the Moguls, established Muhammadan rule over most of India. They produced great architecture, such as the Taj Mahal, and gave India many able and enlightened rulers. By the beginning of the 18th century the Mogul Empire had declined, and European powers were fighting one another for supremacy in the Indian sub-continent. Britain emerged from this struggle, to rule until 1947, when India and Pakistan became autonomous nations.

FAR EAST—CHINA

For centuries China was, geographically, almost inaccessible, and consequently its civilization developed in relative isolation. It absorbed its many invaders, and adapted their ideas to its own traditional culture.

The Chinese, the oldest living civilization, was more than once further advanced and more vigorous than other civilizations. It was practical and humanist, rather than religious. Originating in the Yellow River Valley, it spread north and south, reaching its first golden age in the 6th and 5th centuries B.C. under the Chou Dynasty. During this period the legendary Lao Tse founded Taoism. Later, under the same dynasty, Confucius taught a more active way of wise and righteous living through knowledge and adherence to a strict moral code. Confucianism was developed by Mencius, and became the official state religion under the Han Dynasty 2,000 years ago. The Han Emperors were the first rulers in the world to use a Civil Service (Mandarin class), entry into which was by competitive examination. Their reforms were made possible by the work of their predecessors, the Ch'in Dynasty, who imposed a large measure of central control for the first time, and built the Great Wall for protection against invasion from the north.

Buddhism spread from India to China during the 1st century A.D. It made an immediate appeal to the Chinese who, in turn, passed its teaching on to Korea and Japan.

After a period of disorder, and invasion by the Huns and Tartars, Chinese culture and scholarship flowered again, under the Tang and Sung Dynasties. Mongol invasions interrupted this golden age, but Kublai Khan, grandson of Ghengis Khan and the most enlightened and progressive of the Mongol Emperors, encouraged contact with the outside world. Under the Ming Dynasty, which drove out the Mongol Dynasty, the richness and variety of Chinese life became the envy of foreign traders, travellers and missionaries. But their successors, the Manchus, made a deliberate attempt to isolate China. This led to internal stagnation and, after the "Boxer Rebellion" in 1900, ended in the collapse of Imperial China. Sun-Yat-Sen proclaimed a republic in 1912, and after nearly forty years of almost continual civil strife and of war with Japan, the communists won control in 1949.

THE AMERICAS

No great early Indian civilization is known in North America. In Central and South America many Indian civilizations succeeded one another, as shown in the chart. All were notable for their architecture and art. The last of them, the Aztec and the Inca, were overthrown in the early 16th century by the Spaniards, who then divided the country between themselves and the Portuguese and imposed the Roman Catholic religion on the Indians. From the end of the 15th century North America and parts of South America were gradually colonized by other Europeans, who took with them their own civilization. From subsequent wars and revolutions, Canada, the United States, and the countries of Central and South America emerged as they are today.

D. 100 · 200 · 300 · 400 · 500 · 600 · 700 · 800 · 900 · 1000 · 1100 · 1200 · 1300 · 1400 · 1500 · 1600 · 1700 · 1800 · 1900

Arab-Muslim Civilization in Near East and Spain

Roman supremacy over Near East

Monasticism originates in Near East and spreads to Europe

Islam, influenced by Judaism, teaches, "There is no god but Allah, and Muhammad is His Prophet." Brotherhood of all Muslims: Caliphs extend militant Islam to Indus and Pyrenees but are checked in France and at Constantinople

Islam continues to dominate Near East but wanes in Europe

• Arab government in Spain overthrown

Arab Nationalism Modern Palestine

From Morocco to Persia—Western influence grows, then declines

• Galen. Greek doctor leading medical authority till the 16th century

Arab civilization at Baghdad, Damascus and Cordova. Knowledge of ancient cultures preserved

Neo-Persian Empire

Sassanians rule from Indus to Mediterranean
Zoroastrianism revived as state religion

Study of mathematics, astronomy, alchemy and geography flourishes

Islam invades India, brings back Indian numerals to Near East and Europe

• Averroes: commentaries on Plato and Aristotle

• Battle of Lepanto breaks Turkish sea-power in Mediterranean

• Arab League founded

• Foundation of new state of Israel

• Muhammad at Mecca

• Claudius Ptolemy, of Alexandria, constructs first map on assumption that world is spherical in shape

• Chosroes I successfully defies Roman Empire and rules over a highly developed society until conquered by the Arabs: grants toleration for Christians

• Qurán edited

• Avicenna: philosopher, one of the world's greatest teachers of medicine

• Batuta: traveller and explorer, stimulates study of geography

• Last unsuccessful siege of Vienna marks Islam's final attempt to conquer Europe

Ottoman Empire

Modern Turkey

Paper and block printing introduced from China

Turks, a Central Asian warrior race, embrace Islam, take over Arab Empire, rule from Belgrade to Persian Gulf, block Western trade with Far East

Series of Balkan revolts lead to break-up of Empire

• Turkish Republic founded by Kemal Ataturk

…n Palestine

• Fall of Jerusalem and dispersal of the Jews

…w Testament written

• Seljuk Turks capture Baghdad, fight Crusaders for possession of Holy Land

• Constantinople captured from Greeks

• Suleiman the Magnificent—his reign marks height of Ottoman Empire's power

Early Christian Era · **Dark Ages** · **High Middle Ages** · **Renaissance and Reformation** · **Age of Reason, Industrialism and Socialism**

Despite persecution Christianity steadily grows

• St. Augustine writes "City of God"

…els of St. Paul

• Constantine recognizes Christianity

Civilization rests on concept of "Christendom" and the unity of Europe—Holy Roman Empire. Pope and Emperor contest leadership. The Church serves as guardian of culture. Outlook spiritual rather than material

• Revival of idea of one unified Empire by Charlemagne

Intellectual and artistic revolution. Revived interest in classical knowledge stimulates progress in art, literature, science and philosophy

Friars: Franciscans and Dominicans

Scientific discoveries transform man's understanding of Universe and undermine religious creeds. Industrial revolution causes urbanization, creates new wealth and gives West political and economic hegemony. Political power and education no longer confined to upper classes.

• William Harvey, physician, discovers circulation of blood

• Darwin's law of Evolution

• Einstein's Theory of Relativity

…Empire · **Decline and Fall**

…ax Romana" from …ain to Persia. Creation …advanced system of …v and administration

Gradual military and economic decline in Western part of Empire

Growth of monastic orders and foundation of numerous monasteries: Benedictines and Cistercians

Crusades

Gothic Cathedrals: • Chartres • Rheims

• Giotto

• Dante

• Chaucer

• First printing press

Luther and Calvin break away from the Church of Rome

• Erasmus

• Galileo's telescope and laws of motion

• Faraday, chemist and pioneer of electro-magnetism

• Nuclear fission

• Newton's law of gravity

• Steel first made cheaply and in quantity by Bessemer

• Watt's steam engine

Exploration of Space begins

Missions: • St. Patrick, Ireland

…ugustus, …t Emperor

• Division into Western and Eastern Empires

• St. Colomba, Scotland

• St. Augustine, England

• St. Boniface, Germany

Foundation of Universities: • Bologna • Paris • Oxford

• van Eyck

• Brunelleschi

• Michelangelo

Philosophers: • Descartes • Locke • Kant • Rousseau • Marx

• Freud's psychology

• French Revolution

• Russian Revolution

• Marcus Aurelius

Eastern Roman Empire Byzantine Civilization

Classicism and Romanticism in the Arts

Modern Art:

Painting: • Rembrandt • Hogarth • Goya • Turner • v. Gogh • Picasso

Literature: • Shakespeare • Voltaire • Goethe • Balzac • Tolstoy • J. Joyce

Music: • Bach • Beethoven • Chopin • Verdi • Stravinsky

Spread of Greco-Roman culture throughout Roman Empire. Romans surpass Greeks in architectural achievements

Greek culture, Roman government. Greek Orthodox Church breaks with Roman Papacy. Byzantine Empire defends East against Turks, and its religion and culture penetrate into Russia and Balkans

Expansion of Europe: • Columbus in West Indies

• Vasco da Gama in Africa and India

• Cortez in Mexico

• Cook in Pacific

• Puritans in North America

• Colosseum built

• Justinian codifies Roman Law and builds St. Sophia

Art and architecture of great brilliance—use of mosaics

• Separation of Western and Eastern Churches

Fall of • Constantinople

…ependent States · **Gupta Dynasty** · **Rival States** · **Mohammedan Invasions and Settlements** · **Mogul Empire** · **British Rule** · **Independence**

…auryan Empire …umbles under foreign …vaders who import …eek and Persian …fluences. In its …ace arise a number …short-lived kingdoms

This dynasty once again unifies much of India and marks golden age of Hindu literature, art and science

Gupta Empire breaks up under impact of Hun and early Arab invasions into a number of Hindu kingdoms

Militant Muslim invaders overrun Hindu kingdoms and for first time settle in India, thus beginning the bitter Muslim-Hindu rivalry. Hinduism in turn becomes more militant

Mogul rulers (Muslim) unite most of India, restore law and order

• Britain defeats France in Seven Years War: influence of East India Company supreme

Gandhi leads independence movement through passive resistance

Sanskrit becomes universal literary language

First Muslim dynasty in Punjab

• Babur founds Mogul empire

…nduism asserts …elf as a unifying …ctor in this period …political disunity

Astronomy: Theory of rotation of earth discovered by Hindus

Buddhism progressively disappears from India, its country of origin, but is dominant in the religion and culture of Burma, Siam, Java and Ceylon

Muslim rule spreads over most of north India and the Deccan

• Akbar seeks toleration for all religions. Encourages trade, arts and sciences. Most brilliant period in Muslim India

• Indian Mutiny

India under British Crown, law and order strengthened, roads and railways built, currency unified

• Former Indian Empire attains independence as India and Pakistan

Architecture: shrines, temples and caves

• First Muslim dynasty established at Delhi

• Jesuits welcomed

• Taj Mahal built

Maths—decimal system and use of zero evolved, later brought to Europe by Arabs

Muslim architecture introduced

…ddhism teaches China

• Kalidasa—poet and dramatist

Rivalry between Portuguese, Dutch, French and British traders

…ynasty · **Dark Ages** · **Tang Dynasty** · **Sung Dynasty** · **Mongols** · **Ming Dynasty** · **Manchu Dynasty** · **Republic**

…licy of strengthening …ntral control continues …ns are first to create a …rmanent Civil Service …andarin class)

Period of disorder

Hun and Tartar invasions and disappearance of central control

Central control and a high degree of unity re-established Golden Age of learning, science and art. Traders and scholars make contact with India and Arab countries

China becomes part of Mongol Empire. Kublai Khan encourages trade with outside world. Fails to conquer Japan and Java

Mings drive out Mongols, restore Confucianism and Mandarin class

The Manchus from Manchuria oust the Mings and found a new dynasty. Their Chinese overlordship to Korea, Mongolia, Indo-China and attempt to exclude foreigners from China

• Revolution of Sun-Yat-Sen. Collapse of Manchus and end of Imperial China

• Academy of Letters founded

• Imperial Academy of Painting founded

Renaissance of scholarship and painting

Rapid spread of Buddhism

Block printing, magnetic compass, gunpowder invented

Manufacture of porcelain perfected

European powers seek to open up China

• Communist Revolution

…ddhism comes from India

Neo-Confucianism of Chu Hsi

• Ming Code of Law

First use of paper

Landscape, animal, flower and bird painting thrives

• Kublai Khan visited by Marco Polo

• Jesuit missionaries

• The anti-European Boxer Rising fails

Japanese

Japan remains a closed community until 5th century A.D.; its earlier history is legendary

Buddhism is introduced from China via Korea, and with it Chinese writing

Chinese culture penetrates into Japan and exists side by side with ancient Japanese feudal and religious customs

Painting, architecture and landscape gardening flourish

• Christianity introduced by Francis Xavier

Christianity exterminated, relations with outside world severed

• Com. Perry, U.S. Navy, forces Japan to reopen communication with outside world

Japan becomes modern, industrial state

Pre-Columbian Period · **Colonial Period** · **South and Central America**

• Period of authentic artistic splendour. Elaborate geometricism Purely religious inspiration

• Toltec Indians take over Teotihuacán Building of superb cities such as Tula Temple of the Plumed Serpent

• Aztec Indian civilization Military people who, under Montezuma in early 16th c. dominated Mexico

• Columbus in W. Indies

• Cabot in Labrador and N. America

• Portuguese in Brazil

• Independence generally throughout 19th c.

U.S.A.

• Cortez in Mexico

• Washington President

• Morse

Stock Exchange collapses Roosevelt New Deal

• Monroe Doctrine

• Height of Mayan civilization at Copán in Honduras and Tikal in Guatemala. Development of hieroglyphic writing, arithmetical systems, calendar, expressionist art

• Height of Mayan civilization at Chichen Itzá, Yucatán (Mexico). Knowledge of astronomy, arithmetic grows

Incas rule from Colombia to N.Chile Efficient political system. Temple of the Sun at Cuzco

• Pizarro in Peru

• Slave Trade begins

• English in Newfoundland and Virginia

• B. Franklin

• Boston Tea Party

E. A. Poe

• Lincoln frees slaves: Civil War

Literature: Mark Twain Emerson, Thoreau Longfellow, Walt Whitman

First moon landing

• Declaration of Independence

Kennedy assassinated

• Tiahuanaco Indian civilization in Bolivia at its height

• Pilgrim Fathers

Canada

• Cartier to St. Lawrence

Battle of Quebec

• Canada united

St. Lawrence Seaway opened

• Treaty of Paris

• Dominion established

French in Canada

• Upper and Lower Canada formed

THE GREAT EXPLORATIONS

As cold waters to a thirsty soul,
so is good news from a far country—PROVERBS 25

ONLY a small proportion of the world remains to be explored, for man has always been a wanderer and a searcher for new things.

In 330 B.C., the Greek, Pytheas, sailed round Britain and into the North Sea, but more important than his journey for those who were to come after him was his discovery of a means of calculating latitude.

The most important exploration of this period was made by Alexander the Great in the years 330–323 B.C., when, accompanied by land surveyors and scribes to record details of the countries through which he passed, he marched his armies through Persia to India, and, like a true explorer, returned by a different route.

In the Second and First Centuries B.C., the Romans, in the expansion of their Empire, penetrated up the Nile, as far north as the Baltic, and westwards across Europe.

Westward exploration was extended by the Norsemen, first by their discovery of Iceland about A.D. 867, then Greenland in A.D. 982, and finally by their reaching the mainland of North America about four years later.

At about the same time the Arabs were voyaging far afield in the Indian Ocean, ranging from Spain to China, and as far south as Madagascar. Their greatest traveller was Ibn Batuta, who visited every Moslem country in a remarkable series of journeys that lasted almost thirty years. Buddhist missionaries, passing to and fro from India to China across the deserts of Takla-Makan and Gobi, had come across what came to be known as the Jade Route, along which for centuries traders carried jade from the Himalayas to China in exchange for silk.

In the same period envoys were sent by the Pope to the Great Khan of the Mongol Empire, and thus opened up the way for the Polos, father and son—Venetian jewel merchants and the most famous land travellers of the age—who journeyed twice across Asia.

Meanwhile, ship-building and navigation in Europe had considerably advanced and more extended voyages were possible. By 1487 the Portuguese had coasted down Africa, and in that year the Cape of Good Hope was rounded by Bartholomew Diaz. Thus opened the Great Age of Discovery, and in thirty years all the unknown oceans were crossed—Columbus reaching America in 1492, Vasco da Gama reaching India in 1498, and Magellan sailing across the Pacific and round the whole world in 1521.

Following Columbus, the Portuguese spread down through Brazil, and the Spaniards endeavoured to cross the continent that lay between them and the riches of the East. In 1513 Balboa crossed the Isthmus of Panama, and a few years later Cortez conquered Mexico; by 1540 the Spaniards had reached the Gulf of California. The English and the French gained footings in North America, and, with the Dutch, began to seek a North-West Passage in the Arctic as a route to China. By 1650 the existence of all the continents except Antarctica had been proved, although Australia was not properly understood.

THEN followed the Age of Scientific Discovery, when expeditions by land and sea had exploration for knowledge as their aim. Our greatest leader was Captain Cook who, in three voyages, explored New Zealand, coasted along the eastern shores of Australia, circumnavigated Antarctica, and sailed through the Bering Strait. Exploration by land was slower; it was not until the 19th century that English and American expeditions crossed North America and South America was fully penetrated.

More dramatic achievements came in other parts of the world. The harsh interior of Australia was explored remarkably quickly thanks to men like Stuart and Burke who crossed the continent from south to north in the 1860s. Africa was the last major continent to be crossed. Serious exploration was begun in 1795 by Mungo Park in West Africa, and thirty years later the Lander brothers found the mouth of the river Niger. Great interest was then attached to discovering the sources of the Nile, starting with Burton and Speke. In 1849, David Livingstone, who usually travelled alone and was perhaps the greatest land explorer ever known, began his journeys in Southern and Central Africa: his work was continued after his death by his friend, Stanley, who finally resolved the Nile problem by exploring Lake Edward in 1888.

Major interest was then centred round the north and south Polar regions. In 1909 the American, Peary, was the first to reach the North Pole, and in 1958 the American submarine *Nautilus* travelled *beneath* it. In 1911 the Norwegian, Amundsen, was the first to reach the South Pole, followed a month later by the Englishman, Scott; and in 1955–58, Sir Vivian Fuchs led a British Commonwealth expedition which crossed the Antarctic continent from the Weddell Sea to the Ross Sea.

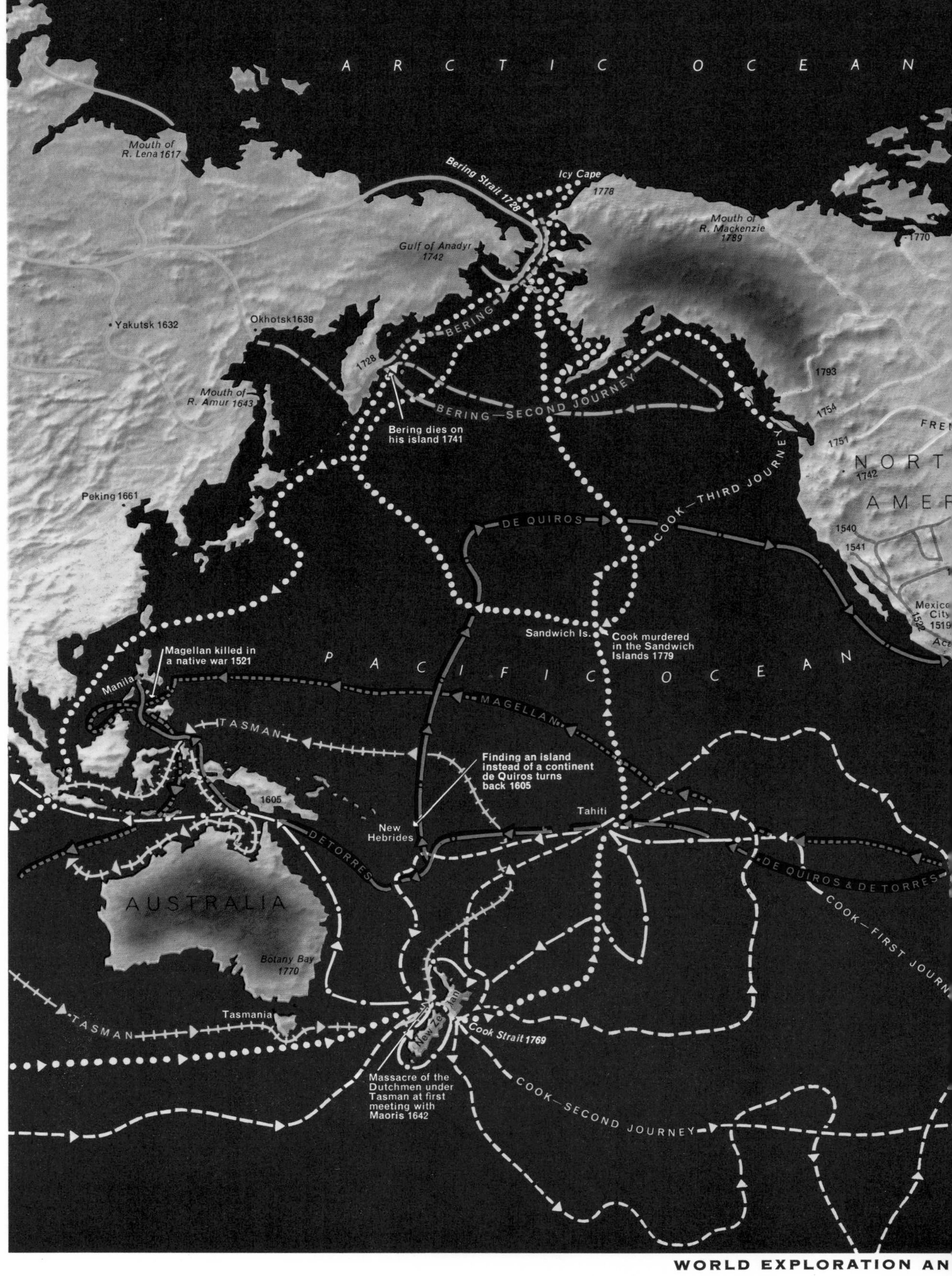

WORLD EXPLORATION AN

SPANISH EXPLORERS		PORTUGUESE EXPLORERS	
⟶	CHRISTOPHER COLUMBUS 1492-1493	⟶	VASCO DA GAMA 1497-1499
⟶	FERDINAND MAGELLAN 1519-1522		PAPAL EXPLORERS
⟶	PEDRO FERNANDES DE QUIROS & LUIS VAEZ DE TORRES 1605-1606	⟶	JOHN GRUEBER & ALBERT D'ORVILLE 1661-1664

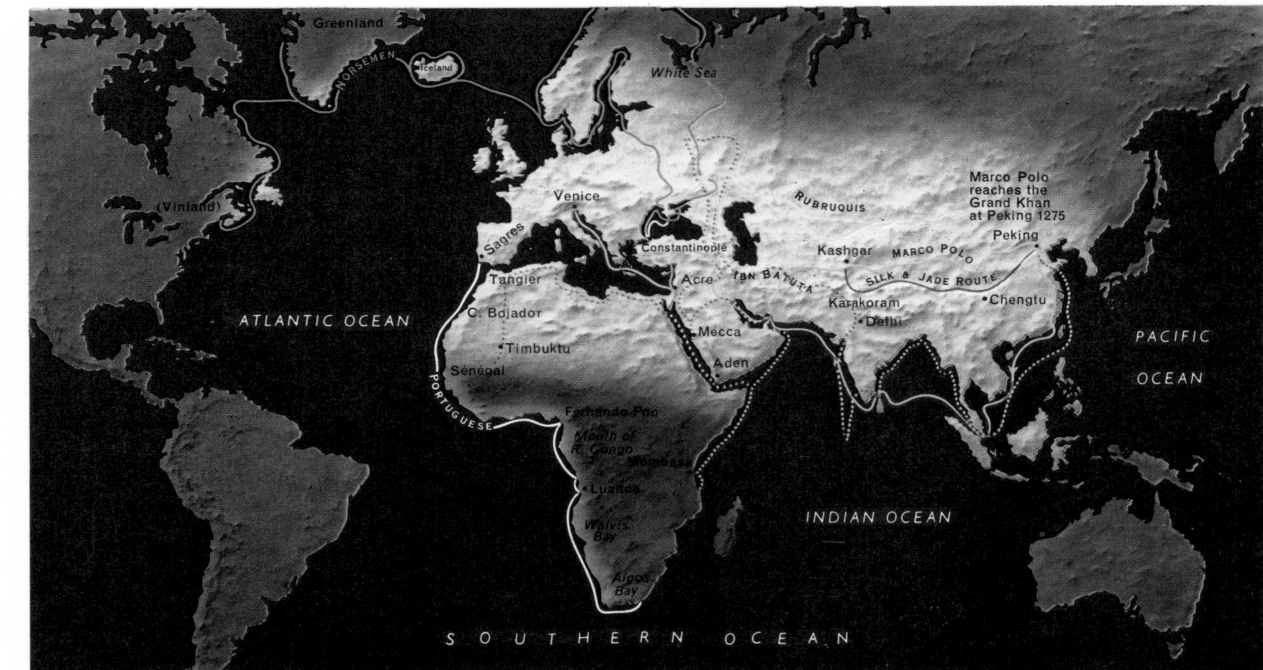

THE WORLD AS KNOWN IN 1490

⟶	SILK & JADE ROUTE	⟶	WILLIAM OF RUBRUCK 1252-1255	⟶	IBN BATUTA 1324-1355
⟶	NORSEMEN C. A.D. 1000	⟶	MARCO POLO 1271-1295	⟶	PORTUGUESE 1420-1487

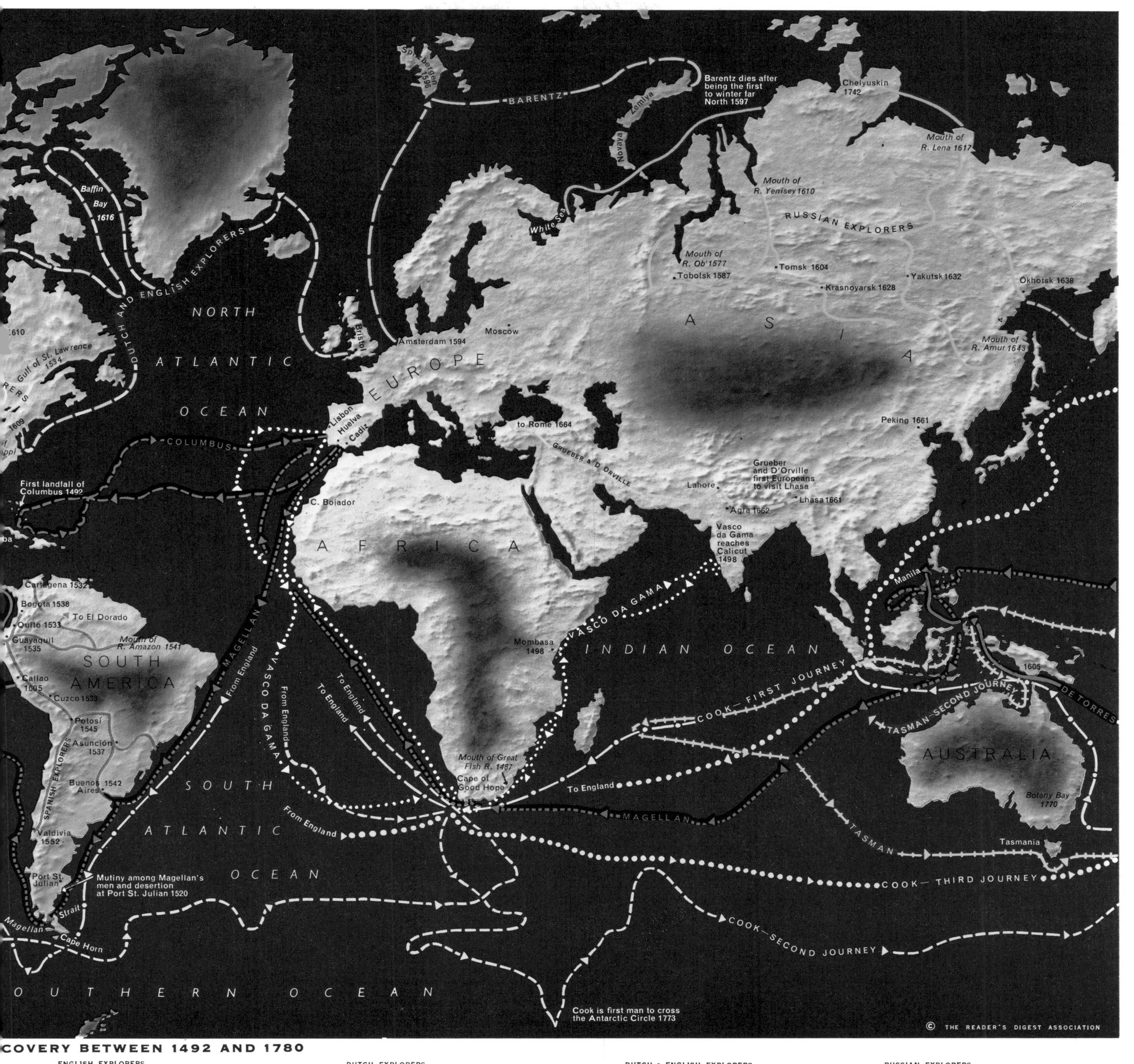

DISCOVERY BETWEEN 1492 AND 1780

ENGLISH EXPLORERS	DUTCH EXPLORERS	DUTCH & ENGLISH EXPLORERS	RUSSIAN EXPLORERS
JAMES COOK—FIRST JOURNEY 1768-1771	WILLIAM BARENTZ 1594-1597		VITUS BERING—FIRST JOURNEY 1728-1729
JAMES COOK—SECOND JOURNEY 1772-1775	ABEL TASMAN 1642-1644	FRENCH EXPLORERS	VITUS BERING—SECOND JOURNEY 1741
JAMES COOK—THIRD JOURNEY 1776-1780			

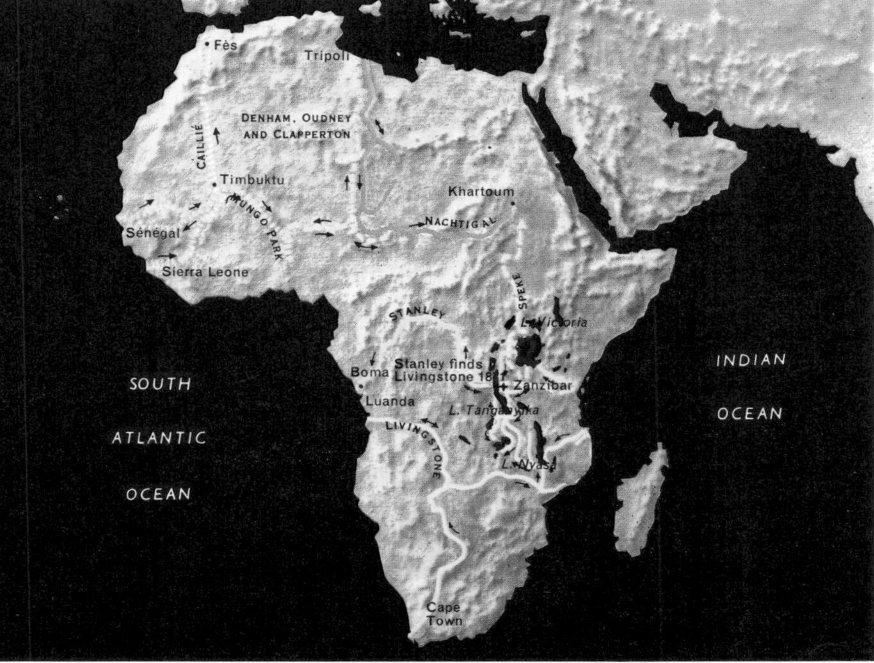

THE OPENING UP OF AFRICA

MUNGO PARK 1795-1797; 1805-1806	RENÉ CAILLIÉ 1827-1828	SPEKE WITH BURTON 1857-1859
DENHAM, OUDNEY AND CLAPPERTON 1822-1824	LIVINGSTONE 1849-1856; 1858-1864; 1866-1873	SPEKE WITH GRANT 1860-1863
	STANLEY 1874-1877	NACHTIGAL 1869-1874

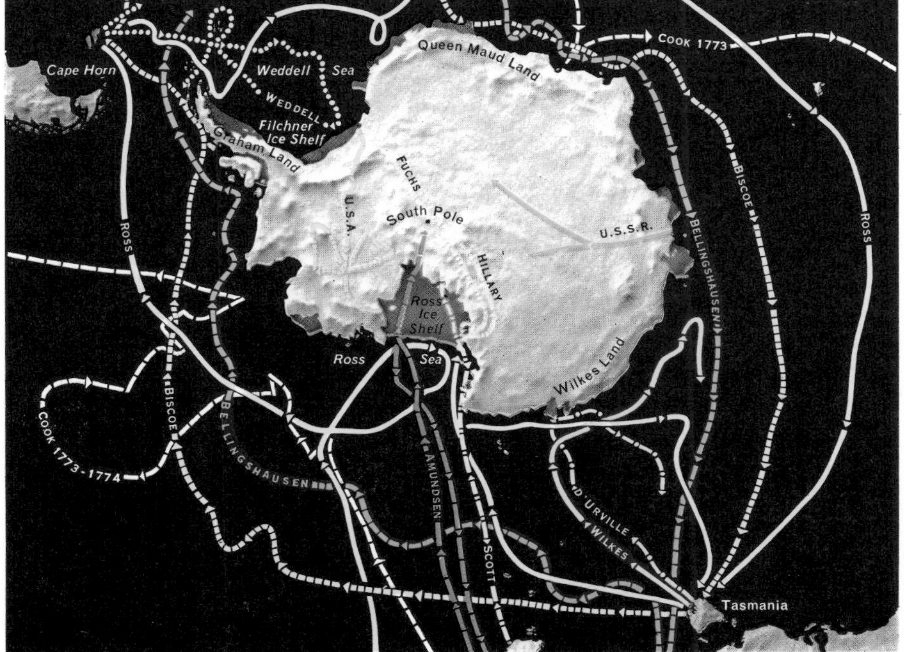

EXPLORATION OF ANTARCTICA

BELLINGSHAUSEN 1819-1822	WILKES 1840	FUCHS 1955-1958
BISCOE 1831-1832	ROSS 1840-1843	HILLARY 1957-1958
WEDDELL 1822-1823	AMUNDSEN 1911-1912	U.S.A. 1957-1960
DUMONT D'URVILLE 1840	SCOTT 1910-1913	U.S.S.R. 1957-1960

135

RELIGIONS—
THEIR ORIGINS AND ADHERENTS

In him we live, and move, and have our being — ACTS 17

RELIGION knows neither frontiers nor geographical barriers. With the exception of tribal religions which, though differing from one another in form and ritual, all seek to explain the mystery of life by insisting that Nature is animated by spirits, most religions have, for one reason or another, spread beyond the lands of their origins.

JUDAISM, which began with Abraham and Moses before the 13th century B.C., when many advanced societies worshipped a multiplicity of gods, is uncompromisingly monotheistic. After

its clash with Imperial Rome and the destruction of Jerusalem in A.D. 70 and 135, the Jews were expelled from the Holy Land, and a Jewish state was not again established in Palestine until 1948—almost 2,000 years later—although the majority of adherents of Judaism remain scattered throughout the world.

HINDUISM, the age-old religion of India, which honours many gods and goddesses—all of whom, however, are regarded as manifestations of the one divine spirit, Brahman—introduced into religious thinking the concept that spiritual peace and happiness can be attained only through physical and mental discipline (*yoga*—yoke). Its rigid caste divisions have been the target of innumerable reformers—among them men like Gandhi, Tagore and Bhave.

BUDDHISM, an offshoot of Hinduism, was founded by Gautama (563–483 B.C.) in North India and insists on rigid moral and

spiritual discipline in order to attain Nirvana, a condition where *karma* (deeds) have perished, the cycle of rebirth on earth has ceased, and supreme peace is attained. It spread widely throughout Asia, developing many local variations of philosophy, form and practice. In Japan, ZEN (meditation) Buddhism teaches enlightenment, while elsewhere many Buddhist teachers hold that salvation for all is possible only through the grace of Buddhas and *Bodhisattvas* (Beings of Enlightenment).

In China, from the 1st century A.D. onwards, Buddhism became mingled with the already established religions of CONFUCIANISM and TAOISM. Confucius' philosophy, which was of little influence in his own lifetime (551–479 B.C.), had been elaborated by subsequent generations of scholars both to provide a moral basis for the political structure of Imperial China and to embrace the hallowed forms of ancestor worship which

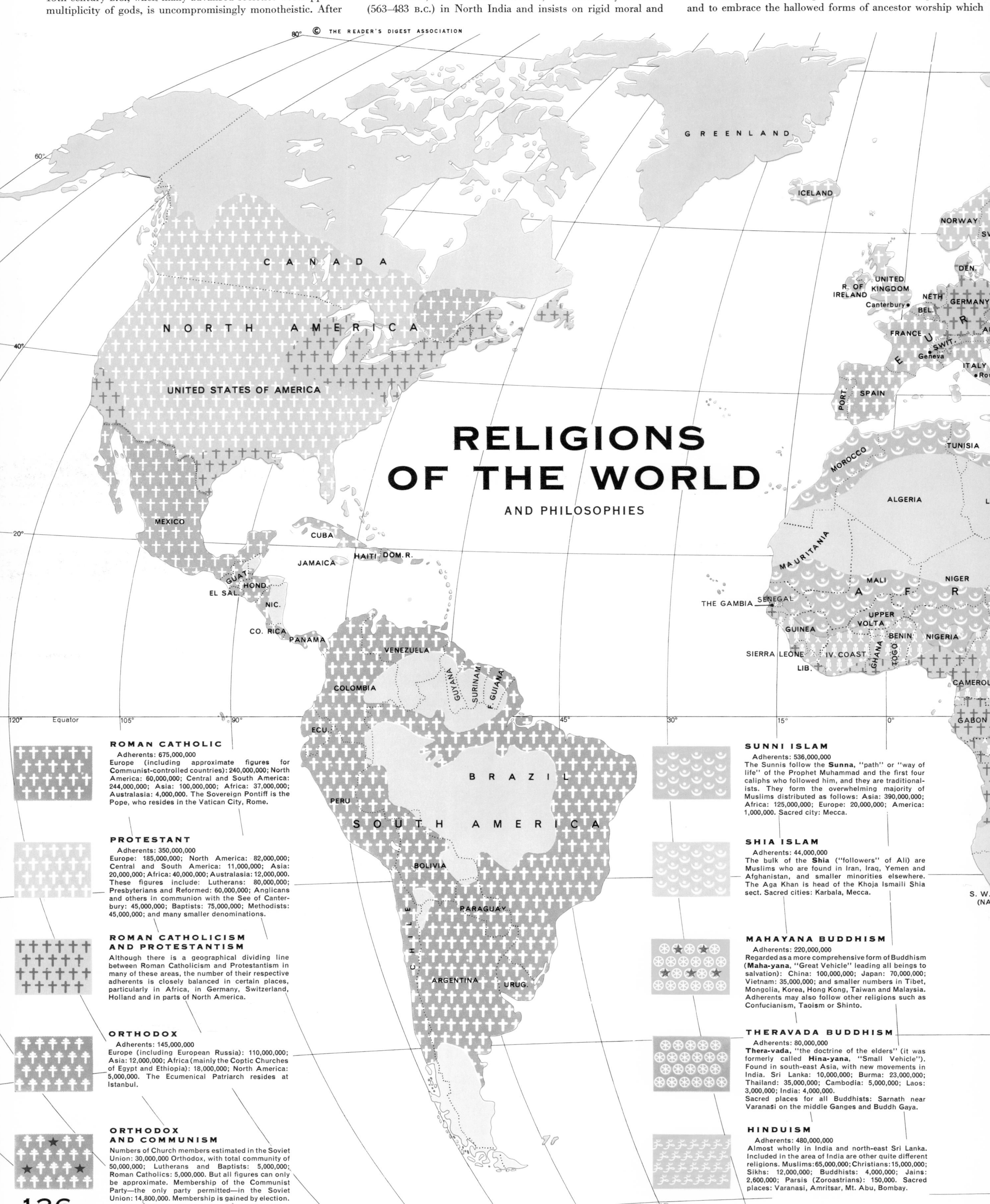

80° © THE READER'S DIGEST ASSOCIATION

RELIGIONS
OF THE WORLD
AND PHILOSOPHIES

ROMAN CATHOLIC
Adherents: 675,000,000
Europe (including approximate figures for Communist-controlled countries): 240,000,000; North America: 60,000,000; Central and South America: 244,000,000; Asia: 100,000,000; Africa: 37,000,000; Australasia: 4,000,000. The Sovereign Pontiff is the Pope, who resides in the Vatican City, Rome.

PROTESTANT
Adherents: 350,000,000
Europe: 185,000,000; North America: 82,000,000; Central and South America: 11,000,000; Asia: 20,000,000; Africa: 40,000,000; Australasia: 12,000,000. These figures include: Lutherans: 80,000,000; Presbyterians and Reformed: 60,000,000; Anglicans and others in communion with the See of Canterbury: 45,000,000; Baptists: 75,000,000; Methodists: 45,000,000; and many smaller denominations.

ROMAN CATHOLICISM AND PROTESTANTISM
Although there is a geographical dividing line between Roman Catholicism and Protestantism in many of these areas, the number of their respective adherents is closely balanced in certain places, particularly in Africa, in Germany, Switzerland, Holland and in parts of North America.

ORTHODOX
Adherents: 145,000,000
Europe (including European Russia): 110,000,000; Asia: 12,000,000; Africa (mainly the Coptic Churches of Egypt and Ethiopia): 18,000,000; North America: 5,000,000. The Ecumenical Patriarch resides at Istanbul.

ORTHODOX AND COMMUNISM
Numbers of Church members estimated in the Soviet Union: 30,000,000 Orthodox, with total community of 50,000,000; Lutherans and Baptists: 5,000,000; Roman Catholics: 5,000,000. But all figures can only be approximate. Membership of the Communist Party—the only party permitted in the Soviet Union: 14,800,000. Membership is gained by election.

SUNNI ISLAM
Adherents: 536,000,000
The Sunnis follow the **Sunna**, "path" or "way of life" of the Prophet Muhammad and the first four caliphs who followed him, and they are traditionalists. They form the overwhelming majority of Muslims distributed as follows: Asia: 390,000,000; Africa: 125,000,000; Europe: 20,000,000; America: 1,000,000. Sacred city: Mecca.

SHIA ISLAM
Adherents: 44,000,000
The bulk of the **Shia** ("followers" of Ali) are Muslims who are found in Iran, Iraq, Yemen and Afghanistan, and smaller minorities elsewhere. The Aga Khan is head of the Khoja Ismaili Shia sect. Sacred cities: Karbala, Mecca.

MAHAYANA BUDDHISM
Adherents: 220,000,000
Regarded as a more comprehensive form of Buddhism (**Maha-yana**, "Great Vehicle" leading all beings to salvation): China: 100,000,000; Japan: 70,000,000; Vietnam: 35,000,000; and smaller numbers in Tibet, Mongolia, Korea, Hong Kong, Taiwan and Malaysia. Adherents may also follow other religions such as Confucianism, Taoism or Shinto.

THERAVADA BUDDHISM
Adherents: 80,000,000
Thera-vada, "the doctrine of the elders" (it was formerly called **Hina-yana**, "Small Vehicle"). Found in south-east Asia, with new movements in India. Sri Lanka: 10,000,000; Burma: 23,000,000; Thailand: 35,000,000; Cambodia: 5,000,000; Laos: 3,000,000; India: 4,000,000.
Sacred places for all Buddhists: Sarnath near Varanasi on the middle Ganges and Buddh Gaya.

HINDUISM
Adherents: 480,000,000
Almost wholly in India and north-east Sri Lanka. Included in the area of India are other quite different religions. Muslims: 65,000,000; Christians: 15,000,000; Sikhs: 12,000,000; Buddhists: 4,000,000; Jains: 2,600,000; Parsis (Zoroastrians): 150,000. Sacred places: Varanasi, Amritsar, Mt. Abu, Bombay.

have always been practised in China: Taoism, based on teachings attributed to Lao Tse in the 6th century B.C., taught a quietist religion of living in the way (tao) of nature.

In Japan, from the 6th century A.D. onwards, Buddhism became mingled with the ancient religion of SHINTO, a nature worship of a multiplicity of deities honoured at shrines like that of Amaterasu, the Sun Goddess, at Ise, and many Japanese still attend the places of worship of both faiths.

One of the most active proselytizing faiths in the history of religion, ISLAM, was carried across Asia and Africa; it swept round the southern shores of the Mediterranean, crossed the Strait of Gibraltar into Spain and entered France within a hundred years of the death of its founder, Muhammad (A.D. 570–632). Almost a thousand years later, Islamic power penetrated far into Central Europe up to the walls of Vienna, and

when the tide eventually receded, it left behind, particularly in the Balkans, innumerable islands of Muslim communities.

The religion with the largest number of adherents and the most pronounced missionary zeal in the world today is CHRISTIANITY. It was founded in the 1st century A.D. by Jesus of Nazareth, who was accepted as the Christ, the Messiah or Anointed One, by his disciples who were then called Christians. His Crucifixion in Jerusalem and his Resurrection furnished the main articles of faith and the Symbol of the Cross.

Christianity spread quickly through the Roman Empire, where it became the official religion in the 4th century A.D., with the Pope in Rome—the successor of St. Peter, Christ's chief disciple—recognized in the West as the supreme authority in a rapidly emerging Church hierarchy. The Eastern Church, which began in the Holy Land before there were any Christians in

Rome, rejected papal authority in the 11th century A.D.; and the Orthodox Church—comprising the historical patriarchal sees of Jerusalem, Antioch, Alexandria and Constantinople, to which was later added the patriarchate of Moscow (the largest today)—continued as a federation of mutually independent churches, standing in full communion with one another and united as equals. The ancient Armenian Jacobite, Syrian, Indian, and Coptic Ethiopian and Egyptian Churches are known, however, as the Oriental Orthodox Churches.

A further rupture in Christian unity came in the 16th century with the Reformation movements of Protestantism, and Protestantism itself is now divided into many denominations. But the settlement of new continents has carried Christianity in one form or another to almost all parts of the world, and strong movements for Christian reunion are now in force.

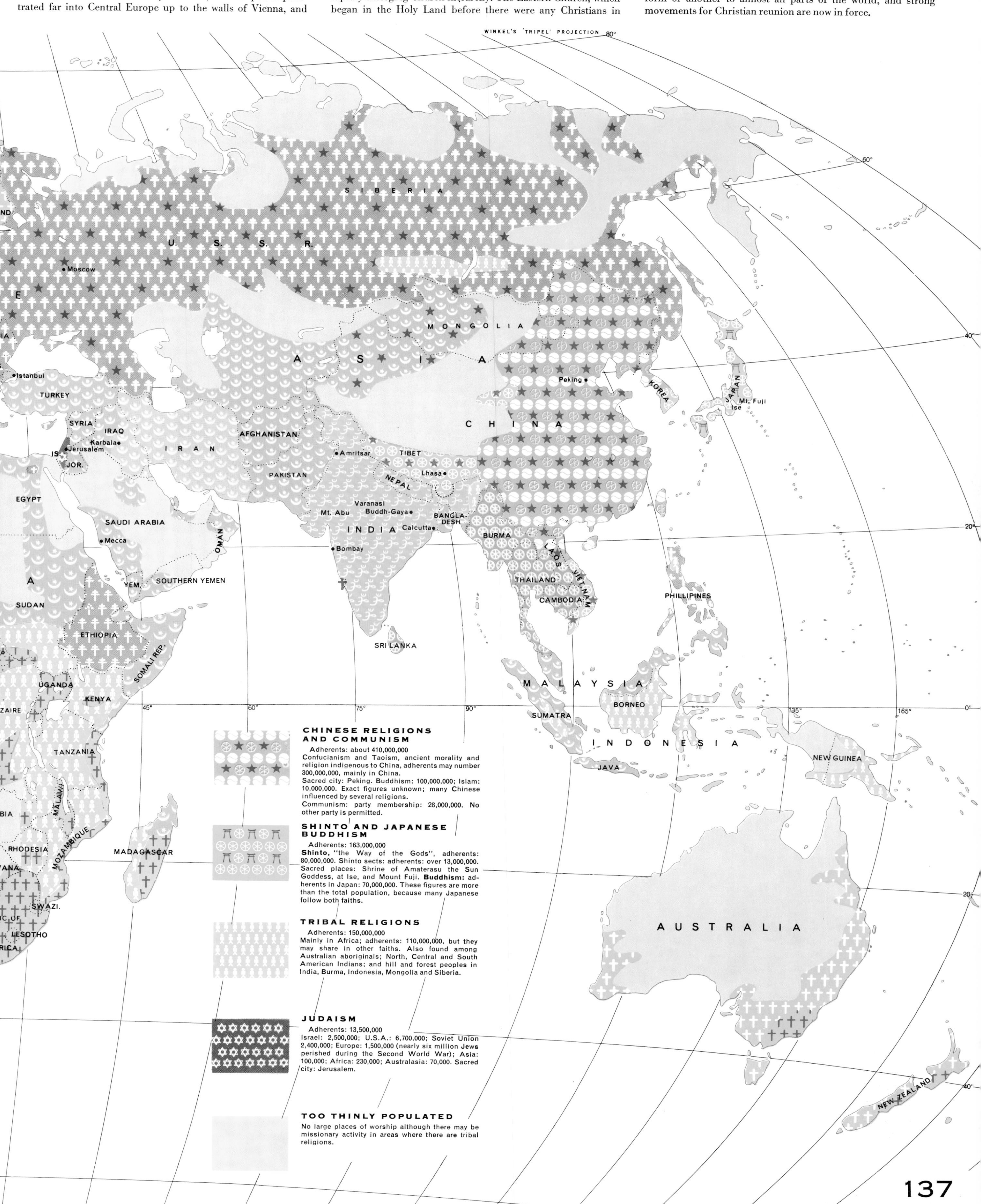

CHINESE RELIGIONS AND COMMUNISM

Adherents: about 410,000,000
Confucianism and Taoism, ancient morality and religion indigenous to China, adherents may number 300,000,000, mainly in China.
Sacred city: Peking. Buddhism: 100,000,000; Islam: 10,000,000. Exact figures unknown; many Chinese influenced by several religions.
Communism: party membership: 28,000,000. No other party is permitted.

SHINTO AND JAPANESE BUDDHISM

Adherents: 163,000,000
Shinto, "the Way of the Gods", adherents: 80,000,000. Shinto sects: adherents: over 13,000,000. Sacred places: Shrine of Amaterasu the Sun Goddess, at Ise, and Mount Fuji. **Buddhism**: adherents in Japan: 70,000,000. These figures are more than the total population, because many Japanese follow both faiths.

TRIBAL RELIGIONS

Adherents: 150,000,000
Mainly in Africa; adherents: 110,000,000, but they may share in other faiths. Also found among Australian aboriginals; North, Central and South American Indians; and hill and forest peoples in India, Burma, Indonesia, Mongolia and Siberia.

JUDAISM

Adherents: 13,500,000
Israel: 2,500,000; U.S.A.: 6,700,000; Soviet Union 2,400,000; Europe: 1,500,000 (nearly six million Jews perished during the Second World War); Asia: 100,000; Africa: 230,000; Australasia: 70,000. Sacred city: Jerusalem.

TOO THINLY POPULATED

No large places of worship although there may be missionary activity in areas where there are tribal religions.

VERTICAL DISTRIBUTION OF CLOUDS

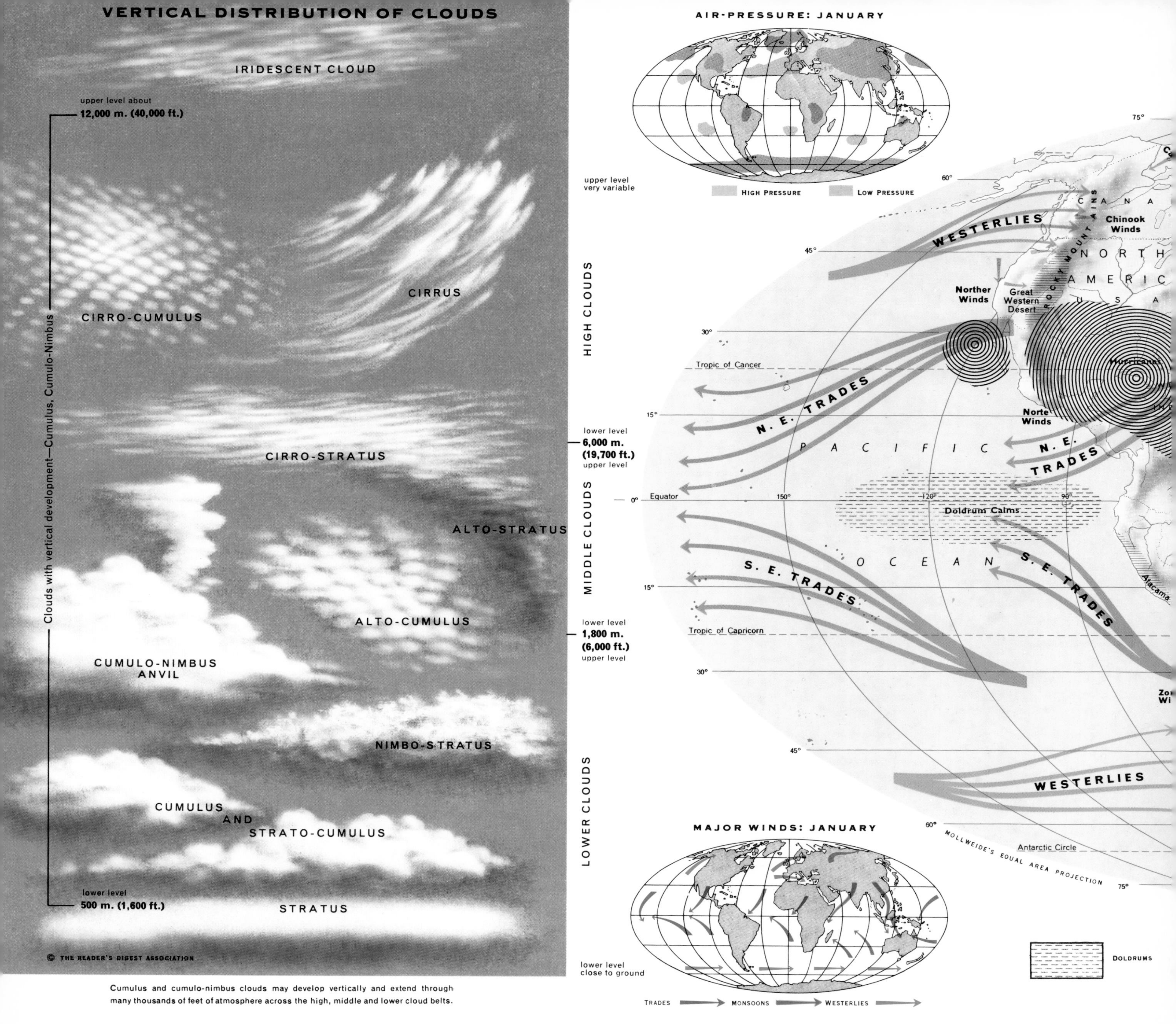

IRIDESCENT CLOUD

upper level about
— 12,000 m. (40,000 ft.)

CIRRUS

CIRRO-CUMULUS

Clouds with vertical development—Cumulus, Cumulo-Nimbus

CIRRO-STRATUS

ALTO-STRATUS

HIGH CLOUDS

upper level
very variable

ALTO-CUMULUS

MIDDLE CLOUDS

lower level
— 6,000 m.
(19,700 ft.)
upper level

CUMULO-NIMBUS
ANVIL

lower level
1,800 m.
(6,000 ft.)
upper level

NIMBO-STRATUS

LOWER CLOUDS

CUMULUS
AND
STRATO-CUMULUS

lower level
500 m. (1,600 ft.)

STRATUS

© THE READER'S DIGEST ASSOCIATION

Cumulus and cumulo-nimbus clouds may develop vertically and extend through
many thousands of feet of atmosphere across the high, middle and lower cloud belts.

AIR-PRESSURE: JANUARY

HIGH PRESSURE   LOW PRESSURE

WESTERLIES   Chinook
                    Winds
Norther
Winds   Great
               Western
               Desert   NORTH
                         AMERICA
                              USA

N. E. TRADES

Norte
Winds

PACIFIC   N. E.
                 TRADES

Tropic of Cancer

Equator   Doldrum Calms

OCEAN   S. E. TRADES

S. E. TRADES

Tropic of Capricorn   Atacama

Zo.
Wi.

WESTERLIES

MOLLWEIDE'S EQUAL AREA PROJECTION
Antarctic Circle

MAJOR WINDS: JANUARY

lower level
close to ground

TRADES ——→   MONSOONS ——→   WESTERLIES ——→

DOLDRUMS

HOW HOT IS IT?

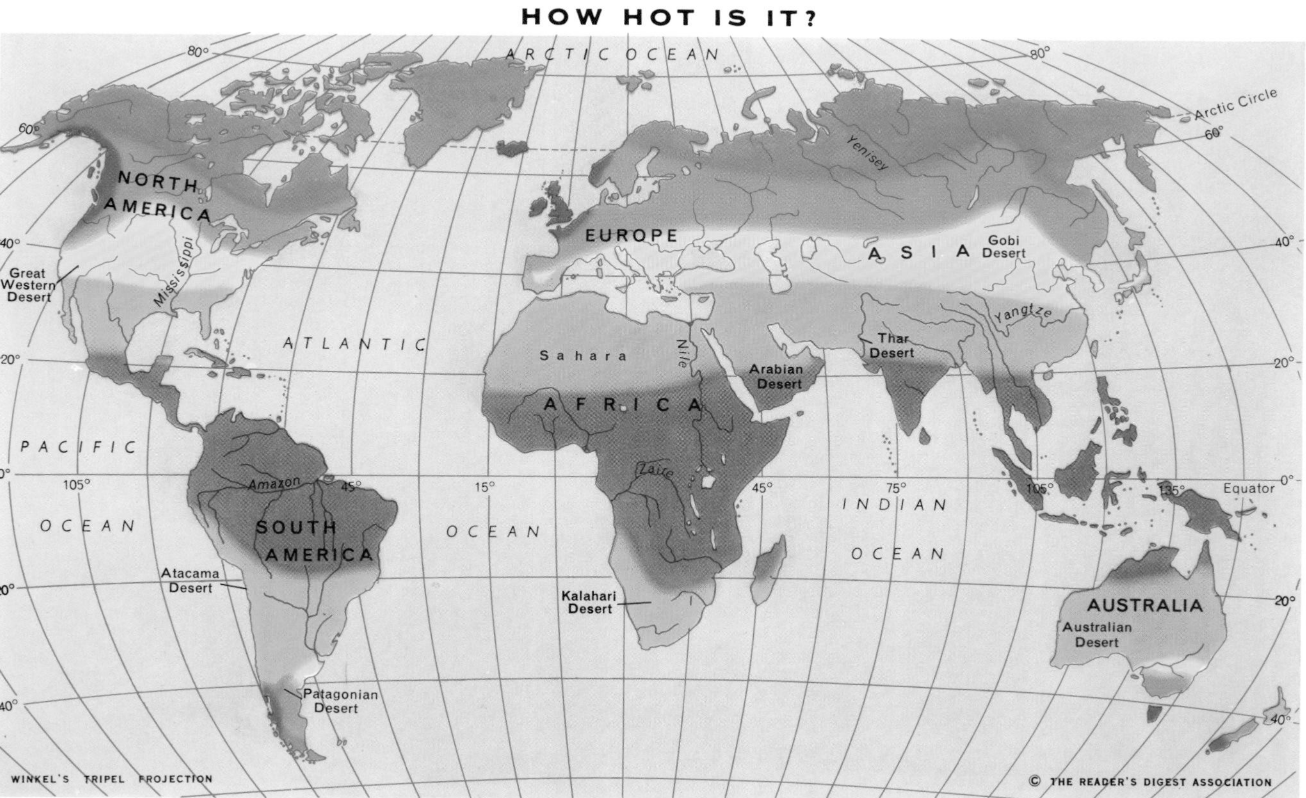

ARCTIC OCEAN   Arctic Circle

NORTH
AMERICA   EUROPE   Yenisey
                                          ASIA   Gobi
Great   Desert
Western   Thar
Desert   ATLANTIC   Sahara   Nile   Desert   Arabian
                                                              Desert
PACIFIC   AFRICA   Yangtze

OCEAN   Amazon   INDIAN
SOUTH   Zaire   OCEAN
AMERICA   OCEAN
Atacama   Kalahari
Desert   Desert   AUSTRALIA
                                                     Australian
                                                     Desert
Patagonian
Desert

WINKEL'S TRIPEL PROJECTION   © THE READER'S DIGEST ASSOCIATION

	ALWAYS COLD
	WARM SUMMER COLD WINTER
	HOT SUMMER COLD WINTER
	COOL SUMMER MILD WINTER
	HOT SUMMER WARM WINTER
	ALWAYS HOT

The difference in temperature between the Tropics and the Poles is not due to the fact that the Poles are fractionally further from the Sun. It is caused by the Earth's curvature. In tropical latitudes the Sun's rays strike the surface of the Earth vertically. Outside them the rays strike the Earth obliquely, so that a 'package' of rays spreads over a greater area of land, as well as being diffused by passing through a greater depth of atmosphere. Air is mainly warmed by contact with the Earth's surface which has absorbed heat from the Sun. The sea warms up less rapidly than the land but retains heat longer, so coastal areas have a more equable climate than those far inland.

Tropical heat is partly dissipated by ocean currents and winds. Because of the warm Gulf Stream and south-westerly winds, Britain enjoys an average temperature of 10°C, whilst Labrador, on the same latitude, averages only 0°C. Altitude also affects temperature which drops about 1°C for every 160 metre rise above sea level.

PATTERNS

*But there went up a mist from the earth, which
watered the whole face of the ground—* GENESIS 2

CLIMATE is determined by latitude and by the average conditions of temperature, humidity, prevailing winds and rainfall of a region. These basic conditions can be modified by the effect of warm or cold ocean currents. The Earth's axis is tilted at an angle of 23·5° from the perpendicular to its orbital plane, which means that during its annual orbit the planet alternately presents its northern and southern hemisphere to the Sun. This causes a seasonal temperature variation which is most marked outside the tropics. The climate within the tropics remains fairly stable because even when the Sun's rays are not directly overhead, the angle at which they hit the Earth does not change significantly and the amount of atmosphere the rays have to penetrate is about the same. This seasonal variation also causes the air-pressure belts to move north and south as shown on the small pressure maps.

The atmosphere is said to have high or low pressure according to the density of the air, and winds are created by differences in pressure. For example, in the equatorial low-pressure areas, air heated by the Sun rises and moves outwards to the north and south. It eventually cools, creating high pressure where it sinks, usually around 30°N and 30°S. This causes winds which blow along the surface of the Earth towards the low pressure in the tropics. These winds are deflected to the left in the southern hemisphere and to the right in the northern hemisphere by the rotation of the Earth. Besides the Trade winds, the other major wind belts are the Westerlies and Polar winds, circulating in a similar way.

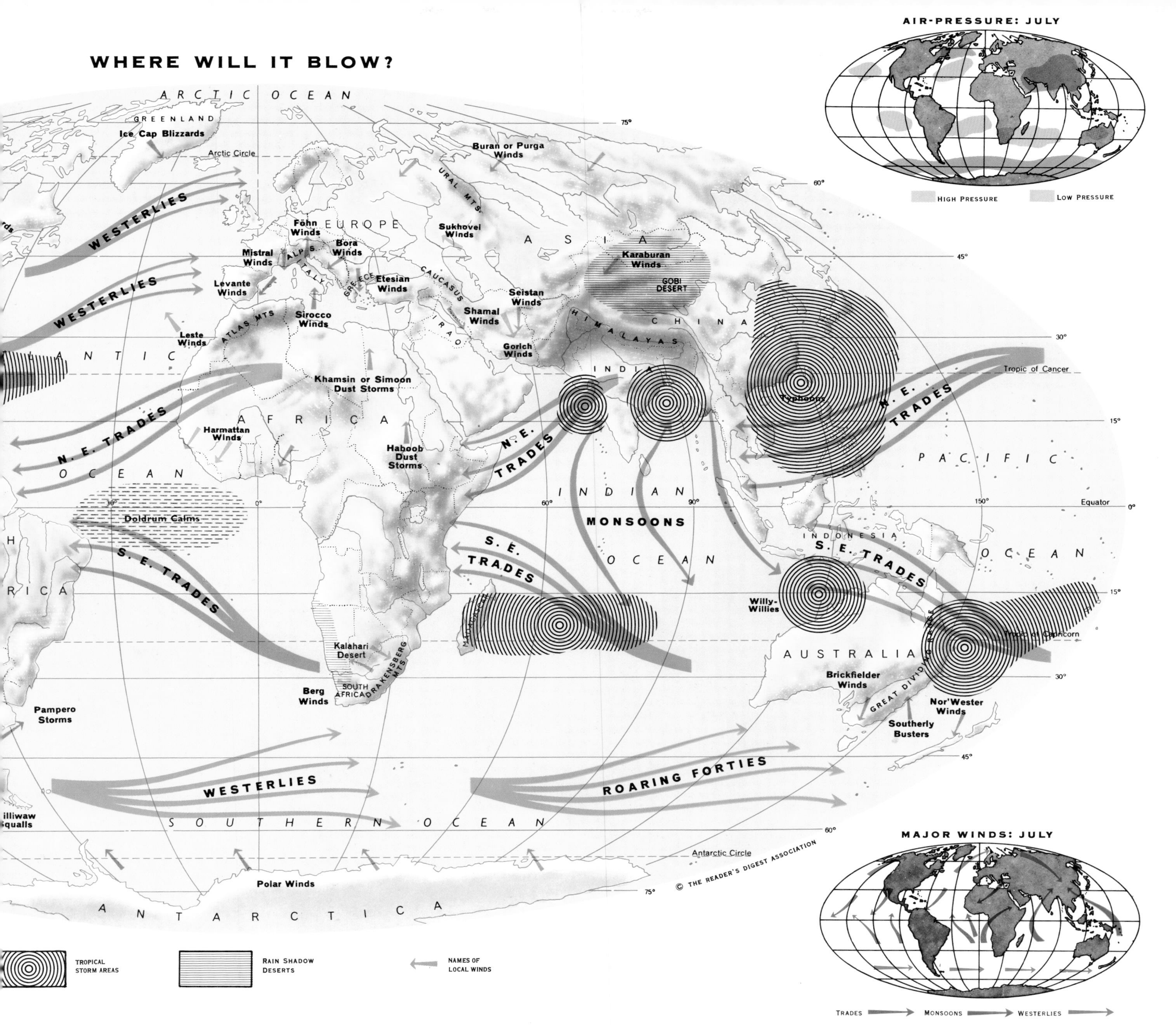

WHERE WILL IT BLOW?

AIR-PRESSURE: JULY

HIGH PRESSURE   LOW PRESSURE

ARCTIC OCEAN
GREENLAND
Ice Cap Blizzards
Arctic Circle
WESTERLIES
WESTERLIES
EUROPE
Föhn Winds
Mistral Winds
Bora Winds
ALPS
Levante Winds
Etesian Winds
GREECE
Leste Winds
ATLAS MTS
Sirocco Winds
ITALY
CAUCASUS
IRAQ
Buran or Purga Winds
URAL MTS
ASIA
Sukhovei Winds
Karaburan Winds
GOBI DESERT
Seistan Winds
Shamal Winds
Gorich Winds
HIMALAYAS
CHINA
Typhoons
N.E. TRADES
Tropic of Cancer
N.E. TRADES
ATLANTIC
N.E. TRADES
AFRICA
Khamsin or Simoon Dust Storms
Harmattan Winds
Haboob Dust Storms
INDIA
N.E. TRADES
PACIFIC
Doldrum Calms
OCEAN
INDIAN OCEAN
MONSOONS
Equator
S.E. TRADES
S.E. TRADES
INDONESIA
S.E. TRADES
OCEAN
AFRICA
Kalahari Desert
SOUTH AFRICA
DRAKENSBERG MTS
Berg Winds
Willy-Willies
AUSTRALIA
Tropic of Capricorn
Brickfielder Winds
GREAT DIVIDING RANGE
Nor'Wester Winds
Pampero Storms
Southerly Busters
WESTERLIES
ROARING FORTIES
Williwaw Squalls
SOUTHERN OCEAN
Antarctic Circle
© THE READER'S DIGEST ASSOCIATION
Polar Winds
ANTARCTICA

TROPICAL STORM AREAS
RAIN SHADOW DESERTS
NAMES OF LOCAL WINDS

MAJOR WINDS: JULY

TRADES   MONSOONS   WESTERLIES

...OF CLIMATE

During the summer months, the land becomes hotter than the sea and the air above rises, causing surface winds to blow in from the sea to take its place. When winter comes, the land quickly loses its heat, becoming cooler than the sea and so winds blow outwards over the sea, towards the areas of low pressure. The same principle applies on a smaller time scale in most coastal areas. During the day, winds come from the sea, but at night, as the land cools, the winds are from land to sea.

The Doldrum Calms are areas of low pressure near the Equator where rising hot air creates calms and variable winds, bringing thunderstorms. Farther from the Equator, occasional violent storms occur known as typhoons in the East, cyclones in the Bay of Bengal and hurricanes in the Caribbean.

In many areas local winds and currents can have a major effect on the climate. The cold Mistral wind, for example, lowers temperatures in the Rhône valley between the Alps and the Central Massif, while the Chinook wind in Canada is warm and helps melt the snows. Similarly, the North Atlantic Drift brings warm waters to the western shores of the British Isles and helps to raise temperatures.

The main types of climate produced by all of these factors are 'humid equatorial' climates, characterized by high temperatures and heavy rainfall; 'desert' climates, which are dry and hot with a wide range of temperature between day and night; 'Mediterranean' climates with mild winters and dry summers; 'temperate maritime' climates, with a small range of temperature and high humidity; 'continental' climates, characterized by strong seasonal variations in temperature; and 'polar' and 'mountain' climates which have low temperatures with either snow or heavy rainfall.

HOW WET IS IT?

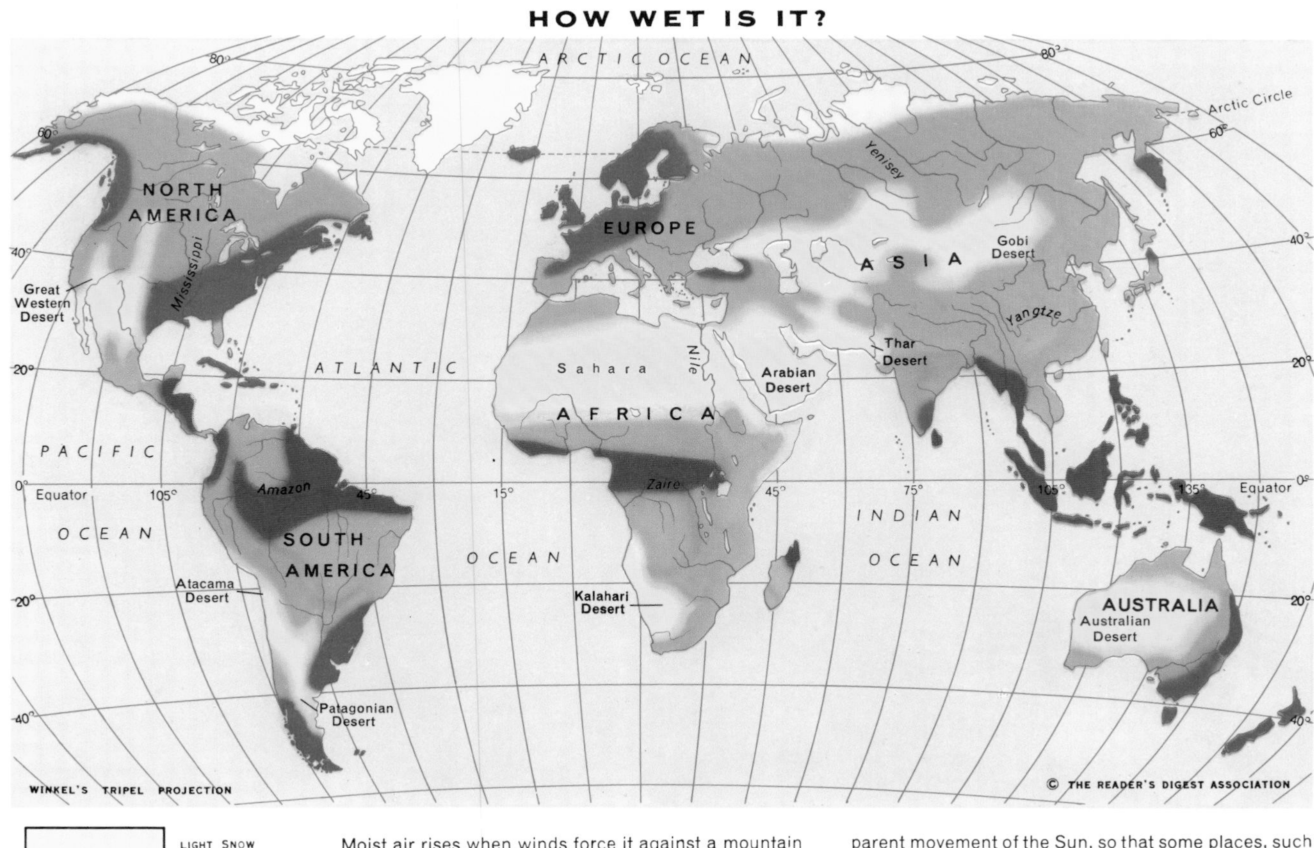

ARCTIC OCEAN
Arctic Circle
NORTH AMERICA
EUROPE
ASIA
Great Western Desert
Gobi Desert
Mississippi
Yenisey
Yangtze
Thar Desert
ATLANTIC
Sahara
Nile
Arabian Desert
PACIFIC OCEAN
AFRICA
Amazon
Equator
Zaire
INDIAN OCEAN
SOUTH AMERICA
Atacama Desert
Kalahari Desert
AUSTRALIA
Australian Desert
Patagonian Desert
WINKEL'S TRIPEL PROJECTION
© THE READER'S DIGEST ASSOCIATION

LIGHT SNOW
SELDOM RAINY
LIGHT SEASONAL RAIN
HEAVY SEASONAL RAIN
MODERATE RAINFALL EVERY MONTH
HEAVY RAINFALL EVERY MONTH

Moist air rises when winds force it against a mountain or blow it over heavier, colder air. As the moist air rises it cools and condenses into minute drops of water, forming clouds. When the droplets in the clouds become too heavy to be sustained, they fall as rain.

Air is most likely to be moist over the sea and where temperatures are high. The wettest places of all are in the Tropics, where the sea air is blown against the windward slopes of high mountains. Rainfall belts move northwards and southwards following the ap-parent movement of the Sun, so that some places, such as the Mediterranean, have most of their rain in the winter, while others, such as the Monsoon regions, have most in the summer.

The driest areas on Earth are where winds have blown for long distances over heated land. But a local dry area may be caused by a range of mountains extracting all the rain on its windward side, leaving what is called a rain-shadow on its leeward side. Such an area is the desert of Northern Chile.

FRONTIERS OF CULTIVATION

DEVELOPMENT OF THE NATURAL AND CULTIVATED AREAS OF THE WORLD

And the earth brought forth grass, herb yielding seed after its kind,
tree bearing fruit, wherein is the seed thereof, after its kind — GENESIS 1

ONLY about one-tenth of the world's land surface is under cultivation and the cultivated areas generally contain the main concentrations of world population. The uncultivated areas are mostly unsuitable for farming because they are too dry or cold, or too unhealthy for settlement. However, the tropical rain forests can be very productive; new technology and the increasing pressures of population are constantly extending the frontiers of cultivation.

The maintenance of soil fertility is of the first importance in cultivated areas, because bad husbandry destroys the natural structure of the soil, turning it into dust, as in the American Dust Bowl of the 1930s. Another danger is deforestation, which can result in the top soil being washed off unprotected slopes by rain, as has been the case in Yugoslavia and Greece, and throughout the tropics.

In Europe, the U.S.S.R., North America and parts of South America, Africa and Australasia, intensive, highly mechanized cultivation is practised on a commercial scale and the farms are often large. Elsewhere in Africa, and even more so in South and East Asia, where there are some of the densest rural populations in the world, farms are small and simple hand tools are used.

In the areas of scattered, less intensive cultivation, traditional methods of farming are often combined with livestock husbandry. Most produce is consumed by the people growing it, but surpluses are marketed.

The areas of shifting cultivation are found in and around the tropical rain forests, where land is cleared as it is needed and, after being denuded of its fertility, is temporarily abandoned. Where the land is cleared and maintained by modern methods, it can support perennial cash crops such as rubber, sugar, tea, oil-palm and cocoa. These forests are a valuable source of timber, though transport costs have limited their exploitation.

Mountain slopes, savannah and scrubland provide grazing for cattle and sheep. In the more temperate parts of these areas, crops such as maize, millet, cotton and groundnuts, or wheat and barley can be grown, but most areas are too dry and are better developed for livestock.

The soils of deserts and semi-arid regions, when irrigated, are often very fertile and productive, as in the Nile Valley, the Indus Plains and lower Colorado. Irrigation has been used as an aid to cultivation since earliest times and water distribution systems built more than 2,000 years ago are still in use in China.

Since the 1960s, there have been considerable technical advances with new varieties of cereals which, combined with artificial fertilizers and a more careful use of water, have resulted in increased yields of up to 100 per cent. The impact has been greatest on the Indian sub-continent, but improvements have also been made in North Africa and Central America.

The methods of increasing food productivity are numerous: the breeding of better, disease-and-pest-resistant varieties of seed; the building up of soil fertility through the use of legumes and crop rotation; forest conservation and afforestation; the better use of organic wastes and artificial fertilizers; improved tools and farm machinery; the reclamation and settlement of new land; the control of pests, such as the locust and tsetse fly; improved livestock husbandry. The future prosperity of mankind depends on the timely and skilful combination of these methods, together with education, land tenure reforms and ecological planning.

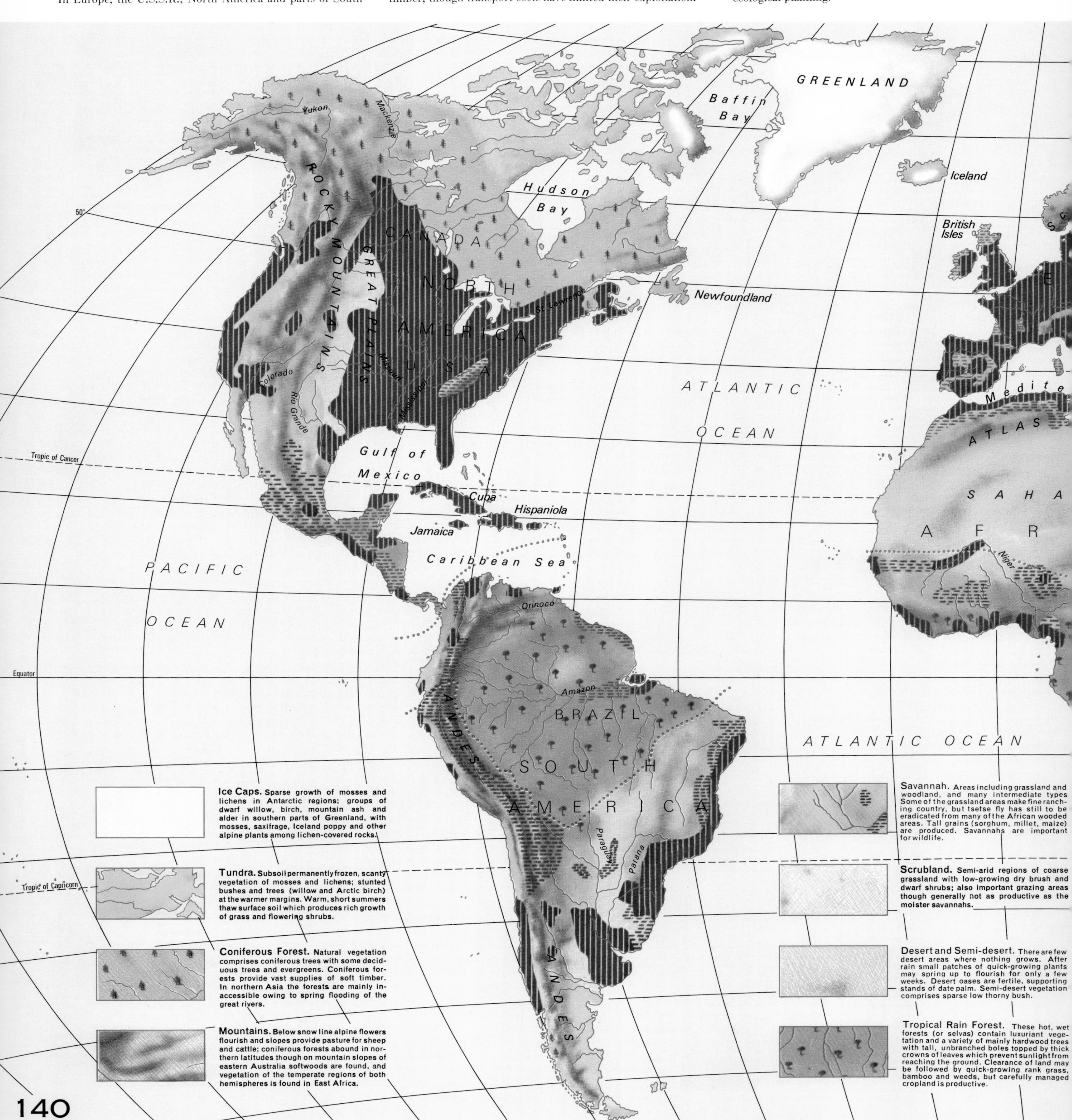

Ice Caps. Sparse growth of mosses and lichens in Antarctic regions; groups of dwarf willow, birch, mountain ash and alder in southern parts of Greenland, with mosses, saxifrage, Iceland poppy and other alpine plants among lichen-covered rocks.

Tundra. Subsoil permanently frozen, scanty vegetation of mosses and lichens; stunted bushes and trees (willow and Arctic birch) at the warmer margins. Warm, short summers thaw surface soil which produces rich growth of grass and flowering shrubs.

Coniferous Forest. Natural vegetation comprises coniferous trees with some deciduous trees and evergreens. Coniferous forests provide vast supplies of soft timber. In northern Asia the forests are mainly inaccessible owing to spring flooding of the great rivers.

Mountains. Below snow line alpine flowers flourish and slopes provide pasture for sheep and cattle; coniferous forests abound in northern latitudes though on mountain slopes of eastern Australia softwoods are found, and vegetation of the temperate regions of both hemispheres is found in East Africa.

Savannah. Areas including grassland and woodland, and many intermediate types. Some of the grassland areas make fine ranching country, but tsetse fly has still to be eradicated from many of the African wooded areas. Tall grains (sorghum, millet, maize) are produced. Savannahs are important for wildlife.

Scrubland. Semi-arid regions of coarse grassland with low-growing dry brush and dwarf shrubs; also important grazing areas though generally not as productive as the moister savannahs.

Desert and Semi-desert. There are few desert areas where nothing grows. After rain small patches of quick-growing plants may spring up to flourish for only a few weeks. Desert oases are fertile, supporting stands of date palm. Semi-desert vegetation comprises sparse low thorny bush.

Tropical Rain Forest. These hot, wet forests (or selvas) contain luxuriant vegetation and a variety of mainly hardwood trees with tall, unbranched boles topped by thick crowns of leaves which prevent sunlight from reaching the ground. Clearance of land may be followed by quick-growing rank grass, bamboo and weeds, but carefully managed cropland is productive.

THE EFFECT OF TEMPERATURE ON VEGETATION

Forests, grasslands and drought-resistant scrublands are the three basic categories of natural vegetation, although very little plant life survives in the extremes of permanent ice and hot, arid deserts. These categories are further subdivided according to the temperature of the region. For example, coniferous forests are typical of the cold northern latitudes of Canada, while tropical rain forests are found in a hot equatorial region like the Amazon basin. Similarly, there are hot deserts such as the Sahara and cold deserts such as the treeless tundra regions of Northern Eurasia. The grasslands also differ between the cold steppe lands and the hot savannah regions. The two main factors controlling plant growth are temperature and rainfall, providing that the soil is fertile, or can be made so.

Generally, temperature varies according to latitude and height above sea level (1°C less for every 500 feet). The amount of moisture available for plant growth does not depend solely on the amount of rain, as drainage and evaporation rates vary considerably, and it is the amount of water retained in the soil which controls the type of vegetation.

The schematic illustration on the right shows the type of vegetation to be found in each of the three main temperature zones and also indicates how altitude affects vegetation in a similar way to latitude. The temperatures of areas within these basic divisions will be further influenced by their proximity to the ocean.

Cold region
Permanent ice caps, the treeless plains of the Tundra and the belt of dense coniferous forest are typical of this region.

Temperate region
Along the Mediterranean coast, pines give way to silver leafed olive trees and oaks. The mixed, mainly deciduous forests extend to the alpine slopes where grazing lands intermingle. Snow does not lie for long in the low-lying areas.

Hot region
Coconut palms grow along the coastal belt with tangled mangroves taking over in swampy river deltas. The dense tropical rain forest thins out away from the equator. Isolated baobab and thorn trees border the dry desert regions where date palms grow in the fertile oases. The permanent snow line is above 15,000 feet.

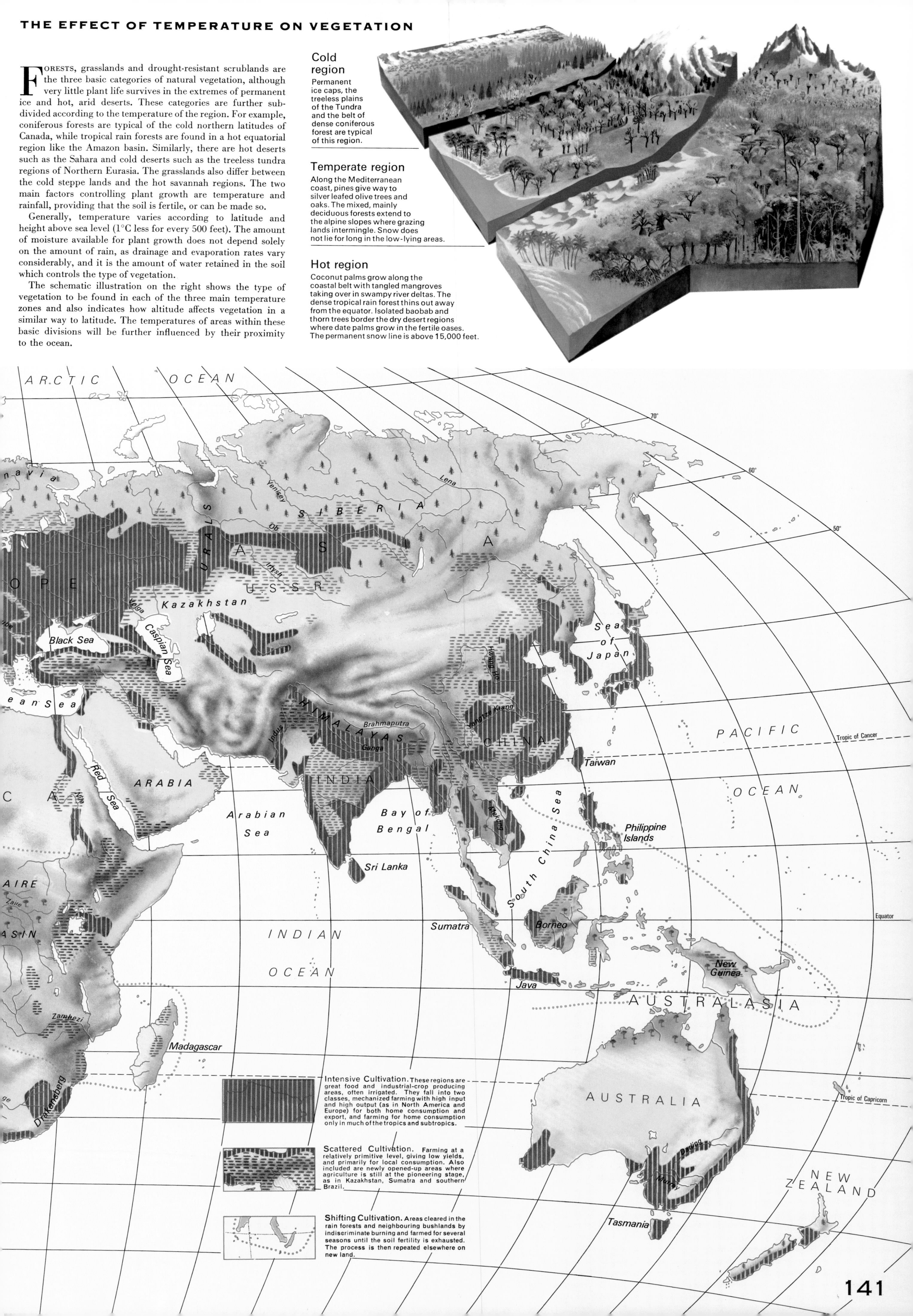

Intensive Cultivation. These regions are great food and industrial-crop producing areas, often irrigated. They fall into two classes, mechanized farming with high input and high output (as in North America and Europe) for both home consumption and export, and farming for home consumption only in much of the tropics and subtropics.

Scattered Cultivation. Farming at a relatively primitive level, giving low yields, and primarily for local consumption. Also included are newly opened-up areas where agriculture is still at the pioneering stage, as in Kazakhstan, Sumatra and southern Brazil.

Shifting Cultivation. Areas cleared in the rain forests and neighbouring bushlands by indiscriminate burning and farmed for several seasons until the soil fertility is exhausted. The process is then repeated elsewhere on new land.

141

WHAT THE WORLD IS EATING

There is nothing better for a man than that he should eat and drink — ECCLESIASTES 2

ENERGY CONSUMPTION PER DAY IN CALORIES

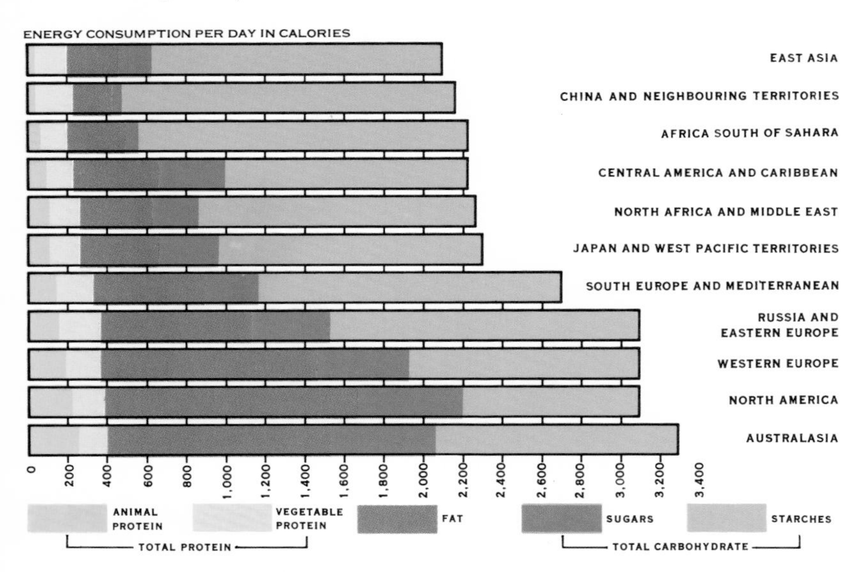

EAST ASIA
CHINA AND NEIGHBOURING TERRITORIES
AFRICA SOUTH OF SAHARA
CENTRAL AMERICA AND CARIBBEAN
NORTH AFRICA AND MIDDLE EAST
JAPAN AND WEST PACIFIC TERRITORIES
SOUTH EUROPE AND MEDITERRANEAN
RUSSIA AND EASTERN EUROPE
WESTERN EUROPE
NORTH AMERICA
AUSTRALASIA

ANIMAL PROTEIN — VEGETABLE PROTEIN — FAT — SUGARS — STARCHES
├─ TOTAL PROTEIN ─┤ ├──── TOTAL CARBOHYDRATE ────┤

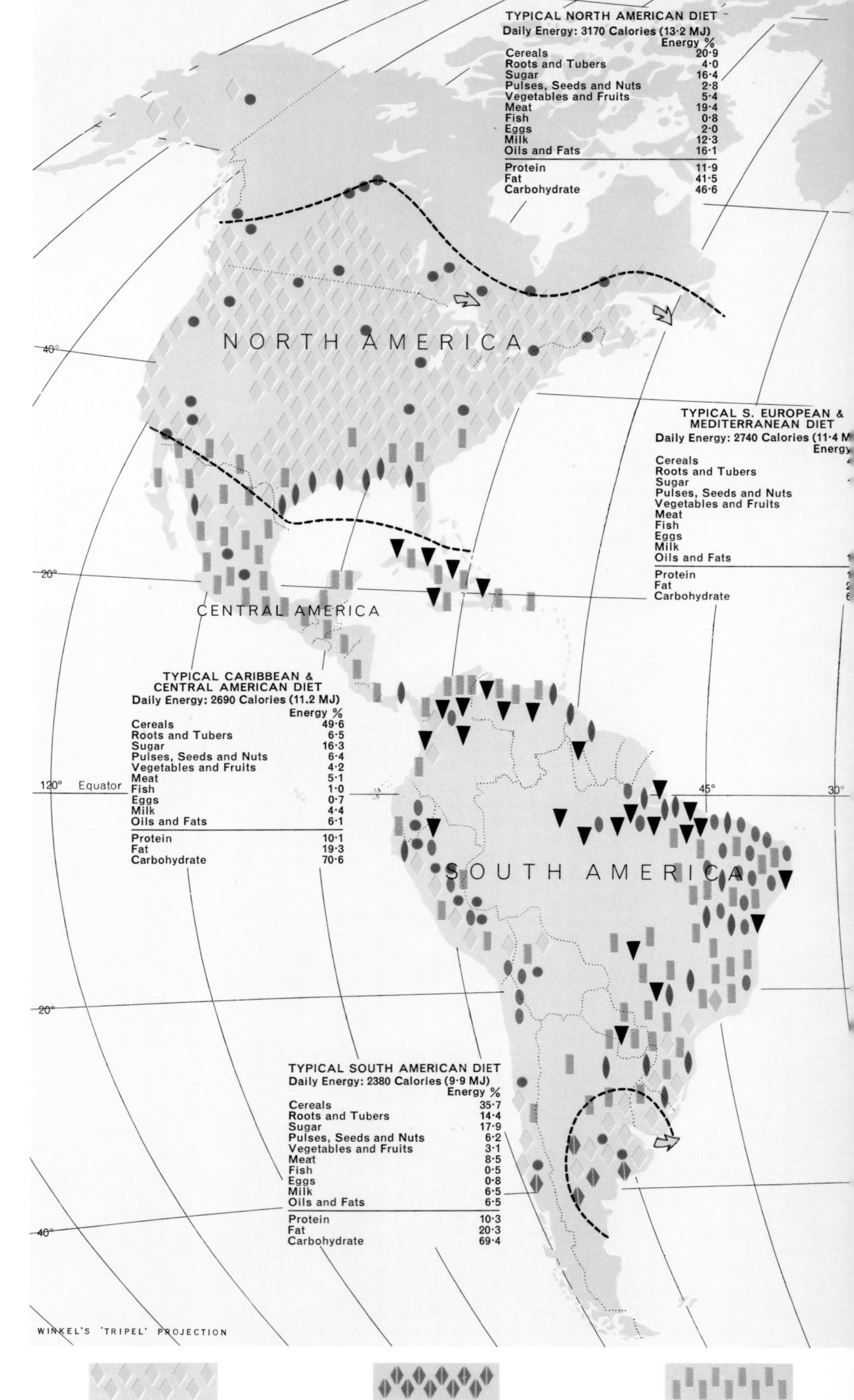

TYPICAL NORTH AMERICAN DIET
Daily Energy: 3170 Calories (13·2 MJ)
	Energy %
Cereals	20·9
Roots and Tubers	4·0
Sugar	16·4
Pulses, Seeds and Nuts	2·8
Vegetables and Fruits	5·4
Meat	19·4
Fish	0·8
Eggs	2·0
Milk	12·3
Oils and Fats	16·1
Protein	11·9
Fat	41·5
Carbohydrate	46·6

NORTH AMERICA

TYPICAL S. EUROPEAN & MEDITERRANEAN DIET
Daily Energy: 2740 Calories (11·4 M
Energy
Cereals
Roots and Tubers
Sugar
Pulses, Seeds and Nuts
Vegetables and Fruits
Meat
Fish
Eggs
Milk
Oils and Fats
Protein
Fat
Carbohydrate

CENTRAL AMERICA

TYPICAL CARIBBEAN & CENTRAL AMERICAN DIET
Daily Energy: 2690 Calories (11.2 MJ)
	Energy %
Cereals	49·6
Roots and Tubers	6·5
Sugar	16·3
Pulses, Seeds and Nuts	6·4
Vegetables and Fruits	4·2
Meat	5·1
Fish	1·0
Eggs	0·7
Milk	4·4
Oils and Fats	6·1
Protein	10·1
Fat	19·3
Carbohydrate	70·6

SOUTH AMERICA

TYPICAL SOUTH AMERICAN DIET
Daily Energy: 2380 Calories (9·9 MJ)
	Energy %
Cereals	35·7
Roots and Tubers	14·4
Sugar	17·9
Pulses, Seeds and Nuts	6·2
Vegetables and Fruits	3·1
Meat	8·5
Fish	0·5
Eggs	0·8
Milk	6·5
Oils and Fats	6·5
Protein	10·3
Fat	20·3
Carbohydrate	69·4

WINKEL'S 'TRIPEL' PROJECTION

E VERY day the world has to find food for more than 3,750 million human beings, and this number is steadily increasing.

The principal constituents of food – proteins, fats and carbohydrates – supply the energy needed for the growth of children, our bodily functions and activities. Food also supplies the building materials for the growth and maintenance of our bodies, one of the principal building materials being protein. If the food supply is inadequate, the building materials will be burnt up to supply energy. Particularly in children, this total inadequacy leads to protein-energy malnutrition. Our diet must also include minerals and vitamins.

Carbohydrates are obtained chiefly from cereals (wheat, maize, rye, oats, barley, rice, sorghums and millets), from roots and tubers (potatoes, sweet potatoes, yams and cassava), and from sugar. Proteins are obtained from meat and fish, from cereals and pulses (dry beans, peas, broad beans, lentils and chick-peas), and from eggs and milk. Fat comes from animal foods and such vegetable foods as nuts, oil-seeds and oil-containing fruit. Vitamins and minerals are obtained from meat, cereals, fresh fruit and vegetables.

Our food consumption was formerly measured by its energy content in calories. Calories are gradually being replaced by megajoules (MJ): 1,000 Calories = 4·2 MJ.

Our requirements for energy depend upon our weight and our activity. An average requirement usually lies between 2,000–3,000 calories (8–13 MJ). The percentage of energy from protein is usually between 10–15% and is the least variable constituent. The percentages of energy from carbohydrates and fat are the most variable. In poorer agricultural countries the carbohydrate content of the diet is high. In the more highly industrialised countries there is usually a greater total consumption with lower percentages of starchy carbohydrate and higher percentage of fat, sugar and animal food. The higher content of animal food helps to improve the quality of the protein, but animal fats increase the risk of heart disease.

Undernutrition, occurring typically as protein-energy malnutrition in the first few years of life, is the most prevalent form of malnutrition in the less well-developed countries of Africa, Asia and South America. Ignorance, with the failure to realise that the relative requirements of young children are much greater than those of adults, is as important a cause of malnutrition as shortage of food. Much is being done today by education, by the spread of scientific and technical knowledge and by the improvement of food crops and methods of agriculture, to improve food supplies for the world's rapidly growing population.

COMPARISON OF POPULATION AND AGRICULTURAL PRODUCTION

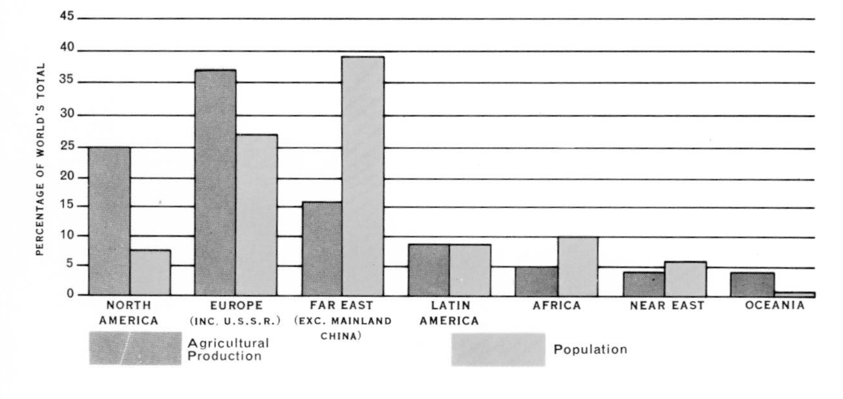

PERCENTAGE OF WORLD'S TOTAL

NORTH AMERICA | EUROPE (INC. U.S.S.R.) | FAR EAST (EXC. MAINLAND CHINA) | LATIN AMERICA | AFRICA | NEAR EAST | OCEANIA

Agricultural Production   Population

WHEAT

WHEAT, of which there are about 650 varieties, is the most important and widely grown of all cereal crops, and is chiefly milled into flour. Wheat products are rich in carbohydrates; the whole grain contains also proteins, fats, minerals and vitamins. It is therefore a major energy food, and highly nutritious. The hard varieties are used mainly for bread, the soft for cakes, biscuits, pastry. One hard species, durum, is manufactured into spaghetti, macaroni, semolina, etc. Flat (unleavened) bread is eaten in much of Africa and Asia. In India wheat is combined with fat and made into pancake-like wafers called *chappatis*. A small part of the world's wheat production is processed into malt, dextrose and alcohol.

RYE, OATS, BARLEY

RYE is mainly produced in the poorer soils and wetter areas of the northern temperate regions, and is consumed largely in central and eastern European countries as "black" bread, which is very nutritious and more warmth-giving than other varieties of bread. OATS are hardy and also flourish in poorer soils. They have a high protein, fat and vitamin B content, and are principally used for breakfast foods, cakes, biscuits, etc. BARLEY thrives in most temperate climates and even under subarctic and subtropical conditions. It is chiefly grown in Europe for the manufacture of beer, though in parts of Scotland and Scandinavia it is made into barley bread. It is the staple food grain of North Africa and parts of Asia, where it is eaten as flatbread, porridge and pearl barley.

MAIZE

MAIZE (Indian corn), one of the most widely distributed food crops, although of great nutritive value, is not as nutritious as wheat. Sometimes the cob is roasted whole, but generally the grain is ground into meal and eaten as porridge, such as the "stirabout" of Ireland, or in cake form, such as the "johnny-cakes" of the U.S.A. It is eaten as a basic food in Mexico and in some parts of South America as *tortilla*, a flat pancake, often in conjunction with soups or fruit or vegetables such as sweet potatoes. In North America it is harvested early and eaten as "sweet corn". In northern Italy it is eaten as "polenta". Corn-flour is prepared from maize by a process of washing. Maize is used industrially as corn-starch, corn-oil and alcohol.

PRODUCTION OF MEAT AND FISH

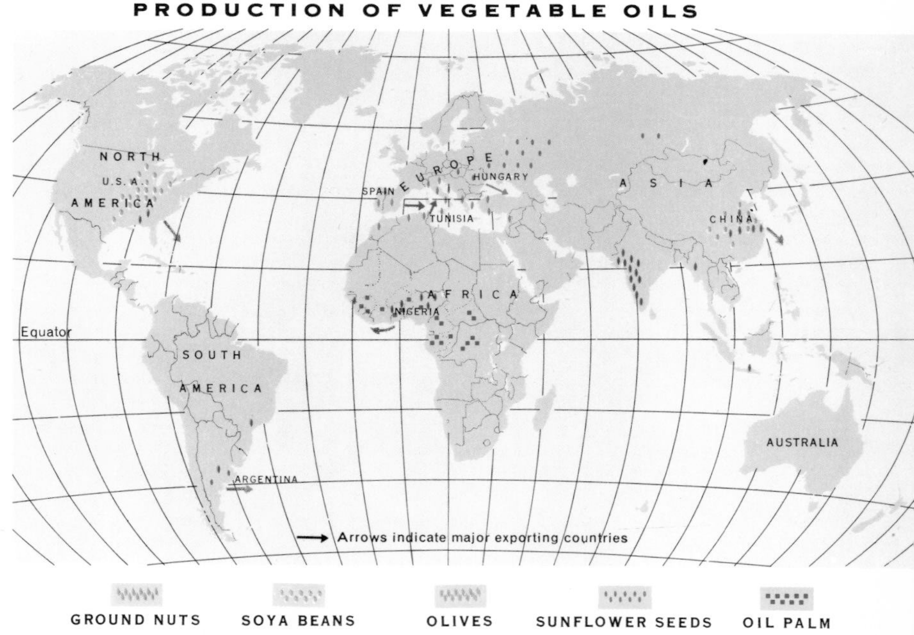

→ Arrows indicate major exporting countries

MEAT   FISH

PRODUCTION OF VEGETABLE OILS

→ Arrows indicate major exporting countries

GROUND NUTS   SOYA BEANS   OLIVES   SUNFLOWER SEEDS   OIL PALM

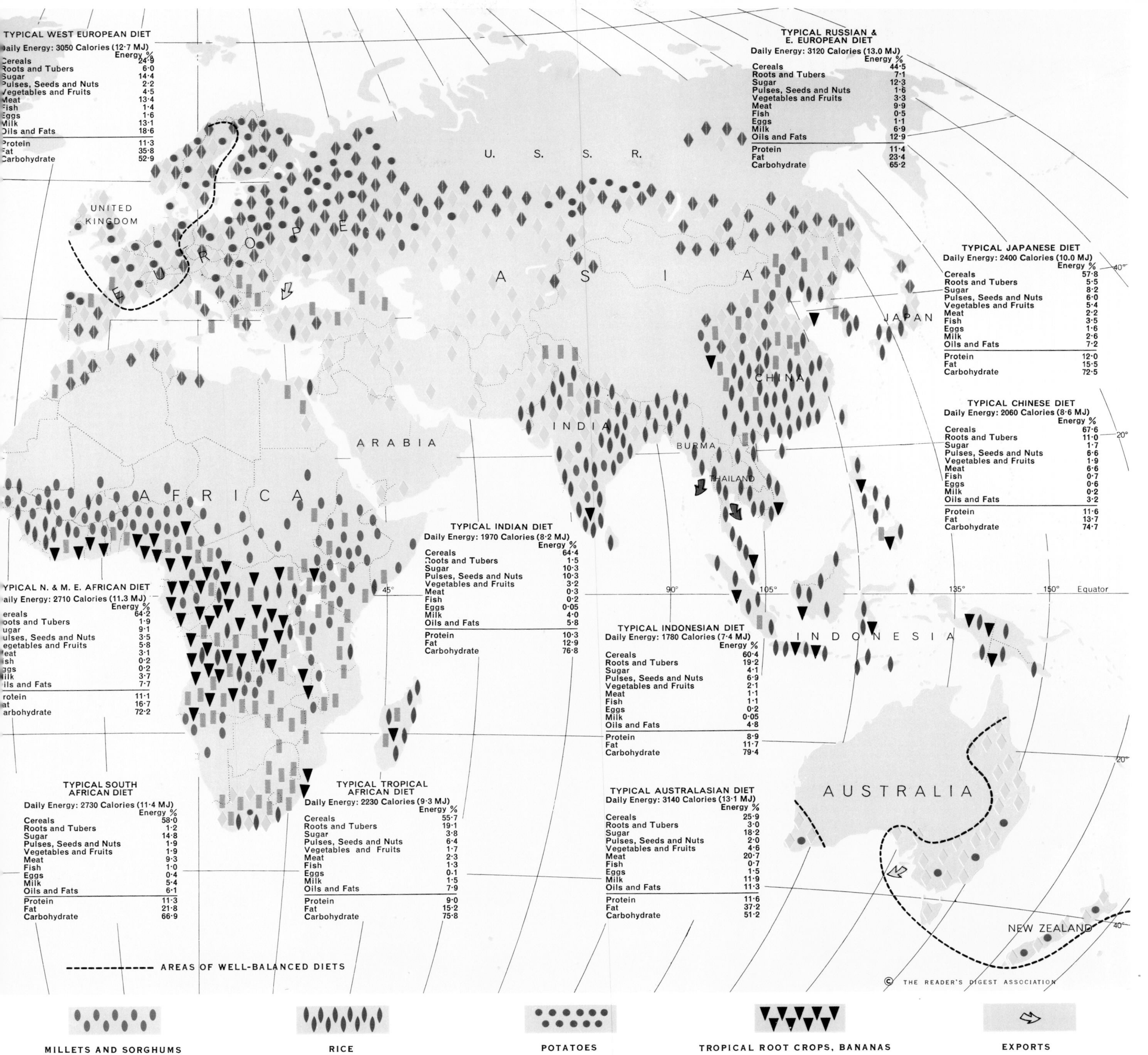

TYPICAL WEST EUROPEAN DIET
Daily Energy: 3050 Calories (12.7 MJ)

	Energy %
Cereals	24.9
Roots and Tubers	6.0
Sugar	14.4
Pulses, Seeds and Nuts	2.2
Vegetables and Fruits	4.5
Meat	13.4
Fish	1.4
Eggs	1.6
Milk	13.1
Oils and Fats	18.6
Protein	11.3
Fat	35.8
Carbohydrate	52.9

TYPICAL RUSSIAN & E. EUROPEAN DIET
Daily Energy: 3120 Calories (13.0 MJ)

	Energy %
Cereals	44.5
Roots and Tubers	7.1
Sugar	12.3
Pulses, Seeds and Nuts	1.6
Vegetables and Fruits	3.3
Meat	9.9
Fish	0.5
Eggs	6.9
Milk	
Oils and Fats	12.9
Protein	11.4
Fat	23.4
Carbohydrate	65.2

TYPICAL JAPANESE DIET
Daily Energy: 2400 Calories (10.0 MJ)

	Energy %
Cereals	57.8
Roots and Tubers	5.5
Sugar	8.2
Pulses, Seeds and Nuts	6.0
Vegetables and Fruits	5.4
Meat	2.2
Fish	3.5
Eggs	1.6
Milk	2.6
Oils and Fats	7.2
Protein	12.0
Fat	15.5
Carbohydrate	72.5

TYPICAL CHINESE DIET
Daily Energy: 2060 Calories (8.6 MJ)

	Energy %
Cereals	67.6
Roots and Tubers	11.0
Sugar	1.7
Pulses, Seeds and Nuts	6.6
Vegetables and Fruits	1.9
Meat	6.6
Fish	0.7
Eggs	0.6
Milk	0.2
Oils and Fats	3.2
Protein	11.6
Fat	13.7
Carbohydrate	74.7

TYPICAL N. & M. E. AFRICAN DIET
Daily Energy: 2710 Calories (11.3 MJ)

	Energy %
Cereals	64.2
Roots and Tubers	1.9
Sugar	9.1
Pulses, Seeds and Nuts	3.5
Vegetables and Fruits	5.8
Meat	3.1
Fish	0.2
Eggs	
Milk	3.7
Oils and Fats	7.7
Protein	11.1
Fat	16.7
Carbohydrate	72.2

TYPICAL INDIAN DIET
Daily Energy: 1970 Calories (8.2 MJ)

	Energy %
Cereals	64.4
Roots and Tubers	1.5
Sugar	10.3
Pulses, Seeds and Nuts	3.2
Vegetables and Fruits	0.3
Meat	0.3
Fish	0.05
Eggs	
Milk	4.0
Oils and Fats	5.8
Protein	10.3
Fat	12.9
Carbohydrate	76.8

TYPICAL INDONESIAN DIET
Daily Energy: 1780 Calories (7.4 MJ)

	Energy %
Cereals	60.4
Roots and Tubers	19.2
Sugar	4.1
Pulses, Seeds and Nuts	6.9
Vegetables and Fruits	2.1
Meat	1.1
Fish	1.1
Eggs	0.2
Milk	0.05
Oils and Fats	4.8
Protein	8.9
Fat	11.7
Carbohydrate	79.4

TYPICAL SOUTH AFRICAN DIET
Daily Energy: 2730 Calories (11.4 MJ)

	Energy %
Cereals	58.0
Roots and Tubers	1.2
Sugar	14.8
Pulses, Seeds and Nuts	1.9
Vegetables and Fruits	1.9
Meat	9.3
Fish	1.0
Eggs	0.4
Milk	5.4
Oils and Fats	6.1
Protein	11.3
Fat	21.8
Carbohydrate	66.9

TYPICAL TROPICAL AFRICAN DIET
Daily Energy: 2230 Calories (9.3 MJ)

	Energy %
Cereals	55.7
Roots and Tubers	19.1
Sugar	3.8
Pulses, Seeds and Nuts	6.4
Vegetables and Fruits	1.7
Meat	2.3
Fish	1.3
Eggs	0.1
Milk	1.5
Oils and Fats	7.9
Protein	9.0
Fat	15.2
Carbohydrate	75.8

TYPICAL AUSTRALASIAN DIET
Daily Energy: 3140 Calories (13.1 MJ)

	Energy %
Cereals	25.9
Roots and Tubers	3.0
Sugar	18.2
Pulses, Seeds and Nuts	2.0
Vegetables and Fruits	4.6
Meat	20.7
Fish	0.7
Eggs	1.5
Milk	11.9
Oils and Fats	11.3
Protein	11.6
Fat	37.2
Carbohydrate	51.2

- - - - - AREAS OF WELL-BALANCED DIETS

© THE READER'S DIGEST ASSOCIATION

MILLETS AND SORGHUMS

MILLETS and SORGHUMS include a number of grain crops that respond to primitive methods of cultivation, and can withstand the drought and poor soil of some of the drier parts of the Tropics. The ear contains small round seeds which are pounded into flour, which is eaten as a gruel or porridge with a seasoned stew of vegetables, but rarely with meat. In West Africa it is made into balls of doughy paste (couscous). These balls, fried in palm or shea-nut oil are known as "beignets" or "galettes" and sold in the streets. In Northern China, millets and sorghums, as well as wheat, form the staple food. When grain is abundant, considerable quantities are brewed into beer; pombe, made from millet, is widely drunk in Africa. A variety of millet (prosbo)—eaten mainly as a thick porridge—is a staple food in the U.S.S.R.

RICE

There are more than 2,500 varieties of rice, more than 1,000 of them in India alone. Rice has a high energy value, though it is relatively poor nutritively. It yields more food per acre than any other grain and is widely grown and widely eaten in China, India, Japan, Burma, etc. It forms a major part of the food in these countries, where, on the whole, the diet is largely deficient in animal proteins. Among the higher income groups, the rice is always accompanied by meat and vegetables. It is commonly eaten with curry, which varies from the hot curries of India, Pakistan and Sri Lanka to the more subtle flavours of Malaysia and Indonesia. In China a favourite combination is with pork. The removal of its outer husk (polishing) deprives rice of much of its goodness. Sake, a popular and potent drink in Japan, Arrak in Java and Chemshu in China are all brewed from rice.

POTATOES

POTATOES, of which there are some 2,000 varieties, are grown in almost every country in the world, though they succeed best in the cooler regions. They contain carbohydrates, proteins, vitamins and mineral salts and are, therefore, a most valuable energy food. Among the white races they form an important part of every diet, and in some parts of Europe they are the staple food. They are generally eaten as a vegetable, but are also turned into flour and used for making bread, pastry and dumplings. Potatoes are also processed into starch and dextrose, and since the middle of the 19th century have replaced grain as a source of alcohol for commercial uses, particularly in Germany. Sweet potatoes are botanically quite different from ordinary potatoes and must be considered a tropical crop, although they have a similar food value.

TROPICAL ROOT CROPS, BANANAS

Three of the principal root crops are CASSAVA (manioc), YAMS and SWEET POTATOES. They are grown mainly in west and central Africa, the Malay Archipelago, and Latin America. The root of sweet cassava can be cooked and eaten directly, but the root of bitter cassava must be soaked in water for a few days before cooking, to extract the prussic acid. The cooked cassava is usually pounded into flour or meal and eaten as a porridge, often accompanied by yams or other vegetables. Sweet potatoes (called yams in America) grow better in drier areas, with less than 50 inches of rain. Although not root crops, BANANAS and PLANTAINS form a staple food in many tropical countries. Bananas are eaten raw and also cooked as a vegetable. Plantains are similar to bananas but contain less sugar and are usually eaten cooked. All these crops are low in protein,

EXPORTS

The arrows indicate those places from which the world's chief food cereals, wheat (yellow) and rice (green) are exported. About 20 per cent of all the wheat produced is exported. Argentina exports one-third of her wheat production, mainly to Brazil, Peru and western Europe; Australia exports two-thirds and Canada one half, principally to Britain, China and Japan; the U.S.A. exports about half her production, mainly to India, Pakistan and Japan. The U.S.S.R. is an important exporter, but in bad harvest years she also becomes a large importer. In most years Britain is the world's largest single importer of wheat. Only about five per cent of the world's production of rice enters international trade, most of which is confined to south and south-east Asia—Burma and Thailand being the major exporters and Japan the largest importer.

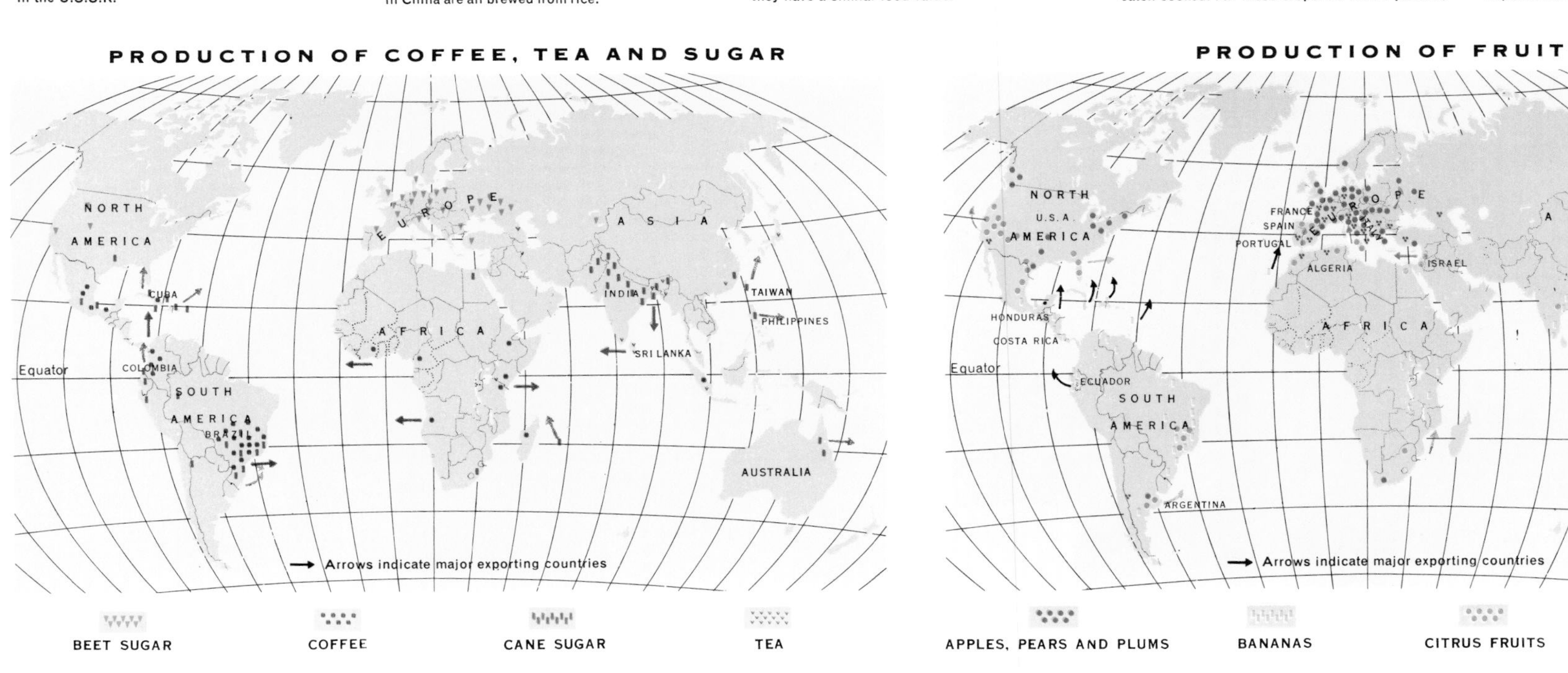

PRODUCTION OF COFFEE, TEA AND SUGAR

→ Arrows indicate major exporting countries

BEET SUGAR   COFFEE   CANE SUGAR   TEA

PRODUCTION OF FRUIT

→ Arrows indicate major exporting countries

APPLES, PEARS AND PLUMS   BANANAS   CITRUS FRUITS   GRAPES

143

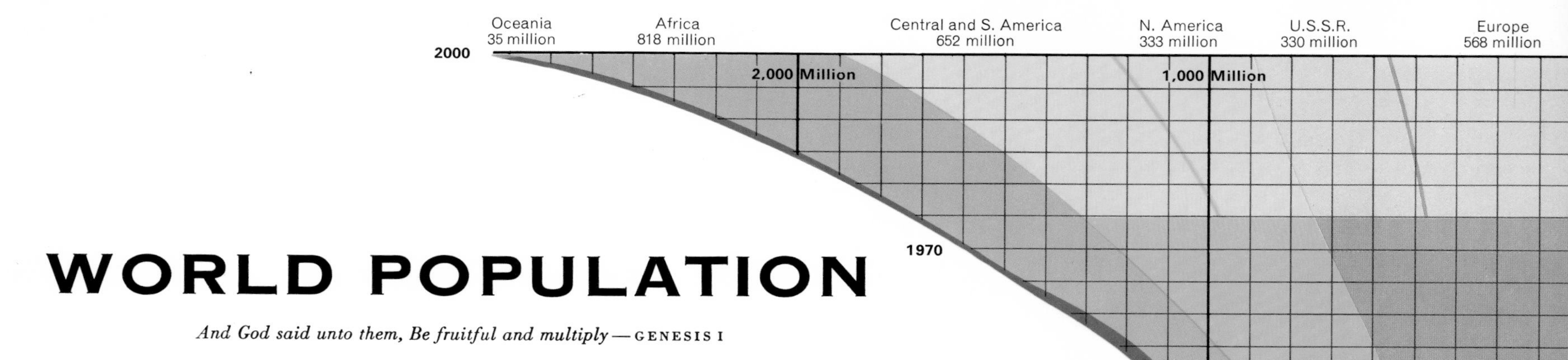

Oceania 35 million	Africa 818 million	Central and S. America 652 million	N. America 333 million	U.S.S.R. 330 million	Europe 568 million

2000

2,000 Million   **1,000 Million**

1970

1950

WORLD POPULATION

And God said unto them, Be fruitful and multiply — GENESIS I

URING the last three centuries, the growth rate of the world's population has accelerated alarmingly—the mushroom effect is shown in the central chart. It is estimated that there were about 500 million people in the world in 1650; 1,000 million in 1850; 2,000 million in 1940; and about 4,000 million by 1976. The doubling of the world's population, which not long ago took about 200 years, now takes place in less than 40 years. These figures substantiate the fear that, if the present rate of increase continues, overcrowding and famine will be inevitable.

The expansion of the population, particularly in parts of Asia and Africa, is largely due to improved standards of health and food production which resulted in a rapid decline in the mortality rate. Natural increase, which is the difference between the birth and death rates, has increased from 0·5 per cent to 2 per cent, resulting in an increase of between 70 and 80 million people each year—the equivalent of ten cities the size of Chicago.

There are still parts of the world for which population statistics are unreliable but, generally, figures are now much more accurate. The first census in China was undertaken in 1953 when it was discovered that previous population assessments had underestimated the true figure by 130 million. This meant that China had a population of 580 million rather than 450 million. The present estimated world population of 4,000 million is very unevenly distributed. The Asian continent contains over 50 per cent of the total, the Americas 15 per cent, Europe and Africa 10 per cent each and the U.S.S.R. 6 per cent. Europe has a greater density of population than any other continent, but the most densely populated rural area in the world is the

Indonesian island of Java where there are over 2,500 people to each square mile.

A major factor affecting population density is the level of urbanization which has risen considerably in recent decades as industrial development increases and the proportion of the population involved in agriculture declines. The highest levels of urbanization occur in North America with 80 per cent, the U.S.S.R. with 65 per cent and Europe with 65 per cent. But this move away from rural life is evident throughout the world and the pace is increasing, particularly in Africa and eastern Asia where urban populations have quadrupled in the last 50 years.

In different parts of the globe, there is a considerable variation in the rate of population growth. In the underdeveloped countries the birth rate is high and, with the help of improved medical facilities which have lowered the mortality rate, the natural increase is now even greater. In Mexico, for example, the birth rate is 4·4 per cent and mortality 0·9 per cent, which has resulted in a rapid increase. One way of maintaining the benefits of improved standards of health and preventing a population explosion is to implement effective methods of birth control. In this way Japan reduced its birth rate from 2·5 per cent in 1946 to 1·7 per cent in 1960, using legalised abortion and an intensive educational campaign.

The rate of population growth is not as important as the actual numbers involved. For example, the large population of India means that despite a growth rate of between 2 and 2·4 per cent—modest by comparison with Malaysia and Indonesia—there will still be many millions of new mouths to feed each year.

1900

1850

NATIONAL POPULATION AND GROWTH RATES

ACH country on the map below has been enlarged or reduced in proportion to the number of inhabitants. It is immediately evident that Asia contains a higher proportion of the world's population than all the other continents put together.

The colour of each country represents the growth rate as a percentage of the total population. The actual increase in a country's population is determined by the difference between the number of births and deaths.

In most countries of Western Europe, the natural increase is low which means the average age of the population is rising. On the other hand, countries such as Mexico, Iran, Kenya and Indonesia have a rapid rate of growth, resulting in a reduction in the average age of the population.

Births vary from 1 to 2 per cent in Finland to about 4 per cent in India. Mortality varies from 0·7 per cent in countries with a high standard of health to 2 per cent or more in some African, South American and Asian countries.

1800

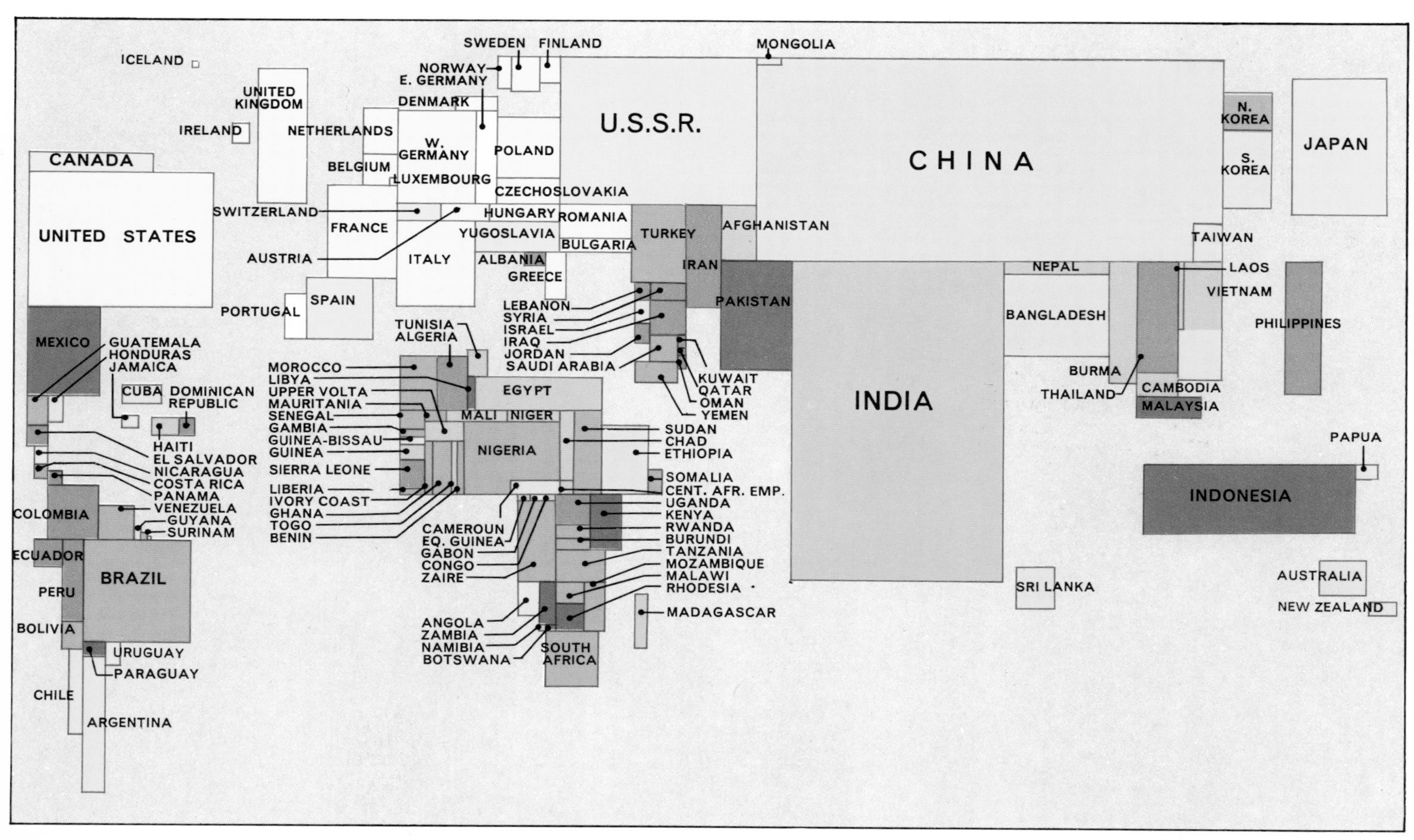

1750

1700

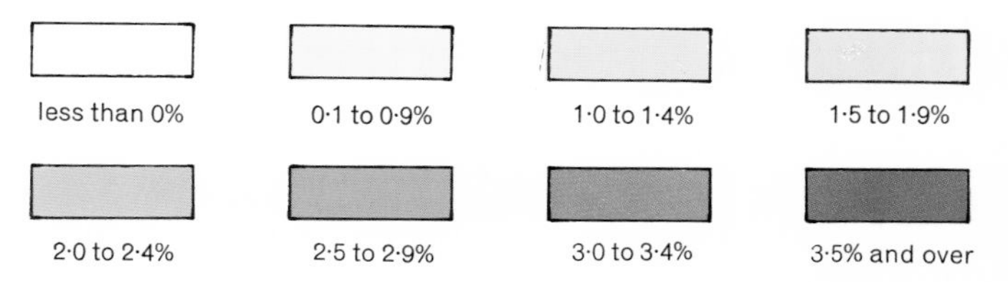

Annual percentage increase in population
(Rates of annual increase based on birth and death rates between 1970 and 1973)

less than 0%	0·1 to 0·9%	1·0 to 1·4%	1·5 to 1·9%

2·0 to 2·4%	2·5 to 2·9%	3·0 to 3·4%	3·5% and over

100 M
50 M
10 M
Population in millions

1650

2000: 6,514 million

Chinese mainland
1,176 million

Rest of Asia
2,602 million

| 1,000 Million | 2,000 Million | 3,000 Million | 2000 |

1970

1950

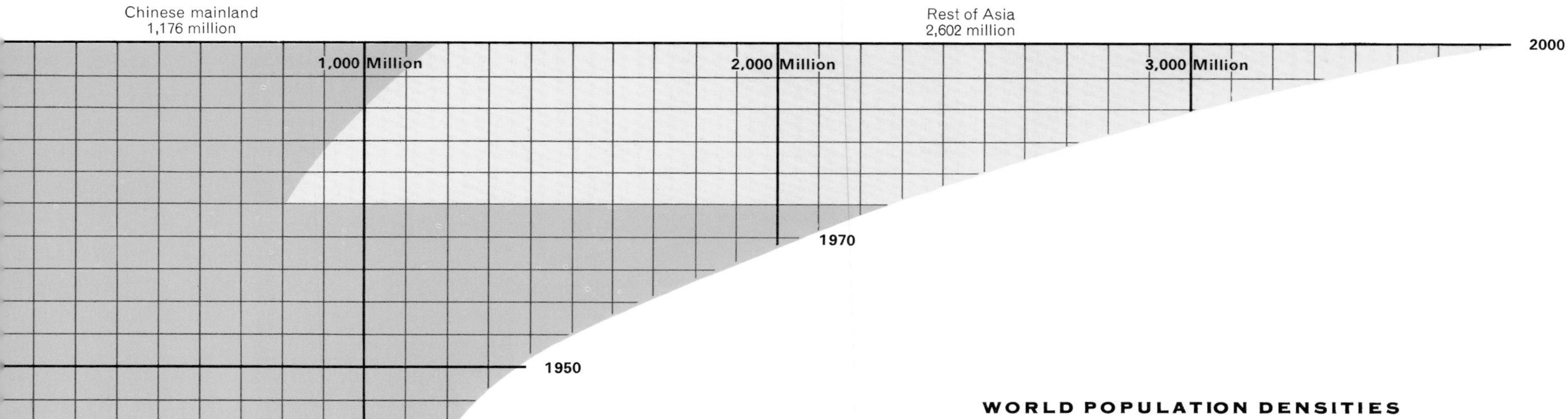

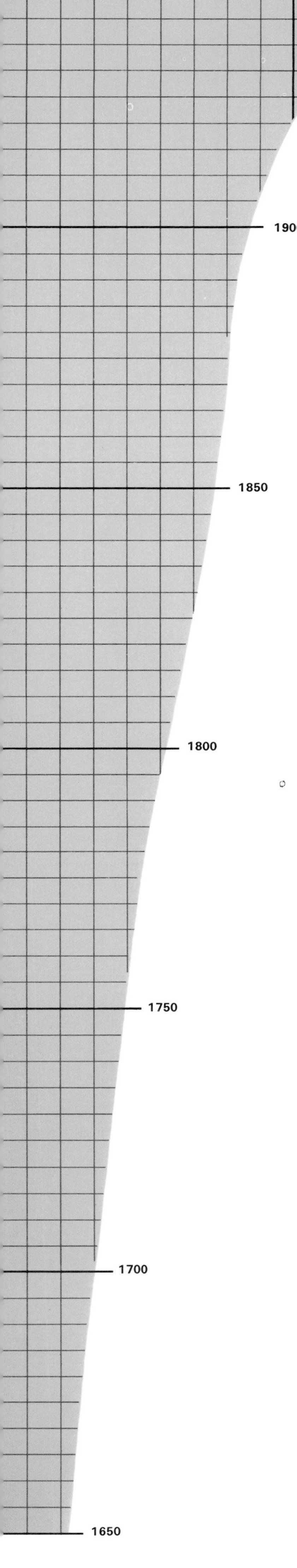

WORLD POPULATION DENSITIES

The Netherlands, with 960 people to the square mile, is the most densely populated country in the world. In Europe, England follows with 895 people to the square mile and Belgium with 809. Taiwan with 921 and South Korea with 765 head the list in Asia; Nigeria with 162 heads the list in Africa; and Puerto Rico with 776 people to the square mile is the most densely populated area in the Caribbean. Australia is over twenty-eight times as large, but less than a sixth as densely populated as New Zealand; the United States of America, with an area slightly less than that of Canada, has almost ten times Canada's population.

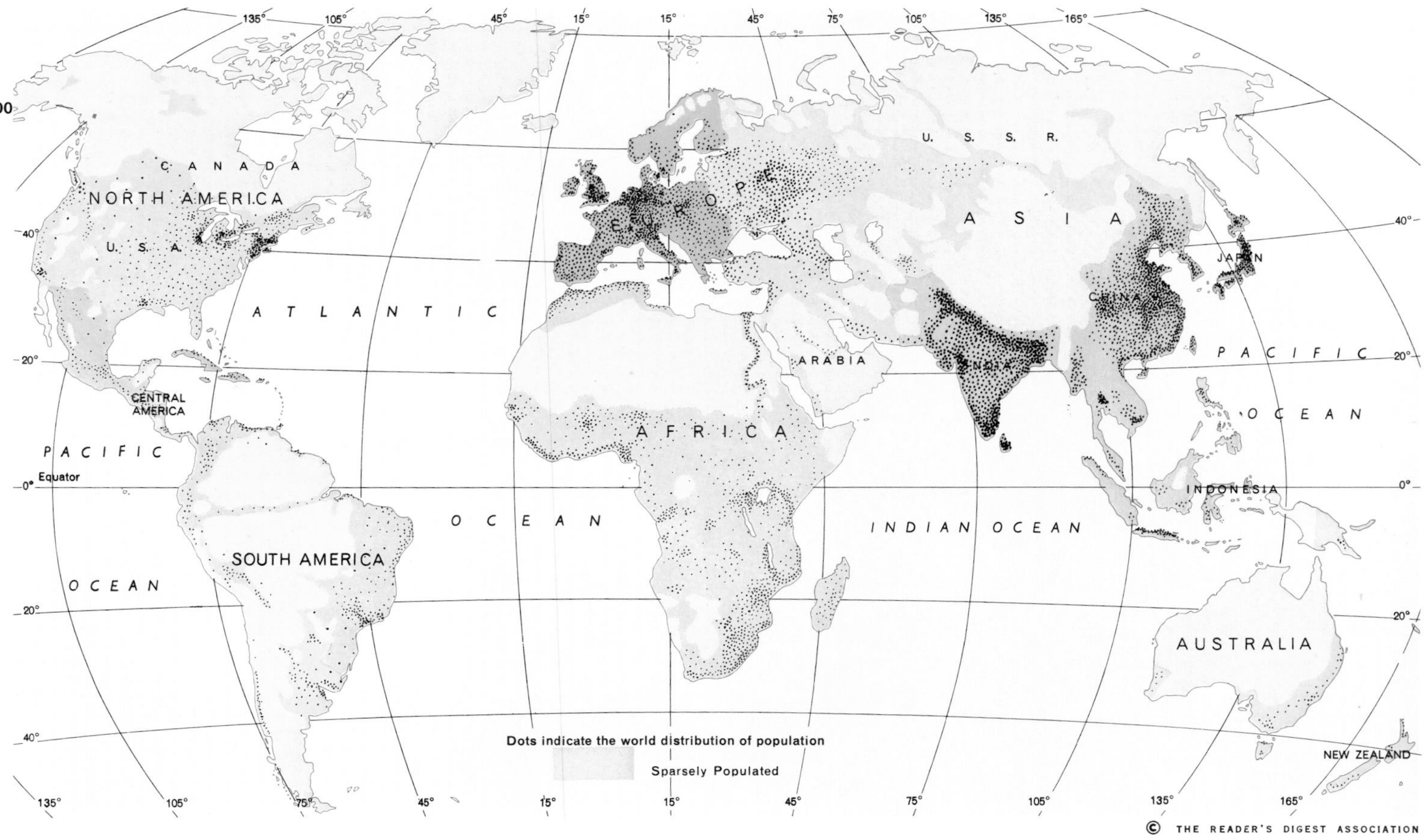

1900

1850

Dots indicate the world distribution of population

Sparsely Populated

© THE READER'S DIGEST ASSOCIATION

1800

GROUP I	GROUP II	GROUP III	GROUP IV
High Density—Moderate Growth	**High Density—Rapid Growth**	**Low Density—Moderate Growth**	**Low Density—Rapid Growth**

GROUP I — High Density—Moderate Growth

Year	Population	% increase over 1974	Persons per sq. mile
1974	581,050,000		269
2000	701,000,000	21%	325

GROUP II — High Density—Rapid Growth

Year	Population	% increase over 1974	Persons per sq. mile
1974	1,980,760,000		247
2000	3,514,000,000	77%	438

GROUP III — Low Density—Moderate Growth

Year	Population	% increase over 1974	Persons per sq. mile
1974	545,900,000		26
2000	761,000,000	39%	36

GROUP IV — Low Density—Rapid Growth

Year	Population	% increase over 1974	Persons per sq. mile
1974	734,040,000		36
2000	1,537,000,000	109%	75

The population growth forecasts for each group are quoted from the 1974 United Nations estimates, which divide the world into more developed regions (Groups I and III leaving out New Guinea and the Pacific Islands) and less developed regions. Groupings are based on broad population trends within large areas. For this reason population density and rate of growth will vary somewhat from country to country within each group.

1750

AGRICULTURAL EMPLOYMENT STRUCTURE

In the highly developed industrial countries of North America and Western Europe only a small percentage of the working population is involved in agriculture—less than 5 per cent in Canada, the United States, Belgium and Switzerland. The situation is reversed in the under-developed Asian and African countries of Indonesia, India and Zaire where 70 per cent or more of the population are employed in agriculture.

The countries in the chart are grouped according to the percentage of the total population who are employed. Mexico has a very low percentage in employment but this does not necessarily imply that there is vast unemployment. Mexico is undergoing a period of very rapid population growth and 50 per cent of the population is below the age of 20, compared with about 30 per cent in the United Kingdom and 38 per cent in the United States. Both Canada and Indonesia have a low percentage of employed population—between 30 and 39 per cent. Canada like Mexico has a young population, but unlike Indonesia it does not suffer from lack of industrial employment facilities for the over 18 age group.

1700

Percentage of total population in employment
- over 49%
- 40 – 49%
- 30 – 39%
- 20 – 29%

Percentage employed in agriculture

Percentage in alternative employment

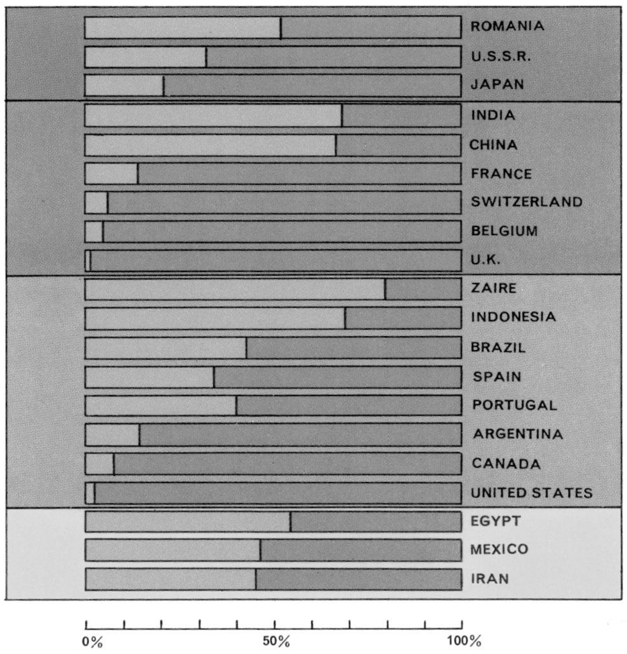

ROMANIA
U.S.S.R.
JAPAN
INDIA
CHINA
FRANCE
SWITZERLAND
BELGIUM
U.K.
ZAIRE
INDONESIA
BRAZIL
SPAIN
PORTUGAL
ARGENTINA
CANADA
UNITED STATES
EGYPT
MEXICO
IRAN

0%   50%   100%

1650

145

WORLD HEALTH

I pray that in all things thou mayest prosper and be in health.—3 JOHN

THE World Health Organization defines health as a state of complete physical, mental and social well-being—not just the absence of illness or infirmity. This ideal state must be the goal, but more tangible factors are used to determine the present state of a nation's health. A principal criterion is the expectation of life at birth.

A nation's life expectancy is determined by the average number of years that a person can expect to survive, taking into consideration the inherent health risks of the country. Generally, the higher the standard of living the longer will be the expectation of life. In the developing countries, which contain three-quarters of the world's population, the average lifespan is 53 years. But, at the lower end of the scale in this group, there are 25 countries with a life expectancy of only 40 years, which was the average for a European in 1850. Today, in the most highly developed areas of Western Europe and the United States, the figure reaches 71, and the problems of extending this span are more dependent on an individual's way of life than on medical discoveries or control. Women have a better chance than men of attaining the average life expectancy limit as they have always lived longer.

Infant mortality is one of the crucial problems in under-developed countries, where the average number of deaths is 14 per cent of live births and may be as high as 20 per cent in some areas. In Europe, the average is 1·5 per cent of live births. This disparity continues into early childhood (one to four years) when the mortality rate frequently reaches 5 per cent in under-developed areas as against 0·1 per cent in Europe. The main cause of high infant-mortality rates is malnutrition. The other main causes of death in developing countries are infectious diseases, diet deficiencies and poor standards of hygiene.

The World Health Organization (a specialized agency of the United Nations Organization) was formed in 1948, and has organized international campaigns against malaria, smallpox and tuberculosis. Smallpox has been eliminated in most countries with the exception of Bangladesh, India, Pakistan and Ethiopia. The malaria campaign has led to eradication in many countries, and has also resulted in the lowering of the mortality rate in areas still infected. Health programmes of this kind improve standards of health and life expectancy in the poorer countries, but economic development is likely to be the governing factor in improving living standards and the general health of a nation.

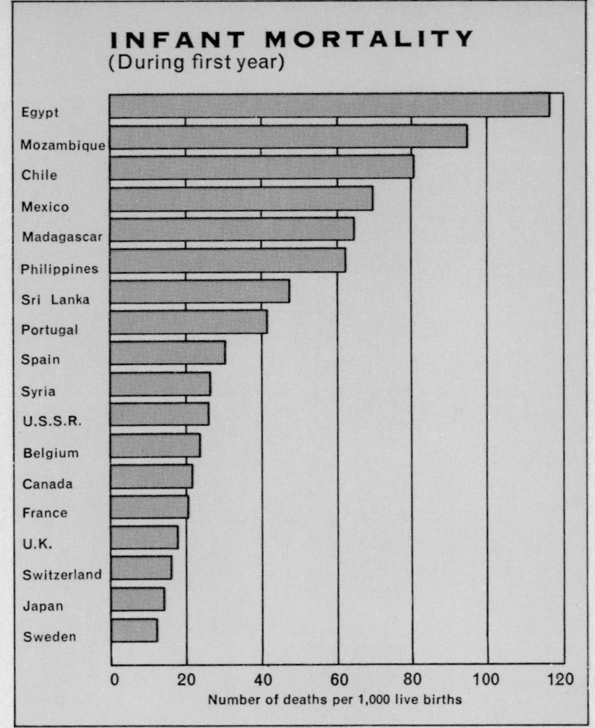

INFANT MORTALITY
(During first year)

Egypt, Mozambique, Chile, Mexico, Madagascar, Philippines, Sri Lanka, Portugal, Spain, Syria, U.S.S.R., Belgium, Canada, France, U.K., Switzerland, Japan, Sweden

Number of deaths per 1,000 live births

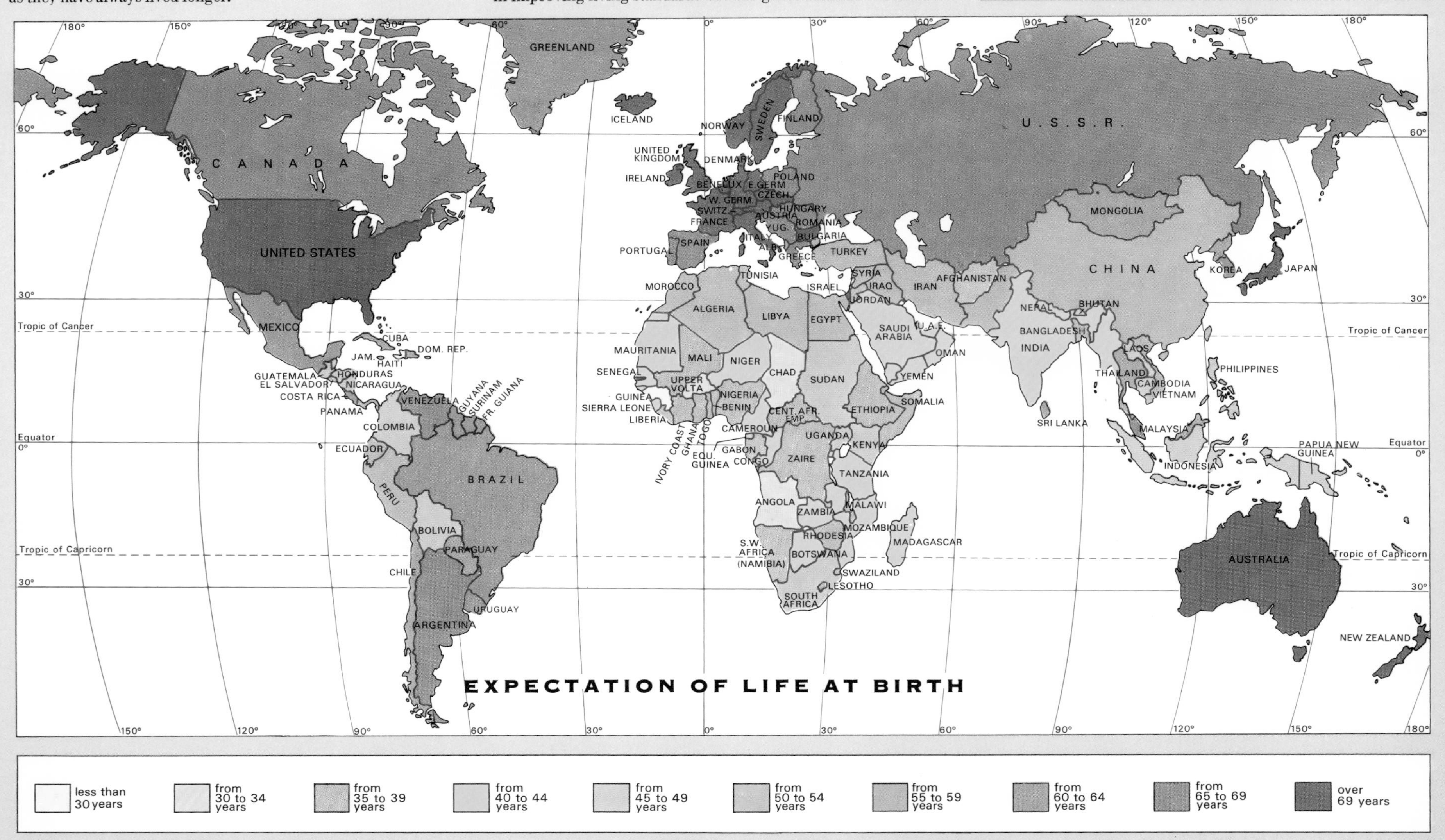

EXPECTATION OF LIFE AT BIRTH

| less than 30 years | from 30 to 34 years | from 35 to 39 years | from 40 to 44 years | from 45 to 49 years | from 50 to 54 years | from 55 to 59 years | from 60 to 64 years | from 65 to 69 years | over 69 years |

PRINCIPAL CAUSES OF DEATH

The most likely cause of death varies considerably from one part of the world to another, and it is therefore necessary to establish the principal causes of death in an area before any effective method of combating disease can be decided. It is not possible to get precise statistics for some of the critical areas because medical records are inadequate in many of the developing countries. In the chart on the right unidentified deaths are part of the grouping "Other causes or causes unknown". This classification also covers accidental deaths.

In countries with a high standard of living, the risk of death is greatest when a person is elderly or very young, and the most likely causes of death amongst the elderly are heart disease and tumours. Between these extremes the greatest proportion of deaths are caused by accidents.

In underdeveloped countries, on the other hand, the mortality rate is high throughout a person's lifespan, with the highest risk from infectious diseases. On the other hand, as life expectancy is relatively short in many Asian and African countries, illnesses associated with old age are obviously far less common.

The chart on the right clearly indicates that the medical problems differ radically between the richer and the poorer areas of the world.

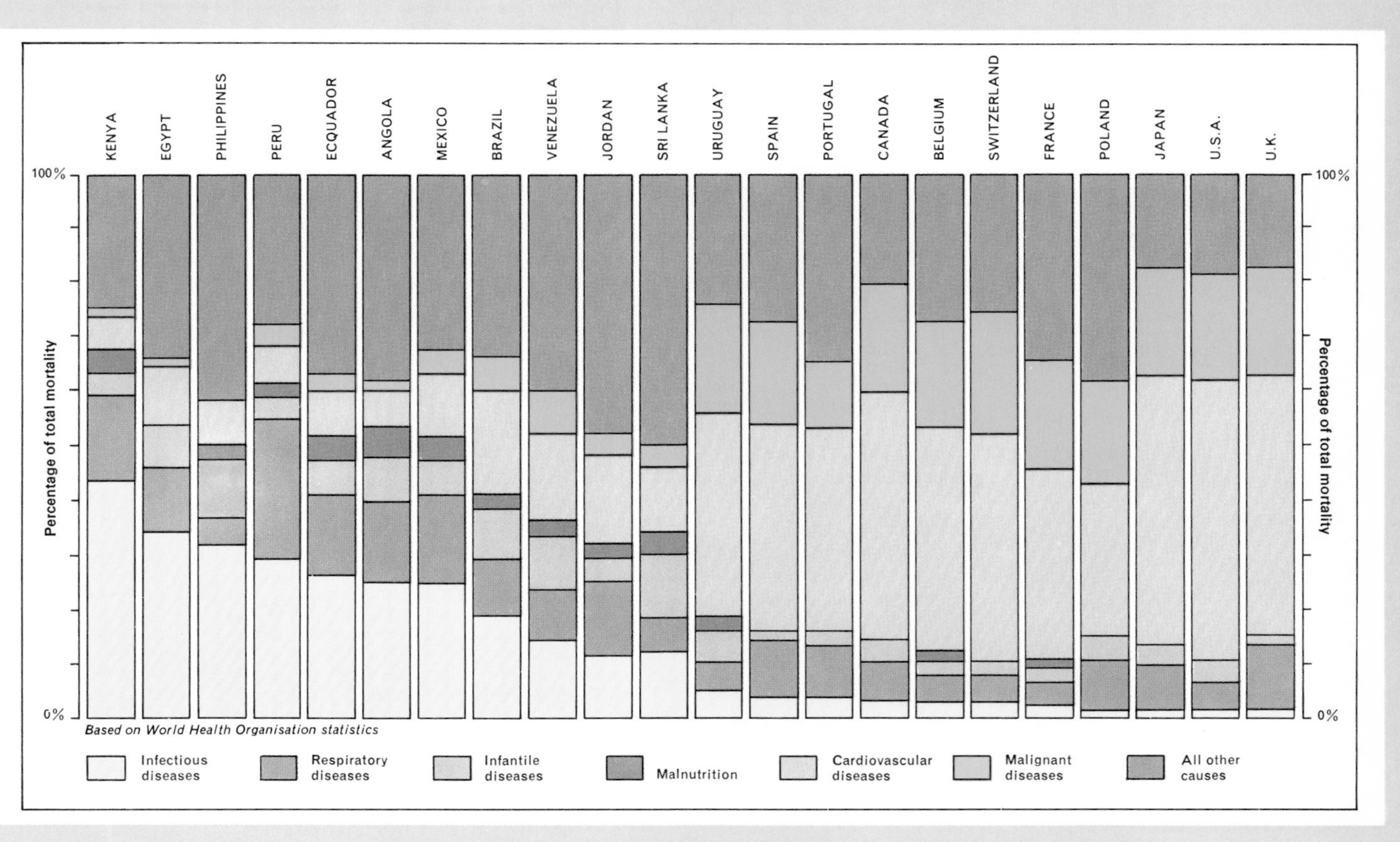

Based on World Health Organisation statistics

Percentage of total mortality

KENYA, EGYPT, PHILIPPINES, PERU, ECUADOR, ANGOLA, MEXICO, BRAZIL, VENEZUELA, JORDAN, SRI LANKA, URUGUAY, SPAIN, PORTUGAL, CANADA, BELGIUM, SWITZERLAND, FRANCE, POLAND, JAPAN, U.S.A., U.K.

| Infectious diseases | Respiratory diseases | Infantile diseases | Malnutrition | Cardiovascular diseases | Malignant diseases | All other causes |

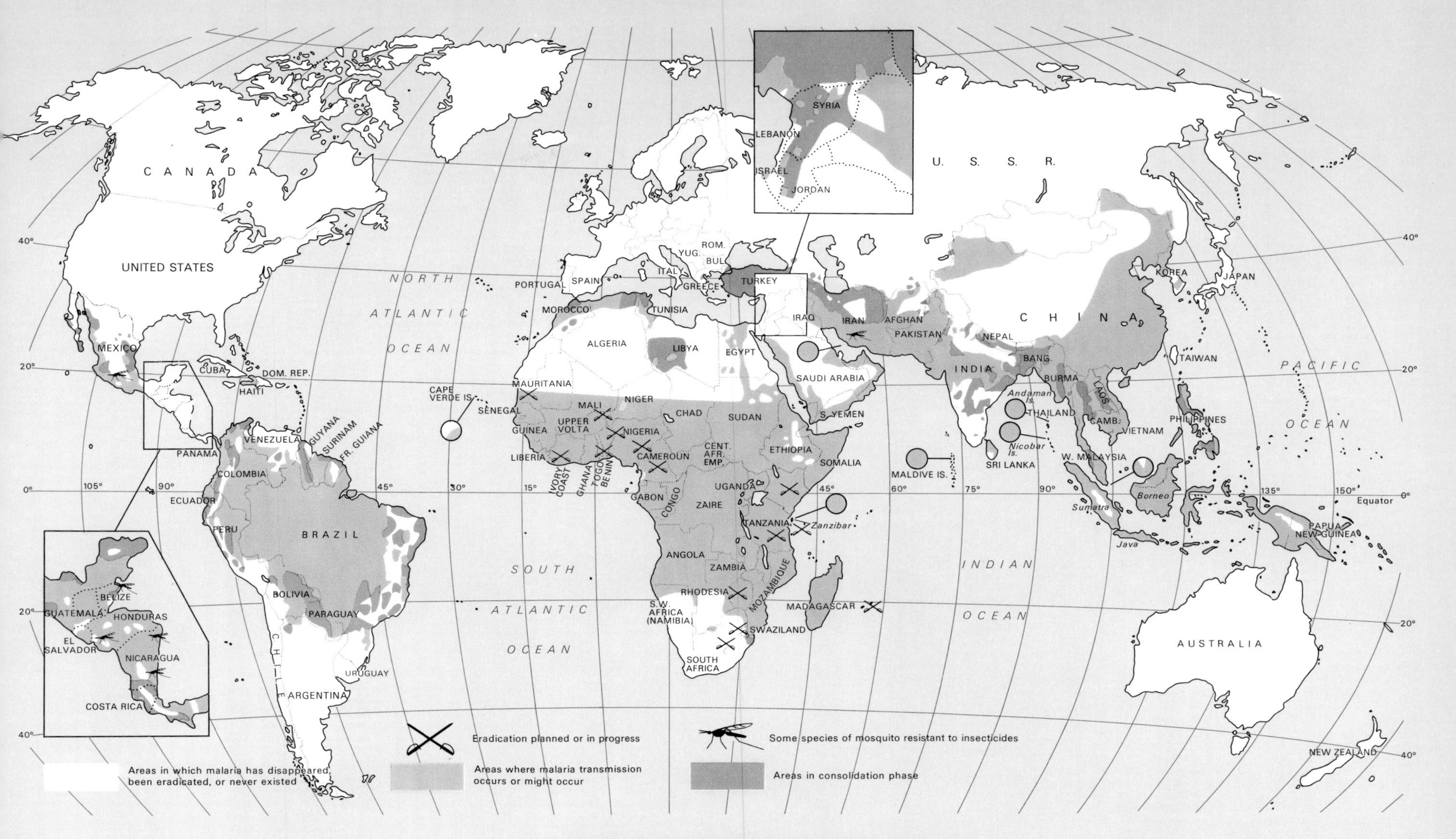

THE FIGHT AGAINST MALARIA

MALARIA, carried and spread by mosquitoes, has been the scourge of man for thousands of years. Although it is now regarded as a tropical disease, it was once prevalent in Europe. Today, it is still one of the most serious problems in the developing world.

There are four species of the malaria parasite which affect man, but only two are of major importance. *Falciparum* malaria causes an acute illness which does not relapse but is highly lethal. *Vivax* malaria causes an acute attack of fever, is not usually fatal, but does relapse, causing considerable debility and chronic ill-health. The economic consequences are considerable in malaria-ridden areas as the disease reduces ability to work—a critical situation in areas where people live at subsistence level and are entirely dependent on the food they produce themselves. In highly malarious zones adults develop immunity, but the infant-mortality rate is very high. Fortunately, there are efficient prophylactic drugs for the protection of visitors to areas where malaria is endemic.

The most important date in the battle against malaria was 1897. In that year Sir Ronald Ross, a British physician born in India, proved conclusively that malaria is transmitted by the bite of the female *Anopheles* mosquito. As a result of Ross's discovery, it became clear that the most effective means of combating malaria was by a direct attack on the mosquito. For

many years successful control was achieved by using various chemicals to destroy the insect in its larval stage, by spraying oil on to the surface of the water where the mosquitoes bred, and by disturbing the breeding sites by intermittent irrigation. These methods were combined with attempts to reduce the number of breeding places by draining swamps, filling in pits and other possible breeding sites.

Although mass control of malaria was not achieved by these methods, they provided effective localized control in areas such as towns, mining camps and plantations. With the discovery of the first of the potent modern insecticides, DDT, the situation was radically improved. It meant that a direct attack could be made on the adult mosquito populations in malarious areas. One method was to spray interior walls with insecticide so that the female mosquito would pick up a lethal dose during its resting phase after consuming blood.

In 1948 the World Health Organization launched a series of spraying campaigns, with the prime objective of eradicating malaria. The disease was eliminated from Europe and North America, most of the Caribbean islands and from large areas of Asia. At one time, Sri Lanka claimed to be totally free of malaria. However, it has proved impossible to maintain eradication in places like India, where malaria is again on the increase. It has also recurred in Sri Lanka. Eradication on a

mass scale was never attempted in tropical Africa because the incidence of malaria there is so high and the problem so enormous.

The campaign against malaria has run into two major problems following its initial success. In many parts of the world where spraying has been carried out, strains of *Anopheles* have emerged which are resistant to DDT. This means that, if the campaign is to be continued, other more expensive insecticides must be used which are much more toxic to man. In addition, many strains of the *Falciparum* parasite have become resistant to the most effective drug, chloroquine. This resistance has developed especially in South East Asia, and also in Central and South America. In these areas, doctors are turning again to quinine—the standard malarial drug. The search for new drugs goes on ceaselessly. Research is also being directed towards the production of a vaccine to give protection against the disease, but the work is in its very early stages and no realistic outcome can be expected for many years.

The concept of eradication for the tropical areas has now been abandoned in favour of selective-control measures with which it is hoped to achieve local eradication. Meantime, malaria remains a killer and a great source of illness and economic loss, causing about a million deaths each year throughout the world. The battle against it is a long way from being won.

STANDARDS OF MEDICAL CARE

In the poorer parts of the world, people do not have the advantage of the standard of medical care which exists in the highly developed countries of Europe and in the United States. The map on the right illustrates this situation by showing medical staff as a proportion of the population in each country.

The World Health Organization has recently assessed the number of doctors for every 10,000 inhabitants on a continental basis. These statistics show that North America has the highest density with 14·98 doctors for every 10,000 inhabitants; Europe is a close second with 14·85, and is followed by Oceania with 11·00, South America with 6·54, Asia with 2·83 and Africa with 1·36.

At the lower end of the scale, the situation is aggravated by the few available medical staff being concentrated almost entirely in capital cities. Since the majority of the population in these areas live in rural communities, they have little or no access to medical care.

The problem of improving medical standards in the poorer countries is extremely difficult because, although the number of doctors increases annually, the increase in population is much greater. Asia will have to more than double its number of medical staff between now and the year 2000 if it is to keep pace with the increase in population.

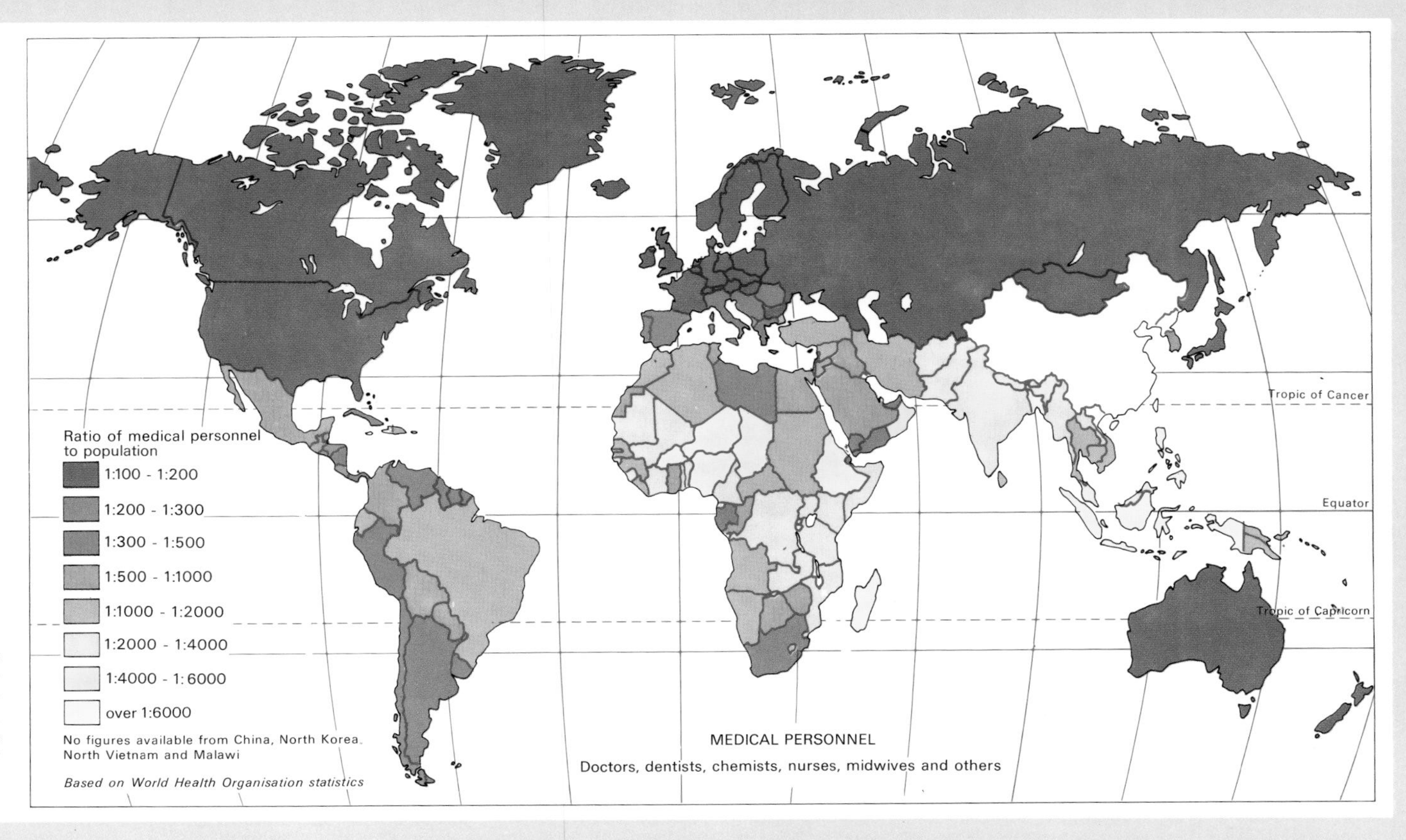

MEDICAL PERSONNEL
Doctors, dentists, chemists, nurses, midwives and others

Ratio of medical personnel to population

- 1:100 - 1:200
- 1:200 - 1:300
- 1:300 - 1:500
- 1:500 - 1:1000
- 1:1000 - 1:2000
- 1:2000 - 1:4000
- 1:4000 - 1:6000
- over 1:6000

No figures available from China, North Korea, North Vietnam and Malawi

Based on World Health Organisation statistics

THE EARTH'S

MINERALS FROM THE

Surely there is a mine for silver, and a place for gold which they refine. Iron is taken out of the earth, and brass is molten out of stone — JOB 28

FROM the prized flints of Stone-Age man to the uranium ores of the atomic scientist, minerals have contributed vitally to the growth of civilization. Man has long recognized their importance as the source of precious metals and precious stones, and of base metals such as copper, lead and zinc. Tomb paintings made in the Nile Valley nearly 5,000 years ago show craftsmen weighing malachite and precious metals, smelting mineral ores and carving emeralds into gems.

Rocks are made up of minerals, and minerals themselves are composed of one or more of the 90-odd natural elements in the Earth's Crust. While a few elements, such as gold, are found in the pure state, the majority occur in chemical combination with other elements. Thus oxides are produced when

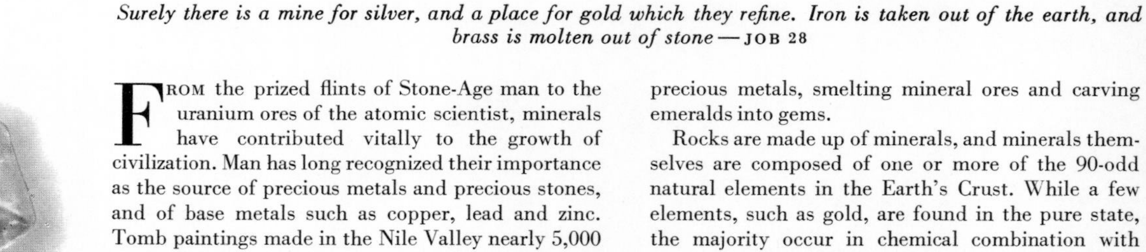

GALENA
Sulphide and chief ore of lead. Leaden pans for holding plants were used in the Hanging Gardens of Babylon. Lead is used in storage batteries, paint pigments, ammunition, solder, type and bearing metal, and as a safety shield with radio-active material. *Missouri, U.S.A.*

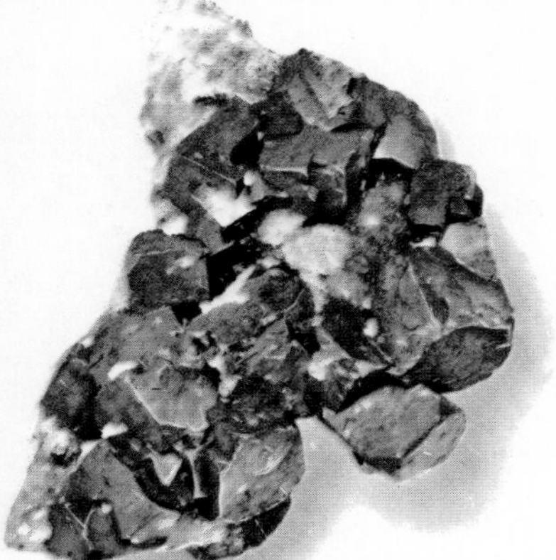

FLUORITE (FLUORSPAR)
Calcium fluoride. Ornamental stone in Victorian times. Raw material for the production of hydrofluoric acid which is used in the aluminium, petroleum, steel and plastic industries; fluorite is used as a flux in steel-making and in the ceramic industry. *Illinois, U.S.A.*

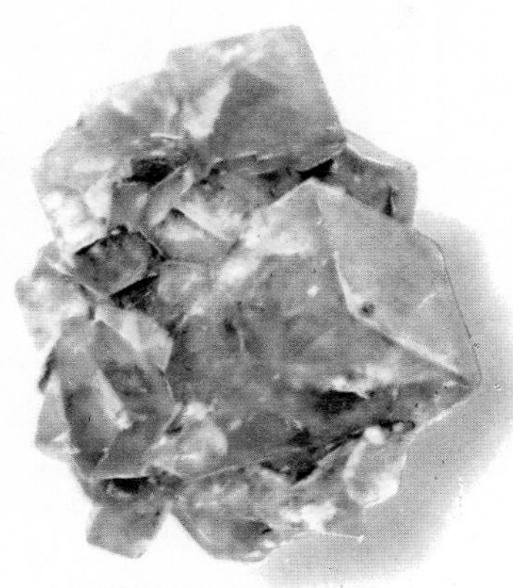

SPHALERITE
Sulphide and chief ore of zinc. Frequently occurs with galena. Zinc is used in die-castings, galvanizing steel, in brasses, dry battery cells; the oxide is used in rubber, paints, ceramics, cosmetics, etc. *Sullivan Mine, British Columbia Canada*

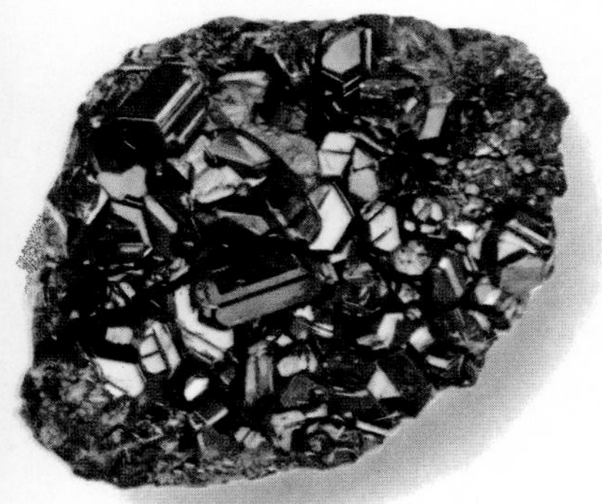

ASBESTOS
A group of fire-resistant, fibrous silicate minerals. The long fibres can be spun into fabrics. The short fibres are mixed with cement to make asbestos board. *Quebec, Canada*

URANIUM MINERALS
Atomic energy developments are based on uranium. Uranium does not occur uncombined in nature but is present in over 150 minerals.

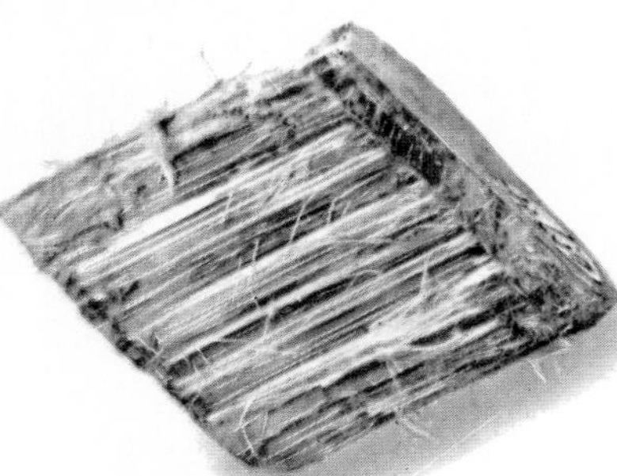

PITCHBLENDE
Uranium oxides with other components. The massive variety of uraninite, the most important ore. *Shinkolobwe, Shaba, Zaire*

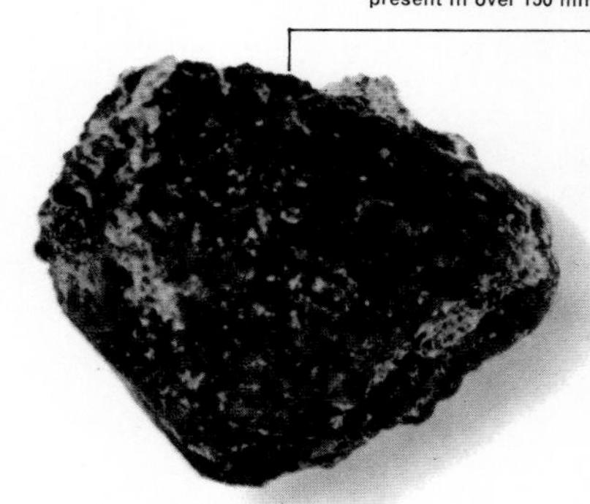

TORBERNITE
Hydrated copper-uranium phosphate. Green plates resemble a mica. *Cornwall, U.K.*

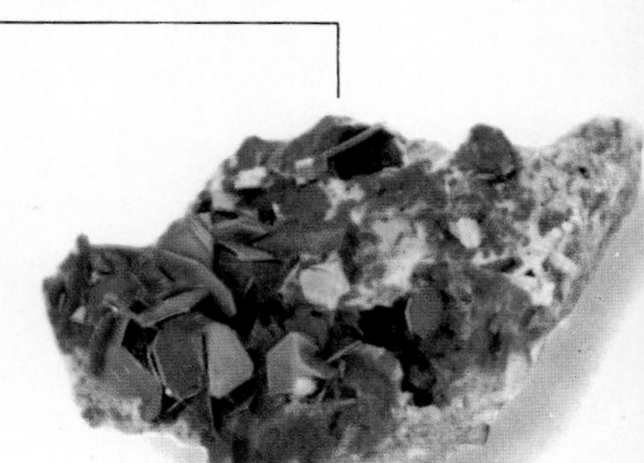

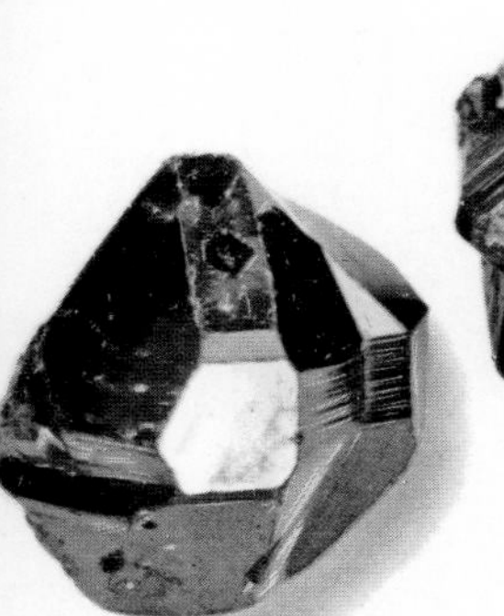

CASSITERITE
Oxide and chief ore of tin. Alloyed with copper, it was the basis of Bronze Age implements. Used in tin-plating, solders, bronze, bearing and type metal, pewter, and die-casting. *Malaysia*

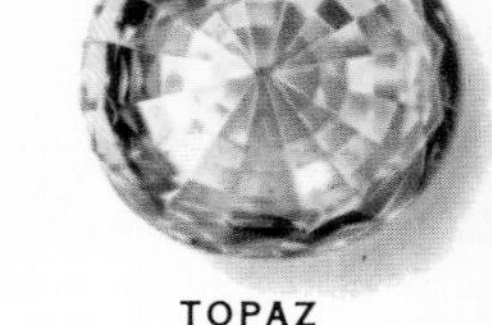

TOPAZ
Silicate of fluorine and aluminium. Used as gemstone and in refractories. *Ouro Preto, Brazil*

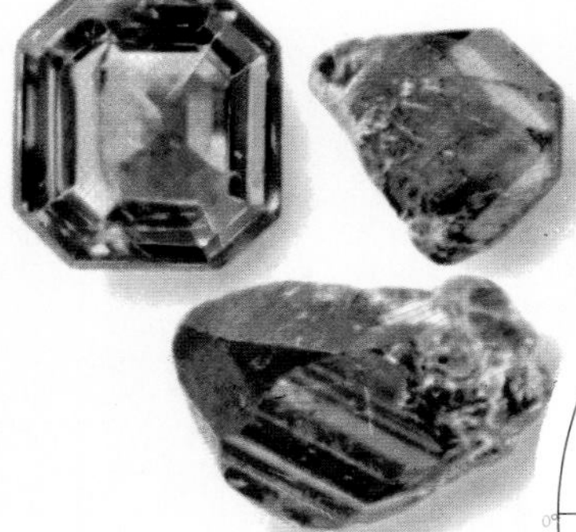

OLIVINE
Magnesium-iron silicate. A common rock-forming mineral. Used as a moulding sand. Peridot is the gem variety. *Zebirget, Egypt*

ALUMINA MINERALS
Although the most abundant metal in the Earth's Crust, aluminium does not occur in the free state, and commercial production did not start until the late 19th century. Alloys are used extensively in motor vehicles, aircraft, ships and domestic goods. Aluminium is used in electric transmission lines. Ruby and sapphire are gem varieties of corundum, a natural aluminium oxide.

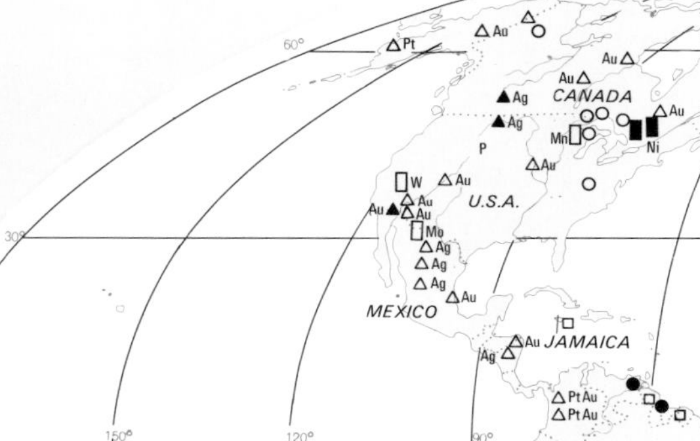

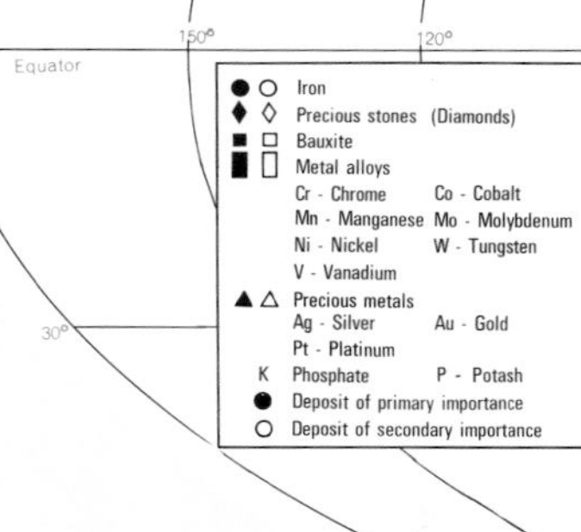

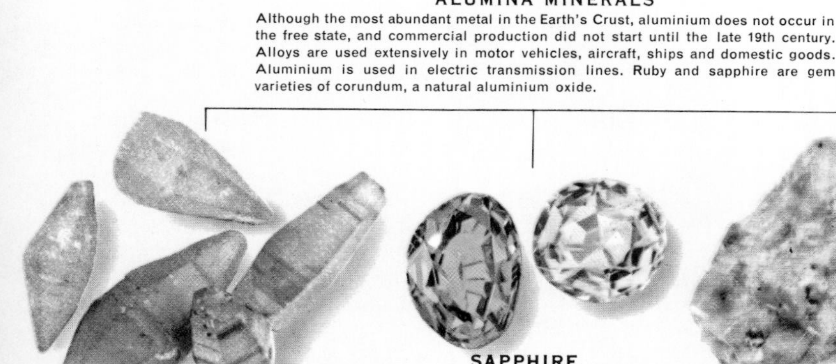

CORUNDUM
Hardness only exceeded by diamond. Used as an abrasive in grinding optical glass. Mixed with magnetite and other minerals to form emery. *Transvaal, South Africa*

SAPPHIRE
Corundum gemstones of whatever colour are sapphires with the exception of red (ruby); commonly blue. *Sri Lanka*

RUBY
"Pigeon-blood" red variety. Large rubies are among the most precious of stones. *Mogok, Burma*

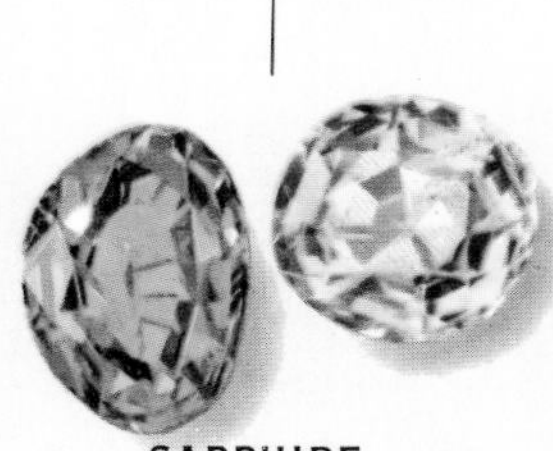

BAUXITE
Rock composed of aluminium hydroxides. Chief ore of aluminium; also used in making abrasives, refractories, chemicals, high-alumina cement, insulating materials, as a catalyst by the oil industry, and as a flux in steel manufacture. *Jamaica*

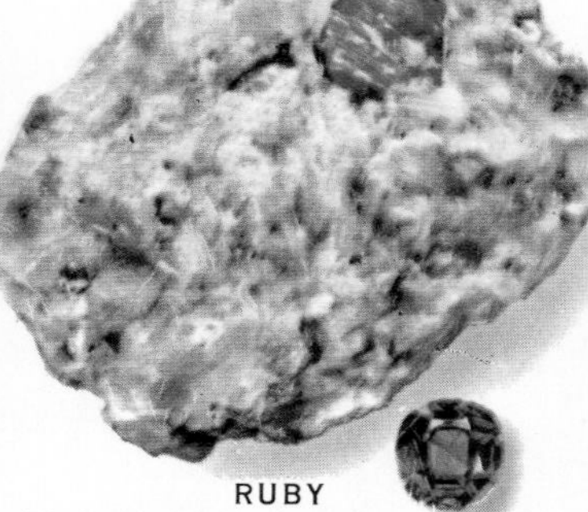

CINNABAR
Sulphide and chief ore of mercury (quicksilver). Mercury is used in the chemical, electrical and metal industries, and in scientific instruments, dental preparations, and detonators. *Almaden, Spain*

COPPER MINERALS
Copper and gold were the first metals used by man. Both occur in the free state and are easily worked. Copper is used extensively in the electrical industry, also in bronze, brass and other alloys. About 12 of the 165 known copper minerals are commercially important.

IRON MINERALS
Iron is industry's indispensable metal. Although iron minerals occur abundantly, pure iron is too soft for use, so man learnt to harden it by adding carbon. Thus the Iron Age followed the Bronze Age in Europe and W. Asia. A moderate amount of carbon produces steel, an excess produces cast-iron.

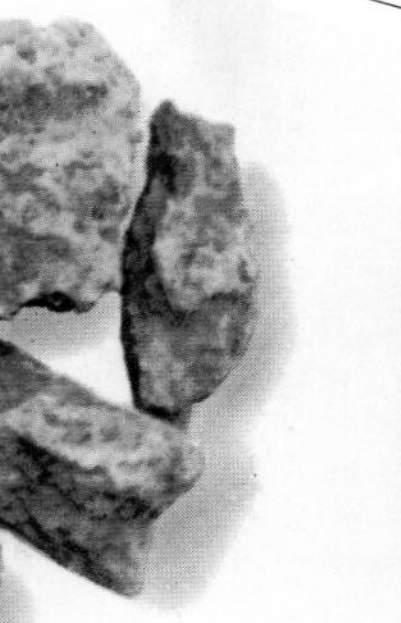

AZURITE
Hydrated copper carbonate. *Shaba, Zaire*

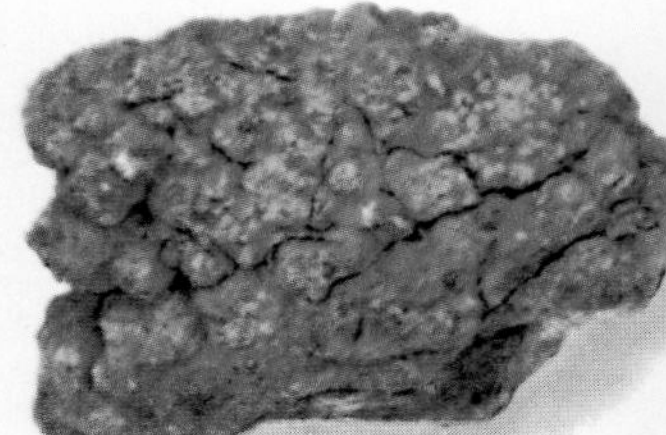

CHALCOPYRITE
Copper-iron-sulphide. Crystals of chalcopyrite and quartz are shown. Most widespread and important ore of copper. *Zambia*

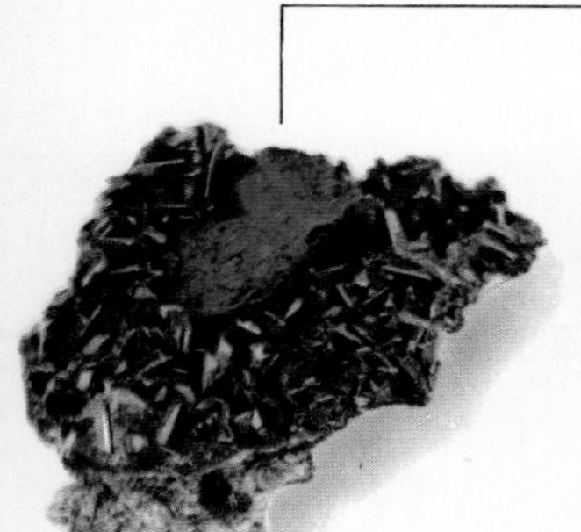

MALACHITE
Hydrated copper carbonate. An ornamental stone as well as a valuable ore. *Shaba, Zaire*

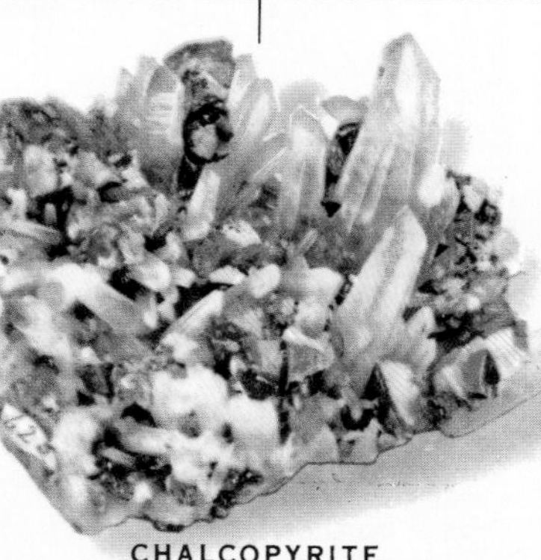

MAGNETITE
Magnetic iron oxide. Crystals show octahedral form. Lodestone (leading-stone), a variety with magnetic polarity, was used in primitive compasses. *Kiruna, Sweden*

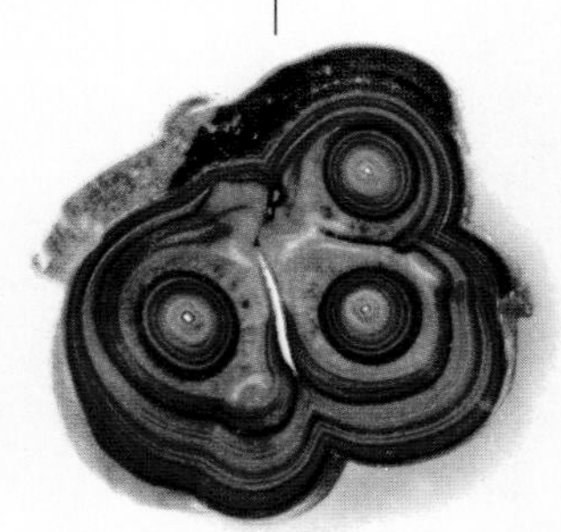

HEMATITE
Oxide of iron. The "kidney-ore" variety is shown. Used as an ornamental stone in signet rings, tie-pins and cuff links. *Minnesota, U.S.A.*

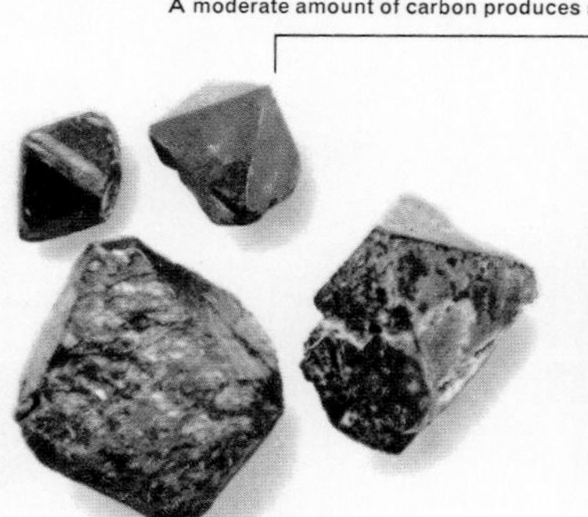
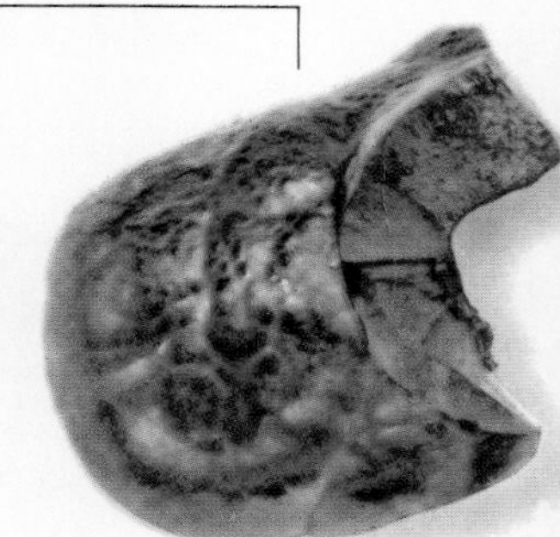

Map legend:

- ● ○ Iron
- ◆ ◇ Precious stones (Diamonds)
- ■ ▢ Bauxite
- ▮ ▯ Metal alloys
  - Cr - Chrome   Co - Cobalt
  - Mn - Manganese Mo - Molybdenum
  - Ni - Nickel   W - Tungsten
  - V - Vanadium
- ▲ △ Precious metals
  - Ag - Silver   Au - Gold
  - Pt - Platinum
- K - Phosphate   P - Potash
- ● Deposit of primary importance
- ○ Deposit of secondary importance

148

TREASURES

EARTH'S CRUST

metals combine with oxygen, and sulphides when metals combine with sulphur. Minerals are formed in various ways, for example, by crystallization from molten lava, rather as ice crystals form when water freezes, and by crystallization from vapours, as in the formation of sulphur crystals by the cooling of sulphur-bearing vapours round active volcanoes.

Some 2,000 minerals have been recorded so far, and, although new minerals are still being discovered, it is unlikely that any large deposit of a new mineral will be found in the accessible parts of the Earth's Crust. At depths below those of the present deepest mine, we may one day find new minerals that are stable at the high pressures and temperatures nearer the centre of the Earth. The advent of space travel opens up the possibility of the discovery of new minerals which would be stable on other planets where conditions are so different from our own.

This small selection of the Earth's minerals shows the variety of their natural forms and colours. The locations of their more commercially important deposits are indicated on the map.

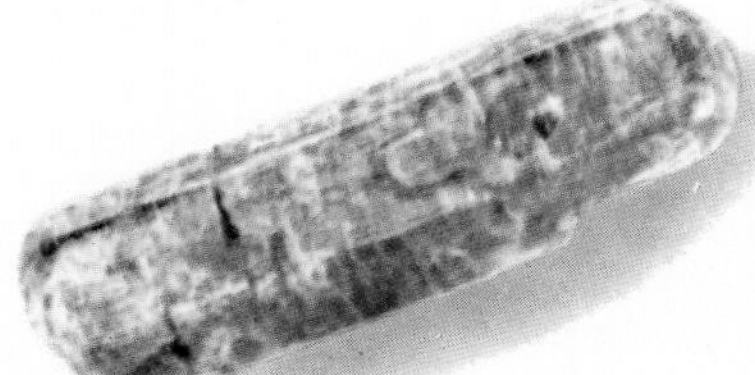

APATITE
Calcium phosphate. Chief constituent of phosphate-rock. Used in manufacture of fertilizers, cleansing products, smoke-bombs, pesticides, and phosphorus alloys.
Kola Peninsula, U.S.S.R.

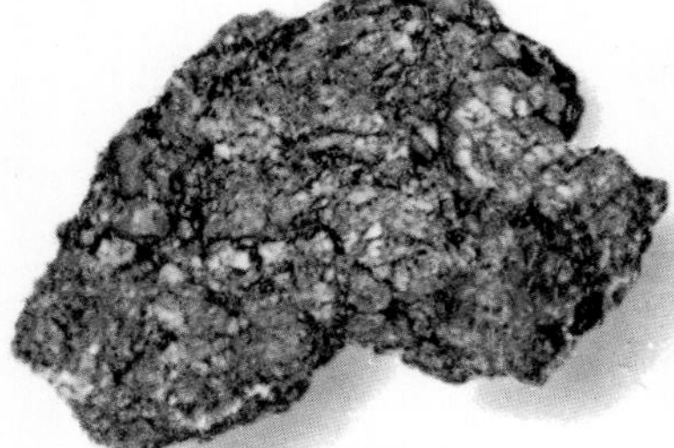

PENTLANDITE
Nickel-iron sulphide. Frequently occurs with chalcopyrite. Used extensively in stainless steels and other alloys; nickel is alloyed with copper to make Britain's "silver" coins and the U.S. five-cent "nickel". *Sudbury, Ontario Canada*

BERYLLIUM MINERALS
Beryllium is unusually light and strong and has valuable metallurgical properties. Used in alloys with copper, nickel, and aluminium, also in X-ray tubes, and nuclear reactors. Beryl is the commercial source of beryllium; aquamarine and emerald are gemstone varieties with similar composition.

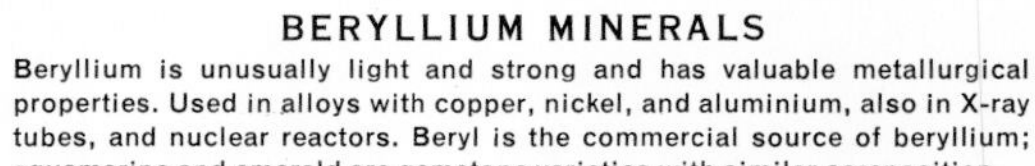

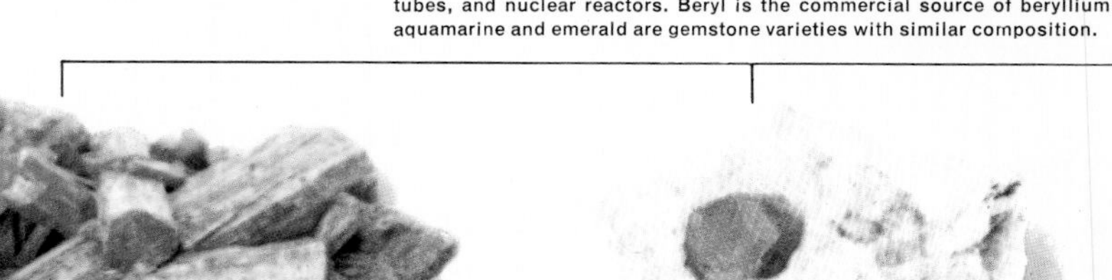

BERYL
Silicate of beryllium and aluminium. Can occur in large crystals up to 25 tons in weight. Gemstone if clear and transparent.
Mozambique

EMERALD
Grass-green, unflawed stones exceeding six carats command high prices. Ranks with diamond and ruby as the most precious stone.
Colombia

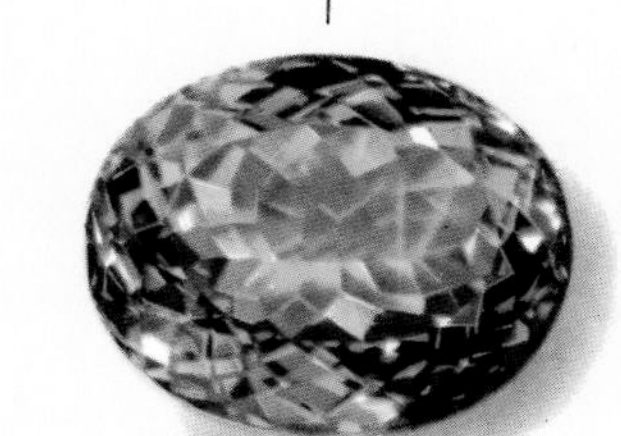

AQUAMARINE
Sea-green variety.
Minas Gerais, Brazil

KAOLIN (CHINA CLAY)
Hydrated aluminium silicate. Used in paper, rubber, ceramics (notably porcelain and china), chemicals, cosmetics, insecticides and petroleum catalysts. *Cornwall, U.K.*

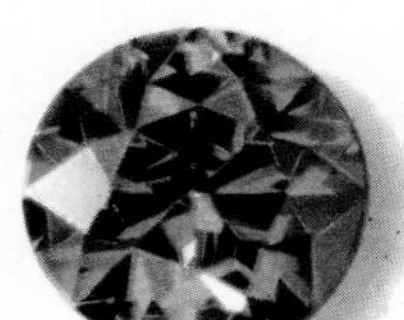

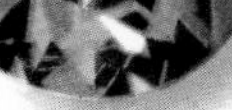

ZIRCON
Zirconium silicate. Besides being a gemstone, zircon in mineral form is used as foundry sand and in abrasives and ceramics. Zirconium metal is used in nuclear reactors, steel alloys, and in the chemical and electrical industries.

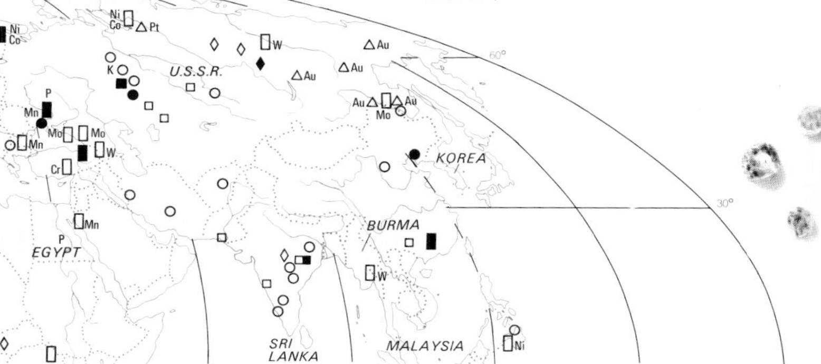

CARBON MINERALS
Native crystalline carbon occurs as two important minerals: diamond and graphite. Coals consist largely of non-crystalline carbon of organic origin. Combination with hydrogen produces the natural hydrocarbons which constitute petroleums and bitumens.

DIAMOND
Hardest known mineral and one of the most valuable gemstones. Crystalized deep down at high temperature and pressure, and brought to surface in volcanic "kimberlite" pipes. Photograph shows a diamond in kimberlite. Most diamonds are minute and imperfect, and are used in industry for cutting or as abrasives.
Kimberley, South Africa

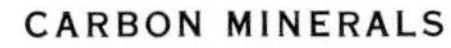

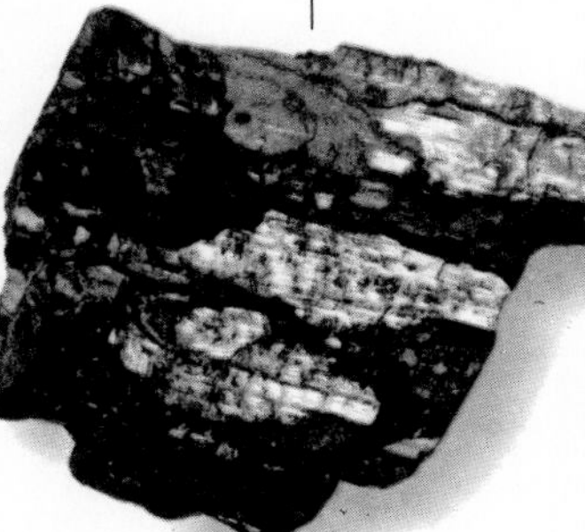

COAL
Bituminous coal showing banded structure. Besides being a fuel, coal is a source of coal gas, coke, tar, ammonia and many hydrocarbon chemicals. *United Kingdom*

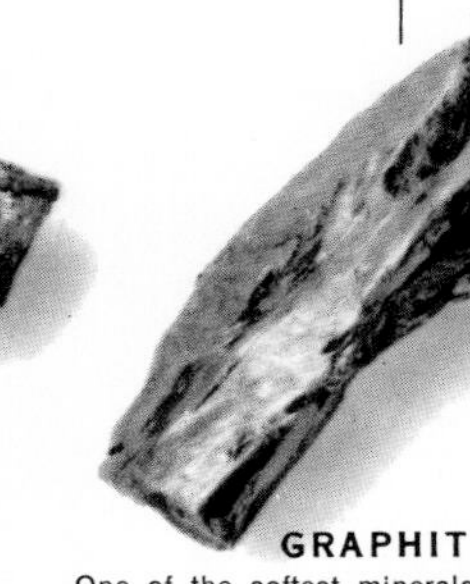

GRAPHITE
One of the softest minerals. The "lead" in lead pencils. Used in foundry facings, steel-making, lubricants, refractory crucibles, electrical equipment, pigments and in atomic piles. *Korea*

SULPHUR (BRIMSTONE)
Native sulphur (illustrated), metallic sulphide ores, "sour" natural and refinery gas, and coal are all commercial sources of sulphur. Used in manufacture of sulphuric acid and many other chemicals, paper, rubber goods, steel, textiles. *Texas, U.S.A.*

GOLD
Man used gold for decoration from early times. It is hardened by alloying with copper, silver, palladium or nickel for use in jewellery, dentistry and scientific equipment. *The Rand, South Africa*

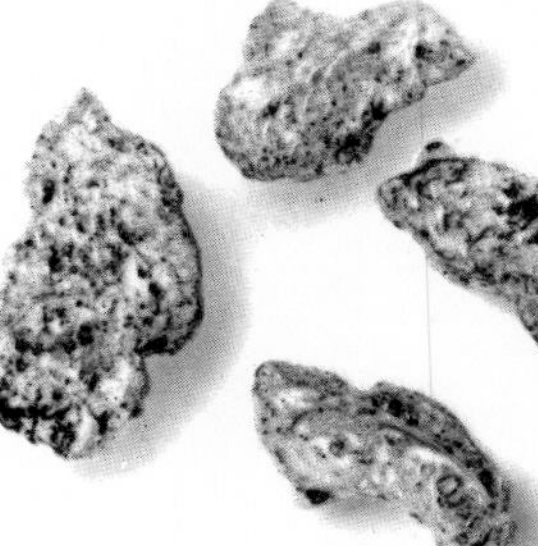

PLATINUM
Native platinum usually contains variable amounts of the other platinum-group metals—palladium, iridium, osmium, rhodium and ruthenium—some of which are employed to harden pure platinum in commercial applications. Platinum is used in anti-corrosive chemical ware, electrical components and laboratory instruments. Platinum and palladium are both used as catalysts, and in jewellery, dentistry and medicine. *Urals, U.S.S.R.*

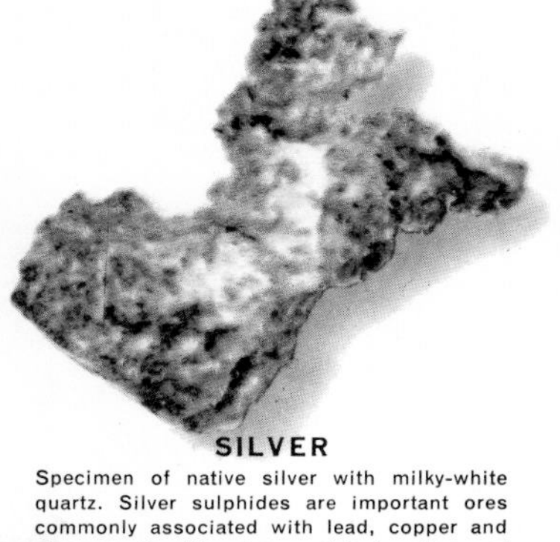

SILVER
Specimen of native silver with milky-white quartz. Silver sulphides are important ores commonly associated with lead, copper and zinc ores. Used in coinage, plate, jewellery and dentistry, and in the photographic, electrical and chemical industries. *Mexico*

SILICA MINERALS
Silicon does not occur uncombined, but its oxide, quartz, and the large group of silicates are the most important rock-forming minerals. Silicon is the most abundant element in the Earth's Crust after oxygen; it is used in electronic components and alloys, and for manufacturing silicones. Chalcedony is a crystalline variety of quartz intimately mixed with opal and other constituents. Flint is a common dark grey-brown variety of chalcedony; precious varieties are shown below.

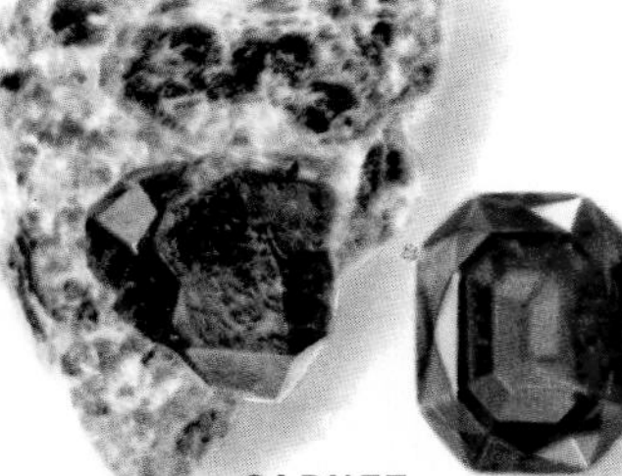

GARNET
Garnet is the name of a group of silicates. The photograph shows crystals in a metamorphic rock; garnet is also a semi-precious gemstone. The iron-aluminium garnet, almandine, is used as an abrasive. *U.S.A.*

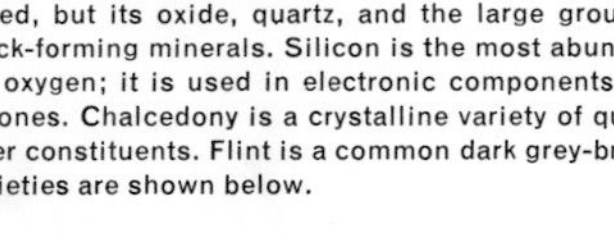

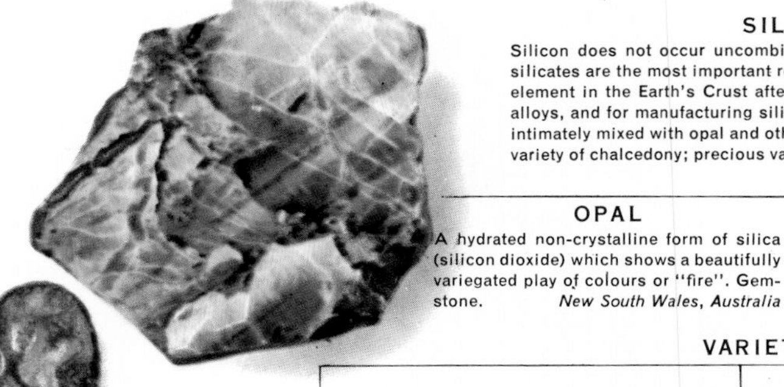

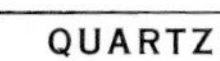

OPAL
A hydrated non-crystalline form of silica (silicon dioxide) which shows a beautifully variegated play of colours or "fire". Gemstone. *New South Wales, Australia*

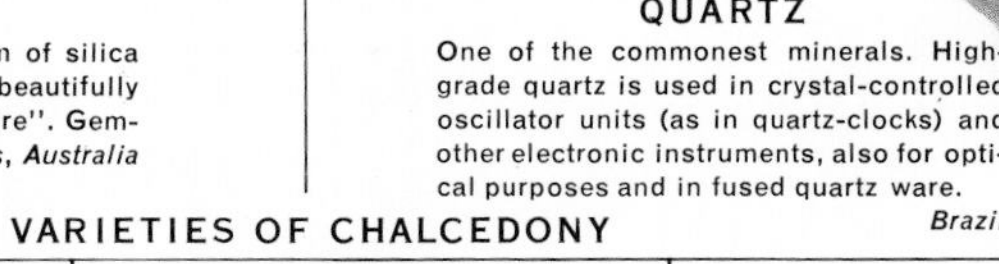

QUARTZ
One of the commonest minerals. High-grade quartz is used in crystal-controlled oscillator units (as in quartz-clocks) and other electronic instruments, also for optical purposes and in fused quartz ware. *Brazil*

VARIETIES OF CHALCEDONY

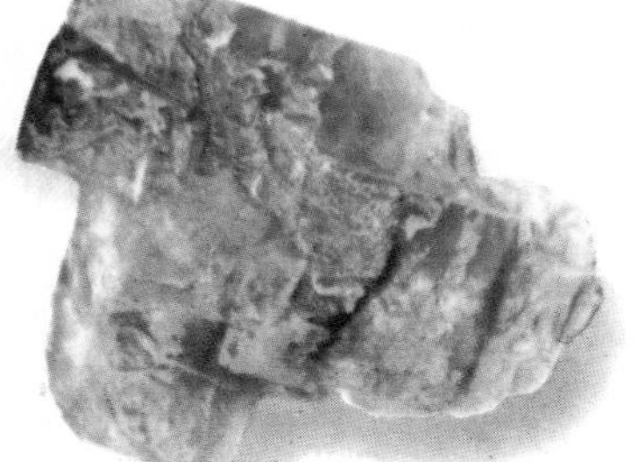

HALITE (ROCK SALT)
Sodium chloride. Man requires about 12 lb. of salt a year. Apart from its use in food-seasoning and preserving, salt is chiefly used by the chemical industry. *Cheshire, U.K.*

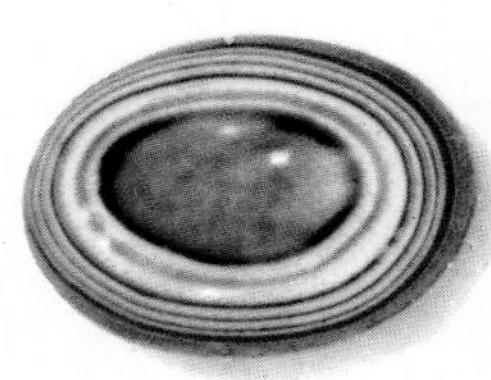

ONYX
An agate with regular bands in sharply contrasted colours.

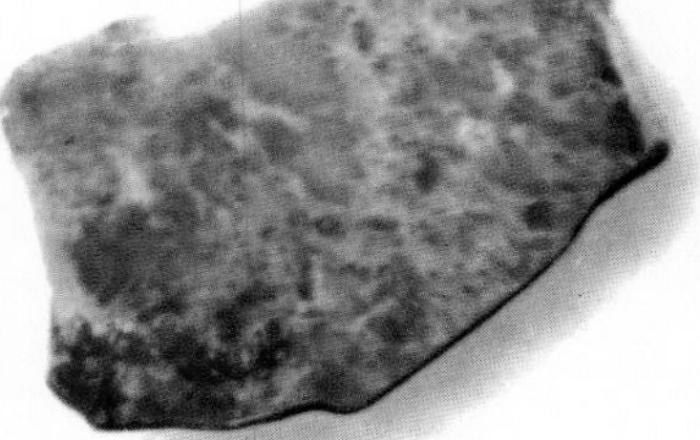

CHRYSOPRASE
Apple-green variety coloured by nickel oxide.

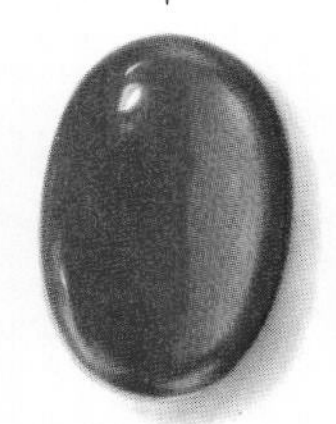

CARNELIAN
Reddish variety coloured by ferric oxide.

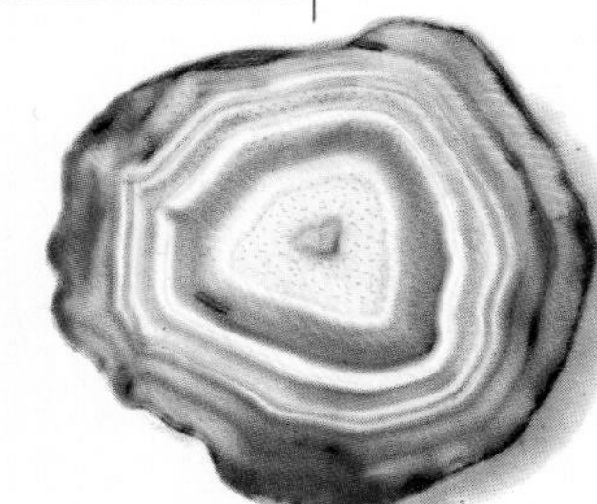

AGATE
Greyish variety in which irregular bands conform to shape of original cavity. Easily stained and used for umbrella handles, brooches, etc., also in laboratory equipment.

149

WORLD ENERGY RESOURCES

As for the earth, out of it cometh bread: and under it is turned up as it were fire.—JOB 28

THE importance of energy supplies to the industrialized countries of the world was strongly emphasized in 1973 and 1974 when oil prices increased to five times the level they were at during the 1960s. The world was still recovering from this crisis when in 1979 the price of crude oil once again more than doubled. As energy is vital for maintaining production in industrialized countries, this rise in oil prices sent the rate of inflation soaring in all the oil-importing countries.

The advance of civilization has depended to a great extent on developments in energy technology. Early man's only source of energy was the food he ate, and he would have needed a daily intake of about 2,500 calories to stay alive. Eventually, man learnt to harness the energy of animals, fire, water, wind and steam. Following the invention of the internal combustion engine in the 19th century, there was a rapid increase in energy consumption. Today, the demand for energy is higher than ever, especially in highly developed societies with their motor vehicles, aircraft, rockets, industrial and domestic needs. The average energy consumption for each man, woman and child in America, for example, is about 250,000,000 calories a day. This trend towards a more energy-intensive lifestyle is not likely to be reversed, even when the world's present reserves of energy run out, for new sources will be exploited.

Oil is the main energy provider today, with coal and natural gas some way behind. The remaining energy is provided by hydro-electric power and nuclear power. Before prices rose, oil was so cheap that other energy sources found it difficult to

compete. It still costs much less to get a barrel of oil out of the ground in the Middle East—source of most of the Western World's oil—than to mine the equivalent amount of coal. But the world's oil reserves are much more limited than coal reserves. At the present rate of energy consumption, reserves of oil and gas will last only a few decades while coal could last for centuries. More oil and gas will be found and more coal too, but the world will still be consuming large quantities of coal long after the oil industry has shrunk from its dominant position.

Nuclear power's contribution to the world's energy supplies is about 6 per cent but this will increase, and soon there could be pressure on uranium reserves. The search for uranium resources has been much less vigorous than the search for other fuels. But, as more nuclear reactors are built, the demand for uranium will rise, and it will become worth while for mining companies to seek new reserves and open up new mines.

There is a type of reactor which could make each tonne of uranium yield around 50 times as much energy as most of the present reactors that are being built. This is called a "breeder" reactor because it can breed more fuel than it uses. This surprising phenomenon is a consequence of the nature of uranium. The uranium excavated from the ground consists of two different types with slightly different atomic weights, but the same chemical composition. The reactors use only the lighter atoms which make up 0·7 per cent of uranium. The remaining 99·3 per cent of heavier atoms are of little value as reactor fuel because they cannot take part in the nuclear reactions. However,

a breeder reactor can turn these heavier atoms of uranium into plutonium, which can be used as reactor fuel.

The first experimental breeder reactors of any size are working in France, Britain, and the Soviet Union. More are being built, and commercial breeder reactors may be much more common around the turn of the century. By then, other sources may be contributing to the world's energy supplies.

Solar energy, wind, wave, hydro-electric and tidal power are not dependent on reserves in the same way as fossil fuels and uranium. These energy sources are virtually inexhaustible, for they derive their power from the Sun and the Moon. Added together they could provide the world with far more energy than it now gets from fossil fuels and nuclear power put together. But the technology needed to extract nature's energy has yet to be fully developed. And even when it is available, the cost of these "free" energy sources may be higher than that of energy from fossil fuels. Only hydro-electric power is now widely used, and there is a limited number of suitable sites for large dams for hydro-electric projects.

Nuclear fusion—the process that powers the hydrogen bomb and the stars, including the Sun—could be the ultimate energy source. A suitable fuel for nuclear fusion could be a rare type of hydrogen which is present in ordinary water, and there is enough of that around to satisfy man's energy needs for hundreds of thousands of years. But more intensive research is needed before the first fusion power station can be built.

ENERGY CONSUMPTION AND PRODUCTION

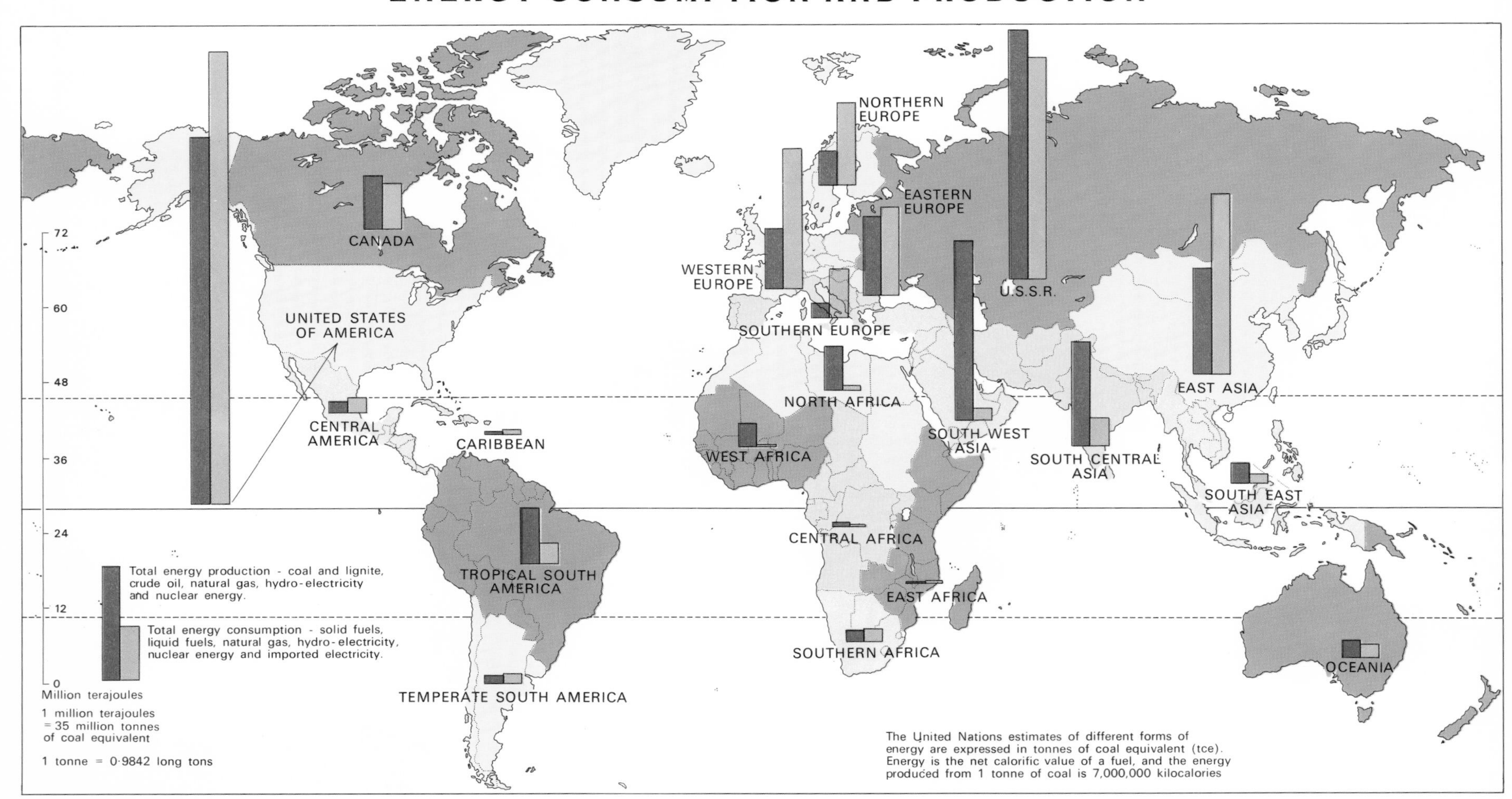

Total energy production - coal and lignite, crude oil, natural gas, hydro-electricity and nuclear energy.

Total energy consumption - solid fuels, liquid fuels, natural gas, hydro-electricity, nuclear energy and imported electricity.

Million terajoules

1 million terajoules
= 35 million tonnes
of coal equivalent

1 tonne = 0·9842 long tons

The United Nations estimates of different forms of energy are expressed in tonnes of coal equivalent (tce). Energy is the net calorific value of a fuel, and the energy produced from 1 tonne of coal is 7,000,000 kilocalories

NATIONAL wealth and high energy consumption seem to go hand in hand. The world's richest country (based on gross national product), the United States of America, contains only about 6 per cent of the world's population but consumes a third of the world's total production of energy. The U.S.A. is a major oil producer, but the level of production began to fall in 1970 and she now relies increasingly on imported oil. Europe is even more dependent on imported energy fuels, although Britain and Norway can look forward to a period of energy self-sufficiency with their oil and natural-gas resources in the North Sea.

The map above shows the level of energy consumption against production for each group of countries. Where the consumption level exceeds production, as in the U.S.A. and Western Europe, energy supplies are obviously being imported. The map also indicates the dramatic variation in energy consumption in different parts of the world. The richer countries consume 20 times as much energy as the poorer areas of the

world. This picture has changed little during recent years.

One aspect of energy which has changed is the demand for the different types of fuel. Two decades ago, coal accounted for just under 50 per cent of all fuel consumed. Oil accounted for less than 33 per cent and natural gas about 10 per cent. Wood and water accounted for about 6 per cent of the world's energy.

Early in the 1960s, coal production went up by about 25 per cent to meet the rising demand for energy and still provided about half of the world's energy. But, by then, oil was providing over a third, with natural gas accounting for 16 per cent of the total output of energy. The production of coal increased by a further 25 per cent in the following decade, but its share of the world's energy market dropped from just under a half to one third. Over the same period, oil production doubled to provide nearly 45 per cent of the world's energy supplies, and the output of natural gas more than doubled to reach 22 per cent.

The rate of increase in the demand for oil was effectively

curbed in 1973 and 1974 when prices soared, and a second bout of massive price increases in 1979 reinforced this trend. Because the industrialized countries have not fully recovered, it is impossible to make accurate assessments for the future. However, the cost of oil is rising faster than the cost of other fuels, so it seems likely that coal will regain a much greater share of the market, and nuclear power will provide a higher proportion of world energy than at present.

The rate of increase in world energy consumption could well slow down as a result of the substantial rise in the cost of all energy. Historically, consumption has doubled every ten years, but this was during a period of falling prices. Attitudes to energy consumption have changed radically since 1973, with more emphasis than before placed on conservation. Investigations have shown that wastage can account for as much as 60 per cent of the energy produced. If conservation is effective, the world's energy resources will last much longer.

THE DISTRIBUTION OF OIL AND NATURAL GAS

A SERIES of biological and geological processes lasting many millions of years turns dead plants and other organisms into oil and natural gas. This decaying matter accumulates on the sea bed and is buried by sediment. Much of the oil and gas produced by this process leaks away, but some is trapped in geological faults in the Earth's crust which form natural underground reservoirs.

There is a flourishing world trade in crude oil because the biggest oil-producing region, the Middle East, is some distance from the main oil-consuming countries.

Natural gas is often found at the same time as oil and used to be just burnt on site as it was a difficult commodity to transport. However, with the development of a method of liquefying the gas for easier transportation, an important international trade has built up.

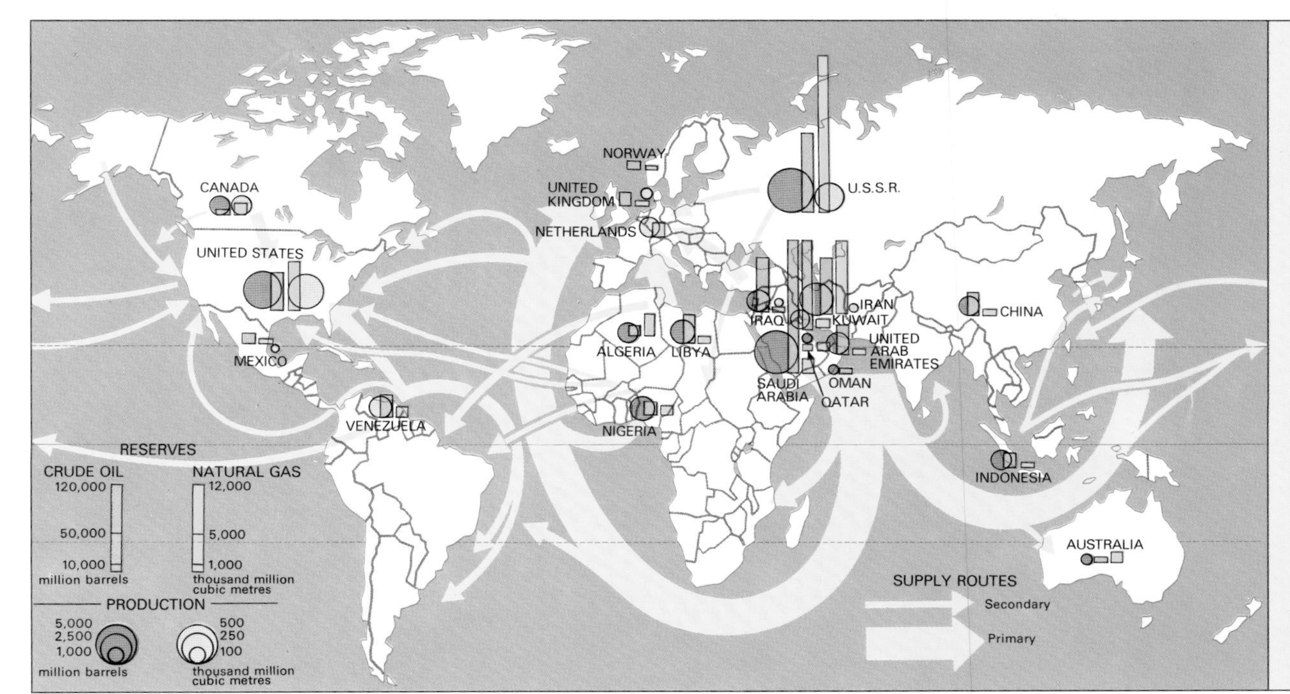

PRODUCTION AND RESERVES OF HYDROCARBONS

Below are listed the world's reserves and the annual production figures for crude oil, in millions of barrels, and the reserves and production of natural gas, in millions of cubic metres. By comparing the annual production figures with the reserves, an estimate can be made of how long reserves will last. The U.S.A., for example, will run out of oil in the 1980s unless more reserves are found, or more oil is available in existing oil fields.

COUNTRY	CRUDE OIL		NATURAL GAS	
	1/1/80 Reserves million barrels	1979 Production million barrels	1/1/80 Reserves thou. million cubic metres	1979 Production thou. million cubic metres
Saudi Arabia	163,350	3,516	2,640	9
Kuwait	71,660	919	1,019	6
U.S.S.R.	67,000	4,268	25,485	407
Iran	58,000	1,087	13,875	14
Iraq	31,000	1,253	779	—
United Arab Emirates	29,411	664	580	—
United States	26,500	3,118	5,493	579
Libya	23,500	751	680	—
China	20,000	778	708	77
Venezuela	17,870	860	1,212	12
Nigeria	17,400	828	1,172	—
United Kingdom	15,400	569	708	48
Indonesia	9,600	580	680	28
Algeria	8,440	391	3,738	10
Canada	6,800	544	2,421	82
Norway	5,750	136	665	—
Qatar	3,760	184	1,699	—
Oman	2,400	108	57	—
Australia	2,130	195	878	8
Ecuador	1,100	83	113	—

COAL RESOURCES

COAL is formed from decayed vegetable matter. The quality of the coal, which determines the amount of energy produced from each tonne, varies from low-quality lignite (brown coal) to anthracite. Its share of the energy market declined during the period when oil was cheaper but, today, coal is again much more competitive. There are vast coal reserves in the world, and large deposits exist in those countries with the highest energy consumption—the U.S.A. and Russia, for example. However, it is not always economically, or environmentally, acceptable to exploit all reserves. Opencast or strip mining, for example, results in extensive damage to the environment.

COAL RESERVES AND PRODUCTION

Coal has two distinct advantages over other fossil fuels: the reserves are very much greater, and the largest deposits are in the countries with the highest energy consumption. However, the dominant position in the energy market if more efficient and economic methods of using it can be found. Petrol for cars and gas with a high heating capacity have been produced from coal, but so far in limited quantities, because of the expense. As the amount of energy produced from coal varies with quality, the figures below are in millions of tonnes of coal equivalent, so that the amounts are comparable, irrespective of the grade of the coal.

COUNTRY	1977 Reserves million tce	1978 Production million tce
United States	177,600	544
U.S.S.R.	109,900	603
China	98,900	618
United Kingdom	45,000	123
West Germany	34,400	127
India	33,700	84
Australia	27,400	83
South Africa	26,900	89
Poland	21,800	205
Canada	9,600	28
* Yugoslavia	8,500	16
* East Germany	7,700	79
* Czechoslovakia	4,800	85
* Bulgaria	2,200	13
Japan	1,000	19
N. Korea	480	42
France	440	23
S. Korea	390	18

* Principally lignite	tce = tonnes of coal equivalent

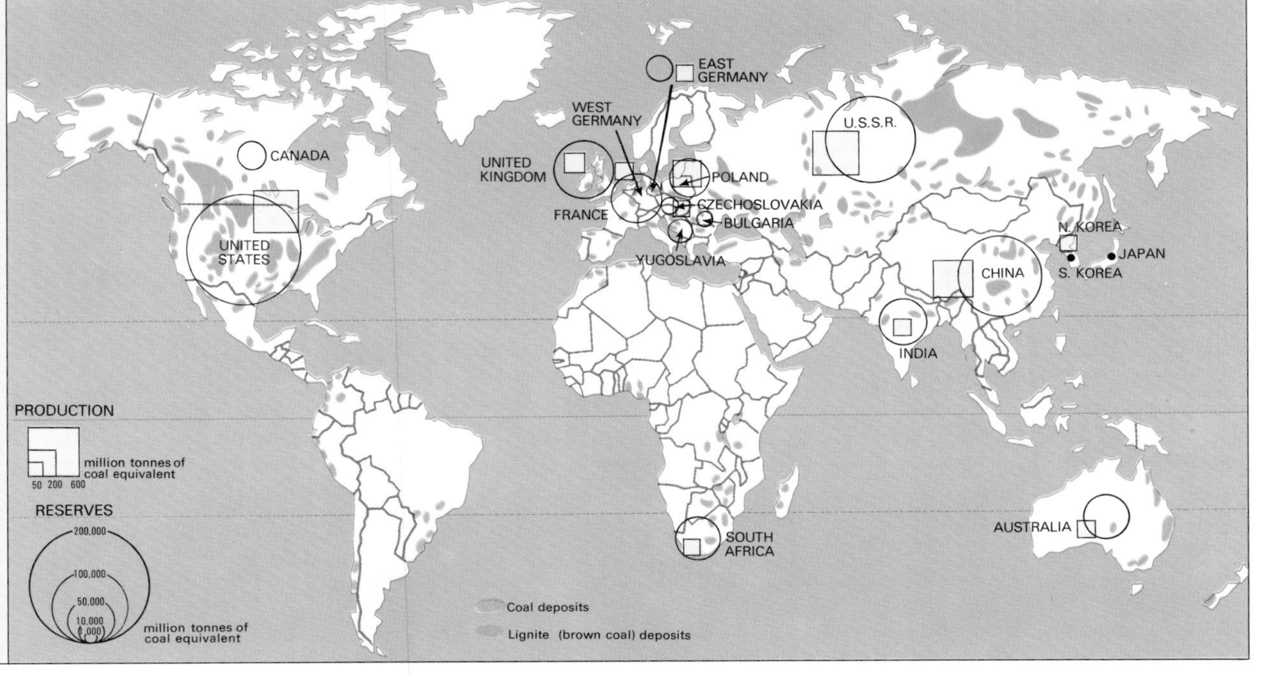

NUCLEAR POWER PROGRAMMES

NUCLEAR power is still in its infancy. In 1978, nuclear reactors were providing only 5·8 per cent of the world's electrical power compared with 22·3 per cent being provided by hydroelectric installations. Only a fraction of the Earth has been surveyed for uranium because, after military needs had been met, the requirements for power stations were so low that the price of uranium dropped, and it was uneconomic to search for new deposits. However, the search was revived as the value of uranium increased in the wake of soaring oil prices. But this effect has been counterbalanced by a fall in demand for electricity and public unease about the risks of nuclear power. The safe disposal of radioactive waste has aroused considerable public concern and is one of the major arguments against expanding nuclear power resources. One of the principal benefits of nuclear power is the high energy output of uranium: 1 kilogram of natural uranium can provide as much energy as 20 tonnes of coal.

NUCLEAR POWER RESOURCES

The U.S.A. has the largest-known deposits of uranium, and this is because surveying has been widespread. Large uranium reserves probably exist in countries other than those listed and now that the search for uranium has been revived substantial new deposits are likely to be found. The reserves listed include only known deposits which can be recovered at a currently acceptable cost.

WORLD URANIUM RESERVES (reasonably assured) 1979		PRINCIPAL NUCLEAR PROGRAMMES (excluding eastern bloc countries)		
COUNTRY	tonnes	COUNTRY	CAPACITY	
			1979 Gigawatts of electricity	1985 estimate Gigawatts of electricity
United States	708,000			
South Africa	391,000			
Sweden	301,000			
Australia	299,000			
Canada	235,000			
Niger	160,000			
Namibia	133,000	United States	55	115
Brazil	74,200	Japan	15	24
France	55,300	United Kingdom	9	10·3
Gabon	37,000	West Germany	9	25
India	29,800	France	9	34
Argentina	28,100	Canada	6	10
Algeria	28,000	Sweden	4	7·4
Denmark (Greenland)	27,000	Belgium	1·7	3·5
Central African Rep.	18,000	Switzerland	2	2·8
Spain	9,800	India	0·64	1·8
Portugal	8,200			
Japan	7,700			

1 gigawatt = 1,000 megawatts = 1,000,000 kilowatts = 1,000,000,000 watts

FACTS ABOUT THE EARTH

Estimated age of the Earth . . at least 4,600 million years
Superficial area 510,100,500 sq. km. (196,950,000 sq. miles)
Land surface . . 148,951,000 sq. km. (57,510,000 sq. miles)
Water surface (71% of total area) . . 361,150,000 sq. km.
(139,440,000 sq. miles)
Equatorial circumference. . . 40,075 km. (24,902 miles)
Meridional circumference . . 40,000 km. (24,860 miles)

Highest point of the Earth's land surface—
Mount Everest . . . . . 8,848 metres (29,028 feet)

Lowest point of the Earth's land surface—
Shores of the Dead Sea, Israel–Jordan . . 396 metres
(1,299 feet) below sea level

Greatest ocean depth—Marianas Trench, east of
the Philippines. . 11,033 m. (36,198 feet) below sea level

The Earth makes one complete revolution round the Sun every
365 days, 5 hours, 48 minutes and 46 seconds.

The Earth makes one complete rotation on its axis in 23 hours
and 56 minutes.

The Earth revolves in its orbit round the Sun at a speed of
107,160 kilometres (66,600 miles) per hour.

The Earth rotates on its axis at an equatorial speed of more
than 1,610 kilometres (1,000 miles) per hour.

CONTINENTS

	Area square km. (square miles)	Mean Elevation metres (feet)	Highest Elevation metres (feet)	Lowest Elevation metres (feet)	Highest Recorded Temperature	Lowest Recorded Temperature
AFRICA	29,785,000 (11,500,000)	580 (1,900)	Mt. Kilimanjaro, *Tanzania* 5,895 (19,340)	Lake Assal, *Djibouti* 150 (492) *below sea level*	Al' Aziziyah, *Libya* 58°C (136·4°F)	Semrir, *Morocco* −23·1°C (−11·4°F)
ANTARCTICA	13,338,500 (5,150,000)	1,830 (6,000)	Vinson Massif 5,140 (16,864)	Sea level	Hope Bay, *Graham Land* 15·2°C (59·4°F)	Nr. Vostok −88·2°C (−126·9°F)
ASIA	44,030,000 (17,000,000)	915 (3,000)	Mt. Everest, *Nepal–Tibet* 8,848 (29,028)	Dead Sea, *Israel–Jordan* 396 (1,299) *below sea level*	Jacobabad, *Pakistan* 52·6°C (127·1°F)	Verkhoyansk, *Siberia* −67·7°C (−89·9°F)
AUSTRALIA	7,686,880 (2,967,909)	305 (1,000)	Mt. Kosciusko, *N. S. Wales* 2,229 (7,313)	Lake Eyre, *South Australia* 16 (52) *below sea level*	Cloncurry, *Queensland* 53°C (127·5°F)	Charlotte Pass, *N. S. Wales* −22·2°C (−8·0°F)
EUROPE*	10,498,000 (4,053,300)	300 (980)	Mt. El'brus, *U.S.S.R.* 5,642 (18,510)	Caspian Sea, *U.S.S.R.* 28 (92) *below sea level*	Seville, *Spain* 51·1°C (124·0°F)	Ust'-Shchugor, *U.S.S.R.* −55°C (−67·0°F)
NORTH AMERICA	24,255,000 (9,365,000)	610 (2,000)	Mt. McKinley, *Alaska* 6,194 (20,320)	Death Valley, *California* 86 (282) *below sea level*	Death Valley, *California* 56·6°C (133·9°F)	Snag, *Yukon* −62·8°C (−81·0°F)
SOUTH AMERICA	17,798,500 (6,872,000)	·550 (1,800)	Mt.Ojos del Salado, *Chile·Arg.* 7,084 (23,240)	Salinas Grandes, *Argentina* 40 (131) *below sea level*	Rivadavia, *Argentina* 48·8°C (120·0°F)	Sarmiento, *Argentina* −33°C (−27·4°F)

*Including U.S.S.R. west of Ural'skiy Khrebet

PRINCIPAL MOUNTAINS OF THE WORLD

	metres	(feet)		metres	(feet)		metres	(feet)
Everest, *Nepal-Tibet*	8,848	(29,028)	Namcha Barwa, *Tibet*	7,756	(25,447)	Aconcagua, *Argentina*	6,960	(22,834)
K2 (Godwin Austen), *Kashmir*	8,611	(28,250)	Gurla Mandhata, *Tibet*	7,728	(25,355)	Bonete, *Argentina*	6,870	(22,541)
Kangchenjunga, *Nepal-Sikkim*	8,600	(28,215)	Muztag, *China*	7,723	(25,338)	Tupungato, *Chile*	6,800	(22,310)
Makalu, *Nepal-Tibet*	8,475	(27,805)	Kongur Shan, *China*	7,719	(25,325)	Huascarán, *Peru*	6,768	(22,205)
Dhaulagiri, *Nepal*	8,172	(26,810)	Tirich Mir, *Pakistan*	7,690	(25,230)	Llullaillaco, *Argentina-Chile*	6,723	(22,057)
Nanga Parbat, *Jammu/Kashmir*	8,126	(26,660)	Gongga Shan (Minya Konka), *China*	7,556	(24,790)	Kangrinboqe Feng (Kailas), *Tibet*	6,714	(22,028)
Annapurna, *Nepal*	8,078	(26,504)	Muztagata, *China*	7,546	(24,757)	Yerupaja, *Peru*	6,632	(21,758)
Gasherbrum, *Jammu/Kashmir*	8,068	(26,470)	Kommunisma (Pik), *U.S.S.R.*	7,495	(24,590)	Sajama, *Bolivia*	6,542	(21,463)
Sisha Pangma (Gosainthan), *Tibet*	8,013	(26,291)	Pobedy (Pik), *U.S.S.R.-China*	7,439	(24,407)	Illampu, *Bolivia*	6,485	(21,276)
Nanda Devi, *India*	7,816	(25,643)	Chomolhari, *Bhutan-Tibet*	7,313	(23,993)	Coropuna, *Peru*	6,425	(21,079)
Rakaposhi, *Jammu/Kashmir*	7,788	(25,551)	Lenina (Pik), *U.S.S.R.*	7,134	(23,406)	Illimani, *Bolivia*	6,402	(21,004)
Kamet, *India-Tibet*	7,756	(25,447)	Ojos del Salado, *Chile-Argentina*	7,084	(23,240)	Chimborazo, *Ecuador*	6,310	(20,701)

PRINCIPAL OCEANS AND SEAS OF THE WORLD

	Area sq. km.	(sq. miles)	Greatest Depth in metres	(feet)		Area sq. km.	(sq. miles)	Greatest Depth in metres	(feet)		Area sq. km.	(sq. miles)	Greatest Depth in metres	(feet)
Pacific Ocean	165,384,000	(63,855,000)	11,033	(36,198)	Bering Sea	2,269,000	(876,000)	5,121	(16,800)	Sea of Japan	1,008,000	(389,000)	3,743	(12,280)
Atlantic Ocean	82,217,000	(31,744,000)	9,200	(30,184)	Caribbean Sea	1,943,000	(750,000)	7,492	(24,580)	North Sea	575,000	(222,000)	661	(2,170)
Indian Ocean	73,481,000	(28,371,000)	8,047	(26,400)	Gulf of Mexico	1,544,000	(596,000)	4,377	(14,360)	Black Sea	461,000	(178,000)	2,243	(7,360)
Arctic Ocean	14,056,000	(5,427,000)	5,450	(17,880)	Sea of Okhotsk	1,528,000	(592,000)	3,475	(11,400)	Red Sea	438,000	(169,000)	2246	(7,370)
Mediterranean	2,505,000	(967,000)	4,846	(15,900)	East China Sea	1,248,000	(482,000)	2,999	(9,840)	Baltic Sea	422,000	(163,000)	439	(1,440)
South China Sea	2,318,000	(895,000)	5,514	(18,090)	Hudson Bay	1,233,000	(476,000)	259	(850)	Yellow Sea	404,000	(156,000)	91	(300)

LONGEST RIVERS OF THE WORLD

	km.	(miles)		km.	(miles)		km.	(miles)
Nile, *Africa*	6,690	(4,160)	Mackenzie, *Canada*	4,241	(2,635)	St. Lawrence, *Canada*	3,058	(1,900)
Amazon, *South America*	6,570	(4,080)	Mekong, *Asia*	4,184	(2,600)	Rio Grande, *U.S.A.-Mexico*	3,034	(1,885)
Mississippi-Missouri, *U.S.A.*	6,212	(3,860)	Niger, *Africa*	4,168	(2,590)	Yukon, *Alaska*	2,897	(1,800)
Irtysh, *U.S.S.R.*	5,570	(3,461)	Yenisey, *U.S.S.R.*	4,129	(2,566)	Orinoco, *South America*	2,897	(1,800)
Chang Jiang (Yangtze), *China*	5,520	(3,430)	Paraná, *South America*	3,943	(2,450)	São Francisco, *S. America*	2,897	(1,800)
Huang He (Yellow), *China*	4,672	(2,903)	Murray-Darling, *Australia*	3,717	(2,310)	Salween, *Burma-China*	2,897	(1,800)
Zaire (Congo), *Africa*	4,667	(2,900)	Volga, *U.S.S.R.*	3,690	(2,293)	Danube, *Europe*	2,848	(1,770)
Amur, *Asia*	4,509	(2,802)	Madeira, *South America*	3,315	(2,060)	Indus, *Asia*	2,736	(1,700)
Lena, *U.S.S.R.*	4,269	(2,653)	Purus, *South America*	3,218	(2,000)	Brahmaputra, *Asia*	2,704	(1,680)

PRINCIPAL LAKES OF THE WORLD

	sq. km.	(sq. miles)		sq. km.	(sq. miles)		sq. km.	(sq. miles)
Caspian Sea, *U.S.S.R.-Iran (salt)*	393,898	(152,084)	Great Slave, *Canada*	28,438	(10,980)	Eyre, *Australia (salt)*	9,583	(3,700)
Superior, *U.S.A.-Canada*	82,814	(31,820)	Erie, *U.S.A.-Canada*	25,745	(9,940)	Rudolf (Turkana), *Kenya (salt)*	9,065	(3,500)
Victoria, *Kenya-Uganda-Tanzania*	69,485	(26,828)	Winnipeg, *Canada*	24,341	(9,398)	Titicaca, *Peru-Bolivia*	9,065	(3,500)
Aral, *U.S.S.R. (salt)*	68,682	(26,518)	Malawi (Nyasa), *Malawi-Mozambique*	23,310	(9,000)	Athabasca, *Canada*	8,081	(3,120)
Huron, *U.S.A.-Canada*	59,596	(23,010)	Ontario, *U.S.A.-Canada*	19,529	(7,540)	Nicaragua, *Nicaragua*	7,697	(2,972)
Michigan, *U.S.A.*	58,016	(22,400)	Balkhash, *U.S.S.R.*	18,260	(7,050)	Reindeer, *Canada*	6,389	(2,467)
Tanganyika, *Tanzania-Zambia-Zaire*	32,893	(12,700)	Ladoga, *U.S.S.R.*	18,130	(7,000)	Issyk-Kul', *U.S.S.R.*	6,190	(2,390)
Great Bear, *Canada*	31,792	(12,275)	Chad, *Nigeria-Niger-Chad*	15,540	(6,000)	Qinghai Hu (Koko Nor), *China (salt)*	5,957	(2,300)
Baykal, *U.S.S.R.*	31,492	(12,159)	Onega, *U.S.S.R.*	9,842	(3,800)	Torrens, *Australia (salt)*	5,698	(2,200)

SECTION FOUR

INDEX

INDEX

LIST OF ABBREVIATIONS

Afghan. Afghanistan
Afr. Africa
Ala. Alabama
Alta. Alberta
Antarc. Antarctica
Arabia. Saudi Arabia
Arch. Archipelago
Arg. Argentina
Ariz. Arizona
Ark. Arkansas
A.S.S.R. Autonomous Soviet Socialist Republic
Atl. Oc. Atlantic Ocean
Aust. Australia
B. Bay, Bahia, Baie, Bucht
Baluch. Baluchistan
B.C. British Columbia
Belg. Belgium, Belgian
Bol. Bolivia
Br. British
Bulg. Bulgaria
C. Cape, Cabo, Cap, Capo
Cal. California
Can. Canada, Canal
Cel. Celebes
Cent. Central
Chan. Channel
Co. County
Col. Colony
Colo. Colorado
Colomb. Colombia
Conn. Connecticut
Cord. Cordillera (mountain chain)
Cr. Creek
Czech. Czechoslovakia
Del. Delaware
Den. Denmark
Dep. Department
Des. Desert
Dist. District
Div. Division
Djib. Djibouti
Dom. Dominican, Dominion
E. East, Eastern
Ecua. Ecuador
E.I. East Indies
Eiln. Eilanden
Eire Republic of Ireland
Emb. Embalse (reservoir)
Eng. England
Equat. Equatorial
Ethio. Ethiopia
Eur. Europe
Fd. Fjord
Fed. Federal, Federation
Fin. Finland
Fla. Florida
Fr. French, France
G. Gulf, Golfe, Golfo, Guba
Ga. Georgia
Geb. Gebirge (mountains)
Ger. Germany
G.F. Goldfield
Gr. Grand
Grp. Group
Gt. Great
Guat. Guatemala
Harb. Harbour
Hd. Head
Hisp. Hispaniola
Hond. Honduras
Hung. Hungary
I., Is. Island, Islands, Ile, Iles
Ia. Iowa
Ida. Idaho
Ill. Illinois
Ind. Indiana
Indon. Indonesia
Intl. International
It. Italian, Italy
Iv. Cst. Ivory Coast
Jeb. Jebel (mountain)
Jct. Junction
Kans. Kansas
Kazakh. Kazakhstan
Kep. Kepulauan (island group)
Kirgiz. Kirghizia
Ky. Kentucky
L. Lake, Loch, Lough, Lago, Lac, Lagoon, Lagos
La. Louisiana
Ld. Land
Leb. Lebanon
Lit. Little
Lith. Lithuania
Lr. Lower
Lt. Ho. Light House
Madag. Madagascar
Man. Manitoba
Mass. Massachusetts
Maur. Mauritania
Md. Maryland
Me. Maine
Medit. Mediterranean
Mex. Mexico
Mich. Michigan
Minn. Minnesota
Miss. Mississippi
Mo. Missouri
Mong. Mongolia
Mont. Montana
Mozamb. Mozambique
Mt., Mte. Mount, Mont, Monte
N. North, Northern, New
Nat. National
N.B. New Brunswick
N.C. North Carolina
N. Dak. North Dakota
Nebr. Nebraska
Neth. Netherlands
Nev. Nevada
Nfld. Newfoundland
N.H. New Hampshire
Nic. Nicaragua
N. Ire. Northern Ireland
N.J. New Jersey
N.Mex. New Mexico
N.S. Nova Scotia
N.S.W. New South Wales
N.W.T. Northwest Territories
N.Y. New York
N.Z. New Zealand
O. Ohio
O., Os. Ostrov (island)
Ova. Ostrova (islands)
Oc. Ocean
O.F.S. Orange Free State
Okla. Oklahoma
Ont. Ontario
Oreg. Oregon
Oz. Ozero (lake)
Pa. Pennsylvania
Pac. Oc. Pacific Ocean
Pak. Pakistan
Pan. Panama
Para. Paraguay
Pass. Passage
P.E.I. Prince Edward Island
Pen. Peninsula, Peninsular
Phil. Philippines
Pk. Peak, Park
Plat. Plateau
Pol. Poland
Port. Portuguese, Portugal
Princip. Principality
Prot. Protectorate
Prov. Province, Provincial
Pt. Point, Pointe
Pta. Punta (point)
Pto. Puerto
Qnsld. Queensland
Que. Quebec
R. River, Rio, Rivière
Ra. Range
Reg. Region
Rep. Republic
Res. Reservoir
R.I. Rhode Island
Rom. Romania
R.S.F.S.R. Russian Soviet Federated Socialist Republic
S. South, Southern
Sa. Serra, Sierra
Sard. Sardinia
Sask. Saskatchewan
S.C. South Carolina
Scot. Scotland
Sd. Sound
S. Dak. South Dakota
S. San, Santo
Set. Settlement
Sol. Solomon
Som. Somali Republic, Somalia
Sp. Spanish, Spain
S.S.R. Soviet Socialist Republic
St., Ste. Saint, Sainte, Santa, Station
Str. Strait
Swed. Sweden
Switz. Switzerland
Tadzhik. Tadzhikstan
Tan. Tanzania
Tenn. Tennessee
Terr. Territory
Tex. Texas
Tg. Tandjung (cape)
Trans. Transvaal
Turkmen. Turkmenistan
U.A.E. United Arab Emirates
Ukr. Ukraine
Up. Upper
U.S.A. United States of America
U.S.S.R. Union of Soviet Socialist Republics
Ut. Utah
Uzbek. Uzbekistan
Va. Virginia
Val. Valley
Vdkhr. Vodokhranilische (reservoir)
Venez. Venezuela
Vict. Victoria
Viet. Vietnam
Vol. Volcano
Vt. Vermont
W. West, Western
Wash. Washington
W.I. West Indies
Wisc. Wisconsin
Wyo. Wyoming
Y.T. Yukon Territory
Yugosl. Yugoslavia

A

Aachen, *W. Germany* 68 Bc
Aaiún,el, *Morocco* 98 Cc
Aalen, *West Germany* 68 Dd
Aalsmeer, *Netherlands* 64 Cb
Aalst, *Belgium* 64 Cd
Aalten, *Netherlands* 64 Ec
Aalter, *Belgium* 64 Bc
Aarau, *Switzerland* 65 Da
Aarberg, *Switzerland* 65 Ca
Aarburg, *Switzerland* 65 Ca
Aardenburg, *Netherlands* 64 Bc
Aare, *Switzerland* 65 Ca
Aargau, *Switzerland* 65 Da
Aarschot, *Belgium* 64 Cd
Aba, *Zaire* 97 Gd
Abacaxis, *Brazil* 52 Fe
Abaco I., Great, *The Bahamas* 51 Da
Abaco I., Little, *The Bahamas* 51 Da
Ābādān, *Iran* 92 Ec
Abadeh, *Iran* 93 Fc
Abaete, *Brazil* 53 Hd
Abagnar Qi, *China* 82 Gb
Abajo Peak, *Utah* 48 Cd
Abakan, *U.S.S.R.* 79 Jc
Abancay, *Peru* 52 Cf
Abarqū, *Iran* 93 Fc
Abashiri, *Japan* 86 Jb
Abau, *Papua New Guinea* 57 Jb
Abaya L., *Ethiopia* 97 Hc
Abbeville, *France* 72 Da
Abbeville, *Georgia, U.S.A.* 45 Fd
Abbeville, *Louisiana* 49 Lh
Abbey, *Saskatchewan* 36 Jh
Abbot Ice Shelf, *Antarctica* 104 Rb
Abbotsford, *B.C.* 39 Ml
Abbottabad, *Pakistan* 90 Cc
Abdul Aziz, Jebel, *Syria* 92 Db
Abdulino, *U.S.S.R.* 81 Ld
Abéché, *Chad* 99 Kf
Abee, *Alberta* 36 Ed
Abele, *Belgium* 64 Ad
Abelessa, *Algeria* 98 Fd
Abengourou, *Ivory Coast* 98 Eg
Abeokuta, *Nigeria* 98 Fg
Aberaeron, *Wales* 63 Eh
Abercorn, *Quebec* 35 Sg
Aberdare, *Wales* 63 Ej
Aberdeen, *Mississippi* 45 Cd
Aberdeen, *Montana* 46 Dc
Aberdeen, *Saskatchewan* 36 Lf
Aberdeen, *Scotland* 62 Fc
Aberdeen, *S. Dakota* 46 Hc
Aberdeen, *Washington* 47 Bb
Aberdeen L., *N.W.T.* 38 Yc
Aberfeldy, *Scotland* 62 Ed
Aberfoyle, *Scotland* 62 Ed
Abergavenny, *Wales* 63 Ej
Abernethy, *Saskatchewan* 37 Oh
Aberystwyth, *Wales* 63 Eh
Abhā, *Arabia* 92 Df
Abidjan, *Ivory Coast* 98 Eg
Ab-i-Istada, *Afghanistan* 93 Jc
Abilene, *Kansas* 49 Jc
Abilene, *Texas* 49 Hf
Abingdon, *Virginia* 45 Gb
Abington, *Massachusetts* 44 Ea
Abisko, *Sweden* 66 Hb
Abitau L., *N.W.T.* 38 Ue
Abitibi, *Ontario* 34 Kc
Abitibi, L., *Ontario* 34 Kd
Abitibi Canyon Dam, *Ont.* 34 Jc
Abitibi R., *Ontario* 34 Jb
Abitibi R., Little, *Ontario* 34 Jb
Abomey, *Benin* 98 Fg
Abound, *Saskatchewan* 37 Mh
Abqaiq, *Arabia* 92 Ed
Abraham, Plains of, *Que.* 35 Sc
Abrantes, *Portugal* 70 Ac
Abrets, les, *France* 72 Fd
Abrud, *Romania* 76 Da
Abruzzi, *Italy* 74 Dd
Abruzzi, Mt., *B.C.* 36 Bh
Abtenau, *Austria* 68 Ee
Abu, *India* 88 Dd
Abu al Abyad, *U.A.E.* 93 Fe
Abu Bahr, *Arabia* 92 Ee
Abu Deleiq, *Sudan* 99 Me
Abu Dhabi, *U.A.E.* 93 Fe
Abu ed Duhur, *Syria* 94 Fb
Abu el Jurdhan, *Jordan* 94 Dg
Abu Jifan, *Arabia* 92 Ee
Abu Kemal, *Syria* 92 Dc
Abumombozi, *Zaire* 96 Ed
Abunã, *Brazil* 52 De
Abu Qurqas, *Egypt* 99 Mc
Abuta, *Japan* 86 Gc
Abuya Myeda, *Ethiopia* 97 Hb
Abu Zabad, *Sudan* 99 Lf
Abyei, *Sudan* 99 Lg
Åbyn, *Sweden* 66 Jd
Abyy, *U.S.S.R.* 79 Pb
Acadia Valley, *Alberta* 36 Gg
Acajutla, *Salvador* 51 Bd
Acambaro, *Mexico* 50 Dc
Acaponeta, *Mexico* 50 Cc
Acapulco de Juárez, *Mexico* 50 Ed
Acará, *Brazil* 53 Hd
Acarigua, *Venezuela* 52 Db
Acatlan, *Mexico* 50 Ed
Accomac, *Virginia* 45 Kb
Accra, *Ghana* 98 Eg
Achaguas, *Venezuela* 52 Db
Achalpur, *India* 88 Ed
Achao, *Chile* 54 Bf
Acheninni L., *Sask.* 37 Pd
Achigan, *Ontario* 34 Ff
Achill I., *Eire* 63 Ag
Achinsk, *U.S.S.R.* 79 Jc
Achray, *Ontario* 35 Ng
Acklins, I., *The Bahamas* 51 Eb
Acme, *Alberta* 36 Dg
Aconcagua, *Argentina* 54 Cd
Açores, *Atlantic Ocean* 98 Aa
Acorizal, *Brazil* 53 Fg
Acoyapa, *Nicaragua* 51 Bd
Acre, *Israel* 94 De
Actaeon, *Tuamotu Arch.* 103 Mk
Acton, *Ontario* 34 Kj
Acton Vale, *Quebec* 35 Sg
Açú, *Brazil* 53 Ke
Ada, *Minnesota* 46 Jb
Ada, *Oklahoma* 49 Je
Adairville, *Kentucky* 45 Db
Adak, *Aleutian Is.* 43 Vm
Adalia. *See* Antalya
Adam, *Oman* 93 Ge
Adamant Mt., *B.C.* 39 Pk
Adamello, *Italy* 74 Cb
Adams, *New York* 40 Hd
Adams, Mt., *Washington* 47 Cb
Adam's Bridge, *India/Sri Lanka* 88 Eg
Adams L., *B.C.* 39 Ok
Adams Peak, *Sri Lanka* 88 Fg
Adamsville, *Quebec* 35 Sg
Adana, *Turkey* 92 Cb
Adanac, *Saskatchewan* 36 Hf
Adapazari, *Turkey* 92 Ba
Adare, *Eire* 63 Bh
Adare, Cape, *Antarctica* 104 Lb
Adavale, *Queensland* 57 He
Ad Dir'iyah, *Arabia* 92 Ee
Addis Abeba, *Ethiopia* 97 Hc
Addis Derra, *Ethiopia* 97 Hb
Addison, *New York* 44 Ba
Ad Diwaniyah, *Iraq* 92 Dc
Adelaer, C., *Greenland* 41 Pc
Adelaide, *Cape Province* 95 Df
Adelaide, *S. Australia* 57 Gf
Adelaide, I., *Antarctica* 104 Sc
Adelaide Pen., *N.W.T.* 38 Za
Adelaide River, *N. Terr.* 56 Fb
Adelboden, *Switzerland* 65 Cb
Ademuz, *Spain* 71 Eb
Aden, *S. Yemen* 92 Eg
Aden, G. of, *Africa* 58 Dg
Adh Dhahiriya, *Jordan* 94 Cf
Adhoi, *India* 88 Dd
Adhra, *Syria* 94 Ed
Adi, *Irian Jaya* 83 Kl
Adi Kaie, *Ethiopia* 97 Hb
Adilabad, *India* 88 Ee
Adirondack Mts., *New York* 40 Jc
Adi Ugri, *Ethiopia* 97 Hb
Adlavik Is., *Nfld.* 31 Og
Admiral, *Saskatchewan* 36 Jj
Admiralty Gulf, *W. Australia* 56 Eb
Admiralty I., *N.W.T.* 38 Xa
Admiralty Inlet, *N.W.T.* 31 Lc
Admiralty Is., *Pacific Ocean* 102 Dh
Adolfo Alsina, *Argentina* 54 De
Adoni, *India* 88 Ee
Adoumre, *Cameroun* 99 Hg
Adour, *France* 73 Ce
Adra, *Spain* 70 Dd
Adraj, *Arabia* 93 Fe
Adrano, *Sicily* 75 Eg
Adrar, *Algeria* 98 Ec
Adria, *Italy* 74 Dc
Adrian, *Michigan* 40 De
Adriatic Sea, *Italy* 74 Ed
Aduwa, *Ethiopia* 97 Hb
Advocate Harbour, *N.S.* 32 Hh
Aegean Sea, *Greece* 77 Ee
AErøskøbing, *Denmark* 67 Dj
Aesch, *Switzerland* 65 Ca
Aetna, *Alberta* 36 Dj
Afferden, *Netherlands* 64 Ec
Affuá, *Brazil* 53 Gd
Afghanistan, *Asia* 93 Hc
Afif, *Arabia* 92 De
Afogados de Ingazeira, *Brazil* 53 Ke
Afognak I., *Alaska* 43 Xm
Afrin, *Syria* 94 Ea
Afula, *Israel* 94 De
Afyon, *Turkey* 92 Bb
Agab Workei, *Ethiopia* 97 Hb
Agadès, *Niger* 98 Ge
Agadir, *Morocco* 98 Db
Again R., *Quebec* 35 Lb
Agartala, *India* 89 Hd
Agassiz, *British Columbia* 39 Nl
Agathla Peak, *Arizona* 48 Bd
Agattu, I., *Aleutian Is.* 43 Um
Agawa, *Ontario* 40 Db
Agawa, R., *Ontario* 34 Fe
Agawa Bay, *Ontario* 34 Fe
Agdam, *Azerbaijan* 92 Ea
Agde, *France* 73 Ee
Agen, *France* 73 Dd
Agiabampo, *Mexico* 50 Cb
Agira, *Sicily* 75 Eg
Agnebilekrou, *Ivory Coast* 98 Eg
Agnes L., *Ontario* 37 Lb
Agno, *Switzerland* 65 Dc
Agordat, *Ethiopia* 97 Ha
Agra, *India* 91 Bb
Agrigento, *Sicily* 75 Dg
Agrihan, *Mariana Is.* 102 Df
Agri Karakose, *Turkey* 92 Db
Agrinion, *Greece* 77 Ce
Agropoli, *Italy* 75 Ee
Agua Clara, *Brazil* 53 Gh
Aguadas, *Colombia* 52 Bb
Aguadilla, *Puerto Rico* 51 Fc
Aguadulce, *Panama* 51 Ce
Aguanish, *Quebec* 33 Kc
Aguanus, Nord-Ouest R., *Quebec* 32 Kb
Aguanus R., *Quebec* 33 Kc
Agua Prieta, *Mexico* 40 Ca
Aguaray, *Argentina* 54 Db
Aguascalientes, *Mexico* 50 Dc
Agudo, *Spain* 70 Cc
Agudos, *Brazil* 53 Hh
Aguilar, *Spain* 70 Cd
Aguilar de Campoó, *Spain* 70 Ca
Aguilas, *Spain* 71 Ed
Aguirre, *Argentina* 54 Cj
Agulhas C., *Cape Province* 95 Cf
Ahar, *Iran* 92 Eb
Ahmadabad, *India* 88 Dd
Ahmadnagar, *India* 88 De
Ahmadpur East, *Pakistan* 90 Bf
Ahmik Lake, *Ontario* 40 Gc
Ahraura, *India* 91 Dc
Ahuachapán, *Salvador* 51 Bd
Ahualulco, *Mexico* 50 Dc
Ahuntsic, *Quebec* 35 Rj
Ahus, *Sweden* 67 Fj
Ahvāz, *Iran* 92 Ec
Ahvenanmaa, *Finland* 67 Hf
Ahwar, *S. Yemen* 92 Eg
Aigle, *Switzerland* 65 Bb
Aigle, l', *France* 72 Db
Aigle, L. à l', *Quebec* 32 Gb
Aihui, *China* 82 Ja
Aikawa, *Japan* 86 Fe
Aileron, *N. Terr.* 57 Fd
Ailsa Craig, *Ontario* 34 Jj
Aim, *U.S.S.R.* 79 Nc
Aimores, *Brazil* 53 Jg
Ain, *France* 72 Fc
Ain Galakka, *Chad* 99 Je
Ain Safra, *Mauritania* 98 Ce
Aïn Sefra, *Algeria* 98 Eb
Ainslie, L., *Nova Scotia* 33 Lg
Ainsworth, *Nebraska* 49 Ha
Airdrie, *Alberta* 36 Cg
Aire, *France* 73 Ce
Aire, R., *England* 63 Gg
Air Force I., *N.W.T.* 31 Md
Airolo, *Switzerland* 65 Db
Aishihik & L., *Y.T.* 38 Ee
Aisne, *France* 72 Eb
Aitkin, *Minnesota* 46 Lb
Aix, *France* 73 Fe
Aix, Mt., *Washington* 47 Cb
Aix-la-Chapelle. *See* Aachen
Aiyansh, *B.C.* 39 Jh
Aiyina, *Greece.* 77 Df
Aiyion, *Greece* 77 De
Aizawl, *India* 89 Hd
Aizpute, *Latvia* 67 Jh
Aizuwakamatsu, *Japan* 86 Gf
Ajaccio, *Corsica* 75 Be
Ajaccio, Golfe d', *Corsica* 75 Be
Ajaigarh, *India* 91 Cc
Ajanta, *India* 88 Ed
Ajanta Ra. *See* Sahiadriparvat Ra.
Ajax, *Ontario* 35 Lj
Ajibba, *Arabia* 92 Dd
Ajigasawa, *Japan* 86 Gd
Ajlun, *Jordan* 94 De
Ajman, *U.A.E.* 93 Gd
Ajmer, *India* 88 Dc
Ajoewa, *Surinam* 53 Fc
Akalkot, *India* 88 Ee
Akan Nat. Park, *Japan* 86 Hc
Akanthou, *Cyprus* 94 Bb
Akaoka, *Japan* 86 Ch
Akarnania & Aitolia, *Greece* 77 Ce
Akaroa, *New Zealand* 55 De
Akashi, *Japan* 86 Dg
Akbarpur, *India* 91 Cb
Akcha, *Afghanistan* 93 Jb
Akhdar, Jeb. al, *Oman* 93 Ge
Akhisar, *Turkey* 92 Ab
Akhterin, *Syria* 94 Fa
Akhtopol, *Bulgaria* 76 Fc
Akhtyrka, *Ukraine* 80 Jf
Akimiski I., *N.W.T.* 31 Lg
Akita, *Japan* 86 Ge
Akkrum, *Netherlands* 64 Da
Aklavik, *N.W.T.* 38 Fa
Ako, *Nigeria* 96 Cb
Akola, *India* 88 Ed
Akpatok I., *N.W.T.* 31 Ne
Akra, Jebel el, *Turkey* 94 Db
Akron, *Colorado* 48 Fb
Akron, *Ohio* 40 Fe
Akron, *Ontario* 34 Fd
Akrotiri, *Crete* 77 Eg
Aksaray, *Turkey* 92 Bb
Aksehir, *Turkey* 92 Bb
Aksha, *U.S.S.R.* 79 Lc
Aksi, *Estonia* 67 Mg
Akti, *Greece* 77 Ed
Aktyubinsk, *Kazakhstan* 78 Ec
Akure, *Nigeria* 98 Gg
Akureyri, *Iceland* 66 Wm
Akyab, *Burma* 89 Hd
Alabama, *U.S.A.* 43 Je
Alabama R., *Alabama* 43 Je
Alaejos, *Spain* 70 Cb
Alagoinhas, *Brazil* 53 Kf
Alagón, *Spain* 71 Eb
Alaja, *Syria* 94 Db
Alajuela, *Costa Rica* 51 Ce
Al Amarah, *Iraq* 92 Ec
Alameda, *California* 47 Bg
Alameda, *Saskatchewan* 37 Pj
Alamogordo, *New Mexico* 48 Ef
Alamogordo Res., *N. Mex.* 48 Ee
Alamos, *Mexico* 50 Cb
Alamosa, *Colorado* 48 Ed
Åland. *See* Ahvenanmaa
Ålans Hav, *Swed./Finland* 67 Hg
Alapayevsk, *U.S.S.R.* 81 Qb
Alapur, *India* 91 Bb
Alasehir, *Turkey* 92 Ab
Al Ashkhirah, *Oman* 93 Ge
Alaska, *U.S.A.* 43 Xl
Alaska, Gulf of, *Alaska* 43 Ym
Alaska Highway, *B.C.* 39 Mg
Alaska Pen., *Alaska* 43 Xm
Alaska Range, *Alaska* 43 Xl
Alatyr, *U.S.S.R.* 81 Hc
Alavus, *Finland* 66 Ke
Al'ayn, *Oman* 93 Gf
Alaysky Khrebet, *Kirghizia* 78 Ge
Alazeyskoye Plat., *U.S.S.R.* 79 Pb
Al'Aziziyah, *Libya* 99 Hb
Albacete, *Spain* 71 Ec
Alba de Tormes, *Spain* 70 Cb
Al Badi, *Arabia* 92 Ee
Al Bahrah, *Kuwait* 92 Ed
Albaida, *Spain* 71 Ec
Alba Iulia, *Romania* 76 Da
Albanel, *Quebec* 35 Sd
Albania, *S. Europe* 76 Cd
Albany, *Georgia, U.S.A.* 45 Ee
Albany, *Kentucky* 45 Eb
Albany, *Missouri* 49 Kb
Albany, *New York* 40 Kd
Albany, *Oregon* 47 Bc
Albany, *W. Australia* 56 Cf
Albany R., *Ontario* 34 Fa
Albarracin, *Spain* 71 Eb
Al Bayda', *Libya* 99 Kb
Albemarle Sound, *N. Carolina* 45 Jb
Albergaria a-Velha, *Port.* 70 Ab
Alberique, *Spain* 71 Ec
Alberni, *British Columbia* 39 Ll
Albert, *New Brunswick* 32 Hh
Albert, Lake, *Zaire* 97 Gd
Alberta, *Canada* 30 Hg
Alberta, Mt., *Alberta* 39 Pj
Albert Edward Mt., *Papua New Guinea* 57 Ja
Albert Lea, *Minnesota* 46 Ld
Alberton, *Prince Edward I.* 32 Hg
Albertville, *France* 72 Gd
Albertville, *Saskatchewan* 37 Me
Albertville. *See* Kalémié
Albi, *France* 73 Ee
Albia, *Iowa* 49 Lb
Albina, *Surinam* 53 Gb
Albion, *Michigan* 40 Dd
Albion, *New York* 44 Aa
Albocácer, *Spain* 71 Eb
Ålborg, *Denmark* 67 Dh
Albreda, *B.C.* 39 Oj
Albufeira, *Portugal* 70 Ad
Albuñol, *Spain* 70 Dd
Albuquerque, *New Mexico* 48 De
Alburquerque, *Spain* 70 Bc
Albury, *New South Wales* 57 Jg
Alcácer do Sal, *Portugal* 70 Ac
Alcalá de Chisvert, *Spain* 71 Fb
Alcalá de Henares, *Spain* 70 Db
Alcamo, *Sicily* 75 Dg
Alcañices, *Spain* 70 Bb
Alcañiz, *Spain* 71 Eb
Alcântara, *Brazil* 53 Jd
Alcántara, *Spain* 70 Bc
Alcántara, Emb. de, *Spain* 70 Bc
Alcantara L., *N.W.T.* 38 Te
Alcantarilla, *Spain* 71 Ed
Alcaraz, *Spain* 71 Dc
Alcázar de San Juan, *Spain* 70 Dc
Alchevsk, *Ukraine* 80 Lg
Alcira, *Spain* 71 Ec
Alcobaça, *Portugal* 70 Ac
Alcolea del Pinar, *Spain* 71 Db
Alcomdale, *Alberta* 36 De
Alcoutim, *Portugal* 70 Bd
Alcoy, *Spain* 71 Ec
Aldabra Is., *Indian Ocean* 97 Ka
Al Dāli, *S. Yemen* 92 Dg
Aldama, *Chihuahua, Mexico* 50 Cb
Aldama, *Tamaulipas, Mexico* 50 Ec
Aldan, *U.S.S.R.* 79 Mc
Aldeburgh, *England* 63 Jh
Alderney, *Channel Is.* 63 Ak
Aldershot, *England* 63 Gj
Alderson, *Alberta* 36 Fh
Aldersyde, *Alberta* 36 Dh
Al Dola, *S. Yemen* 92 Eg
Aledo, *Illinois* 49 Mb
Alegrete, *Brazil* 54 Ec
Alejandro Selkirk, *Chile* 103 Sl
Aleksandrov, *U.S.S.R.* 80 Lc
Aleksandrovsk Sakhalinskiy, *U.S.S.R.* 79 Pc
Aleksandry, Zemlya, *U.S.S.R.* 78 Da
Alekseyevka, *Kazakhstan* 78 Gc
Alekseyevka, *U.S.S.R.* 81 Hd
Alençon, *France* 72 Db
Alenquer, *Brazil* 53 Gd
Alenquer, *Portugal* 70 Ac
Aleppo, *Syria* 94 Fa
Alert, *N.W.T.* 31 Na
Alert Bay, *B.C.* 39 Kk
Alès, *France* 73 Fd
Aleshki, *U.S.S.R.* 81 Ee
Alessandria, *Italy* 74 Bc
Ålestrup, *Denmark* 67 Ch
Ålesund, *Norway* 66 Be
Aletschhorn, *Switz.* 65 Cb
Aleutian Is., *Bering Sea* 43 Um
Aleutian Ra., *Alaska* 41 Ad
Alexander, *Manitoba* 37 Rj
Alexander Arch., *Alaska* 43 Zm
Alexander C., *N.W.T.* 38 Ua
Alexander City, *Alabama* 45 Ed
Alexander I. I., *Antarctica* 104 Sc
Alexandra, *New Zealand* 55 Bf
Alexandra Falls, *N.W.T.* 38 Pe
Alexandretta. *See* Iskenderun
Alexandria, *B.C.* 39 Mj
Alexandria, *Egypt* 99 Lb
Alexandria, *Louisiana* 49 Lg
Alexandria, *Minnesota* 46 Kc
Alexandria, *Ontario* 35 Qg
Alexandria, *Virginia* 44 Bc
Alexandrina, L., *S. Aust.* 57 Gg
Alexandroúpolis, *Greece* 77 Ed
Alexikovo, *U.S.S.R.* 81 Fe
Alexis Bay, *Nfld.* 31 Og
Alexis Creek, *B.C.* 39 Mj
Alexis R., *Nfld.* 33 Pa
Alexo, *Alberta* 36 Bf
Aleysk, *U.S.S.R.* 78 Hc
Alfaro, *Spain* 71 Ea
Al Fāw, *Iraq* 92 Ed
Alfred, *Maine* 44 Ea
Al Fujayrah, *Arabia* 93 Gd
Alga, *Kazakhstan* 78 Ed
Algård, *Norway* 67 Ag
Algarrobo del Aguila, *Arg.* 54 Ce
Algeciras, *Spain* 70 Cd
Alger, *Algeria* 73 Nh
Algeria, *N.W. Africa* 98 Eb
Al Ghail, *Yemen* 92 Ef
Alghero, *Sardinia* 75 Be
Algiers. *See* Alger
Algoa B., *Cape Province* 95 Df
Algoma, *Ontario* 34 Hf
Algoma, *Wisconsin* 40 Cc
Algona, *Iowa* 49 Ka
Algonquin Provincial Park, *Ontario* 35 Mg
Alguada Reef, *Burma* 89 He
Alhama de Granada, *Spain* 70 Dd
Al Hammām, *Iraq* 92 Dc
Al Hasa, *Arabia* 92 Ed
Al Hayy, *Iraq* 92 Ec
Al Hillah, *Iraq* 92 Dc
Al Hoceima, *Morocco* 70 De
Alhucemas, *Spain* 70 De
Alia, *Sicily* 75 Dg
Aliaga, *Spain* 71 Eb
Alibag, *India* 88 De
Alicante, *Spain* 71 Ec
Alice, *Texas* 48 Hj
Alice Arm, *B.C.* 39 Jh
Alice Springs, *N. Terr.* 57 Fd
Aliceville, *Alabama* 49 Nf
Alicudi, *Italy* 75 Ef
Alida, *Saskatchewan* 37 Qj
Aliganj, *India* 91 Bb
Aligarh, *India* 90 Fg
Ali Khel, *Afghanistan* 93 Jc
Alimnia, *Greece* 77 Ff
Aling Kangri, *China* 88 Fb
Alingsås, *Sweden* 67 Eh

Alipur, India 91 Gb
Alipur, India 91 Gd
Alipur, Pakistan 90 Bf
Alipura, India 91 Bc
Alirajpur, India 88 Dd
Alivérion, Greece 77 Ee
Alix, Alberta 36 Df
Al Jaghbub, Libya 99 Kc
Al Jawf, Libya 99 Kd
Al Jesab, Arabia 92 Eg
Aljustrel, Portugal 70 Ad
Alken, Belgium 64 Dd
Al Khābūrah, Oman 93 Ge
Al Khums, Libya 99 Hb
Alkmaar, Netherlands 64 Cb
Al Kut, Iraq 92 Ec
Allahabad, India 91 Cc
Allan, Saskatchewan 36 Lg
Allanmyo, Burma 89 Je
Allan Water, Ontario 37 Na
Allard, Montana 46 Eb
Allard, L., Quebec 32 Jc
Allard, R., Quebec 35 Nc
Allardville, N.B. 32 Gf
Allariz, Spain 70 Ba
Allaykha, U.S.S.R. 79 Pa
Alle, Belgium 64 Ce
Allegan, Michigan 40 Dd
Allegheny Mts., U.S.A. 43 Kd
Allegheny R., Pa. 44 Aa
Allenby Bridge, Jordan 94 Df
Allenford, Ontario 34 Jh
Allen L., Eire 63 Bf
Allentown, Pennsylvania 44 Cb
Alleppey, India 88 Eg
Allgäuer Alpen, Austria 68 De
Alliance, Alberta 36 Ff
Alliance, Nebraska 48 Fa
Alliance, Ohio 40 Fe
Allier, France 72 Ec
Allier, R., France 72 Ed
Allison Harbour, B.C. 39 Kk
Alliston, Ontario 35 Lh
Alloa, Scotland 62 Ed
All Pines, Belize 51 Bc
Al Luhayyah, Yemen 92 Df
Allumettes, I. des, Que. 35 Ng
Ally, Quebec 35 Rc
Alma, Michigan 40 Dd
Alma, New Brunswick 32 Hh
Alma, Quebec 35 Td
Alma Ata, Kazakhstan 78 Gd
Almadén, Spain 70 Cc
Almagro, Spain 70 Dc
Al Maḥmūdīyah, Iraq 92 Dc
Almansa, Spain 71 Ec
Alma Pk., B.C. 39 Kg
Al Marj (Barce), Libya 99 Kb
Almazán, Spain 71 Db
Almeirim, Brazil 53 Gd
Almeirim, Portugal 70 Ac
Almelo, Netherlands 64 Eb
Almendra, Emb. de, Spain 70 Bb
Almeria, Spain 71 Dd
Almeria, Golfo de, Spain 71 Dd
Almirante, Panama 51 Ce
Almiropótamos, Greece 77 Ee
Almirós, Greece 77 De
Almodôvar, Portugal 70 Bd
Almodóvar, Spain 70 Cc
Almont, N. Dakota 46 Gb
Almonte, Ontario 35 Og
Almora, India 91 Ba
Almorox, Spain 70 Cb
Almudébar, Spain 71 Ea
Al Mukalla, S. Yemen 92 Eg
Almunia de Doña Godina, la, Spain 71 Eb
Al Musayyib, Iraq 92 Dc
Al Muwailih, Arabia 92 Cd
Alness, Scotland 62 Ec
Alnwick, England 62 Fe
Alocén, Spain 71 Db
Aloja, Latvia 67 Lh
Alon, Burma 89 Jd
Alón. See Iliodhrómia
Alonsa, Manitoba 37 Th
Alor, Indonesia 83 Hm
Alora, Spain 70 Cd
Alor Setar, Pen. Malaysia 87 Ce
Aloysius, Mt., W. Australia 56 Ee
Alpena, Michigan 40 Ec
Alpes de Haute Provence, France 73 Gd
Alpes-Maritimes, Fr. 73 Ge
Alphen, Netherlands 64 Cb
Alpine, Texas 42 Fe
Alps, Cent. Europe 61 Jg
Al Qatrun, Libya 99 Hd
Al Qunfidhah, Arabia 92 Df
Al Qurnah, Iraq 92 Ec
Als, I., Denmark 67 Cj
Alsask, Saskatchewan 36 Hg
Alsek, R., B.C. 38 Ef
Alsten, Norway 66 Ed
Alston, England 63 Ff
Alšvanga, Latvia 67 Jh
Alta Gracia, Argentina 54 Dd
Altagracia, Venezuela 52 Ca
Altagracia de Orituco, Venezuela 52 Db
Altai, Central Asia 78 Hc
Altamachi, Bolivia 52 Dg
Altamaha R., Georgia, U.S.A. 43 Ke
Altamira, Brazil 53 Gd
Altamura, Italy 75 Fe
Altanbulag, Mongolia 79 Kc
Altar, Mexico 50 Ba
Altario, Alberta 36 Gg
Altata, Mexico 50 Cc
Altdorf, Switzerland 65 Db
Altea, Spain 71 Ec
Altenburg, E. Germany 68 Ec
Altin Köprü, Iraq 92 Db
Altmark, E. Germany 68 Db
Alto Araguaia, Brazil 53 Gg
Alto Longa, Brazil 53 Je
Alto Madeira, Brazil 52 Ee
Alto Molocue, Mozambique 97 Hh
Alton, Illinois 49 Mc
Alton, Missouri 45 Bb
Altona, Manitoba 37 Uj
Altona, New York 40 Kc
Altona, W. Germany 68 Cb
Altoona, Pennsylvania 44 Ab
Altstätten, Switzerland 65 Ea
Altun Shan, China 58 He
Alturas, California 47 Ce
Altus, Oklahoma 49 He
Altus L., Oklahoma 49 He
Al Udayliyah, Arabia 92 Ed
Al Ugla, Arabia 92 Cd
Al 'Uj, Arabia 92 Ee
Alūksne, Latvia 67 Mh
Alùla, Somalia 97 Lb
Aluminé, Argentina 54 Be
Alupka, U.S.S.R. 80 Jj
Al 'Uqaylah, Libya 99 Jb
Alushta, U.S.S.R. 80 Jj
Alva, Oklahoma 49 Hd
Alvarado, Mexico 50 Ed
Alvear, Argentina 54 De
Alvena, Saskatchewan 36 Lf
Alverstone, Mt., Y.T. 38 De
Alvesta, Sweden 67 Fh
Älvho, Sweden 67 Ff
Alvin, Texas 49 Kh
Alvinston, Ontario 34 Jk
Alvito, Portugal 70 Bc
Alvord, L., Oregon 47 Dd
Al Wajh, Arabia 92 Cd
Alwar, India 90 Eg
Alyab, Sudan 99 Me
Alytus, Lithuania 67 Lj
Amadeus L., N. Terr. 56 Ed
Amadi, Sudan 99 Mg
Amadiyah, Iraq 92 Db
Amadjuak L., N.W.T. 31 Md
Amaila Falls, Guyana 52 Fb
Amakusa nada, Japan 86 Ah
Åmål, Sweden 67 Eg
Amalfi, Italy 75 Ee
Amaliás, Greece 77 Cf
Amami Gunto, Japan 86 Nn
Amanalco, Mexico 50 Ed
Amantea, Italy 75 Ff
Amapá, Brazil 53 Gc
Amapala, Honduras 51 Bd
Amarante, Brazil 53 Je
Amaranth, Manitoba 37 Th
Amarapura, Burma 89 Jd
Amargosa, Brazil 53 Kf
Amarillo, Texas 48 Ge
Amasra, Turkey 92 Ba
Amasya, Turkey 92 Ca
Amatique, B. de, Guatemala 50 Gd
Amatitlán, Guatemala 50 Fe
Amazon, Saskatchewan 37 Mg
Amazon, Mths. of the, Brazil 53 Hc
Amazonas, Brazil 53 Gd
Ambala, India 90 Ee
Ambalavoa, Madagascar 97 Nl
Ambam, Cameroun 96 Cd
Ambar, Iran 93 Gc
Ambarchik, U.S.S.R. 79 Rb
Ambato, Ecuador 52 Bd
Ambato-Boéni, Madag. 97 Nk
Amberg, West Germany 68 Dd
Ambergris Cay, Belize 51 Bc
Ambergris Cay, The Bahamas 51 Eb
Ambérieu, France 72 Fc
Amberley, Ontario 34 Jh
Ambert, France 72 Ed
Ambikapur, India 91 Dd
Ambilobe, Madagascar 97 Nj
Ambition Mtn., B.C. 39 Hg
Amblève, Belgium 64 Ed
Ambohimahasoa, Madag. 97 Nl
Ambon, Indonesia 83 Jl
Ambositra, Madagascar 97 Nl
Ambrim, Vanuatu 102 Fj
Ambriz, Angola 96 Cf
Ambrizete, Angola 96 Cf
Amchitka, Aleutian Is. 43 Um
'Amd, South Yemen 92 Ef
Amderma, U.S.S.R. 78 Fb
Ameca, Mexico 50 Dc
Ameland, Netherlands 64 Da
Amelia, Virginia 45 Jb
American Falls, Utah 48 Aa
American Fork, Utah 48 Bb
American Samoa, terr., Pacific Ocean 102 Hj
Americus, Georgia, U.S.A. 43 Ke
Amerongen, Netherlands 64 Db
Amersfoort, Netherlands 64 Db
Ames, Iowa 49 La
Amesbury, Alberta 36 Ec
Amesbury, Massachusetts 44 Ea
Amesdale, Ontario 36 Ka
Ameson, Ontario 34 Fc
Amethi, India 91 Cb
Amfiklia, Greece 77 De
Amfilokhia, Greece 77 Ce
Amga, U.S.S.R. 79 Nb
Amgu, U.S.S.R. 79 Nd
Amherst, Massachusetts 44 Da
Amherst, Nova Scotia 32 Hh
Amherst. See Kyaikkami
Amherstburg, Ontario 34 Gk
Amherst I., Ontario 35 Oh
Amiens, France 72 Eb
Amindivi Is., Indian Ocean 88 Df
Amingnon, India 89 Hc
Aminuis, Namibia 95 Bd
Amirante Is., Indian Ocean 100 De
Amisk, Alberta 36 Ff
Amisk L., Saskatchewan 37 Pd
Amisquioumisca, L., Que. 35 Ob
Amistad Res., Texas 48 Gh
Amlwch, Wales 63 Eg
Amm Adam, Sudan 99 Ne
Amman, Jordan 94 Df
Amol, Iran 93 Fb
Amorgós, Greece 77 Ef
Amos, Quebec 35 Md
Amoy. See Xiamen
Amparo, Brazil 53 Hh
Amqui, Quebec 32 Ee
Amraho, Sudan 99 Me
Amrān, Yemen 92 Df
Amravati, India 88 Ed
Amreli, India 88 Dd
Amriswil, Switzerland 65 Ea
Amritsar, India 90 Ee
Amroha, India 91 Ba
Amstelveen, Netherlands 64 Cb
Amsterdam, Netherlands 64 Cb
Amsterdam, New York 44 Ca
Amsterdam, I., Indian Ocean 100 Fh
Am Timan, Chad 99 Kf
Amu Dar'ya, Turkmenistan 78 Fd
Amund Ringnes I., N.W.T. 31 Kb
Amundsen G., N.W.T. 38 La
Amundsen Sea, Antarctica 104 Qb
Amundson, Alberta 39 Oh
Amur, U.S.S.R./China 79 Mc
Amyot, Ontario 34 Fd
Amyun, Lebanon 94 Dc
An, Burma 89 He
Anabta, Jordan 94 De
Anaconda, Montana 47 Gb
Anadarko, Oklahoma 49 He
Anadyr, U.S.S.R. 79 Sb
Anadyrskiy Zaliv, U.S.S.R. 79 Tb
Anáfi, Greece 77 Ef
Anah, Iraq 92 Dc
Anahim Lake, B.C. 39 Lj
Anai, Libya 99 Hd
Anaimalai Hills, India 88 Ef
Anakapalle, India 89 Fe
Analalava, Madagascar 97 Nj
Anama, Brazil 52 Ed
Anama Bay, Manitoba 37 Tg
Anambas, Indonesia 83 Ek
Anamizu, Japan 86 Ef
Anamosa, Iowa 49 Ma
Anandpur, India 90 Ee
Anantapur, India 88 Ef
Anápolis, Brazil 53 Hg
Anar, Iran 93 Gc
Anarak, Iran 93 Fc
Anardara, Afghanistan 93 Hc
Anatolia, Turkey 92 Bb
Añatuya, Argentina 54 Dc
Anchorage, Alaska 43 Yl
Anchuras, Spain 70 Cc
Ancohuma, Bolivia 52 Dg
Ancón, Peru 52 Bf
Ancona, Italy 74 Dd
Ancud, Chile 54 Bf
Andacollo, Argentina 54 Be
Andalgala, Argentina 54 Cc
Åndalsnes, Norway 66 Be
Andalucia, Spain 70 Cd
Andaman Is. & Str., Bay of Bengal 89 Hf
Andaman Sea, Bay of Bengal 89 Hf
Andeer, Switzerland 65 Eb
Andelfingen, Switzerland 65 Da
Andenne, Belgium 64 Dd
Andermatt, Switzerland 65 Db
Anderson, Indiana 40 De
Anderson, S. Carolina 45 Fc
Anderson, R., N.W.T. 38 Ja
Anderson B., N.W.T. 38 Va
Andes, Cord. de los, South America 54 Cc
And Fd., Norway 66 Gb
Andhra Pradesh, India 88 Ee
Andikíthira, Greece 77 Dg
Andilly, L., Quebec 33 Mc
Andímilos, Greece 77 Ef
Andíparos, Greece 77 Ef
Andizhan, Uzbekistan 78 Gd
Andkhui, Afghanistan 93 Jb
Andoas, Ecuador 52 Bd
Andorra, Pyrenees 71 Fa
Andover, Massachusetts 44 Ea
Andover, New Brunswick 32 Eg
Andover, S. Dakota 46 Jc
Andøy, Norway 66 Fb
Andreanof Is., Aleutian Is. 43 Vm
Andreas, C., Cyprus 94 Cb
Andrew, Alberta 36 Ee
Andreyevka, Ukraine 80 Jg
Andria, Italy 75 Fe
Andriba, Madagascar 97 Nk
Andritsaina, Greece 77 Cf
Andros, Greece 77 Ef
Androscoggin R., Maine 32 Bj
Andros I., The Bahamas 51 Db
Anegada, Virgin Is. 51 Gc
Anegada, Bahia, Argentina 54 Df
Anelo, Argentina 54 Ce
Anerley, Saskatchewan 36 Kg
Aneroid, Saskatchewan 36 Kj
Aneta, N. Dakota 46 Jb
Aney, Niger 99 He
Anfa, Lebanon 94 Dc
Angangueo, Mexico 50 Dd
Angel de la Guarda, Mexico 50 Bb
Angel Falls, Venezuela 52 Eb
Angelholm, Sweden 67 Eh
Angers, France 72 Cc
Angikuni L., N.W.T. 30 Ke
Angkor, Kampuchea 87 Cd
Anglesey, Wales 63 Eg
Anglia, Saskatchewan 36 Jg
Angliers, Quebec 35 Le
Angmagssalik, Greenland 41 Nc
Angoche, Mozambique 97 Hh
Angol, Chile 54 Be
Angola, New York 44 Aa
Angola, W. Africa 96 Dg
Angora. See Ankara
Angoulême, France 72 Dd
Angoumois, France 72 Dd
Angra, Brazil 53 Jh
Anguilla, Leeward Is. 51 Gc
Anguille, C. & Mts., Nfld. 33 Nf
Angul, India 89 Gd
Anguo, China 84 Gc
Angus, Ontario 35 Lh
Angusville, Manitoba 37 Qh
Anholt, Denmark 67 Dh
Anhui, China 84 Hf
Aniai, Japan 86 Ge
Animas Range, New Mexico 48 Cg
Anina, Romania 76 Cb
Anita, Montana 46 Dc
Anjengo, India 88 Eg
Anjou, France 72 Cc
Anjou, Quebec 35 Sh
Anjouan, Comoros 97 Jg
Anjozorobe, Madagascar 97 Nk
Ankacho, U.S.S.R. 79 Kb
Ankang, China 84 Df
Ankara, Turkey 92 Ba
Ankober, Ethiopia 97 Hc
Anlier, Belgium 64 De
Anlu. See Zhongxiang
Anna, Illinois 45 Cb
Anna, U.S.S.R. 81 Ee
Annaba, Algeria 99 Ga
Annai, Guyana 52 Fc
An Najaf, Iraq 92 Dc
Annam, Vietnam 87 Dc
Annan, Scotland 62 Ee
Annapolis, Maryland 44 Bc
Annapolis R., Nova Scotia 32 Gj
Annapolis Royal, N.S. 32 Gj
Annapurna, Nepal 89 Fc
Ann Arbor, Michigan 40 Ed
An Nasiriyah, Iraq 92 Ec
Ann Cape, Antarctica 104 Ec
Ann Cape, Massachusetts 44 Ea
Annecy, France 72 Gd
Annecy, Lac d', France 72 Gd
An Nhon, Vietnam 87 Dd
Annieopsquotch Mts., Nfld. 33 Pe
Anniston, Alabama 45 Ed
Annobōn I. See Pagalu
Annonay, France 73 Fd
Anoka, Minnesota 46 Lc
Anole, Somalia 97 Je
Anō Viánnos, Crete 77 Eg
Anqing, China 85 Hg
Anrelândia, Brazil 53 Jh
Ansariye, Jebel el, Syria 94 Eb
Ansbach, W. Germany 68 Dd
Anse-au-Griffon, Quebec 32 He
Anshan, China 82 Hb
Anshun, China 85 Bj
Anson B., N. Terr. 56 Eb
Ansongo, Mali 98 Fe
Ansonia, Connecticut 44 Db
Ansonville, Ontario 34 Kd
Anta, Peru 52 Cf
Antakya, Turkey 94 Ea
Antalo, Ethiopia 97 Hb
Antalya, Turkey 92 Bb
Antarctic Pen., Antarctic 104 Sc
Antelope, Saskatchewan 36 Jh
Antelope I., Utah 48 Ab
Antequera, Paraguay 54 Eb
Antequera, Spain 70 Cd
Anthony, Kansas 49 Hd
Anthony Lagoon, N. Terr. 57 Gc
Antibes, France 73 Ge
Anticosti, Ile d', Quebec 32 Jd
Antigo, Wisconsin 40 Bc
Antigonish, Nova Scotia 33 Kh
Antigua, Leeward Is. 51 Gc
Antilhue, Chile 54 Be
Antilla, Cuba 51 Db
Antilles, Greater, W.I. 51
Antilles, Lesser, W.I. 51
Antioch. See Antakya
Antioquia, Colombia 52 Bb
Antipodes Is., Pacific Ocean 102 Gm
Antivari. See Bar
Antler, Saskatchewan 37 Qj
Antler R., Man./Sask. 37 Qj
Antlers, Oklahoma 49 Ke
Antofagasta, Chile 54 Bb
Antofagasta de la Sierra, Argentina 54 Cc
Antofalla, Argentina 54 Cc
Antoing, Belgium 64 Bd
Antongil, B. d', Madagascar 97 Nk
Antonito, Colorado 48 Dd
Antrain, France 72 Cb
Antrim, N. Ireland 63 Cf
Antrim Hills, N. Ireland 62 Ce
Antsirabe, Madagascar 97 Nk
Antsla, Estonia 67 Mh
Antwerp. See Antwerpen
Antwerpen, Belg. 64 Cc
Anupgarh, India 90 Cf
Anupshahr, India 91 Ba
Anuradhapura, Sri Lanka 88 Fg
Anvers. See Antwerpen
Anville, Quebec 35 Pc
Anxi, China 82 Cb
Anxin, China 84 Gc
Anyang, China 84 Gd
Anykščiai, Lithuania 67 Lj
Anyox, B.C. 39 Jh
Anzac, Alberta 39 Sg
Anzhero Sudzhensh, U.S.S.R. 78 Hc
Aomori, Japan 86 Gd
Aonla, India 91 Ba
Aorangi Mts., N.Z. 55 Ed
Aosta, Italy 74 Ac
Aouderas, Niger 98 Ge
Apache L., Arizona 48 Bf
Apakova, U.S.S.R. 81 Jc
Apalachee B., Florida 45 Ef
Apalachicola, Florida 45 Ef
Apalachicola B., Florida 45 Ef
Apalachicola R., Florida 43 Kf
Aparri, Philippines 83 Hg
Apataki, Tuamotu Arch. 103 Lj
Apatin, Yugoslavia 76 Bb
Ape, Latvia 67 Mh
Apeganau, L., Manitoba 37 Sc
Apeldoorn, Netherlands 64 Db
Apennines, Italy 61 Kh
Api, Mt., Nepal 91 Ca
Apia, Western Samoa 102 Hj
Apiai, Brazil 54 Gb
Apodi, Brazil 53 Ke
Apolo, Bolivia 52 Df
Apostle Is., Wisconsin 40 Ab
Apostoles, Argentina 54 Ec
Apoteri, Guyana 52 Fc
Apozai, Pakistan 88 Cb
Appalachian Mts., U.S.A. 43 Kd
Appenzell, Switz. 65 Ea
Applecross, Scotland 62 Dc
Apple River, Nova Scotia 32 Hh
Appleton, Wisconsin 40 Bc
Appleton City, Missouri 49 Kc
Apsley, Ontario 35 Mh
Apt, France 73 Fe
Apuka, U.S.S.R. 79 Rb
'Aqaba, Jordan 94 Dh
Aqarbat, Syria 94 Fb
'Aqda, Iran 93 Fc
Aqiq, Sudan 97 Ha
Aqraba, Jordan 94 De
Aquidauana, Brazil 53 Fh
Aquila, L', Italy 74 Dd
Aquin, Haiti 51 Ec
Arabian L., Quebec 33 Nc
Arabian Sea, S. Asia 58 Fg
Aracajú, Brazil 53 Kf
Aracatí, Brazil 53 Kd
Aracruz, Brazil 53 Jg
Araçuaí, Brazil 53 Jg
Arad, Romania 76 Ca
Arada, Chad 99 Ke
Arafura Sea, Indonesia 83 Km
Aragon, Spain 71 Eb
Araguacema, Brazil 53 He
Aragua de Barcelona, Venezuela 52 Eb
Araguaia, R., Brazil 53 He
Araguari, Brazil 53 Hg
Arak, Iran 92 Ec
Arakaka, Guyana 52 Fb
Arakan Yoma, Burma 89 Hd
Araks, Iran 78 De
Ara L., Ontario 34 Cb
Aral'sk, Kazakhstan 78 Fd
Aral'skoye More, Kazakhstan/Uzbekistan 78 Ed
Aramac, Queensland 57 Jd
Arambagh, India 91 Fd
Aranda de Duero, Spain 70 Db
Arandu, Pakistan 90 Bc
Arani, Bolivia 52 Dg
Aran Is., Eire 63 Ag
Aranjuez, Spain 70 Db
Aransas B., Texas 48 Jh
Aranya, Thailand 87 Cd
Arapey, Uruguay 54 Ed
Arapkir, Turkey 92 Cb
Arapuni, New Zealand 55 Ec
Araranguá, Brazil 54 Gc
Ararat, Victoria 57 Hg
Ararat, Mt., Turkey 92 Db
Araria, India 91 Fb
Arati, Brazil 52 Ce
Arauca, Colombia 52 Cb
Arauco, Chile 54 Be
Aravalli Ra., India 88 Dc
Araxá, Brazil 53 Hg
Arbatax, Sardinia 75 Bf
Arbil, Iraq 92 Db
Arboga, Sweden 67 Fg
Arbois, France 72 Fc
Arbon, Switzerland 65 Ea
Arbonne L.d', Louisiana 45 Ad
Arborfield, Saskatchewan 37 Oe
Arborg, Manitoba 37 Uh
Arbroath, Scotland 62 Fd
Arbuckle, L. of the, Okla. 49 Je
Arcade, New York 40 Gd
Arcadia, Alberta 36 Ac
Arcadia, Michigan 40 Cc
Arcadia, Wisconsin 46 Mc
Arcen, Netherlands 64 Ec
Archbald, Pennsylvania 44 Cb
Archerwill, Saskatchewan 37 Of
Archidona, Spain 70 Cd
Archive, Saskatchewan 37 Mh
Arcola, Saskatchewan 37 Pj
Arcot, India 88 Ef
Arctic Bay, N.W.T. 31 Lc
Arctic Ocean, 41
Arctic Red River, N.W.T. 38 Gb
Ardabil, Iran 92 Eb
Ardahan, Turkey 92 Da
Ardakan, Iran 93 Fc
Ardal, Iran 93 Fc
Årdal, Norway 67 Bf
Ardath, Saskatchewan 36 Kg
Ardatov, U.S.S.R. 81 Fc
Ardbeg, Ontario 34 Kg
Ardèche, France 73 Fd
Arden, Manitoba 36 Sh
Arden, Ontario 35 Oh
Ardennes, Belgium 72 Fa
Ardennes, France 72 Fb
Ardestan, Iran 93 Fc
Ardez, Switzerland 65 Fb
Ardglass, N. Ireland 63 Df
Ardill, Saskatchewan 37 Mj
Ardino, Bulgaria 76 Ed
Ardley, Alberta 36 Df
Ardmore, Alberta 36 Gd
Ardmore, Oklahoma 49 Je
Ardrishaig, Scotland 62 De
Ardrossan, Alberta 36 De
Ardrossan, Scotland 62 De
Ardud, Romania 69 Ke
Arecibo, Puerto Rico 51 Fc
Areia Branco, Brazil 53 Kd
Arelee, Saskatchewan 36 Kf
Arenales, Argentina 54 Dd
Arenales, Mt., Chile 54 Bg
Arenas de San Pedro, Spain 70 Cb
Arendal, Norway 67 Cg
Arenys de Mar, Spain 71 Gb
Arequipa, Peru 52 Cg
Areré, Brazil 53 Gd
Arévalo, Spain 70 Cb
Arezzo, Italy 74 Cd
Argent, R. à l', Quebec 32 Cc
Argenta, B.C. 39 Pk
Argentan, France 72 Cb
Argentat, France 73 Dd
Argentia, Newfoundland 33 Sf
Argentina, S. America 54
Argentino, L., Argentina 54 Bh
Argent-sur-Sauldre, France 72 Ec
Argo, Sudan 99 Me
Argolís, G. of, Greece 77 Df
Argonne, France 72 Fb
Argos, Greece 77 Df
Arguedas, Spain 71 Ea
Argun, U.S.S.R./Manchuria 79 Lc
Argungu, Nigeria 98 Ff
Argyle, Nova Scotia 32 Gk
Århus, Denmark 67 Dh
Ariano Irpino, Italy 75 Ee
Arica, Chile 54 Ba
Arica, Colombia 52 Cd
Arichat, Nova Scotia 33 Mh
Ariège, France 73 De
Arilje, Yugoslavia 76 Cc
Arima, Brazil 52 Ee
Arinda, Guyana 52 Fc
Aripuana, Brazil 52 Ee
Ariquemes, Brazil 52 Ee
Arisaig, Scotland 62 Dd
Aristazabal I., B.C. 39 Jj
Arivechi, Mexico 50 Cb
Ariza, Spain 71 Db
Arizona, Argentina 54 Ce
Arizona, U.S.A. 42 De
Arizona Plat., Arizona 48 Be
Arizpe, Mexico 50 Ba
Arka, U.S.S.R. 79 Pb
Arkabutla Res., Mississippi 49 Me
Arkadelphia, Arkansas 49 Le
Arkadhía, Greece 77 Df
Arkalyk, Kazakhstan 78 Fc
Arkansas, U.S.A. 43 He
Arkansas City, Arkansas 45 Bd
Arkansas City, Kansas 49 Jd
Arkansas R., Arkansas 49 Me
Arkell, Mt., Y.T. 38 Fe
Arkhangel'sk, U.S.S.R. 78 Db
Arklow, Eire 63 Ch
Arkoi, Greece 77 Ff
Arkona, Ontario 34 Jj
Arles, France 73 Fe
Arlon, Belgium 64 De
Arltunga, N. Terr. 57 Fd
Armada, Alberta 36 Eh
Armagh, N. Ireland 63 Cf
Armagh, Quebec 32 Bg
Armark L., N.W.T. 38 Xb
Armenia, Colombia 52 Bc
Armenia. See Armyanskaya S.S.R.
Armentières, France 72 Ea
Armidale, N.S.W. 57 Kf
Armirós, B. of, Crete 77 Eg
Armit, Saskatchewan 37 Qf
Armley, Saskatchewan 37 Ne
Armori, India 88 Fd
Arms, Ontario 34 Dc
Armstrong, B.C. 39 Ok
Armstrong, Ontario 37 Oa
Armstrong, Mt., Y.T. 38 Gd
Armyanskaya S.S.R., U.S.S.R 78 Dd
Arnaud, Manitoba 37 Uj
Arnaud (Payne) R., Que. 31 Mf
Arnaudville, Louisiana 45 Be
Arnauti, C., Cyprus 94 Ab
Arnhem, Netherlands 64 Dc
Arnhem, C., N. Terr. 57 Gb
Arnhem Land, N. Terr. 56 Fb
Arni, India 88 Ef
Arnissa, Greece 77 Cd
Arnot, Manitoba 37 Vc
Arnøy, Norway 66 Ja
Arnprior, Ontario 35 Og
Arnsberg, W. Germany 68 Cc
Arnstadt, E. Germany 68 Dc
Arnstein, Ontario 35 Lg
Arntfield, Quebec 35 Ld
Aroe Eiln. See Aru Kep.
Arolla, Switzerland 65 Cb
Aroostook, N.B. 32 Eg
Arorae, Kiribati 102 Gh
Arosa, Switzerland 65 Eb
Aroya, Colorado 48 Fc
Arpin, Ontario 34 Kd
Arrah, India 91 Ec
Arraias, Brazil 53 Hf
Ar Ramadi, Iraq 92 Dc
Arran, Saskatchewan 37 Qg
Arran, Isle of, Scotland 62 De
Arrandale, B.C. 39 Jh
Arras, France 72 Ea
Arroba, Spain 70 Cc
Arromanches, France 72 Cb
Arronches, Portugal 70 Bc
Arrowhead, B.C. 39 Pk
Arrow L., Eire 63 Bf
Arrow L., Ontario 37 Nb
Arrow L., Upper, B.C. 39 Pk
Arrow Lake, Lower, B.C. 39 Ol
Arrow Park, B.C. 39 Ok
Arrowtown, New Zealand 55 Bf
Arrowwood, Alberta 36 Dh
Arroyito, Argentina 54 Dd
Arroyo, Puerto Rico 51 Fc
Års, Denmark 67 Ch
Arsenault L., Sask. 36 Jc
Arseno L., N.W.T. 38 Qc
Arsk, U.S.S.R. 81 Jb
Artā, Greece 77 Ce
Artawiya, Arabia 92 Ed
Artemovsk, Ukraine 80 Kg
Artemovsk, U.S.S.R. 79 Jc
Artemovskiy, U.S.S.R. 79 Lc
Artemovskiy, U.S.S.R. 81 Qb
Artenay, France 72 Db
Artesia, New Mexico 48 Ef
Arthabaska, Quebec 35 Tf
Arthur, Ontario 34 Kj
Artibonite, R., Haiti 51 Ec
Artigas, Uruguay 54 Ed
Artillery L., N.W.T. 38 Td
Artland, Saskatchewan 36 Hf
Artois, France 72 Ea
Artur de Paiva, Angola 96 Dg
Artvin, Turkey 92 Da
Aru, Zaire 97 Gd
Aruanã, Brazil 53 Gf
Aruba, Caribbean 51 Fd
Aru Kep., Indonesia 83 Km
Arumá, Brazil 52 Ed
Arunachal Pradesh, India 89 Hc
Arundel, Quebec 40 Jc
Aruppukkottai, India 88 Eg
Arusha, Tanzania 97 He
Aru Tso, China 89 Fb
Arvada, Wyoming 46 Dc
Arvayheer, Mongolia 82 Da
Arvida, Quebec 35 Td
Arvika, Sweden 67 Eg
Arvilla, N. Dakota 46 Jb
Arzamas, U.S.S.R. 81 Fc
Arzew, Algeria 98 Ea
Arzúa, Spain 70 Aa
As, Belgium 64 Dc
Aš, Czechoslovakia 68 Ec
Asahigawa, Japan 86 Hc
Asansol, India 91 Fd
Åsarna, Sweden 66 Fe
Asbestos, Quebec 35 Tg
Asbury Park, New Jersey 44 Db
Ascención, Mexico 50 Ca
Ascensión, Bolivia 52 Eg
Ascension, B. de la, Mexico 50 Gd
Ascension I., Atlantic Ocean 101 Jj
Aschaffenburg, W. Germany 68 Cd
Ascoli Piceno, Italy 74 Dd
Ascona, Switzerland 65 Db
Ascotán, Chile 54 Cb
Åseda, Sweden 67 Fh
Åsele, Sweden 66 Gd
Åsen, Sweden 67 Ef
Asenovgrad, Bulgaria 76 Ed
Ashārādeh ye Bozorg, Iran 93 Fb
Ashburton, New Zealand 55 Ce
Ashburton, R., W. Aust. 56 Cd
Ashcroft, B.C. 39 Nk
Ashdod, Israel 94 Cf
Asheboro, N. Carolina 45 Hc
Ashern, Manitoba 37 Tg
Asheville, N. Carolina 45 Fc
Ash Fork, Arizona 48 Ae
Ashkhabad, Turkmenistan 78 Ee
Ashland, Kansas 49 Hd
Ashland, Kentucky 45 Fa
Ashland, Maine 32 Dg
Ashland, Montana 46 Dc
Ashland, Ohio 40 Ee
Ashland, Oregon 47 Bd
Ashland, Pennsylvania 44 Bb
Ashland, Virginia 45 Jb
Ashland, Wisconsin 40 Ab
Ashland City, Tennessee 45 Db
Ashley, N. Dakota 46 Hb
Ashmont, Alberta 36 Fd
Ashqelon, Israel 94 Cf
Ash Shihr, S. Yemen 92 Eg
Ashtabula, Ohio 40 Fe
Ashtabula L., N. Dakota 46 Hb
Ashton, Ontario 35 Og
Ashuanipi, L., Nfld. 31 Ng
Ashville, Alabama 45 Dd
Asinara, Sardinia 75 Be
Asinara, Golfo di, Sardinia 75 Be
Asino, U.S.S.R. 78 Hc
Asir, Arabia 92 Df
Askersund, Sweden 67 Fg
Askvoll, Norway 67 Af
Aslanduz, Iran 92 Eb
Asmara, Ethiopia 97 Ha

Aspern, Austria 69 Gd
Aspinaje, Brazil 53 Hf
Aspiring, Mt., New Zealand 55 Bf
Aspres-sur-Buech, France 73 Fd
Aspro, C., Cyprus 94 Ac
Aspy B., Nova Scotia 33 Mg
Asquith, Saskatchewan 36 Kf
Assab, Ethiopia 97 Jb
As Safa, Arabia 92 Ed
Assal, Lake, Djibouti 97 Jb
As Salamiyah, Arabia 92 Ee
Assam, India 89 Hc
As Samāwah, Iraq 92 Ec
Assaye, India 88 Ed
Asse, Belgium 64 Cd
Assean L., Manitoba 37 Vb
Assen, Netherlands 64 Ea
Asshur, Iraq 92 Db
Assigny, L., Quebec 32 Gb
Assiniboia, Saskatchewan 37 Mj
Assiniboine, Mt., B.C./Alta. 39 Qk
Assiniboine R., Man./Sask. 37 Tj
Assinica, L., Quebec 35 Pb
Assisi, Italy 74 Dd
As Sulayyil, Arabia 92 Ee
Assumar, Portugal 70 Bc
As Suwayḥ, Oman 93 Ge
As Suwayq, Oman 93 Ge
As Suwayrah, Iraq 92 Dc
Asten, Netherlands 64 Dc
Asti, Italy 74 Bc
Astipálaia, Greece 77 Ff
Astor, Kashmir 90 Dc
Astorga, Spain 70 Ba
Astoria, Oregon 47 Bb
Astorville, Ontario 35 Lf
Astrakhan, U.S.S.R. 78 Dd
Åsträsk, Sweden 66 Hd
Astros, Greece 77 Df
Astudillo, Spain 70 Ca
Asunción, Paraguay 54 Ec
Aswan, Egypt 99 Md
Aswan High Dam, Egypt 99 Md
Asyût, Egypt 99 Mc
Atacama, Chile 54 Cb
Atakpame, Togo 98 Fg
Atalaia, Brazil 53 Ke
Atalándi, Greece 77 De
Atalaya, Peru 52 Cf
Atalèh, Somalia 97 Kd
Atambua, Timor I., Indon. 83 Hm
Atar, Mauritania 98 Cd
Atara, Yemen 92 Eg
Ataran, Burma 89 Je
Ataúba, Brazil 52 Ed
Atbara, Sudan 99 Me
Atbasar, Kazakhstan 78 Fc
Atchafalaya B., Louisiana 49 Mh
Atchison, Kansas 49 Kc
Ateca, Spain 71 Eb
Ath, Belgium 64 Bd
Athabasca, Alberta 36 Dd
Athabasca, L., Sask./Alta. 38 Tf
Athabasca, R., Alberta 39 Sg
Athapap, Manitoba 37 Qd
Athapapuskow L., Man. 37 Qd
Athboy, Eire 63 Cg
Athenry, Eire 63 Bg
Athens, Georgia, U.S.A. 45 Fd
Athens, Ontario 35 Ph
Athens. See Athínai
Athens, Tennessee 45 Ec
Atherley, Ontario 35 Lh
Atherton, Queensland 57 Hc
Atherton Plat., Queensland 57 Hc
Athínai, Greece 77 Df
Athlone, Eire 63 Bg
Athna, Cyprus 94 Bb
Athol, Massachusetts 44 Da
Athol, New Zealand 55 Bf
Athy, Eire 63 Ch
Atico, Peru 52 Cg
Aticonipi L., Quebec 33 Nb
Atienza, Spain 70 Db
Atik, Manitoba 37 Qd
Atikameg, Alberta 36 Bc
Atikokan, Ontario 36 Lb
Atikonak L., Nfld. 32 Ha
Atikwa L., Ontario 36 Ja
Atka, Aleutian Is. 43 Vm
Atka, U.S.S.R. 79 Qb
Atkarsk, U.S.S.R. 81 Ge
Atkinson Pt., N.W.T. 38 Ha
Atlanta, Georgia, U.S.A. 45 Ed
Atlanta, Michigan 40 Dc
Atlantic, Iowa 49 Kb
Atlantic City, New Jersey 44 Cc
Atlee, Alberta 36 Gh
Atlin & L., B.C. 38 Gf
Atlit, Israel 94 Ce
Atnarko, B.C. 39 Lj
Atoka, Oklahoma 49 Je
Atrauli, India 91 Bb
At Tā'if, Saudi Arabia 92 De
Attalla, Alabama 45 Dc
Attawapiskat, Ontario 31 Lg
Attawapiskat, R., Ontario 31 Lg
Attica, Indiana 49 Ob
Attica, New York 44 Aa
Attiki, Greece 77 De
Attleboro, Massachusetts 44 Eb
Attock, Pakistan 90 Cd
Attopeu, Laos 87 Dd
Attu, Aleutian Is. 43 Um
Atupi, Brazil 53 Gc
Atwater, Saskatchewan 37 Ph
Atwood, Ontario 34 Kj
Aube, France 72 Fb
Aubel, Belgium 64 Dd
Aubenas, France 73 Fd
Aubonne, Switzerland 65 Bb
Aubry L., N.W.T. 38 Kb
Auburn, Alabama 45 Ed
Auburn, Indiana 40 De
Auburn, Maine 32 Bj
Auburn, Nebraska 49 Kb
Auburn, New York 44 Ba
Aubusson, France 72 Ed
Auce, Latvia 67 Kh
Auch, France 73 De
Auckland, New Zealand 55 Eb
Auckland Is., Pacific Ocean 102 Fn
Aude, France 73 Ee
Audeghle, Somalia 97 Jd
Auden, Ontario 34 Cb
Audenarde, Belgium 64 Bd
Audierne, B. d', France 72 Ac
Audubon, Iowa 49 Kb
Aufa, Lebanon 94 Df
Augathella, Queensland 57 Je
Augsburg, West Germany 68 Dd
Augusta, Arkansas 45 Bc
Augusta, Georgia, U.S.A. 45 Gd
Augusta, Kansas 49 Jd
Augusta, Kentucky 45 Fa
Augusta, Maine 32 Cj
Augusta, Sicily 75 Eg
Augusta, Wisconsin 40 Ac
Augusta Mt., Y.T. 38 Ce
Augustów, Poland 69 Kb
Augustus, Mt., W. Australia 56 Cd
Auletta, Italy 75 Ee
Aulneau Pen., Ontario 36 Ha
Aunis, France 72 Cc
Aurangabad, Bihar, India 91 Ec
Aurangabad, Maharashtra, India 88 Ee
Auray, France 72 Bc
Aurillac, France 73 Ed
Aurora, Illinois 49 Nb
Aurora, New York 44 Ba
Aurora, Ontario 35 Lj
Aus, Namibia 95 Be
Au Sable, Michigan 40 Ec
Au Sable Forks, New York 40 Kc
Austin, Minnesota 46 Ld
Austin, Nevada 47 Ef
Austin, Texas 49 Jg
Austin, L., W. Australia 56 Ce
Australia, 56
Australian Alps, Victoria/N.S.W. 57 Jg
Austria, rep., C. Europe 61 Lg
Auteuil, L. D', Quebec 33 Lc
Authier, Quebec 35 Md
Autlan, Mexico 50 Dd
Autun, France 72 Fc
Auvergne, France 73 Ed
Auxerre, France 72 Ec
Aux Sources, Mt., Lesotho 95 De
Ava, Burma 89 Jd
Avallon, France 72 Ec
Avalon Pen., Newfoundland 33 Tf
Avanoas, Namibia 95 Ac
Avaré, Brazil 53 Hh
Avaviken, Sweden 66 Hd
Aveiro, Brazil 53 Fd
Aveiro, Portugal 70 Ab
Avelgem, Belgium 64 Bd
Avellanada, Argentina 54 Ed
Avellino, Italy 75 Ee
Avenir, French Guiana 53 Gc
Averøy, Norway 66 Be
Aversa, Italy 75 Ee
Avesnes, France 72 Ea
Avesta, Sweden 67 Gf
Aveyron, France 73 Ed
Avezzano, Italy 75 De
Aviá Teria, Argentina 54 Dc
Aviemore, Scotland 62 Ec
Avigliano, Italy 75 Ee
Avignon, France 73 Fe
Ávila, Spain 70 Cb
Aviz, Portugal 70 Bc
Avoca, Iowa 49 Kb
Avola, B.C. 39 Ok
Avola, Sicily 75 Eg
Avon, England 63 Fj
Avonlea, Saskatchewan 37 Mh
Avranches, France 72 Cb
Awaji Shima, Japan 86 Dg
Awakino, New Zealand 55 Ec
Awbārī, Libya 99 Hc
Awe L., Scotland 62 Dd
Awjilah, Libya 99 Kc
Awry L., N.W.T. 38 Qd
Awusa L., Ethiopia 97 Hc
Axat, France 73 Ee
Axel, Netherlands 64 Bc
Axel Heiberg I., N.W.T. 31 Ka
Axinim, Brazil 52 Fd
Axminster, England 63 Ek
Ayabaca, Peru 52 Bd
Ayacucho, Argentina 54 Ee
Ayacucho, Peru 52 Cf
Ayaguz, Kazakhstan 78 Hd
Ayamonte, Spain 70 Bd
Ayan, U.S.S.R. 79 Nc
Ayancik, Turkey 92 Ba
Ayaviri, Peru 52 Cf
Aydin, Turkey 92 Ab
Ayerbe, Spain 71 Ea
Ayia, Greece 77 De
Ayion Oros, Greece 77 Ed
Ayios Evstrátios, Greece 77 Ee
Aykathonisi, Greece 77 Ff
Aylen L., Ontario 35 Ng
Aylesbury, England 63 Gj
Aylesbury, Saskatchewan 37 Mh
Aylesford, Nova Scotia 32 Hh
Aylesworth, Mt., B.C. 38 Df
Aylmer, Ontario 34 Kk
Aylmer, Quebec 35 Pg
Aylmer, Mt., Alberta 36 Bg
Aylmer L., N.W.T. 38 Tc
Aylsham, Saskatchewan 37 Oe
Aylwin, Quebec 35 Og
Ayodhya, India 91 Db
Ayon, Ostrov, U.S.S.R. 79 Ra
Ayora, Spain 71 Ec
Ayr, Queensland 57 Jc
Ayr, Scotland 62 De
Ayun, Arabia 92 Dd
Ayutla, Guatemala 50 Fe
Ayutla, Mexico 50 Ed
Ayvalik, Turkey 92 Ab
Aywaille, Belgium 64 Dd
Azaila, Spain 71 Eb
Azamgarh, India 91 Db
Azare, Nigeria 99 Hf
Azaz, Syria 94 Fa
Azerbaydzhanskaya S.S.R., U.S.S.R. 78 Dd
Azogues, Ecuador 52 Bd
Azores Is. See Açores, Is.
Azov, Sea of, U.S.S.R. 80 Kj
Azpeitia, Spain 73 Be
Aztec, New Mexico 42 Ed
Azua, Dominican Rep. 51 Ec
Azuaga, Spain 70 Cc
Azufre, Chile 54 Cc
Azul, Argentina 54 Ee
Azzan, S. Yemen 92 Eg
Az Zubayr, Iraq 92 Ec

B

Baalbek, Lebanon 94 Ec
Baarle-Hertog, Belgium 64 Cc
Baarle Nassau, Netherlands 64 Cc
Baarn, Netherlands 64 Db
Babahoya, Ecuador 52 Bd
Babar, Indonesia 83 Jm
Babati, Tanzania 97 He
Babbage, R., Y.T. 38 Da
Bab el Mandeb, Red Sea 97 Jb
Babenna, Syria 94 Eb
Babine, British Columbia 39 Kh
Babine, R., B.C. 39 Kh
Babine L., B.C. 39 Lh
Babine Ra., B.C. 39 Kh
Bābōl, Iran 93 Fb
Babura, Nigeria 96 Bb
Babuyan Is., Philippines 82 Hg
Babylon, Iraq 92 Dc
Bacabal, Brazil 53 Fe
Bacadehuachi, Mexico 50 Cb
Bacalar, Mexico 50 Gd
Bacan, Indonesia 83 Jl
Bacău, Romania 76 Fa
Bac Can, Vietnam 85 Bl
Baccaro Pt., Nova Scotia 32 Gk
Bacerac, Mexico 50 Ca
Bac Giang, Vietnam 85 Cm
Bache Pen., N.W.T. 31 Mb
Bačka Topola, Yugoslavia 76 Bb
Backbone Mts., W.Va./Md. 44 Ac
Backbone Ranges, N.W.T. 38 Jd
Bäckefors, Sweden 67 Eg
Backergunge, Bangladesh 89 Hd
Back L., N.W.T. 38 Td
Back R., N.W.T. 38 Zb
Bac-Ninh, Vietnam 87 Db
Bacoachic, Mexico 50 Ca
Bacolod, Philippines 83 Hh
Bada, Arabia 92 Cd
Badajos, Brazil 53 Hd
Badajoz, Spain 70 Bc
Badalona, Spain 71 Gb
Badarma, U.S.S.R. 79 Kc
Badas, Brunei 83 Fk
Bad Axe, Michigan 40 Ed
Baddeck, Nova Scotia 33 Mg
Baden, Manitoba 37 Qf
Baden, Switzerland 65 Da
Baden, West Germany 68 Cd
Baden-Baden, W. Germany 68 Cd
Badger, Manitoba 36 Fa
Badger, Newfoundland 33 Qe
Badin, Pakistan 88 Cd
Badiyah, Oman 93 Ge
Bad Kissingen, W. Germany 68 Dc
Bad Lands, U.S.A. 42 Fc
Badon, Senegal 98 Cf
Bad Ragaz, Switzerland 65 Ea
Badrinath, India 88 Eb
Baduen, Somalia 97 Kc
Badulla, Sri Lanka 88 Fg
Baena, Spain 70 Cd
Baffin Bay, N.W.T. 31 Mc
Baffin I., N.W.T. 31 Lc
Bafia, Cameroun 99 Hh
Bafoulabé, Mali 98 Cf
Baf'q, Iran 93 Gc
Bafra, Turkey 92 Ca
Bafra Burun, Turkey 92 Ca
Baft, Iran 93 Gd
Bafwasende, Zaire 96 Fd
Bagata, Zaire 96 De
Bagdarin, U.S.S.R. 79 Lc
Bage, Brazil 54 Fd
Bagerhat, Bangladesh 91 Gd
Baghdād, Iraq 92 Dc
Baghin, Iran 93 Gc
Baghpat, India 90 Ef
Bagley, Minnesota 46 Kb
Bagnara Calabra, Italy 75 Ef
Bagnell Dam, Missouri 45 Aa
Bagnols-sur-Céze, France 73 Fd
Bagong Co, Kashmir/China 88 Eb
Bagotville, Quebec 32 Be
Bagra Kote, India 91 Gb
Bagrationovsk, U.S.S.R. 69 Ja
Baguio, Philippines 83 Hg
Bahaar-i-Gaz, Iran 93 Fb
Bahadurgarh, India 90 Ef
Bahama I., Grand, The Bahamas 51 Da
Bahawalpur, Pakistan 90 Bf
Baheri, India 91 Ba
Bahia. See Salvador
Bahía Blanca, Argentina 54 De
Bahía de Caráquez, Ecuador 52 Ad
Bahía Laura, Argentina 54 Cg
Bahía Negra, Paraguay 54 Eb
Bahraich, India 91 Cb
Bahrain, Persian Gulf 93 Fd
Bahr el Ghazal, Sudan 96 Fc
Bahret el Ateibe, Syria 94 Ed
Bahret el Hijane, Syria 94 Ed
Bahret Homs, Syria 94 Ec
Bahu Kalat, Iran 93 Hd
Baiao, Brazil 53 Hd
Baibokoum, Chad 99 Jg
Baicheng, China 82 Ha
Baie-Carrière, Quebec 35 Me
Baie-Comeau, Quebec 32 Dd
Baie-des-Ha! Ha!, Quebec 33 Oc
Baie-des-Sables, Quebec 32 Ee
Baie-du-Poste, Quebec 31 Mg
Baie-du-Renard, Que. 33 Ld
Baie-Johan-Beetz, Quebec 32 Kc
Baie-Ste-Catherine, Que. 32 Ce
Baie-Ste-Clair, Quebec 32 Hd
Baie-St-Paul, Quebec 32 Bf
Baie-Trinité, Quebec 32 Ed
Baie Verte, Newfoundland 33 Qd
Baihe, China 84 Ef
Baiji, Iraq 92 Dc
Baile Atha Cliath (Dublin), Eire 63 Cg
Bailén, Spain 70 Dc
Baillie-Hamilton I., N.W.T. 30 Kb
Baillie Is., N.W.T. 38 Ja
Baillie R., N.W.T. 38 Vc
Baimak Tanalykovo, U.S.S.R. 81 Nd
Bainbridge, Georgia, U.S.A. 45 Ee
Bainville, Montana 46 Ea
Bairnsdale, Victoria 57 Jg
Baital Faqih, Yemen 92 Dg
Baixo Longa, Angola 95 Bc
Baja, Hungary 76 Ba
Baja California, Mex. 50 Bb
Baján, Mexico 50 Db
Bajmok, Yugoslavia 76 Bb
Bakal, U.S.S.R. 80 Hj
Bakaly, U.S.S.R. 81 Lc
Bakel, Senegal 98 Cf
Baker, Montana 46 Eb
Baker, Oregon 47 Ec
Baker, Mt., Washington 42 Bb
Baker Butte, Arizona 48 Be
Baker Foreland, N.W.T. 31 Ke
Baker I., Pacific Ocean 102 Hg
Baker L., N.W.T. 30 Ke
Baker Lake, N.W.T. 30 Ke
Bakersfield, California 47 Dh
Bakhasar, India 88 Dd
Baklansk, U.S.S.R. 81 Sc
Bakloh, India 90 Dd
Bako, Ethiopia 97 Hc
Bakonyerdo, Hungary 69 Ge
Baku, Azerbaijan 78 Dd
Bala, Ontario 35 Lh
Bala, Wales 63 Eh
Balabac Str., Philippines 83 Gj
Balagnat, India 88 Fd
Balaguer, Spain 71 Fb
Balakhta, U.S.S.R. 79 Jc
Balaklava, U.S.S.R. 80 Hj
Balama, Mozambique 97 Hg
Bala Murghab, Afghanistan 93 Hb
Balancan, Mexico 50 Fd
Balashov, U.S.S.R. 81 Fe
Balasore, India 89 Gd
Balat, Egypt 99 Lc
Balaton, Hungary 69 Ge
Balazote, Spain 71 Dc
Balboa, Panama 51 De
Balbriggan, Eire 63 Cg
Balcarce, Argentina 54 Ee
Balcarres, Saskatchewan 37 Oh
Balchik, Bulgaria 76 Gc
Balclutha, New Zealand 55 Bg
Bald Knob, Arkansas 45 Bc
Bald Knob, W. Virginia 45 Ga
Baldock L., Manitoba 37 Tb
Baldwin, Illinois 45 Ca
Baldwin, Michigan 40 Dd
Baldwinsville, New York 44 Ba
Baldwinton, Saskatchewan 36 Hf
Baldy Mt., Manitoba 37 Rg
Baldy Peak, Arizona 42 Ee
Baldy Pk, New Mexico 48 Ee
Baleares, Is., Medit. Sea 71 Gc
Balearic Is. See Baleares
Baleine, I. à la, Quebec 33 Pb
Baleine, R., Quebec 31 Nf
Balen, Belgium 64 Dc
Baler, Philippines 83 Hg
Balestrand, Norway 67 Bf
Baley, U.S.S.R. 79 Lc
Balfour, B.C. 39 Pl
Balfour, N. Dakota 46 Gb
Balgonie, Saskatchewan 37 Nh
Bal Haf, S. Yemen 92 Eg
Bali, Indonesia 83 Fm
Balikesir, Turkey 92 Ab
Balikpapan, Borneo (Kalimantan) 83 Gl
Baljennie, Saskatchewan 36 Kf
Balk, Netherlands 64 Db
Balkans, The, Europe 76
Balkhash, Kazakh. 78 Gd
Balkhash, Oz., U.S.S.R. 78 Gd
Ball, Mt., Alberta 36 Bg
Ballabgarh, India 90 Ef
Ballachulish, Scotland 62 Dd
Balladonia, W. Australia 56 Df
Ballaghaderreen, Eire 63 Bg
Ballantrae, Scotland 62 De
Ballantyne Str., N.W.T. 30 Hb
Ballarat, Victoria 57 Hg
Ballater, Scotland 62 Ec
Ballé, Mali 98 De
Ballenas, B. de, Mexico 50 Bb
Ballenas Channel, Mexico 50 Bb
Balleny Is., Antarctica 104 Lc
Ballia, India 91 Ec
Ballina, Eire 63 Af
Ballinasloe, Eire 63 Bg
Ballinrobe, Eire 63 Ag
Ballinskelligs B., Eire 63 Aj
Ballston Spa, New York 44 Da
Ballycastle, N. Ireland 62 Ce
Ballymahon, Eire 63 Bg
Ballymena, N. Ireland 63 Cf
Ballymoney, N. Ireland 62 Ce
Ballyshannon, Eire 63 Bf
Balmoral, Manitoba 37 Uh
Balotra, India 88 Dc
Balrampur, India 91 Db
Balranald, N.S.W. 57 Hf
Balsam L., Ontario 35 Mh
Balsas, Brazil 53 He
Balta, Ukraine 80 Fh
Baltanás, Spain 70 Cb
Baltasar Brum, Uruguay 54 Ed
Baltic Sea, N.-W. Europe 67
Baltim, Egypt 99 Mb
Baltimore, Eire 63 Aj
Baltimore, Maryland 40 Hf
Baltistan, Kashmir 90 Dc
Baltit, Kashmir 90 Db
Baltiysk, U.S.S.R. 67 Hj
Baluchistan, Pakistan 88 Bc
Balurghat, India 91 Gc
Balzac, Alberta 36 Dg
Bam, Iran 93 Gd
Bama, Nigeria 99 Hf
Bamako, Mali 98 Df
Bambari, Cent. Afr. Rep. 99 Kg
Bamberg, West Germany 68 Dd
Bambui, Brazil 53 Hh
Bamenda, Cameroun 99 Gg
Bamfield, B.C. 39 Ll
Bamfield, Michigan 40 Ec
Bamiyan, Afghanistan 93 Jc
Bampton, England 63 Ek
Bampur, Iran 93 Hd
Bam Tso, China 89 Gc
Bananal, I. do, Brazil 53 Gf
Banaras, India 91 Dc
Banat, Romania 76 Cb
Banayyan, Arabia 93 Fe
Banbury, England 63 Gh
Banchory, Scotland 62 Fc
Bancroft, Ontario 35 Ng
Banda, India 91 Cc
Banda Aceh, Sumatra 83 Cj
Banda Beila, Somalia 97 Lc
Bandar. See Machilipatham
Bandar 'Abbās, Iran 93 Gd
Bandar Anzalī, Iran 92 Eb
Bandarawela, Sri Lanka 88 Fg
Bandar-e Deylam, Iran 93 Fc
Bandar-e Lengeh, Iran 93 Fd
Bandar-e Pahlavi. See Bandar Anzalī
Bandar-e Rig, Iran 93 Fd
Bandar-e Shāh, Iran 93 Fb
Bandar-e Shāhpūr. See Bandar Khomeynī
Bandar Khomeynī, Iran 92 Ec
Bandar Seri Begawan, Brunei 83 Fk
Banda Sea, Indonesia 83 Jm
Bandera, Argentina 54 Dc
Banderas, B., Mexico 50 Cc
Bandiagara, Mali 98 Ef
Bandikui, India 88 Ec
Bandirma, Turkey 92 Aa
Bandol, France 73 Fe
Bandon, Eire 63 Bj
Band Qir, Iran 92 Ec
Bandundu, Zaire 96 De
Bandung, Java 83 Em
Baneh, Iran 92 Eb
Banes, Cuba 51 Db
Bañeza, La, Spain 70 Ca
Banff, Alberta 39 Qk
Banff, Scotland 62 Fc
Banff Nat. Park, Alberta 39 Pk
Bangada, Zaire 97 Fd
Bangalore, India 88 Ef
Bangārapet, India 88 Ef
Bangassou, Cent. Afr. Rep. 99 Kh
Bangka, Indonesia 83 El
Bangkok, Thailand 83 Dh
Bangkok, Bight of, Thailand 87 Cd
Bangladesh, S. Asia 89 Gd
Bang Mun Nak, Thailand 83 Dg
Bangor, Maine 32 Dj
Bangor, N. Ireland 63 Df
Bangor, Pennsylvania 44 Cb
Bangor, Saskatchewan 37 Ph
Bangor, Wales 63 Eg
Bang Saphan Yai, Thailand 87 Bd
Bangui, Cent. Afr. Rep. 99 Jh
Bangweulu L., Zambia 97 Gg
Ban Houei Sai, Laos 87 Cb
Bani, Dominican Rep. 51 Ec
Bania, Cent. Afr. Rep. 96 Dd
Bani Bu 'Ali, Oman 93 Ge
Baniyas, Syria 94 Dd
Baniyas, Syria 94 Db
Banja Luka, Yugoslavia 74 Fc
Banjarmasin, Borneo (Kalimantan) 83 Fl
Ban. Jaruga, Yugoslavia 74 Fc
Banjul, Gambia 98 Bf
Banka, India 91 Fc
Banka Pahari, India 91 Cc
Banki, India 89 Gd
Bankipore, India 91 Ec
Banks I., B.C. 39 Hj
Banks I., N.W.T. 30 Gc
Banks I., Queensland 57 Hb
Banks Is., Vanuatu 102 Fj
Banks Pen., New Zealand 55 De
Banks Str., Tasmania 57 Jh
Bankura, India 91 Fd
Bannockburn, Ontario 35 Nh
Bann R., N. Ireland 63 Cf
Bannu, Pakistan 90 Bd
Bañolas, Spain 71 Ga
Baños de Montemayor, Sp. 70 Bb
Bansda, India 88 Dd
Bansi, India 91 Db
Banswara, India 88 Dd
Ban tha Uthen, Thailand 87 Cc
Bantry, Eire 63 Aj
Banu, Afghanistan 93 Jb
Banur, India 90 Ee
Banyak Kep., Indonesia 83 Ck
Banyo, Cameroun 99 Hg
Banyuwangi, Java 83 Fm
Banzare Coast, Antarctica 104 Jb
Banzyville. See Yasanyama
Baoding, China 84 Gc
Baoji, China 84 Ce
Baoshan, China 82 Ce
Baotou, China 84 Db
Bapaume, France 72 Ea
Baptiste, Ontario 35 Mg
Baq'a, Arabia 92 Dd
Ba'qubah, Iraq 92 Dc
Bar, Yugoslavia 76 Bc
Bara, Sudan 99 Mf
Barabanki, India 91 Cb
Barabinsk, U.S.S.R. 78 Gc
Baraboo, Wisconsin 40 Bd
Barachois-de-Malbaie, Quebec 32 He
Baracoa, Cuba 51 Eb
Barad, Syria 94 Fb
Barahona, Dominican Rep. 51 Eb
Barahona, Spain 71 Db
Barail Ra., India 89 Hc
Barak R., India 89 Hd
Baramula, Kashmir 90 Dc
Baranagar, India 91 Gd
Baranof I., Alaska 43 Zm
Baranovichi, U.S.S.R. 80 Ee
Baranów, Poland 69 Jc
Baraque Michel, Belgium 64 Ed
Barataria B., Louisiana 49 Mh
Baraunda, India 91 Cc
Baraut, India 90 Ef
Barbacena, Brazil 53 Jh
Barbacoas, Colombia 52 Bc
Barbadillo del Mercado, Sp. 70 Da
Barbados, Windward Is. 51 Hd
Barbara L., Ontario 34 Cc
Barbastro, Spain 71 Fa
Barbel, L., Quebec 32 Db
Barbezieux, France 72 Cd
Barbosa, Colombia 52 Cb
Barbuda, Leeward Is. 51 Gc
Barca d'Alva, Portugal 70 Bb
Barcaldine, Queensland 57 Jd
Barcarrota, Spain 70 Bc
Barcellona Pozza di Gotto, Sicily 75 Ef
Barcelona, Spain 71 Gb
Barcelona, Venezuela 52 Ea
Barcelonnette, France 73 Gd
Barcelos, Brazil 52 Ed
Barcelos, Portugal 70 Ab
Barco de Avila, El, Spain 70 Cb
Barcoo, R., Queensland 57 Hd
Bardera, Somalia 97 Jd
Bardi, India 91 Dc
Bardiyah, Libya 99 Lb
Bardoux, L., Quebec 32 Eb
Bardsey, I., Wales 63 Dh
Bardstown, Kentucky 45 Eb
Bareilly, India 91 Ba
Barentsøya, Arctic Ocean 78 Ba
Barents Sea, Arctic Ocean 78 Ba
Bares, C. de, Spain 70 Ba
Barga, China 88 Fb
Bargal, Somalia 97 Lb
Barh, India 91 Ec
Barhaj, India 91 Db
Bar Harbor, Maine 32 Dj
Bari, India 91 Ab
Bari, Italy 75 Fe
Bari Doab, Pakistan 90 Ce
Barinas, Venezuela 52 Cb
Baring, C., N.W.T. 38 Pa
Barisal, Bangladesh 89 Hd
Barito, Borneo (Kalimantan) 83 Fl
Barkā, Oman 93 Ge
Barkald, Norway 67 Df
Barkerville, B.C. 39 Nj
Barkhan, Pakistan 90 Af
Bark L., Ontario 34 Hf
Barkly Tableland, Australia 57 Gc
Bar-le-Duc, France 72 Fb
Barlee, L., W. Australia 56 Ce
Barlee Ra., W. Australia 56 Cd
Barletta, Italy 75 Fe
Barlow L., N.W.T. 38 Wd
Barmer, India 88 Dc
Barmouth, Wales 63 Eh
Barnaba, Pacific Ocean 102 Fh
Barnaby River, N.B. 32 Gg
Barnard Castle, England 63 Ff
Barnaul, U.S.S.R. 78 Hc
Barnegat B., New Jersey 40 Jf
Barne Inlet, Antarctica 104 La
Barnes Ice Cap, N.W.T. 31 Mc
Barnesville, Minnesota 46 Jb
Barneveld, Netherlands 64 Db
Barn Mt., Quebec 32 Fe
Barnsley, England 63 Gg
Barnstable, Massachusetts 44 Eb
Barnstaple, England 63 Ej
Barnwell, Alberta 36 Ej
Baroda. See Vadodara
Barons, Alberta 36 Dj
Barpeta, India 89 Hc
Barquinha, Portugal 70 Ac
Barquisimeto, Venezuela 52 Da
Barra, Arabia 92 Ee
Barra, Brazil 53 Jf
Barra, I., Scotland 62 Cd
Barra, Sound of, Scotland 62 Bc
Barrackpore, India 91 Gd
Barra do Bugres, Brazil 52 Ff
Barra do Corda, Brazil 53 He
Barra do Pirai, Brazil 53 Jh
Barrage-Gilardo, Quebec 35 Re
Barra Head, Scotland 62 Bd
Barra Mansa, Brazil 53 Jh
Barranca, Peru 52 Bd
Barrancabermeja, Colombia 52 Cb
Barrancas, Venezuela 52 Eb
Barrancos, Portugal 70 Bc
Barranqueras, Argentina 54 Ec
Barranquilla, Colombia 52 Ca
Barraute, Quebec 35 Nd
Barre, Vermont 40 Kc
Barreiras, Brazil 53 Hf
Barreirinha, Brazil 53 Fd
Barreirinhas, Brazil 53 Jd
Barreiro, Portugal 70 Ac
Barreiros, Brazil 53 Ke
Barrême, France 73 Ge
Barren River, Kentucky 45 Db
Barrhead, Alberta 36 Cd
Barrie, Ontario 35 Lh
Barrie I., Ontario 34 Hf
Barrière, B.C. 39 Nk
Barrier I., Great, N.Z. 55 Eb
Barrier I., Little, N.Z. 55 Eb
Barrington, Nova Scotia 32 Gk
Barrington, Mt., N.S.W. 57 Kf
Barrington L., Manitoba 37 Ra
Barrington Passage, N.S. 32 Gk
Barringun, N.S.W. 57 Je
Barron, Wisconsin 46 Mc
Barrow, Argentina 54 De
Barrow Creek, N. Terr. 57 Fd
Barrow-in-Furness, England 63 Ef
Barrow R., Eire 63 Ch
Barrows, Manitoba 37 Qf
Barrow Str., N.W.T. 31 Kc
Barry, Wales 63 Ej
Barry's Bay, Ontario 35 Ng
Barsi, India 88 Ee
Bar-sur-Aube, France 72 Fb
Bar-sur-Seine, France 72 Fb
Bartibog, N.B. 32 Gf
Bartica, Guyana 52 Fb
Bartle Frere, Mt., Queensland 57 Hc
Bartlesville, Oklahoma 49 Jd
Bartlett L., N.W.T. 38 Od
Bartletts Harbour, Nfld. 33 Pc
Bartouille, Quebec 35 Nd
Baruch, India 88 Dd
Baruva, India 89 Fe
Barvaux, Belgium 64 Dd
Barwa, India 91 Ed
Barwani, India 88 Dd
Barwick, Ontario 36 Hb
Barwon, R., N.S.W. 57 Je
Basel (Basle), Switzerland 65 Ca
Baselland, Switz. 65 Ca
Bashaw, Alberta 36 Ef
Bashi, Iran 93 Fc
Bashi Chan., Phil./Taiwan 85 Km
Bashkirskaya A.S.S.R., U.S.S.R. 78 Ec
Basia, India 91 Ed
Basilan, Philippines 83 Hj
Basilicata, Italy 75 Ee
Basingstoke, England 63 Gj
Basin L., Saskatchewan 37 Mf
Baskatong, Rés., Quebec 35 Pf
Båsmo, Norway 66 Fc
Basongo, Zaire 96 Ee
Basra, Iraq 92 Ec
Bas-Rhin, France 72 Gb
Bassano, Alberta 36 Eh
Bassein, Burma 89 He
Bassein, India 88 De
Basses, Gt. & Lit., Sri Lanka 88 Fg
Basseterre, Leeward Is. 51 Gc
Bassevelde, Belgium 64 Bc
Bass River, Nova Scotia 32 Jh
Bass Str., Tasmania/Victoria 57 Jg
Basswood, Manitoba 37 Rh
Basswood L., Minn./Ont. 36 Lb
Båstad, Sweden 67 Eh
Bastak, Iran 93 Fd
Baṣṭam, Iran 93 Gb
Basti, India 91 Db
Bastia, Corsica 74 Bd
Bastille, L., Quebec 32 Db
Bastogne, Belgium 64 De
Bastrop, Louisiana 49 Mf
Bata, Equatorial Guinea 96 Bd
Bataan Corregidor, Philippines 83 Hh
Batacosa, Mexico 50 Cb
Batala, India 90 De
Batalha, Portugal 70 Ac
Batang, China 82 Ce

Batangas, Philippines 83 Hh
Batan Is., Philippines 82 Hf
Batavia, Argentina 54 Cd
Batavia, New York 44 Aa
Bataysk, U.S.S.R. 81 Dg
Batchawana, Ontario 34 Ff
Batchelor, N. Terr. 56 Fb
Bateman, Saskatchewan 36 Lj
Batenburg, Netherlands 64 Dc
Batesburg, S. Carolina 45 Gd
Batesville, Arkansas 49 Me
Batesville, Mississippi 45 Cc
Bath, England 63 Fj
Bath, Maine 32 Ck
Bath, New Brunswick 32 Eg
Bath, New York 44 Ba
Bathurst, New Brunswick 32 Gf
Bathurst, N.S.W. 57 Jf
Bathurst. See Banjul
Bathurst, C., N.W.T. 38 Ka
Bathurst I., N. Terr. 56 Eb
Bathurst I., N.W.T. 30 Jb
Bathurst Inlet, N.W.T. 38 Ub
Bathurst Inlet, N.W.T. 38 Tb
Batie, Upper Volta 98 Eg
Batiscan, Quebec 35 Sf
Batiscan, L., Quebec 35 Te
Batna, Algeria 98 Ga
Batoche, Saskatchewan 37 Lf
Baton Rouge, Louisiana 49 Mg
Batopilas, Mexico 50 Cb
Batraki, U.S.S.R. 81 Jd
Batrun, Lebanon 94 Dc
Battambang, Kampuchea 87 Cd
Batticaloa, Sri Lanka 88 Fg
Battice, Belgium 64 Dd
Battih, South Yemen 92 Ef
Battle Creek, Michigan 40 Dd
Battle Creek, Sask. 36 Hj
Battleford, Saskatchewan 36 Jf
Battle Harbour, Nfld. 33 Ra
Battle Mountain, Nevada 47 Ee
Battle R., Alberta 36 Ff
Battrum, Saskatchewan 36 Jh
Batu, Indonesia 83 Cl
Batumi, Georgia, U.S.S.R. 78 Dd
Baturadja, Sumatra 83 Dl
Baturité, Brazil 53 Kd
Baubau, Celebes (Sulawesi) 83 Hm
Bauchi, Nigeria 99 Gf
Baud, India 89 Fd
Baudette, Minnesota 46 Ka
Baudó, Colombia 52 Bb
Baudouinville. See Moba
Bauge, France 72 Cc
Bauld, C., Newfoundland 33 Rb
Baunt, U.S.S.R. 79 Lc
Baures, Bolivia 52 Ef
Bauru, Brazil 53 Hh
Baus, Brazil 53 Gg
Bauska, Latvia 67 Lh
Bautzen, East Germany 68 Fc
Bavispe, Mexico 50 Ca
Bawal, India 90 Ef
Bawean, Indonesia 83 Fm
Bawiti, Egypt 99 Lc
Bawk, Ontario 34 Dc
Bawku, Ghana 98 Ef
Bawlf, Alberta 36 Ef
Ba Xian, China 84 Hc
Bayamo, Cuba 51 Db
Bayana, India 91 Ab
Bayan Aul, Kazakhstan 78 Gc
Bayandzurh, Mongolia 82 Ea
Bayan Har Shan, China 82 Cd
Bayan Obo, China 84 Db
Bay Bulls, Newfoundland 33 Uf
Bayburt, Turkey 92 Da
Bay City, Michigan 40 Ed
Bay City, Texas 49 Kh
Baydaratskaya B., U.S.S.R. 78 Fb
Bay de Verde, Nfld. 33 Ue
Bay du Nord, Nfld. 33 Rf
Bay du Vin, N.B. 32 Gf
Bayern, West Germany 68 Dd
Bayeux, France 72 Cb
Bayfield, Ontario 34 Jj
Bayfield I., Quebec 33 Ob
Bayfield Mt., Quebec 32 Fe
Bayhān al Qasāb, S. Yemen 92 Eg
Bayir, Jordan 94 Eg
Bay Is., Honduras 51 Bc
Baykal, Ozero, U.S.S.R. 79 Kc
Baykonyr, Kazakhstan 78 Fd
Bay L'Argent, Nfld. 33 Sf
Bay Minette, Alabama 45 De
Bayona, Spain 70 Aa
Bayonne, France 73 Ce
Bayovar, Peru 52 Ae
Bayram Ali, Turkmenistan 78 Fe
Bayreuth, West Germany 68 Dd
Bayrischer Wald., W. Ger. 68 Ed
Bay Roberts, Newfoundland 33 Tf
Bays, L. of, Ontario 35 Lg
Baysville, Ontario 35 Lg
Baytik Shan, China 82 Bb
Baza, Sa. de, Spain 71 Dd
Bazaruto I., Mozambique 95 Fd
Bazas, France 73 Cd
Bazhong, China 84 Cg
Bazias, Romania 76 Cb
Bazin, R., Quebec 35 Qe
Bazman, Iran 93 Gd
Beach, N. Dakota 46 Fb
Beachburg, Ontario 35 Og
Beachy Head, England 63 Hk
Beacon, New York 44 Db
Beacon Hill, Saskatchewan 36 Hd
Beale, C., B.C. 39 Ll
Beal Ra., Queensland 57 He
Beamsville, Ontario 35 Lj
Bear Creek, Y.T. 38 Ee
Beardmore, Ontario 34 Cc
Beardmore Gl., Antarctica 104 La
Bear Hills, The, Sask. 36 Jg
Bear I., N.W.T. 31 Lg
Bear Is. See Medvezhi Osa.
Bear Island, Ontario 34 Kf
Bear L., Indiana/Utah 48 Ba
Bear L., Manitoba 37 Vc
Bear Lake, B.C. 39 Kg
Bearn, France 73 Ce
Béarn, Quebec 35 Le
Bear Paw Mts., Montana 46 Ca
Bear R., Indiana/Utah 48 Ba
Bear River, Nova Scotia 32 Gj
Bearskin Lake, Ontario 31 Kg
Beata, I., Dominican Rep. 51 Ec
Beatenberg, Switzerland 65 Cb
Beatrice, Nebraska 49 Jb
Beatton R., B.C. 39 Ng
Beatton River, B.C. 39 Ng
Beatty, Saskatchewan 37 Nf
Beattyville, Kentucky 45 Fb
Beattyville, Quebec 35 Nd
Beaucanton, Quebec 35 Lc
Beauceville, Quebec 32 Bg
Beauchêne, L., Quebec 35 Mf
Beaudry, Quebec 35 Ld
Beaufort, S. Carolina 45 Gd
Beaufort Sea, Canada 30 Ec
Beaufort West, Cape Prov. 95 Cf
Beaugency, France 72 Dc
Beauharnois, Quebec 35 Rg
Beauharnois Power Canal, Quebec 35 Qg
Beauly, Scotland 62 Dc
Beaumont, Belgium 64 Cd
Beaumont, France 72 Eb
Beaumont, New Zealand 55 Bf
Beaumont, Quebec 35 Se
Beaumont, Texas 49 Kg
Beaune, France 72 Fc
Beauport, Quebec 35 Ta
Beauraing, Belgium 64 Cd
Beauséjour, Manitoba 36 Ea
Beauvais, France 72 Eb
Beauvais Lake Provincial Park, Alberta 36 Cj
Beauval, Saskatchewan 30 Jf
Beauval, Saskatchewan 36 Kc
Beauvallon, Alberta 36 Fe
Beauvoir-sur-Mer, France 72 Bc
Beaver, Oklahoma 48 Gd
Beaver, Utah 47 Gf
Beaver, R., Y.T. 38 Le
Beaverbank, Nova Scotia 32 Jj
Beaver Brook, N.B. 32 Gf
Beaver Creek, Y.T. 38 Cd
Beaver Dam, Wisconsin 40 Bd
Beaverdell, B.C. 39 Ol
Beaver Falls, Pennsylvania 40 Fe
Beaverhead Mts., Idaho 47 Gc
Beaverhill L., Alberta 36 Ee
Beaverhill L., N.W.T. 39 Vd
Beaver I., Michigan 40 Dc
Beaverlodge, Alberta 39 Oh
Beavermouth, B.C. 39 Pk
Beaver R., Alberta 36 Fd
Beaver R., Saskatchewan 36 Kd
Beaver R., Utah 47 Gf
Beaver Res., Arkansas 49 Kd
Beaverton, Ontario 35 Lh
Beawar, India 88 Dc
Beazley, Argentina 54 Cd
Bebedouro, Brazil 53 Hh
Becej, Yugoslavia 76 Bb
Becerrea, Spain 70 Ba
Béchar, Algeria 98 Eb
Beclean, Romania 69 Le
Bédar, Spain 71 Ed
Bede, Manitoba 37 Rj
Bedford, England 63 Gh
Bedford, Nova Scotia 32 Jj
Bedford, Pennsylvania 44 Ac
Bedford, Quebec 35 Sg
Bedfordshire, England 63 Gh
Bedourie, Queensland 57 Gd
Bedretto, Switzerland 65 Db
Bedzin, Poland 69 Hc
Beechey L., N.W.T. 38 Uc
Beechwood Hydro-Electric Sta., New Brunswick 32 Ef
Beechy, Saskatchewan 36 Kh
Beek, Netherlands 64 Dc
Beek, Netherlands 64 Dd
Beekbergen, Netherlands 64 Db
Beerlegem, Belgium 64 Bd
Beer Menuha, Israel 94 Dg
Beernem, Belgium 64 Bc
Beers, Netherlands 64 Dc
Beersheba, Israel 94 Cf
Beeville, Texas 48 Jh
Befale, Zaire 96 Ed
Befandriana, Madagascar 97 Nk
Bega, New South Wales 57 Kg
Behbehan, Iran 93 Fc
Beho, Belgium 64 Dd
Bei'an, China 82 Ja
Beidha, Arabia 92 Ce
Beihai, China 85 Dm
Beijing, China 84 Hc
Beilen, Netherlands 64 Eb
Beilul, Ethiopia 97 Jb
Beinwil, Switzerland 65 Da
Beira, Mozambique 95 Fc
Beirût (Beyrouth), Lebanon 94 Dd
Beiseker, Alberta 36 Dg
Beitbridge, Zimbabwe 95 Ed
Beit-et-Din, Lebanon 94 Dd
Beius, Romania 76 Da
Beizhen, China 84 Kb
Beja, Portugal 70 Bc
Bejaia, Golfe de, Algeria 73 Ph
Bejaïa (Bougie), Algeria 73 Ph
Béjar, Spain 70 Cb
Bejestān, Iran 93 Gc
Bejucal, Cuba 51 Cb
Békéscsaba, Hungary 69 Je
Bela, Pakistan 88 Cc
Belagunj, India 91 Dc
Belair, Louisiana 45 Cf
Belang, Celebes (Sulawesi) 83 Hk
Bélanger Pt., Manitoba 37 Ue
Bélanger R., Manitoba 37 Ue
Bela Palanka, Yugoslavia 76 Dc
Belaya Tserkov, Ukraine 80 Gg
Belcher Chan., N.W.T. 30 Kb
Belcher Is., N.W.T. 31 Mf
Belcher Is. N., N.W.T. 31 Mf
Belchiragh, Afghanistan 93 Jb
Belchite, Spain 71 Eb
Belcourt, Quebec 35 Nd
Beldanga, India 91 Gd
Belebey, U.S.S.R. 81 Mc
Belém, Brazil 53 Hd
Belèm, Mexico 50 Bb
Belén, Argentina 54 Cc
Belen, New Mexico 48 De
Belén, Panama 51 Ce
Belfast, Maine 32 Cj
Belfast, N. Ireland 63 Df
Belfast Lough, N. Ireland 63 Df
Belfeld, Netherlands 64 Ec
Belfield, N. Dakota 46 Fb
Belford, England 62 Fe
Belfort, France 72 Gc
Belgaum, India 88 De
Belgium, Cent. Eur. 61 Jf
Belgorod, U.S.S.R. 80 Kf
Belgorod Dnestrovskiy, Ukraine 80 Gh
Belgrade. See Beograd
Belgrano, Argentina 54 Ee
Belin, France 73 Cd
Belitung, Indonesia 83 El
Belize, Belize 51 Bc
Belize, Central America 51 Bc
Bell, R., Quebec 35 Nc
Bell, R., Yukon Territory 38 Eb
Bella Bella, B.C. 39 Jj
Bellac, France 72 Dc
Bella Coola, B.C. 39 Kj
Bellaire, Michigan 40 Dc
Bellaire, Ohio 40 Fe
Bellary, India 88 Ee
Bellavista, Peru 52 Be
Bellburns, Newfoundland 33 Pc
Belle B., Newfoundland 33 Rf
Bellefontaine, Ohio 40 Ee
Bellefonte, Pennsylvania 44 Bb
Belle Fourche, S. Dakota 46 Fc
Belle I., Newfoundland 33 Rb
Belle Ile, France 72 Bc
Belle Isle, Strait of, 33 Qb
Bellême, France 72 Db
Belleoram, Newfoundland 33 Rf
Belle Plain, Saskatchewan 37 Mh
Belle Plaine, Iowa 49 Lb
Belle Rivière, L. de la, Quebec 35 Td
Belleterre, Quebec 35 Me
Belleville, France 72 Fc
Belleville, Illinois 49 Mc
Belleville, Kansas 49 Jc
Belleville, Ontario 35 Nh
Bellevue, Alberta 36 Cj
Bellevue, Iowa 49 Ma
Bellevue, Ohio 40 Ee
Bellevue, Ontario 40 Db
Belley, France 72 Fd
Belle Yella, Liberia 98 Cg
Bell I., Conception Bay, Newfoundland 33 Tf
Bell I., White Bay, Nfld. 33 Rc
Bellingham, England 62 Fe
Bellingham, Washington 42 Bb
Bellingshausen Sea, Antarc. 104 Rc
Bellin (Payne), Quebec 31 Ne
Bellinzona, Switzerland 65 Eb
Bellis, Alberta 36 Ed
Bellows Falls, Vermont 44 Da
Bell Pen., N.W.T. 31 Le
Bellsite, Manitoba 37 Qf
Belluno, Italy 74 Db
Bell Ville, Argentina 54 Dd
Belly R., Alberta 36 Dj
Bélmez, Spain 70 Cc
Belmond, Iowa 49 La
Belmont, Manitoba 37 Sj
Belmont, Missouri 45 Cb
Belmont, New York 44 Ba
Belmont, Nova Scotia 32 Jh
Belmont, Ontario 34 Jk
Belmonte, Brazil 53 Kg
Belmonte, Portugal 70 Bb
Belmonte, Spain 71 Dc
Belmont L., Pennsylvania 44 Cb
Belmopan, Belize 51 Bc
Belmullet, Eire 63 Af
Belo Horizonte, Brazil 53 Jg
Beloit, Kansas 49 Hc
Beloit, Wisconsin 49 Na
Belomorsk, U.S.S.R. 78 Cb
Belopol'ye, Ukraine 80 Jf
Belorado, Spain 70 Da
Beloretsk, U.S.S.R. 81 Pd
Belorusskaya S.S.R. See Byelorussia
Belostok. See Bialystok
Belot, L., N.W.T. 38 Kb
Beloye More, U.S.S.R. 78 Cb
Beloye Ozero, U.S.S.R. 80 Ka
Belp, Switzerland 65 Cb
Belt, Lille, Denmark 67 Cj
Belt, Store, Denmark 67 Dj
Belterra, Brazil 53 Gd
Belvedere Marittimo, Italy 75 Ef
Belver, Portugal 70 Bc
Belvidere, Illinois 49 Na
Belvidere, New Jersey 44 Cb
Belyy, Ostrov, U.S.S.R. 78 Fa
Bemidji, Minnesota 46 Kb
Benalla, Victoria 57 Jg
Benalto, Alberta 36 Cf
Benapol, India 91 Gd
Benares. See Varanasi
Benavente, Spain 70 Cb
Benbecula I., Scotland 62 Cc
Bencubbin, W. Australia 56 Cf
Bend, Oregon 47 Cc
Ben Dearg, Scotland 62 Dc
Bender, Saskatchewan 37 Ph
Bendery, Moldavia 80 Fh
Bendigo, Victoria 57 Hg
Benevento, Italy 75 Ee
Bengal, B. of, India 89 Ge
Bengal, West, India 91 Fd
Ben Gardane, Tunisia 99 Hb
Bengbu, China 84 Hf
Bengbu, China 85 Jl
Benghāzi, Libya 99 Kb
Bengough, Saskatchewan 37 Mj
Benguela, Angola 96 Cg
Benha, Egypt 99 Mb
Ben Hope, Scotland 62 Db
Beni, R., Bolivia 52 Df
Beni-Abbès, Algeria 98 Eb
Beniah L., N.W.T. 38 Rd
Benicarló, Spain 71 Fb
Benidorm, Spain 71 Ec
Beni Mazar, Egypt 99 Mc
Benin, W. Africa 98 Fg
Benin, Bight of, W. Africa 98 Fh
Benin City, Nigeria 98 Gg
Beni Saf, Algeria 98 Ea
Beni Suef, Egypt 99 Mc
Benito, Equat. Guinea 96 Bd
Benito, Manitoba 37 Qg
Benjamin Constant, Brazil 52 Cd
Benkelman, Nebraska 48 Gb
Benkovac, Yugoslavia 74 Ec
Ben Lomond, N.S.W. 57 Ke
Ben Macdui, Scotland 62 Ed
Ben More Assynt, Scotland 62 Db
Bennett, B.C. 38 Ff
Bennett L., B.C. 38 Ff
Bennettsville, S. Carolina 45 Hc
Ben Nevis, Scotland 62 Dd
Bennington, Vermont 44 Da
Benny, Ontario 34 Jf
Benson, Arizona 48 Bg
Benson, Minnesota 46 Kc
Benson, Saskatchewan 37 Oj
Benson Mines, New York 40 Jc
Bent, Iran 93 Gd
Bentinck I., Burma 89 Jf
Bentley, Alberta 36 Cf
Bento Goncalves, Brazil 54 Fc
Benton, Alberta 36 Gg
Benton, Arkansas 45 Ac
Benton, New Brunswick 32 Eg
Benton Harbor, Michigan 40 Cd
Benue, Nigeria 98 Gg
Benwee Head, Eire 63 Af
Ben Wyvis, Scotland 62 Dc
Beograd, Yugoslavia 76 Cb
Beppu, Japan 86 Bh
Berar, India 88 Ed
Berat, Albania 77 Bd
Berber, Sudan 99 Me
Berbera, Somalia 97 Kb
Berbérati, Cent. Afr. Rep. 99 Jh
Berchtesgaden, Germany 68 Ee
Berdichev, Ukraine 80 Fg
Berdigestyakh, U.S.S.R. 79 Mb
Berdyansk, Ukraine 80 Kh
Berens, I., Manitoba 37 Uf
Berens R., Manitoba 37 Vf
Berens River, Manitoba 37 Vf
Beresford, Manitoba 37 Rj
Beresford, S. Dakota 46 Jd
Beresti, Romania 76 Fa
Berezniki, U.S.S.R. 78 Ec
Berezovo, U.S.S.R. 78 Fb
Berg, Norway 66 Gb
Berga, Spain 71 Fa
Bergamo, Italy 74 Bc
Bergeijk, Netherlands 64 Dc
Bergen, East Germany 68 Ea
Bergen, Norway 67 Af
Bergen, West Germany 68 Cb
Bergen-op-Zoom, Netherlands 64 Cc
Bergerac, France 73 Dd
Bergisch Gladbach, W. Ger. 68 Bc
Bergland, Ontario 36 Hb
Bergün, Switzerland 65 Eb
Berhampore, India 89 Gd
Berhampur, India 89 Fe
Berhampur, India 91 Gc
Beri, India 90 Ef
Beringen, Belgium 64 Dc
Bering Sea, Asia/America 43 Ul
Bering Strait, Asia/America 43 Vl
Berislav, Ukraine 80 Hh
Berkåk, Norway 66 De
Berkeley, California 47 Bg
Berkeley, C., N.W.T. 30 Jc
Berkley, Virginia 45 Jb
Berkovitsa, Bulgaria 76 Dc
Berkshire (Berks), Eng. 63 Gj
Berkshire Hills, Mass. 44 Da
Berland, R., Alberta 39 Ph
Berlin, Germany 68 Eb
Berlin, New Hampshire 40 Lc
Berlin, Wisconsin 40 Bc
Berlinguet Inlet, N.W.T. 31 Lc
Bermillo de Sáyago, Spain 70 Bb
Bermudas, Is., Atlantic Oc. 43 Pe
Bern, Switzerland 65 Cb
Bernalillo, New Mexico 48 De
Bernard, Saskatchewan 36 Kh
Bernard, L., Quebec 32 Jc
Bernard I., N.W.T. 30 Gc
Bernasconi, Argentina 54 De
Bernay, France 72 Db
Bernburg, East Germany 68 Dc
Berne. See Bern
Berneau, Belgium 64 Dd
Berneck, Switzerland 65 Ea
Berner Alpen, Switzerland 65 Cb
Bernier B., N.W.T. 31 Lc
Bernina, Passo del, Switz. 65 Eb
Beromünster, Switzerland 65 Da
Berri, France 72 Ec
Berry, Quebec 35 Md
Berry Is., The Bahamas 51 Da
Berryville, Virginia 44 Ac
Bersillies, Belgium 64 Cd
Berté, L., Quebec 32 Dc
Berthierville, Quebec 35 Rf
Berthold, N. Dakota 46 Ga
Bertoua, Cameroun 99 Hh
Bertraghboy B., Eire 63 Ag
Bertrix, Belgium 64 De
Beru, Kiribati 102 Gh
Berwick, Nova Scotia 32 Hh
Berwick, Pennsylvania 44 Bb
Berwick, Scotland 62 Fe
Berwick-upon-Tweed., Eng. 62 Fe
Berwyn, Alberta 39 Pg
Berwyn Mts., Wales 63 Eh
Berzee, Belgium 64 Cd
Besançon, France 72 Gc
Beskidy Zachodnie, Central Europe 69 Hd
Besnard L., Saskatchewan 37 Mc
Besni, Turkey 92 Cb
Bessemer, Alabama 45 Dd
Bessemer, Ontario 35 Ng
Best, Netherlands 64 Dc
Betanzos, Spain 70 Aa
Betbetti, Sudan 99 Ke
Betchie, L., Quebec 32 Cd
Bethanie, Namibia 95 Be
Bethany, Missouri 49 Kb
Bethany, Ontario 35 Mh
Bethel, Maine 32 Bj
Bethlehem, Jordan 94 Df
Bethlehem, O.F.S. 95 De
Bethlehem, Pennsylvania 44 Cb
Béthoulat, L., Quebec 32 Ab
Bethune, Saskatchewan 37 Mh
Betling Sib, India 89 Hd
Betsiamites (Bersimis), Que. 32 De
Betsiamites (Bersimis), R., Quebec 32 Cd
Bettiah, India 91 Eb
Beugen, Netherlands 64 Dc
Beulah, Manitoba 37 Qh
Beveland, Noord, Neth. 64 Bc
Beveland, Zuid, Neth. 64 Bc
Beveren, Belgium 64 Cc
Beverley, Saskatchewan 36 Jh
Beverlo, Belgium 64 Dc
Beverly, Massachusetts 44 Ea
Beverly L., N.W.T. 38 Xc
Beverst, Belgium 64 Dd
Bex, Switzerland 65 Cb
Bexly, C., N.W.T. 38 Qa
Beyla, Guinea 98 Dg
Beypazari, Turkey 92 Ba
Beypore, India 88 Ef
Beysehir, Turkey 92 Bb
Beyt Guvrin, Israel 94 Cf
Beyt Shean, Israel 94 De
Bezdán, Yugoslavia 76 Bb
Bezhitsa, U.S.S.R. 80 He
Béziers, France 73 Ee
Bhabua, India 91 Dc
Bhadarwah, Kashmir 90 Dd
Bhadaur, India 90 De
Bhadaura, India 91 Ac
Bhadohi, India 91 Dc
Bhadra, India 90 Df
Bhadreswar, India 91 Gd
Bhagalpur, India 91 Fc
Bhakkar, Pakistan 90 Be
Bhamo, Burma 89 Jd
Bhandara, India 88 Ed
Bhannis, Lebanon 94 Dd
Bhanrer Range, India 91 Bd
Bharatpur, India 91 Ab
Bhatgaon, Nepal 91 Eb
Bhatinda, India 90 De
Bhatpara, India 91 Gd
Bhaunagar, India 88 Dd
Bhawani Patna, India 89 Fe
Bhera, Pakistan 90 Cd
Bhilwara, India 88 Dc
Bhima R., India 88 Ee
Bhind, India 91 Bb
Bhir (Bir), India 88 Ee
Bhiwani, India 90 Ef
Bhopal, India 91 Ad
Bhuj, India 88 Cd
Bhusawal, India 88 Ed
Bhutan, Himalayas 89 Hc
Biafra, Bight of, W. Africa 96 Bd
Biak, Irian Jaya 83 Ll
Bialogard, Poland 69 Ga
Bialowieza, Poland 69 Kb
Bialystok, Poland 69 Kb
Biarritz, France 73 Ce
Biberach, West Germany 68 Cd
Bibon, Wisconsin 40 Ab
Bic, Quebec 32 De
Bic, I. du, Quebec 32 De
Biche, L. la, Alberta 36 Ed
Bicknell, Indiana 40 Cf
Bida, Nigeria 98 Gg
Bidar, India 88 Ee
Biddeford, Maine 44 Ea
Bideford, England 63 Ej
Bidesir, India 90 Dg
Biel, Switzerland 65 Ca
Bield, Manitoba 37 Qg
Bielefeld, West Germany 68 Cb
Bieler See, Switzerland 65 Ca
Bielsk Podlaski, Poland 69 Kb
Bienfait, Saskatchewan 37 Pj
Bienne. See Biel
Bienville, Quebec 35 Tb
Bienville, L., Quebec 31 Mf
Bière, Switzerland 65 Bb
Bietschhorn, Switz. 65 Cb
Biga, Turkey 92 Aa
Big Bar Creek, B.C. 39 Mk
Big Beaver, Saskatchewan 37 Mj
Big Beaver Falls, Ontario 34 Hc
Big Beaver House, Ontario 31 Lg
Big Bell, W. Australia 56 Ce
Big Belt Mts., Montana 47 Hb
Big Bend Nat. Park, Texas 48 Fh
Big Blue R., Kansas/Nebraska 49 Jb
Big Creek, B.C. 39 Mk
Bigelow, Maine 40 Lc
Biggar, Saskatchewan 36 Kf
Bigger, Mt., B.C. 38 Ef
Big Hatchet Mts., New Mexico 48 Cg
Bighorn L., Montana 46 Cc
Big Horn Mts., Wyoming 46 Dc
Big Horn R., Montana/Wyo. 42 Ec
Big I., N.W.T. 38 Pe
Big I., N.W.T. 31 Me
Big. I., Ontario 36 Ga
Big Kalzas L., Y.T. 38 Fd
Big L., Arkansas 49 Me
Big L., N.W.T. 38 Rc
Big Lake, Ontario 34 Jg
Big Muddy L., Sask. 37 Mj
Bignasco, Switzerland 65 Db
Bignona, Senegal 98 Bf
Big Pond, Nova Scotia 33 Mh
Big Rapids, Michigan 40 Dd
Big River, Saskatchewan 36 Ke
Big Salmon, Y.T. 38 Fe
Big Salmon, R., Y.T. 38 Fe
Big Sandy L., Sask. 37 Nd
Big Sandy R., Kentucky 45 Fa
Bigsby I., Ontario 36 Ja
Big Spring, Texas 48 Gf
Bigstick L., Saskatchewan 36 Hh
Bigstone L., Manitoba 37 We
Bigstone R., Manitoba 37 Wc
Bigtimber, Montana 46 Cc
Big Trout L., Ontario 31 Lg
Big Trout Lake, Ontario 31 Lg
Big Valley, Alberta 36 Ef
Bigwood, Ontario 34 Kf
Bihac, Yugoslavia 74 Ec
Bihar, India 89 Gd
Bihar, India 91 Ec
Biharamulo, Tanzania 97 Ge
Bihorului, Mts., Romania 76 Da
Bijagós, Arquipelago dos, Guinea-Bissau 98 Bf
Bijapur, India 88 Ee
Bijar, Iran 92 Eb
Bijawar, India 91 Bc
Bijeljina, Yugoslavia 76 Bb
Bijna, India 91 Bc
Bijnabad, Iran 93 Gd
Bijnor, India 90 Ff
Bikaner, India 90 Cf
Bikin, U.S.S.R. 79 Nd
Bikini, Marshall Is. 102 Ff
Bikoro, Zaire 96 De
Bilaspur, India 89 Fd
Bilaspur, India 91 Cd
Bilauktaung Range, Burma/Thailand 83 Ch
Bilbao, Spain 70 Da
Bileća, Yugoslavia 76 Bc
Bilecik, Turkey 92 Aa
Bílé Karpaty, Czech. 69 Gd
Bilin, Burma 89 Je
Bilisht, Albania 77 Cd
Billings, Montana 46 Cc
Billiton, I. See Belitung
Bilma, Niger 99 He
Biloela, Queensland 57 Jd
Bilo Goro, Yugoslavia 74 Fc
Biloxi, Mississippi 45 Ce
Bilsi, India 91 Ba
Bilta, Norway 66 Jb
Bilthoven, Netherlands 64 Db
Bilugyun, Burma 89 Je
Bilyarsk, U.S.S.R. 81 Kc
Bilzen, Belgium 64 Dd
Bimbe, Angola 96 Dg
Bimini Is., The Bahamas 43 Lf
Bimlipatam, India 89 Fe
Bina, India 91 Bc
Binaija, Seram I., Indon. 83 Jl
Binalud, Iran 93 Gb
Binche, Belgium 64 Cd
Bindki, India 91 Cb
Bindloss, Alberta 36 Gh
Bindura, Zimbabwe 95 Ec
Binefar, Spain 71 Fb
Bingen, West Germany 68 Bd
Bingerville, Ivory Coast 98 Eg
Bingham, Maine 32 Ch
Bingham Canyon, Utah 48 Ab
Binghamton, New York 44 Ca
Bingle, Ontario 34 Kd
Bingöl, Turkey 92 Db
Binn, Switzerland 65 Db
Binscarth, Manitoba 37 Qh
Bintan, Riouw Arch., Indonesia 83 Dk
Bint Jubeil, Lebanon 94 Dd
Bir Ali, South Yemen 92 Eg
Birch Hills, Saskatchewan 37 Me
Birch I., Manitoba 37 Sf
Birch L., Alberta 36 Fe
Birch L., N.W.T. 38 Pd
Birch L., Saskatchewan 36 Je
Birch Mts., Alberta 39 Rg
Birch R., Alberta 39 Rf
Birch River, Manitoba 37 Qf
Birchwood, New Zealand 55 Af
Bird, Manitoba 30 Kf
Bird Cove, Newfoundland 33 Qb
Birdsboro, Pennsylvania 44 Cb
Birdsville, Queensland 57 Ge
Birdum, N. Terr. 56 Fc
Birecik, Turkey 92 Cb
Birein, Syria 94 Eb
Bir Fadhil, Arabia 92 Ee
Bir Gara, Chad 99 Jf
Birhan, Ethiopia 97 Hb
Birjand, Iran 93 Gc
Birkenhead, England 63 Eg
Bîrlad, Romania 76 Fa
Bir Malusi, Iraq 92 Cc
Bir Maqran, Arabia 92 Ee
Birmingham, Alabama 45 Dd
Birmingham, England 63 Fh
Birmingham, Michigan 40 Ed
Birmingham, Saskatchewan 37 Ph
Birney, Montana 46 Dc
Birnie, Manitoba 37 Sh
Birnin Kebbi, Nigeria 98 Ff
Birni-n'Konni, Niger 98 Gf
Birobidzhan, U.S.S.R. 79 Nd
Birq, Arabia 92 Df
Birr, Eire 63 Bg
Birsay, Saskatchewan 36 Lg
Birsilpur, India 90 Cf
Birsk, U.S.S.R. 81 Mc
Birtle, Manitoba 37 Qh
Biryusa R., U.S.S.R. 79 Jc
Biržai, Lithuania 67 Lh
Bisalpur, India 91 Ba
Bisauli, India 91 Ba
Bisbal, la, Spain 71 Gb
Bisbee, Arizona 48 Cg
Bisbee, N. Dakota 46 Ha
Biscay, B. of, France/Spain 61 Fg
Bischofszell, Switzerland 65 Ea
Biscoe, B., Antarctica 104 Nb
Biscoe, Is., Antarctica 104 Sc
Biscotasi, L., Ontario 34 He
Biscotasing, Ontario 34 He
Bishnath, India 89 Hc
Bishnupur, India 91 Fd
Bishop Auckland, England 63 Ff
Bishop L., N.W.T. 38 Pc
Bishop Mt., Wyoming 46 Ce
Bishopric, Saskatchewan 37 Mh
Bishop's Falls, Nfld. 33 Rd
Bishops Stortford, England 63 Hj
Bishri, Jebel el, Syria 92 Cb
Bisina, L., Uganda 97 Gd
Bisisthal, Switzerland 65 Db
Biskia, Ethiopia 97 Ha
Bismarck, N. Dakota 46 Gb
Bismarck Arch., Pacific Oc. 102 Dh
Bismarck C., Greenland 41 Mb
Bison, S. Dakota 46 Fc
Bison L., Alberta 39 Pg
Bissau, Guinea-Bissau 98 Bf
Bissau, India 90 Df
Bistcho L., Alberta 38 Of
Biswan, India 91 Cb
Bithur, India 91 Cb
Bitlis, Turkey 92 Db
Bitola, Yugoslavia 76 Cd
Bitonto, Italy 75 Fe
Bitterfeld, East Germany 68 Ec
Bittern L., Saskatchewan 37 Me
Bittern Lake, Alberta 36 De
Bitter Root Mts., Idaho 47 Fb
Bitumount, Alberta 39 Sg
Bivio, Switzerland 65 Eb
Biwa Ko, Japan 86 Dg
Biysk, U.S.S.R. 78 Hc
Bizerte, Tunisia 99 Ga
Bjelovar, Yugoslavia 74 Fc
Björkö, Sweden 67 Hg
Bjorli, Norway 66 Ce
Björna, Sweden 66 He
Bjørnør, Norway 66 Dd
Bjørnøya, Barents Sea 78 Aa
Blache, L. De La, Quebec 32 Cc
Blackall, Queensland 57 Jd
Black B., Ontario 34 Bd
Black B., Saskatchewan 38 Tf
Black Bear Island L., Sask. 37 Mc
Black Birch L., Sask. 39 Ug
Blackburn, England 63 Fg
Blackburn, Mt., Alaska 30 Ee
Black Diamond, Alberta 36 Ch
Black Dome, B.C. 39 Kj
Blackdown Hills, England 63 Ek
Blackfoot, Alberta 36 Ge
Blackfoot, Idaho 47 Gd
Black Hawk, Ontario 36 Hb
Blackhead B., Nfld. 33 Te
Black Hills, S. Dakota 42 Fc
Black I., Manitoba 37 Vg
Blackie, Alberta 36 Dh
Black Isle, Scotland 62 Ec
Black L., Saskatchewan 38 Vf
Black Lake, Quebec 35 Tf
Black Mt., Pakistan 90 Cc
Black Mts., Arizona 47 Fh

Black Mts., *New Brunswick* 32 Ef
Black Mts., *Wales* 63 Ej
Black Pines, *B.C.* 39 Nk
Black Pool, *B.C.* 39 Nk
Blackpool, *England* 63 Eg
Black R., *Arkansas/Missouri* 49 Me
Black Range, *New Mexico* 48 Df
Blackriver, *Michigan* 40 Ec
Black River Falls, *Wisconsin* 40 Ac
Black Rock, *Arkansas* 45 Bb
Black Rock Des., *Nevada* 47 De
Black Sea, *Europe/Asia* 58 Cd
Blacks Harbour, *N.B.* 32 Fh
Blacksod B., *Eire* 63 Af
Blackstone, R., *Y.T.* 38 Ec
Black Sturgeon, L., *Ont.* 34 Bc
Black Sugar Loaf, Mt., *New South Wales* 57 Kf
Blackville, *New Brunswick* 32 Gg
Blackville, *S. Carolina* 45 Gd
Black Volta R., *Ghana* 98 Eg
Blackwater L., *N.W.T.* 38 Mc
Blackwater R., *Eire* 63 Bh
Blackwell, *Oklahoma* 49 Jd
Bladworth, *Saskatchewan* 36 Lg
Blagoevgrad, *Bulgaria* 76 Dc
Blagoveshchensk, *U.S.S.R.* 79 Mc
Blagoveshchensk, *U.S.S.R.* 81 Mc
Blaine Lake, *Saskatchewan* 36 Lf
Blair, *Nebraska* 49 Jb
Blair Atholl, *Scotland* 62 Ed
Blairgowrie, *Scotland* 62 Ed
Blairmore, *Alberta* 36 Cj
Blaj, *Romania* 76 Da
Blanc, C., *Mauritania* 98 Bd
Blanc, le, *France* 72 Dc
Blanc, Mt., *France/Italy* 72 Gd
Blanca, B., *Argentina* 54 De
Blanca, Sierra, *New Mexico* 48 Ef
Blanca Peak, *Colorado* 42 Ed
Blanche, *Ontario* 34 Eb
Blanche, *Quebec* 35 Pg
Blanche, L., *S. Australia* 57 Ge
Blanco, C., *Oregon* 47 Ad
Blanco, Pico, *Costa Rica* 51 Ce
Blanc-Sablon, *Quebec* 33 Pb
Bland, *Virginia* 45 Gb
Blandford, *England* 63 Fk
Blanes, *Spain* 71 Gb
Blangpidie, *Sumatra* 83 Ck
Blangy, *France* 72 Db
Blankenberge, *Belgium* 64 Bc
Blantyre, *Malawi* 97 Hh
Blaregnies, *Belgium* 64 Bd
Blaton, *Belgium* 64 Bd
Blaye, *France* 73 Cd
Blazowa, *Poland* 69 Kd
Bleharies, *Belgium* 64 Bd
Blenheim, *New Zealand* 55 Dd
Blenheim, *Ontario* 34 Jk
Bleu, L., *Quebec* 35 Mf
Blewett, *Saskatchewan* 37 Oj
Blida, *Algeria* 98 Fa
Blind River, *Ontario* 34 Hf
Blitta, *Togo* 98 Fg
Block I., *Rhode Island* 44 Eb
Bloedel, *British Columbia* 39 Lk
Bloemfontein, *O.F.S.* 95 De
Blois, *France* 72 Dc
Blokzijl, *Netherlands* 64 Eb
Bloody Foreland, *Eire* 62 Be
Bloomfield, *Indiana* 40 Cf
Bloomfield, *Iowa* 49 Lb
Bloomfield, *Ontario* 35 Nh
Bloomington, *Illinois* 49 Nb
Bloomington, *Indiana* 85 Jd
Bloomsburg, *Pennsylvania* 44 Bb
Blossburg, *Pennsylvania* 44 Bb
Blount Springs, *Alabama* 45 Dc
Blow, R., *Y.T.* 38 Ea
Blucher, *Saskatchewan* 36 Lf
Blueberry R., *B.C.* 39 Ng
Blue Earth, *Minnesota* 46 Kd
Bluefield, *W. Virginia* 45 Gb
Bluefields, *Nicaragua* 51 Cd
Blue Hills of Couteau, *Nfld.* 33 Of
Blue Mesa Res., *Colorado* 48 Dc
Blue Mt., *India* 89 Hd
Blue Mts., *Jamaica* 51 Dc
Blue Mts., *N.S.W.* 57 Kf
Blue Mts., *Oregon* 47 Dc
Blue Mts., *Pennsylvania* 44 Cb
Blue Nile, *Sudan* 97 Gb
Bluenose, L., *N.W.T.* 38 Oa
Blue R., *British Columbia* 38 Jf
Blue Ridge, *Alberta* 36 Bd
Blue Ridge, Mts., *U.S.A.* 43 Kd
Blue River, *B.C.* 39 Oj
Blue Sea Lake, *Quebec* 35 Of
Blue Stack Mts., *Eire* 63 Bf
Bluff, *New Zealand* 55 Bg
Bluff, *Utah* 42 Ed
Bluff Knoll, *W. Australia* 56 Cf
Bluffton, *Alberta* 36 Cf
Blumenau, *Brazil* 54 Gc
Blumenhof, *Saskatchewan* 36 Kh
Blyth, *England* 62 Ge
Blyth, *Ontario* 34 Jj
Blytheville, *Arkansas* 49 Ne
Bo, *Sierra Leone* 98 Cg
Boac, *Philippines* 83 Hh
Boaco, *Nicaragua* 51 Bd
Boa Fé, *Brazil* 52 Ce
Bo'ai, *China* 84 Fe
Boakview, *Ontario* 34 Kg
Boardman, *N. Carolina* 45 Hc
Boa Vista, *Brazil* 52 Ec
Bobcaygeon, *Ontario* 35 Mh
Bobo Dioulasso, *Upper Volta* 98 Ef
Bobolice, *Poland* 69 Gb
Bobonong, *Botswana* 95 Dd
Bobrov, *U.S.S.R.* 81 Ee
Bobruysk, *Byelorussia* 80 Fe
Boca do Acre, *Brazil* 52 De
Boca do Copana, *Brazil* 52 Ee
Bocas del Toro, *Panama* 51 Ce
Bochnia, *Poland* 69 Jd
Bocholt, *Belgium* 64 Dc
Bocholt, *West Germany* 68 Bc
Bochum, *West Germany* 68 Bc
Bodaybo, *U.S.S.R.* 79 Lc
Boden, *Sweden* 66 Jd
Boden See, *Switz./Germany* 65 Ea
Boderg L., *Eire* 63 Bg
Bodmin, *England* 63 Dk
Bodmin Moor, *England* 63 Dk
Bodo, *Alberta* 36 Gf
Bodø, *Norway* 66 Fc
Boende, *Zaire* 96 Ee
Boertange, *Netherlands* 64 Ea
Bogalusa, *Louisiana* 49 Ng
Bogandé, *Upper Volta* 98 Ef
Bogart, Mt., *Alberta* 36 Bh
Bogbonga, *Zaire* 96 Dd
Bogda Shan, *China* 82 Ab
Boggeragh Mts., *Eire* 63 Ah
Boggy Creek, *Oklahoma* 49 Je
Bogong, Mt., *Victoria* 57 Jg
Bogor, *Java* 83 Em
Bogorodsk, *U.S.S.R.* 81 Jd
Bogorodskoye, *U.S.S.R.* 79 Pc
Bogotá, *Colombia* 52 Cc
Bogotal, *U.S.S.R.* 78 Hc
Bogra, *Bangladesh* 91 Gc
Bo Hai, *China* 84 Jc
Boharm, *Saskatchewan* 37 Mh
Bohemia, *Czechoslovakia* 68 Ed
Böhmer Wald, *Ger./Czech.* 68 Ed
Bohol, *Philippines* 83 Hj
Boiacu, *Brazil* 52 Ed
Boiestown, *New Brunswick* 32 Fg
Boigu, I., *Torres Str., Qnsld.* 57 Ha
Boim, *Brazil* 53 Fd
Bois, L. des, *N.W.T.* 38 Lb
Bois Blanc I., *Michigan* 40 Dc
Boisdale, *Nova Scotia* 33 Mg
Boisé, *Idaho* 47 Ed
Boise City, *Oklahoma* 48 Fd
Boissevain, *Manitoba* 37 Rj
Bojnurd, *Iran* 93 Gb
Bokaro, *India* 91 Ed
Boké, *Guinea* 98 Cf
Bokki, *Cameroun* 99 Hg
Bokn Fd., *Norway* 67 Ag
Bokoro, *Chad* 99 Jf
Bolangir, *India* 89 Fd
Bolan Pass, *Pakistan* 88 Cc
Bolbee, *France* 72 Db
Bole, *Ghana* 98 Eg
Bölebyn, *Sweden* 66 Jd
Bolger, *Quebec* 35 Od
Bolgrad, *Ukraine* 80 Fj
Bolintin, *Romania* 76 Eb
Bolívar, *Argentina* 54 De
Bolívar, *Colombia* 52 Bc
Bolivar, *Missouri* 49 Ld
Bolivia, *S. America* 52 Dg
Bolkow, *Ontario* 34 Gd
Bollon, *Queensland* 57 Je
Bollstabruk, *Sweden* 66 Ge
Bolmen, L., *Sweden* 67 Eh
Bolobo, *Zaire* 96 De
Bologna, *Italy* 74 Cc
Bologoye, *U.S.S.R.* 80 Jc
Bolomba, *Zaire* 96 Dd
Bolotnoye, *U.S.S.R.* 78 Hc
Bolsena, L. di, *Italy* 74 Cd
Bolsheretsk, *U.S.S.R.* 79 Qc
Bol'shevik, Ostrov, *U.S.S.R.* 79 Ka
Bolshoy Lyakhovskiy, Ostrov, *U.S.S.R.* 79 Pa
Boltana, *Spain* 71 Fa
Bolton, *England* 63 Fg
Bolton, *Ontario* 35 Lj
Bolton L., *Manitoba* 37 Wd
Bolu, *Turkey* 92 Ba
Bolzano, *Italy* 74 Cb
Bomal, *Belgium* 64 Dd
Bombala, *New S. Wales* 57 Jg
Bombarral, *Portugal* 70 Ac
Bombay, *India* 88 De
Bom Futuro, *Brazil* 52 Ef
Bomhus, *Sweden* 67 Gf
Bom Jesus, *Brazil* 53 Je
Bømlo, *Norway* 67 Ag
Bomnak, *U.S.S.R.* 79 Mc
Bomoseen, L., *Vermont* 44 Da
Bon Accord, *Alberta* 36 De
Bonaduz, *Switzerland* 65 Eb
Bonaire, *Neth. Antilles* 51 Fd
Bonanza, *Nicaragua* 51 Cd
Bonarlaw, *Ontario* 35 Nh
Bonaventure, *Quebec* 32 Ge
Bonaventure, I. de, *Que.* 32 He
Bonavista & B., *Nfld.* 33 Te
Bondo, *Zaire* 96 Ed
Bondoukou, *Ivory Coast* 98 Eg
Bône. *See* Annaba
Bone, Teluk, *Celebes (Sulawesi)* 83 Hl
Bonfield, *Ontario* 35 Lf
Bongor, *Chad* 99 Jf
Bonham, *Texas* 49 Jf
Bonifacio, *Corsica* 75 Be
Bonin Is., *Pacific Ocean* 82 Me
Bonn, *West Germany* 68 Bc
Bonne Bay, *Newfoundland* 33 Pd
Bonne-Espérance, *Quebec* 33 Pb
Bonne Terre, *Missouri* 45 Bb
Bonnet Plume, R., *Y.T.* 38 Fc
Bonneval, *France* 72 Db
Bonneville Salt Flats, *Utah* 48 Ab
Bonnie Rock, *W. Australia* 56 Cf
Bonny, *France* 72 Ec
Bonny, *Nigeria* 98 Gh
Bonny River, *N.B.* 32 Fh
Bonnyville, *Alberta* 36 Gd
Bononi Mhai, *Vietnam* 87 Dd
Boom, *Belgium* 64 Cc
Boone, *Iowa* 49 La
Boone, *N. Carolina* 45 Gb
Booneville, *Mississippi* 45 Cc
Boon Tsagaan Nuur, *Mongolia* 82 Ca
Boonville, *Missouri* 49 Lc
Boonville, *New York* 44 Ca
Boothia, Gulf of, *N.W.T* 31 Ld
Boothia Pen., *N.W.T.* 30 Kc
Bopeechee, *S. Australia* 57 Ge
Bophuthatswana, *S. Africa* 95 Ce
Boquerón, *Cuba* 51 Dc
Boquete, *Panama* 51 Ce
Boramo, *Somalia* 97 Jc
Borås, *Sweden* 67 Eh
Borba, *Brazil* 52 Fd
Bordeaux, *France* 73 Cd
Bordeaux, *Quebec* 35 Rj
Borden, *P.E.I.* 32 Jg
Borden, *Saskatchewan* 36 Kf
Borden I., *N.W.T.* 30 Hb
Borden Pen., *N.W.T.* 31 Lc
Borders, reg., *Scotland* 62 Fe
Bordertown, *S. Australia* 57 Gg
Borgå, *Finland* 66 Fd
Børgefjell, *Norway* 66 Ed
Borger, *Netherlands* 64 Eb
Borger, *Texas* 48 Ge
Borgholm, *Sweden* 67 Gh
Borikhone, *Laos* 87 Cc
Borisoglebsk, *U.S.S.R.* 81 Ee
Borisov, *Byelorussia* 80 Fd
Bo River Post, *Sudan* 99 Lg
Borja, *Spain* 71 Eb
Borjas Blancas, *Spain* 71 Fb
Borkum, *West Germany* 68 Bb
Borlänge, *Sweden* 67 Ff
Borneo (Kalimantan), *Indonesia* 83 Fk
Bornholm, I., *Denmark* 67 Fj
Borodino, *U.S.S.R.* 80 Jd
Borogontsy, *U.S.S.R.* 79 Nb
Borongan, *Philippines* 83 Jh
Borovichi, *U.S.S.R.* 80 Hb
Borroloola, *N. Terr.* 57 Gc
Borskoye, *U.S.S.R.* 81 Kd
Borūjerd, *Iran* 92 Ec
Bor Yuryakh, *U.S.S.R.* 79 La
Borzya, *U.S.S.R.* 79 Lc
Bosaso, *Somalia* 97 Kb
Bósco, *Switzerland* 65 Db
Boscobel, *Wisconsin* 40 Ad
Bose, *China* 85 Cl
Boshan, *China* 84 Hd
Bosiljgrad, *Yugoslavia* 76 Dc
Boskoop, *Netherlands* 64 Cb
Bosna-Hercegovina, *Yugosl.* 76 Ab
Bosobolo, *Zaire* 96 Dd
Bōso Hanto, *Japan* 86 Gg
Bosoli, *Botswana* 95 Dd
Bosporus, *Turkey* 92 Aa
Bossier City, *Louisiana* 49 Lf
Bosso, *Niger* 99 Hf
Bostan, *Pakistan* 88 Cb
Boston, *England* 63 Hh
Boston, *Massachusetts* 40 Ld
Boston Bar, *B.C.* 39 Nl
Boston Mts., *Arkansas* 49 Le
Boswarlos, *Newfoundland* 33 Oe
Boswell, *B.C.* 39 Pl
Botera, *Angola* 96 Cg
Botha, *Alberta* 36 Ef
Bothaville, *O.F.S.* 95 De
Bothnia, G. of, *N.-W. Europe* 67 Hf
Bothwell, *Ontario* 34 Jk
Botswana, *S. Africa* 95 Cd
Botten, *Alberta* 39 Oh
Botucatu, *Brazil* 53 Hh
Botwood, *Newfoundland* 33 Rd
Bouaké, *Ivory Coast* 98 Eg
Bouar, *Cent. Afr. Rep.* 99 Jg
Bou Arfa, *Morocco* 98 Eb
Boucher, L., *Quebec* 33 Nb
Boucherville, *Quebec* 35 Th
Boucherville, Iles de, *Que.* 35 Th
Bouches-du-Rhône, *France* 73 Fe
Bouchette, *Quebec* 35 Pf
Bou Djébéha, *Mali* 98 Ee
Boudry, *Switzerland* 65 Bb
Bougainville, *Solomon Is.* 102 Eh
Bougaroun C., *Algeria* 98 Ga
Bougie & G. of. *See* Bejaïa
Bougouni, *Mali* 98 Df
Bouillon, *Belgium* 64 De
Boulain, L., *Quebec* 33 Lc
Boulder, *Colorado* 48 Eb
Boulder, *W. Australia* 56 Df
Bouleau, L. au, *Quebec* 35 Ne
Boulia, *Queensland* 57 Gd
Boulogne, *France* 72 Da
Bouna, *Ivory Coast* 98 Eg
Boundary B., *B.C.* 39 Hm
Boundary Bay, *B.C.* 39 Hm
Boundary Mts., *Me./Que.* 32 Bh
Boundary Plat., *Mont./Sask.* 36 Jj
Bountiful, *Utah* 48 Bb
Bounty, *Saskatchewan* 36 Kg
Bounty Is., *Pacific Ocean* 102 Gm
Bourbonnais, *France* 72 Ec
Bourem, *Mali* 98 Ee
Bourg, *France* 72 Fc
Bourg Argental, *France* 73 Fd
Bourges, *France* 72 Ec
Bourget, L. du, *France* 72 Fd
Bourgmont, *Quebec* 35 Pd
Bourgogne, *France* 72 Fc
Bourg St. Pierre, *Switz.* 65 Cc
Bourke, *N.S.W.* 57 Jf
Bourkes, *Ontario* 34 Kd
Bourlamaque, *Quebec* 35 Nd
Bourne, C., *N.W.T.* 31 Ka
Bournemouth, *England* 63 Fk
Bouvet I., *Atlantic Ocean* 104 Cd
Bovigny, *Belgium* 64 Dd
Bovino, *Italy* 75 Ee
Bowbells, *N. Dakota* 46 Fa
Bowden, *Alberta* 36 Cg
Bowen, *Queensland* 57 Jc
Bowen I., *B.C.* 39 Ml
Bowie, *Texas* 49 Jf
Bow Island, *Alberta* 36 Fj
Bowling Green, *Kentucky* 45 Db
Bowling Green, *Missouri* 49 Mc
Bowling Green, *Ohio* 40 Ee
Bowling Green, *Virginia* 45 Ja
Bowman, *N. Dakota* 46 Fb
Bowman B., *N.W.T.* 31 Md
Bowman I., *Antarctica* 104 Hc
Bowmanville, *Ontario* 35 Mj
Bowness, *Alberta* 36 Cg
Bow R., *Alberta* 36 Dh
Bowron Lake Prov. Park, *B.C.* 39 Nj
Bowron R., *B.C.* 39 Nj
Bowser L., *B.C.* 39 Jg
Bowsman, *Manitoba* 37 Qf
Bowyer I., *B.C.* 39 Gk
Box Elder, *Montana* 46 Ba
Boxholm, *Sweden* 67 Fg
Boxmeer, *Netherlands* 64 Dc
Boxtel, *Netherlands* 64 Dc
Boyang, *China* 85 Hh
Boyd, *Manitoba* 37 Vc
Boyd L., *N.W.T.* 38 We
Boyd's Cove, *Nfld.* 33 Sd
Boyle, *Alberta* 36 Ed
Boylston, *Nova Scotia* 33 Lh
Boyne, R., *Eire* 63 Cg
Boyne City, *Michigan* 40 Dc
Boyoma Falls, *Zaire* 96 Fd
Bozeman, *Montana* 46 Bc
Bozoum, *Cent. Afr. Rep.* 99 Jg
Bra, *Italy* 74 Ac
Brabant, *Belgium* 64 Cd
Brabant, Noord, *Netherlands* 64 Dc
Brabant I., *Saskatchewan* 37 Ob
Brac, *Yugoslavia* 74 Fd
Bracadale L., *Scotland* 62 Cc
Bracebridge, *Ontario* 35 Lg
Brach, *Libya* 99 Hc
Bräcke, *Sweden* 66 Fe
Bracken, *Saskatchewan* 36 Jj
Bracken L., *Manitoba* 37 Se
Brad, *Romania* 76 Da
Braddock, *N. Dakota* 46 Gb
Braddock, *Pennsylvania* 44 Ab
Bradford, *England* 63 Fg
Bradford, *Ontario* 35 Lh
Bradford, *Pennsylvania* 44 Ab
Bradore Bay, *Quebec* 33 Pb
Brador Hills, *Quebec* 33 Pb
Bradwardine, *Manitoba* 37 Rj
Bradwell, *Saskatchewan* 36 Lg
Braemar, *Scotland* 62 Ed
Braga, *Portugal* 70 Ab
Bragado, *Argentina* 54 De
Bragança, *Portugal* 70 Bb
Bragança Paulista, *Brazil* 53 Hh
Brahmanbaria, *Bangladesh* 89 Hd
Brahmaputra, *India* 89 Hc
Braidwood, *Illinois* 40 Be
Brail, *Switzerland* 65 Fb
Brăila, *Romania* 76 Fb
Braine l'Alleud, *Belgium* 64 Cd
Braine le Comte, *Belgium* 64 Cd
Brainerd, *Minnesota* 46 Kb
Bralorne, *B.C.* 39 Mk
Brampton, *Ontario* 35 Lj
Branch, *Newfoundland* 33 Tg
Branchville, *S. Carolina* 45 Gd
Brandenburg, *East Germany* 68 Eb
Brandon, *Manitoba* 37 Sj
Brandon Head, *Eire* 63 Ah
Brandsen, *Argentina* 54 Ee
Brandvlei, *Cape Province* 95 Cf
Branford, *Florida* 45 Ff
Braniewo, *Poland* 69 Ha
Bransfield Str., *Antarctica* 104 Tc
Brańsk, *Poland* 69 Kb
Brant, *Alberta* 36 Dh
Brantford, *Ontario* 34 Kj
Brantôme, *France* 73 Dd
Bras d'Or, *Nova Scotia* 33 Mg
Bras d'Or L., *Nova Scotia* 33 Mh
Brasília, *Brazil* 53 Hg
Brasília Legal, *Brazil* 53 Fd
Braşov, *Romania* 76 Eb
Brassus, le, *Switzerland* 65 Bb
Bratislava, *Czechoslovakia* 69 Gd
Bratsk, *U.S.S.R.* 79 Kc
Bratten, *Alberta* 39 Oh
Brattleboro, *Vermont* 44 Da
Braunau, *Austria* 68 Ed
Braunlage, *West Germany* 68 Dc
Braunschweig, *W. Germany* 68 Db
Braunwald, *Switzerland* 65 Db
Brava, *Somalia* 97 Jd
Brawley, *California* 47 Fj
Bray, *Eire* 63 Cg
Bray Head, *Eire* 63 Aj
Bray I., *N.W.T.* 31 Md
Brazeau, *Alberta* 39 Pj
Brazeau, Mt., *Alberta* 39 Pj
Brazeau R., *Alberta* 39 Pj
Brazil, *Indiana* 49 Oc
Brazil, *S. America* 53
Brazil Lake, *Nova Scotia* 32 Gk
Brazos R., *Texas* 49 Kh
Brazos Santiago, *Texas* 48 Jj
Brazzaville, *Congo* 96 De
Brčko, *Yugoslavia* 76 Bb
Bream B., *New Zealand* 55 Ea
Brébeuf, L., *Quebec* 32 Be
Brechin, *Ontario* 35 Lh
Brechin. *Scotland* 62 Fd
Breckenridge, *Minnesota* 46 Jb
Brecknock, *Chile* 54 Bh
Břeclav, *Czechoslovakia* 69 Gd
Brecon, *Wales* 63 Ej
Brecon Beacons, *Wales* 63 Ej
Breda, *Netherlands* 64 Cc
Bredasdorp, *Cape Province* 95 Cf
Bredenbury, *Saskatchewan* 37 Ph
Bredene, *Belgium* 64 Ac
Bredy, *U.S.S.R.* 81 Qd
Bree, *Belgium* 64 Dc
Breidha fjördhur, *Iceland* 66 Tm
Breil, *France* 73 Ge
Breithorn, *Switzerland* 65 Cb
Brejo, *Brazil* 53 Jd
Bremangerland, *Norway* 66 Af
Bremen, *West Germany* 68 Cb
Bremerhaven, *W. Germany* 68 Cb
Bremerton, *Washington* 47 Bb
Bremgarten, *Switzerland* 65 Da
Brenham, *Texas* 49 Jg
Brenner Pass, *Austria/Italy* 74 Cb
Breno, *Italy* 74 Cc
Brent, *Ontario* 35 Mf
Brescia, *Italy* 74 Cc
Breskens, *Netherlands* 64 Bc
Breslau. *See* Wroclaw
Bressay I., *Scotland* 62 Qb
Bressuire, *France* 72 Cc
Brest, *France* 72 Ab
Brest (Brest-Litovsk), *Byelorussia* 80 Ce
Bretagne, *France* 72 Bb
Breţcu, *Romania* 76 Fa
Breton, *Alberta* 36 Ce
Breton, C., *Nova Scotia* 33 Nh
Breton Sound, *Louisiana* 49 Nh
Breugel, *Netherlands* 64 Dc
Breuil-Cervinia, *Italy* 65 Cc
Brevard, *N. Carolina* 45 Fc
Brevik, *Norway* 67 Cg
Brewarrina, *N.S.W.* 57 Je
Brewer, *Maine* 32 Dj
Brewster Mt., *Antarctica* 104 Lb
Brewton, *Alabama* 45 De
Brežice, *Yugoslavia* 74 Ec
Březová, *Czechoslovakia* 69 Gd
Bria, *Cent. Afr. Rep.* 99 Kg
Briançon, *France* 73 Gd
Briare, *France* 72 Ec
Briçonnet, L., *Quebec* 33 Mb
Bridgehampton, *New York* 44 Db
Bridgeport, *Connecticut* 40 Ke
Bridgeport, *Nebraska* 48 Fb
Bridgeport L., *Texas* 49 Jf
Bridge R., *B.C.* 39 Mk
Bridgeton, *New Jersey* 44 Cc
Bridgetown, *Nova Scotia* 32 Gj
Bridgeville, *Nova Scotia* 32 Kh
Bridgewater, *Nova Scotia* 32 Hj
Bridgman C., *Arctic Ocean* 41 Na
Bridgton, *Maine* 32 Bj
Bridgwater, *England* 63 Ej
Bridgwater Bay, *England* 63 Ej
Bridlington, *England* 63 Gf
Brielle, *Netherlands* 64 Cc
Brienz, *Switzerland* 65 Db
Brienzer See, *Switzerland* 65 Cb
Briercrest, *Saskatchewan* 37 Mh
Briereville, *Alberta* 36 Fd
Brier I., *Nova Scotia* 32 Fj
Brig, *Switzerland* 65 Cb
Brigden, *Ontario* 34 Hk
Brigels, *Switzerland* 65 Eb
Brigham, *Utah* 48 Ab
Brigham, *Utah* 47 Ge
Brighton, *Colorado* 48 Eb
Brighton, *England* 63 Gk
Brighton, *Ontario* 35 Nh
Brignoles, *France* 73 Ge
Brindaban, *India* 90 Eg
Brindisi, *Italy* 75 Ge
Brinkley, *Arkansas* 45 Bc
Brione, *Switzerland* 65 Db
Brion I., *Quebec* 33 Lf
Brioude, *France* 73 Ed
Brisbane, *Queensland* 57 Ke
Brissago, *Switzerland* 65 Db
Bristol, *England* 63 Fj
Bristol, *New Brunswick* 32 Eg
Bristol, *Pennsylvania* 44 Cb
Bristol, *Quebec* 35 Og
Bristol, *Rhode Island* 44 Eb
Bristol, *Tennessee* 45 Fb
Bristol Bay, *Alaska* 43 Wm
Bristol Channel, *England* 63 Di
Bristol I., *S. Sandwich Is.* 104 Ad
Britannia Beach, *B.C.* 39 Ml
British Columbia, *Canada* 30 Gf
British Empire Range, *N.W.T.* 31 La
British Honduras. *See* Belize
British Isles, *N.-W. Europe* 60 Ee
Brito, *Nicaragua* 51 Bd
Briton Cove, *Nova Scotia* 33 Mg
Britstown, *Cape Province* 95 Cf
Britt, *Ontario* 34 Kg
Brive-la-Gaillarde, *France* 73 Dd
Briviesca, *Spain* 70 Da
Brno, *Czechoslovakia* 69 Gd
Broach, L., *Quebec* 32 Dc
Broadacres, *Saskatchewan* 36 Jf
Broadalbin, *New York* 40 Jd
Broad B., *Scotland* 62 Cb
Broadback, R., *Quebec* 35 Pb
Broadback R., *Quebec* 31 Mg
Broadford, *Pennsylvania* 44 Ab
Broadford, *Scotland* 62 Dc
Broadus, *Montana* 46 Ec
Broadview, *Saskatchewan* 37 Ph
Brochet, *Manitoba* 37 Qa
Brochet, L., *Manitoba* 38 Xf
Brochet, L. au, *Quebec* 32 Cd
Brock, *Saskatchewan* 36 Jg
Brock, R., *Quebec* 35 Qb
Brocket, *Alberta* 36 Dj
Brock I., *N.W.T.* 30 Hb
Brockton, *Massachusetts* 44 Ea
Brockville, *Ontario* 35 Ph
Brod, *Yugoslavia* 76 Cd
Brod, *Yugoslavia* 76 Ab
Broderick, *Saskatchewan* 36 Lg
Brodeur Peninsula, *N.W.T.* 31 Lc
Brodhead, *Wisconsin* 40 Bd
Brodick, *Scotland* 62 De
Broek-in-Waterland, *Netherlands* 64 Db
Broglio, *Switzerland* 65 Db
Broken Bow, *Nebraska* 49 Hb
Broken Bow Res., *Oklahoma* 49 Ke
Broken Hill, *N.S.W.* 57 Hf
Bromberg. *See* Bydgoszcz
Bromhead, *Saskatchewan* 37 Oj
Bromptonville, *Quebec* 40 Lc
Bronte, *Ontario* 35 Lj
Bronte, *Sicily* 75 Eg
Brookfield, *Missouri* 49 Lc
Brookfield, *Nova Scotia* 32 Jh
Brookhaven, *Mississippi* 49 Mg
Brooking, *Saskatchewan* 37 Nj
Brookings, *Oregon* 47 Ad
Brookings, *S. Dakota* 46 Jc
Brooklin, *Ontario* 35 Mj
Brooklyn, *Iowa* 49 Lb
Brooklyn, *New York* 44 Db
Brooklyn, *Nova Scotia* 32 Hj
Brookmere, *B.C.* 39 Nl
Brooks, *Alberta* 36 Fh
Brooks Brook, *Y.T.* 38 Ge
Brooksby, *Saskatchewan* 37 Ne
Brook's Point, *Philippines* 83 Gj
Brooks Range, *Alaska* 43 Xl
Brookville, *Pennsylvania* 44 Ab
Broom, L., *Scotland* 62 Dc
Broom B., *Quebec* 33 Kd
Broome, *W. Australia* 56 Dc
Brora, *Scotland* 62 Eb
Brossard, *Quebec* 35 Tk
Brothers, The, *Red Sea* 92 Bd
Broughty Ferry, *Scotland* 62 Fd
Broumov, *Czechoslovakia* 69 Gc
Brouwershaven, *Neth.* 64 Bc
Brown, Mt., *S. Australia* 57 Gf
Browning, *Saskatchewan* 37 Pj
Brownlee, *Saskatchewan* 37 Mh
Brownrigg, *Ontario* 34 Jc
Brownsburg, *Quebec* 35 Qg
Brown's Valley, *Minnesota* 46 Jc
Brownsville, *Tennessee* 45 Cc
Brownsville, *Texas* 48 Jk
Brownville Jct., *Maine* 32 Ch
Brownwood, *Texas* 49 Hg
Brownwood, L., *Texas* 49 Hg
Brozas, *Spain* 70 Bc
Bruce, *Alberta* 36 Ee
Bruce, Mt., *W. Australia* 56 Cd
Brucefield, *Ontario* 34 Jj
Bruce Mines, *Ontario* 34 Gf
Bruce Pen., *Ontario* 34 Jg
Bruck, *Austria* 68 Ee
Bruck an der Mur, *Austria* 68 Fe
Bruederheim, *Alberta* 36 Ee
Bruges, *Belgium* 64 Bc
Brugg, *Switzerland* 65 Da
Brugge. *See* Bruges
Bruin Pk., *Utah* 48 Bc
Brûlé, *Alberta* 39 Oj
Brûlé, L., *Quebec* 35 Nf
Brûlé, L., *Quebec* 32 Ja
Bruly, *Belgium* 64 Ce
Brumado, *Brazil* 53 Jf
Brummen, *Netherlands* 64 Eb
Brunei, *Borneo (Kalimantan)* 83 Fk
Brunette, I., *Newfoundland* 33 Rf
Brunette Downs, *N. Terr.* 57 Gc
Brunflo, *Sweden* 66 Fe
Brunkild, *Manitoba* 37 Uj
Brunn. *See* Brno
Brunnen, *Switzerland* 65 Da
Brunner, *New Zealand* 55 Ce
Bruno, *Saskatchewan* 37 Mf
Brunssum, *Netherlands* 64 Dd
Brunswick, *Georgia, U.S.A.* 45 Ge
Brunswick, *Maine* 32 Bk
Brunswick, *Maryland* 44 Bc
Brunswick. *See* Braunschweig
Brunswick, Pen. de, *Chile* 54 Bh
Brunswick B., *W. Australia* 56 Dc
Brunswick L., *Ontario* 34 Gc
Bruny I., *Tasmania* 57 Jh
Brusartsi, *Bulgaria* 76 Dc
Brush, *Colorado* 48 Fb
Brusio, *Switzerland* 65 Fb
Brussel, *Belgium* 64 Cd
Brussels, *Ontario* 34 Jj
Bruzual, *Venezuela* 52 Db
Bryan Coast, *Antarctica* 104 Rb
Bryansk, *U.S.S.R.* 80 Je
Bryce Canyon Nat. Park, *Utah* 47 Gg
Bryson, *Quebec* 40 Hc
Bryson, L., *Quebec* 35 Of
Bryson City, *N. Carolina* 45 Fc
Brzeg, *Poland* 69 Gc
Brzesko, *Poland* 69 Jd
Bsharri, *Lebanon* 94 Dc
Bua, *Angola* 96 Cf
Buayan, *Philippines* 83 Jj
Bubasa, *Ethiopia* 97 Jc
Bubiyan, *Persian Gulf* 92 Ed
Bubulu, *Uganda* 97 Gd
Bucaramanga, *Colombia* 52 Cb
Buchach, *Ukraine* 80 Dg
Buchanan, *Liberia* 98 Cg
Buchanan, *Saskatchewan* 37 Pg
Buchanan, L., *Queensland* 57 Jd
Buchanan L., *Texas* 49 Hg
Buchan G., *N.W.T.* 31 Mc
Buchan Ness, *Scotland* 62 Fc
Buchans, *Newfoundland* 33 Qe
Buchans Junction, *Nfld.* 33 Qe
Buchardo, *Argentina* 54 Dd
Bucharest. *See* Bucuresti
Buchs, *Switzerland* 65 Ea
Buckhannon, *West Virginia* 40 Ff
Buckie, *Scotland* 62 Fc
Buckingham, *Eng.* 63 Gj
Buckingham, *Quebec* 35 Pg
Buckingham, *Quebec* 40 Jc
Buck L., *Alberta* 36 Ce
Buckland L., *Manitoba* 37 Va
Bucksport, *Maine* 32 Dj
Buctouche, *N.B.* 32 Hg
Bucuresti, *Romania* 76 Fb
Bud, *Norway* 66 Bc
Buda, *Texas* 49 Jg
Budaia, *Arabia* 92 De
Budapest, *Hungary* 69 He
Budaun, *India* 91 Ba
Bud Bud, *India* 91 Fd
Buddh Gaya, *India* 91 Ec
Bude, *England* 63 Dk
Budeşti, *Romania* 76 Fb
Budhana, *India* 90 Ef
Budva, *Yugoslavia* 76 Bc
Buea, *Cameroun* 99 Gh
Buenaventura, *Colombia* 52 Bc
Buenaventura, *Mexico* 50 Cb
Buena Vista, *Georgia, U.S.A.* 45 Ed
Buena Vista, *Virginia* 45 Hb
Buenos Aires, *Argentina* 54 Ed
Buenos Aires, *Colombia* 52 Cd
Buenos Aires, L., *Chile/Argentina* 54 Bg
Bufa, *Mexico* 50 Dc
Buffalo, *Alberta* 36 Gh
Buffalo, *Minnesota* 46 Lc
Buffalo, *Missouri* 45 Ab
Buffalo, *New York* 40 Gd
Buffalo, *S. Dakota* 46 Fc
Buffalo, *Wyoming* 46 Dc
Buffalo, R., *Alta./N.W.T.* 38 Qf
Buffalo Gap, *Saskatchewan* 37 Mj
Buffalo L., *Alberta* 36 Ef
Buffalo L., *N.W.T.* 38 Qe
Buffalo Narrows, *Sask.* 36 Jc
Buffalo River, *N.W.T.* 38 Qe
Buff City, *Tennessee* 45 Fb
Bug, *Poland/Byelorussia* 69 Jb
Buga, *Colombia* 52 Bc
Bugti, *Pakistan* 88 Cc
Bugulchan, *U.S.S.R.* 81 Md
Bugulma, *U.S.S.R.* 81 Lc
Buguruslan, *U.S.S.R.* 81 Ld
Builth Wells, *Wales* 63 Eh
Buinsk, *U.S.S.R.* 81 Jc
Buique, *Brazil* 53 Ke
Buir Nur, *China* 82 Ga
Buitenpost, *Netherlands* 64 Ea
Bujumbura, *Burundi* 97 Fe
Buka, *Solomon Is.* 102 Eh
Bukama, *Zaire* 96 Ff
Bukavu, *Zaire* 97 Fe
Bukene, *Tanzania* 97 Ge
Bukhara, *Uzbekistan* 78 Fe
Bukoba, *Tanzania* 97 Ge
Buksa Duar, *India* 91 Gb
Bukwimba, *Tanzania* 97 Ge
Bula, *Seram I., Indonesia* 83 Kl
Bülach, *Switzerland* 65 Da
Bulan, *Philippines* 83 Hh
Bulandshahr, *India* 90 Ef
Bulawayo, *Zimbabwe* 95 Dd
Bulgan, *Mongolia* 82 Da
Bulgaria, *S. Europe* 61 Nh
Bulkley R., *B.C.* 39 Kh
Bullange, *Belgium* 64 Ed
Bullen, R., *N.W.T.* 38 Wc
Buller R., *New Zealand* 55 Cd
Bullfinch, *W. Australia* 56 Cf
Bulloo Creek, *Queensland* 57 He
Bull R., *B.C.* 36 Bj
Bull Shoals L., *Arkansas* 49 Ld
Bulnes, *Chile* 54 Be
Bulo Burti, *Somalia* 97 Kd
Bulsar, *India* 88 Dd
Bulu, *Borneo (Kalimantan)* 83 Gk
Bulun, *U.S.S.R.* 79 Ma
Bulwark, *Alberta* 36 Ff
Bulyea, *Saskatchewan* 37 Nh
Bumba, *Zaire* 96 Ed
Bumpus, Mt., *N.W.T.* 38 Ra
Buna, *Kenya* 97 Hd
Buna, *Papua New Guinea* 57 Ja
Bunbah, *Libya* 99 Kb
Bunbah, G. of, *Libya* 99 Kb
Bunbury, *W. Australia* 56 Cf
Buncrana, *Eire* 62 Ce
Bundaberg, *Queensland* 57 Kd
Bundi, *India* 88 Ec
Bundooma, *N. Terr.* 57 Fd
Bundoran, *Eire* 63 Bf
Bungay, *England* 63 Hh
Bungo, *Angola* 96 Df
Bungo Suidō, *Japan* 86 Ch
Bunguran Kep., *Indonesia* 83 Ek

Bunker, Missouri 45 Bb
Bunkie, Louisiana 49 Lg
Buntok, Borneo (Kalimantan) 83 Gl
Buochs, Switzerland 65 Db
Buol, Celebes (Sulawesi) 83 Hk
Buolkalakh, U.S.S.R. 79 La
Buorkhaya, Guba, U.S.S.R. 79 Na
Buraimi, United Arab Emirates 93 Ge
Bur Akaba, Somalia 97 Jd
Buram, Sudan 99 Lf
Burang, China 88 Fb
Burao, Somalia 97 Kc
Buraq, Syria 94 Ed
Buraydah, Arabia 92 Dd
Burd, Jebel, Arabia 92 Cd
Burdekin, R., Queensland 57 Jc
Burden, Mt., B.C. 39 Mg
Burdett, Alberta 36 Fj
Burdia, Sudan 99 Lf
Burdur, Turkey 92 Bb
Burdwan, India 91 Fd
Bureå, Sweden 66 Jd
Bureinskiy Khrebet, U.S.S.R. 79 Nd
Buren, Netherlands 64 Dc
Büren, Switzerland 65 Ca
Bureya, U.S.S.R. 79 Nd
Burford, Ontario 34 Kj
Burgas, Bulgaria 76 Fc
Bur Gavo, Somalia 97 Je
Burgaw, N. Carolina 45 Jc
Burgdorf, Switzerland 65 Ca
Burgenland, Austria 69 Ge
Burgeo, Newfoundland 33 Pf
Burgersdorp, Cape Prov. 95 Df
Burgh, Netherlands 64 Bc
Burgos, Spain 70 Da
Burhanpur, India 88 Ed
Buria, India 90 Ee
Burias, Philippines 83 Hh
Burin & Pen., Nfld. 33 Rf
Buriti, Brazil 53 Jd
Burke Channel, B.C. 39 Kj
Burkesville, Kentucky 45 Eb
Burketown, Queensland 57 Gc
Burkeville, Virginia 45 Hb
Burk's Falls, Ontario 35 Lg
Burley, Idaho 48 Aa
Burlington, Colorado 48 Fc
Burlington, Iowa 49 Mb
Burlington, Newfoundland 33 Rd
Burlington, New Jersey 44 Cb
Burlington, Ontario 35 Lj
Burlington, Vermont 40 Kc
Burlington, Wisconsin 40 Bd
Burlyuk, U.S.S.R. 80 Hj
Burma, S. Asia 89 Hd
Burmis, Alberta 36 Cj
Burnaby, & L., B.C. 39 Hl
Burnak, U.S.S.R. 81 Ee
Burnie, Tasmania 57 Jh
Burnley, England 63 Fg
Burns, Oregon 47 Dd
Burnside, R., N.W.T. 38 Tb
Burns Lake, B.C. 39 Lh
Burnsville, New Brunswick 32 Gf
Burnt River, Ontario 35 Mh
Burntwood L. & R., Manitoba 37 Rc
Burqin, China 82 Aa
Burr, Saskatchewan 37 Mf
Burrard Inlet, B.C. 39 Gi
Burriana, Spain 71 Ec
Burrinjuck Res., N.S.W. 57 Jg
Burrundie, N. Terr. 56 Fb
Bursa, Turkey 92 Aa
Burstall, Saskatchewan 36 Hh
Burt L., Michigan 40 Dc
Burtonport, Eire 62 Bf
Burton-upon-Trent, England 63 Fh
Burträsk, Sweden 66 Jd
Burtscheid, W. Germany 64 Ed
Burtts Corner, N.B. 32 Fg
Buru, Indonesia 83 Jl
Burullus L., Egypt 99 Mb
Burum, South Yemen 92 Eg
Burundi, Central Africa 97 Fe
Burutu, Nigeria 98 Gg
Burwash, Ontario 34 Kf
Burwash Landing, Y.T. 38 De
Bury, England 63 Fg
Bury, Quebec 35 Tg
Buryatskaya A.S.S.R., U.S.S.R. 79 Kc
Bury St Edmunds, England 63 Hh
Busby, Alberta 36 De
Busembatia, Uganda 97 Gd
Būshehr (Bushire), Iran 93 Fd
Bushell, Saskatchewan 38 Tf
Bushnell, Florida 45 Ff
Bushnell, Ontario 35 Lf
Businga, Zaire 96 Ed
Busra, Syria 94 Ee
Bussa, Nigeria 98 Ff
Busselton, W. Australia 56 Cf
Bussum, Netherlands 64 Db
Busu Djanoa, Zaire 96 Ed
Buta, Zaire 96 Ed
Butana, India 90 Ef
Buta Ranquil, Argentina 54 Ce
Butare, Rwanda 97 Fe
Butaritari, Kiribati 102 Gg
Butedale, B.C. 39 Jj
Bute I., Scotland 62 De
Bute Inlet, B.C. 39 Lk
Bütgenbach, Belgium 64 Ed
Buthidaung, Burma 89 Hd
Butler, Missouri 49 Kc
Butler, Pennsylvania 40 Ge
Butschwil, Switzerland 65 Ea
Butte, Montana 47 Gc
Buttes, Switzerland 65 Bb
Buttle L., B.C. 39 Ll
Button Is., N.W.T. 31 Ne
Butuan, Philippines 83 Jj
Butung, Indonesia 83 Hl
Buturlinovka, U.S.S.R. 81 Ee
Buxar, India 91 Ec
Buxton, England 63 Fg
Buy, U.S.S.R. 80 Mb
Buyaga, U.S.S.R. 79 Mc
Buyck, Minnesota 36 Kb
Buzancais, France 72 Dc
Buzău, Romania 76 Fb
Buzuluk, U.S.S.R. 81 Ld
Buzzards B., Massachusetts 44 Eb
Byam Martin Channel, N.W.T. 30 Jb
Byam Martin I., N.W.T. 30 Jb
Bydgoszcz, Poland 69 Gb
Byelaya, R., U.S.S.R. 81 Lc
Byelokatay, U.S.S.R. 81 Pc
Byelorussia (Belorusskaya S.S.R.), U.S.S.R. 80 Ee
Byelozersk, U.S.S.R. 80 Ka
Byemoor, Alberta 36 Ef
Byers Mt., Ontario 34 Jd
Bygland, Norway 67 Bg
Byglandsfjord, Norway 67 Bg
Bylot I., N.W.T. 31 Mc
Byng Inlet, Ontario 34 Kg
Byrd Land, Antarctica 104 Pb
Byron, C., N.S.W. 57 Ke
Byron B., N.W.T. 38 Ta
Byske, Sweden 66 Jd
Bytom, Poland 69 Hc
Bytów, Poland 69 Ga

C

Caaguazu, Paraguay 54 Ec
Caballococha, Peru 52 Cd
Caballo Res., New Mexico 48 Df
Caballos, Sierra de los, New Mexico 48 Df
Cabañas, Cuba 51 Cb
Cabanatuan, Philippines 83 Hg
Cabano, Quebec 32 Df
Cabar, Yugoslavia 74 Ec
Cabedelo, Brazil 53 Le
Cabeza del Buey, Spain 70 Cc
Cabezas, Bolivia 52 Eg
Cabinda, Angola 96 Cf
Cabo Blanco, Argentina 54 Cg
Cabo Frio, Brazil 53 Jh
Cabonga, Rés., Quebec 35 Oe
Cabora Bassa Dam, Mozamb. 95 Ec
Cabo Raso, Argentina 54 Cf
Caborca, Mexico 50 Ba
Cabot Head, Ontario 34 Jg
Cabot Str., Nfld./N.S. 33 Mf
Cabra, Spain 70 Cd
Cabrera, Balearic Is. 71 Gc
Cabri, Saskatchewan 36 Jh
Cabrobo, Brazil 53 Ke
Cabuérniga, Spain 70 Ca
Cabure, Venezuela 52 Da
Cabusa I., Burma 89 Jf
Čačak, Yugoslavia 76 Cc
Cacaoui L., Quebec 32 Fc
Cacapon R., W. Virginia 44 Ac
Cacequi, Brazil 54 Fc
Caceres, Brazil 53 Fg
Cáceres, Spain 70 Bc
Cache Bay, Ontario 34 Kf
Cachinal, Chile 54 Cb
Cachisca, L., Quebec 35 Qb
Cachoeira, Brazil 53 Kf
Cachoeira do Iguacu, Arg. 54 Fc
Cachoeira do Sul, Brazil 54 Fd
Caconda, Angola 96 Dg
Cacouna, Quebec 32 Cf
Cactus Lake, Sask. 36 Hf
Cadaqués, Spain 71 Ga
Caddo L., Louisiana 49 Lf
Cadereyta, Mexico 50 Eb
Cader Idris, Wales 63 Eh
Cadillac, Michigan 40 Dc
Cadillac, Quebec 35 Md
Cadillac, Saskatchewan 36 Kj
Cádiz, Spain 70 Bd
Cádiz, Gulf of, Spain 70 Bd
Cadogan, Alberta 36 Gf
Cadomin, Alberta 39 Pj
Cadotte, R., Alberta 39 Pg
Cadzand, Netherlands 64 Bc
Caen, France 72 Cb
Caernarfon, Wales 63 Eg
Caernarfon B., Wales 63 Dg
Cagayan, Philippines 83 Hj
Cagayan Sulu, Phil. 83 Gj
Cagliari, Sardinia 75 Bf
Caguas, Puerto Rico 51 Fc
Caha Mts., Eire 63 Aj
Cahore Pt., Eire 63 Ch
Cahors, France 73 Dd
Caiapônia, Brazil 53 Gg
Caibarién, Cuba 51 Db
Caicara, Bolivar, Venezuela 52 Db
Caicara, Monagas, Venez. 52 Eb
Caicos Is., The Bahamas 51 Eb
Cailloma, Peru 52 Cg
Caillou B., Louisiana 49 Mh
Caimanera, Cuba 51 Dc
Cains R., New Brunswick 32 Gg
Caird Coast, Antarctica 104 Ab
Cairngorms, Scotland 62 Ec
Cairns, Queensland 57 Jc
Cairo, Egypt 99 Mb
Cairo, Georgia, U.S.A. 45 Ee
Cairo, Illinois 45 Cb
Caizi Hu, China 84 Hg
Cajamarca, Peru 52 Be
Cajazeiras, Brazil 53 Ke
Cakovec, Yugoslavia 74 Fb
Cala, Spain 70 Bd
Calabar, Nigeria 98 Gg
Calabogie, Ontario 35 Og
Calabozo, Venezuela 52 Db
Calabria, Italy 75 Ff
Calacoto, Bolivia 52 Dg
Calafat, Romania 76 Dc
Calafate, Argentina 54 Bh
Calais, France 72 Da
Calais, Maine 32 Eh
Calama, Brazil 52 Ee
Calama, Chile 54 Cb
Calamar, Colombia 52 Cc
Calamar, Colombia 52 Ca
Calamian Group, Phil. 83 Gh
Calamocha, Spain 71 Eb
Calanaque, Brazil 52 Ed
Calang, Sumatra 83 Ck
Calatayud, Spain 71 Eb
Calava C., Sicily 75 Ef
Calbuco, Chile 54 Bf
Calcasieu L., Louisiana 49 Lh
Calceta, Ecuador 52 Bd
Calçhaqui, Argentina 54 Dc
Calcoene, Brazil 53 Gc
Calcutta, India 89 Gd
Caldas da Rainha, Portugal 70 Ac
Calder, Saskatchewan 37 Qg
Caldera, Chile 54 Bc
Caldwell, Idaho 47 Ed
Caldwell, Texas 49 Jg
Caledonia, Minnesota 46 Md
Caledonia, Nova Scotia 32 Gj
Caledonia, Nova Scotia 33 Kh
Caledonia, Ontario 34 Lj
Calella, Spain 71 Gb
Calenzana, Corsica 73 Jf
Caleta Buena, Chile 54 Ba
Caleta Junin, Chile 54 Ba
Caleta Olivia, Argentina 54 Cg
Calgary, Alberta 36 Cg
Cali, Colombia 52 Bc
Calicut, India 88 Ef
California, U.S.A. 42 Bd
California, G. of, Mexico 50 Bb
Calimalli, Mexico 50 Bb
Calingasta, Argentina 54 Cd
Callabonna L., S. Australia 57 He
Callander, Ontario 35 Lf
Callander, Scotland 62 Ed
Callao, Peru 52 Bf
Calling, L., Alberta 36 Dc
Calling Lake, Alberta 36 Dc
Calling River, Alberta 36 Dc
Callison Ranch, B.C. 39 Hf
Callosa de Ensarriá, Spain 71 Ec
Calm, L., Ontario 36 Lb
Calmar, Alberta 36 De
Calmon, Brazil 54 Fc
Calstock, Ontario 34 Fc
Caltagirone, Sicily 75 Eg
Caltanissetta, Sicily 75 Eg
Calulo, Angola 96 Dg
Calumet, Quebec 35 Qg
Calumet, I. du Grand, Quebec 40 Hc
Calunda, Angola 96 Eg
Calvados, France 72 Cb
Calvert I., B.C. 39 Jk
Calverton, Virginia 45 Ja
Calvillo, Mexico 50 Dc
Calvinia, Cape Province 95 Bf
Camabatela, Angola 96 Df
Camachigama, L., Quebec 35 Oe
Camagüey, Cuba 51 Db
Camagüey, Arch. de, Cuba 51 Db
Camaná, Peru 52 Cg
Camara, Brazil 52 Ed
Camarat C., France 73 Ge
Camargo, Bolivia 52 Dh
Camargo, Mexico 50 Eb
Camarones, Argentina 54 Cf
Ca-Mau. See Mui Bai Bung
Cambados, Spain 70 Aa
Cambodia. See Kampuchea 87 Cd
Cambodia, C. See Mui Bai Bung
Cambona, Mozambique 97 Hg
Cambrai, France 72 Ea
Cambrian Mts., Wales 63 Eh
Cambridge, England 63 Gh
Cambridge, Massachusetts 44 Ea
Cambridge, New Zealand 55 Eb
Cambridge, Ontario 34 Kj
Cambridge Bay, N.W.T. 38 Va
Cambridge G., W. Australia 56 Eb
Cambridgeshire, England 63 Gh
Camden, Arkansas 49 Lf
Camden, Delaware 44 Cc
Camden, Maine 32 Cj
Camden, New Jersey 44 Cc
Camden, New York 40 Jd
Camden, S. Carolina 45 Gc
Camedo, Switzerland 65 Db
Cameron, Missouri 49 Kc
Cameron, Texas 49 Jg
Cameron Falls, Ontario 34 Bc
Cameron Hills, Alberta 38 Of
Cameron Mts., New Zealand 55 Ag
Camerota, Italy 75 Ee
Cameroun, Cent. Africa 99 Hg
Cameroun Mt., Cameroun 96 Bd
Cametá, Brazil 53 Hd
Camilla, Georgia, U.S.A. 45 Ee
Camina, Chile 54 Ca
Caminha, Portugal 70 Ab
Caminreal, Spain 71 Eb
Camlaren, N.W.T. 38 Rd
Camoa, Mexico 50 Cb
Camocim, Brazil 53 Jd
Camooweal, Queensland 57 Gd
Camopi, Fr. Guiana 53 Gc
Camorta, Nicobar Is. 89 Hg
Camousitchouane, L., Que. 35 Pa
Campana, Argentina 54 Ed
Campana, I., Chile 54 Ag
Campania, Italy 75 Ee
Campania I., B.C. 39 Jj
Campbell, Missouri 45 Bb
Campbell, L., N.W.T. 38 Ud
Campbell, L., N.W.T. 38 Ga
Campbell B., N.W.T. 38 Va
Campbellford, Ontario 35 Nh
Campbell I., Pacific Ocean 102 Fn
Campbell Island, B.C. 39 Jj
Campbellpore, Pakistan 90 Cd
Campbell River, B.C. 39 Ll
Campbell's Bay, Quebec 35 Og
Campbellton, N.B. 32 Ff
Campbellton, Nfld. 33 Sd
Campbeltown, Scotland 62 De
Campeche, Mexico 50 Fd
Campeche, G. of, Mexico 50 Fd
Camperville, Manitoba 37 Rg
Campiglia Marittima, Italy 74 Cd
Campillos, Spain 70 Cd
Campina Grande, Brazil 53 Ke
Campinas, Brazil 53 Hh
Camp-Mercier, Quebec 35 Te
Campoalegre, Colombia 52 Bc
Campobasso, Italy 75 Ee
Campobello I., N.B. 32 Fj
Campo Belo, Brazil 53 Hh
Campo Formosa, Brazil 53 Jf
Campo Gallo, Argentina 54 Dc
Campo Grande, Brazil 53 Gh
Campo Maior, Brazil 53 Jd
Campo Maior, Portugal 70 Bc
Campos, Brazil 53 Jh
Campos Novos, Brazil 54 Fc
Campos Sales, Brazil 53 Je
Camrose, Alberta 36 Ee
Camsell, L., N.W.T. 38 Pd
Camsell Portage, Sask. 38 Tf
Camsell Ra., N.W.T. 38 Md
Canaan, New Brunswick 32 Gg
Canaan Pk., Utah 48 Bd
Canaan R., N.B. 32 Gh
Canada Bay, Newfoundland 33 Rc
Cañada de Gomez, Arg. 54 Dd
Canadian, Texas 48 Ge
Canadian R., U.S.A. 49 Je
Canakkale, Turkey 92 Aa
Canal Flats, B.C. 39 Qk
Canama, Brazil 52 Ce
Canandaigua, New York 44 Ba
Canandaigua L., New York 44 Ba
Cananea, Mexico 50 Ba
Cananeia, Brazil 54 Gc
Canarias, Islas, Atlantic Oc. 98 Bc
Canarreos, Arch. de los, Cuba 51 Cb
Canary Is. See Canarias
Canas, Portugal 70 Bb
Canaseraga, New York 44 Ba
Canatlan, Mexico 50 Dc
Cañaveral, Spain 70 Bc
Canaveral, C., Florida 45 Jf
Cañaveras, Spain 71 Db
Canavieiras, Brazil 53 Kg
Canberra, Australia 57 Jg
Canby, Minnesota 46 Jc
Candasnos, Spain 71 Fb
Candia. See Iráklion
Candiac, Saskatchewan 37 Oh
Candle L., Saskatchewan 37 Me
Candle Lake, Sask. 37 Me
Cando, Saskatchewan 36 Jf
Canea. See Khania
Canela, Brazil 54 Fc
Canelones, Uruguay 54 Ed
Cañete, Chile 54 Be
Canete, Peru 52 Bf
Cañete, Spain 71 Eb
Cangamba, Angola 96 Dg
Cangandala, Angola 96 Df
Cangas, Spain 70 Ba
Canguaretama, Brazil 53 Le
Cangzhou, China 84 Hd
Canha, Portugal 70 Ac
Caniapiscau L., Quebec 31 Ng
Caniapiscau R., Quebec 31 Nf
Canica, Ile, Quebec 35 Nc
Canicatti, Sicily 75 Dg
Canim L., B.C. 39 Nk
Çankiri, Turkey 92 Ba
Canmore, Alberta 36 Bg
Canna, Scotland 62 Cc
Cannanore, India 88 Ef
Cannelton, Indiana 45 Db
Cannes, France 73 Ge
Canning, Nova Scotia 32 Hh
Cannington, Ontario 35 Lh
Cannon Ball, N. Dakota 46 Gb
Canoe, L., Saskatchewan 36 Jc
Canoe R., B.C. 39 Oj
Canon City, Colorado 48 Ec
Canora, Saskatchewan 37 Pg
Canosa, Italy 75 Fe
Canso, Nova Scotia 33 Mh
Canso, C., Nova Scotia 33 Mh
Canso, Strait of, N.S. 33 Lh
Cantábrica, Cord., Spain 70 Ca
Cantal, France 73 Ed
Cantanhede, Portugal 70 Ab
Cantaur, Saskatchewan 36 Jh
Canterbury, England 63 Hj
Canterbury, N.B. 32 Eh
Canterbury Bight, N.Z. 55 Df
Canterbury Plains, N.Z. 55 Cf
CanTho, Vietnam 87 De
Canton, Mississippi 49 Nf
Canton, New York 40 Jc
Canton, Ohio 40 Fe
Canton, S. Dakota 46 Jd
Canton. See Guangzhou
Canton-Bégin, Quebec 35 Td
Canton I., Phoenix Is. 102 Hh
Canton Res., Oklahoma 49 Hd
Canuelas, Argentina 54 Ee
Canutama, Brazil 52 Ee
Canwood, Saskatchewan 36 Le
Canyon, Ontario 34 Fe
Canyon, Y.T. 38 Ee
Canyon Creek, Alberta 36 Bc
Canyon Dam Res., Texas 49 Hh
Canyon de Chelly Nat. Mon., Arizona 48 Cd
Canyon Ras., N.W.T. 38 Kd
Cao Bang, Vietnam 87 Db
Caopacho L., Quebec 32 Fa
Caopacho R., Quebec 32 Fb
Caopatina, L., Quebec 35 Qc
Caotibi, L., Quebec 32 Ec
Capabarida, Venezuela 52 Ca
Capão Bonito, Brazil 54 Gb
Capasin, Saskatchewan 36 Ke
Cap-aux-Meules, I. du, Que. 33 Lf
Cap-Chat, Quebec 32 Fd
Cap-de-la-Madeleine, Que. 35 Sf
Cap-d'Espoir, Quebec 32 He
Cape Barren I., Tasmania 57 Jh
Cape Breton Highlands National Park, N.S. 33 Mg
Cape Breton I., N.S. 33 Ng
Cape Broyle, Nfld. 33 Uf
Cape Charles, Nfld. 33 Ra
Cape Charles, Virginia 45 Kb
Cape Coast, Ghana 98 Eg
Cape Cod B., Massachusetts 44 Eb
Cape Dorset, N.W.T. 31 Me
Cape Dyer, N.W.T. 31 Nd
Cape Fear R., N. Carolina 45 Hc
Cape Girardeau, Missouri 45 Cb
Cape La Hune, Nfld. 33 Pf
Capelinha, Brazil 53 Jg
Capelle, la, France 72 Eb
Cape May, New Jersey 44 Cc
Cape May Court House, N.J. 44 Cc
Cape Parry, N.W.T. 38 La
Cape Province (Cape of Good Hope), S. Africa 95 Cf
Cape Race, Nfld. 33 Tg
Cape Ray, Newfoundland 33 Nf
Cape Sable I., N.S. 32 Gk
Cape St. Mary Lt. Ho., N.S. 32 Fj
Cape Tormentine, N.B. 32 Jg
Cape Town, Cape Province 95 Bf
Cape Verde Is., Atlantic Oc. 98 Bh
Cape York Pen., Queensland 57 Hb
Cap Haïtien, Haiti 51 Ec
Capilla, Argentina 54 Ed
Capilla del Monte, Arg. 54 Dd
Capim, Brazil 53 Hd
Capitachouane, R., Que. 35 Oe
Capitan Mts., New Mexico 48 Ef
Caplan, Quebec 32 Ge
Capraia, Italy 74 Bd
Capreol, Ontario 34 Kf
Caprera, Sardinia 75 Be
Capri, Italy 75 Ee
Capricorn Chan., Qnsld. 57 Kd
Caprivi Strip, Namibia 95 Cc
Capstick, Nova Scotia 33 Mg
Carabaya, Cord. de, Peru 52 Cf
Caracaraí, Brazil 52 Ec
Caracas, Venezuela 52 Da
Caracol, Brazil 53 Je
Caraguatay, Paraguay 54 Eb
Caramat, Ontario 34 Dc
Caransebes, Romania 76 Db
Carapegua, Paraguay 54 Ec
Caraquet & B., N.B. 32 Hf
Caras, Peru 52 Be
Caratasca Lag., Honduras 51 Cc
Caratinga, Brazil 53 Jg
Carauari, Brazil 52 Dd
Caravaca, Spain 71 Ec
Caravelas, Brazil 53 Kg
Caraveli, Peru 52 Cg
Carballino, Spain 70 Aa
Carballo, Spain 70 Aa
Carberry, Manitoba 37 Sj
Carbon, Alberta 36 Dg
Carbonara C., Sardinia 75 Bf
Carbondale, Alberta 36 De
Carbondale, Illinois 49 Nd
Carbondale, Pennsylvania 44 Cb
Carbonear, Newfoundland 33 Tf
Carbon Hill, Alabama 45 Dd
Carcajou, Alberta 39 Pg
Carcajou, R., N.W.T. 38 Jc
Carcassonne, France 73 Ee
Carcross, Y.T. 38 Fe
Cardale, Manitoba 37 Rh
Cardamomes, Chaine des, Mts., Kampuchea 89 Kf
Cardamom Hills, India 88 Eg
Cárdenas, Cuba 51 Cb
Cardenas, Mexico 50 Ec
Cardiel, L., Argentina 54 Bg
Cardiff, Wales 63 Ej
Cardigan, P.E.I. 32 Kg
Cardigan, Wales 63 Dh
Cardigan B., P.E.I. 32 Kg
Cardigan Bay, Wales 63 Dh
Cardinal, Ontario 35 Ph
Cardona, Spain 71 Fb
Cardross, Saskatchewan 37 Mj
Cardston, Alberta 36 Dj
Cardwell, Queensland 57 Jc
Carey, L., W. Australia 56 De
Carey L., N.W.T. 38 Wd
Cargill, Ontario 34 Jh
Carhaix, France 72 Bb
Carhué. See Adolfo Alsina
Caribbean Sea, West Indies 51 Dd
Cariboo Mts., B.C. 39 Nj
Caribou, Maine 32 Dg
Caribou, R., Y.T. 38 Fb
Caribou Hide, B.C. 39 Kg
Caribou I., Nova Scotia 32 Kh
Caribou I., Ontario 34 Ee
Caribou Is., N.W.T. 38 Re
Caribou L., Ontario 34 Ab
Caribou Mts., Alberta 39 Qf
Caribou R., N.W.T. 38 Ke
Carichic, Mexico 50 Cb
Carievale, Saskatchewan 37 Qj
Carillon, Quebec 35 Qg
Cariñena, Spain 71 Eb
Carinhanha, Brazil 53 Jf
Caripito, Venezuela 52 Ea
Carius, Brazil 53 Ke
Carl, L., Oklahoma 49 Jd
Carlet, Spain 71 Ec
Carleton, Quebec 32 Fe
Carleton, Mt., N.B. 32 Ff
Carleton, Pte, Quebec 32 Kd
Carleton Place, Ontario 35 Og
Carlingford L., Eire 63 Dg
Carlinville, Illinois 49 Nc
Carlisle, England 63 Ff
Carlisle, Kentucky 45 Ea
Carlisle, Pennsylvania 44 Bb
Carlisle, S. Carolina 45 Gc
Carlos Casares, Argentina 54 De
Carlow, Eire 63 Ch
Carlsbad, New Mexico 48 Ef
Carlsbad Caverns Nat. Park, New Mexico 42 Fe
Carlton, Minnesota 46 Lb
Carlton, Saskatchewan 36 Lf
Carlyle, Saskatchewan 37 Pj
Carmacks, Y.T. 38 Ed
Carman, Manitoba 37 Uj
Carmangay, Alberta 36 Dh
Carmanville, Nfld. 33 Sd
Carmarthen, Wales 63 Ej
Carmarthen B., Wales 63 Dj
Carmaux, France 73 Ed
Carmel, New York 44 Db
Carmel, Saskatchewan 37 Mf
Carmel, Mt., Israel 94 De
Carmelo, Uruguay 54 Ed
Carmen, Bolivia 52 Df
Carmen, Colombia 52 Bb
Carmen, Mexico 50 Fd
Carmen Alto, Chile 54 Cb
Carmen de Patagones, Argentina 54 Df
Carmen I., Mexico 50 Bb
Carmensa, Argentina 54 Ce
Carmi, Illinois 45 Ca
Carmichael, Sask. 36 Jh
Carmona, Spain 70 Cd
Carnamah, W. Australia 56 Ce
Carnarvon, Cape Province 95 Cf
Carnarvon, W. Australia 56 Bd
Carndonagh, Eire 62 Ce
Carnduff, Saskatchewan 37 Qj
Carnegie L., W. Australia 56 De
Carnot, Cent. Afr. Rep. 99 Jh
Carnsore Pt., Eire 63 Ch
Carnwath, R., N.W.T. 38 Jb
Caro, Michigan 40 Ed
Carolina, Brazil 53 He
Carolina, Transvaal 95 Ee
Caroline, Alberta 36 Cf
Caroline I., Pacific Ocean 103 Kh
Caroline Is., Pacific Ocean 102 Dg
Caron, Saskatchewan 37 Mh
Carora, Venezuela 52 Ca
Carp, Ontario 35 Og
Carpathian Mts., Cent. Europe 61 Nf
Carpatii Meridionali, Romania 76 Db
Carpentaria, G. of, Aust. 57 Gb
Carp L., British Columbia 39 Mh
Carragana, Saskatchewan 37 Of
Carrara, Italy 74 Cc
Carreño, Spain 70 Ca
Carrickmacross, Eire 63 Cg
Carrick-on-Shannon, Eire 63 Bg
Carrick-on-Suir, Eire 63 Ch
Carrière, L., Quebec 35 Ne
Carrington, N. Dakota 46 Hb
Carrión-de-los-Condes, Spain 70 Ca
Carrizo Mts., Arizona 48 Cd
Carrizo Springs, Texas 48 Hh
Carroll, Iowa 49 Ka
Carroll, Manitoba 37 Rj
Carrollton, Alabama 45 Cd
Carrollton, Missouri 49 Lc
Carrot R., Manitoba 37 Vd
Carrot R., Saskatchewan 37 Ne
Carrot River, Sask. 37 Oe
Carrowmore L., Eire 63 Af
Carroz, le, Switzerland 65 Bb
Carruthers, Saskatchewan 36 Hf
Carsamba, Turkey 92 Ca
Carseland, Alberta 36 Dh
Carson City, Nevada 47 Df
Carson Sink, Nevada 47 Df
Carstairs, Alberta 36 Cg
Carstairs, Scotland 62 Ee
Carstensz, Mt. See Puncak Jaja
Carswell L., Sask. 39 Tf
Cartagena, Colombia 52 Ba
Cartagena, Spain 71 Ed
Cartago, Colombia 52 Bc
Cartago, Costa Rica 51 Ce
Cartaxo, Portugal 70 Ac
Cartaya, Spain 70 Bd
Carter, Wyoming 46 Be
Carteret, France 72 Cb
Cartersville, Georgia, U.S.A. 45 Ec
Carterton, New Zealand 55 Ed
Carthage, Illinois 49 Mb
Carthage, Missouri 43 Hd
Carthage, N. Carolina 45 Hc
Carthage, New York 40 Jd
Carthage, Tennessee 45 Eb
Cartier, Ontario 34 Jf
Cartierville, Quebec 35 Rj
Cartierville Airport, Que. 35 Qj
Cartwright, Manitoba 37 Sj
Cartwright, Nfld. 31 Og
Cartyville, Nfld. 33 Oe
Carúpano, Venezuela 52 Ea
Carutaperá, Brazil 53 Hd
Caruthersville, Missouri 49 Nd
Carvoeiro, Brazil 52 Ed
Casablanca, Chile 54 Bd
Casablanca. See Dar-el-Beida
Casaccia, Switzerland 65 Eb
Casa Grande, Arizona 48 Bf
Casas Grandes, Mexico 50 Ca
Casas Ibáñez, Spain 71 Ec
Cascade, B.C. 39 Ol
Cascade, Montana 46 Bb
Cascade Mts., Canada/U.S.A. 39 Nl
Cascade Range, Oregon/Wash. 42 Bc
Cascais, Portugal 70 Ac
Cascapédia R., Quebec 32 Fe
Caserta, Italy 75 Ee
Caseville, Michigan 40 Ed
Casey, Quebec 35 Qe
Cashel, Eire 63 Bh
Casilda, Argentina 54 Dd
Casilda, Cuba 51 Db
Casino, N.S.W. 57 Ke
Casma, Peru 52 Be
Casmalia, California 47 Ch
Caspe, Spain 71 Eb
Casper, Wyoming 46 Dd
Caspian Sea, Europe/Asia 78 Dd
Cassai, Angola 96 Eg
Cassamba, Angola 96 Eg
Cassel, France 72 Ea
Casselman, Ontario 35 Pg
Casselton, N. Dakota 46 Jb
Cassiar, British Columbia 38 Hf
Cassiar Mts., B.C. 38 Hf
Cassinga, Angola 95 Bc
Cassino, Brazil 54 Fd
Cassino, Italy 75 De
Cassis, France 73 Fe
Cassopolis, Michigan 40 Ce
Cassville, Missouri 49 Ld
Castanhal, Brazil 52 Ee
Castanheiro, Brazil 52 Dd
Castaño, Argentina 54 Cd
Castasegna, Switzerland 65 Eb
Casteljaloux, France 73 Cd
Castellammare, Sicily 75 Df
Castellammare di Stabia, Italy 75 Ee
Castellane, France 73 Ge
Castellar de Santiago, Spain 70 Dc
Castelli, Argentina 54 Ee
Castellón de la Plana, Spain 71 Ec
Castellote, Spain 71 Eb
Castelnaudary, France 73 Ee
Castelo Branco, Portugal 70 Bc
Castelo de Vide, Portugal 70 Bc
Castelsarrasin, France 73 De
Castelvetrano, Sicily 75 Dg
Castets, France 73 Ce
Castilletes, Colombia 52 Ca
Castillo, Mt., Chile 54 Bg
Castine, Maine 32 Dj
Castlebar, Eire 63 Ag
Castle Douglas, Scotland 63 Ef
Castlegar, B.C. 39 Pl
Castlerea, Eire 63 Bg
Castlereagh, R., N.S.W. 57 Jf
Castle Rock, Utah 48 Bb
Castle Rock, Mt., Oregon 47 Dc
Castle Rock Buttes, S. Dakota 46 Fc
Castor, Alberta 36 Ff
Castres, France 73 Ee
Castro, Brazil 54 Fb
Castro, Chile 54 Bf
Castro Marin, Portugal 70 Bd
Castropol, Spain 70 Ba
Castrovillari, Italy 75 Ff
Castuera, Spain 70 Cc
Catabola, Angola 96 Dg
Catahoula L., Louisiana 49 Lg
Catalina, Newfoundland 33 Te
Catamaran, Tasmania 57 Jh
Catamarca, Argentina 54 Cc
Catanduanes, Philippines 83 Hh
Catania, Sicily 75 Eg
Catanzaro, Italy 75 Ff
Catarman, Philippines 83 Hh
Catastrophe, C., S. Australia 57 Gg
Cateau, le, France 72 Ea
Cater, Saskatchewan 36 Je
Cathedral Mt., Texas 48 Fg
Cathedra Provincial Park, B.C. 39 Nl
Cat I., The Bahamas 51 Db
Cat Lake, Ontario 31 Kg
Catlettsburg, Kentucky 45 Fa
Catonsville, Maryland 44 Bc
Catorce, Mexico 50 Dc
Catrilo, Argentina 54 De
Catskill, New York 44 Ca
Cattaraugus, New York 44 Aa

Catuna, *Argentina* 54 Cd
Caucasus, Mts. *See* Kavkaz
Cauchon L., *Manitoba* 37 Vc
Caughnawaga, *Quebec* 35 Rg
Caughnawaga Indian Reservation, *Quebec* 35 Rk
Caungula, *Angola* 96 Df
Cauquenes, *Chile* 54 Be
Causapscal, *Quebec* 32 Ee
Cauto, *Cuba* 51 Db
Cauvery, *India* 88 Ef
Cavalcante, *Brazil* 53 Hf
Cavallo Pass, *Texas* 48 Jh
Cavan, *Eire* 63 Cg
Cave, *New Zealand* 55 Cf
Cavell, *Ontario* 34 Cb
Cavell, *Saskatchewan* 36 Jf
Cavendish, *Alberta* 36 Gh
Cavergno, *Switzerland* 65 Db
Cavers, *Ontario* 34 Cd
Caviana, *Brazil* 53 Gc
Cawnpore. *See* Kanpur
Caxias, *Brazil* 52 Cd
Caxias, *Brazil* 53 Jd
Caxias do Sul, *Brazil* 54 Fc
Cayambe, *Ecuador* 52 Bc
Cayenne, *French Guiana* 53 Gc
Cayes, Les, *Haiti* 51 Ec
Cayley, *Alberta* 36 Dh
Cayman Is., *W. Indies* 51 Cc
Cayo, *Belize* 51 Bc
Cayuga, *Ontario* 34 Lk
Cayuga L., *New York* 44 Ba
Cazaje, *Angola* 96 Eg
Cazalla de la Sierra, *Spain* 70 Cd
Cazenovia, *New York* 44 Ca
Cazin, *Yugoslavia* 74 Ec
Cazorla, *Spain* 70 Dd
Ceanannus Mór, *Eire* 63 Cg
Ceara Mirim, *Brazil* 53 Ke
Ceba, *Saskatchewan* 37 Pe
Cebaco, I., *Panama* 51 Ce
Cebollar, *Argentina* 54 Cc
Cebollera, Sa., *Spain* 71 Db
Cebu, *Philippines* 83 Hh
Cecil, *Georgia, U.S.A.* 45 Fe
Ceclavín, *Spain* 70 Bc
Cedar, *Utah* 48 Bc
Cedarburg, *Wisconsin* 40 Cd
Cedar City, *Utah* 47 Gg
Cedar Creek Res., *Texas* 49 Jf
Cedar Falls, *Iowa* 49 La
Cedar Key, *Florida* 43 Kf
Cedar L., *Manitoba* 37 Re
Cedar L., *Texas* 48 Ff
Cedar Mts., *Oregon* 47 Ed
Cedar Ra., *Utah* 47 Ge
Cedar Rapids, *Iowa* 49 Mb
Cedar Springs, *Michigan* 40 Dd
Cedar Springs, *Ontario* 34 Hk
Cedoux, *Saskatchewan* 37 Oj
Cedral, *Mexico* 50 Dc
Cedros, I., *Mexico* 50 Ab
Ceduna, *S. Australia* 57 Ff
Cefalù, *Sicily* 75 Ef
Cegléd, *Hungary* 69 He
Cehegín, *Spain* 71 Ec
Ceiba, La, *Honduras* 50 Gd
Cejal, *Colombia* 52 Dc
Cejita Blanca, *New Mexico* 48 Dd
Celanova, *Spain* 70 Ba
Celaya, *Mexico* 50 Dc
Celebes Sea, *Indonesia* 83 Hk
Celebes (Sulawesi), *Indonesia* 83 Gl
Celje, *Yugoslavia* 74 Eb
Cella, *Spain* 71 Eb
Celle, *West Germany* 68 Db
Celles, *Belgium* 64 Bd
Çemisgezek, *Turkey* 92 Cb
Cenis, Mt., *France* 74 Ac
Center, *Alabama* 45 Ec
Center, *Texas* 49 Kg
Centerville, *Alabama* 45 Dd
Centerville, *Iowa* 49 Lb
Centerville, *Missouri* 45 Bb
Centerville, *Tennessee* 45 Dc
Central, Cord., *Dom. Rep.* 51 Ec
Central, Cord., *Peru* 52 Be
Central, reg., *Scotland* 62 Ed
Central African Republic, *Africa* 99 Jg
Central America, 51 Bd
Central Butte, *Sask.* 36 Lh
Central City, *Nebraska* 49 Hb
Centralia, *Illinois* 49 Nc
Centralia, *Ontario* 34 Jj
Centralia, *Washington* 47 Bb
Central Lake, *Michigan* 40 Dc
Central Russian Uplands, *U.S.S.R.* 80 Jd
Central Siberian Tableland. *See* Sibirskoye Ploskogor'ye
Centreville, *N.B.* 32 Eg
Centreville, *Nova Scotia* 32 Fj
Cephalonia. *See* Kefallinia
Ceram Sea, *Indonesia* 83 Jl
Cereal, *Alberta* 36 Gg
Cerf, L. du, *Quebec* 35 Pf
Cerignola, *Italy* 75 Ee
Cerigo. *See* Kithira
Cerigotto. *See* Andikithira
Cerknica, *Yugoslavia* 74 Ec
Çermik, *Turkey* 92 Cb
Cerralvo, *Mexico* 50 Eb
Cerralvo, I., *Mexico* 50 Cc
Cerreto Sannita, *Italy* 75 Ee
Cerro de Pasco, *Peru* 52 Bf
Cervera de Pisuerga, *Spain* 70 Ca
Cesena, *Italy* 74 Dc
Cesis, *Latvia* 67 Lh
Česká Lípa, *Czechoslovakia* 68 Fc
České Budějovice, *Czech.* 68 Fd
Cessford, *Alberta* 36 Fg
Cessnock, *N.S.W.* 57 Kf
Cetinje, *Yugoslavia* 76 Bc
Cetraro, *Italy* 75 Ef
Ceuta, *N. Africa* 98 Da
Ceuta, B. de, *Mexico* 50 Cc
Cevennes, *France* 73 Ee
Cevio, *Switzerland* 65 Db
Ceylon, *Saskatchewan* 37 Nj
Ceylon. *See* Sri Lanka
Chablis, *France* 72 Ec
Chacabuco, *Argentina* 54 Dd
Chacance, *Chile* 54 Cb
Chachapoyas, *Peru* 52 Be
Chachoengsao, *Thailand* 87 Cd
Chaco R., *New Mexico* 48 Cd
Chad L., *Chad* 99 Hf
Chad rep., *Africa* 99 Jf
Chadron, *Nebraska* 48 Fa
Chadwick, *Missouri* 45 Ab
Chagai, *Pakistan* 88 Bc
Chagda, *U.S.S.R.* 79 Nc
Chagny, *France* 72 Fc
Chagode, *U.S.S.R.* 80 Jb
Chagos Arch., *Indian Ocean* 100 Fe
Chaguaramas, *Trinidad* 52 Ea
Chāh Bahār, *Iran* 93 Hd
Chaibassa, *India* 91 Ed
Chaise Dieu, *France* 73 Ed
Chakansur, *Afghanistan* 93 Hc
Chakia, *India* 91 Dc
Chakwal, *Pakistan* 90 Cd
Chala, *Peru* 52 Cg
Chalchihuites, *Mexico* 50 Dc
Chaleurs, B. des, *Que./N.B.* 32 Gf
Chalham, I., *Chile* 54 Bh
Chalhuanca, *Peru* 52 Cf
Chaling, *China* 85 Fj
Chalisgaon, *India* 88 Dd
Chalk River, *Ontario* 35 Nf
Challapata, *Bolivia* 52 Dg
Challenger Mts., *N.W.T.* 31 La
Chalna, *Bangladesh* 91 Gd
Châlons-sur-Marne, *France* 72 Fb
Châlon-sur-Saône, *France* 72 Fc
Châlus, *France* 72 Dd
Cham, *W. Germany* 68 Ed
Chama, *New Mexico* 48 Dd
Chaman, *Pakistan* 88 Cb
Chamba, *India* 90 Ed
Chamba, *Tanzania* 97 Hg
Chambal, *India* 88 Ec
Chamberlain, *Sask.* 37 Mh
Chamberlain, *S. Dakota* 46 Hd
Chamberlain L., *Maine* 32 Cg
Chambersburg, *Pa.* 44 Bc
Chambéry, *France* 72 Fd
Chambica, *Brazil* 53 He
Chambord, *Quebec* 35 Sd
Chamical, *Argentina* 54 Cd
Chamo, L., *Ethiopia* 97 Hc
Chamonix, *France* 72 Gd
Champa, *India* 91 De
Champagne, *France* 72 Eb
Champaign, *Illinois* 49 Nb
Champerico, *Guatemala* 50 Fe
Champion, *Alberta* 36 Dh
Champion, *Belgium* 64 Dd
Champlain, *Quebec* 35 Sf
Champlain L., *N.Y./Vermont* 40 Kc
Champlitte, *France* 72 Fc
Champneuf, *Quebec* 35 Nd
Chamusca, *Portugal* 70 Ac
Chana, *Thailand* 87 Ce
Chañaral, *Chile* 54 Bc
Chanco, *Chile* 54 Be
Chancy, *Switzerland* 65 Ab
Chandarnagar, *India* 91 Gd
Chandausi, *India* 91 Ba
Chandeleur Is., *Louisiana* 49 Nh
Chanderi, *India* 91 Bc
Chandigarh, *India* 90 Ee
Chandler, *Quebec* 32 He
Chandod, *India* 88 Dd
Chandpur, *Bangladesh* 89 Hd
Chandpur, *India* 91 Ba
Chandrakona, *India* 91 Fd
Chandrapur, *India* 88 Ee
Chanduria, *Bangladesh* 91 Gd
Chanf, *Iran* 93 Hd
Chang-chia-kou. *See* Zhangjiakou
Changchun, *China* 82 Jb
Changde, *China* 85 Eh
Change Islands, *Nfld.* 33 Sd
Changhua, *Taiwan* 85 Kk
Chang Jiang, *China* 84 Eg
Changjiang, *Hainan, China* 82 Eg
Changle, *China* 84 Jd
Changping, *China* 84 Hb
Changsha, *China* 85 Fh
Changshan, *China* 85 Jh
Changshun, *China* 85 Cj
Changte. *See* Anyang
Changting, *China* 85 Hk
Changzhi, *China* 84 Fd
Changzhou, *China* 84 Jg
Channel Is., *California* 42 Be
Channel Is., *English Channel* 63 Al
Channel-Port aux Basques, *Newfoundland* 33 Nf
Chantada, *Spain* 70 Ba
Chanthaburi, *Thailand* 87 Cd
Chantilly, *France* 72 Eb
Chanute, *Kansas* 49 Kd
Chany, Ozero, *U.S.S.R.* 78 Gc
Chao, *Thailand* 83 Dg
Chao'an, *China* 85 Hl
Chao Hu, *China* 84 Hg
Chapais, *Quebec* 35 Qc
Chapala, L., *Mexico* 50 Dc
Chapayevsk, *U.S.S.R.* 81 Jd
Chapeau, *Quebec* 35 Ng
Chapleau, *Ontario* 34 Ge
Chapleau, R., *Ontario* 34 Gd
Chaplin, *Saskatchewan* 36 Lh
Chapman, Mt., *B.C.* 39 Ok
Chapman Is., *N.W.T.* 38 Ta
Chapra, *India* 91 Ec
Chaput Hughes, *Ontario* 34 Kd
Char, *Mauritania* 98 Cd
Chara, *U.S.S.R.* 79 Lc
Charagua, *Bolivia* 52 Eg
Charaña, *Bolivia* 52 Dg
Charco Azul, B., *Panama* 51 Ce
Charcot I., *Antarctica* 104 Sc
Chard, *Alberta* 39 Sh
Chardzhou, *Turkmenistan* 78 Fe
Charente, *France* 72 Dd
Charente, *France* 72 Cd
Charente-Maritime, *France* 72 Cd
Chari, *Chad* 99 Jf
Charikar, *Afghanistan* 93 Jc
Charité, la, *France* 72 Ec
Chariton, *Iowa* 49 Lb
Charkhari, *India* 91 Bc
Charleroi, *Belgium* 64 Cd
Charlesbourg, *Quebec* 35 Ra
Charles C., *Virginia* 43 Ld
Charles City, *Iowa* 49 La
Charles I., *N.W.T.* 31 Me
Charles L., *Alberta* 38 Sf
Charles L., *Louisiana* 43 He
Charles R., *Massachusetts* 44 Ea
Charleston, *Illinois* 49 Nc
Charleston, *Mississippi* 45 Bc
Charleston, *Missouri* 45 Cb
Charleston, *S. Carolina* 45 Hd
Charleston, *W. Virginia* 45 Ga
Charleston Pk., *Nevada* 47 Fg
Charles Town, *W. Virginia* 44 Bc
Charleville, *Queensland* 57 Je
Charleville-Mézières, *Fr.* 72 Fb
Charlevoix, *Michigan* 40 Dc
Charlie Lake, *B.C.* 39 Ng
Charlotte, *Michigan* 40 Dd
Charlotte, *N. Carolina* 45 Gc
Charlotte, *New York* 40 Hd
Charlotte Amalie, *Virgin Is.* 51 Gc
Charlotte Harbour, *Florida* 45 Fg
Charlotte L., *B.C.* 39 Lj
Charlottenburg, *W. Berlin* 68 Eb
Charlottesville, *Virginia* 45 Ha
Charlottetown, *P.E.I.* 32 Jg
Charlton, *Ontario* 34 Ke
Charlton, *Victoria* 57 Hg
Charlton I., *N.W.T.* 31 Mg
Charmey, *Switzerland* 65 Cb
Charny, *Quebec* 32 Ag
Charolles, *France* 72 Fc
Charrote, Sierra, *Texas* 48 Fg
Charsadda, *Pakistan* 90 Bc
Charters Towers, *Qnsld.* 57 Jd
Chartierville, *Quebec* 32 Ah
Chartres, *France* 72 Db
Chartreuse, *France* 72 Fd
Charvonnex, *France* 65 Bc
Chascomus, *Argentina* 54 Ee
Chase, *B.C.* 39 Ok
Chaska, *Minnesota* 46 Lc
Chasm, *B.C.* 39 Nk
Chasse, I. à la, *Quebec* 32 Jc
Chasseneuil, *France* 72 Dd
Chatanooga, *Tennessee* 45 Ec
Châteaubriant, *France* 72 Cc
Château Chinon, *France* 72 Ec
Château-du-Loir, *France* 72 Dc
Châteaudun, *France* 72 Db
Château Gontier, *France* 72 Cc
Château-la-Vallière, *France* 72 Dc
Châteaulin, *France* 72 Ab
Châ teauneuf-en-Thimerais, *France* 72 Db
Châteaurenault, *France* 72 Dc
Château-Richer, *Quebec* 32 Ag
Châteauroux, *France* 72 Dc
Château-Salins, *France* 72 Gb
Château Thierry, *France* 72 Eb
Châteauvert, L., *Quebec* 35 Re
Châteauvillain, *France* 72 Fb
Chateh, *Alberta* 39 Of
Châtelet, *Belgium* 64 Cd
Châtellerault, *France* 72 Dc
Châtel-St Denis, *Switz.* 65 Bb
Chatfield, *Manitoba* 37 Uh
Chatfield, *Minnesota* 46 Ld
Chatham, *England* 63 Hj
Chatham, *New Brunswick* 32 Gf
Chatham, *Ontario* 34 Hk
Chatham, *Virginia* 45 Hb
Chatham Is., *Pacific Ocean* 102 Hm
Chatham Sd., *B.C.* 39 Hh
Châtillon-sur-Seine, *France* 72 Fc
Chatra, *India* 91 Ec
Chatrapur, *India* 89 Ge
Châtre, la, *France* 72 Ec
Chatsworth, *Ontario* 34 Kh
Chattahoochee R., *Ga., U.S.A.* 43 Ke
Chattanooga, *Tennessee* 43 Jd
Chaudière Falls, *Ontario/Quebec* 34 Dh
Chauka R., *India* 91 Cb
Chaumont-en-Bassigny, *France* 72 Fb
Chaunskaya Guba, *U.S.S.R.* 79 Rb
Chau Phu, *Vietnam* 87 Cd
Chausa, *India* 91 Dc
Chautauqua L., *New York* 44 Aa
Chauvin, *Alberta* 36 Gf
Chaux de Fonds, la, *Switz.* 65 Ba
Chaves, *Brazil* 53 Hd
Chaves, *Portugal* 70 Bb
Chayu, *China* 82 Ce
Chazón, *Argentina* 54 Dd
Cheadle, *Alberta* 36 Dg
Cheb, *Czechoslovakia* 68 Ec
Cheboksary, *U.S.S.R.* 81 Hb
Cheboygan, *Michigan* 40 Dc
Chedabucto B., *N.S.* 33 Lh
Cheduba, *Burma* 89 He
Cheecham, *Alberta* 39 Sg
Cheepash, R., *Ontario* 34 Jb
Cheepay R., *Ontario* 34 Ga
Cheeseman L., *Ontario* 37 Oa
Che foo. *See* Yantai
Chehalis, *Washington* 47 Bb
Cheju-do, *Korea* 82 Jd
Chekunda, *U.S.S.R.* 79 Nc
Chelan, *Saskatchewan* 37 Of
Chelforó, *Argentina* 54 Ce
Chelkar, *Kazakhstan* 78 Ed
Chelm, *Poland* 69 Kc
Chelmsford, *England* 63 Hj
Chelmsford, *Ontario* 34 Jf
Chelsea, *Vermont* 40 Kc
Chelsea, *Wisconsin* 40 Ac
Cheltenham, *England* 63 Fj
Chelva, *Spain* 71 Ec
Chelyabinsk, *U.S.S.R.* 81 Qc
Chemainus, *B.C.* 39 Ml
Chemba, *Mozambique* 95 Ec
Chembar, *U.S.S.R.* 81 Fd
Chemnitz. *See* Karl-Marx-Stadt
Chemquasabamticook L., *Maine* 32 Cg
Chenab R., *Pakistan* 90 Be
Chenchow. *See* Huaiyang
Chenesht, *Iran* 93 Gc
Chénéville, *Quebec* 35 Pg
Cheney Res., *Kansas* 49 Jd
Chenfan. *See* Minqin
Chengde, *China* 84 Hb
Chengdu, *China* 84 Bg
Chengshan Tow, *China* 82 Hc
Chenier, *Quebec* 35 Of
Chenil, L., *Quebec* 33 Nb
Chenoa, *Illinois* 40 Be
Chensagi, L., *Quebec* 35 Ob
Chen Xian, *China* 85 Fk
Chepén, *Peru* 52 Be
Chepes, *Argentina* 54 Cd
Cher, *France* 72 Ec
Cherbourg, *France* 72 Cb
Cherchell, *Algeria* 98 Fa
Cheremkhovo, *U.S.S.R.* 79 Kc
Cherepovets, *U.S.S.R.* 80 Lb
Cherhill, *Alberta* 36 Ce
Cherkassy, *Ukraine* 80 Hg
Chermoz, *U.S.S.R.* 78 Ec
Chernigov, *Ukraine* 80 Gf
Chernikovsk, *U.S.S.R.* 81 Nc
Chernovsk, *U.S.S.R.* 81 Ja
Chernovtsy, *Ukraine* 80 Dg
Chernyakhovsk, *U.S.S.R.* 67 Jj
Cherokee, *Iowa* 49 Ka
Cherokees, L. o' the, *Okla.* 49 Kd
Cherra Punji, *India* 89 Hc
Cherryfield, *Maine* 32 Dj
Cherry Point, *Alberta* 39 Og
Cherskogo, Khrebet, *U.S.S.R.* 79 Pb
Chertkovo, *Ukraine* 80 Lg
Chervenbryag, *Bulgaria* 76 Ec
Chesapeake B., *Maryland* 43 Ld
Cheshire, *England* 63 Fg
Cheshskaya Guba, *U.S.S.R.* 78 Db
Chesley, *Ontario* 34 Jh
Chester, *England* 63 Fg
Chester, *Illinois* 45 Cb
Chester, *Nova Scotia* 32 Hj
Chester, *Pennsylvania* 44 Cc
Chester, *S. Carolina* 45 Gc
Chester Basin, *Nova Scotia* 32 Hj
Chesterfield, *England* 63 Gg
Chesterfield, *S. Carolina* 45 Gc
Chesterfield Inlet, *N.W.T.* 31 Ke
Chesterfield Is., *Pacific Oc.* 102 Ej
Chestertown, *Maryland* 44 Bc
Chesterville, *Ontario* 35 Pg
Chesuncook L., *Maine* 32 Ch
Chéticamp, *Nova Scotia* 33 Lg
Chetumal, *Mexico* 50 Gd
Chetumal B., *Mexico* 51 Bc
Cheviot, *New Zealand* 55 De
Cheviot, *Saskatchewan* 36 Lf
Cheviot, The, *England* 62 Fe
Cheviot Hills, *Eng./Scot.* 62 Fe
Cheyenne, *Wyoming* 46 Ee
Cheyenne, *Wyoming* 42 Fc
Cheyenne R., *S. Dakota* 46 Gc
Chhachrauli, *India* 90 Ee
Chhata, *India* 90 Eg
Chhatarpur, *India* 91 Bc
Chhibramau, *India* 91 Bb
Chhindwara, *India* 91 Bd
Chia-i, *Taiwan* 85 Kl
Chia-mu-ssu. *See* Jiamusi
Chiang-hsi. *See* Jiangxi
Chiang Khan, *Thailand* 87 Cc
Chiang Mai, *Thailand* 87 Bc
Chiang Rai, *Thailand* 87 Bc
Chiang-su. *See* Jiangsu
Chiapa, *Mexico* 50 Fd
Chiapas, *Mexico* 50 Fd
Chiasso, *Switzerland* 65 Ec
Chiavari, *Italy* 74 Bc
Chiba, *Japan* 86 Gg
Chibougamau, *Quebec* 35 Qc
Chibougamau, R., *Quebec* 35 Pc
Chicago, *Illinois* 49 Ob
Chic-Chocs, Monts, *Quebec* 32 Fe
Chichagof I., *Alaska* 43 Zm
Chichester, *England* 63 Gk
Ch'i-ch'i-ha-erh. *See* Qiqihar
Chickasha, *Oklahoma* 49 Je
Chiclayo, *Peru* 52 Be
Chico, *California* 47 Cf
Chicoana, *Argentina* 54 Cc
Chicobi, L., *Quebec* 35 Md
Chicopee, *Massachusetts* 44 Da
Chicoutai, Pte., *Quebec* 33 Lc
Chicoutimi, *Quebec* 32 Ae
Chicoutimi, R., *Quebec* 35 Te
Chicoutimi-Nord, *Quebec* 32 Be
Chicualacula, *Mozambique* 95 Ed
Chicuma, *Angola* 96 Cg
Chidambaram, *India* 88 Ef
Chidley, C., *N.W.T.* 31 Ne
Chiefs Pt., *Ontario* 34 Jh
Chiete, *Italy* 74 Ed
Chièvres, *Belgium* 64 Bd
Chifeng, *China* 84 Ja
Chignecto B., *N.S./N.B.* 32 Hh
Chignik, *Alaska* 41 Ad
Chigoubiche, *Quebec* 35 Rc
Chigubo, *Mozambique* 95 Ed
Chihchow. *See* Guichi
Chihli, G. of. *See* Bo Hai
Chihuahua, *Mexico* 50 Cb
Chik-Ballapur, *India* 88 Ef
Chikmagalur, *India* 88 Ef
Chikwawa, *Malawi* 97 Gh
Chilas, *Kashmir* 90 Dc
Chilca, Pta. de, *Peru* 52 Bf
Chilcotin, R., *B.C.* 39 Mk
Childress, *Texas* 48 Ge
Chile, *S. America* 54 Bf
Chilecito, *Argentina* 54 Cc
Chilete, *Peru* 52 Be
Chilia Veche, *Romania* 76 Gb
Chililabombwe, *Zambia* 95 Db
Chilka L., *India* 89 Ge
Chilko, R., *B.C.* 39 Mk
Chilko L., *B.C.* 39 Lk
Chillán, *Chile* 54 Be
Chillicothe, *Missouri* 49 Lc
Chillicothe, *Ohio* 40 Ef
Chilliwack, *B.C.* 39 Nl
Chiloé, I. de, *Chile* 54 Bf
Chilonga, *Zambia* 97 Gg
Chilpancingo, *Mexico* 50 Ed
Chiltern Hills, *England* 63 Gj
Chilton, *Wisconsin* 40 Bc
Chiluane, *Mozambique* 95 Fd
Chilubula, *Zambia* 97 Gg
Chilumba, *Malawi* 95 Eb
Chilung, *Taiwan* 85 Kk
Chilwa L., *Malawi* 97 Hh
Chimay, *Belgium* 64 Cd
Chimbay, *Uzbekistan* 78 Ed
Chimborazo, *Ecuador* 52 Bd
Chimbote, *Peru* 52 Be
Chimkent, *Kazakhstan* 78 Fd
Chin, *Alberta* 36 Ej
Chin, C., *Ontario* 34 Jg
Chin, rep., *India* 59 Ke
Chinan. *See* Jinan
Chinandega, *Nicaragua* 51 Bd
Chincha, *Peru* 52 Bf
Chinchaga, R., *Alberta* 39 Of
Chin-chiang. *See* Qingjiang
Chinchón, *Spain* 70 Db
Chindwin, *Burma* 89 Jc
Chingleput, *India* 88 Ff
Chingtao. *See* Qingdao
Chinguetta, *Mauritania* 98 Cd
Ch'ing-yuan. *See* Baoding
Chin Hills, *Burma* 89 Hd
Chin-hua. *See* Jinhua
Chin-ning. *See* Jining
Chiniot, *Pakistan* 90 Ce
Chinju, *Korea* 82 Jc
Chinook, *Alberta* 36 Gg
Chinook, *Montana* 46 Ca
Chinsura, *India* 91 Gd
Chioggia, *Italy* 74 Dc
Chios, I. *See* Khíos
Chipata, *Zambia* 97 Gg
Chipewyan L., *Manitoba* 37 Ta
Chipewyan Lake, *Alberta* 38 Rg
Chipili, *Zambia* 97 Fg
Chip L., *Alberta* 36 Be
Chip Lake, *Alberta* 36 Be
Chipman, *New Brunswick* 32 Gg
Chipman L., *Ontario* 34 Dc
Chipoka, *Malawi* 95 Eb
Chippawa, *Ontario* 35 Lj
Chippenham, *England* 63 Fj
Chippewa, R., *Wisconsin* 43 Hb
Chippewa Falls, *Wisconsin* 46 Mc
Chipping Norton, *England* 63 Fj
Chiputneticook Lakes, *Maine/New Brunswick* 32 Eh
Chiquián, *Peru* 52 Bf
Chiquimula, *Guatemala* 50 Ge
Chiquinquira, *Colombia* 52 Cb
Chiras, *Afghanistan* 93 Jb
Chirawa, *India* 90 Df
Chiricahua Nat. Mon., *Arizona* 48 Cf
Chiriquí, Lag. de, *Panama* 51 Ce
Chiriqui Grande, *Panama* 51 Ce
Chirpan, *Bulgaria* 76 Ec
Chirripo, Mt., *Costa Rica* 51 Ce
Chisamba Falls, *Zambia* 97 Gg
Chishmy, *U.S.S.R.* 81 Mc
Chisholm, *Alberta* 36 Cd
Chisimaio, *Somalia* 97 Je
Chisinau. *See* Kishinev
Chistopol', *U.S.S.R.* 81 Kc
Chita, *U.S.S.R.* 79 Lc
Chitambo, *Zambia* 97 Gg
Chitek, *Saskatchewan* 36 Ke
Chitek L., *Manitoba* 37 Sf
Chitila, *Romania* 76 Eb
Chitipa, *Malawi* 95 Ea
Chitorgarh, *India* 88 Dd
Chitradurga, *India* 88 Ef
Chitral, *Pakistan* 90 Bc
Chitre, *Panama* 51 Ce
Chittagong, *Bangladesh* 89 Hd
Chittoor, *India* 88 Ef
Chiusi, *Italy* 74 Cd
Chiuta, L., *Malawi* 97 Hg
Chiva, *Spain* 71 Ec
Chivasso, *Italy* 74 Ac
Chivay, *Peru* 52 Cg
Chivilcoy, *Argentina* 54 Dd
Chivoto, Sierra, *New Mexico* 48 De
Chiwanda, *Tanzania* 97 Gg
Chmielnik, *Poland* 69 Jc
Choapam, *Mexico* 50 Ed
Choban Bey, *Syria* 94 Fa
Chocaya, *Bolivia* 52 Dh
Choceň, *Czechoslovakia* 69 Gc
Chochocouane, R., *Quebec* 35 Oe
Choco, *Colombia* 52 Bb
Choconta, *Colombia* 52 Cb
Choele Choel, *Argentina* 54 Ce
Choiceland, *Saskatchewan* 37 Ne
Choiseul, *Solomon Islands* 102 Eh
Choix, *Mexico* 50 Cb
Chojna, *Poland* 68 Fb
Chojnice, *Poland* 69 Gb
Choke Mts., *Ethiopia* 97 Hb
Cholet, *France* 72 Cc
Cholon, *Vietnam* 87 Dd
Choluteca, *Honduras* 51 Bd
Choma, *Zambia* 95 Dc
Chomolhari, *Bhutan* 91 Fa
Chomutov, *Czechoslovakia* 68 Ec
Chone, *Ecuador* 52 Ad
Chong'an, *China* 85 Hj
Chongjin, *Korea* 82 Jb
Chong Kal, *Kampuchea* 87 Cd
Chongming, *China* 84 Kg
Chongqing, *China* 85 Ch
Chongzuo, *China* 82 Ef
Chonos, Arch. de los, *Chile* 54 Bf
Chorillos, *Peru* 52 Bf
Chorrera, *Panama* 51 De
Chorzele, *Poland* 69 Jb
Chorzow, *Poland* 69 Hc
Choshi, *Japan* 86 Gg
Chos Malal, *Argentina* 54 Be
Chota, *Peru* 52 Be
Chown Mt., *Alberta* 39 Oj
Christchurch, *New Zealand* 55 De
Christian, C., *N.W.T.* 31 Nc
Christian I., *Ontario* 34 Kh
Christianshab, *Greenland* 31 Od
Christie B., *N.W.T.* 38 Sd
Christie L., *Manitoba* 37 Vb
Christina L., *Alberta* 36 Fc
Christina R., *Alberta* 36 Gb
Christmas, I., *Pacific Ocean* 103 Kg
Christmas I., *Indian Ocean* 83 En
Christopher Falls, *Ontario* 34 Hb
Chrudim, *Czechoslovakia* 69 Fd
Chrzanów, *Poland* 69 Hc
Chuali L., *Mozambique* 95 Ed
Chubut R., *Argentina* 54 Cf
Chuchow. *See* Lishui
Chucul, *Argentina* 54 Dd
Chudleigh, *Ontario* 34 Kf
Chudovo, *U.S.S.R.* 80 Gb
Chudskoye Ozero, *Estonia/U.S.S.R.* 67 Mg
Chukai, *Pen. Malaysia* 83 Dk
Chukhloma, *U.S.S.R.* 81 Fa
Chukotskiy Khrebet, *U.S.S.R.* 79 Sb
Chul'man, *U.S.S.R.* 79 Mc
Chulym, *U.S.S.R.* 78 Hc
Chumikan, *U.S.S.R.* 79 Nc
Chumphon, *Thailand* 87 Bd
Chuna, *U.S.S.R.* 79 Jc
Chunan, *Taiwan* 85 Kk
Chunar, *India* 91 Dc
Chunchŏn, *Korea* 82 Jc
Chung-ch'ing. *See* Chongqing
Chung-yang Shan-mo, *Taiwan* 85 Kl
Chunian, *Pakistan* 90 Ce
Chunya, *Tanzania* 97 Gf
Chuquibambilla, *Peru* 52 Cf
Chuquicamata, *Chile* 54 Cb
Chur, *Switzerland* 65 Eb
Churapcha, *U.S.S.R.* 79 Nb
Churchbridge, *Sask.* 37 Qh
Churchill, *Manitoba* 30 Kf
Churchill, C., *Manitoba* 31 Kf
Churchill, R., *Nfld.* 31 Ng
Churchill Falls, *Nfld.* 31 Ng
Churchill L., *Sask.* 36 Jb
Churchill Peak, *B.C.* 39 Lf
Churchill R., *Sask./Man.* 30 Jf
Churchill R., Lit., *Man.* 37 Wb
Church Point, *Nova Scotia* 32 Fj
Church's Ferry, *N. Dakota* 46 Ha
Churia Ghati Hills, *Nepal* 91 Eb
Churia Range, *Nepal* 91 Ca
Churu, *India* 90 Df
Chusca, Sierra, *New Mexico* 48 Cd
Chusovoy, *U.S.S.R* 78 Ec
Chute-aux-Outardes, *Quebec* 32 Dd
Chute-des-Passes Dam, *Quebec* 32 Ad
Chuvashskaya, *A.S.S.R.*, *U.S.S.R.* 78 Dc
Chuxiong, *China* 82 De
Chwan Ho. *See* Chang Jiang
Cicero, *Illinois* 49 Ob
Cidones, *Spain* 71 Db
Ciechanów, *Poland* 69 Jb
Ciego de Avila, *Cuba* 51 Db
Cienaga, *Colombia* 52 Ca
Cienfuegos, *Cuba* 51 Cb
Cierfs, *Switzerland* 65 Fb
Cieszyn, *Poland* 69 Hd
Cieza, *Spain* 71 Ec
Cifuentes, *Spain* 71 Db
Cijara, Emb. de, *Spain* 70 Cc
Cilacap, *Java* 83 Em
Cili, *China* 85 Eh
Cimaltepec, *Mexico* 50 Ed
Cimarron R., *U.S.A.* 42 Fd
Cimpulung, *Romania* 76 Eb
Cincinnati, *Ohio* 40 Df
Cioara, *Romania* 76 Fb
Ciotat, La, *France* 73 Fe
Circeo C., *Italy* 75 De
Circle, *Alaska* 43 Yl
Circle, *Montana* 46 Eb
Circleville, *Ohio* 40 Ef
Cirebon, *Java* 83 Em
Cirencester, *England* 63 Fj
Ciro, *Italy* 75 Ff
Citlaltepetl, *Mexico* 50 Ed
Citrusdal, *Cape Province* 95 Bf
Citta del Vaticano, *Italy* 75 De
Cittanova, *Italy* 75 Ff
Ciudad Bolívar, *Venezuela* 52 Eb
Ciudad Bolivia, *Venezuela* 52 Cb
Ciudad Camargo, *Mexico* 50 Cb
Ciudad Guzmán, *Mexico* 50 Dd
Ciudad Juárez, *Mexico* 50 Ca
Ciudad Madero, *Mexico* 50 Ec
Ciudad Real, *Spain* 70 Dc
Ciudad Rodrigo, *Spain* 70 Bb
Ciudad Victoria, *Mexico* 50 Ec
Civitanova Marche, *Italy* 74 Dd
Civitavecchia, *Italy* 74 Cd
Civray, *France* 72 Dc
Civril, *Turkey* 92 Ab
Cizre, *Turkey* 92 Db
Clacton-on-Sea, *England* 63 Hj
Clair, *New Brunswick* 32 Df
Clair, *Saskatchewan* 37 Nf
Claire, L., *Alberta* 39 Rf
Clamecy, *France* 72 Ec
Clandonald, *Alberta* 36 Ge
Clanwilliam, *Manitoba* 37 Sh
Clara I., *Burma* 89 Jf
Clare, *Eire* 63 Ah
Clare, *Michigan* 40 Dd
Clare I., *Eire* 63 Ag
Claremont, *New Hampshire* 44 Da
Claremore, *Oklahoma* 49 Kd
Claremorris, *Eire* 63 Bg
Clarence, *Chile* 54 Bh
Clarence I., *Antarctica* 104 Tc
Clarence R., *New Zealand* 55 De
Clarence Str., *N. Terr.* 56 Fb
Clarendon, *Arkansas* 45 Bc
Clarendon Station, *Ont.* 35 Oh
Clarenville, *Newfoundland* 33 Se
Claresholm, *Alberta* 36 Dh
Clarinda, *Iowa* 49 Kb
Clarion, *Iowa* 49 La
Clarion, *Pennsylvania* 44 Ab
Clarion R., *Pennsylvania* 44 Ab
Clark, *S. Dakota* 46 Jc
Clark, Mt., *N.W.T.* 38 Lc
Clark, Pt., *Ontario* 34 Jh
Clarke, R., *N.W.T.* 38 Wd
Clarke City, *Quebec* 32 Fc
Clarke L., *Saskatchewan* 36 Kd
Clarkesville, *Texas* 49 Kf
Clarksburg, *West Virginia* 40 Ff
Clarksdale, *Mississippi* 45 Bc
Clark's Harbour, *N.S.* 32 Gk
Clarkson, *Ontario* 35 Lj
Clarksville, *Tennessee* 49 Oc
Claro, *Switzerland* 65 Eb
Clausthal, *West Germany* 68 Dc
Clavet, *Saskatchewan* 36 Lf
Clay Center, *Kansas* 49 Jc
Claydon, *Saskatchewan* 36 Hj
Clay L., *Ontario* 36 Ja
Clayoquot, *B.C.* 39 Kl
Clayton, *Alabama* 45 Ee
Clayton, *New Mexico* 48 Fd
Clear, C., *Eire* 63 Aj
Clear, L., *Ontario* 35 Ng
Clear Creek, *Oklahoma* 49 Je
Clearfield, *Pennsylvania* 44 Ab
Clear Hills, *Alberta* 39 Og
Clear L., *California* 47 Bf
Clear L., *Manitoba* 37 Sh
Clear Lake, *Iowa* 49 La
Clearmont, *Wyoming* 46 Dc
Clearwater, *B.C.* 39 Nk
Clearwater, R., *Alberta* 39 Sg
Clearwater L., *Manitoba* 37 Qa
Clearwater R., *Alberta* 36 Bf
Clearwater R., *Idaho* 47 Fb
Clearwater Res., *Missouri* 49 Md
Cleburne, *Texas* 49 Jf
Cleeves, *Saskatchewan* 36 He
Clements Markham Inlet, *Northwest Territories* 31 Na
Clementsport, *N.S.* 32 Gj
Clementsvale, *N.S.* 32 Gj
Cléricy, *Quebec* 35 Md
Clermont, *Quebec* 32 Bf
Clermont, *Queensland* 57 Jd
Clermont-Ferrand, *France* 72 Ed
Clerval, *Quebec* 35 Ld
Cleveland, *England* 63 Gf
Cleveland, *Ohio* 40 Fe
Cleveland, *Tennessee* 45 Ec
Cleveland, *Texas* 49 Kg
Clew Bay, *Eire* 63 Ag
Clifden, *Eire* 63 Ag
Clifford, *Ontario* 34 Kj
Clifton, *Arizona* 48 Cf

Clifton, *Tennessee* 45 Cc
Clifton Forge, *Virginia* 45 Hb
Clifton Hills, *S. Australia* 57 Ge
Clifton Pt., *N.W.T.* 38 Oa
Clifton Ville, *Wisconsin* 40 Bc
Climax, *Saskatchewan* 36 Jj
Clinch Mts., *Tenn./Va.* 45 Fb
Cline Mt., *Alberta* 39 Pj
Clinton, *Arkansas* 45 Ac
Clinton, *B.C.* 39 Nk
Clinton, *Illinois* 49 Nb
Clinton, *Iowa* 49 Mb
Clinton, *Massachusetts* 44 Ea
Clinton, *Missouri* 49 Lc
Clinton, *Oklahoma* 49 He
Clinton, *Ontario* 34 Jj
Clinton-Colden L., *N.W.T.* 38 Ud
Clinton Dam, *Tennessee* 45 Eb
Clipperton, *Pacific Ocean* 103 Qf
Clisson, *France* 72 Cc
Clive, *Alberta* 36 Df
Clive L., *N.W.T.* 38 Od
Cliza, *Bolivia* 52 Dg
Cloan, *Saskatchewan* 36 Jf
Clonakilty, *Eire* 63 Bj
Cloncurry, *Queensland* 57 Hd
Clones, *Eire* 63 Cf
Clonmel, *Eire* 63 Bh
Clo-oose, *B.C.* 39 Ll
Cloquet, *Minnesota* 46 Lb
Clorinda, *Argentina* 54 Ec
Cloud Peak, *Wyoming* 42 Ec
Cloutier, *Quebec* 35 Ld
Clova, *Quebec* 35 Pd
Clover, *Virginia* 45 Hb
Clovis, *New Mexico* 48 Fe
Cluj, *Romania* 76 Da
Cluny, *Alberta* 36 Eh
Clusone, *Italy* 74 Bc
Clute, *Ontario* 34 Kc
Clut L., *N.W.T.* 38 Pc
Clwyd, *Wales* 63 Eg
Clyde, *Alberta* 36 Dd
Clyde, *New Zealand* 55 Bf
Clyde, *N.W.T.* 31 Nc
Clyde, Firth of, *Scotland* 62 De
Clyde Forks, *Ontario* 35 Og
Clyde Inlet, *N.W.T.* 31 Nc
Clyde R., *Nova Scotia* 32 Gk
Clyde R., *Scotland* 62 Ee
Coacoachou L., *Quebec* 33 Mc
Coahuila, *Mexico* 50 Db
Coalcomán, *Mexico* 50 Dd
Coaldale, *Alberta* 36 Ej
Coalhurst, *Alberta* 36 Ej
Coal R., *Y.T.* 38 Ke
Coal River, *B.C.* 38 Kf
Coamo, *Puerto Rico* 51 Fc
Coari, *Brazil* 52 Ed
Coast Mts., *B.C.* 39 Gg
Coast Range, *Oregon* 30 Gj
Coatbridge, *Scotland* 62 Ee
Coatepec, *Mexico* 50 Ed
Coatepeque, *Guatemala* 50 Fe
Coatesville, *Pennsylvania* 44 Cc
Coaticook, *Quebec* 34 Tg
Coats I., *N.W.T.* 31 Le
Coats Land, *Antarctica* 104 Bb
Coatzacoalcos, *Mexico* 50 Fd
Cobalt, *Ontario* 35 Le
Cobàn, *Guatemala* 50 Fd
Cobar, *N.S.W.* 57 Jf
Cobb, Mt., *New Zealand* 55 Dd
Cobden, *Ontario* 35 Og
Cobequid B. & Mts., *N.S.* 32 Jh
Cóbh, *Eire* 63 Bj
Cobija, *Bolivia* 52 Df
Cobleskill, *New York* 40 Jd
Coboconk, *Ontario* 35 Mh
Cobourg, *Ontario* 35 Mj
Cobourg Pen., *N. Terr.* 56 Fb
Cobre, El, *Cuba* 51 Dc
Coburg, *W. Germany* 68 Dc
Coburg I., *N.W.T.* 31 Mb
Cocahacra, *Peru* 52 Cg
Cocamá, *Peru* 52 Cf
Cochabamba, *Bolivia* 52 Dg
Cochin, *India* 88 Eg
Cochin China, *Vietnam* 87 Dd
Cochinoca, *Argentina* 54 Cb
Cochran, *Georgia, U.S.A.* 45 Fd
Cochrane, *Alberta* 36 Cg
Cochrane, *Chile/Arg.* 54 Bg
Cochrane, *Ontario* 34 Jc
Cochrane, R., *Sask.* 38 Wf
Cockburn, *S. Australia* 57 Hf
Cockburn, Canal, *Chile* 54 Bh
Cockburn I., *Ontario* 34 Gf
Cockburn Island, *Ontario* 34 Gg
Coco, I. del, *Pacific Ocean* 103 Sg
Cocos Is., *Indian Ocean* 100 Hf
Cocula, *Mexico* 50 Dc
Cocumbi, *Angola* 96 Dg
Cocuy, *Colombia* 52 Cb
Cod, C., *Massachusetts* 44 Ea
Codajás, *Brazil* 52 Ed
Coderre, *Saskatchewan* 36 Lh
Codette, *Saskatchewan* 37 Ne
Codfish I., *New Zealand* 55 Ag
Cod I., *Newfoundland* 31 Nf
Codó, *Brazil* 53 Jd
Codroy, *Newfoundland* 33 Nf
Codroy Pond, *Nfld.* 33 Oe
Cod's Head, *Eire* 63 Aj
Cody, *Wyoming* 46 Cc
Codys, *New Brunswick* 32 Gh
Coe Hill, *Ontario* 35 Nh
Coen, *Queensland* 57 Hb
Coeur d'Alene, *Idaho* 47 Eb
Coevorden, *Netherlands* 64 Eb
Coeymans, *New York* 44 Da
Coffee Creek, *Y.T.* 38 Dd
Coffeyville, *Kansas* 49 Kd
Coff's Harbour, *N.S.W.* 57 Kf
Cognac, *France* 72 Cd
Cogolludo, *Spain* 70 Db
Cohoes, *New York* 44 Da
Coiba I., *Panama* 51 Ce
Coihaique, *Chile* 54 Bg
Coimbatore, *India* 88 Ef
Coimbra, *Portugal* 70 Ab
Coin, *Spain* 70 Cd
Coire. *See* Chur
Cojimies, *Ecuador* 52 Ac
Colac, *Victoria* 57 Hg
Colair L., *India* 88 Fe
Colbeck Arch., *Antarctica* 104 Fc
Colborne, *Ontario* 35 Nh
Colby, *Kansas* 48 Gc
Colcha, *Bolivia* 52 Dh
Colchester, *England* 63 Hj
Cold L., *Alberta* 36 Gd
Cold Lake, *Alberta* 36 Gd
Cold Lake, *Manitoba* 37 Qc
Coldwater, *Ontario* 35 Lh
Coldwell, *Ontario* 34 Dd
Colebrook, *New Hampshire* 40 Lc
Coleman, *Alberta* 36 Cj
Coleman, *Texas* 49 Hg
Coleraine, *N. Ireland* 62 Ce
Coleraine, *Quebec* 35 Tg
Coleridge, L., *New Zealand* 55 Ce
Coleville, *Saskatchewan* 36 Hg
Colfax, *Saskatchewan* 37 Oj
Colgate, *Saskatchewan* 37 Oj
Colgong, *India* 91 Fc
Colhué Huapi, L., *Argentina* 54 Cg
Colima, *Mexico* 50 Dd
Colinas, *Brazil* 53 Je
Colinton, *Alberta* 36 Dd
Coll, I., *Scotland* 62 Cd
Collaguasi, *Chile* 54 Cb
Collie, *W. Australia* 56 Cf
Collier B., *W. Australia* 56 Dc
Collines-de-Normandie, *France* 72 Cb
Collingwood, *Ontario* 34 Kh
Collingwood, *Queensland* 57 Hd
Collins, *Ontario* 37 Oa
Collins, Mt., *Ontario* 34 Ke
Collinson Pen., *N.W.T.* 38 Xa
Collinsville, *Queensland* 57 Jd
Collo, *Algeria* 98 Ga
Colmar, *France* 72 Gb
Colmars, *France* 73 Gd
Colmena, *Argentina* 54 Dc
Colmenar, *Spain* 70 Cd
Colmenar de Oreja, *Spain* 70 Db
Colmenar Viejo, *Spain* 70 Db
Colne R., *England* 63 Hj
Cologne, *West Germany* 68 Bc
Colombia, *Brazil* 53 Hh
Colombia, *S. America* 52 Cc
Colombier, *Switzerland* 65 Bb
Colombière, *Quebec* 35 Nd
Colombo, *Sri Lanka* 88 Eg
Colón, *Argentina* 54 Dd
Colón, *Argentina* 54 Ed
Colón, *Cuba* 51 Cb
Colón, *Panama* 51 De
Colón, *Venezuela* 52 Cb
Colonelganj, *India* 91 Cb
Colonia, *Uruguay* 54 Ed
Colonia Alvear, *Argentina* 54 Cd
Colonsay, *Saskatchewan* 37 Mg
Colonsay, *Scotland* 62 Cd
Colorado, *Texas* 48 Gf
Colorado, *U.S.A.* 42 Ed
Colorado, R., *Argentina* 54 De
Colorado Des., *Wyoming* 46 Cd
Colorado Desert, *California* 47 Eh
Colorado Plat., *Arizona* 48 Bd
Colorado R., *Texas* 49 Jh
Colorado R., *Utah/Arizona* 48 Cc
Colorado R., *Utah/Colo.* 42 Dd
Colorado R., Little, *Arizona* 48 Be
Colorados, Arch. de los, *Cuba* 51 Cb
Colorado Springs, *Colorado* 48 Ec
Colotlán, *Mexico* 50 Dc
Colpoy B., *Ontario* 34 Kh
Colquechaca, *Bolivia* 52 Dg
Colton, *California* 47 Eh
Columbia, *Alabama* 45 Ee
Columbia, *Indiana* 40 De
Columbia, *Kentucky* 45 Eb
Columbia, *Louisiana* 45 Ad
Columbia, *Maryland* 44 Bb
Columbia, *Mississippi* 43 Je
Columbia, *Missouri* 49 Lc
Columbia, *Pennsylvania* 44 Bb
Columbia, *S. Carolina* 45 Gc
Columbia, *Tennessee* 45 Dc
Columbia, C., *N.W.T.* 31 Ma
Columbia, Mt., *B.C.* 39 Pj
Columbia Lake, *B.C.* 39 Qk
Columbiana, *Alabama* 45 Dd
Columbia Plat., *Wash./Oregon/Idaho* 42 Cb
Columbia R., *B.C.* 39 Pk
Columbus, *Georgia, U.S.A.* 45 Ed
Columbus, *Indiana* 40 Df
Columbus, *Kansas* 49 Kd
Columbus, *Mississippi* 49 Nf
Columbus, *Montana* 46 Cc
Columbus, *Nebraska* 49 Jb
Columbus, *Ohio* 40 Ef
Columbus, *Texas* 49 Jh
Colville, C., *New Zealand* 55 Eb
Colville L., *N.W.T.* 38 Lb
Colville Mts., *N.W.T.* 38 Qa
Colwyn Bay, *Wales* 63 Eg
Comacchio, *Italy* 74 Dc
Comai, *China* 89 Hc
Comalcalco, *Mexico* 50 Fd
Comana, *Romania* 76 Fb
Comayagua, *Honduras* 51 Bd
Combarbala, *Chile* 54 Bd
Comber, *Ontario* 34 Hk
Combermere, *Ontario* 35 Ng
Comblain, *Belgium* 64 Dd
Comencho, L., *Quebec* 35 Pb
Comeragh Mts., *Eire* 63 Bh
Comino C., *Sardinia* 75 Be
Comiso, *Sicily* 75 Eg
Comitán, *Mexico* 50 Fd
Commanda, *Ontario* 35 Lg
Commentry, *France* 72 Ec
Commissaires, L. des, *Que.* 35 Sd
Committee B., *N.W.T.* 31 Ld
Commonwealth Range, *Antarctica* 104 Na
Como, *Italy* 74 Bc
Como, L., *Ontario* 40 Eb
Como, L. di, *Italy* 74 Bc
Comodoro Rivadavia, *Arg.* 54 Cg
Comondu, *Mexico* 50 Bb
Comorin, C., *India* 88 Eg
Comoros, *Ind. Ocean* 97 Jg
Compeer, *Alberta* 36 Gg
Compiègne, *France* 72 Eb
Comporta, *Portugal* 70 Ac
Compostela, *Mexico* 50 Dc
Conakry, *Guinea* 98 Cg
Conceicao do Araguaya, *Brazil* 53 He
Concepción, *Argentina* 54 Cc
Concepción, *Bolivia* 52 Df
Concepción, *Chile* 54 Be
Concepción, *Paraguay* 54 Eb
Concepción del Oro, *Mexico* 50 Dc
Concepción del Uruguay, *Argentina* 54 Ed
Conception, Pt., *California* 42 Be
Conception B., *Nfld.* 33 Uf
Conception Harbour, *Nfld.* 33 Tf
Conception I., *The Bahamas* 51 Db
Conchas Res., *New Mexico* 48 Ee
Conche, *Newfoundland* 33 Rc
Conchi, *Chile* 54 Cb
Concord, *Massachusetts* 44 Ea
Concord, *N. Carolina* 45 Gc
Concord, *New Hampshire* 44 Ea
Concordia, *Argentina* 54 Ed
Concordia, *Chile* 54 Ba
Concordia, *Kansas* 49 Jc
Concordia, *Mexico* 50 Cc
Condobolin, *N.S.W.* 57 Jf
Condom, *France* 73 De
Condor, Cord. del, *Peru* 52 Bd
Conemaugh, *Pennsylvania* 44 Ab
Conesa, *Argentina* 54 Df
Coney Arm, *Nfld.* 33 Qd
Coney I., *New York* 44 Db
Confolens, *France* 72 Dc
Confusion B., *Nfld.* 33 Rc
Congo, People's Rep. of the, *Africa* 96 Ee
Congo (Brazzaville). *See* Congo, Rep.
Congo (Kinshasa). *See* Zaire Rep. of
Congo R., *Congo/Zaire* 96 De
Congress, *Saskatchewan* 36 Lj
Coniston, *England* 63 Ef
Coniston, *Ontario* 34 Kf
Conklin, *Alberta* 39 Sh
Conlin, *Montana* 46 Eb
Connacht, *Eire* 63 Ag
Connaught, *Ontario* 34 Kd
Connecticut, *U.S.A.* 43 Mc
Connecticut R., *U.S.A.* 44 Da
Connellsville, *Pennsylvania* 44 Ab
Connemara, Mts. of, *Eire* 63 Ag
Conn L., *Eire* 63 Af
Connors, *New Brunswick* 32 Df
Conquest, *Saskatchewan* 36 Kg
Conrad, *Montana* 46 Ba
Conroe, *Texas* 49 Kg
Consecon, *Ontario* 35 Nj
Conselheiro Lafaiete, *Brazil* 53 Jh
Conshohocken, *Pa.* 44 Cb
Con Son Is., *Vietnam* 87 De
Consort, *Alberta* 36 Gf
Constance. *See* Konstanz
Constance, L. *See* Boden See
Constancia do Baetas, *Brazil* 52 Ee
Constanța, *Romania* 76 Gb
Constantine, *Algeria* 98 Ga
Constantine, Mt, *Y.T.* 38 Ce
Constitución, *Chile* 54 Be
Consuegra, *Spain* 70 Dc
Consul, *Saskatchewan* 36 Hj
Contamana, *Peru* 52 Ce
Conthey, *Switzerland* 65 Cb
Contrecoeur, *Quebec* 35 Rg
Contreras I., *Chile* 54 Ah
Control, *Alberta* 36 Fg
Contwoyto L., *N.W.T.* 38 Sc
Convención, *Colombia* 52 Cb
Conway, *Arkansas* 49 Le
Conway, *Missouri* 49 Ld
Conway, *New Hampshire* 40 Lc
Conway, *S. Carolina* 45 Hd
Conway, *Wales* 63 Eg
Coober Pedy, *S. Australia* 57 Fe
Cooch Behar, *India* 91 Gb
Cook, B. de, *Chile* 54 Bj
Cook, C., *B.C.* 39 Kk
Cook, Mt., *New Zealand* 55 Ce
Cooking L., *Alberta* 36 De
Cook Inlet, *Alaska* 43 Xm
Cook Is., *Pacific Ocean* 102 Jj
Cook's Harbour, *Nfld.* 33 Rb
Cookshire, *Quebec* 35 Tg
Cook's Passage, *Queensland* 57 Jb
Cookstown, *Ontario* 35 Lh
Cook Str., *New Zealand* 55 Ed
Cooktown, *Queensland* 57 Jc
Coolgardie, *W. Australia* 56 Df
Cooma, *N.S.W.* 57 Jg
Coonamble, *N.S.W.* 57 Jf
Coonoor, *India* 88 Ef
Cooper Mt., *B.C.* 39 Pk
Coopers Creek, *S. Australia* 57 Ge
Cooperstown, *New York* 44 Ca
Cooroy, *Queensland* 57 Ke
Coos Bay, *Oregon* 47 Ad
Cootamundra, *N.S.W.* 57 Jf
Cootehill, *Eire* 63 Cf
Copenhagen, *Denmark* 67 Ej
Copetonas, *Argentina* 54 De
Copiapó, *Chile* 54 Bc
Coporaque, *Peru* 52 Cf
Coppell, *Ontario* 34 Gc
Copper Cliff, *Ontario* 34 Jf
Coppermine, *N.W.T.* 38 Qb
Coppermine Pt., *Ontario* 34 Ff
Coppermine R., *N.W.T.* 38 Qb
Copper Mountain, *B.C.* 39 Nl
Coppet, *Switzerland* 65 Bb
Copp L., *N.W.T.* 38 Qe
Coquart, *Quebec* 40 Ja
Coquimbo, *Chile* 54 Bc
Coquitlam, *B.C.* 39 Jl
Corabia, *Romania* 76 Ec
Coraçoes, *Brazil* 53 Hh
Coral, *Ontario* 34 Jb
Coral Harbour, *N.W.T.* 31 Le
Corato, *Italy* 75 Fe
Corazon, Sierra, *Texas* 48 Fh
Corbetton, *Ontario* 34 Kh
Corbin Hd., *Newfoundland* 33 Rg
Corcaigh. *See* Cork
Corcovado, G. del, *Chile* 54 Bf
Corcovado, Mt., *Chile* 54 Bf
Corcubión, *Spain* 70 Aa
Cordell, *Oklahoma* 49 He
Córdoba, *Argentina* 54 Dd
Córdoba, *Mexico* 50 Ed
Córdoba, *Spain* 70 Cd
Cordova, *Alaska* 43 Yl
Córdova, *Peru* 52 Cf
Cordova Mines, *Ontario* 35 Nh
Corfu. *See* Kérkira
Corfu, Str. of, *Greece* 77 Ce
Coria, *Spain* 70 Bb
Corigliano Calabro, *Italy* 75 Ff
Coringa, *India* 89 Fe
Corinth, *Mississippi* 45 Cc
Corinth, *New York* 44 Da
Corinth. *See* Kórinthos
Corinto, *Brazil* 53 Jg
Corinto, *Nicaragua* 51 Bd
Cork, *Eire* 63 Bj
Cork Harb., *Eire* 63 Bj
Corleone, *Sicily* 75 Dg
Cormack, *Newfoundland* 33 Pd
Cormack, Mt., *Nfld.* 33 Qe
Cormier, L., *Quebec* 33 Lb
Cormorant, & L., *Man.* 37 Rd
Cormorant, Pte. au, *Que.* 33 Ld
Corner Brook, *Nfld.* 33 Pe
Corning, *Iowa* 49 Kb
Corning, *New York* 44 Ba
Corning, *Saskatchewan* 37 Pj
Cornwall, *England* 63 Dk
Cornwall, *New York* 44 Cb
Cornwall, *Ontario* 35 Qg
Cornwall I., *N.W.T.* 30 Kb
Cornwallis I., *N.W.T.* 30 Kb
Coro, *Venezuela* 52 Da
Coroata, *Brazil* 53 Jd
Corocoro, *Bolivia* 52 Dg
Coroico, *Bolivia* 52 Dg
Coromandel Range, *N.Z.* 55 Eb
Coronach, *Saskatchewan* 37 Mj
Coronada, B., *Costa Rica* 51 Ce
Coronation, *Alberta* 36 Ff
Coronation G., *N.W.T.* 38 Ra
Coronation I., *Antarctica* 104 Tc
Coronel, *Chile* 54 Be
Coronel Pringles, *Argentina* 54 De
Coronel Suarez, *Argentina* 54 De
Coronie, *Surinam* 53 Fb
Coropuna, Mt., *Peru* 52 Cg
Corozal, *Belize* 51 Bc
Corpen Aiken, *Argentina* 54 Cg
Corpus Christi and B., *Texas* 48 Jj
Corpus Christi L., *Texas* 48 Jh
Corpus Christi Pass, *Texas* 48 Jj
Corque, *Bolivia* 52 Dg
Corrales, *Uruguay* 54 Ed
Corralitos, *Mexico* 50 Ca
Corregidor Bataan, *Philippines* 83 Hh
Corrèze, *France* 73 Dd
Corribelle, *Quebec* 35 Oc
Corrib L., *Eire* 63 Ag
Corrientes, *Argentina* 54 Ec
Corrientes, C., *Argentina* 54 Ee
Corrientes, C., *Mexico* 50 Cc
Corrigin, *W. Australia* 56 Cf
Corry, *Pennsylvania* 44 Ab
Corse, *France* 74 Bd
Corse-du-Sud, *Corsica* 73 Jg
Corsewall Point, *Scotland* 62 De
Corsica. *See* Corse
Corsicana, *Texas* 49 Jf
Cortés, C., *Cuba* 51 Cb
Cortland, *New York* 44 Ba
Cortona, *Italy* 74 Cd
Coruche, *Portugal* 70 Ac
Coruh, *Turkey* 92 Da
Çorum, *Turkey* 92 Ca
Corumbá, *Brazil* 53 Fg
Corunna. *See* La Coruña
Corvallis, *Oregon* 47 Bc
Corwen, *Wales* 63 Eh
Corwin, *Alaska* 43 Wl
Corydon, *Iowa* 49 Lb
Cosalo, *Mexico* 50 Cc
Coscurita, *Spain* 71 Db
Cosenza, *Italy* 75 Ff
Cosigüina, Vol., *Nicaragua* 51 Bd
Cosquin, *Argentina* 54 Dd
Cossonay, *Switzerland* 65 Bb
Costa Blanca, *Spain* 71 Ec
Costa Brava, *Spain* 71 Gb
Costa del Azahar, *Spain* 71 Fc
Costa Dorada, *Spain* 71 Fb
Costa Rica, *Central America* 51 Cd
Costebelle, L., *Quebec* 33 Kc
Costigan Mts., *N.B.* 32 Fg
Costillo Pk., *New Mexico* 48 Ed
Cotabato, *Philippines* 83 Hj
Cotagaita, *Bolivia* 52 Dh
Cotahuasi, *Peru* 52 Cg
Côteau, La Station-du-, *Que.* 35 Qg
Coteau, The, plat., *Sask.* 36 Kg
Cote Blanche B., *Louisiana* 49 Mh
Côte-d'or, *France* 72 Fc
Côtes-du-Nord, *Fr.* 72 Bb
Côte-St.-Luc, *Quebec* 35 Rk
Cotonou, *Benin* 98 Fg
Cotswold Hills, *England* 63 Fj
Cottbus, *East Germany* 68 Fc
Cottel I., *Newfoundland* 33 Te
Cottica, *Surinam* 53 Gc
Cotton L., *Manitoba* 37 Vc
Cotulla, *Texas* 48 Hh
Coudersport, *Pennsylvania* 44 Bb
Coudres, I. aux, *Quebec* 32 Bf
Coulman, I., *Antarctica* 104 Lb
Coulonge, R., *Quebec* 35 Of
Coulter, *Manitoba* 37 Qj
Council Bluffs, *Iowa* 49 Kb
Council Grove, *Kansas* 49 Jc
Couper Is., *N.W.T.* 38 Qb
Courageous L., *N.W.T.* 38 Sc
Courantyne R., *Guyana* 53 Fc
Courcelles, *Quebec* 32 Bh
Couronne C., *France* 73 Fe
Courtenay, *B.C.* 39 Ll
Courtenay, *N. Dakota* 46 Hb
Courtmacsherry, *Eire* 63 Bj
Courtrai. *See* Kortrijk
Courtright, *Ontario* 34 Hk
Court-St Etienne, *Belgium* 64 Cd
Courval, *Saskatchewan* 36 Lh
Couta Magalhães, *Brazil* 53 He
Couterne, *France* 72 Cb
Couthuin, *Belgium* 64 Dd
Coutts, *Alberta* 36 Fj
Couvin, *Belgium* 64 Cd
Cove I., *Ontario* 34 Jg
Coventry, *England* 63 Fh
Covilhã, *Portugal* 70 Bb
Covington, *Kentucky* 40 Df
Covington, *Tennessee* 45 Cc
Covington, *Virginia* 45 Hb
Cowan, *Manitoba* 37 Rf
Cowan, L., *W. Australia* 56 Df
Cowan L., *Saskatchewan* 36 Kd
Cowan R., *Saskatchewan* 36 Kd
Cowansville, *Quebec* 35 Sg
Cowdenbeath, *Scotland* 62 Ed
Cowell, *S. Australia* 57 Gf
Cowes, *England* 63 Gk
Cow Head, *Newfoundland* 33 Pd
Cowichan L., *B.C.* 39 Ll
Cowley, *Alberta* 36 Dj
Cowra, *N.S.W.* 57 Jf
Coxipi L., *Quebec* 33 Ob
Coxsackie, *New York* 44 Da
Cox's Bazar, *Bangladesh* 89 Hd
Cox's Cove, *Newfoundland* 33 Od
Coyame, *Mexico* 50 Cb
Coyuca, *Mexico* 50 Dd
Cozumel, *Mexico* 50 Gc
Cozumel, I., *Mexico* 50 Gc
Cracow. *See* Kraków
Craig, *Colorado* 48 Db
Craig, Mt., *Y.T.* 38 Ce
Craigmyle, *Alberta* 36 Eg
Craigville, *Minnesota* 46 Lb
Craik, *Saskatchewan* 37 Mg
Craiova, *Romania* 76 Db
Cranberry Portage, *Man.* 37 Qd
Cranbrook, *B.C.* 39 Ql
Crandall, *Manitoba* 37 Rh
Crandon, *Wisconsin* 40 Bc
Crane L., *Saskatchewan* 36 Hh
Crane Lake, *Minnesota* 36 Kb
Crane Valley, *Sask.* 37 Mj
Crans, *Switzerland* 65 Cb
Crater L., *Oregon* 47 Bd
Crater Lake Nat. Park, *Oregon* 47 Bd
Crateús, *Brazil* 53 Je
Crato, *Brazil* 52 Ee
Crato, *Brazil* 53 Ke
Craven, *Saskatchewan* 37 Nh
Crawford, *Nebraska* 48 Fa
Crazy Mts., *Montana* 46 Bb
Crean L., *Saskatchewan* 36 Ld
Cree, R., *Saskatchewan* 39 Uf
Cree L., *Saskatchewan* 39 Ug
Cree Lake, *Saskatchewan* 39 Ug
Creelman, *Saskatchewan* 37 Oj
Creemore, *Ontario* 34 Kh
Cree River, *Saskatchewan* 30 Jf
Creighton, *Ontario* 34 Jf
Creighton, *Sask.* 37 Pd
Cremona, *Alberta* 36 Cg
Cremona, *Italy* 74 Cc
Crerar, *Ontario* 34 Kf
Cres, *Yugoslavia* 74 Ec
Cresco, *Iowa* 49 La
Cressday, *Alberta* 36 Gj
Crest, *Quebec* 40 Gb
Cresta, *Switzerland* 65 Eb
Creston, *B.C.* 39 Pl
Creston, *Iowa* 49 Kb
Crestwynd, *Saskatchewan* 37 Mh
Crete, *Nebraska* 49 Jb
Crete. *See* Kriti
Crete, Sea of, *Greece* 77 Eg
Creuse, *France* 72 Dc
Creusot, le, *France* 72 Fc
Crewe, *England* 63 Fg
Crichton, *Saskatchewan* 36 Kj
Crieff, *Scotland* 62 Ed
Crilly, *Ontario* 36 Kb
Crimea, pen., *U.S.S.R.* 80 Hj
Crimmitschau, *E. Germany* 68 Ec
Crimson Lake Provincial Park, *Alberta* 36 Cf
Cripple Creek, *Colorado* 48 Ec
Crisana, *Romania* 76 Ca
Cristóbal, *Panama* 51 De
Crna Gora, *Yugoslavia* 76 Bc
Crockett, *Texas* 49 Kg
Croisic, le, *France* 72 Bc
Croix, L. à la, *Quebec* 32 Bb
Croker, C., *Ontario* 34 Kh
Croker, R., *N.W.T.* 38 Oa
Croker I., *N. Terr.* 56 Fb
Cromarty, *Scotland* 62 Ec
Cromer, *England* 63 Hh
Cromer, *Manitoba* 37 Qj
Cromwell, *New Zealand* 55 Bf
Crooked I., *The Bahamas* 51 Eb
Crooked Island Passage, *The Bahamas* 51 Eb
Crooked L., *Newfoundland* 33 Qe
Crooked R., *B.C.* 39 Mh
Crooked River, *Sask.* 37 Of
Crookston, *Minnesota* 46 Jb
Croque, *Newfoundland* 33 Rb
Crosse, Ile-à-la-, *Sask.* 39 Th
Crosse, Lac Ile-à-la-, *Sask.* 39 Uh
Cross Fell, *England* 63 Ff
Crossfield, *Alberta* 36 Cg
Cross L., *Manitoba* 37 Ud
Cross Lake, *Manitoba* 37 Ud
Crossley Lakes, *N.W.T.* 38 Ja
Crotch L., *Ontario* 35 Oh
Crotone, *Italy* 75 Ff
Crow Agency, *Montana* 46 Dc
Crowduck L., *Manitoba* 36 Fa
Crowley, *Louisiana* 49 Lg
Crown Prince Frederik I., *Northwest Territories* 31 Ld
Crown Prince Olav Land, *Antarctica* 104 Ec
Crown Princess Martha Ld., *Antarctica* 104 Bb
Crowsnest Pass, *Alta./B.C.* 36 Cj
Croydon, *England* 63 Gj
Croydon, *Queensland* 57 Hc
Crozet Is., *Indian Ocean* 100 Dj
Crozier, C., *Antarctica* 105 Lb
Crozier Chan., *N.W.T.* 30 Hb
Cruz, *Utah* 47 Gf
Cruz Alta, *Argentina* 54 Dd
Cruz Alta, *Brazil* 54 Fc
Cruz del Eje, *Argentina* 54 Dd
Cruzeiro do Sul, *Brazil* 52 Ce
Cruz Grande, *Chile* 54 Bc
Cruz Grande, *Mexico* 50 Ed
Cry L., *B.C.* 39 Jf
Crysdale, Mt., *B.C.* 39 Mh
Crystal City, *Manitoba* 37 Tj
Crystal Falls, *Michigan* 40 Bb
Crystal Falls, *Ontario* 34 Lf
Crystal Springs, *Mississippi* 45 Be
Crystal Springs, *Sask.* 37 Mf
Cuamba, *Mozambique* 95 Fb
Cuangar, *Angola* 95 Bc
Cuango, *Angola* 96 Df
Cuanza R., *Angola* 96 Cf
Cuatro Ciénegas, *Mexico* 50 Db
Cuba, *New Mexico* 48 De
Cuba, *New York* 40 Gd
Cuba, *Portugal* 70 Bc
Cuba, *W. Indies* 51 Cb
Cub Hills, *Saskatchewan* 37 Nd
Cuchi, *Angola* 96 Dg
Cuchillo-Co., *Argentina* 54 De
Cuchillo Parado, *Mexico* 50 Db
Cúcuta, *Colombia* 52 Cb
Cudahy, *Wisconsin* 40 Cd
Cuddalore, *India* 88 Ef
Cuddapah, *India* 88 Ef
Cudworth, *Saskatchewan* 37 Mf
Cue, *W. Australia* 56 Ce
Cuéllar, *Spain* 70 Cb
Cuenca, *Ecuador* 52 Bd
Cuenca, *Spain* 71 Db
Cuencame, *Mexico* 50 Dc
Cuernavaca, *Mexico* 50 Ed
Cuero, *Texas* 49 Jh
Cuevo, *Bolivia* 52 Eh
Cuff L., *Quebec* 33 Nb
Cuglieri, *Sardinia* 75 Be
Cuiabá, *Brazil* 53 Fg
Cuiabá, *Brazil* 52 Fe
Cuiculaia, *Nicaragua* 51 Cd
Cuillin Hills, *Scotland* 62 Cc
Cuiña, P. de, *Spain* 70 Ba
Cuito Cuanavale, *Angola* 95 Bc
Culcairn, *N.S.W.* 57 Jg
Culebra, I., *West Indies* 51 Fc
Culemborg, *Netherlands* 64 Dc
Culgoa, R., *Qnsld./N.S.W.* 57 Je
Culiacán, *Mexico* 50 Cc
Cullera, *Spain* 71 Ec
Cully, *Switzerland* 65 Bb
Culmi, *Honduras* 51 Bc
Culpeper, *Virginia* 45 Ha
Culverden, *New Zealand* 55 De
Cumanà, *Venezuela* 52 Ea
Cumaria, *Peru* 52 Ce
Cumberland, *B.C.* 39 Ll
Cumberland, *Maryland* 44 Ac
Cumberland, *Virginia* 45 Hb
Cumberland, *Wisconsin* 46 Lc
Cumberland House, *Sask.* 37 Pe
Cumberland I., *Georgia, U.S.A.* 45 Ge
Cumberland L., *Sask.* 37 Pd
Cumberland Mts., *Tenn.* 45 Fb
Cumberland Peninsula, *Northwest Territories* 31 Nd
Cumberland Plat., *Tenn.* 35 Ec
Cumberland R., *Ky./Tenn.* 43 Jd
Cumberland Sound, *N.W.T.* 31 Nd
Cumbria, *England* 63 Ff
Cumbrian Mts., *England* 63 Ef
Cumbum, *India* 88 Ee
Cummins, *S. Australia* 57 Gf
Cumpas, *Mexico* 50 Ca
Cunene, *Angola* 95 Ac
Cuneo, *Italy* 74 Ac
Cunnamulla, *Queensland* 57 Je
Cupar, *Saskatchewan* 37 Nh
Cupar, *Scotland* 62 Ed
Cuprija, *Yugoslavia* 76 Cc
Cura, *Venezuela* 52 Da
Curaçá, *Brazil* 53 Ke
Curacao, *Caribbean Sea* 52 Da
Curaglia, *Switzerland* 65 Db
Curiapo, *Venezuela* 52 Eb
Curico, *Chile* 54 Bd
Curiplaya, *Colombia* 52 Cc
Curitiba, *Brazil* 54 Gc
Curitibanos, *Brazil* 54 Fc
Curlew Pt., *Quebec* 33 Lc
Currais Novos, *Brazil* 53 Ke
Curralinho, *Brazil* 53 Hd
Currie L., *Manitoba* 37 Ua
Currituck, *N. Carolina* 45 Kb
Curtis, I., *Pacific Ocean* 102 Hl
Curuai, L. Gde. do, *Brazil* 53 Fd
Curuca, *Brazil* 53 Hd
Curuzú Cuatia, *Argentina* 54 Ec
Curwensville, *Pennsylvania* 44 Ab
Cushing, *Oklahoma* 49 Je
Custer, *S. Dakota* 46 Fd
Cut Bank, *Montana* 46 Aa
Cutbank, R., *Alberta* 39 Oh
Cut Beaver L., *Sask.* 37 Pe
Cuthbert, *Georgia, U.S.A.* 45 Ee
Cut Knife, *Saskatchewan* 36 Jf
Cutler, *Ontario* 34 Hf
Cuttack, *India* 89 Gd
Cuxhaven, *West Germany* 68 Cb
Cuzco, *Peru* 52 Cf
Cyclades. *See* Kikládhes
Cygnet L., *Manitoba* 37 Wb
Cynthiana, *Kentucky* 45 Ea
Cynthia Oil Fields, *Alberta* 36 Be
Cypress Hills, *Sask.* 36 Hj
Cypress Hills Prov. Park, *Alberta/Sask.* 36 Gj
Cypress L., *Saskatchewan* 36 Hj
Cypress River, *Manitoba* 37 Sj
Cyprus, I., rep., *Medit. Sea* 94 Bb
Cyrenaica, *Libya* 99 Kc
Cyrus Field B., *N.W.T.* 31 Ne
Czar, *Alberta* 36 Gf
Czarnkow, *Poland* 69 Gb
Czechoslovakia, rep., *Europe* 61 Lf
Czersk, *Poland* 69 Hb
Częstochowa, *Poland* 69 Hc
Czlopa, *Poland* 69 Gb
Czyzewo, *Poland* 69 Kb

D

Da, R., *Vietnam* 87 Cb
Daaquam, *Quebec* 32 Cg
Dabā, *United Arab Emirates* 93 Gd
Dabakala, *Ivory Coast* 98 Eg
Dabaro, *Somalia* 97 Kc
Daba Shan, *China* 84 Df
Dabeiba, *Colombia* 52 Bb
Dębie, *Poland* 68 Fb
Dabola, *Guinea* 98 Cf
Dąbrowa Górnicza, *Poland* 69 Hc
Dacca, *Bangladesh* 89 Hd
Dachangtu Shan, *China* 85 Lg
Dadanawa, *Guyana* 52 Fc
Dade City, *Florida* 45 Ff
Dadri, *India* 90 Ef
Daedalus Reef, *Red Sea* 92 Ce
Dafang, *China* 85 Bj
Dafoe, *Saskatchewan* 37 Ng
Dagana, *Senegal* 98 Be
Dagash, *Sudan* 99 Me
Dagda, *Latvia* 67 Mh
Dagupan, *Philippines* 83 Hg
Dahadinni, R., *N.W.T.* 38 Ld
Da Hinggan Ling, *China* 82 Ha
Dahlak, Arch., *Ethiopia* 97 Ja
Dahomey. *See* Benin
D'Ailleboust, L., *Quebec* 32 Ad
Daimiel, *Spain* 70 Dc
Daireaux, *Argentina* 54 De
Dairut, *Egypt* 99 Mc
Daisetsuzan Nat. Park, *Japan* 86 Hc
Dai Shan, *China* 85 Lg
Daishoji. *See* Kaga
Dai Xian, *China* 84 Fc
Dajarra, *Queensland* 57 Gd
Dakar, *Senegal* 98 Bf
Dakhla, *Mauritania* 98 Bd
Dakovica, *Yugoslavia* 76 Cc
Dal, *Norway* 67 Df
Dala, *Angola* 96 Eg
Dalälvan, *Sweden* 67 Gf

Dalandzadagad, Mongolia 82 Db
DaLat, Vietnam 87 Dd
Dalbandin, Pakistan 88 Bc
Dalbosjön, Sweden 67 Eg
Dalby, Queensland 57 Ke
Dalby, Sweden 67 Ef
Dalemead, Alberta 36 Dh
Dalen, Netherlands 64 Eb
Dalen, Norway 67 Bg
Dalhart, Texas 42 Fd
Dalhousie, India 90 Ed
Dalhousie, N.B. 32 Fe
Dalhousie, C., N.W.T. 38 Ja
Dali, China 82 Ce
Dali, China 84 De
Dallas, Manitoba 37 Ug
Dallas, Oregon 47 Bc
Dallas, Texas 49 Jf
Dalles, The, Oregon 47 Cc
Dalmacio Velez, Argentina 54 Dd
Dalmatia, Yugoslavia 74 Ed
Dalmatovo, U.S.S.R. 81 Rb
Dalmau, India 91 Cb
Dalmeny, Saskatchewan 36 Lf
Dal'nerechensk, U.S.S.R. 79 Nd
Daloa, Ivory Coast 98 Dg
Dalou Shan, China 82 Ee
Dalquier, Quebec 35 Md
Dalroy, Alberta 36 Dg
Dalrymple, Mt., Queensland 57 Jd
Dalton, Ontario 34 Fd
Daltongani, India 91 Ec
Daly, R., N. Terr. 56 Fb
Daly L., Saskatchewan 39 Vg
Daly Waters, N. Terr. 56 Fc
Dam, Surinam 53 Fc
Daman, India 88 Dd
Damanhur, Egypt 99 Mb
Damant L., N.W.T. 38 Ve
Damar, Indonesia 83 Jm
Damascus. See Damas
Damas (Damascus), Syria 92 Cc
Damāvand, Iran 93 Fb
Damba, Angola 96 Df
Dambacha, Ethiopia 97 Hb
Damghan, Iran 93 Fb
Damiya, Jordan 94 De
Dammam, Ad, Arabia 93 Fd
Damoh, India 91 Bd
Dampier Arch., W. Aust. 56 Cd
Dampier Land, W. Aust. 56 Dc
Dampier Str., Irian Jaya 83 Kl
Damqawt, S. Yemen 93 Ff
Dan, C., Greenland 41 Nc
Dana, Saskatchewan 37 Mf
Dana, L., Quebec 35 Nb
Dana, Mt., California 47 Dg
Da Nang, Vietnam 87 Dc
Danapur, India 91 Ec
Danbury, Connecticut 44 Db
Danby, California 47 Fh
Dancing Point, Manitoba 37 Tf
Dandeldhura, Nepal 91 Ca
Dandenong, Victoria 57 Hg
Dandong, China 84 Mb
Dandurand, L., Quebec 35 Qe
Danford L., Quebec 35 Og
Danforth, Maine 32 Eh
Danger Pt., Cape Province 95 Bf
Dangshan, China 84 He
Dangtu, China 84 Jg
Daniel-Johnson Dam, Quebec 32 Dc
Daniel's Harbour, Nfld. 33 Pc
Daniels L., Ontario 36 Ja
Danilov, U.S.S.R. 80 Mb
Dankaz, Ethiopia 97 Hb
Danmark Fd., Greenland 41 Na
Dannevirke, New Zealand 55 Fd
Danskøya, Svalbard 41 Lb
Dansville, New York 44 Ba
Dante (Hafun), Somalia 97 Lb
Danube, R., Cent. Europe 61 Mg
Danville, Illinois 49 Pb
Danville, Kentucky 45 Eb
Danville, Pennsylvania 44 Bb
Danville, Quebec 35 Sg
Danville, Virginia 45 Hb
Danzig. See Gdańsk
Danzig, G. of, Poland 69 Ha
Dapp, Alberta 36 Dd
Daqq e Patargan, Afghan./Iran 93 Hc
Daraban Kalan, Pakistan 90 Be
Daran, Iran 93 Fc
Daraw, Egypt 99 Md
Darb, Arabia 92 Df
Darbhanga, India 91 Eb
D'Arcy, Saskatchewan 36 Jg
Dardanelle Res., Arkansas 49 Le
Dardanelles, Turkey 92 Ab
Dar-el-Beida, Morocco 98 Db
Darende, Turkey 92 Cb
Dar es Salaam, Tanzania 97 Hf
Darfur, Northern, Sudan 96 Eb
Darfur, Southern, Sudan 96 Eb
Dargai, Pakistan 90 Bc
Dargaon, India 89 Fd
Dargaville, New Zealand 55 Da
Darhan, Mongolia 79 Kd
Darien, Georgia, U.S.A. 45 Ge
Darjeeling, India 91 Gb
Darke Lake Provincial Park, British Columbia 39 Ol
Darling, L., N. Dakota 46 Ga
Darling, R., N.S.W. 57 Hf
Darling Downs, Queensland 57 Je
Darlingford, Manitoba 37 Tj
Darling Pen., N.W.T. 31 Mb
Darling Range, W. Australia 56 Cf
Darlington, S. Carolina 45 Hc
Darlington, Wisconsin 49 Ma
Darlowo, Poland 69 Ga
Darmody, Saskatchewan 36 Lh
Darmstadt, West Germany 68 Cd
Darnah, Libya 99 Kb
Darnley B., N.W.T. 38 La
Daroca, Spain 71 Eb
Darreh Gaz, Iran 93 Gb
Dart, C., Antarctica 104 Pb
Dart, R., England 63 Ek
Dartmoor, England 63 Ek
Dartmouth, England 63 Ek
Dartmouth, Nova Scotia 32 Jj
Dartmouth R., Quebec 32 Hd
Daru, Papua New Guinea 57 Ha
Daruvar, Yugoslavia 74 Fc
Darwin, N. Terr. 56 Fb
Darwin, Mt., Zimbabwe 95 Ec
Daryabad, India 91 Cb
Daryāchehye Bakhtegān, L., Iran 93 Fd
Daryācheh-ye-Rezā'Iyeh L., Iran 92 Eb
Dasara, Bangladesh 91 Hd
Dasht Ab, Iran 93 Gd
Dasht R., Pakistan 88 Bc
Dashwood, Ontario 34 Jj
Daska, Pakistan 90 Dd
Daspalla, India 89 Fd
Daspur, India 91 Fe
Dasuya, India 90 De
Dataganj, India 91 Ba
Datia, India 91 Bc
Datong, China 84 Fb
Datong He, China 82 Dc
Daudnagar, India 91 Ec
Daugavpils, Latvia 67 Mj
Daulatabad, Afghanistan 93 Jb
Daulatabad, India 88 Ed
Daulat Yar, Afghanistan 93 Jc
Daule, Ecuador 52 Ad
Dauphin, Manitoba 37 Rg
Dauphiné, France 73 Fd
Dauphin L., Manitoba 37 Sg
Davangus, Quebec 35 Md
Davao, Philippines 83 Jj
Davar Panah, Iran 93 Hd
Daveluyville, Quebec 35 Sf
Davenport, Iowa 49 Mb
Davenport Range, N. Terr. 57 Fd
David, Panama 51 Ce
David City, Nebraska 49 Jb
Davidson, Saskatchewan 37 Mg
Davies Gilbert, Mt., Y.T. 38 Ea
Davignab, Namibia 95 Be
Davin, Saskatchewan 37 Nh
Davin L., Saskatchewan 39 Wg
Davis, Saskatchewan 37 Me
Davis Inlet, Nfld. 31 Nf
Davis Mts., Texas 48 Eg
Davis Sea, Antarctica 104 Gc
Davis Str., Greenland 41 Pc
Davis Strait, Greenland/Canada 31 Od
Davos Dorf, Switzerland 65 Eb
Davos Platz, Switzerland 65 Eb
Davy L., Saskatchewan 38 Tf
Davy Sd., Greenland 41 Nb
Dawna Ra., Burma 89 Je
Dawson, Georgia, U.S.A. 45 Ee
Dawson, Minnesota 46 Jc
Dawson, N. Dakota 46 Hb
Dawson, New Mexico 48 Ed
Dawson, Y.T. 38 Dc
Dawson, Mt., B.C. 39 Pk
Dawson, R., Queensland 57 Je
Dawson B., Manitoba 37 Rf
Dawson Creek, B.C. 39 Nh
Dawson Landing, N.W.T. 38 Qe
Dawson Ra., Y.T. 38 Dd
Dawsonville, Georgia, U.S.A. 45 Ec
Dawu, China 82 Dd
Dax, France 73 Ce
Daxian, China 84 Cg
Dayong, China 85 Eh
Daysland, Alberta 36 Ef
Dayton, Ohio 40 Df
Dayton, Tennessee 45 Ec
Daytona Beach, Florida 45 Gf
Dayu, China 85 Gk
De Aar, Cape Province 95 Cf
Dead Sea, Jordan/Israel 94 Df
Deadwood, S. Dakota 42 Fc
Deal, England 63 Hj
Dean Channel, B.C. 39 Kj
Dean Funes, Argentina 54 Dd
Dean R., B.C. 39 Lj
Dease, R., B.C. 38 Jf
Dease, R., N.W.T. 38 Ob
Dease Arm, N.W.T. 38 Nb
Dease L., B.C. 39 Hf
Dease Lake, B.C. 38 Hf
Dease Str., N.W.T. 38 Ta
Deas I., B.C. 39 Hm
Death Valley, California 47 Eg
Deauville, France 72 Db
Debao, China 85 Cl
Debar, Yugoslavia 76 Cd
Debden, Saskatchewan 36 Le
Debec, New Brunswick 32 Eg
Debesy, U.S.S.R. 81 Lb
Dębica, Poland 69 Jc
Dęblin, Poland 69 Jc
Dębno, Poland 68 Fb
Debra Markos, Ethiopia 97 Hb
Debrecen, Hungary 69 Je
Decatur, Alabama 45 Dc
Decatur, Georgia, U.S.A. 45 Ed
Decatur, Illinois 49 Nc
Decaturville, Tennessee 45 Cc
Deccan, India 88 Ef
Decelles, Rés., Quebec 35 Me
Deception, I., S. Shetlands 104 Sc
Dechêne, L., Quebec 32 Eb
Decimal, Manitoba 36 Ga
Děčín, Czechoslovakia 68 Fc
Decize, France 72 Ec
Decker, Manitoba 37 Rh
Dedeagach. See Alexandroúpolis
Dédougou, Upper Volta 98 Ef
Dedza, Malawi 97 Gg
Deep Brook, Nova Scotia 32 Gj
Deep Creek L., Maryland 44 Ac
Deep River, Ontario 35 Nf
Deep Rose L., N.W.T. 38 Yc
Dee R., Scotland 62 Fc
Dee R., Wales 63 Eg
Deer I., Maine 32 Dj
Deer I., New Brunswick 32 Fj
Deer Lake, Newfoundland 33 Pd
Deerlijk, Belgium 64 Bd
Deer Lodge, Montana 47 Gb
Deer Park, B.C. 39 Ol
Deerpass B., N.W.T. 38 Mc
Deer River, Minnesota 46 Lb
Deesa, India 88 Dd
Defferrari, Argentina 54 Ee
De Funiak Springs, Florida 45 De
Degana, India 88 Dc
Degerfors, Sweden 66 Hd
de Gerlache Str., Antarctica 104 Sc
De Gray Res., Arkansas 49 Le
De Grey, R., W. Australia 56 Cd
Deh Bid, Iran 93 Fc
Dehdez, Iran 93 Fc
Dehra Dun, India 90 Fe
Deim Zubeir, Sudan 99 Lg
Deinze, Belgium 64 Bd
Deir Abu Said, Jordan 94 De
Deir 'Ali, Syria 94 Ed
Deir Atiye, Syria 94 Ec
Deir ez Zor, Syria 92 Cb
Deir Hafir, Syria 94 Fa
Deir Shemil, Syria 94 Eb
Déj, Romania 69 Ke
Dekalb, Illinois 49 Nb
De Kalb, Mississippi 45 Cd
De Kastri, U.S.S.R. 79 Pc
Dekoven, Kentucky 45 Cb
Delano Peak, Utah 48 Ac
Delaronde L., Sask. 36 Ld
Delavan, Wisconsin 40 Bd
Delaware, Ohio 40 Ee
Delaware, U.S.A. 43 Ld
Delaware B., Del./N.J. 44 Cc
Delaware City, Delaware 44 Cc
Delaware R., U.S.A. 44 Cb
Delburne, Alberta 36 Df
Delden, Netherlands 64 Eb
Deleau, Manitoba 37 Rj
Deleitosa, Spain 70 Cc
De Lemmer, Netherlands 64 Db
Delémont, Switzerland 65 Ca
Delft, Netherlands 64 Cb
Delfzijl, Netherlands 64 Ea
Delgerhet, Mongolia 82 Fa
Delgo, Sudan 99 Md
Delhi, India 88 Ec
Delhi, New York 44 Ca
Delhi, Ontario 34 Kk
Delia, Alberta 36 Eg
Delisle, Saskatchewan 36 Kg
Dellenbaugh, Mt., Arizona 47 Gg
Dellys, Algeria 98 Fa
Delmas, Saskatchewan 36 Jf
Delmenhorst, W. Germany 68 Cb
Del Norte, Colorado 48 Dd
Deloraine, Manitoba 37 Rj
Del Rio, Texas 48 Gh
Delta, Colorado 48 Cc
Delta, Louisiana 45 Bd
Delta, Missouri 45 Cb
Delta, Pennsylvania 44 Bc
Delta, Utah 48 Ac
Delta, district, B.C. 39 Hm
Delta Beach, Manitoba 37 Th
Demaine, Saskatchewan 36 Kh
Demanda, Sa. de la, Spain 70 Da
Demchok, China 88 Eb
Deming, New Mexico 48 Df
Demmin, E. Germany 68 Eb
Demopolis, Alabama 45 Dd
Denare Beach, Saskatchewan 37 Pd
Denbigh, Ontario 35 Ng
Denbigh, Wales 63 Eg
Denderleeuw, Belgium 64 Cd
Dendermonde, Belgium 64 Cc
Dendi, Ethiopia 97 Hc
Dendron, Saskatchewan 36 Kh
Denekamp, Netherlands 64 Eb
Den Haag. See 's Gravenhage
Den Helder, Netherlands 64 Cb
Denholm, Saskatchewan 36 Jf
Denia, Spain 71 Fc
Deniau, Quebec 32 Cf
Deniliquin, N.S.W. 57 Jg
Denison, Iowa 49 Ka
Denison, Texas 49 Jf
Denizli, Turkey 92 Ab
Denmark, Nova Scotia 32 Jh
Denmark, S. Carolina 45 Gd
Denmark, W. Eur. 67 Cj
Denmark Str., Greenland 41 Nc
Denmark Strait, Greenland/Iceland 31 Qd
Den Oever, Netherlands 64 Db
Denpasar, Indonesia 83 Gm
Dent Blanche, Mt., Switz. 65 Cb
Denton, Maryland 40 Jf
Denton, Texas 49 Jf
D'Entrecasteaux, Is., Papua New Guinea 57 Ka
D'Entrecasteaux Pt., W. Aust. 56 Cf
Denver, Colorado 48 Ec
Denzil, Saskatchewan 36 Hf
Deoband, India 90 Ef
Deobhog, India 89 Fd
Deogarh, India 89 Fd
Deoghar, India 91 Fc
Deolia, India 88 Dd
Deori, India 91 Bd
De Panne, Belgium 64 Ac
De Pere, Wisconsin 40 Bc
Deposit, New York 40 Jd
Dépôt-de-l'Aigle, Quebec 35 Of
Dépôt-du-Chapeau-de-Paille, Quebec 35 Re
Depot Harbour, Ontario 34 Kg
Dépôt Michomis, Quebec 35 Pe
De Queen, Arkansas 49 Kf
Dera, Syria 94 Ee
Dera Bugti, Pakistan 88 Cc
Dera Ghazi Khan, Pakistan 90 Be
Dera Ismail Khan, Pakistan 90 Be
Dera Nanak, India 90 Dd
Derbent, U.S.S.R. 78 Dd
Derby, England 63 Fh
Derby, W. Australia 56 Dc
Derbyshire, England 63 Fh
Derecske, Hungary 69 Je
Derg L., Eire 63 Bf
Derg L., Eire 63 Bh
De Ridder, Louisiana 49 Lg
De Rijp, Netherlands 64 Cb
Dermott, Arkansas 49 Mf
Dernberg C., Namibia 95 Be
Derravaragh L., Eire 63 Cg
Derudeb, Sudan 99 Ne
De Ruyter, New York 44 Ca
Derventa, Yugoslavia 74 Fc
Derwent, Alberta 36 Fe
Derwent Water, England 63 Ef
Des Arc, Arkansas 45 Bc
Desbarats, Ontario 34 Ff
Descalvados, Brazil 53 Fg
Deschaillons-sur-St-Laurent, Quebec 35 Sf
Deschambault L., Sask. 37 Od
Deschambault Lake, Sask. 37 Od
Deschênes, Quebec 34 Cj
Deschênes Rapids & L., Quebec/Ontario 34 Bj
Deseado, Argentina 54 Cg
Deseado, R., Argentina 54 Cg
Deseronto, Ontario 35 Oh
Désert, L., Quebec 35 Of
Desmarais, Alberta 36 Dc
Desmaraisville, Quebec 35 Oc
Des Moines, Iowa 49 Lb
Desna, Ukraine 80 Gf
Desolación, I., Chile 54 Bh
Desolation C., Greenland 41 Pc
De Soto, Missouri 49 Mc
Dessau, East Germany 68 Ec
Destruction Bay, Y.T. 38 De
Deta, Romania 76 Cb
Detlor, Ontario 35 Ng
Detroit, Michigan 40 Ed
Detroit Lakes, Minnesota 46 Kb
Dett, Zimbabwe 95 Dc
Deurne, Netherlands 64 Dc
Deux Décharges, L. aux, Que. 32 Bb
Deux Montagnes, L. des, Quebec 40 Jc
Deux-Rivières, Ontario 35 Mf
Deux-Sèvres, France 72 Cc
Déva, Romania 76 Db
Dévávanya, Hungary 76 Ca
Deventer, Netherlands 64 Eb
Devenyns, L., Quebec 40 Kb
Deveron R., Scotland 62 Fc
Devils Lake, N. Dakota 46 Ha
Devin, Bulgaria 76 Ed
Devizes, England 63 Fj
Devli, India 88 Ec
Devon, Alberta 36 De
Devon, England 63 Ek
Devon I., N.W.T. 31 Lb
Devonport, England 63 Ek
Devonport, New Zealand 55 Eb
Devonport, Tasmania 57 Jh
Dewangiri, Bhutan 89 Hc
Dewar Lake, Saskatchewan 36 Hg
Dewberry, Alberta 36 Ge
De Winton, Alberta 36 Ch
De Witt, Arkansas 45 Bc
Dexter, Maine 32 Ch
Dexter, Missouri 45 Cb
Deyhuk, Iran 93 Gc
Dezadeash, L., Y.T. 38 Ee
Dezfūl, Iran 92 Ec
Dezhou, China 82 Hd
Dhahran, Arabia 93 Fd
Dhak, Pakistan 90 Cd
Dhamār, Yemen 92 Dg
Dhampur, India 91 Ba
Dhamra, India 89 Gd
Dhamtari, India 88 Fd
Dhangain, India 91 Ec
Dhankuta, Nepal 91 Fb
Dharmjaygarh, India 91 Dd
Dharmkot, India 90 De
Dharmsala, India 90 Ed
Dharwar, India 88 Ee
Dhaulagiri, Mt., Nepal 91 Da
Dhaulpur, India 91 Ab
Dhayd, United Arab Emirates 93 Gd
Dhiban, Jordan 94 Df
Dhidhimótikhon, Greece 76 Fd
Dhilos, Greece 77 Ef
Dhionisiadhes. See Yianisadhes
Dholera, India 88 Dd
Dhond, India 88 De
Dhubāb, Yemen 92 Dg
Dhubri, India 91 Hb
Dhula, S. Yemen 92 Eg
Dhule, India 88 Dd
Dhurma, Arabia 92 Ee
Dhurwai, India 91 Bc
Dia, Crete 77 Eg
Diamante, Argentina 54 Dd
Diamantina, Brazil 53 Jg
Diamantina, R., Queensland 57 Hd
Diamantino, Brazil 53 Ff
Diamond, I., Burma 89 He
Diamond City, Alberta 36 Ej
Diamond Harbour, India 91 Gd
Dian Chi, China 82 Df
Dianópolis, Brazil 53 Hf
Dibbah, Jebel, Arabia 92 Cd
Dibbéla, Niger 99 He
Dibete, Botswana 95 Dd
Dibrugarh, India 89 Hc
Dickinson, N. Dakota 46 Fb
Dickson, Tennessee 45 Db
Didsbury, Alberta 36 Cg
Didyme, Quebec 35 Sd
Die, France 73 Fd
Diefenbaker, L., Sask. 36 Kh
Diego Suarez, Madag. 97 Nj
Dien Bien Phu, Vietnam 87 Cb
Dieppe, France 72 Db
Diest, Belgium 64 Dd
Dieverbrug, Netherlands 64 Eb
Dig, India 90 Eg
Digby, Nova Scotia 32 Gj
Digby Neck, pen., N.S. 32 Fj
Dighal, S. Yemen 92 Eg
Digne, France 73 Gd
Digoin, France 72 Ec
Digul, Irian Jaya 83 Lm
Dijon, France 72 Fc
Diksmuide, Belgium 64 Ac
Dikson, U.S.S.R. 41 Gb
Dikwa, Nigeria 99 Hf
Dilam, Arabia 92 Ee
Dili, Timor I., Indonesia 83 Jm
Dilke, Saskatchewan 37 Mh
Dillon, Montana 47 Gc
Dillon, Saskatchewan 36 Jc
Dillon R., Saskatchewan 36 Hc
Dilolo, Angola 96 Eg
Dilolo, Zaire 96 Eg
Dimbokro, Ivory Coast 98 Eg
Dimgarpur, India 88 Dd
Dimitrovgrad, Yugoslavia 76 Dc
Dimla, Bangladesh 91 Gb
Dimona, Israel 94 Df
Dimotika. See Dhidhimótikhon
Dinagat, Philippines 83 Jh
Dinajpur, Bangladesh 91 Gc
Dinan, France 72 Bb
Dinanagar, India 90 Dd
Dinant, Belgium 64 Cd
Dinar, Turkey 92 Bb
Dinard, France 72 Bb
Dinarske Planina, Yugosl. 74 Fc
Dindigul, India 88 Ef
Dingle, Eire 63 Ah
Dingnan, China 85 Gk
Dingwall, Scotland 62 Dc
Ding Xian, China 84 Gc
Dinorwic L., Ontario 36 Ka
Dinosaur Nat. Mon., Colorado 48 Cb
Dinosaur Prov. Park, The, Alberta 36 Fh
Dinsmore, Saskatchewan 36 Kg
Dinteloord, Netherlands 64 Cc
Diourbel, Senegal 98 Bf
Dipalpur, Pakistan 90 Ce
Dipton, New Zealand 55 Bf
Dir, Pakistan 90 Bc
Direction, C., Queensland 57 Hb
Diredawa, Ethiopia 97 Jc
Diriamba, Nicaragua 51 Bd
Dirk Hartogs I., W. Aust. 56 Be
Dirksland, Netherlands 64 Cc
Dirranbandi, Queensland 57 Je
Disappointment, C., Wash. 47 Ab
Disappointment, L., W. Aust. 56 Dd
Disappointment Is., Tuamotu Arch. 103 Lj
Disentis, Switzerland 65 Db
Disko, I., Greenland 41 Pc
Disko B., Greenland 41 Pc
Disley, Saskatchewan 37 Mh
Dismal Lakes, N.W.T. 38 Pb
Disna, Byelorussia 80 Fd
Dison, Belgium 64 Dd
Disraëli, Quebec 35 Tg
Dissimieux, L., Quebec 32 Cd
Diu, India 88 Dd
Diver, Ontario 35 Lf
Dividing Range, Australia 57 Je
Diviso, Colombia 52 Bc
Divrigi, Turkey 92 Cb
Dix, Quebec 35 Od
Dix Milles, L. des, Quebec 35 Qe
Dixmude, Belgium 64 Ac
Dixon, Illinois 49 Nb
Dixon, Kentucky 45 Db
Dixon Entrance, Str., B.C./Alaska 39 Gh
Dixonville, Alberta 39 Pg
Dixville, Quebec 35 Tg
Diyarbakir, Turkey 92 Db
Djambi. See Telanaipura
Djelfa, Algeria 98 Fb
Djeneien, Tunisia 99 Gb
Djerba, I., Tunisia 99 Hb
Djibouti, N.E. Africa 97 Jb
Djidjelli, Algeria 98 Ga
Djolu, Zaire 96 Ed
Djougou, Benin 98 Fg
Djursholm, Sweden 67 Gg
Dmitriya Lapteva, U.S.S.R. 79 Pa
Dnepr, Ukraine 80 Gf
Dneprodzerzhinsk, Ukraine 80 Jg
Dnepropetrovsk, Ukraine 80 Jg
Dnestr, Ukraine 80 Fh
Dnieper R. See Dnepr
Dniester R. See Dnestr
Doaktown, N.B. 32 Fg
Dobbyn, Queensland 57 Hc
Dobele, Latvia 67 Kh
Doberan, East Germany 68 Da
Dobra, Czechoslovakia 69 Jd
Dobřany, Czechoslovakia 68 Ed
Dobrich. See Tolbukhin
Dobříš, Czechoslovakia 68 Fd
Dobruja, Romania 76 Gb
Dobryanski, U.S.S.R. 81 Na
Dobrzyń, Poland 69 Hb
Doctor Arroyo, Mexico 50 Dc
Doda, L., Quebec 35 Pc
Dodds, Alberta 36 Ee
Dodecanese, Greece 77 Ff
Dodge City, Kansas 49 Hd
Dodgeville, Wisconsin 49 Ma
Dodman Point, England 63 Dk
Dodoma, Tanzania 97 Hf
Dodsland, Saskatchewan 36 Jg
Dodson, Montana 46 Ca
Doel, Belgium 64 Cc
Doesburg, Netherlands 64 Eb
Doetinchem, Netherlands 64 Ec
Dog Creek, B.C. 39 Mk
Dogger Bank, North Sea 60 He
Dog L., Manitoba 37 Tg
Dog L., Ontario 34 Fd
Dog L., Ontario 37 Oa
Dogpound, Alberta 36 Cg
Doha, Qatar, Persian Gulf 93 Fd
Dohad, India 88 Dd
Doheny, Quebec 35 Se
Doka, Arabia 92 Df
Dokkum, Netherlands 64 Ea
Dol, France 72 Cb
Dolbeau, Quebec 35 Sd
Dôle, France 72 Fc
Dolent, Mt., Switzerland 65 Cc
Dolgellau, Wales 63 Eh
Dollard, Saskatchewan 36 Jj
Dollard L., Quebec 32 Fc
Dolo, Ethiopia 97 Jd
Dolomitiche, Alpi, Italy 74 Cb
Dolores, Argentina 54 Ee
Dolores, Mexico 50 Bb
Dolores, Spain 71 Ec
Dolphin, C., Falkland Is. 54 Eh
Dolphin and Union Str., Northwest Territories 38 Pa
Dolunnor. See Duolun
Dom, Mt., Irian Jaya 83 Ll
Domagaya L., Nfld. 32 Hb
Domain, Manitoba 37 Uj
Domariaganj, India 91 Db
Domburg, Netherlands 64 Bc
Dome Creek, B.C. 39 Nj
Domel I., Burma 89 Jf
Dome Rock Mts., Arizona 47 Fj
Domfront, France 72 Cb
Dominica, West Indies 51 Gc
Dominican Rep., W. Indies 51 Ec
Dominion, Nova Scotia 33 Ng
Dominion, C., N.W.T. 31 Md
Dominion City, Manitoba 37 Uj
Dominion L., Nfld. 33 La
Domino, Newfoundland 31 Og
Dömitz, East Germany 68 Db
Dom Pedrito, Brazil 54 Fd
Domremy, Saskatchewan 37 Mf
Domuyo, Argentina 54 Be
Domvraina, Greece 77 De
Don, U.S.S.R. 78 Cc
Don, R., Scotland 62 Ec
Donaghadee, N. Ireland 63 Df
Donald, Ontario 35 Mh
Donalda, Alberta 36 Ef
Donaldson, Louisiana 49 Mg
Donau (Danube), Central Europe 68 Ed
Donaueschingen, W. Ger. 68 Ce
Donavon, Saskatchewan 36 Kg
Don Benito, Spain 70 Cc
Doncaster, England 63 Gg
Dondo, Angola 96 Cf
Donegal, Eire 63 Bf
Donegal B., Eire 63 Bf
Donets, U.S.S.R. 81 Eg
Donetsk, U.S.S.R. 80 Kh
Donga, Nigeria 99 Hg
Dong'an, China 85 Ej
Dongara, W. Australia 56 Be
Dongargarh, India 88 Fd
Dongchuan, China 85 Aj
Donggala, Celebes (Sulawesi) 83 Gl
Dongguan, China 85 Fl
Dong Hai, S.E. Asia 82 Jd
Donghai Dao, China 85 Em
Dong-Hoi, Vietnam 87 Dc
Dongo, Angola 96 Dg
Dongola, Sudan 99 Me
Dongtai, China 84 Kf
Dongting Hu, China 85 Fh
Donjek, R., Y.T. 38 Dd
Donji Miholjac, Yugoslavia 74 Gc
Dønna, Norway 66 Ec
Donnacona, Quebec 35 Tf
Donnelly, Alberta 39 Ph
Donnellys Crossing, N.Z. 55 Da
Doolittle, L., Quebec 35 Of
Doon L., Scotland 62 Ee
Doorn, Netherlands 64 Db
Dora, L., W. Australia 56 Dd
Doranda, India 91 Ed
Doran L., N.W.T. 38 Te
Dorat, le, France 72 Dc
Dorchester, England 63 Fk
Dorchester, N.B. 32 Hh
Dorchester, C., N.W.T. 31 Md
Dordogne, France 73 Dd
Dordogne, France 73 Cd
Dordrecht, Netherlands 64 Cc
Doré, Lac le, Quebec 33 Lb
Dore, Mt., France 72 Ed
Doré L., Saskatchewan 36 Kd
Doré Lake, Saskatchewan 39 Uh
Dorenlee, Alberta 36 Ef
Dori, Upper Volta 98 Ef
Dorintosh, Saskatchewan 39 Th
Dorion, Ontario 37 Pa
Dorion, Quebec 35 Qg
Dornoch, Scotland 62 Ec
Dorokhsh, Iran 93 Gc
Dorotea, Sweden 66 Gd
Dorothy, Alberta 36 Eg
Dorrego, Argentina 54 De
Dorset, England 63 Fk
Dorset, Ontario 35 Mg
Dorsey, Montana 46 Bb
Dortmund, West Germany 68 Bc
Dorval & I., Quebec 35 Qk
Dos Bahias, C., Argentina 54 Cf
Doshi, Afghanistan 93 Jb
Dospat, Bulgaria 76 Ed
Dosquet, Quebec 35 Tf
Dosso, Niger 98 Ff
Dossor, Kazakhstan 78 Ed
Dothan, Alabama 45 Ee
Doting Cove, Nfld. 33 Td
Douai, France 72 Ea
Douala, Cameroun 99 Gh
Douarnenez, France 72 Ab
Doubs, France 72 Gc
Doubtless B., New Zealand 55 Da
Douglas, Arizona 48 Cg
Douglas, Cape Province 95 Ce
Douglas, Georgia, U.S.A. 45 Fe
Douglas, Isle of Man 63 Ef
Douglas, Ontario 35 Og
Douglas, Wyoming 46 Ed
Douglas Channel, B.C. 39 Jj
Douglas Pt., Ontario 34 Jh
Douglas Station, Man. 36 Aa
Douglastown, N.B. 32 Gf
Douglastown, Quebec 32 Hg
Douglasville, Georgia, U.S.A. 45 Ed
Doullens, France 72 Ea
Doume, Cameroun 96 Cd
Douro, Spain/Portugal 70 Ab
Dover, Delaware 44 Cc
Dover, England 63 Hj
Dover, New Hampshire 44 Ea
Dover, New Jersey 44 Cb
Dover, Ohio 40 Fe
Dover, L., Tennessee 45 Db
Dover, Str. of, Eng./France 72 Da
Dover Foxcroft, Maine 32 Ch
Dovrefjell, Norway 66 Ce
Dowa, Malawi 97 Gg
Dow L., Botswana 95 Cd
Dowling, Alberta 36 Fg
Dowling L., Alberta 36 Eg
Down, N. Ireland 63 Ef
Downpatrick, N. Ireland 63 Df
Downsview Airport (Military), Ontario 34 Cj
Downton, Mt., B.C. 39 Lj
Dow Polān, Iran 93 Fc
Doylestown, Pa. 44 Cb
Dozois, Rés., Quebec 35 Ne
Drăgăsani, Romania 76 Eb
Draguignan, France 73 Ge
Drake, Saskatchewan 37 Mg
Drakensberg Mts., S. Africa 95 Df
Drake Str., Antarctica 104 Sd
Dráma, Greece 76 Ed
Drammen, Norway 67 Dg
Dranov, Romania 76 Gb
Dras, Kashmir 90 Dc
Drawsko, Poland 69 Fb
Drayton, N. Dakota 46 Ja
Drayton, Ontario 34 Kj
Drayton Valley, Alberta 36 Be
Drazinda, Pakistan 90 Ae
Drenthe, Netherlands 64 Eb
Dresden, East Germany 68 Ec
Dresden, Ontario 34 Hk
Dreux, France 72 Db
Driftpile, Alberta 36 Bc
Driftwood, Ontario 34 Jc
Drina, Yugoslavia 76 Bc
Drin G., Albania 76 Bd
Drinkwater, Saskatchewan 37 Mh
Drøbak, Norway 67 Dg
Drogheda, Eire 63 Cg
Droitwich, England 63 Fh
Drôme, France 73 Fd
Drongen, Belgium 64 Bc
Dropmore, Manitoba 37 Qg
Drowning, R., Ontario 34 Eb
Druid, Saskatchewan 36 Jg
Drumbo, Ontario 34 Kj
Drumheller, Alberta 36 Eg
Drummond I., Michigan 40 Ec
Drummondville, Quebec 35 Sg
Drunen, Netherlands 64 Dc
Drunken Pt., cape, Man. 37 Vh
Drury L., Y.T. 38 Fd

Druten, *Netherlands* 64 Dc
Druz, Jeb. ed., *Syria* 94 Ee
Dryberry, L., *Ontario* 36 Ha
Drybrough, *Manitoba* 37 Qb
Dryden, *Ontario* 36 Ka
Drygalski I., *Antarctica* 104 Gc
Drylake, *Nfld.* 32 Fa
Dschang, *Cameroun* 96 Cc
Duba, *Arabia* 92 Cd
Dubawnt, R., *N.W.T.* 38 Yc
Dubawnt L., *N.W.T.* 38 Xd
Dubayy, *United Arab Emirates* 93 Gd
Dubbo, *New S. Wales* 57 Jf
Dublin, *Eire* 63 Cg
Dublin, *Georgia, U.S.A.* 43 Ke
Dublin, *Ontario* 34 Jj
Dublin, *Texas* 49 Hf
Dubno, *Ukraine* 80 Df
Du Bois, *Pennsylvania* 44 Ab
Dubrovnik, *Yugoslavia* 76 Bc
Dubuc, *Saskatchewan* 37 Ph
Dubuque, *Iowa* 49 Ma
Duchcov, *Czechoslovakia* 68 Ec
Duchesne, *Utah* 48 Bb
Duchess, *Alberta* 36 Fh
Ducie I., *Pacific Ocean* 103 Nk
Duck Bay, *Manitoba* 37 Rf
Duck I., Great, *Ontario* 34 Hg
Duck I., West, *Ontario* 34 Hg
Duck Lake, *Saskatchewan* 36 Lf
Duck Mountain Provincial Park, *Manitoba* 37 Rg
Duck Mountain Provincial Park, *Saskatchewan* 37 Qg
Duck Mt., *Manitoba* 37 Qg
Duck River, *Manitoba* 37 Rg
Dudinka, *U.S.S.R.* 78 Hb
Dudley, *England* 63 Fh
Duero, *Spain* 70 Cb
Duff, *Saskatchewan* 37 Oh
Duffel, *Belgium* 64 Cc
Duffield, *Alberta* 36 Ce
Dufresne, L., *Quebec* 32 Gb
Dufresne Lake, *Quebec* 32 Gb
Dugi Otok, *Yugoslavia* 74 Ec
Duhamel, *Alberta* 36 Ef
Duifken Point, *Queensland* 57 Hb
Duisburg, *West Germany* 64 Ec
Duisburg, *West Germany* 68 Bc
Dujana, *India* 90 Ef
Duke of Gloucester Grp., *Tuamotu Archipelago* 103 Lk
Duke of York Archipelago, *Northwest Territories* 38 Ra
Duk Faiwil, *Sudan* 99 Mg
Dulan, *China* 82 Cc
Dulce, G., *Costa Rica* 51 Ce
Duluth, *Minnesota* 46 Lb
Duma, *Syria* 94 Ed
Dumas, *Arkansas* 45 Bd
Dumas, *Texas* 48 Ge
Dumbarton, *Scotland* 62 Ee
Dum-Dum, *India* 91 Gd
Dumeir, *Syria* 94 Ed
Dumfries, *Scotland* 62 Ee
Dumfries & Galloway, *Scotland* 62 Ee
Dumka, *India* 91 Fc
Dummer, *Saskatchewan* 37 Nj
Dumoine, L., *Quebec* 35 Nf
Dumont, L., *Quebec* 35 Of
Dumraon, *India* 91 Ec
Dumyat (Damietta), *Egypt* 99 Mb
Dunarea (Danube) R., *Cent. Europe* 61 Pg
Dunaújváros, *Hungary* 76 Ba
Dunblane, *Saskatchewan* 36 Lg
Duncan, *Arkansas* 45 Bc
Duncan, *B.C.* 39 Ml
Duncan, *Oklahoma* 49 Je
Duncan L., *N.W.T.* 38 Rd
Duncan Pass., *Andaman Is.* 89 Hf
Duncansby Head, *Scotland* 62 Fb
Dunchurch, *Ontario* 34 Lg
Dundalk, *Eire* 63 Cf
Dundalk, *Ontario* 34 Kh
Dundalk B., *Eire* 63 Cg
Dundas, *Greenland* 31 Nb
Dundas, *Ontario* 34 Kj
Dundas I., *B.C.* 39 Hh
Dundas Pen., *N.W.T.* 30 Hc
Dundas Str., *N. Terr.* 56 Fb
Dún Dealgan. *See* Dundalk
Dundee, *Natal* 95 Ee
Dundee, *Scotland* 62 Fd
Dundee I., *Antarctica* 104 Tc
Dundrum B., *N. Ireland* 63 Df
Dundurn, *Saskatchewan* 37 Mg
Dundwa Ra., *Nepal* 91 Db
Dunedin, *New Zealand* 55 Cf
Dunfermline, *Scotland* 62 Ed
Dungannon, *Ontario* 34 Jj
Dungarven, *Eire* 63 Bh
Dungbure Range, *China* 89 Ga
Dungeness, *England* 63 Hk
Dungu, *Zaire* 97 Fd
Dunhuang, *China* 82 Bb
Dunkeld, *Scotland* 62 Ed
Dunkerque, *France* 72 Ea
Dunkirk, *New York* 44 Aa
Dunkirk, *Saskatchewan* 37 Mh
Dunkur, *Ethiopia* 97 Hb
Dunkwa, *Ghana* 98 Eg
Dúnlaoghaire, *Eire* 63 Cg
Dunlap, *Iowa* 49 Kb
Dunlop, *Manitoba* 37 Td
Dunlop, *Ontario* 34 Jj
Dunmanway, *Eire* 63 Aj
Dunmara, *N. Terr.* 57 Fc
Dunmore, *Alberta* 36 Gj
Dunn, *N. Carolina* 45 Hc
Dunnet Head, *Scotland* 62 Eb
Dunnottar, *Manitoba* 37 Vh
Dunns Valley, *Ontario* 34 Gf
Dunnville, *Ontario* 35 Lk
Dunrankin, *Ontario* 34 Gd
Dunrea, *Manitoba* 37 Sj
Duns, *Scotland* 62 Fe
Dunster, *B.C.* 39 Nj
Duntroon, *Ontario* 34 Kh
Dunvegan L., *N.W.T.* 38 Ue
Duolun, *China* 84 Ha
Duparquet, *Quebec* 35 Ld
Duparquet, L., *Quebec* 35 Ld
Dupuy, *Quebec* 35 Ld
Duquoin, *Illinois* 45 Ca
Duque de York, I., *Chile* 54 Ah
Dura, *Jordan* 94 Df
Durango, *Colorado* 48 Dd
Durango, *Mexico* 50 Dc
Durant, *Mississippi* 45 Cd
Durant, *Oklahoma* 49 Jf
Durazno, *Uruguay* 54 Ed
Durazzo. *See* Durrës
Durban, *Manitoba* 37 Qg
Durban, *Natal* 95 Ee
Durbe, *Latvia* 67 Jh
Durbuy, *Belgium* 64 Dd
Durdevac, *Yugoslavia* 74 Fb
Durdureh, *Somalia* 97 Kb
Dureikish, *Syria* 94 Ec
Düren, *West Germany* 68 Bc
Durga Str., *Irian Jaya* 57 Ga
Durham, *England* 63 Ff
Durham, *N. Carolina* 45 Hb
Durham, *Ontario* 34 Kh
Durham Bridge, *N.B.* 32 Fg
Durham-Sud, *Quebec* 35 Sg
Durness, *Scotland* 62 Db
Durocher, L., *Quebec* 33 Lc
Durrës, *Albania* 76 Bd
Dursey, I., *Eire* 63 Aj
Duruh, *Iran* 93 Hc
D'Urville I., *New Zealand* 55 Dd
Duryea, *Pennsylvania* 44 Cb
Dusey, R., *Ontario* 34 Da
Dushanbe, *Tadzhikstan* 78 Fe
Dushore, *Pennsylvania* 44 Bb
Dusky Sound, *New Zealand* 55 Af
Düsseldorf, *West Germany* 68 Bc
Dussen, *Netherlands* 64 Cc
Duszniki Zdrój, *Poland* 69 Gc
Dutch Harb., *Aleutian Is.* 43 Wm
Dutton, *Ontario* 34 Jk
Dutton, Mt., *Utah* 48 Ac
Duval, *Saskatchewan* 37 Ng
Duval, L., *Quebec* 35 Of
Duvan, *U.S.S.R.* 81 Nc
Duwadami, *Arabia* 92 De
Duwwāh, *Oman* 93 Ge
Duyun, *China* 85 Cj
Dvina, R., *Latvia* 67 Lh
Dyatkovo, *U.S.S.R.* 80 Je
Dyce, *Manitoba* 37 Rd
Dyer, C., *N.W.T.* 31 Nd
Dyer B., *N.W.T.* 30 Gb
Dyer B., *Ontario* 34 Jg
Dyer Bay, *Ontario* 34 Jg
Dyersburg, *Tennessee* 45 Cb
Dyfed, *Wales* 63 Ej
Dyle R., *Belgium* 64 Cd
Dyment, *Ontario* 36 Ka
Dysart, *Saskatchewan* 37 Nh
Dyurtyuli, *U.S.S.R.* 81 Mc
Dzamïn Üüd, *Mongolia* 82 Fb
Dzep, *Yugoslavia* 76 Dc
Dzerzhinsk, *Byelorussia* 80 Ee
Dzerzhinsk, *U.S.S.R.* 81 Fb
Dzhagdy, Khrebet, *U.S.S.R.* 79 Mc
Dzhalal Abad, *Kirghizia* 78 Gd
Dzhalinda, *U.S.S.R.* 79 Mc
Dzhambul, *Kazakhstan* 78 Gd
Dzhezkazgan, *Kazakhstan* 78 Fd
Dzhugdzhur Khrebet, *U.S.S.R.* 79 Nc
Dzhungarskiy Ala-Tau., *Kazakhstan* 78 Gd
Dzhusaly, *Kazakhstan* 78 Fd
Dzierzoniow, *Poland* 69 Gc

E

Eabamet L., *Ontario* 31 Lg
Eagle, *Alaska* 43 Yl
Eagle Grove, *Iowa* 49 La
Eaglehead L., *Ontario* 37 Oa
Eagle I., *Manitoba* 37 Te
Eagle L., *Maine* 32 Cg
Eagle L., *Ontario* 36 Ja
Eagle Lake, *Maine* 32 Df
Eagle Mountain L., *Texas* 49 Jf
Eagle Pass, *Texas* 48 Gh
Eagle R., *Y.T.* 38 Eb
Eagle River, *Ontario* 36 Ja
Eagle River, *Wisconsin* 40 Bc
Eahamas, *West Indies* 51 Db
Earl Grey, *Saskatchewan* 37 Nh
Earlton, *Ontario* 35 Le
Earlville, *New York* 44 Ca
Earn L., *Scotland* 62 Ed
Earn L., *Y.T.* 38 Fd
East Angus, *Quebec* 35 Tg
East Aurora, *New York* 44 Aa
East Bay, *Nova Scotia* 33 Mg
Eastbourne, *England* 63 Hk
Eastbourne, *New Zealand* 55 Ed
East Braintree, *Manitoba* 36 Fa
East Broughton, *Que.* 32 Ag
East Butte, Mt., *Montana* 36 Fk
East China Sea. *See* Dong Hai
East Coulee, *Alberta* 36 Eg
East Dereham, *England* 63 Hh
Eastend, *Saskatchewan* 36 Jj
Easter I., *Pacific Ocean* 103 Qk
Eastern B., *Maryland* 44 Bc
Eastern Meelpaeg, *Nfld.* 33 Se
East Florenceville, *N.B.* 32 Eg
Eastford, *Ontario* 34 Kc
East Grand Forks, *Minn.* 46 Jb
East Jeddore, *N.S.* 32 Kj
East Jordan, *Nova Scotia* 32 Gk
East Kemptville, *N.S.* 32 Gj
Eastland, *Texas* 49 Hf
East Liverpool, *Ohio* 40 Fe
East London, *Cape Province* 95 Df
Eastmain, *Quebec* 31 Mg
Eastmain, R., *Quebec* 31 Mg
Eastman, *Quebec* 35 Sg
Easton, *Maryland* 44 Bc
Easton, *Pennsylvania* 44 Cb
East Pine, *B.C.* 39 Nh
East Poplar, *Sask.* 37 Mj
Eastport, *Maine* 32 Ej
East Pt., *Nova Scotia* 33 Nk
East Pt., *Ontario* 35 La
East Pt., *P.E.I.* 33 Lg
East Pubnico, *Nova Scotia* 32 Gk
East Retford, *England* 63 Gg
East Saint Louis, *Illinois* 49 Mc
East Sioux Falls, *S. Dakota* 46 Jd
East Sussex, *England* 63 Hk
East Trout L., *Sask.* 37 Md
Eastville, *Virginia* 45 Kb
East York, *Ontario* 34 Dj
Eatonia, *Saskatchewan* 36 Hg
Eaton Rapids, *Michigan* 40 Dd
Eau Claire, *Wisconsin* 46 Mc
Eau Claire, L., *Quebec* 31 Mf
Eau-Claire, L. à l', *Nfld.* 32 Ga
Eau Jaune, L. à l', *Quebec* 35 Qc
Ebbw Vale, *Wales* 63 Ej
Ebenezer, *Saskatchewan* 37 Pg
Ebensburg, *Pennsylvania* 44 Ab
Eberswalde, *East Germany* 68 Eb
Eboli, *Italy* 75 Ee
Ebolowa, *Cameroun* 96 Cd
Ebro, *Spain* 71 Ea
Ecaussines, *Belgium* 64 Cd
Echallens, *Switzerland* 65 Bb
Echo Bay, *Ontario* 34 Ff
Echo Bay (Port Radium), *N.W.T.* 38 Pb
Echo Cliffs, *Arizona* 48 Bd
Échouani, L., *Quebec* 35 Pe
Echt, *Netherlands* 64 Dc
Echten, *Netherlands* 64 Eb
Echternach, *Luxembourg* 68 Bd
Echuca, *Victoria* 57 Hg
Eckville, *Alberta* 36 Cf
Eclipse Sound, *N.W.T.* 31 Mc
Écorces, L. aux, *Quebec* 35 Te
Écorces, L. de l', *Quebec* 35 Oe
Ecuador, *S. America* 52 Bd
Ecum Secum, *Nova Scotia* 33 Kj
Edam, *Netherlands* 64 Db
Edam, *Saskatchewan* 36 Je
Eday, I., *Orkney Is.* 62 Fa
Edberg, *Alberta* 36 Ef
Ed Damer, *Sudan* 99 Me
Ed Damur, *Lebanon* 94 Dd
Ed Debba, *Sudan* 99 Me
Eddies Cove, *Nfld.* 33 Qb
Eddies Cove West, *Nfld.* 33 Pc
Eddrachillis B., *Scotland* 62 Db
Ed Dueim, *Sudan* 99 Mf
Ede, *Netherlands* 64 Db
Edebäck, *Sweden* 67 Ef
Eden, *Manitoba* 37 Sh
Eden, *New York* 44 Aa
Edenburg, *Orange Free State* 95 De
Edendale, *New Zealand* 55 Bg
Edenderry, *Eire* 63 Cg
Edenhurst, *Ontario* 34 Jh
Eden L., *Manitoba* 37 Rb
Eden R., *England* 63 Ff
Edenton, *N. Carolina* 45 Jb
Edenwold, *Saskatchewan* 37 Nh
Edgeley, *N. Dakota* 46 Hb
Edgeley, *Saskatchewan* 37 Oh
Edgell I., *N.W.T.* 31 Ne
Edgemont, *S. Dakota* 46 Fd
Edgeøya, *Arctic Ocean* 78 Ba
Edgerton, *Alberta* 36 Gf
Edgerton, *Wisconsin* 40 Bd
Edgewood, *B.C.* 39 Ol
Édhessa, *Greece* 77 Dd
Edievale, *New Zealand* 55 Bf
Edina, *Missouri* 49 Lb
Edinburg, *Texas* 48 Hj
Edinburgh, *Scotland* 62 Ee
Edirne, *Turkey* 92 Aa
Edith Cavell, Mt., *Alberta* 39 Pj
Edmonton, *Alberta* 36 De
Edmundston, *N.B.* 32 Df
Edremit, *Turkey* 92 Ab
Edrengiyn Nuruu, *Mongolia* 82 Cb
Edsele, *Sweden* 66 Ge
Edson, *Alberta* 39 Pj
Eduni, Mt., *N.W.T.* 38 Jc
Edwand, *Alberta* 36 Ed
Edward, L., *Uganda* 97 Fe
Edward I., *Ontario* 34 Bd
Edwards, *New York* 40 Jc
Edwards Plat., *Texas* 48 Gg
Edwardsville, *Illinois* 49 Nc
Edziza Peak, *B.C.* 39 Hg
Eeklo, *Belgium* 64 Bc
Efate, *Vanuatu* 102 Fj
Eferding, *Austria* 68 Ed
Effingham, *Illinois* 40 Bf
Egadi Is., *Sicily* 75 Dg
Egan, *S. Dakota* 46 Jc
Egaña, *Argentina* 54 Ee
Eganville, *Ontario* 35 Ng
Eger, *Hungary* 69 Je
Eger. *See* Cheb
Egersund, *Norway* 67 Bg
Eggenfelden, *West Germany* 68 Ed
Eghezée, *Belgium* 64 Cd
Eglinton I., *N.W.T.* 30 Hb
Egmont, Mt., *New Zealand* 55 Ec
Egmont B., *P.E.I.* 32 Hg
Egremont, *Alberta* 36 Dd
Egridir, *Turkey* 92 Bb
Egypt, *N. Africa* 99 Lc
Eibergen, *Netherlands* 64 Eb
Eichstätt, *West Germany* 68 Dd
Eide, *Norway* 67 Bf
Eidsvoll, *Norway* 67 Df
Eifel, *West Germany* 68 Bc
Eigg I., *Scotland* 62 Cd
Eights Coast, *Antarctica* 104 Rb
Eighty Mile Beach, *W. Aust.* 56 Dc
Eijsden, *Netherlands* 64 Dd
Eil, *Somalia* 97 Kc
Eileen L., *N.W.T.* 38 Ud
Eindhoven, *Netherlands* 64 Dc
Ein Yahav, *Israel* 94 Dg
Eire. *See* Ireland, Rep. of
Eirunepé, *Brazil* 52 Ce
Eisenach, *East Germany* 68 Dc
Eisenerz, *Austria* 68 Fe
Eisenhower, Mt., *Alberta* 36 Bg
Eisleben, *East Germany* 68 Dc
Ejutla, *Mexico* 50 Ed
Eke, *Belgium* 64 Bd
Ekeren, *Belgium* 64 Cc
Eketahuna, *New Zealand* 55 Ed
Ekhinádbes, *Greece* 77 Ce
Ekka I., *N.W.T.* 38 Mb
Eksjö, *Sweden* 67 Fh
Ekträsk, *Sweden* 66 Hd
Ekwan, R., *Ontario* 31 Lg
El Abde, *Lebanon* 94 Dc
Elafónisi Chan., *Greece* 77 Df
Élafos I., *Greece* 77 Df
El Agheila. *See* Al'uqaylah
El Aina, *Jordan* 94 Dg
El Alamein, *Egypt* 99 Lb
El Asnam, *Algeria* 98 Fa
Elasson, *Greece* 77 De
Elat, *Israel* 94 Ch
Elâzi, *Turkey* 92 Cb
Elba, *Italy* 74 Cd
El Bab, *Syria* 94 Fa
El Bahluiye, *Syria* 94 Db
El Banco, *Colombia* 52 Cb
El Barco de Valdeorras, *Spain* 70 Ba
Elbasan, *Albania* 76 Cd
El Baul, *Venezuela* 52 Db
El-Bayadh, *Algeria* 98 Fb
Elbe, *West Germany* 68 Cb
Elbert, Mt., *Colorado* 42 Ed
Elbeuf, *France* 72 Db
El-Birka, *Arabia* 92 De
Elbistan, *Turkey* 92 Cb
Elblag, *Poland* 69 Ha
Elbow, *Saskatchewan* 36 Lg
Elbow R., *Alberta* 36 Ch
El Br'aij, *Syria* 94 Ec
El'brus, *U.S.S.R.* 78 Dd
El Buheyrat, *Sudan* 97 Fc
Elburg, *Netherlands* 64 Db
Elburz Mts., *Iran* 93 Fb
El Callao, *Venezuela* 52 Eb
El Centro, *California* 47 Fj
Elche, *Spain* 71 Ec
El Chorro, *Argentina* 54 Db
El Cuy, *Argentina* 54 Ce
El Dab, *Somalia* 97 Kc
El Diwân, *Egypt* 99 Md
Eldon, *P.E.I.* 32 Kg
El Donfar, *Somalia* 97 Kb
Eldora, *Iowa* 49 La
Eldorado, *Arkansas* 45 Ad
El Dorado, *Kansas* 49 Jd
El Dorado, *Mexico* 50 Cc
Eldorado, *Saskatchewan* 38 Tf
El Dorado, *Venezuela* 52 Eb
Eldoret, *Kenya* 97 Hd
El Encanto, *Colombia* 52 Cd
Elephant Butte Res., *New Mexico* 48 Df
Elephant I., *Antarctica* 104 Tc
Eleşkirt, *Turkey* 92 Db
Eleuthera I., *The Bahamas* 51 Da
Elewijt, *Belgium* 64 Cd
El Faiyum, *Egypt* 99 Mc
El Fasher, *Sudan* 99 Lf
El Ferrol del Caudillo, *Spain* 70 Aa
Elfros, *Saskatchewan* 37 Og
El Fuwara, *Arabia* 92 Dd
El Geteina, *Sudan* 99 Mf
El Gezira, *Sudan* 97 Gb
Elgg, *Switzerland* 65 Da
Elghena, *Ethiopia* 97 Ha
El-Ghobbe, *Arabia* 92 Ce
Elgin, *Illinois* 49 Na
Elgin, *Manitoba* 37 Rj
Elgin, *New Brunswick* 32 Gh
Elgin, *Scotland* 62 Ec
El Giza, *Egypt* 99 Mb
El Golea, *Algeria* 98 Fb
Elgon, Mt., *Uganda* 97 Gd
El Hamra, *Syria* 94 Fb
El Hamrat, *Syria* 94 Ec
El-Harrach, *Algeria* 98 Fa
El Haseke, *Syria* 92 Db
El-Hayath, *Arabia* 92 Dd
El Hijane, *Syria* 94 Ed
El Hilla, *Sudan* 99 Lf
Elie, *Manitoba* 37 Uj
Elista, *U.S.S.R.* 78 Dd
Elizabeth, *New Jersey* 44 Cb
Elizabeth, *West Virginia* 40 Ff
Elizabeth, Mt., *N.B.* 32 Ff
Elizabeth City, *N. Carolina* 45 Jb
Elizabeth I., *Massachusetts* 44 Eb
Elizabethtown, *Kentucky* 45 Eb
Elizondo, *Spain* 71 Ea
El-Jadida, *Morocco* 98 Db
El Jafr, *Jordan* 94 Eg
Elk, *Poland* 69 Kb
Elk City, *Oklahoma* 49 He
El Kef, *Tunisia* 99 Ga
El Kharga, *Egypt* 99 Mc
Elkhart, *Indiana* 40 De
Elkhead Mts., *Colorado* 48 Db
Elkhorn, *Manitoba* 37 Qj
Elkhorn, Mt., *Idaho* 47 Gd
El Khushniye, *Syria* 94 Dd
Elkins, *West Virginia* 40 Gf
Elk Island National Park, *Alta.* 36 Ee
Elk Lake, *Ontario* 34 Ke
Elk Mts., *New Mexico* 48 Cf
Elko, *B.C.* 39 Ql
Elko, *Nevada* 47 Fe
Elk Point, *Alberta* 36 Ge
Elk Point, *S. Dakota* 46 Jd
Elk R., *B.C.* 39 Ql
Elk River, *Minnesota* 46 Lc
Elkton, *Maryland* 44 Cc
El Lädhiqîya. *See* Latakia
Ellas, *Greece* 77 De
Ellef Ringnes I., *N.W.T.* 30 Jb
Ellen, Mt., *Utah* 48 Bc
Ellenabad, *India* 90 Df
Ellendale, *N. Dakota* 46 Hb
Ellensburg, *Washington* 47 Cb
Ellesmere, L., *New Zealand* 55 De
Ellesmere I., *N.W.T.* 31 Lb
Ellezelles, *Belgium* 64 Bd
Ellice, R., *N.W.T.* 38 Vb
Ellice Is. *See* Tuvalu
Ellicott City, *Maryland* 44 Bc
Elliot, *Cape Province* 95 Df
Elliot, *Northern Territory* 57 Fc
Elliot Group, *China* 84 Lc
Elliot L., *Ontario* 34 Hf
Elliot Lake, *Ontario* 34 Hf
Ellis, B., *Quebec* 32 Hd
Elliston, *Newfoundland* 33 Ue
Ellora, *India* 88 Ed
Ellscott, *Alberta* 36 Ed
Ellsworth, *Maine* 32 Dj
Ellsworth, L., *Oklahoma* 49 He
Ellsworth Highland, *Antarctica* 104 Ra
Elm, *Switzerland* 65 Eb
Elma, *Manitoba* 36 Fa
El Ma'arra, *Syria* 94 Ea
Elma Dagh, *Turkey* 92 Bb
El Madhiq, *Arabia* 92 Ce
El Mansura, *Egypt* 99 Mb
El Mazar, *Jordan* 94 Df
El Mazra'a, *Jordan* 94 Df
Elm Creek, *Manitoba* 37 Uj
El Menzil, *Jordan* 94 Ef
El Minya, *Egypt* 99 Mc
Elmira, *New York* 44 Ba
Elmira, *Ontario* 34 Kj
Elmira, *P.E.I.* 33 Kg
Elm L., *S. Dakota* 46 Hc
El Molar, *Spain* 70 Db
Elmsdale, *Nova Scotia* 32 Jj
Elmsvale, *Nova Scotia* 32 Jh
El Muwaqqar, *Jordan* 94 Ef
Elmvale, *Ontario* 34 Lh
Elmwood, *Ontario* 34 Jh
El Nahud, *Sudan* 99 Lf
El Negro, *Venezuela* 52 Eb
Elnora, *Alberta* 36 Dg
El Obeid, *Sudan* 99 Mf
El Odaiya, *Sudan* 99 Lf
Elora, *Ontario* 34 Kj
Elora, *Tennessee* 45 Dc
El Pardo, *Spain* 70 Db
El Paso, *Illinois* 49 Nb
El Paso, *Texas* 42 Ee
Elphinstone, *Manitoba* 37 Rh
Elphinstone I., *Burma* 89 Jf
El Pico, *Bolivia* 52 Eg
El Pintado, *Argentina* 54 Db
El Portugues, *Peru* 52 Be
El Puente del Arzobispo, *Spain* 70 Cc
El Qadmus, *Syria* 94 Eb
El Qanawat, *Syria* 94 Ee
El Qaryatein, *Syria* 94 Fc
El Qatrana, *Jordan* 94 Ef
El Quds esh Sherif. *See* Jerusalem
El Quneitra, *Syria* 94 Dd
El Quseir, *Syria* 94 Ec
El Quweira, *Jordan* 94 Dh
El Reno, *Oklahoma* 49 Je
Elrose, *Saskatchewan* 36 Jg
Elroy, *Wisconsin* 40 Ad
Elsa, *Y.T.* 38 Fd
El Sadi. *See* Wajir
El Salvador, *Cent. America* 51 Bd
Elsas, *Ontario* 34 Hd
El Seibo, *Dominican Rep.* 51 Fc
Elsenborn, *Belgium* 64 Ed
Elsloo, *Netherlands* 64 Dd
Elspeet, *Netherlands* 64 Db
Elst, *Netherlands* 64 Dc
Elsterwerda, *E. Germany* 68 Ec
Elstow, *Saskatchewan* 36 Lg
Eltham, *New Zealand* 55 Ec
El Tigre, *Venezuela* 52 Eb
El Tocuyo, *Venezuela* 52 Cb
El Toro, *Spain* 71 Eb
El Transito, *Chile* 54 Bc
Eltrut L., *Ontario* 36 Ka
Elu Inlet, *N.W.T.* 38 Ua
Eluru, *India* 88 Fe
Elva, *Manitoba* 37 Qj
El Valle, *Colombia* 52 Bb
Elvas, *Portugal* 70 Bc
El Vigia, *Venezuela* 52 Cb
Ely, *England* 63 Hh
Ely, *Minnesota* 46 Mb
Ely, *Nevada* 47 Ff
Ely, Isle of, *England* 63 Hh
Emamrūd, *Iran* 93 Gb
Emangulova, *U.S.S.R.* 81 Md
Emba R., *Kazakhstan* 78 Ed
Embar, *Nfld.* 32 Ga
Embarcación, *Argentina* 54 Db
Embarras Portage, *Alberta* 39 Sf
Embóna, *Greece* 77 Ff
Embro, *Ontario* 34 Kj
Embrun, *France* 73 Gd
Embrun, *Ontario* 35 Pg
Emden, *West Germany* 68 Bb
Emerald, *Queensland* 57 Jd
Emerald I., *N.W.T.* 30 Hb
Emerson, *Manitoba* 37 Uj
Emilia-Romagna, *Italy* 74 Cc
Eminabad, *Pakistan* 90 Dd
Eminence, *Missouri* 45 Bb
Emmaste, *Estonia* 67 Kg
Emmeline L., *Sask.* 36 Lc
Emmen, *Netherlands* 64 Eb
Emmetsburg, *Iowa* 49 Ka
Emmons, Mt., *Utah* 48 Bb
Emo, *Ontario* 36 Jb
Emory Peak, *Texas* 48 Fh
Empalme, *Mexico* 50 Bb
Empedrado, *Argentina* 54 Ec
Empire, *Michigan* 40 Cc
Emporia, *Kansas* 49 Jc
Emporia, *Virginia* 45 Jb
Emporium, *Pennsylvania* 44 Ab
Empress, *Alberta* 36 Gh
Emptinne, *Belgium* 64 Dd
Ems, Bad, *West Germany* 68 Bc
Emsdale, *Ontario* 35 Lg
Enard B., *Scotland* 62 Db
Encantada, Cerro de la, *Mexico* 50 Aa
Encarnación, *Paraguay* 54 Ec
Enchant, *Alberta* 36 Eh
Encontrados, *Venezuela* 52 Cb
Encounter B., *S. Australia* 57 Gg
Encruzilhada, *Brazil* 54 Fd
Endako, *B.C.* 39 Lh
Ende, *Flores I., Indonesia* 83 Hm
Endeavour, *Saskatchewan* 37 Pf
Enderbury I., *Phoenix Is.* 102 Hh
Enderby, *B.C.* 39 Ok
Enderby Land, *Antarctica* 104 Ec
Enderlin, *N. Dakota* 46 Jb
Endicott, *New York* 44 Ba
Endicott Mts., *Alaska* 43 Xl
Endo, *Ontario* 34 Fd
Enez, *Turkey* 92 Aa
Enez, G. of, *Greece* 77 Ed
Enfield, *Nova Scotia* 32 Jj
Engaño, C., *Philippines* 83 Hg
Engelberg, *Switzerland* 65 Db
Engel's, *U.S.S.R.* 81 He
Enggaño, *Indonesia* 83 Dm
Enghien, *Belgium* 64 Cd
Engineer, *B.C.* 38 Ff
England, *Great Britain* 63 Fh
Englee, *Newfoundland* 33 Qc
Englefield, *Saskatchewan* 37 Nf
Englehart, *Ontario* 35 Le
Englewood, *B.C.* 39 Kk
Englewood, *New Jersey* 44 Db
English B., *B.C.* 39 Gl
English Bazar, *India* 91 Gc
English Channel, *France/England* 61 Gf
English Coast, *Antarctica* 104 Sb
English Harbour West, *Nfld.* 33 Rf
English River, *Ontario* 37 Ma
Enid, *Oklahoma* 49 Jd
Enilda, *Alberta* 36 Ac
Enkhuizen, *Netherlands* 64 Db
Enköping, *Sweden* 67 Gg
Enna, *Sicily* 75 Eg
Ennadai, *N.W.T.* 38 Xe
Ennadai L., *N.W.T.* 38 Xe
En Naqura, *Lebanon* 94 Dd
En Nebk, *Syria* 94 Ec
Ennell L., *Eire* 63 Cg
Ennis, *Eire* 63 Bh
Enniscorthy, *Eire* 63 Ch
Enniskillen, *N. Ireland* 63 Bf
Ennistymon, *Eire* 63 Ah
Enns, *Austria* 68 Fd
Enns, *Austria* 68 Fe
Enontekiö, *Finland* 66 Kb
Enriquillo, L., *Dom. Rep.* 51 Ec
Ensanche Sarmiento, *Arg.* 54 Bg
Enschede, *Netherlands* 64 Eb
Ensenada, *Argentina* 54 Ed
Ensenada, *Mexico* 50 Aa
Enshi, *China* 85 Dg
Ensign, *Alberta* 36 Dh
Entebbe, *Uganda* 97 Ge
Enterprise, *Mississippi* 49 Nf
Enterprise, *Ontario* 35 Oh
Entraygues, *France* 73 Ed
Entrée, I. d', *Quebec* 33 Lf
Entre Rios, *Brazil* 53 Kf
Entre Rios, *Brazil* 53 Ge
Entwistle, *Alberta* 36 Ce
Eokuk L., *N.W.T.* 38 Rb
Eolie, Isole, *Italy* 75 Ef
Epe, *Netherlands* 64 Db
Epernay, *France* 72 Eb
Ephraim, *Utah* 48 Bc
Episkopi & B., *Cyprus* 94 Ac
Epping, *England* 63 Hj
Equatoria, Eastern, *Sudan* 97 Gc
Equatoria, Western, *Sudan* 97 Fc
Equatorial Guinea, *W. Africa* 96 Bd
Equeipa, *Venezuela* 52 Eb
Erciş, *Turkey* 92 Db
Erciyas Daği, *Turkey* 92 Cb
Erd, *Hungary* 69 He
Erebus, Mt., *Antarctica* 104 Lb
Erebus B., *N.W.T.* 38 Ya
Erebus Gulf, *Antarctica* 104 Tc
Ereğli, *Turkey* 92 Ba
Ereğli, *Turkey* 92 Bb
Erenhot, *China* 82 Fb
Erepecú L., *Brazil* 53 Fd
Eressós, *Greece* 77 Ee
Erexim, *Brazil* 54 Fc
Erfurt, *East Germany* 68 Dc
Ergani, *Turkey* 92 Cb
Er Hai, *China* 82 De
Ericht L., *Scotland* 62 Ed
Erickson, *Manitoba* 37 Sh
Éric L., *Quebec* 32 Gb
Erie, L., *U.S.A./Can.* 43 Kc
Erieau, *Ontario* 34 Jk
Eriha, *Syria* 94 Eb
Eriksdale, *Manitoba* 37 Th
Erikson, *Manitoba* 37 Sh
Erimo saki, Cape, *Japan* 86 Hd
Erin, *Ontario* 34 Kj
Erlach, *Switzerland* 65 Ca
Erlangen, *West Germany* 68 Dd
Erlenbach, *Switzerland* 65 Cb
Erling L., *Arkansas* 49 Lf
Ermelo, *Netherlands* 64 Db
Ermenek, *Turkey* 92 Bb
Ernakulam, *India* 88 Ef
Ernée, *France* 72 Cb
Erne L., *N. Ireland* 63 Bf
Erne L., Upper, *N. Ireland* 63 Bf
Ernfold, *Saskatchewan* 36 Lh
Erromanga, *Vanuatu* 102 Fj
Erquelinnes, *Belgium* 64 Bd
Er Rabba, *Jordan* 94 Df
Er Rahad, *Sudan* 99 Mf
Er Rastan, *Syria* 94 Ec
Errigal, *Eire* 62 Be
Erris Head, *Eire* 63 Af
Er Roseires, *Sudan* 99 Mf
Er Rumman, *Jordan* 94 De
Erskine, *Alberta* 36 Ef
Erval, *Brazil* 54 Fd
Erwood, *Saskatchewan* 37 Pf
Erz Geb., *East Germany* 68 Ec
Erzincan, *Turkey* 92 Cb
Erzurum, *Turkey* 92 Db
Erzviljkas, *Lithuania* 67 Kj
Esashi, *Japan* 86 Hb
Esbjerg, *Denmark* 67 Cj
Escada, *Brazil* 53 Ke
Escala, La, *Spain* 71 Ga
Escalante, *Utah* 48 Bd
Escalón, *Mexico* 50 Db
Escanaba, *Michigan* 40 Cc
Escaut, *Belgium* 64 Bd
Esch, *Luxembourg* 68 Ad
Escholzmatt, *Switzerland* 65 Cb
Escravos, R., *Nigeria* 98 Fg
Escudo de Veraguas, *Pan.* 51 Ce
Escuinapa, *Mexico* 50 Cc
Escuintla, *Guatemala* 50 Fe
Escuminac, *Quebec* 32 Fe
Escuminac, Pt., *N.B.* 32 Hf
Esfahān, *Iran* 93 Fc
Eshowe, *Natal* 95 Ee
Eskbank, *Saskatchewan* 36 Lh
Eskdale, *New Zealand* 55 Fc
Eskilstuna, *Sweden* 67 Gg
Eskimo Lakes, *N.W.T.* 38 Ga
Eskimo Point, *N.W.T.* 30 Ke
Eskişehir, *Turkey* 92 Bb
Esla, *Spain* 70 Cb
Esla, Emb. del, *Spain* 70 Cb
Eslöv, *Sweden* 67 Ej
Esmeralda, I., *Chile* 54 Ag
Esmeraldas, *Ecuador* 52 Bc
Esnagami L., *Ontario* 34 Db
Esnagi L., *Ontario* 34 Fd
Espalion, *France* 73 Ed
Espanola, *Ontario* 34 Jf
Esperance, *W. Australia* 56 Df
Esperanza, *Argentina* 54 Dd
Espiel, *Spain* 70 Cc
Espinho, *Portugal* 70 Ab
Espinosa de los Monteros, *Spain* 70 Da
Espírito Santo, *Brazil* 53 Jh
Espíritu Santo, *Vanuatu* 102 Fj
Espíritu Santo, B. del, *Mex.* 50 Gd
Espíritu Santo, C., *Argentina* 54 Ch
Espíritu Santo, I., *Mexico* 50 Bc
Espoir, B. d', *Nfld.* 33 Rf
Esquel, *Argentina* 54 Bf
Esquina, *Argentina* 54 Ed
Es Salt, *Jordan* 94 De
Es Samra, *Jordan* 94 Ee
Es Sanamein, *Syria* 94 Ed
Essaouira, *Morocco* 98 Db
Esse & Älv, *Finland* 66 Ke
Es-Sekhira, *Tunisia* 99 Hb
Essen, *Belgium* 64 Cc
Essen, *West Germany* 68 Bc
Essequibo, *Guyana* 52 Fb
Essex, *England* 63 Hj
Essex, *Ontario* 34 Hk
Essex Mt., *Wyoming* 42 Ec
Esslingen, *West Germany* 68 Cd
Es Sukhne, *Syria* 92 Cc
Es Suweidīya, *Syria* 94 Ee
Est, I. de l', *Quebec* 33 Lf

Est, Pte. de l', Quebec 33 Lf
Estabutchie, Mississippi 45 Ce
Estados, I. de los, Argentina 54 Dh
Estaire, Ontario 34 Kf
Estância, Brazil 53 Kf
Estavayer, Switzerland 65 Bb
Estcourt, Natal 95 De
Esteli, Nicaragua 51 Bd
Esterhazy, Saskatchewan 37 Ph
Esternay, France 72 Eb
Estevan, Saskatchewan 37 Oj
Estevan Group, B.C. 39 Jj
Estevan Point, B.C. 39 Kl
Esther, Alberta 36 Gg
Estherville, Iowa 49 Ka
Estlin, Saskatchewan 37 Nh
Eston, Saskatchewan 36 Jg
Estonia (Estonskaya S.S.R.), U.S.S.R. 80 Db
Estoril, Portugal 70 Ac
Estreito, Brazil 54 Fd
Estremoz, Portugal 70 Bc
Estrondo, Sa. des, Brazil 53 He
Estuary, Saskatchewan 36 Hh
Etadunna, S. Australia 57 Ge
Etah, India 91 Bb
Etalle, Belgium 64 De
Étamamiou, Quebec 33 Nc
Étamamiou, R., Quebec 33 Nc
Étampes, France 72 Eb
Étang-du-Nord, Quebec 33 Kf
Étaples, France 72 Da
Etawah, India 91 Bb
Etawney L., Manitoba 37 Va
Eternity Range, Antarctica 104 Sb
Ethe, Belgium 64 De
Ethelbert, Manitoba 37 Rg
Ethel Creek, W. Australia 56 Dd
Ethelton, Saskatchewan 37 Nf
Ethiopia, E. Africa 97 Hc
Etivaz, l', Switzerland 65 Cb
Etive L., Scotland 62 Dd
Etna Mt., Sicily 75 Eg
Etobicoke, Ontario 34 Bk
Etomami, Saskatchewan 37 Pf
Eton, Ontario 34 Fe
Ettelbrück, Luxembourg 68 Bd
Etten, Netherlands 64 Cc
Ettrick, New Zealand 55 Bf
Etzikom, Alberta 36 Fj
Etzikom Coulee, R., Alta. 36 Fj
Euboea. See Évvoia
Eucla, W. Australia 56 Ef
Eudistes, L. des, Quebec 32 Gc
Eufaula, Alabama 43 Je
Eufaula, Oklahoma 49 Ke
Eugene, Oregon 47 Bc
Eugmö, Finland 66 Ke
Eugondo, Uganda 97 Gd
Eunice, Louisiana 49 Lg
Eupen, Belgium 64 Ed
Euphrates, Iraq 92 Ec
Eure, France 72 Db
Eure-et-Loir, France 72 Db
Eureka, California 47 Ae
Eureka, Kansas 49 Jd
Eureka, Nevada 47 Ff
Eureka, Nova Scotia 32 Kh
Eureka, N.W.T. 31 La
Eureka, Utah 47 Gf
Eureka River, Alberta 39 Og
Eureka Sd., N.W.T. 31 Lb
Eursinge, Netherlands 64 Eb
Eutaw, Alabama 45 Dd
Eutin, West Germany 68 Da
Eutsuk, L., B.C. 39 Kj
Evale, Angola 95 Bc
Evans, C., N.W.T. 31 La
Evans, L., Quebec 35 Ob
Evans, Mt., Alberta 39 Oj
Evansburg, Alberta 36 Ce
Evans Str., N.W.T. 31 Le
Evanston, Illinois 49 Oa
Evanston, Wyoming 46 Be
Evansville, Indiana 45 Da
Evansville, Minnesota 46 Kb
Evansville, Ontario 34 Hg
Evaux-les-Bains, France 72 Ec
Eveleth, Minnesota 46 Lb
Everard, Ontario 34 Bd
Everard, L., S. Australia 57 Ff
Everest, Nepal/China 89 Gc
Everett, Washington 42 Bb
Evergem, Belgium 64 Bc
Everglades, The, Florida 43 Kf
Everglades Nat. Park, Fla. 45 Gh
Evergreen, Alabama 45 De
Evesham, England 63 Fh
Evesham, Saskatchewan 36 Hf
Evijärvi, Finland 66 Ke
Evje, Norway 67 Bg
Evolène, Switzerland 65 Cb
Evora, Portugal 70 Bc
Evreux, France 72 Db
Evros, Greece 77 Fd
Evrykhou, Cyprus 94 Ab
Évvoia, Greece 77 De
Évvoia, G. of, Greece 77 De
Ewarton, Jamaica 51 Dc
Ewe L., Scotland 62 Dc
Exaltación, Bolivia 52 Df
Excel, Alberta 36 Gg
Exeter, England 63 Ek
Exeter, New Hampshire 44 Ea
Exeter, Ontario 34 Jj
Exeter L., N.W.T. 38 Sc
Exloo, Netherlands 64 Eb
Exmoor, England 63 Ej
Exmouth, England 63 Ek
Exmouth G., W. Australia 56 Bd
Exmouth L., N.W.T. 38 Qc
Expanse, Saskatchewan 37 Mj
Expedition Range, Queensland 57 Jd
Exploits R., Newfoundland 33 Re
Exshaw, Alberta 36 Bg
Exuma Is., The Bahamas 51 Db
Exuma Sound, The Bahamas 51 Db
Eyasi, L., Tanzania 97 Ge
Eyeberry L., N.W.T. 39 Vd
Eyebrow, Saskatchewan 36 Lh
Eyemouth, Scotland 62 Fe
Eymoutiers, France 72 Dd
Eyre, Saskatchewan 36 Hg
Eyre, W. Australia 56 Ef
Eyre, L., S. Australia 57 Ge
Eyre Cr., S. Australia 57 Ge
Eyre Pen., S. Australia 57 Gf
Eyrie L., Manitoba 37 Ra
Eyzies, les, France 73 Dd
Ezcaray, Spain 73 Be

F

Faber L., N.W.T. 38 Pd
Fåborg, Denmark 67 Dj
Fabre, Quebec 35 Le
Facatativa, Colombia 52 Cc
Fada, Chad 99 Ke
Fadan'Gourma, Upper Volta 98 Ff
Faddeyevskiy, Os., U.S.S.R. 79 Pa
Faenza, Italy 74 Cc
Faeróerne, N. Atlantic Ocean 41 Mc
Faeroes. See Faeróerne
Fafa, Mali 98 Fe
Făgăras, Romania 76 Eb
Fagerli, Norway 66 Fc
Fagernes, Norway 67 Cf
Fagnano, L., Argentina 54 Ch
Faid, Arabia 92 Dd
Faido, Switzerland 65 Db
Faifo. See Hoi An
Faillon, L., Quebec 35 Od
Fairbanks, Alaska 43 Yl
Fairbury, Illinois 40 Be
Fairbury, Nebraska 49 Jb
Fairfield, Illinois 45 Ca
Fairfield, Iowa 49 Mb
Fairfield, Maine 32 Cj
Fairford, Manitoba 37 Tg
Fairhaven, Massachusetts 44 Eb
Fair Head, N. Ireland 62 Ce
Fairholme, Saskatchewan 36 Je
Fair I., Scotland 62 Fa
Fairlie, New Zealand 55 Cf
Fairlight, Saskatchewan 37 Qj
Fairmont, Minnesota 46 Kd
Fairmont, West Virginia 40 Ff
Fairmont Hot Springs, British Columbia 39 Qk
Fairmount, Saskatchewan 36 Hg
Fair Ness, N.W.T. 31 Me
Fairview, Alberta 39 Og
Fairweather, Mt., Alaska 43 Zm
Fairy Glen, Saskatchewan 37 Ne
Faith, S. Dakota 46 Fc
Faizabad, Afghanistan 93 Kb
Faizabad dist., India 91 Db
Fajr, Arabia 92 Cd
Fakfak, Irian Jaya 83 Kl
Fakiya, Bulgaria 76 Fc
Falaise L., N.W.T. 38 Pe
Falam, Burma 89 Hd
Falama, Guinea 98 Df
Fălciu, Romania 76 Ga
Falconbridge, Ontario 34 Kf
Falcone, C., Sardinia 75 Be
Falcon Res., Texas 48 Hj
Falher, Alberta 39 Ph
Falkenberg, Sweden 67 Eh
Falkirk, Scotland 62 Ee
Falkland, B.C. 39 Ok
Falkland Is., S. Atlantic Ocean 54 Dh
Falkland Sound, Falkland Is. 54 Dh
Falköping, Sweden 67 Eg
Fall River, Massachusetts 44 Eb
Falls City, Nebraska 49 Kb
Falmagne, Belgium 64 Cd
Falmouth, England 63 Dk
Falmouth, Jamaica 51 Dc
Falmouth, Kentucky 40 Df
False B., (Valsbaai), Cape Prov. 95 Bf
False Point, India 89 Gd
Falset, Spain 71 Fb
Falso, C., Mexico 50 Bc
Falster. I., Denmark 67 Dj
Falun, Sweden 67 Ff
Famagusta & B., Cyprus 94 Bb
Famatina, Argentina 54 Cc
Fannich L., Scotland 62 Dc
Fanning I., Pacific Ocean 103 Kg
Fannūj, Iran 93 Gd
Fanny Bay, B.C. 39 Ll
Fannystelle, Manitoba 37 Uj
Fanö, I., Denmark 67 Cj
Fanö Bugt, Denmark 67 Cj
Faradje, Zaire 97 Fd
Farafangana, Madagascar 97 Nl
Farah, Afghanistan 93 Hc
Farajah, Arabia 93 Fe
Faranah, Guinea 98 Cf
Farasān, Red Sea 92 Df
Faraulep, Caroline Is. 102 Dg
Farewell C., Greenland 41 Pd
Fargo, N. Dakota 46 Jb
Faribault, Minnesota 46 Lc
Faridabad, India 90 Ef
Faridkot, India 90 De
Faridpur, Bangladesh 91 Gd
Faridpur, India 91 Ba
Farīmān, Iran 93 Gb
Farlane, Ontario 36 Ha
Farley, Quebec 35 Pf
Farmington, B.C. 39 Nh
Farmington, Maine 32 Bj
Farmington, Missouri 45 Bb
Farmington, New Mexico 48 Cd
Farmington, Utah 48 Bb
Farmville, Virginia 45 Hb
Farne Is., England 62 Fe
Farnes, Norway 67 Bf
Farnham, Quebec 35 Rg
Farnham, Mt., B.C. 39 Pk
Faro, Brazil 53 Fd
Faro, Portugal 70 Bd
Faro, Y.T. 30 Fe
Fårön, I., Sweden 67 Hh
Farrellton, Quebec 35 Og
Farrerdale, Saskatchewan 37 Mg
Farrukhabad, India 91 Bb
Farrukhnagar, India 90 Ef
Fársala, Greece 77 De
Farsi, Afghanistan 93 Hc
Farsund, Norway 67 Bg
Farwell, Michigan 40 Dd
Farwell, Texas 42 Fe
Fasā, Iran 93 Fd
Fatehabad, India 90 Df
Fatehgarh, India 91 Bb
Fatehpur, Uttar Prad., India 91 Cb
Fatehpur, dist., India 91 Cc
Father, L., Quebec 35 Pc
Fatmomakke, Sweden 66 Fd
Fatshan. See Foshan
Fatu Hiva, Marquêsas Is. 103 Mj
Fauquier, B.C. 39 Pl
Faust, Alberta 36 Bc
Fawcett, Alberta 36 Dc
Fawcett L., Alberta 36 Dc
Fawn, R., Ontario 31 Lg
Faxaflói, Iceland 66 Um
Faya. See Largeau
Fayette, Alabama 49 Of
Fayette, Missouri 49 Lc
Fayetteville, Arkansas 49 Kd
Fayetteville, N. Carolina 45 Hc
Fayetteville, Pa. 43 Bc
Fayetteville, W. Virginia 45 Ga
Fazilka, India 90 De
Fdérik, Mauritania 98 Cd
Feale R., Eire 63 Ah
Fear, C., N. Carolina 43 Le
Fécamp, France 72 Db
Federación, Argentina 54 Ed
Fehmarn, Germany 68 Da
Feijó, Brazil 52 Ce
Feilding, New Zealand 55 Ed
Feira de Santana, Brazil 53 Kf
Feldbach, Austria 69 Fe
Feldkirch, Austria 68 Ce
Felipe Carrillo Puerto, Mexico 50 Gd
Felix, C., N.W.T. 38 Za
Felix, Rio, New Mexico 48 Ef
Felix U Gomez, Mexico 50 Ca
Femund, L., Norway 66 De
Fenelon Falls, Ontario 35 Mh
Fenghuang, China 85 Dj
Fengjie, China 84 Dg
Feng Xian, China 84 He
Fengxiang, China 84 Ce
Fengyang, China 84 Hf
Fengzhen, China 84 Fb
Fenton, Michigan 40 Ed
Fenton, Saskatchewan 37 Me
Fenwick, Ontario 35 Lj
Fenwood, Saskatchewan 37 Og
Fenyang, China 84 Ed
Feodosiya, U.S.S.R. 80 Hd
Ferdow, Iran 93 Gc
Fergus, Ontario 34 Kj
Fergus Falls, Minnesota 46 Jb
Ferguson, Missouri 45 Ba
Ferguson, Quebec 40 Kb
Ferguson, Saskatchewan 38 Va
Fergusson I., Papua New Guinea 57 Ka
Ferintosh, Alberta 36 Ef
Ferland, Ontario 34 Bb
Fermanagh, N. Ireland 63 Bf
Ferme-Neuve, Quebec 35 Pf
Fermoy, Eire 63 Bh
Fernando Poo. See Bioko
Fernie, British Columbia 39 Ql
Ferolle Pt., Nfld. 33 Pb
Ferrara, Italy 74 Cc
Ferrar Glacier, Antarctica 104 Kb
Ferrato C., Sardinia 75 Bf
Ferreira do Zezere, Portugal 70 Ac
Ferreira Gomes, Brazil 53 Gc
Ferru, L., Quebec 33 Nb
Ferryland, Newfoundland 33 Ud
Fertile, Minnesota 46 Jb
Fertö tó. See Neusiedler See
Fès, Morocco 98 Db
Festus, Missouri 45 Ba
Fethard, Eire 63 Bh
Fethiye, Turkey 92 Ab
Fetlar I., Zetland 62 Ja
Feu, L. du, Quebec 33 Mc
Feudal, Saskatchewan 36 Kg
Feuilles, R., Quebec 31 Mf
Fiambala, Argentina 54 Cc
Ficalho, Portugal 70 Bd
Fichtel Geb., West Germany 68 Dc
Fideris, Switzerland 65 Eb
Fidler L., Manitoba 37 Va
Field, Ontario 34 Lf
Fielding, Saskatchewan 36 Kf
Fier, Albania 77 Bd
Fiesch, Switzerland 65 Db
Fife, Scotland 62 Ed
Fife L., Saskatchewan 37 Mj
Fife Lake, Saskatchewan 37 Mj
Fife Ness, Scotland 62 Fd
Figeac, France 73 Ed
Figline Valdarno, Italy 74 Cd
Figueira de Castelo Rodrigo, Portugal 70 Bb
Figueras, Spain 71 Ga
Figuig, Morocco 98 Eb
Fiji, Pacific Ocean 102 Gj
Fil'akovo, Czechoslovakia 69 Hd
Filchner Ice Shelf, Antarc. 104 Tb
File L., Manitoba 37 Rd
Filiátes, Greece 77 Ce
Filicudi, Italy 75 Ef
Filipow, Poland 69 Ka
Filisur, Switzerland 65 Eb
Fillmore, Saskatchewan 37 Oj
Filonovsk, U.S.S.R. 81 Fe
Fincastle, Virginia 45 Hb
Finch, Ontario 35 Pg
Findhorn R., Scotland 62 Ec
Findlater, Saskatchewan 37 Mh
Findlay, Ohio 40 Ee
Findlay, Mt., B.C. 39 Pk
Fingal, N. Dakota 46 Jb
Finger L., Ontario 30 Kg
Finhaut, Switzerland 65 Bb
Finistère, France 72 Ab
Finisterre, C., Spain 70 Aa
Finke, R., N. Terr. 57 Ge
Finland, rep., N. Europe 66 Le
Finland G. of, N.-W. Europe 67 Lg
Finlay, R., B.C. 39 Kg
Finmark, Ontario 37 Nb
Finnegan, Alberta 36 Eg
Finschhafen, New Guinea 57 Ja
Finspång, Sweden 67 Fg
Finsteraarhorn, Switzerland 65 Db
Fintona, N. Ireland 63 Cf
Fionnay, Switzerland 65 Cb
Fiq, Syria 94 De
Firat, Turkey 92 Cb
Firebag R., Alberta 39 Sg
Firenze, Italy 74 Cd
Fire River, Ontario 34 Gd
Firmat, Argentina 54 Dd
Fir Mountain, Sask. 36 Lj
Firozabad, India 91 Bb
Firozpur, India 90 De
Firozpur Jhirka, India 90 Eg
Firth, R., Y.T. 38 Ca
Firūzabad, Iran 93 Fd
Fisher, Quebec 35 Nd
Fisher B., Manitoba 37 Ug
Fisher Branch, Manitoba 37 Ug
Fisher Str., N.W.T. 31 Le
Fishguard, Wales 63 Dj
Fishing Ls., The, Sask. 37 Nh
Fish L., N.W.T. 38 Md
Fishtrap Res., Kentucky 45 Fb
Fiske, Saskatchewan 36 Jg
Fitchburg, Massachusetts 44 Ea
Fitful Head, Zetland 62 Hb
Fitzcarrald, Peru 52 Cf
Fitz Hugh Sd., B.C. 39 Kk
Fitzpatrick, Alabama 45 Ed
Fitzpatrick, Quebec 35 Se
Fitzroy, R., Queensland 57 Jd
Fitzroy, R., W. Australia 56 Dc
Fitzroy Crossing, W. Australia 56 Ec
Fitzroy Harbour, Ontario 35 Og
Fitzwilliam I., Ontario 34 Jg
Fiume. See Rijeka
Five Islands, Nova Scotia 32 Hh
Fjällåsen, Sweden 66 Jc
Flagstaff, Arizona 48 Be
Flagstaff, Arizona 42 Dd
Flamborough Head, England 63 Gf
Flaming Gorge Res., Wyo. 48 Cb
Flamingo B., Irian Jaya 83 Lm
Flanders, Ontario 36 Lb
Flat, Alaska 43 Xl
Flat Bay, Newfoundland 33 Oe
Flatbush, Alberta 36 Cd
Flathead L., Montana 47 Fb
Flat L., Alberta 36 Ed
Flat R., N.W.T. 38 Ke
Flattery, C., Queensland 57 Jb
Flattery C., Washington 42 Bb
Flaxcombe, Saskatchewan 36 Hg
Flèche, la, France 72 Cc
Fleet, Alberta 36 Ff
Fleetwood, England 63 Eg
Flekkefjord, Norway 67 Bg
Fleming, Saskatchewan 37 Qh
Flemington, New Jersey 44 Cb
Flensburg, West Germany 68 Ca
Flers, France 72 Cb
Flesherton, Ontario 34 Kh
Fletcher L., N.W.T. 38 Td
Fleurance, France 73 De
Fleur de Lys, Nfld. 33 Rc
Fleur-de-May, L., Nfld. 32 Hb
Fleurier, Switzerland 65 Bb
Fleurus, Belgium 64 Cd
Flims, Switzerland 65 Eb
Flinders, R., Queensland 57 Hc
Flinders I., S. Australia 57 Ff
Flinders I., Tasmania 57 Jg
Flinders Range, S. Australia 57 Gf
Flin Flon, Manitoba 37 Qd
Flint, Michigan 40 Ed
Flint, Wales 63 Eg
Flint I., Pacific Ocean 103 Kj
Flint L., Ontario 34 Ec
Flintoft, Saskatchewan 36 Lj
Flint R., Georgia, U.S.A. 43 Ke
Flisa, Norway 67 Ef
Flora, Illinois 49 Nc
Florac, France 73 Ed
Floreffe, Belgium 64 Cd
Florence, Alabama 45 Dc
Florence, Arizona 48 Bf
Florence, Colorado 48 Ec
Florence, S. Carolina 45 Hc
Florence. See Firenze
Florence, Wisconsin 40 Bc
Florencia, Argentina 54 Ec
Florencia, Argentina 54 Db
Florencia, Colombia 52 Bc
Florennes, Belgium 64 Cd
Florenville, Belgium 64 Dd
Flores, Guatemala 50 Gd
Flores, Indonesia 83 Hm
Flores I., Atlantic Ocean 98 Aa
Flores I., B.C. 39 Kl
Flores Sea, Indonesia 83 Hm
Floriano, Brazil 53 Je
Floriano Peixoto, Brazil 52 De
Florianópolis, Brazil 54 Gc
Florida, Uruguay 54 Ed
Florida, U.S.A. 43 Je
Florida B., Florida 43 Kg
Florida C., Florida 43 Kf
Florida City, Florida 43 Kf
Florida Keys, Florida 45 Gh
Florida Mts., New Mexico 48 Df
Floridia, Sicily 75 Eg
Florina, Greece 77 Cd
Flörö, Norway 66 Af
Flotten L., Saskatchewan 36 Jd
Flower's Cove, Nfld. 33 Qb
Floydada, Texas 48 Gf
Flüelen, Switzerland 65 Db
Flushing, New York 44 Db
Flushing. See Vlissingen
Fly, R., New Guinea 57 Ha
Flying Fish C., Antarctica 104 Rb
Foam Lake, Saskatchewan 37 Og
Foča, Yugoslavia 76 Bc
Focsani, Romania 76 Fb
Fofa Cahuel, Argentina 54 Bf
Foggia, Italy 75 Ee
Fogo, Newfoundland 33 Sd
Fogo I., Newfoundland 33 Td
Föhr, West Germany 68 Ca
Foix, France 73 De
Fokis, Greece 77 De
Folda, Fd.,*Norway 66 Fc
Folégandros, Greece 77 Ef
Foleyet, Ontario 34 Hd
Foley I., N.W.T. 31 Md
Foligno, Italy 74 Dd
Folkestone, England 63 Hj
Folkston, Georgia, U.S.A. 45 Fe
Folkstone, N. Carolina 45 Jc
Fonda, New York 44 Ca
Fond du Lac, Minnesota/Wisconsin 40 Ab
Fond-du-Lac, Sask. 38 Uf
Fond du Lac, Wisconsin 40 Bd
Fond du Lac R., Sask. 38 Vf
Fonsagrada, Spain 70 Ba
Fonseca, G., Honduras 51 Bd
Fontaine, Belgium 64 Cd
Fontainebleau, France 72 Eb
Fontaine L., Saskatchewan 38 Uf
Fontana, L., Argentina 54 Bf
Fontas, B.C. 39 Nf
Fontas, R., B.C. 39 Nf
Fontenay-le-Comte, France 72 Cc
Fonteneau, L., Quebec 33 Lb
Fontenelle, Quebec 32 He
Foothills, Alberta 39 Pj
Forbes, New South Wales 57 Jf
Forbes, Mt., Alberta 39 Pk
Forcados, Nigeria 98 Gg
Forcalquier, France 73 Fe
Førde, Norway 67 Af
Ford Ranges, Antarctica 104 Pb
Fordyce, Arkansas 49 Lf
Forel, Mt., Greenland 41 Nc
Foremost, Alberta 36 Fj
Forest, Ontario 34 Hj
Forestburg, Alberta 36 Ef
Forestville, Quebec 32 De
Forfar, Scotland 62 Fd
Forgan, Saskatchewan 36 Kg
Forget, Quebec 35 Od
Forget, Saskatchewan 37 Pj
Fork, R., N., Idaho 42 Dc
Fork River, Manitoba 37 Sg
Forli, Italy 74 Dc
Formentera, Balearic Is. 71 Fc
Formia, Italy 75 De
Formiga, Brazil 53 Hh
Formosa, Argentina 54 Ec
Formosa, Brazil 53 Hg
Formosa. See Taiwan
Formosa Str. See Taiwan Haixia
Fornos d'Algôdres, Portugal 70 Bb
Forres, Scotland 62 Ec
Forrest, W. Australia 56 Ef
Forrest City, Arkansas 49 Me
Forrest L., Saskatchewan 39 Tg
Forrest Station, Manitoba 36 Aa
Forsa, Sweden 67 Gf
Forsayth, Queensland 57 Hc
Forsnäs, Sweden 66 Hc
Forssa, Finland 67 Kf
Forsyth, Montana 46 Db
Forsythe, Quebec 35 Od
Fort Albany, Ontario 31 Lg
Fortaleza, Brazil 53 Kd
Fortaleza, Terr. do Acre, Brazil 52 De
Fort Ann, New York 44 Da
Fort Anne Nat. Hist. Park, Nova Scotia 32 Gj
Fort Archambault. See Sarh
Fort Assiniboine, Alberta 39 Qh
Fort Atkinson, Wisconsin 49 Na
Fort Atkinson, Wisconsin 40 Bd
Fort Augustus, Scotland 62 Dc
Fort Beaufort, Cape Prov. 95 Df
Fort Beauséjour Nat. Hist. Park, New Brunswick 32 Hh
Fort Bennett, S. Dakota 46 Gc
Fort Benton, Montana 46 Bb
Fort Black, Saskatchewan 36 Kc
Fort Bragg, California 47 Bf
Fort-Chimo, Quebec 31 Nf
Fort Chipewyan, Alberta 39 Sf
Fort Cobb Res., Oklahoma 49 He
Fort Collins, Colorado 48 Eb
Fort-Coulonge, Quebec 35 Og
Fort Crampel, Central African Rep. 99 Jg
Fort Dauphin, Madagascar 97 Nm
Fort Dodge, Iowa 49 Ka
Forteau, Newfoundland 33 Pb
Fort Erie, Ontario 35 Lk
Fortescue, R., W. Australia 56 Cd
Fort Fairfield, Maine 32 Eg
Fort Fitzgerald, Alberta 38 Sf
Fort Flatters, Algeria 98 Gc
Fort Frances, Ontario 36 Jb
Fort Franklin, N.W.T. 38 Mc
Fort Fraser, B.C. 39 Lh
Fort Garry, Manitoba 37 Uh
Fort George, Quebec 31 Mg
Fort Good Hope, N.W.T. 38 Jb
Forth, Firth of, Scotland 62 Fd
Fort Hope, Ontario 31 Lg
Fort Howard, Wisconsin 40 Bc
Forth R., Scotland 62 Ed
Fort Hunter, New York 44 Ca
Fortierville, Quebec 35 Tf
Forties Settlement, N.S. 32 Hj
Fortin, L., Quebec 32 Ec
Fortin Avalos Sanchez, Paraguay 54 Eb
Fortin General Diaz, Para. 54 Db
Fortin Lopez, Paraguay 54 Db
Fort Kent, Alberta 36 Gd
Fort Kent, Maine 32 Df
Fort Keogh, Montana 46 Eb
Fort Lallemand, Algeria 98 Gb
Fort Lamy. See N'Djamena
Fort Langley, B.C. 39 Kl
Fort Laramie, Wyoming 46 Ed
Fort Liard, N.W.T. 38 Me
Fort MacKay, Alberta 39 Sg
Fort Macleod, Alberta 36 Dj
Fort McMurray, Alberta 39 Sg
Fort McPherson, N.W.T. 38 Fb
Fort Madison, Iowa 49 Mb
Fort Maginnis, Montana 46 Cb
Fort Morgan, Alabama 45 De
Fort Morgan, Colorado 48 Fb
Fort Munro, Pakistan 90 Af
Fort Nelson, B.C. 39 Mf
Fort Nelson R., B.C. 39 Mf
Fort Norman, N.W.T. 38 Lc
Fort Ogden, Florida 45 Gg
Fort Peck, Montana 46 Db
Fort Peck Res., Montana 46 Db
Fort Pierre, S. Dakota 46 Gc
Fort Plain, New York 44 Ca
Fort Polignac. See Illizi
Fort Portal, Uganda 97 Gd
Fort Providence, N.W.T. 38 Pe
Fort Qu'Appelle, Sask. 37 Oh
Fort Randall, Alaska 41 Bd
Fort Resolution, N.W.T. 38 Re
Fortress of Louisbourg National Historic Park, N.S. 33 Mh
Fort Rice, N. Dakota 46 Gb
Fortrose, Scotland 62 Ec
Fort Rupert, Ontario 31 Ma
Fort Saint George. See Madras
Fort Saint James, B.C. 39 Lh
Fort Saint John, B.C. 39 Ng
Fort Sandeman, Pakistan 90 Ae
Fort Saskatchewan, Alta. 36 De
Fort Scott, Kansas 49 Kd
Fort Severn, Ontario 31 Lf
Fort Sibut, Cent. Afr. Rep. 99 Jg
Fort Sill, Oklahoma 49 He
Fort Simpson, N.W.T. 38 Ne
Fort Smith, Arkansas 49 Ke
Fort Smith, N.W.T. 38 Se
Fort Stockton, Texas 48 Fg
Fort Sumner, New Mexico 48 Ee
Fortuna, California 47 Ae
Fortuna, Spain 71 Ec
Fortune & B., Nfld. 33 Rf
Fort Valley, Georgia, U.S.A. 45 Fd
Fort Vermilion, Alberta 39 Qf
Fort Victoria, Zimbabwe 95 Ed
Fort Warren, Wyoming 46 Ee
Fort Wayne, Indiana 40 De
Fort William, Scotland 62 Dd
Fort Worth, Texas 49 Jf
Fort Yates, N. Dakota 46 Gb
Forty Mile, Y.T. 38 Cc
Fort Yukon, Alaska 43 Yl
Forville, Belgium 64 Cd
Forward, Saskatchewan 37 Nj
Foshan, China 85 Fl
Fosheim Pen., N.W.T. 31 Lb
Fosse, Belgium 64 Cd
Foss Res., Oklahoma 49 He
Fosston, Saskatchewan 37 Of
Foster, Quebec 35 Sg
Foster Ls., Saskatchewan 39 Vg
Foster R., Saskatchewan 39 Vg
Fosterton, Saskatchewan 36 Jh
Fougères, France 72 Cb
Foula, I., Scotland 62 Ha
Foul B., Egypt 99 Nd
Foul I., Burma 89 He
Foulness I., England 63 Hj
Fouly, la, Switzerland 65 Cc
Fourchu, Nova Scotia 33 Mh
Fournel, L., Quebec 33 Pb
Fournier, L., Quebec 32 Gb
Foúrnoi, Greece 77 Ff
Foveaux Strait, New Zealand 55 Ag
Fowchow. See Fulin
Fowlers B., S. Australia 56 Ff
Fox, R., Manitoba 30 Kf
Foxe Basin, N.W.T. 31 Ld
Foxe Chan., N.W.T. 31 Ld
Foxe Pen., N.W.T. 31 Me
Foxford, Saskatchewan 37 Me
Fox Harbour, Nfld. 33 Ra
Fox Is., Aleutian Is. 43 Wm
Fox R., B.C. 39 Lg
Foxton, New Zealand 55 Ed
Fox Valley, Saskatchewan 36 Hh
Foxwarren, Manitoba 37 Qh
Foyle L., N. Ireland 62 Ce
Foynes, Eire 63 Ah
Fóz do Aripuana, Brazil 52 Ee
Foz do Cunene, Angola 95 Ac
Foz do Jordão, Brazil 52 Ce
Foz do Jutai, Brazil 52 Dd
Foz do Pauini, Brazil 52 De
Foz Embira, Brazil 52 Ce
Fraire, Belgium 64 Cd
Frameries, Belgium 64 Bd
Framingham, Massachusetts 44 Ea
Franca, Brazil 53 Hh
Francavilla Fontana, Italy 75 Fe
France, W. Europe 61 Hg
Frances L., Y.T. 38 Je
Frances Lake, Y.T. 38 Je
Frances R., Y.T. 38 Je
Franceville, Gabon 96 Ce
Franche-Comté, Fr. 72 Gc
Francis, Manitoba 37 Oh
Francis Case L., S. Dakota 46 Hd
Francis Harbour, Nfld. 33 Ra
Francistown, Botswana 95 Dd
François, Newfoundland 33 Qf
François L., B.C. 39 Lh
Frankford, Ontario 35 Nh
Frankfort, Kansas 49 Jc
Frankfort, Kentucky 45 Ea
Frankfort, Michigan 40 Cc
Frankfurt am Main, W. Ger. 68 Cc
Frankfurt-an-der-Oder, Ger. 68 Fb
Fränkischer Jura, W. Ger. 68 Dd
Franklin, Louisiana 49 Mh
Franklin, N. Carolina 45 Fc
Franklin, New Hampshire 44 Ea
Franklin, New Jersey 44 Cb
Franklin, Pennsylvania 44 Ab
Franklin, Tasmania 57 Jh
Franklin, Tennessee 45 Dc
Franklin, Virginia 45 Jb
Franklin, W. Virginia 45 Ha
Franklin, Dist. of, N.W.T. 30 Hc
Franklin, I., Antarctica 104 Lb
Franklin B., N.W.T. 38 Ka
Franklin City, Virginia 45 Kb
Franklin I., Ontario 34 Kg
Franklin L., N.W.T. 38 Zb
Franklin Mts., N.W.T. 38 Kc
Franklin Str., N.W.T. 30 Kc
Frantsa Iosifa, Zemlya, Arctic Ocean 78 Da
Franz, Ontario 34 Fd
Franz Josef Fd., Greenland 41 Nb
Franz Josef Land. See Frantsa Iosifa, Zemlya
Fraser, R., B.C. 39 Oj
Fraserburg, Cape Province 95 Cf
Fraserburgh, Scotland 62 Fc
Fraserdale, Ontario 34 Jc
Frasertown, New Zealand 55 Fc
Fraserwood, Manitoba 37 Uh
Frasnes, Belgium 64 Bd
Frater, Ontario 34 Fe
Frauenfeld, Switzerland 65 Da
Fray Bentos, Uruguay 54 Ed
Frazer L., Ontario 34 Cc
Fredericia, Denmark 67 Cj
Frederick, Maryland 44 Bc
Frederick, Oklahoma 49 He
Frederick, S. Dakota 46 Hc
Frederick House, R., Ont. 34 Jc
Fredericksburg, Virginia 45 Ja
Fredericktown, Missouri 45 Bb
Fredericton, N.B. 32 Fh
Fredericton Jct., N.B. 32 Fh
Frederikshåb, Greenland 41 Pc
Frederikshavn, Denmark 67 Dh
Fredonia, Colombia 52 Bb
Fredonia, Kansas 49 Kd
Fredonia, New York 44 Aa
Fredrika, Sweden 66 Hd
Fredrikstad, Norway 67 Dg
Freehold, New Jersey 44 Cb
Freeman R., Alberta 36 Bd
Freeport, Illinois 49 Na
Freeport, Nova Scotia 32 Fj
Freeport, Pennsylvania 44 Ab
Freetown, P.E.I. 32 Jg
Freetown, Sierra Leone 98 Cg
Fregenal de la Sierra, Spain 70 Bc
Fréhel C., France 72 Bb
Freiberg, East Germany 68 Ec
Freiburg, West Germany 68 Bd
Freirina, Chile 54 Bc
Freistadt, Austria 68 Fd
Freital, East Germany 68 Ec
Frexiel, Portugal 70 Bb
Freixo, Portugal 70 Bb
Fremantle, W. Australia 56 Cf
Fremont, Nebraska 49 Jb

Fremont, Ohio 40 Ee
Fremont Mts., Oregon 47 Cd
Fremont Pk., Wyoming 46 Cd
Fremont R., Utah 42 Dd
French Guiana, S. America 53 Gc
Frenchman Butte, Sask. 36 He
Frenchman's Cove, Nfld. 33 Od
French R., Ontario 40 Fb
French Territory of the Afars and Issas. See Djibouti
Fresco, Ivory Coast 98 Dg
Freshwater, Newfoundland 33 Tf
Fresnillo, Mexico 50 Dc
Fresno, California 47 Dg
Fresno Res., Montana 46 Ca
Frewena, N. Terr. 57 Gc
Fria C., Namibia 95 Ac
Frías, Spain 70 Da
Fribourg, Switz. 65 Cb
Fridtjof Nansen, Antarc. 104 La
Friedland, East Germany 68 Eb
Friend, Nebraska 49 Jb
Friesische Is., Nord, W. Ger. 67 Cj
Friesische Is., Ost., W. Ger. 68 Ab
Friesland, Netherlands 64 Da
Friuli-Venezia Giulia, Italy 74 Db
Frobisher, Saskatchewan 37 Pj
Frobisher Bay, N.W.T. 31 Ne
Frobisher L., Saskatchewan 39 Tg
Frog L., Alberta 36 Ge
Frohavet, Norway 66 Ce
Frome, England 63 Fj
Frome, L., S. Australia 57 Hf
Fronteira, Portugal 70 Bc
Frontera, Mexico 50 Fd
Fronteras, Mexico 50 Ca
Frontier, Saskatchewan 36 Jj
Front Range, Colorado 48 Eb
Front Royal, Virginia 44 Ac
Frosinone, Italy 75 De
Frostburg, Maryland 44 Ac
Frotet, L., Quebec 35 Qb
Froude, Saskatchewan 37 Oj
Frøya, Norway 66 Ce
Frunze, Kirghizia 78 Gd
Frutigen, Switzerland 65 Cb
Frutuoso, Brazil 52 Ef
Frývaldov, Czechoslovakia 69 Gc
Fthiótis, Greece 77 De
Fu-chou. See Fuzhou
Fuente-Alamo de Murcia, Sp. 71 Ed
Fuente del Arco, Spain 70 Cc
Fuentes de Oñoro, Spain 70 Bb
Fuerte, El, Mexico 50 Cb
Fuerte, R., Mexico 50 Cb
Fuerteventura, Canary Is. 98 Cc
Fujian, China 85 Hj
Fuji san, Japan 86 Fg
Fuka, Egypt 97 Lb
Fukuei Chiao, Taiwan 85 Kk
Fukui, Japan 86 Ef
Fukuoka, Japan 86 Bh
Fukushima, Japan 86 Gf
Fukuyama. See Matsumae
Fulda, West Germany 68 Cc
Fuling, China 85 Ch
Fullerton, Nebraska 49 Jb
Fulton, Kentucky 45 Cb
Fulton, Mississippi 45 Cc
Fulton, Missouri 49 Mc
Fulton, New York 44 Ba
Fulton Chain Ls., New York 44 Ca
Funchal, Madeira I. 98 Bb
Fundão, Portugal 70 Bb
Fundy, B. of, N.S./N.B. 32 Gj
Fundy Nat. Pk., N.B. 32 Gh
Funing, China 84 Jf
Fuping, China 84 Gc
Furg, Iran 93 Gd
Furneaux Grp., Tasmania 57 Jh
Furnes. See Veurne
Furness, Saskatchewan 36 He
Furqlus, Syria 94 Fc
Fürth, West Germany 68 Dd
Fury & Hecla Str., N.W.T. 31 Ld
Fusagasuga, Colombia 52 Cc
Fushih. See Yan'an
Fushun, China 84 Lb
Fusilier, Saskatchewan 36 Hg
Fusio, Switzerland 65 Db
Fuxin, China 82 Ka
Fuxin, China 84 Ka
Fuyang, China 84 Gf
Fuyu, China 82 Ha
Fuzhou, China 85 Hh
Fuzhou, China 85 Jj
Fyn, Denmark 67 Dj
Fyne L., Scotland 62 Dd

G

Gabarus, N.S. 33 Mh
Gabarus B., N.S. 33 Mh
Gabès, & G. of, Tunisia 99 Hb
Gąbin, Poland 69 Hb
Gable Mt., B.C. 39 Kj
Gabon, Central Africa 96 Ce
Gaborone, Botswana 95 Dd
Gabriel y Galán, Emb., Spain 70 Bb
Gabrovo, Bulgaria 76 Ec
Gach Saran, Iran 93 Fc
Gadag, India 88 Ee
Gadsby, Alberta 36 Ef
Gadsden, Alabama 45 Ec
Gael Hamkes B., Greenland 41 Mb
Găeşti, Romania 76 Eb
Gaeta, Italy 75 De
Gafsa, Tunisia 99 Gb
Gagarin, U.S.S.R. 80 Jd
Gage, C., P.E.I. 32 Hg
Gagetown, New Brunswick 32 Fh
Gagnon, Quebec 32 Db
Gagnon, L., Quebec 35 Qf
Gaibanda, Bangladesh 91 Gc
Gaillac, France 73 De
Gaillarbois, L., Quebec 32 Ea
Gaimán, Argentina 54 Cf
Gainesboro, Tennessee 45 Eb
Gainesville, Alabama 45 Cd
Gainesville, Florida 45 Ff
Gainesville, Georgia, U.S.A. 45 Fc
Gainesville, Missouri 45 Ab
Gainesville, Texas 49 Jf
Gainsborough, England 63 Gg
Gainsborough, Sask. 37 Qj
Gairdner, L., S. Australia 57 Gf
Gairloch, Scotland 62 Dc
Galahad, Alberta 36 Ff
Galangue, Angola 96 Dg
Galápagos Is., Pacific Ocean 103 Rg
Galashiels, Scotland 62 Fe
Galatea, New Zealand 55 Fc
Galathea B., Nicobar Is. 89 Hg
Galati, Romania 76 Gb
Galax, Virginia 45 Gb
Galdhøpiggen, Mt., Norway 67 Cf
Galeana, Mexico 50 Ca
Galeana, Mexico 50 Ec
Galeh Dar, Iran 93 Fd
Galena, Illinois 49 Ma
Galesburg, Illinois 49 Mb
Galeton, Pennsylvania 44 Bb
Galiano I., B.C. 39 Ml
Galich, U.S.S.R. 81 Fa
Galilee, L., Queensland 57 Jd
Galilee, Sea of. See Tiberias L.
Galissonnière, Lac la, Que. 32 Kb
Galiuro Mts., Arizona 48 Bf
Gallacaio, Somalia 97 Kc
Gallatin, Tennessee 45 Db
Galle, Sri Lanka 88 Fg
Gallego, Mexico 48 Dh
Gallegos, Argentina 54 Bh
Gallet, L., Quebec 33 Ob
Gallichan, Quebec 35 Ld
Gallipoli, Italy 75 Fe
Gallipoli. See Gelibolu
Gällivare, Sweden 66 Jc
Gallo Mts., New Mexico 48 Ce
Galloway, Mull of, Scotland 63 Df
Gallup, New Mexico 48 Ce
Galty Mts., Eire 63 Bh
Galva, Illinois 40 Ae
Galveston, Texas 49 Kh
Galvez, Argentina 54 Dd
Galway B., Eire 63 Ag
Galway (Gaillimh), Eire 63 Ag
Gamba, China 89 Gc
Gambaga, Ghana 98 Ef
Gambia, The, N.W. Africa 98 Bf
Gambo, Newfoundland 33 Se
Gams, Switzerland 65 Ea
Ganane, Somalia 97 Jd
Gananoque, Ontario 35 Oh
Gand, Belgium 64 Be
Gandak R., India 91 Eb
Gandava, Pakistan 88 Cc
Gander, L. & R., Nfld. 33 Se
Gander & airport, Nfld. 33 Se
Gander Bay South, Nfld. 33 Sd
Gandesa, Spain 71 Fb
Gandhinagar, India 88 Dd
Gandhi Sagar Dam, India 88 Ed
Gandía, Spain 71 Ec
Ganga, R., India 91 Ec
Ganganagar, India 90 Cf
Gangaw, Burma 89 Hd
Ganges. See Ganga
Gangoh, India 90 Ef
Gangtok, India 91 Gb
Ganjam, India 89 Ge
Gan Jiang, China 82 Ge
Gannat, France 72 Ec
Gannett Pk., Wyoming 46 Cd
Gansu, China 84 Be
Gantheaume B., W. Australia 56 Be
Ganyu, China 84 Je
Ganzhou, China 85 Gk
Gao, Mali 98 Ee
Gao'an, China 85 Gh
Gaomi, China 84 Jd
Gaoual, Guinea 98 Cf
Gao Xian, China 82 De
Gaoyi, China 84 Gd
Gaoyou, China 84 Jf
Gaoyou Hu, China 84 Jf
Gar, China 88 Fb
Garachiné, Panama 51 De
Gara L., Eire 63 Bg
Garanhuns, Brazil 53 Ke
Garba Tula, Kenya 97 Hd
García de Sola, Emb. de, Spain 70 Cc
Gard, dep., France 73 Fd
Garda, L. di., Italy 74 Cc
Gardafui, C., Somalia 97 Lb
Garde L., N.W.T. 38 Ud
Garden, Michigan 40 Cc
Garden City, Kansas 48 Gd
Garden River, Ontario 34 Ff
Gardenton, Manitoba 37 Vj
Gardiner, Maine 32 Cj
Gardiner, Montana 46 Bc
Gardiner, Ontario 34 Kc
Gardiner, Oregon 47 Ad
Gardiners, B., N.Y. 44 Db
Gardner Canal, B.C. 39 Jj
Gardner I., Hawaiian Is. 102 Je
Gardo, Somalia 97 Kc
Garfield, Utah 48 Ab
Gargantua, C., Ontario 34 Ee
Garha, India 91 Bc
Garhmuktesar, India 90 Ff
Garhshankar, India 90 Ee
Garibaldi, B.C. 39 Ml
Garibaldi, Brazil 54 Fc
Garibaldi Prov. Park, B.C. 39 Mk
Garies, Cape Province 95 Bf
Garissa, Kenya 97 He
Garland, Manitoba 37 Rg
Garland, Montana 46 Dc
Garm, Tadzhikistan 78 Ge
Garmsār, Iran 93 Fb
Garneau R., Quebec 32 Jb
Garnet B., N.W.T. 31 Mb
Garo Hills, India 89 Hc
Garonne, France 73 De
Garoua, Cameroun 99 Hg
Garraway, Liberia 98 Dh
Garrick, Saskatchewan 37 Ne
Garrison, N. Dakota 46 Gb
Garrovillas, Spain 70 Bc
Garry L., N.W.T. 38 Fa
Garry L., N.W.T. 38 Xb
Garsen, Kenya 97 Je
Garson L., Alberta 36 Gb
Gary, Indiana 40 Ce
Garyasa, China 88 Fb
Garza, Argentina 54 Dc
Garza Little Elm Res., Texas 49 Jf
Garzon, Colombia 52 Bc
Gasan Kuli, Turkmenistan 78 Ee
Gascogne, France 73 De
Gascogne, G. de, Fr./Sp. 73 Be
Gasconade R., Missouri 45 Ba
Gascoyne, R., W. Australia 56 Ce
Gasherbrum, Mt., Kashmir 90 Ec
Gasht, Iran 93 Hd
Gaspé, C. de, Quebec 32 He
Gaspé & B. de, Quebec 32 He
Gaspé Pén., Quebec 32 Ge
Gaspereau Forks, N.B. 32 Gg
Gaspésie, Parc prov. de la, Quebec 32 Fe
Gasselte, Netherlands 64 Eb
Gaston, L., North Carolina 45 Jb
Gastonia, N. Carolina 45 Gc
Gastre, Argentina 54 Cf
Gata, Spain 70 Bb
Gata, C., Cyprus 94 Bc
Gataga, R., B.C. 39 Kf
Gate City, Virginia 45 Fb
Gateshead, England 62 Ff
Gateshead I., N.W.T. 38 Xa
Gatineau, Quebec 35 Pg
Gatineau, Parc de la, Quebec 35 Pg
Gatineau, R., Quebec 35 Pe
Gatooma, Zimbabwe 95 Dc
Gatun L., Panama 51 Ce
Gaud-i-Zirreh, Afghanistan 93 Hd
Gaudreault, L., Quebec 33 Kc
Gauer L., Manitoba 37 Ua
Gauhati, India 89 Hc
Gauribidanūr, India 88 Ef
Gaurihar, India 91 Cc
Gāvbandī, Iran 93 Fd
Gavdhos, I., Crete 77 Eg
Gavião, Portugal 70 Bc
Gāv Koshī, Iran 93 Gd
Gävle, Sweden 67 Gf
Gävlebukten, Sweden 67 Gf
Gāvur Daglari, Turkey 92 Cb
Gawler Range, S. Australia 57 Gf
Gaya, India 91 Ec
Gaya, Niger 98 Ff
Gayaza, Uganda 97 Ge
Gaylord, Michigan 40 Dc
Gaza, Cent. Afr. Rep. 99 Jh
Gaza, Egypt 94 Cf
Gaziantep, Turkey 92 Cb
Gdańsk, Poland 69 Ha
Gdynia, Poland 69 Ha
Gebeit, Sudan 99 Ne
Gedaref, Sudan 99 Nf
Gedinne, Belgium 64 Ce
Geel, Belgium 64 Cc
Geelong, Victoria 57 Hg
Geikie, I., Ontario 34 Bb
Geikie, R., Saskatchewan 39 Vg
Gejui, China 82 Df
Gela, Sicily 75 Eg
Gelderland, Netherlands 64 Db
Geldrop, Netherlands 64 Dc
Gelert, Ontario 35 Mh
Gelib, Somalia 97 Jd
Gelibolu, Turkey 92 Aa
Gelinden, Belgium 64 Dd
Gelsenkirchen, W. Germany 68 Bc
Gem, Alberta 36 Eh
Gemas, Pen. Malaysia 87 Cf
Gembloux, Belgium 64 Cd
Gemena, Zaire 96 Dd
Gemert, Netherlands 64 Dc
Gemmenich, Belgium 64 Dd
Gemmi Pass, Switzerland 65 Cb
Gempe, Belgium 64 Cd
Gendringen, Netherlands 64 Ec
Geneina, Sudan 99 Kf
Genemuiden, Netherlands 64 Eb
General Acha, Argentina 54 De
General Alvarado, Arg. 54 Ee
General Alvear, Arg. 54 De
General Capdevila, Arg. 54 Dc
General Guido, Argentina 54 Ee
General José de San Martin, Argentina 54 Ec
General La Madrid, Arg. 54 De
General Lavalle, Arg. 54 Ee
General Madariaga, Arg. 54 Ee
General Pico, Argentina 54 De
General Pinto, Argentina 54 Dd
General Roca, Argentina 54 Ce
General Viamonte, Arg. 54 De
General Villegas, Arg. 54 De
Geneseo, New York 44 Ba
Geneva, Nebraska 49 Jb
Geneva, New York 44 Ba
Geneva, L. of. See Léman, Lac
Génève, Switz. 65 Bb
Genier, Ontario 34 Kc
Genk, Belgium 64 Dd
Genkai nada, Japan 86 Ah
Gennargentu, Mte. del, Sardinia 75 Be
Gennep, Netherlands 64 Dc
Genoa. See Genova
Genova, Italy 74 Bc
Genova, G. di, Italy 74 Bc
Gent. See Gand
Geographe B., W. Australia 56 Cf
Geographe Chan., W. Aust. 56 Bd
Georga Zemlya, Arctic Oc. 78 Da
George, C., N.S. 33 Lh
George, L., New S. Wales 57 Jg
George, L., Ontario 34 Ff
George L., New York 44 Da
Georgetown, Ascension I. 96 Ag
Georgetown, Delaware 40 Jf
Georgetown, Georgia, U.S.A. 45 Ee
George Town, Gr. Cayman, West Indies 51 Cc
Georgetown, Guyana 52 Fb
Georgetown, Kentucky 45 Ea
Georgetown, Ontario 34 Lj
Georgetown, P.E.I. 32 Kg
George Town, Pen. Malaysia 87 Ce
Georgetown, Queensland 57 Hc
Georgetown, S. Carolina 45 Hd
Georgetown, Virginia 44 Bc
Georgeville, Quebec 35 Sg
Georgia. See Gruzinskaya S.S.R.
Georgia, U.S.A. 43 Ke
Georgia, Str. of, B.C. 39 Ll
Georgian B., Ontario 34 Jg
Georgian Bay Is. National Park, Ontario 34 Jg
Georgina, R., Queensland 57 Gd
Georgiu Dezh, U.S.S.R. 81 De
Georgiyevsk, U.S.S.R. 78 Dd
Gera, East Germany 68 Ec
Geraardsbergen, Belgium 64 Bd
Gerald, Saskatchewan 37 Qh
Geraldine, New Zealand 55 Cf
Geraldton, Ontario 34 Dc
Geraldton, W. Australia 56 Be
Gérgal, Spain 71 Dd
Gerlach, Nevada 47 De
Germain, Grand L., Que. 32 Fb
Germania, Argentina 54 Dd
Germania Ld., Greenland 41 Mb
Germansen Landing, B.C. 39 Lh
Germany, East, Europe 60 Lf
Germany, W., Europe 60 Kf
Gerona, Spain 71 Ga
Gers, France 73 De
Gerze, Turkey 92 Ca
Getafe, Spain 70 Db
Gethsémani, Quebec 33 Mc
Gettysburg, Pennsylvania 44 Bc
Gettysburg, S. Dakota 46 Hc
Getz Ice Shelf, Antarctica 104 Pb
Gevgelija, Yugoslavia 76 Dd
Ghabaghib, Syria 94 Ed
Ghāghara, R., India 91 Db
Ghaida, S. Yemen 92 Eg
Ghail, Arabia 92 Ee
Ghana, W. Africa 98 Eg
Ghantur, Syria 94 Fc
Ghanzi, Botswana 95 Cd
Gharandal, Jordan 94 Dg
Ghardaïa, Algeria 98 Fb
Gharyān, Libya 99 Hb
Ghatal, India 91 Fd
Ghatampur, India 91 Cb
Ghat (Gat), Libya 99 Hd
Ghatghat, Arabia 92 Ee
Ghats, Eastern, India 88 Fe
Ghats, Western, India 88 De
Ghazaouet, Algeria 98 Ea
Ghaziabad, India 90 Ef
Ghazipur, India 91 Dc
Ghazir, Lebanon 94 Dc
Ghazni, Afghanistan 93 Jc
Gheorgheni, Romania 76 Ea
Ghislenghien, Belgium 64 Bd
Ghizao, Afghanistan 93 Jc
Ghorak, Afghanistan 93 Jc
Ghorian, Afghanistan 93 Hc
Ghost L., N.W.T. 38 Qd
Ghost Mt., B.C. 39 Pj
Ghost River, Ontario 36 La
Ghotki, Pakistan 88 Cc
Ghubreh, Oman 93 Ge
Ghudāmis, Libya 99 Gb
Giarre, Sicily 75 Eg
Gibara, Cuba 51 Db
Gibeon, Namibia 95 Be
Gibraltar, Spain 70 Cd
Gibraltar, Str. of, Spain 70 Ce
Gibraltar Point, Ontario 34 Dk
Gibson Desert, W. Aust. 56 Dd
Gibsons, B.C. 39 Ml
Giddings, Texas 49 Jg
Gidole, Ethiopia 97 Hc
Gien, France 72 Ec
Giessen, West Germany 68 Cc
Giffard, Quebec 35 Sa
Giffard, L., Quebec 35 Oa
Gifhorn, West Germany 68 Db
Gifu, Japan 86 Eg
Giganta, La, Mexico 50 Bb
Gijón, Spain 70 Ca
Gila, R., Arizona/New Mexico 48 Cf
Gila Desert, Arizona 50 Ba
Gila Desert, Arizona 42 De
Gilău, Romania 76 Da
Gilbert, R., Queensland 57 Hc
Gilbert Is. See Kiribati
Gilbert Mt., B.C. 39 Lk
Gilberton, Queensland 57 Hc
Gilbert Plains, Manitoba 37 Rg
Gilbués, Brazil 53 Je
Gilgit & R., Kashmir 90 Dc
Gil I., British Columbia 39 Jj
Gillam, Manitoba 30 Kf
Gillett, Arkansas 45 Bc
Gillette, Wyoming 46 Ec
Gilmour, Ontario 35 Nh
Gilroy, Saskatchewan 36 Lh
Gimel, Switzerland 65 Bb
Gimli, Manitoba 37 Vh
Ginir, Ethiopia 97 Jc
Ginzo, Spain 70 Ba
Gioia, G. di, Italy 75 Ef
Giornico, Switzerland 65 Db
Girardot, Colombia 52 Cc
Girdle Ness, Scotland 62 Fc
Giresun, Turkey 92 Ca
Girga, Egypt 99 Mc
Giridih, India 91 Fc
Girishk, Afghanistan 93 Hc
Gironde, France 72 Cd
Gironde, France 73 Cd
Giroux, Manitoba 37 Vj
Girvan, Scotland 62 De
Girvin, Saskatchewan 37 Mg
Gisborne, New Zealand 55 Gc
Gisborne L., Newfoundland 33 Sf
Giscome, B.C. 39 Mh
Gisenyi, Rwanda 97 Fe
Gisors, France 72 Db
Giswil, Switzerland 65 Db
Gitch, Mt., Ethiopia 97 Hb
Giuba, Somalia 97 Jd
Giulietti, L., Ethiopia 97 Jb
Giurgiu, Romania 76 Ec
Givry, Belgium 64 Cd
Gizhiga, U.S.S.R. 79 Rb
Giżycko, Poland 69 Ja
Gjirokastër, Albania 77 Cd
Gjoa Haven, N.W.T. 38 Za
Gjøvik, Norway 67 Df
Glabbeek, Belgium 64 Cd
Glace Bay, Nova Scotia 33 Ng
Glacier, B.C. 39 Pk
Glacier Nat. Park, B.C. 39 Ok
Glacier Str., N.W.T. 31 Mb
Gladmar, Saskatchewan 37 Nj
Gladstone, Manitoba 37 Th
Gladstone, Michigan 40 Cc
Gladstone, Queensland 57 Kd
Gladwin, Michigan 40 Dd
Gladys L., B.C. 38 Gf
Glamoc, Yugoslavia 74 Fc
Glamorgan, Wales 63 Ej
Glärnisch, Switzerland 65 Db
Glarus, Switz. 65 Ea
Glasgow, Kentucky 45 Eb
Glasgow, Montana 46 Da
Glasgow, Scotland 62 Ee
Glaslyn, Saskatchewan 36 Je
Glasnevin, Saskatchewan 37 Mj
Glassboro, New Jersey 44 Cc
Glauchau, East Germany 68 Ec
Glazov, U.S.S.R. 81 La
Gleichen, Alberta 36 Dh
Glen, New Hampshire 40 Lc
Glen Affric, Scotland 62 Dc
Glen Afton, New Zealand 55 Eb
Glénan, France 72 Ac
Glenavon, Saskatchewan 37 Oh
Glenbain, Saskatchewan 36 Kj
Glenboro, Manitoba 37 Sj
Glenburnie, Nfld. 33 Pd
Glenbush, Saskatchewan 36 Ke
Glen Canyon, National Recreation Area, Utah 48 Bd
Glencoe, Minnesota 46 Kc
Glencoe, Ontario 34 Jk
Glendale, Arizona 48 Af
Glendale, California 47 Dh
Glendale Cove, B.C. 39 Lk
Glendive, Montana 46 Eb
Glendon, Alberta 36 Fd
Glendo Res., Wyoming 46 Ed
Glenella, Manitoba 37 Sh
Glen Ewen, Saskatchewan 37 Pj
Glen Falls, New York 40 Kd
Glen Garry, Scotland 62 Ed
Glenhope, New Zealand 55 Dd
Glen Innes, N.S.W. 57 Ke
Glen Kerr, Saskatchewan 36 Kh
Glenora, B.C. 39 Hg
Glen Robertson, Ontario 35 Qg
Glenrock, Wyoming 46 Ed
Glenside, Saskatchewan 36 Lg
Glenties, Eire 63 Bf
Glentworth, Sask. 36 Lj
Glenvale, Ontario 34 Ke
Glenville, West Virginia 40 Ff
Glenwood, Alberta 36 Dj
Glenwood, Iowa 49 Kb
Glenwood, Minnesota 46 Kc
Glenwood, Nfld. 33 Re
Glenwood Springs, Colorado 48 Dc
Gletsch, Switzerland 65 Db
Glidden, Saskatchewan 36 Hg
Glittertind, Mt., Norway 67 Cf
Gliwice, Poland 69 Hc
Globe, Arizona 48 Bf
Głogów, Poland 69 Gc
Gloppen, Norway 66 Bf
Gloria, Brazil 53 Ke
Gloucester, England 63 Fj
Gloucester, Massachusetts 44 Ea
Gloucester, New Jersey 44 Cc
Gloucester, Virginia 45 Jb
Gloucestershire, England 63 Fj
Glover I., Newfoundland 33 Pe
Gloversville, New York 44 Ca
Glovertown, Nfld. 33 Te
Glukhov, Ukraine 80 Hf
Gmünd, Austria 68 Ee
Gmünd, West Germany 68 Cd
Gmunden, Austria 68 Ee
Gniezno, Poland 69 Gb
Goa, Daman & Diu, India 88 De
Goalpara, India 89 Hc
Goalundo Ghat, Bangladesh 91 Gd
Gobabis, Namibia 95 Bd
Gobi, desert, E. Asia 79 Kd
Gobindpur, India 91 Fd
Godavari, India 88 Ee
Godbout & R., Quebec 32 Ed
Godda, India 91 Fc
Godech, Bulgaria 76 Dc
Goderich, Ontario 34 Jj
Godfrey, Ontario 35 Oh
Godhra, India 88 Dd
Gods L., Manitoba 30 Kg
Godthåb, Greenland 41 Pc
Goéland, L. au, Quebec 35 Oc
Goéland, L. du, Quebec 32 Ad
Goéolands, L., Quebec 31 Nf
Goes, Netherlands 64 Bc
Goesi, Irian Jaya 83 Kl
Gogama, Ontario 34 Je
Gogebic Range, Michigan 40 Bb
Gog Magog Hills, England 63 Hh
Gogrial, Sudan 99 Lg
Gohana, India 90 Ef
Goiânia, Brazil 53 Hg
Goiás, Brazil 53 Gg
Goirle, Netherlands 64 Dc
Gökçeada I., Turkey 92 Aa
Gökçeağac, Turkey 92 Ba
Goksun, Turkey 92 Cb
Golaghat, India 89 Hc
Golchikha, U.S.S.R. 78 Ha
Golconda, Illinois 45 Cb
Golconda, India 88 Ee
Goldap, Poland 69 Ka
Goldboro, Nova Scotia 33 Lh
Golden, B.C. 39 Pk
Golden, Colorado 48 Ec
Golden B., New Zealand 55 Dd
Golden Lake, Ontario 35 Ng
Golden Prairie, Sask. 36 Hh
Goldenville, Nova Scotia 33 Kh
Goldfield, Nevada 47 Eg
Gold Rock, Ontario 36 Ka
Goldsand L., Manitoba 37 Qa
Goldsboro, N. Carolina 45 Jc
Goldsworthy, W. Australia 56 Cd
Goleniów, Poland 68 Fb
Golmud, China 82 Cc
Goltva, Ukraine 80 Hg
Gomal Pass, Pakistan 90 Bd
Gombe, Nigeria 99 Hf
Gomel, Byelorussia 80 Ge
Gomera, I., Canary Is. 98 Bc
Gómez Farias, Mexico 50 Dc
Gómez Palacio, Mexico 50 Db
Gonaïves, Haiti 51 Ec
Gonâve, I. de la, Haiti 51 Ec
Gonbad-e-Kavus, Iran 93 Gb
Gonda, India 91 Db
Gondal, India 88 Dd
Gondo, Switzerland 65 Db
Gönen, Turkey 77 Fd
Gonggar, China 89 Hc
Gongga Shan, China 82 De
Gongga Ling, China 82 De
Goniądz, Poland 69 Kb
Gonzales, Texas 49 Jh
Goodenough I., New Guinea 57 Ka
Gooderham, Ontario 35 Mh
Goodeve, Saskatchewan 37 Og
Good Hope, Cape of, Cape Prov. 95 Bf
Good Hope, Mt., B.C. 39 Lk
Goodland, Kansas 48 Gc
Goodlands, Manitoba 37 Rj
Goodrich, Wisconsin 40 Ac
Goodsir, Mt., B.C. 39 Pk
Goodsoil, Saskatchewan 36 Hd
Good Spirit L., Sask. 37 Pg
Good Spirit Lake Prov. Park, Saskatchewan 37 Pg
Goodwater, Saskatchewan 37 Oj
Goodwin, Ontario 35 Ld
Goole, England 63 Gg
Goomalling, W. Australia 56 Cf
Goonyella, Queensland 57 Jd
Goor, Netherlands 64 Eb
Goose Bay, Nfld. 31 Ng
Gooseberry Lake Provincial Park, Alberta 36 Gf
Goose Cove, Nfld. 33 Rb
Goose L., Manitoba 37 Qd
Goose L., Oregon/Cal. 47 Ce
Goose L., Saskatchewan 37 Pe
Goose L., Saskatchewan 36 Kg
Goose R., Alberta 39 Ph
Gopalpur, India 89 Fe
Göppingen, W. Germany 68 Cd
Gor, Spain 70 Dd
Gora, China 82 Ce
Gorakhpur, India 91 Db
Gordola, Switzerland 65 Db
Gordon, Nebraska 48 Fa
Gordon L., Alberta 36 Gb
Gordon L., N.W.T. 38 Rd
Gordon Landing, Y.T. 38 Fd
Gordonsville, Virginia 45 Ha
Gordonvale, Queensland 57 Jc
Goré, Chad 99 Jg
Gore, Ethiopia 97 Hc
Gore, New Zealand 55 Bg
Gore Bay, Ontario 34 Hg
Gorey, Eire 63 Ch
Gorgān, Iran 93 Fb
Gorgona, Italy 74 Bd
Gorinchem, Netherlands 64 Cc
Gorizia, Italy 74 Dc
Gor'kiy, U.S.S.R. 81 Gb
Gorlice, Poland 69 Jd
Görlitz, East Germany 68 Fc
Gorlovka, Ukraine 80 Lg
Gorodetz, U.S.S.R. 81 Fb
Gorodishche, U.S.S.R. 81 Gd
Gorodnitsa, Ukraine 80 Ef
Gorontalo, Celebes (Sulawesi) 83 Hk
Gorrahei, Ethiopia 97 Jc
Gorrie, Ontario 34 Jj
Gorssel, Netherlands 64 Eb
Gorzów Wielkopolski, Poland 68 Fb
Gosainthan. See Sisha Pangma
Göschenen, Switzerland 65 Db
Goshanak, Pakistan 88 Bc
Goshen, New York 44 Cb
Gospić, Yugoslavia 74 Ec
Gosport, England 63 Gk
Gossa, Norway 66 Be
Gossau, Switzerland 65 Ea
Gosselies, Belgium 64 Cd
Gostivar, Yugoslavia 76 Cd
Göta Alv, Sweden 67 Eg
Göteborg, Sweden 67 Dh
Gotha, East Germany 68 Dc
Gothenburg, Nebraska 48 Gb
Gothenburg. See Göteborg
Gotland, I., Sweden 67 Hh
Goto Retto, Japan 86 Ah
Gotska Sandön, Sweden 67 Hg
Göttingen, West Germany 68 Cc
Gott Pk., B.C. 39 Mk
Gottwaldov, Czechoslovakia 69 Gd
Gouda, Netherlands 64 Cb
Goudreau, Ontario 34 Fd
Goudswaard, Netherlands 64 Cc
Gough I., Atlantic Ocean 101 Kn
Gough L., Alberta 36 Ef
Gouin, Rés., Quebec 35 Qd
Goukou, China 82 Ha
Goulais River, Ontario 34 Ff
Goulburn, N.S.W. 57 Jf
Gould, Quebec 35 Tg
Goundam, Mali 98 Ee
Gouré, Niger 99 Hf
Gourlay L., Ontario 34 Fd
Gournay, France 72 Db
Gouverneur, New York 40 Jc
Gouverneur, Sask. 36 Kj
Govan, Saskatchewan 37 Ng
Govenlock, Saskatchewan 36 Hj
Governor L., Nova Scotia 32 Kh
Gowanda, New York 40 Gd
Gowganda, Ontario 34 Ke
Gowna L., Eire 63 Bg
Goya, Argentina 54 Ec
Goyelle, L., Quebec 33 Mc
Gozo, Medit. Sea 75 Eg
Graaff Reinet, Cape Prov. 95 Cf
Grabów, Poland 69 Hc
Gračac, Yugoslavia 74 Ec
Gracefield, Quebec 35 Of
Gracias, Honduras 51 Bd
Gracias a Dios, Nicaragua 51 Cd
Gradets, Bulgaria 76 Fc
Grado, Spain 70 Ba
Grafton, N. Dakota 46 Ja
Grafton, N.S.W. 57 Ke
Grafton, W. Virginia 40 Ff
Grafton Is., Chile 54 Bh
Graham, Ontario 37 Ma
Graham, Texas 49 Hf
Graham Bell, Os., Arctic Oc. 78 Fa
Graham I., B.C. 39 Gj
Graham I., N.W.T. 31 Kb
Graham L., Alberta 36 Cb
Graham Land, Antarctica 104 Sc
Graham R., B.C. 39 Mg
Grahamstown, Cape Prov. 95 Df
Grainger, Alberta 36 Dg
Grajewo, Poland 69 Kb
Grampian, reg., Scotland 62 Fc
Grampian Mts., Scotland 62 Dd
Gramsbergen, Netherlands 64 Eb
Granada, Nicaragua 51 Bd
Granada, Spain 70 Dd
Granby, Quebec 35 Sg
Granby, L., Colorado 48 Eb
Gran Canaria I., Canary Is. 98 Bc
Gran Chaco, Argentina 54 Dc
Grand, L., Louisiana 49 Lh
Grand, R., Colorado 48 Dc
Grand, R., Ontario 34 Lj
Grand B., Ontario 34 Bc
Grand Bank, Nfld. 33 Rf
Grand Bassam, Ivory Coast 98 Eg
Grand Bay, N.B. 32 Fh
Grand Beach, Manitoba 37 Vh
Grand Beach Provincial Park, Manitoba 37 Vh
Grand Bend, Ontario 34 Jj
Grand Bruit, Nfld. 33 Of
Grand Can., China 82 Gc
Grand Canyon, Arizona 42 Dd
Grand Canyon Nat. Pk., Arizona 42 Dd
Grand Cayman, W. Indies 51 Cc
Grand Centre, Alberta 36 Gd

Grand Coulee Dam, Wash. 42 Cb
Grande, B., Argentina 54 Ch
Grande, Rio, Brazil 53 Gg
Grande-Anse, N.B. 32 Gf
Grande-Baie, Quebec 32 Be
Grande Baleine, Quebec 31 Mf
Grande Comore, I., Comoros 97 Jg
Grande de Santiago, Mex. 50 Dc
Grande Entrée, I. de la, Quebec 33 Lf
Grande-Gascapédia, Quebec 32 Ge
Grande-Grève, Quebec 32 He
Grande Ile, Quebec 32 Jc
Grande Passe, I. de la, Quebec 33 Ob
Grande Prairie, Alberta 39 Oh
Grande-Rivière, Quebec 32 He
Grande-Rivière L., Que. 31 Mg
Grandes-Bergeronnes, Quebec 32 Ce
Grandes-Piles, Quebec 35 Sf
Grand-Étang, N.S. 33 Lg
Grande-Vallée, Quebec 32 Gd
Grand Falls, N.B. 32 Ef
Grand Falls, Newfoundland 33 Re
Grand Falls L., Maine/New Brunswick 32 Eh
Grand Forks, B.C. 39 Ol
Grand Forks, N. Dakota 46 Jb
Grand Harbour, N.B. 32 Fj
Grand Haven, Michigan 40 Cd
Grand I., Michigan 40 Cb
Grand I., New York 35 Mj
Grandin, L., N.W.T. 38 Oc
Grand Island, Nebraska 49 Hb
Grand Junction, Colorado 48 Cc
Grand Junction, Tennessee 45 Cc
Grand L., Maine 32 Eh
Grand L., New Brunswick 32 Fh
Grand L., Newfoundland 33 Pd
Grand Lahou, Ivory Coast 98 Dg
Grand Ledge, Michigan 40 Dd
Grand L. Victoria, Que. 35 Ne
Grand Manan I., N.B. 32 Fj
Grand Marais, Minnesota 40 Ab
Grandmenil, Belgium 64 Dd
Grand-Mère, Quebec 35 Sf
Grand Mesa, Colorado 48 Dc
Grandmesnil, L., Quebec 32 Eb
Grand Mt., B.C. 39 Pk
Grandois, Nfld. 33 Rb
Grandola, Portugal 70 Ac
Grand R., Michigan 40 Dd
Grand R., S. Dakota 42 Fb
Grand Rapids, Manitoba 37 Se
Grand Rapids, Michigan 40 Dd
Grand Rapids, Minnesota 46 Lb
Grand-Remous, Quebec 35 Pf
Grandrieu, Belgium 64 Cd
Grand River, N.S. 33 Mh
Grandson, Switzerland 65 Bb
Grand Teton Mt., Wyoming 42 Dc
Grand Tower, Illinois 45 Cb
Grand Valley, Ontario 34 Kj
Grandview, Manitoba 37 Rg
Grane, Norway 66 Ed
Granet, L., Quebec 35 Ne
Granger, Wyoming 46 Be
Granite Bay, B.C. 39 Lk
Granite City, Illinois 49 Mc
Granite Falls, Minnesota 46 Kc
Granity, New Zealand 55 Cd
Granja, Brazil 53 Jd
Grankulla, Finland 67 Lf
Granollers, Spain 71 Gb
Granön, Sweden 66 Hd
Grant, Ontario 34 Db
Grant City, Missouri 46 Ke
Grantham, England 63 Gh
Grant L., N.W.T. 38 Pc
Granton, Ontario 34 Jj
Grantown-on-Spey, Scotland 62 Ec
Grant Range, Nevada 47 Ff
Grants, New Mexico 48 De
Grants Pass, Oregon 47 Bd
Grantsville, Utah 48 Ab
Granum, Alberta 36 Dj
Granville, N. Dakota 46 Ga
Granville, New York 44 Da
Granville, Y.T. 38 Dd
Granville Ferry, N.S. 32 Gj
Granville L., Manitoba 37 Rb
Gras, L. de, N.W.T. 38 Sc
Grasett, Ontario 40 Da
Graskop, Transvaal 95 Ed
Gräsö, Sweden 67 Hf
Grassano, Italy 75 Fe
Grasse, France 73 Ge
Grasset, L., Quebec 35 Mc
Grassier, Switzerland 65 Bb
Grass R., Manitoba 37 Tc
Grassy Island L., Alberta 36 Gg
Grassy Lake, Alberta 36 Fj
Grates Cove, Nfld. 33 Ue
Graubünden, Switz. 65 Eb
Graus, Spain 71 Fa
Gravarne, Sweden 67 Dg
Grave, Netherlands 64 Dc
Gravelbourg, Sask. 36 Lj
Gravel Hill L., N.W.T. 38 Vd
Gravenhurst, Ontario 35 Lh
Gray, France 72 Fc
Gray, Saskatchewan 37 Nh
Gray L., N.W.T. 38 Te
Grayling, Michigan 40 Dc
Grayling, R., B.C. 38 Lf
Grayson, Saskatchewan 37 Ph
Grayville, Illinois 45 Ca
Graz, Austria 69 Fe
Greasy L., N.W.T. 38 Md
Great Australian Bight, Aust. 56 Ef
Great Barrier Reef, Aust. 57 Jc
Great Barrington, Mass. 44 Da
Great Basin, Nevada 42 Cc
Great Bear, R., N.W.T. 38 Lc
Great Bear L., N.W.T. 38 Nb
Great Bend, Kansas 49 Hc
Great Blasket I., Eire 63 Ah
Great Burnt L., Nfld. 33 Qe
Great Colinet I., Nfld. 33 Tg
Great Deer, Sask. 36 Kf
Great Dividing Range, Aust. 57 Jd
Greater London, Eng. 63 Gj
Greater Manchester, Eng. 63 Fg
Great Falls, Montana 46 Bb
Great Geysir, Iceland 66 Vm
Great Grimsby, England 63 Gg
Great Harbour Deep, Newfoundland 33 Qc
Great Karoo, Cape Prov. 95 Cf
Great Lake. See Tonle Sap
Great N. Mts., W. Va./Virginia 44 Ac
Great Pt., Massachusetts 44 Eb
Great Pubnico L., N.S. 32 Gk
Great Salt Lake, Utah 47 Ge
Great Salt Lake Des., Utah 47 Ge
Great Salt Plains Res., Oklahoma 49 Oc
Great Sand Dunes Nat. Mon., Colorado 48 Ed
Great Sandy Des., W. Aust. 56 Dd
Great Sandy I. (Fraser I.), Queensland 57 Ke
Great Slave L., N.W.T. 38 Qe
Great Smoky Mts., Tenn. 45 Fc
Great Smoky Mts. Nat. Park, Tennessee 45 Fc
Great Snow Mt., B.C. 39 Lg
Great South B., New York 44 Db
Great Torrington, England 63 Ek
Great Victoria Desert, W. Aust. 56 Ee
Great Village, N.S. 32 Jh
Great Wass I., Maine 32 Ej
Great Yarmouth, England 63 Jk
Grebbestad, Sweden 67 Dg
Greco C., Cyprus 94 Cc
Greece, S. Europe 61 Nj
Greeley, Colorado 48 Eb
Greely Fiord, N.W.T. 31 La
Green B., Wisconsin 40 Cc
Green Bay, Wisconsin 40 Cc
Greencastle, Indiana 49 Oc
Green Court, Alberta 36 Bd
Green Cr., Ontario 34 Eh
Greenfield, Indiana 40 Df
Greenfield, Iowa 49 Kb
Greenfield, Massachusetts 40 Kd
Greenfield Park, Quebec 35 Tj
Green I., Newfoundland 33 Qb
Greening, Quebec 35 Qd
Green L., B.C. 39 Nk
Green Lake, Sask. 36 Kd
Greenland, N. America 41 Pb
Greenland Sea, Arctic Oc. 31 Sb
Greenly I., Quebec 33 Pb
Green Mts., Vermont 40 Kd
Green Mts., Wyoming 46 Dd
Greenock, Scotland 62 De
Greenport, New York 40 Ke
Green R., Kentucky 45 Db
Green R., N.B. 32 Df
Green R., Utah 48 Bc
Green River, Wyoming 46 Ce
Greensboro, Georgia, U.S.A. 45 Fd
Greensboro, N. Carolina 45 Hb
Greensburg, Kansas 49 Hd
Greensburg, Kentucky 45 Eb
Greensburg, Pennsylvania 44 Ab
Greenspond, Nfld. 33 Td
Greenvale, Queensland 57 Hc
Greenville, Alabama 45 De
Greenville, Illinois 49 Nc
Greenville, Kentucky 45 Db
Greenville, Liberia 98 Dg
Greenville, Maine 32 Ch
Greenville, Michigan 40 Dd
Greenville, Mississippi 45 Bd
Greenville, Missouri 45 Bb
Greenville, N. Carolina 45 Jc
Greenville, S. Carolina 45 Fc
Greenville, Tennessee 45 Fb
Greenville, Texas 49 Jf
Greenwater L., Ontario 37 Mb
Greenwater Lake Provincial Park, Saskatchewan 37 Of
Greenway, Manitoba 37 Sj
Greenwich, Connecticut 44 Db
Greenwich, England 63 Hj
Greenwich, Rhode Island 44 Eb
Greenwood, Mississippi 45 Bd
Greenwood, S. Carolina 45 Fc
Greenwood, Wisconsin 40 Ac
Greenwood L., N.Y./N.J. 44 Cb
Greer's Ferry Res., Arkansas 45 Ac
Greeson, L., Arkansas 49 Le
Gregg, Manitoba 37 Sj
Gregoire L., Alberta 36 Fb
Gregory, S. Dakota 46 Hd
Gregory Range, Queensland 57 Hc
Greifen See, Switzerland 65 Da
Greifswald, East Germany 68 Ea
Grein, Austria 68 Fd
Greiz, East Germany 68 Ec
Grenå, Denmark 67 Dh
Grenada, Mississippi 45 Cd
Grenada, Windward Is. 51 Gd
Grenadines, Windward Is. 51 Gd
Grenchen, Switzerland 65 Ca
Grenfell, Saskatchewan 37 Ph
Grenoble, France 73 Fd
Grenora, N. Dakota 46 Fa
Grenville, C., Queensland 57 Hb
Grenville, Mt., B.C. 39 Lk
Grenville Chan., B.C. 39 Jj
Gretna, Louisiana 45 Bf
Gretna, Manitoba 37 Uj
Gretna, Virginia 45 Hb
Grevelingen, Netherlands 64 Cc
Grevená, Greece 77 Cd
Grey, Alberta 39 Oj
Greybull, Wyoming 46 Cc
Greycliff, Montana 46 Cc
Grey Hunter Pk., Y.T. 38 Fd
Grey Is., Newfoundland 33 Rc
Grey Islands Harbour, Newfoundland 33 Rc
Greylock Mt., Massachusetts 44 Da
Greymouth, New Zealand 55 Ce
Grey R., Newfoundland 33 Qe
Grey Range, Qnsld./N.S.W. 57 He
Grey Reservoir, Newfoundland 33 Qe
Greystones, Eire 63 Cg
Greytown, New Zealand 55 Ed
Griesalp, Switzerland 65 Cb
Griffin, Georgia, U.S.A. 45 Ed
Griffith, N.S.W. 57 Jf
Griffith I., N.W.T. 30 Kc
Grim, C., Tasmania 57 Hh
Grimsby, England 63 Gg
Grimsby, Ontario 35 Lj
Grimshaw, Alberta 39 Pg
Grimstad, Norway 67 Cg
Grindelwald, Switzerland 65 Db
Grindstone, Michigan 40 Ec
Grindstone Pt., Man. 37 Vg
Grinnell, Iowa 49 Lb
Grinnell Pen., N.W.T. 31 Kb
Griquatown, Cape Province 95 Ce
Griquet, Newfoundland 33 Rb
Grise Fiord, N.W.T. 31 Lb
Grīva, Latvia 67 Mj
Grizzly Bear Mt., N.W.T. 38 Nc
Groais I., Newfoundland 33 Rc
Grobiņa, Latvia 67 Jh
Gröbming, Austria 68 Ee
Grodno, Byelorussia 80 Ce
Grodzisk, Poland 69 Gb
Groenlo, Netherlands 64 Eb
Groix, I. de, France 72 Bc
Groningen, Neth. 64 Ea
Gronlid, Saskatchewan 37 Ne
Grono, Switzerland 65 Eb
Gronton, S. Dakota 46 Hc
Groote Eylandt, N. Terr. 57 Gb
Grootfontein, Namibia 95 Be
Grootfontein, Namibia 95 Bc
Groot Natuna I. See Bunguran Kep.
Gros-Morne, Quebec 32 Gd
Gros Morne, pk., Nfld. 33 Pd
Gros Pate, pk., Nfld. 33 Pc
Grosse Boule I., Quebec 32 Fc
Grosse I., Quebec 33 Lf
Grossevichi, U.S.S.R. 79 Nd
Gross Glockner, Austria 68 Ee
Groton, New York 44 Ba
Grouard, Alberta 36 Ac
Groundhog, R., Ontario 34 Hd
Grouse Mt., B.C. 39 Hk
Grovedale, Alberta 39 Oh
Groznyy, U.S.S.R. 78 Dd
Grudziądz, Poland 69 Hb
Grues, I. aux, Quebec 32 Bf
Grüsch, Switzerland 65 Eb
Grude, Yugoslavia 76 Bc
Gruzinskaya S.S.R., U.S.S.R. 78 Dd
Grybów, Poland 69 Jd
Gsteig, Switzerland 65 Cb
Guabito, Panama 51 Ce
Guacanayabo, G. de, Cuba 51 Db
Guachipas, Argentina 54 Cc
Guadalaja, Spain 70 Db
Guadalajara, Mexico 50 Dc
Guadalcanal, Solomon Is. 102 Eh
Guadalcanal, Spain 70 Cc
Guadalcazar, Mexico 50 Dc
Guadalquivir, Spain 70 Cd
Guadalupe, Mexico 50 Dc
Guadalupe I., Mexico 50 Ab
Guadalupe Mts., New Mexico/Texas 48 Ef
Guadalupe R., Texas 42 Gf
Guadalupe y Calvo, Mexico 50 Cb
Guadarrama, Spain 70 Cb
Guadarrama, Sa. de, Spain 70 Db
Guadeloupe, Leeward Is. 51 Gc
Guadiana, Spain 70 Bc
Guadix, Spain 70 Dd
Guafo, Chile 54 Bf
Guairá, Brazil 53 Gh
Guaitecas, Is., Chile 54 Bf
Guajar-á-Mirim, Brazil 52 Df
Guajaratuba, Brazil 52 Ee
Gualeguaychu, Argentina 54 Ed
Guam, Pacific Ocean 102 Df
Guamá, Brazil 53 Hd
Guamini, Argentina 54 De
Guamo, Colombia 52 Cc
Guanabaçoa, Cuba 51 Cb
Guanacevi, Mexico 50 Cb
Guanahacabibes, Pen. de, Cuba 51 Cb
Guanajuato, Mexico 50 Dc
Guanare, Venezuela 52 Db
Guanarito, Venezuela 52 Db
Guandacol, Argentina 54 Cc
Guane, Cuba 51 Cb
Guangchang, China 85 Hj
Guangdong, China 85 Fl
Guangnan, China 85 Bk
Guangxi, China 85 Cl
Guangzhou, China 85 Fl
Guánica, Puerto Rico 51 Fc
Guanta. See Puerto La Cruz
Guantánamo, Cuba 51 Db
Guapi, Colombia 52 Bc
Guapiles, Costa Rica 51 Cd
Guaporé, Brazil 52 Ef
Guaporé, Brazil 54 Fc
Guaporé, R., Brazil/Bolivia 52 Ef
Guaqui, Bolivia 52 Dg
Guarapuava, Brazil 54 Fc
Guarda, Portugal 70 Bb
Guasdualito, Venezuela 52 Cb
Guasipati, Venezuela 52 Eb
Guatemala, Cent. America 50 Fe
Guatemala, Guatemala 50 Fe
Guatrache, Argentina 54 De
Guaviare, Colombia 52 Dc
Guaxupé, Brazil 53 Hh
Guayabal, Venezuela 52 Db
Guayama, Puerto Rico 51 Fc
Guayaquil, Ecuador 52 Bd
Guaymas, Mexico 50 Bb
Gubin, Poland 68 Fc
Gudiyatam, India 88 Ef
Guéguen, L., Quebec 35 Nd
Guelma, Algeria 98 Ga
Guelph, Ontario 34 Kj
Guemes, Argentina 54 Cb
Guénette, Quebec 35 Pf
Guéret, France 72 Dc
Guérin, Quebec 35 Le
Guernsey, Channel Is. 72 Bb
Guernsey, Saskatchewan 37 Mg
Guernsey Res., Wyoming 46 Ed
Guerrero, Mexico 50 Dd
Guerrero, Mexico 50 Cb
Guest Pen., Antarctica 104 Nb
Gugera, Pakistan 90 Ce
Guiana Highlands, S. America 52 Ec
Guichi, China 84 Hg
Guide, China 84 Ad
Guiges, Quebec 35 Ld
Guija, Mozambique 95 Ed
Guildford, England 63 Gj
Guildford, Maine 32 Ch
Guilin, China 85 Ek
Guillaumes, France 73 Gd
Guimaraes, Brazil 53 Jd
Guimarães, Portugal 70 Ab
Guinea, West Africa 98 Cf
Guinea, G. of, N.W. Africa 96 Ad
Guinea-Bissau, N.W. Africa 98 Bf
Guinecourt, L., Quebec 32 Cc
Güines, Cuba 51 Cb
Guingamp, France 72 Bb
Guiping, China 85 El
Guiria, Venezuela 52 Ea
Guisanbourg, Fr. Guiana 53 Gc
Guise, France 72 Eb
Guisisil, Vol., Nicaragua 51 Bd
Guixi, China 85 Hh
Guiyang, China 85 Cj
Guiyang, China 85 Fk
Guizhou, China 85 Bj
Gujarat, India 88 Dd
Gujar Khan, Pakistan 90 Cd
Gujranwala, Pakistan 90 Dd
Gujrat, Pakistan 90 Dd
Gulbarga, India 88 Ee
Gulbene, Latvia 67 Mh
Gulfport, Mississippi 49 Ng
Gulin, China 85 Bh
Gulistan, Pakistan 88 Cb
Gul Koh, Afghanistan 93 Jc
Gull L., Alberta 36 Df
Gull Lake, Saskatchewan 36 Jh
Gull R., Ontario 37 Oa
Gulpen, Netherlands 64 Dd
Gulran, Afghanistan 93 Hb
Gulu, Uganda 97 Gd
Gumel, Nigeria 99 Gf
Gummersbach, W. Germany 68 Bc
Gümüsane, Turkey 92 Ca
Guna, India 91 Ac
Gunchu, Japan 86 Ch
Gunflint L., Minnesota 37 Mb
Gunisao L., Manitoba 37 Ve
Gunisao R., Manitoba 37 Ue
Gunnar, Saskatchewan 38 Tf
Gunnbjørn, Greenland 41 Nc
Gunnedah, N.S.W. 57 Kf
Gunnison, Colorado 48 Dc
Gunnison, Utah 48 Bc
Gunnison, R., Colorado 48 Dc
Gunnworth, Sask. 36 Jg
Guntakal, India 88 Ee
Guntersville, Ala. 45 Dc
Gunton, Manitoba 37 Uh
Guntur, India 88 Fe
Gurais, Kashmir 90 Dc
Gurdaspur, India 90 Dd
Gurdon, Arkansas 49 Lf
Gurgaon, India 90 Ef
Gurgl, Austria 68 De
Gurha, India 88 Dc
Gurkha, Nepal 91 Eb
Gurla Mandhata, China 88 Fb
Gurnigel, Switzerland 65 Cb
Gurskøy, Norway 66 Ae
Gurué, Mozambique 95 Fc
Gurupá, Brazil 53 Gd
Guru Sikhar, India 88 Dd
Gur'yev, Kazakhstan 78 Ed
Gusev, Lithuania 67 Kj
Gųspini, Sardinia 75 Bf
Gustav Holm, Kap, Greenland 41 Nc
Güstrow, East Germany 68 Eb
Guthrie, Iowa 49 Kb
Guthrie, Kentucky 45 Db
Guthrie, Oklahoma 49 Je
Guthrie L., Manitoba 37 Rc
Guttannen, Switzerland 65 Db
Guyana, S. America 52 Fc
Guyang, China 84 Eb
Guyenne, France 73 Dd
Guyenne, Quebec 35 Md
Guymon, Oklahoma 48 Gd
Guysborough, Nova Scotia 33 Lh
Gwa, Burma 89 He
Gwadar, Iran 93 Hd
Gwadar, Pakistan 88 Bc
Gwalior, India 91 Bb
Gwanda, Zimbabwe 95 Dd
Gweebarra B., Eire 63 Bf
Gwelo, Zimbabwe 95 Dc
Gwent, Wales 63 Fj
Gwynedd, Wales 63 Eg
Gwynne, Alberta 36 Df
Gyangzê, China 89 Gc
Gyaring Hu, China 82 Cd
Gydanskiy Pol., U.S.S.R. 78 Ga
Gyirong, China 91 Ea
Gympie, Queensland 57 Ke
Győr, Hungary 69 Ge
Gypsum Pt., N.W.T. 38 Qe
Gypsumville, Manitoba 37 Tg
Gyula, Hungary 69 Je

H

Haacht, Belgium 64 Cd
Haag, Switzerland 65 Ea
Haaksbergen, Netherlands 64 Eb
Haarlem, Netherlands 64 Cb
Habana, Cuba 51 Cb
Habay, Alberta 39 Of
Habban, S. Yemen 92 Eg
Habbaniyah, Iraq 92 Dc
Habiganj, Bangladesh 89 Hd
Haboro, Japan 86 Gb
Hache, Lac la, B.C. 39 Nk
Hachiman, Japan 86 Eg
Hachinohe, Japan 86 Gd
Hackett, Alberta 36 Ef
Hadasan, Mongolia 82 Da
Hadda, Arabia 92 Ce
Haddington, Scotland 62 Fe
Hadera, Israel 94 Ce
Haderslev, Denmark 67 Cj
Hadley B., N.W.T. 30 Jc
Haeju, Korea 82 Jc
Hafar, Arabia 92 Ed
Hafford, Saskatchewan 36 Kf
Hafnarfjördhur, Iceland 66 Vm
Hagen, Saskatchewan 37 Mf
Hagen, West Germany 68 Bc
Hageri, Estonia 67 Lg
Hagerstown, Maryland 44 Bc
Hagersville, Ontario 34 Kj
Hagi, Japan 86 Bg
Hague, Saskatchewan 36 Lf
Hague, C. de la, France 72 Cb
Hague, The. See 's Gravenhage
Hahnville, Louisiana 45 Bf
Haicheng, China 84 Lb
Haifa, Israel 94 Ce
Haig, W. Australia 56 Ef
Haikang, China 85 Em
Haikou, China 85 Em
Hā'il, Arabia 92 Dd
Hailar, China 82 Ga
Haileybury, Ontario 34 Le
Hailun, China 82 Ja
Hailuoto, Finland 66 Ld
Hainan Dao, China 85 En
Hainaut, Belgium 64 Bd
Haines, Alaska 30 Ff
Haines Junction, Y.T. 38 Ee
Haiphong, Vietnam 87 Db
Hair, Arabia 92 Ee
Hairy Hill, Alberta 36 Fe
Haiti, West Indies 51 Ec
Hajdúböszörmény, Hungary 69 Je
Hajima, Jebel, Arabia 92 Ce
Hajipur, India 91 Ec
Haka, Burma 89 Hd
Hakkâri, Turkey 92 Db
Hakodate, Japan 86 Gd
Hala, Pakistan 88 Cc
Halacho, Mexico 50 Fc
Halaib, Sudan 92 Ce
Halba, Lebanon 94 Ec
Halberstadt, East Germany 68 Dc
Halbrite, Saskatchewan 37 Oj
Halcyon Hot Springs, B.C. 39 Ok
Haldane, R., N.W.T. 38 Nb
Halden, Norway 67 Dg
Haleb, Syria 92 Cb
Halen, Belgium 64 Dc
Halfway, R., B.C. 39 Mg
Hali, Arabia 92 Df
Halia, India 91 Dc
Haliburton, Ontario 35 Mg
Halifax, England 63 Fg
Halifax, N. Carolina 45 Jb
Halifax, Nova Scotia 32 Jj
Halifax B., Queensland 57 Jc
Halkett C., Alaska 43 Xk
Halkirk, Alberta 36 Ef
Hall, West Germany 68 Cd
Hall Beach, N.W.T. 31 Ld
Hallboro, Manitoba 37 Sh
Halle, Belgium 64 Cd
Halle, East Germany 68 Dc
Hallebourg, Ontario 34 Gc
Hallein, Austria 68 Ee
Hallen, Sweden 66 Fe
Halley, B., Antarctica 104 Ab
Halliday L., N.W.T. 38 Te
Hall Is., Caroline Is. 102 Eg
Halliste, Estonia 67 Lg
Hall Ld., Greenland 41 Pa
Hällnäss, Sweden 66 Hd
Hallock, Minnesota 46 Ja
Hallonquist, Saskatchewan 36 Kh
Hall Pen., N.W.T. 31 Ne
Halls Creek, W. Australia 56 Ec
Hallstavik, Sweden 67 Hf
Halmahera, Indonesia 83 Jk
Halmstad, Sweden 67 Eh
Halsa, Norway 66 Ce
Halton Hills, Ontario 34 Kj
Halvorgate, Saskatchewan 36 Lh
Hama, Syria 94 Eb
Hamada, Japan 86 Cg
Hamadān, Iran 92 Ec
Hamam, Arabia 92 Ee
Hamamatsu, Japan 86 Eg
Hamar, Arabia 92 Ee
Hamar, Norway 67 Df
Hama Tonbetsu, Japan 86 Hb
Hambantota, Sri Lanka 88 Fg
Hamber Prov. Park, B.C. 39 Oj
Hamburg, Iowa 49 Kb
Hamburg, New York 44 Aa
Hamburg, Pennsylvania 44 Cb
Hamburg, S. Carolina 45 Gd
Hamburg, West Germany 68 Db
Hamdānīya, Syria 94 Eb
Hämeenlinna, Finland 67 Lf
Hameln, West Germany 68 Cb
Hamersley Range, W. Aust. 56 Cd
Hamhung, Korea 82 Jc
Hami, China 82 Bb
Hamidan, Arabia 93 Fe
Hamidiya, Syria 94 Dc
Hamilton, Alabama 45 Dc
Hamilton, N. Carolina 45 Jc
Hamilton, New York 44 Ca
Hamilton, New Zealand 55 Eb
Hamilton, Ohio 40 Df
Hamilton, Ontario 35 Lj
Hamilton, Scotland 62 Ee
Hamilton, Victoria 57 Hg
Hamilton, L., Arkansas 49 Le
Hamilton Inlet, Nfld. 31 Og
Hamilton Sound, Nfld. 33 Sd
Hamina, Finland 67 Mf
Hamiota, Manitoba 37 Rh
Hamirpur, India 91 Cc
Hamlet, N. Carolina 45 Hc
Hamm, West Germany 68 Bc
Hamme, Belgium 64 Cc
Hammerdal, Sweden 66 Fe
Hammerfest, Norway 66 Ka
Hammond, Indiana 40 Ce
Hammond, Louisiana 45 Be
Hammondvale, N.B. 32 Gh
Hammonton, New Jersey 44 Cc
Ham-Nord, Quebec 35 Tg
Hamont, Belgium 64 Dc
Hampden, N. Dakota 46 Ha
Hampden, New Zealand 55 Cf
Hampden, Nfld. 33 Qd
Hampshire, England 63 Gj
Hampstead, N.B. 32 Fh
Hampton, Arkansas 45 Ad
Hampton, Iowa 49 La
Hampton, N.B. 32 Gh
Hampton, S. Carolina 45 Gd
Hamun-i-Helmand, Iran/Afghanistan 93 Hc
Hamun-i-Lora, Pakistan 88 Bc
Hamun-i-Puzak, Afghanistan 93 Hc
Han, Belgium 64 Dd
Hanau, West Germany 68 Cc
Hanbury, Ontario 35 Le
Hancock, Michigan 43 Jb
Hancock, New York 44 Cb
Handan, China 84 Gd
Handegg, Switzerland 65 Db
Handel, Saskatchewan 36 Jf
Handeni, Tanzania 97 Hf
Handsworth, Sask. 37 Pj
Hanford, California 47 Dg
Hanford, Washington 47 Db
Hangayn Nuruu, Mongolia 59 Jd
Hangchow B. See Hangzhou Wan
Hangu, Pakistan 90 Bd
Hangzhou, China 85 Kg
Hangzhou Wan, China 84 Kg
Hankinson, N. Dakota 46 Jb
Hankö B., Finland 67 Kg
Hankow. See Wuhan
Hanle, Kashmir 88 Eb
Hanley, Saskatchewan 36 Lg
Hanlon, Alberta 39 Oj
Hanmer, New Zealand 55 De
Hanmer, Ontario 34 Jf
Hanna, Alberta 36 Fg
Hanna, Wyoming 46 Ee
Hannah B., Ontario 34 La
Hannibal, Missouri 49 Mc
Hannover, West Germany 68 Cb
Hannut, Belgium 64 Dd
Hanöbukten, Sweden 67 Fj
Hanoi, Vietnam 87 Db
Hanover, Ontario 34 Kh
Hanover, Pennsylvania 44 Bc
Hanover, Virginia 45 Jb
Hanover, I., Chile 54 Bh
Hansard, B.C. 39 Nh
Hansen, Ontario 34 Gc
Hanshou, China 85 Eh
Han Shui, China 82 Ed
Hansi, India 90 Ef
Hanson L., Saskatchewan 37 Pd
Hansweert, Netherlands 64 Cc
Hantsport, Nova Scotia 32 Hh
Hanumangarh, India 90 Df
Hanyang, China 85 Gg
Hanyin, China 84 Df
Hanzhong, China 84 Cf
Hao, Tuamotu Arch. 103 Lj
Haparanda, Sweden 66 Ld
Happy Valley, Nfld. 31 Ng
Hapur, India 90 Ef
Haqal, Arabia 92 Bd
Haraiya, India 91 Db
Harak, Arabia 92 Cd
Haranomachi, Japan 86 Gf
Harar, Ethiopia 97 Jc
Harardera, Somalia 97 Kd
Harbin, China 82 Ja
Harbor Beach, Michigan 40 Ed
Harbor Springs, Michigan 40 Dc
Harbour Breton, Nfld. 33 Rf
Harbour Buffett, Nfld. 33 Tf
Harbour Grace, Nfld. 33 Tf
Harbour Mille, Nfld. 33 Sf
Harbourville, Nova Scotia 32 Gh
Harburg, Ger. 68 Cb
Harcourt, N.B. 32 Gg
Harcus, Manitoba 37 Th
Harda, India 88 Ed
Hardanger Fd., Norway 67 Bf
Hardangervidda, Norway 67 Bf
Hardenberg, Netherlands 64 Eb
Harderwijk, Netherlands 64 Db
Hardin, Montana 46 Dc
Harding, Natal 95 Df
Harding, R., N.W.T. 38 Pa
Harding L., Manitoba 37 Tb
Hardisty, Alberta 36 Ff
Hardisty L., N.W.T. 38 Pc
Hardoi, India 91 Cb
Hardwar, India 90 Ff
Hardy, Saskatchewan 37 Nj
Hardy, Pen., Chile 54 Cj
Hare, I. See Lièvres, I. aux
Hare B., Newfoundland 33 Rb
Hare Bay, Newfoundland 33 Se
Hareidland, Norway 66 Ae
Harelbeke, Belgium 64 Bd
Hargeisa, Somalia 97 Jc
Hargrave, Manitoba 37 Qj
Hargrave L., Manitoba 37 Sd
Hari, Sumatra 83 Dl
Harib, Arabia 92 Ef
Harihar, India 88 Ef
Harim, Syria 94 Ea
Haripur, Pakistan 90 Cd
Hariq, Arabia 92 Ee
Harishpur, India 89 Gd
Harlan, Iowa 49 Kb
Harlan, Kentucky 43 Kd
Harlem, Montana 46 Ca
Harlequin Hills, Nevada 47 De
Harlingen, Netherlands 64 Da
Harlingen, Texas 48 Jj
Harlowton, Montana 46 Cb
Harney Basin, Oregon 42 Bc
Harney L., Oregon 47 Dd
Harney Pk., S. Dakota 46 Fd
Härnösand, Sweden 66 Ge
Harper, Liberia 98 Dh
Harper, Mt., Y.T. 38 Cc
Harper Cr., Alberta 39 Qf
Harptree, Saskatchewan 37 Mj
Harran, Turkey 92 Cb
Harricana R., Quebec 35 Lb
Harrington Harbour, Que. 33 Nc
Harriott L., Saskatchewan 37 Pb
Harris, Saskatchewan 36 Kg
Harris, Scotland 62 Cc
Harrisburg, Arkansas 45 Bc
Harrisburg, Illinois 45 Cb
Harrisburg, Pennsylvania 44 Bb
Harris Hill, Ontario 36 Hb
Harrison, Arkansas 49 Ld
Harrison, Michigan 40 Dc
Harrison, C., Nfld. 31 Og
Harrisonburg, Louisiana 45 Be
Harrisonburg, Virginia 45 Ha
Harrison L., B.C. 39 Nl
Harrisonville, Missouri 49 Kc
Harriston, Ontario 34 Kj
Harrisville, Michigan 40 Ec
Harrodsburg, Kentucky 45 Eb
Harrogate, England 63 Fg
Harrow, Ontario 34 Gk
Harrowby, Manitoba 37 Qh
Harry S. Truman Res., Missouri 49 Lc
Har Sagī, Israel 94 Cg
Harsprånget, Sweden 66 Jc
Harstad, Norway 66 Gb
Hart, Michigan 40 Cd
Hart, Saskatchewan 37 Mj
Hart, R., Y.T. 38 Ec
Hartell, Alberta 36 Ch
Hartford, Connecticut 44 Db
Hart Jaune R., Quebec 32 Db
Hartland, New Brunswick 32 Eg
Hartlepool, England 63 Gf
Hartley Bay, B.C. 39 Jj
Hart Mt., Manitoba 37 Qf
Hartney, Manitoba 37 Rj
Hartsville, Tennessee 45 Db
Hartville, Missouri 45 Ab
Harty, Ontario 34 Hc
Har Us Nuur, Mongolia 82 Ba
Harvard, Illinois 40 Bd
Harvard, Mt., Colorado 42 Ed
Harvey, N. Dakota 46 Hb
Harvey Station, N.B. 32 Fh
Harwich, England 63 Hj
Haryana, state, India 90 Ef
Harz, Mts., Germany 68 Dc
Hasā, Jordan 94 Dg
Hasan D., Turkey 92 Bb
Hasanpur, India 91 Ba

Hasbaya, Lebanon 94 Dd
Hashimoto, Japan 86 Dg
Hassan, India 88 Ef
Hassel Sd., N.W.T. 30 Kb
Hasselt, Belgium 64 Dd
Hasselt, Netherlands 64 Eb
Hastière, Belgium 64 Cd
Hastings, England 63 Hk
Hastings, Michigan 40 Dd
Hastings, Minnesota 46 Lc
Hastings, Nebraska 49 Hb
Hastings, New Zealand 55 Fc
Hastings, Ontario 35 Mh
Hatay, Turkey 92 Cb
Hatchet L., Saskatchewan 38 Wf
Hateg, Romania 76 Db
Hatfield, Saskatchewan 37 Mg
Hatgal, Mongolia 79 Kc
Hatha, Arabia 92 De
Hathras, India 91 Bb
Hat I., N.W.T. 38 Xa
Ha-Tinh, Vietnam 87 Dc
Hatteras, C., N. Carolina 45 Kc
Hattiesburg, Mississippi 45 Ce
Hatton, Saskatchewan 36 Hh
Hatvan, Hungary 69 He
Hat Yai, Thailand 83 Dj
Haudères, les, Switzerland 65 Cb
Haugesund, Norway 67 Ag
Haukipudas, Finland 66 Ld
Hauki vesi, Finland 66 Ne
Haura, S. Yemen 92 Eg
Hauraki Gulf, New Zealand 55 Eb
Hauroko, L., New Zealand 55 Af
Hausa, Jordan 94 Fh
Hausstock, Switzerland 65 Eb
Haut, Ile au, Maine 32 Dj
Hauta, Arabia 92 Ee
Haute Atlas, Mts., Morocco 98 Db
Haute-Corse, Corsica 73 Jf
Haute-Garonne, France 73 De
Haute-Loire, France 73 Ed
Hautes, Alpes, France 73 Gd
Haute Saône, France 72 Gc
Haute-Savoie, France 72 Gc
Hautes-Pyrénées, Fr. 73 De
Haute Vienne, France 72 Dd
Haut-Marne, France 72 Fb
Haut-Rhin, France 72 Gc
Hautrive, Quebec 32 Dd
Havasu L., Cal./Arizona 47 Fh
Havelange, Belgium 64 Dd
Havelland, East Germany 68 Eb
Havelock, New Brunswick 32 Gh
Havelock, Ontario 35 Mh
Havelock I., Andaman Is. 89 Hf
Havelock North, N.Z. 55 Fc
Haverfordwest, Wales 63 Dj
Haverhill, Massachusetts 44 Ea
Haverstraw, New York 44 Cb
Havré, Belgium 64 Cd
Havre, Montana 46 Ca
Havre, I. du, Quebec 32 Jc
Havre-Aubert, Quebec 33 Kf
Havre-Aubert (Amherst), I.-du-, Quebec 33 Kf
Havre-aux-Maisons, Que. 33 Lf
Havre aux Maisons, I. du (Alright I.), Quebec 33 Lf
Havre Boucher, N.S. 33 Lh
Havre de Grace, Maryland 44 Bc
Havre-St-Pierre, Quebec 32 Jc
Hawaii, Pacific Oc. 103 Kf
Hawaiian Is., Pacific Ocean 102 Je
Hawarden, Iowa 49 Ja
Hawarden, Saskatchewan 36 Lg
Hawea Flat, New Zealand 55 Bf
Hawera, New Zealand 55 Ec
Hawesville, Kentucky 45 Db
Hawick, Scotland 62 Fe
Hawke B., New Zealand 55 Fc
Hawkesbury, Ontario 35 Qg
Hawk Junction, Ontario 34 Fd
Hawk Lake, Ontario 36 Ha
Hawr al Hammar, Iraq 92 Ec
Hawr Saniya, Iraq 92 Ec
Hay, New South Wales 57 Hf
Hay, R., Alberta/B.C. 39 Nf
Hayatpur, India 91 Fc
Hayes Halvø, Greenland 41 Qb
Hayes R., Manitoba 37 Vd
Hay L., Alberta 39 Of
Hay Lakes, Alberta 36 De
Hayneville, Alabama 45 Dd
Hay River, N.W.T. 38 Qe
Hays, Alberta 36 Fh
Hays, Kansas 49 Hc
Hayter, Alberta 36 Gf
Hayward, Wisconsin 46 Mb
Haywood, Manitoba 37 Tj
Hazara Highlands, Afghan. 93 Hc
Hazard, Kentucky 45 Fb
Hazaribagh, India 91 Ed
Hazaribagh Ra., India 91 Dd
Hazawza, Arabia 92 Cc
Hazelhurst, Georgia, U.S.A. 45 Fe
Hazelridge, Manitoba 37 Vj
Hazelton, B.C. 39 Kh
Hazen L., N.W.T. 31 Na
Hazenmore, Sask. 36 Kj
Hazen Str., N.W.T. 30 Hb
Hazeva, Israel 94 Dg
Hazleton, Pennsylvania 44 Cb
Hazro, Pakistan 90 Cd
Head Harbour I., Maine 32 Ej
Heard I., Indian Ocean 100 Fk
Hearne, Saskatchewan 37 Mh
Hearne, C., N.W.T. 38 Qa
Hearne L., N.W.T. 38 Rd
Hearst, Ontario 34 Gc
Heart L., Alberta 36 Fd
Heart R., Alberta 36 Ab
Heart's Content, Nfld. 33 Tf
Heart's Delight, Nfld. 33 Tf
Heath, Pte., Quebec 33 Ld
Heatherton, Nfld. 33 Oe
Heavener, Oklahoma 49 Ke
Hebbronville, Texas 48 Hj
Hebei, China 84 Gc
Heber, Utah 48 Bb
Heber Springs, Arkansas 45 Ac
Hébert, L., Quebec 35 Pc
Hébertville-Station, Quebec 35 Td
Hebi, China 84 Ge
Hebrides, Outer, Scotland 62 Bc
Hebron, Jordan 94 Df
Hebron, N. Dakota 46 Fb
Hebron, Nebraska 49 Jb
Hebron, Newfoundland 31 Nf
Hebron, Nova Scotia 32 Fk
Hecate Str., B.C 39 Hj
Hecelchakan, Mexico 50 Fc
Hechingen, West Germany 68 Cd
Hechtel, Belgium 64 Dc
Hechuan, China 85 Cg
Hecla & Griper B., N.W.T. 30 Hb
Hecla & I., Manitoba 37 Vg
Hectanooga, Nova Scotia 32 Fj
Hector, Mt., Alberta 39 Pk
Hector, Mt., New Zealand 55 Ed
Hede, Sweden 66 Ee
Hedemora, Sweden 67 Ff
Hedley, B.C. 39 Nl
Heemstede, Netherlands 64 Cb
Heer, Netherlands 64 Dd
Heerenveen, Netherlands 64 Db
Heerlen, Netherlands 64 Dd
Hefei, China 84 Hg
Heffley, B.C. 39 Nk
Heide, West Germany 68 Ca
Heidelberg, West Germany 68 Cd
Heidelburg, Transvaal 95 De
Heiden, Switzerland 65 Ea
Heijen, Netherlands 64 Dc
Heilbronn, West Germany 68 Cd
Heinola, Finland 67 Mf
Heinsburg, Alberta 36 Ge
Heisler, Alberta 36 Ef
Heist, Belgium 64 Bc
Hejaz, Arabia 92 Ce
Hekla, Mt., Iceland 66 Wn
Hekou, China 85 Al
Helan Shan, China 82 Dc
Helchteren, Belgium 64 Dc
Helder, Den, Netherlands 64 Cb
Helena, Arkansas 45 Bc
Helena, Montana 47 Gb
Helene L., Saskatchewan 36 Je
Helen L., Ontario 34 Bc
Helensburgh, Scotland 62 Dd
Helensville, New Zealand 55 Eb
Helgoland, West Germany 68 Ba
Helgoländer Bucht, W. Ger. 68 Ba
Hellin, Spain 71 Ec
Helmand, Afghanistan 93 Hc
Helme, Estonia 67 Lh
Helmond, Netherlands 64 Dc
Helmsdale, Scotland 62 Eb
Helsingborg, Sweden 67 Eh
Helsingfors. See Helsinki
Helsingør, Denmark 67 Eh
Helsinki, Finland 67 Lf
Helston, England 63 Dk
Hemaruka, Alberta 36 Fg
Hemelum, Netherlands 64 Db
Heming Lake, Manitoba 37 Qd
Hemmingford, Quebec 35 Rg
Hemnes, Norway 66 Ec
Hemse, Sweden 67 Hh
Henan, China 84 Fe
Hendaye, France 73 Ce
Henderson, Kentucky 49 Od
Henderson, Minnesota 46 Lc
Henderson, N. Carolina 45 Hb
Henderson, New York 40 Hd
Henderson, Tennessee 45 Cc
Henderson I., Pacific Ocean 103 Nk
Hendersonville, N. Carolina 45 Fc
Hendon, Saskatchewan 37 Of
Hengam, Iran 93 Gd
Hengelo, Netherlands 64 Eb
Hengshan, China 85 Fj
Heng Xian, China 85 Dl
Hengyang, China 85 Fj
Henley Harbour, Nfld. 33 Rb
Henley-on-Thames, England 63 Gj
Henlopen, C., New Jersey 44 Cc
Hennebont, France 72 Bc
Henri, Mt., B.C. 39 Lg
Henribourg, Sask. 37 Me
Henrietta, Texas 49 Hf
Henrietta Maria, C., Ont. 31 Lf
Henrique de Carvalho, Angola 96 Ef
Henryetta, Oklahoma 49 Je
Henry Kater Pen., N.W.T. 31 Nd
Henry Mts., Utah 48 Bc
Henrys, Idaho 46 Bc
Hensall, Ontario 34 Jj
Henzada, Burma 89 Je
Hepburn, Saskatchewan 36 Lf
Hepburn I., N.W.T. 38 Sb
Hepu, China 85 Dm
Hepworth, Ontario 34 Jh
Heran, Yemen 92 Df
Herat, Afghanistan 93 Hc
Hérault, France 73 Ee
Herbert, N. Zealand 55 Cf
Herbert, Saskatchewan 36 Kh
Herbertville, New Zealand 55 Fd
Herbesthal, Belgium 64 Ed
Herb Lake, Manitoba 37 Sd
Herceg Novi, Yugoslavia 76 Bc
Herchmer, Manitoba 30 Kf
Heredia, Costa Rica 51 Cd
Hereford, England 63 Fh
Hereford, Texas 48 Fe
Hereford & Worcester, England 63 Fh
Hereheretue, Pacific Oc. 103 Lj
Herford, West Germany 68 Cb
Heriot Bay, B.C. 39 Lk
Herisau, Switzerland 65 Ea
Herkimer, New York 44 Ca
Herma Ness, Shetland 62 Ja
Hermann, Missouri 49 Mc
Hermil, Lebanon 94 Ec
Hermitage, Nfld. 33 Rf
Hermitage B., Nfld. 33 Qf
Hermite, Is., Chile 54 Cj
Hermon, Mt. See Sheikh
Hermosillo, Mexico 50 Bb
Herne, Belgium 64 Cd
Herning, Denmark 67 Ch
Héron, Belgium 64 Dd
Heron Bay, Ontario 34 Dd
Heron I., Queensland 57 Kd
Hérons, I. aux, Quebec 35 Sk
Herowabad, Iran 92 Eb
Herräng, Sweden 67 Hf
Herrera, Argentina 54 Dc
Herrera di Pisuerga, Spain 70 Ca
Herring Neck, Nfld. 33 Sd
Herrington, Kansas 49 Jc
Herriot, Manitoba 37 Qb
Herschel, Saskatchewan 36 Jg
Herschel I., Y.T. 38 Da
Herselt, Belgium 64 Cc
Hersey, Michigan 40 Dd
Hertford, England 63 Gj
Hertford, N. Carolina 45 Jb
Hertfordshire, England 63 Gj
Hervás, Spain 70 Cb
Herve, Belgium 64 Dd
Hervey, B., Queensland 57 Kd
Hervey Is., Cook Is. 102 Jj
Hervey-Jonction, Quebec 35 Sf
Herzberg, East Germany 68 Ec
Herzliyya, Israel 94 Ce
Herzogenbuchsee, Switz. 65 Ca
Hesdin, France 72 Ea
Hess Mts., Y.T. 38 Gd
Hess R., Y.T. 38 Gd
Heughlin, Mt., N. Terr. 56 Fd
Heusden, Netherlands 64 Dc
Hève, C. de la, France 72 Db
Heward, Saskatchewan 37 Oj
Hexham, England 62 Ff
He Xian, China 85 Ek
Heyuan, China 82 Ff
Heze, China 84 Ge
Hiawatha, Kansas 49 Kc
Hibbard, Quebec 35 Qe
Hibbing, Minnesota 46 Lb
Hickman's Harbour, Nfld. 33 Te
Hicks Bay, New Zealand 55 Gb
Hicks L., N.W.T. 38 Ye
Hickson, Ontario 34 Kj
Hidalgo, Mexico 50 Eb
Hidalgo, Mexico 50 Ec
Hieflau, Austria 68 Fe
Hierro, I., Canary Is. 98 Bc
High Hill L., Manitoba 37 Wc
Highland, reg., Scotland 62 Dc
Highland Park, Illinois 49 Oa
Highmore, S. Dakota 46 Hc
High Point, N. Carolina 45 Gc
High Point, Saskatchewan 36 Kh
High Prairie, Alberta 39 Ph
High River, Alberta 36 Dh
Highrock & L., Manitoba 37 Rc
Highrock L., Sask. 39 Vg
Highwood Mts., Montana 46 Bb
Hiiumaa, Estonia 67 Kg
Híjar, Spain 71 Eb
Hikone, Japan 86 Eg
Hilda, Alberta 36 Gh
Hildesheim, West Germany 68 Cb
Hill City, Kansas 49 Hc
Hill City, Minnesota 46 Lb
Hillcrest Mines, Alberta 36 Cj
Hilliard, Alberta 36 Ee
Hill Island L., N.W.T. 38 Te
Hillman, Michigan 40 Ec
Hillmond, Saskatchewan 36 He
Hillsboro, Illinois 49 Nc
Hillsboro, N. Carolina 45 Hb
Hillsboro, Texas 49 Jf
Hillsborough, N.B. 32 Hh
Hillsborough B., P.E.I. 32 Jg
Hillsburgh, Ontario 34 Kj
Hillsdale, Michigan 40 De
Hillsdale, Ontario 35 Lh
Hillsport, Ontario 34 Ec
Hillston, N.S.W. 57 Jf
Hillsville, Virginia 45 Gb
Hilton Beach, Ontario 34 Ff
Hilversum, Netherlands 64 Db
Hilyan, Arabia 92 De
Himachal Pradesh, India 90 Ee
Himalayan Ra., India 88 Eb
Himanka, Finland 66 Kd
Himara, Albania 77 Bd
Himeji, Japan 86 Dg
Hinchliffe, Saskatchewan 37 Pf
Hinckley, Minnesota 46 Lb
Hindeloopen, Netherlands 64 Db
Hindman, Kentucky 45 Fb
Hinds Hill, pk., Nfld. 33 Qd
Hindubagh, Pakistan 88 Cb
Hindu Kush, Afghan./Pakistan 88 Da
Hindupur, India 88 Ef
Hindville, Alberta 36 Ge
Hines Creek, Alberta 39 Og
Hingan. See Ankang
Hinganghat, India 88 Ed
Hingham, Montana 46 Ba
Hinghwa. See Putian
Hinglaj, Pakistan 88 Cc
Hingol, Pakistan 88 Cc
Hingoli, India 88 Ee
Hinis, Turkey 92 Db
Hinnöy, Norway 66 Fb
Hinsdale, Montana 46 Da
Hinsdale, New Hampshire 44 Da
Hinton, Alberta 39 Pj
Hinton, W. Virginia 45 Gb
Hiroo, Japan 86 Hc
Hirosaki, Japan 86 Gd
Hiroshima, Japan 86 Cg
Hîrşova, Romania 76 Fb
Hisar, India 90 Df
Hisaronu, Turkey 92 Ba
Hisban, Jordan 94 Df
Hispaniola, West Indies 51 Ec
Hissmofors, Sweden 66 Fe
Hissua, India 91 Ec
Hisya, Syria 94 Ec
Hit, Iraq 92 Dc
Hitchcock, Saskatchewan 37 Oj
Hitra, Norway 66 Ce
Hiva Oa, Marquêsas Is. 103 Mh
Hiwasa, Japan 86 Dh
Hjälmaren, L., Sweden 67 Fg
Hjørring, Denmark 67 Ch
Hoadley, Alberta 36 Cf
Hobart, Oklahoma 49 He
Hobart, Tasmania 57 Jh
Hobbema, Alberta 36 Df
Hobbs, New Mexico 48 Ff
Hoboken, Belgium 64 Cc
Hobro, Denmark 67 Ch
Ho Chi Minh. See Saigon
Hodal, India 90 Eg
Hodeida, Yemen 92 Dg
Hodges Hill, pk., Nfld. 33 Qd
Hodgeville, Saskatchewan 36 Lh
Hodgson, Manitoba 37 Ug
Hódmezövásárhely, Hungary 69 Je
Hoek van Holland, Neth. 64 Cc
Hoey, Saskatchewan 37 Mf
Hof, West Germany 68 Dc
Hoff, Alberta 39 Oj
Hofn, Iceland 66 Ym
Hofra, Libya 99 Jc
Höfs Jökull, Iceland 66 Wm
Höganäs, Sweden 67 Eh
Hogarth, Ontario 34 Bc
Hogg L., Manitoba 37 Va
Hohe Tauern, Austria 68 Ee
Hohhot, China 84 Eb
Hoh Xil Shan, China 89 Fa
Hoi An, Vietnam 87 Dc
Hokianga Harbour, N.Z. 55 Da
Hokitika, New Zealand 55 Ce
Hokkaidō, Japan 86 Gc
Holbaek, Denmark 67 Dj
Holberg, B.C. 39 Jk
Holbrook, Arizona 48 Be
Holden, Alberta 36 Ee
Holdenville, Oklahoma 49 Je
Holdfast, Saskatchewan 37 Mh
Holdredge, Nebraska 49 Hb
Holguín, Cuba 51 Db
Holland, Manitoba 37 Tj
Holland, Michigan 40 Cd
Holland, New York 44 Aa
Holland, Noord, Neth. 64 Cb
Holland, Parts Of, England 63 Gh
Holland, Zuid, Neth. 64 Cb
Holland Centre, Ontario 34 Kh
Hollange, Belgium 64 De
Hollidaysburg, Pennsylvania 44 Ab
Hollis, Oklahoma 49 He
Hollogne, Belgium 64 Dd
Holly, Colorado 48 Fc
Holly, Michigan 40 Ed
Hollyburn Mt., B.C. 39 Gk
Holly Springs, Mississippi 49 Ne
Hollywood, California 47 Dh
Holm, Norway 66 Ed
Holman, N.W.T. 38 Pa
Holmes L., Manitoba 37 Va
Holmestrand, Norway 67 Dg
Holmfield, Manitoba 37 Sj
Holmsund, Sweden 66 Je
Holstebro, Denmark 67 Ch
Holstein, Ontario 34 Kh
Holsteinsborg, Greenland 41 Pc
Holten, Netherlands 64 Eb
Holter, L., Montana 46 Ab
Holton, Kansas 49 Kc
Holtyre, Ontario 34 Kd
Holwerd, Netherlands 64 Da
Holy Cross, Alaska 43 Wl
Holy Cross, Mt. of the, Colo. 42 Ed
Holyhead, Wales 63 Dg
Holy I., England 62 Fe
Holy I., Wales 63 Dg
Holyoke, Alberta 36 Gd
Holyoke, Colorado 48 Fb
Holyoke, Massachusetts 40 Kd
Holyrood, Newfoundland 33 Tf
Home B., N.W.T. 31 Nd
Homer, Alaska 43 Xm
Homer, Louisiana 49 Lf
Homer, New York 40 Hd
Homestead, Pennsylvania 40 Ge
Homfray Str., Andaman Is. 89 Hf
Hommelvik, Norway 66 De
Homs. See Al Khums
Homs, Syria 94 Ec
Honda, Colombia 52 Cb
Honda, B., Cuba 51 Cb
Hondo, Alberta 36 Cc
Hondo, Mexico 50 Db
Honduras, C. America 51 Bd
Honduras, C., Honduras 51 Bc
Honduras, G. of, Belize 51 Bc
Hønefoss, Norway 67 Df
Honesdale, Pennsylvania 44 Cb
Honeywood, Ontario 34 Kh
Honfleur, France 72 Db
Hong, Vietnam 87 Cb
Honghai Wan, China 85 Gl
Hong Kong, S.E. Asia 85 Gl
Honguedo, Détroit d', Quebec 32 Hd
Hongze Hu, China 84 Jf
Honolulu, Hawaiian Is. 103 Ke
Honor, Michigan 40 Cc
Honshū, Japan 86 Cg
Hood, Mt., Oregon 47 Cc
Hood R., N.W.T. 38 Tb
Hoofdplaat, Netherlands 64 Bc
Hoogersmilde, Netherlands 64 Eb
Hoogeveen, Netherlands 64 Eb
Hoogezand-Sappemeer, Netherlands 64 Ea
Hooghalen, Netherlands 64 Eb
Hooghly, India 91 Gd
Hooghly R., India 91 Ge
Hook Hd., Eire 63 Ch
Hoopeston, Illinois 40 Ce
Hooping Harbour, Nfld. 33 Qc
Hoorn, Netherlands 64 Db
Hoosick Falls, New York 40 Kd
Hoosier, Saskatchewan 36 Hg
Hoover Dam, Arizona 47 Fh
Hope, Arkansas 49 Lf
Hope, British Columbia 39 Nl
Hope C., N.W.T. 38 Pa
Hopedale, Nfld. 31 Nf
Hopen, Barents Sea 78 Ba
Hopes Advance, C., Que. 31 Ne
Hopetoun, W. Australia 56 Df
Hopetown, Cape Province 95 Ce
Hopewell, Virginia 45 Jb
Hopewell Is., N.W.T. 31 Mf
Hopkinsville, Kentucky 45 Db
Hoppner, R., N.W.T. 38 Pa
Hoquiam, Washington 47 Bb
Horaždovice, Czech. 68 Ed
Horburg, Alberta 36 Bf
Horcasitas, Mexico 50 Bb
Horgen, Switzerland 65 Da
Horinger, China 84 Eb
Horizon, Saskatchewan 37 Mj
Horka, East Germany 68 Fc
Hormoz, Iran 93 Fd
Hormoz, Iran 93 Gd
Hormuz, Str. of, Arabia/Iran 93 Gd
Horn, Austria 69 Fd
Horn, Iceland 66 Ul
Horn, Netherlands 64 Dc
Horn, C. See Hornos, C. de
Hornaday, R., N.W.T. 38 Ma
Hornavan, Sweden 66 Gc
Hornby, New Zealand 55 De
Hörnefors, Sweden 66 He
Hornell, New York 44 Ba
Hornepayne, Ontario 34 Fc
Hornopiren, Chile 54 Bf
Hornos, C. de, Chile 54 Cj
Horn Plateau, N.W.T. 38 Od
Hornsea, England 63 Gg
Horonobe, Japan 86 Gb
Horqin Youyi Qianqi, China 82 Ha
Horqueta, Paraguay 54 Eb
Horsefly, B.C. 39 Nj
Horseheads, New York 44 Ba
Horse Is., Newfoundland 33 Rc
Horse Islands, Nfld. 33 Rc
Horsens, Denmark 67 Cj
Horse R., Alberta 36 Fb
Horse Shoe, W. Australia 56 Ce
Horseshoe Bay, B.C. 39 Gk
Horseshoe L., Arizona 48 Be
Horsham, England 63 Gj
Horsham, Saskatchewan 36 Hh
Horsham, Victoria 57 Hg
Horšovský Týn, Czech. 68 Ed
Horst, Netherlands 64 Ec
Horten, Norway 67 Dg
Horton, Kansas 49 Kc
Horton, Montana 46 Db
Horton, R., N.W.T. 38 Ka
Horwood L., Ontario 34 Hd
Hoşap, Turkey 92 Db
Hose Ra., Sarawak 83 Fk
Hoshangabad, India 91 Ad
Hoshiarpur, India 90 De
Hospel, India 88 Ee
Hospenthal, Switzerland 65 Db
Hossegor, France 73 Ce
Hoste, Chile 54 Cj
Hosur, India 88 Ef
Hotagen, Sweden 66 Fe
Hotan, China 78 Ge
Hotchkiss, Alberta 39 Pg
Hot Springs, N. Carolina 45 Fc
Hot Springs, S. Dakota 46 Fd
Hot Springs Nat. Pk., Ark. 49 Le
Hottah L., N.W.T. 38 Oc
Hotton, Belgium 64 Dd
Houdelaincourt, France 72 Fb
Houffalize, Belgium 64 Dd
Houghton L., Michigan 40 Dc
Houlton, Maine 32 Eg
Houma, China 84 Ee
Houma, Louisiana 49 Mh
Hourn L., Scotland 62 Dc
Housatonic, R., Connecticut 44 Db
House R., Alberta 36 Ec
House Range, Utah 48 Ac
Houston, B.C. 39 Kh
Houston, Mississippi 45 Cd
Houston, Missouri 45 Bb
Houston, Texas 49 Kh
Houtman Abrolhos, W. Aust. 56 Be
Hovd, Mongolia 82 Ba
Hövsgöl Nuur, L., Mongolia 79 Kc
Howard, Michigan 40 Dd
Howard, Pennsylvania 44 Bb
Howard, S. Dakota 46 Jc
Howard L., N.W.T. 38 Ud
Howell, Michigan 40 Ed
Howe Sd., B.C. 39 Ml
Howick, Natal 95 Ee
Howick, Quebec 35 Rg
Howland I., Pacific Ocean 102 Hg
Howley, Newfoundland 33 Pd
Howrah, India 91 Gd
Howser, B.C. 39 Pk
Hoyes, Spain 70 Bb
Hoy I., Orkney 62 Eb
Hoyle, Ontario 34 Jd
Hoyt, N.B. 32 Fh
Hozat, Turkey 92 Cb
Hrubieszów, Poland 69 Kc
Hsenwi, Burma 89 Jd
Hsi-an. See Xi'an
Hsi-ch'ang. See Xichang
Hsinchu, Taiwan 85 Kk
Hsi-ning. See Xining
Hsinking. See Changchun
Hsipaw, Burma 89 Jd
Hsuchow. See Xuchang
Huacho, Peru 52 Bf
Huacrachuco, Peru 52 Be
Huai'an, China 84 Jf
Huaibei, China 84 Hf
Huai-pei, China 84 He
Huairen, China 84 Fc
Huaiyang, China 84 Gf
Hualgayoc, Peru 52 Be
Hualien, Taiwan 85 Kl
Huambo, Angola 96 Dg
Huanay, Bolivia 52 Dg
Huancabamba, Peru 52 Be
Huancane, Peru 52 Dg
Huancavelica, Peru 52 Bf
Huancayo, Peru 52 Bf
Huanchaca, Bolivia 52 Dh
Huanchaco, Peru 52 Be
Huanggang, China 84 Gg
Huang He, China 82 Gc
Huanghe Kou, China 84 Jc
Huangshi, China 85 Gg
Huang Xian, China 84 Kd
Huanta, Peru 52 Cf
Huanuco, Peru 52 Be
Huan Xian, China 84 Cd
Huaonta, Nicaragua 51 Cd
Huara, Chile 54 Ca
Huáraz, Peru 52 Be
Huariaca, Peru 52 Bf
Huario, Peru 52 Bf
Huarmey, Peru 52 Bf
Huascarán, Peru 52 Be
Huasco, Chile 54 Bc
Hua Xian, China 85 Fl
Huaylas, Peru 52 Be
Hubbard, Saskatchewan 37 Og
Hubbard, Mt., Y.T. 38 De
Hubbards, Nova Scotia 32 Hj
Hubei, China 84 Fg
Huberdeau, Quebec 35 Qg
Hubli, India 88 Ee
Huddersfield, England 63 Fg
Hudiksvall, Sweden 67 Gf
Hudson, New York 44 Da
Hudson, Ontario 36 Ka
Hudson, Wisconsin 46 Lc
Hudson B., Canada 31 Lf
Hudson Bay, Sask. 37 Pf
Hudson Falls, New York 40 Kd
Hudson Hope, B.C. 39 Ng
Hudson L., Oklahoma 49 Kd
Hudson R., New York 44 Da
Hudson Strait, Canada 31 Me
Hudwin L., Manitoba 37 We
Hue, Vietnam 87 Dc
Hueco Mts., New Mex./Texas 48 Ef
Huedin, Romania 76 Da
Huehuetenango, Guatemala 50 Fd
Huejutla, Mexico 50 Ec
Huelva, Spain 70 Bd
Huércal Overa, Spain 71 Ed
Huete, Spain 71 Db
Hufūf, Al, Arabia 92 Ed
Hughenden, Alberta 36 Ff
Hughenden, Queensland 57 Hd
Hughes R., Manitoba 37 Rb
Hughton, Saskatchewan 36 Kg
Hugo, Oklahoma 49 Ke
Huiarau Range, New Zealand 55 Fc
Hŭichŏn, Korea 82 Jb
Huimin, China 84 Hd
Huinan, China 82 Jb
Huizhou, China 85 Gl
Hukawng Valley, Burma 89 Jc
Hukou, China 82 Ge
Hukuntsi, Botswana 95 Cd
Hulah Res., Oklahoma 49 Jd
Hula L., Israel 94 Dd
Hulin, China 82 Ka
Hull, Quebec 35 Pg
Hull, Kingston on, England 63 Gg
Hulst, Netherlands 64 Cc
Hulun Nur, China 82 Ga
Huma, China 79 Mc
Humacao, Puerto Rico 51 Fc
Humaitá, Brazil 52 Ee
Humaita, Paraguay 54 Ec
Humansdorp, Cape Prov. 95 Cf
Humay, Peru 52 Bf
Humbe, Angola 95 Ac
Humber B., Ontario 34 Ck
Humber R., England 63 Hg
Humberside, England 63 Gg
Humboldt, Iowa 49 Ka
Humboldt, Saskatchewan 37 Mf
Humboldt, Tennessee 45 Cc
Humboldt B., California 42 Bc
Humboldt Glacier, Greenl'd. 41 Nb
Humboldt R., Nevada 47 De
Hume, R., N.W.T. 38 Jc
Humenné, Czechoslovakia 69 Jd
Hume Res., N.S.W. 57 Jg
Humphreys, Mt., California 47 Dg
Humphreys Peak, Arizona 48 Be
Hun, Libya 99 Jc
Hunafloi, Iceland 66 Vm
Hunan, China 85 Ej
Hundred Mile House, B.C. 39 Nk
Hungary, Cent. Europe 61 Mg
Hungnam, Korea 82 Jc
Hunjiang, China 82 Jb
Hunsrück, W. Ger. 68 Bd
Hunt, Mt., Y.T. 38 Je
Hunta, Ontario 34 Jc
Hunter I., B.C. 39 Jk
Hunter Is., Tasmania 57 Hh
Hunter River, P.E.I. 32 Jg
Huntersville, W. Virginia 45 Ga
Huntingburg, Indiana 45 Da
Huntingdon, England 63 Gh
Huntingdon, Pennsylvania 44 Ab
Huntingdon, Quebec 35 Qg
Huntington, Indiana 40 De
Huntington, New York 44 Db
Huntington, Utah 48 Bc
Huntington, W. Virginia 45 Fa
Huntley, Montana 46 Cc
Huntly, New Zealand 55 Eb
Huntly, Scotland 62 Fc
Hunts Point, Nova Scotia 32 Hk
Huntsville, Alabama 45 Dc
Huntsville, Ontario 35 Lg
Huntsville, Tennessee 45 Eb
Huntsville, Texas 49 Kg
Hunucma, Mexico 50 Fc
Hunyuan, China 84 Fc
Huon Is., Pacific Ocean 102 Fj
Huon Pen., Papua New Guinea 57 Ja
Huo Xian, China 84 Ed
Hurd C., Ontario 34 Jg
Hurghada, Egypt 99 Mc
Hurkett, Ontario 34 Bd
Huron, S. Dakota 46 Hc
Huron, L., U.S.A./Can. 43 Kc
Hurtsboro, Alabama 45 Ed
Huskvarna, Sweden 67 Fh
Hussar, Alberta 36 Eg
Husum, West Germany 68 Ca
Hutchinson, Kansas 49 Jc
Hutchinson, Minnesota 46 Kc
Hüttenberg, Austria 68 Fe
Hutton, B.C. 39 Nh
Huttwil, Switzerland 65 Ca
Huxley, Alberta 36 Dg
Huy, Belgium 64 Dd
Hvar, Yugoslavia 74 Fd
Hvargas Nuur, L., Mongolia 79 Jd
Hwaiking. See Qinyang
Hwaining. See Anqing
Hwaiyih. See Qingjiang
Hwang-Hai. See Huang Hai
Hweichow. See She Xian
Hyas, Saskatchewan 37 Pg
Hybla, Ontario 35 Ng
Hyden, Kentucky 45 Fb
Hyden, W. Australia 56 Cf
Hyde Park, Vermont 40 Kc
Hyderabad, India 88 Ee
Hyderabad, Pakistan 88 Cc
Hyères, France 73 Ge
Hyères, Is. d', France 73 Ge
Hyland, R., Y.T. 38 Je
Hyland Post, B.C. 39 Jg
Hylo, Alberta 36 Ed
Hyndman Peak, Idaho 42 Dc
Hyrum, Utah 48 Bb
Hyrynsalmi, Finland 66 Nd
Hythe, Alberta 39 Oh
Hythe, England 63 Hj

I

Iasi, Romania 80 Eh
Iauarete, Colombia 52 Dc
Ibadan, Nigeria 98 Fg
Ibagué, Colombia 52 Bc
Ibarra, Ecuador 52 Bc
Ibb, Yemen 92 Dg
Ibembo, Zaire 96 Ed
Iberville, Quebec 35 Rg
Ibicuí, Brazil 54 Ec
Ibiza I., Balearic Is. 71 Fc
Ibresi, U.S.S.R. 81 Hc
Ibri, Oman 93 Ge
Içá, Brazil 52 Dd
Içá, Peru 52 Bf
Içana, Brazil 52 Dc
Içel, Turkey 92 Bb
Iceland, N. Atl. Oc. 60 Cb
Ichak, India 91 Ec
Ichihusa, Japan 86 Bh
Idabel, Oklahoma 49 Kf
Ida Grove, Iowa 49 Ka
Idah, Nigeria 98 Gg
Idaho, U.S.A. 42 Cc
Idaho Falls, Idaho 47 Gd
Iddesleigh, Alberta 36 Fh
Ideles, Algeria 98 Gd
Idfu, Egypt 99 Md
Ídhra, Greece 77 Df

Idi Amin Dada, L. See Edward, L.
Idlib, Syria 94 Eb
Idutywa, Cape Province 95 Df
Ieper, Belgium 64 Ad
Ierissós, G. of, Greece 77 Dd
Ifakara, Tanzania 97 Hf
Iférouane, Niger 98 Ge
Igan, Sarawak 83 Fk
Igarapé Miri, Brazil 53 Hd
Igarka, U.S.S.R. 78 Hb
Ighil-Izane, Algeria 98 Fa
Iglesias, Sardinia 75 Bf
Igli, Algeria 98 Eb
Igloolik, N.W.T. 31 Ld
Ignace, Ontario 36 La
Igoma, Tanzania 97 Gf
Igra, U.S.S.R. 81 Lb
Iguaçú, Brazil 54 Fc
Iguala, Mexico 50 Ed
Iguapé, Brazil 54 Gb
Iguatu, Brazil 53 Ke
Igumira, Tanzania 97 Gf
Ihosy, Madagascar 97 Nl
Ihtiman, Bulgaria 76 Dc
Iida, Japan 86 Eg
Iisalmi, Finland 66 Me
Ijebu-Ode, Nigeria 98 Fg
IJmuiden, Netherlands 64 Cb
IJselmonde, Netherlands 64 Cc
IJselmuiden, Netherlands 64 Db
IJselstein, Netherlands 64 Db
IJsselmeer, Netherlands 64 Db
IJssel R., Netherlands 64 Eb
Ijui, Brazil 54 Fc
IJzendijke, Netherlands 64 Bc
Ikaria, Greece 77 Ff
Ikla, Estonia 67 Lh
Ikushumbet, Japan 86 Gc
Ilagan, Philippines 83 Hg
Ilam, Iran 92 Ec
Ilam, Nepal 91 Fb
Ilan, Taiwan 85 Kk
Ilanz, Switzerland 65 Eb
Ilawa, Poland 69 Hb
Ilbunga, S. Australia 57 Ge
Ilderton, Ontario 34 Jj
Ile-à-la-Crosse, Sask. 36 Jc
Ile-à-la-Crosse, L., Sask. 36 Kc
Ile au Castor, L. de l', Que. 33 Nb
Ilebo, Zaire 96 Ee
Ile-de-France, France 72 Eb
Ile Mayotte, Comoros 97 Kg
Iles, L. des, Sask. 36 Hd
Ilford, Manitoba 37 Wb
Ilfracombe, England 63 Ej
Ilhavo, Portugal 70 Ab
Ilhéus, Brazil 53 Kf
Ilia, Greece 77 Cf
Ilic, Turkey 92 Cb
Ilich, Kazakhstan 78 Fd
Ilimsk, U.S.S.R. 79 Kc
Iliodhrómia, Greece 77 De
Ilion, New York 44 Ca
Illampu, Bolivia 52 Dg
Illapel, Chile 54 Bd
Ille-et-Vilaine, France 72 Cb
Illescas, Spain 70 Db
Illimani, Bolivia 52 Dg
Illinois, U.S.A. 43 Hd
Illinois, R., Illinois 49 Mc
Illora, Spain 70 Dd
Ilmen Ozero, U.S.S.R. 80 Gb
Ilo, Peru 52 Cg
Iloilo, Philippines 83 Hh
Ilorin, Nigeria 98 Fg
Il'pyrskiy, U.S.S.R. 79 Rc
Imabari, Japan 86 Cg
Imandra, Ozero, U.S.S.R. 78 Cb
Imerimandroso, Madagascar 97 Nk
Imi, Ethiopia 97 Jc
Immendingen, W. Germany 68 Ce
Imperatriz, Amaz., Brazil 52 De
Imperatriz, Maran., Brazil 53 He
Imperia, Italy 74 Bd
Imperial, Saskatchewan 37 Mg
Imperial Dam, Arizona 42 De
Imperoyal, Nova Scotia 32 Jj
Imphal, India 89 Hd
Imroz, I. See Gökçeada I.
Imtan, Syria 94 Ee
Inagua, Great, The Bahamas 51 Eb
Inagua, Little, The Bahamas 51 Eb
Inari & L., Finland 66 Mb
Inchkeith, Scotland 62 Ed
Inch'ŏn, Korea 82 Jc
Incourt, Belgium 64 Cd
Indaal, L., Scotland 62 Ce
Indalsälven, Sweden 66 Ge
Indaw, Burma 89 Jd
Indawgyi L., Burma 89 Jc
Independence, Iowa 49 Ma
Independence, Kansas 49 Kd
Independence, Missouri 49 Kc
Independencia, Arg. 54 Cd
India, S. Asia 88
Indian, R., Y.T. 38 Dd
Indiana, Pennsylvania 44 Ab
Indiana, U.S.A. 43 Jc
Indianapolis, Indiana 40 Cf
Indian Arm, B.C. 39 Hk
Indian Brook, N.S. 33 Mg
Indian Cabins, Alberta 38 Pf
Indian Desert. See Thar Desert
Indian Harbour, Nfld. 31 Og
Indian Harbour, N.S. 32 Jj
Indian Head, Saskatchewan 37 Oh
Indian L., New York 44 Ca
Indian L., Northern, Man. 37 Ua
Indian L., Southern, Man. 37 Ta
Indianola, Iowa 49 Lb
Indicateur L., Quebec 32 Ab
Indiga, U.S.S.R. 78 Db
Indigirka, U.S.S.R. 79 Pb
Indin L., N.W.T. 38 Qc
Indonesia, S.E. Asia 83 Fl
Indore, India 88 Ed
Indre, France 72 Dc
Indre-et-Loire, France 72 Dc
Indur. See Nizamabad
Indus, Pakistan/India 88 Cd
Inebolu, Turkey 92 Ba
Inez, Kentucky 45 Fb
Ingalls L., N.W.T. 38 Ve
Ingelmunster, Belgium 64 Bd
Ingenika, R., B.C. 39 Lg
Ingersoll, Ontario 34 Kj
Ingham, Queensland 57 Jc
Inglefield Inlet, Greenland 41 Qb
Inglefield Ld., Greenland 41 Qb
Inglewood, New Zealand 55 Ec
Inglis, Manitoba 37 Qh
Ing. Luiggi, Argentina 54 De
Ingolf, Ontario 36 Ga
Ingolstadt, West Germany 68 Dd
Ingonish, Nova Scotia 33 Mg
Ingramport, Nova Scotia 32 Hj
Ingray L., N.W.T. 38 Pc
Ingrid Christensen Coast, Antarctica 104 Fb
Inhambane, Mozambique 95 Fd
Inishark, Eire 63 Ag
Inishbofin, Eire 63 Ag
Inishkea, Eire 63 Af
Inishman, Eire 63 Ag
Inishmore, Eire 63 Ag
Inishmurray, Eire 63 Bf
Inishtrahull, Eire 62 Ce
Inishturk, Eire 63 Ag
Injune, Queensland 57 Je
Inkerman, New Brunswick 32 Hf
Inklin, British Columbia 38 Gf
Inklin R., B.C. 38 Gf
Inman, R., N.W.T. 38 Oa
Innertkirchen, Switzerland 65 Db
Innisfail, Alberta 36 Df
Innisfail, Queensland 57 Jc
Innisfree, Alberta 36 Fe
Innsbruck, Austria 68 De
Inoucdjouac (Port Harrison), Quebec 31 Mf
Inowroclaw, Poland 69 Hb
Inquisivi, Bolivia 52 Dg
Ins, Switzerland 65 Ca
In Salah, Algeria 98 Fc
Insar, U.S.S.R. 81 Gd
Insein, Burma 89 Je
In Shan. See Yin Shan
Insinger, Saskatchewan 37 Og
Insterburg. See Chernyakhovsk
Instow, Saskatchewan 36 Jj
Intelewa, Surinam 53 Fc
Interlaken, Switzerland 65 Cb
International Falls, Minn. 46 La
International Peace Garden, Canada/U.S.A. 37 Rk
Intersection Mt., Alberta/B.C. 39 Oj
Interview I., Andaman Is. 89 Hf
Intragna, Switzerland 65 Db
Inutil, B., Chile 54 Ch
Inuvik, N.W.T. 38 Ga
Inveraray, Scotland 62 Dd
Invercargill, New Zealand 55 Bg
Inverell, N.S.W. 57 Ke
Invermay, Saskatchewan 37 Og
Invermere, B.C. 39 Pk
Inverness, Nova Scotia 33 Lg
Inverness, Quebec 35 Tf
Inverness, Scotland 62 Ec
Inverurie, Scotland 62 Fc
Investigator Strait, S. Aust. 57 Gg
Inwood, Ontario 34 Jk
Inyati, Zimbabwe 95 Dc
Inza, U.S.S.R. 81 Hd
Inzer, U.S.S.R. 81 Nc
Ioannina, Greece 77 Ce
Iola, Kansas 49 Kd
Iona, Nova Scotia 33 Mh
Iona, Scotland 62 Cd
Ionia, Michigan 40 Dd
Ionia, Montana 46 Dc
Ionian Is., Greece 77 Be
Ionian Sea, Italy 75 Ff
Ionishkis, Lithuania 67 Kh
Ios, Greece 77 Ef
Iowa, U.S.A. 43 Hc
Iowa City, Iowa 49 Mb
Iowa Falls, Iowa 49 La
Ipala, Mexico 50 Cc
Ipameri, Brazil 53 Hg
Ipiales, Colombia 52 Bc
Ipiros, Greece 77 Ce
Ipoh, Pen. Malaysia 87 Cf
Ipperwash Provincial Park, Ontario 34 Jj
Ippy, Cent. Afr. Rep. 99 Kg
Ipswich, England 63 Hh
Ipswich, Queensland 57 Ke
Ipswich, S. Dakota 46 Hc
Ipu, Brazil 53 Jd
Iquique, Chile 54 Bb
Iquitos, Peru 52 Cd
Iracoubo, French Guiana 53 Gb
Iráklia, Greece 77 Ef
Iráklion, Crete 77 Eg
Iran, Asia 93 Fc
Irapa, Venezuela 52 Ea
Irapuato, Mexico 50 Dc
Iraq, Asia 92 Dc
Irazu, Costa Rica 51 Cd
Irbid, Jordan 94 De
Irbit, U.S.S.R. 81 Rb
Ireland, Rep. of, Eire 63 Bg
Irendyk Mts., U.S.S.R. 81 Ne
Irgiz, Kazakhstan 78 Fd
Irian Jaya, Indonesia 59 Nj
Irikinskiy, U.S.S.R. 81 Pe
Iringa, Tanzania 97 Hf
Irish Sea, British Isles 63 Dg
Irkutsk, U.S.S.R. 79 Kc
Irma, Alberta 36 Ff
Iron Bridge, Ontario 34 Gf
Iron City, Tennessee 45 Ac
Irondale, Ontario 35 Mh
Iron Knob, S. Australia 57 Gf
Iron Mountain, Michigan 40 Cc
Iron Mt., Missouri 45 Bb
Iron River, Michigan 40 Bb
Iron River, Wisconsin 46 Mb
Ironside, Quebec 34 Cg
Ironton, Missouri 49 Md
Ironton, Ohio 45 Fa
Ironwood, Michigan 40 Ab
Iroquois, Ontario 35 Ph
Iroquois Falls, Ontario 34 Kd
'Irqah, South Yemen 92 Eg
Irrawaddy, Burma 89 He
Irrawaddy, R., Burma 89 He
Irricana, Alberta 36 Dg
Irtysh, R., U.S.S.R. 78 Fc
Irumu, Zaire 97 Fd
Irvine, Alberta 36 Gj
Isaac L., British Columbia 39 Nj
Isaac's Harbour, N.S. 33 Lh
Isabela I., Galapagos Is. 103 Rh
Isabella, Manitoba 37 Rh
Isaccea, Romania 76 Gb
Isachsen, N.W.T. 30 Jb
Isachsen, C., N.W.T. 30 Jb
Isafjördhur, Iceland 66 Ul
Isa Khel, Pakistan 90 Bd
Isangi, Zaire 96 Ed
Isari, Greece 77 Df
Ischia, Italy 75 De
Iscia Baidao, Somalia 97 Jd
Ise, Japan 86 Eg
Iselin, Pennsylvania 44 Ab
Iseltwald, Switzerland 65 Cb
Isère, France 73 Fd
Isernia, Italy 75 Ee
Ise wan, Japan 86 Eg
Ishikari wan, Japan 86 Gc
Ishim, U.S.S.R. 78 Fc
Ishimbai, U.S.S.R. 81 Nd
Ishinomaki wan, Japan 86 Ge
Ishkamish, Afghanistan 93 Jb
Ishkashim, Afghanistan 93 Kb
Ishpeming, Michigan 40 Cb
Isil Kul, U.S.S.R. 78 Gc
Isiolo, Kenya 97 Hd
Isiro, Zaire 97 Fd
Isisford, Queensland 57 Hd
Iskenderun, Turkey 92 Cb
Iskilip, Turkey 92 Ba
Iskitim, U.S.S.R. 78 Hc
Iskut, R., B.C. 39 Hg
Iskwatam L., Sask. 37 Oc
Islamabad, Kashmir 90 Dd
Islamabad, Pakistan 90 Cd
Islampur, India 91 Ec
Island, R., N.W.T. 38 Ne
Island Falls, Ontario 34 Jc
Island Falls, Saskatchewan 37 Pc
Island L., Ontario 34 Kg
Island Lake, Nfld. 33 Qe
Island Pond, Vermont 40 Lc
Islands, B. of, New Zealand 55 Ea
Islands, B. of, Nfld. 33 Od
Islay, Alberta 36 Ge
Islay, Scotland 62 Ce
Isle aux Morts, Nfld. 33 Of
Isle-Maligne, Quebec 32 Ae
Isle of Wight, Eng. 63 Gk
Isleta, New Mexico 48 De
Ismâ'ilîya, Egypt 99 Mb
Isna, Egypt 99 Mc
Isoka, Zambia 97 Gg
Isparta, Turkey 92 Bb
Israel, S.W. Asia 94 Ce
Isriya, Syria 94 Fb
Issoudun, France 72 Dc
Issyk Kul', Ozero, Kirghizia 78 Gd
Istanbul, Turkey 92 Aa
Isthmus B., Ontario 34 Jg
Istmina, Colombia 52 Bb
Istra, Yugoslavia 74 Dc
Itabaiana, Brazil 53 Ke
Itacare, Brazil 53 Kf
Itacoatiara, Brazil 52 Fd
Itaete, Brazil 53 Jf
Itaituba, Brazil 53 Fd
Itajaí, Brazil 54 Gc
Itajuí, Brazil 53 Hf
Italy, S. Europe 61 Kh
Itapaci, Brazil 53 Hf
Itapajé, Brazil 53 Kd
Itapecuru-mirim, Brazil 53 Jd
Itapemirim, Cachoeiro de, Brazil 53 Jh
Itapetininga, Brazil 53 Hh
Itapeva, Brazil 53 Hh
Itaqui, Brazil 54 Ec
Itarsi, India 88 Ed
Itasca, L., Minnesota 42 Gb
Itatubu, Brazil 52 Ee
Itauna, Brazil 53 Jh
Itchen L., N.W.T. 38 Rc
Itéa, Greece 77 De
Ithaca, Michigan 40 Dd
Ithaca, New York 44 Ba
Ithâci. See Ithaka
Ithaka, Greece 77 Ce
Itiés, Greece 77 Cd
Ituaçu, Brazil 53 Jf
Itubera, Brazil 53 Kf
Itula, Zaire 97 Fe
Ituna, Saskatchewan 37 Og
Iturbe, Arg. 54 Cb
Iturup, Kuril Is. 41 De
Ivailovgrad, Bulgaria 76 Fd
Ivanhoe, N.S.W. 57 Hf
Ivanhoe, R., Ontario 34 Hd
Ivanic Grad, Yugoslavia 74 Fc
Ivano-Frankovsk, U.S.S.R. 80 Dg
Ivanovka, U.S.S.R. 81 Kd
Ivanovo, U.S.S.R. 80 Mc
Ivdel, U.S.S.R. 78 Fb
Ivory Coast, W. Africa 98 Dg
Ivugivik, Quebec 31 Me
Iwakuni, Japan 86 Cg
Iwaniska, Poland 69 Jc
Ixiamas, Bolivia 52 Df
Ixtla, Mexico 50 Ed
Ixtlán de Juarez, Mexico 50 Ed
Iyo nada, Japan 86 Bh
Izabal, Guatemala 50 Gd
Izegem, Belgium 64 Bd
Izhevsk, U.S.S.R. 81 Lb
Izhma, U.S.S.R. 78 Eb
Izki, Oman 93 Ge
Izmail, Ukraine 80 Fj
Izmir, Turkey 92 Ab
Izmit, Turkey 92 Aa
Izra, Syria 94 Ee
Iztapa, Guatemala 50 Fe
Izu Hanto, Japan 86 Fg
Izu Shotō, Japan 86 Fg
Izyum, Ukraine 80 Kg

J

Jabalpur, India 91 Cd
Jabbeke, Belgium 64 Bc
Jabbul, Syria 94 Fa
Jablonec, Czechoslovakia 68 Fc
Jaboti, Brazil 52 Fd
Jabrin Oasis, Arabia 92 Ee
Jaburú, Brazil 52 Dd
Jaca, Spain 71 Ea
Jacarezinho, Brazil 53 Hh
Jachal, Arg. 54 Cd
Jaci Paraná, Brazil 52 Ee
Jack Fish, Ontario 34 Dd
Jackfish L., Saskatchewan 36 Je
Jackfish River, Alberta 38 Rf
Jackhead Harbour, Man. 37 Ug
Jacksboro, Tennessee 45 Eb
Jackson, Kentucky 45 Fb
Jackson, Louisiana 49 Mg
Jackson, Michigan 40 Dd
Jackson, Minnesota 46 Kd
Jackson, Mississippi 45 Bd
Jackson, Missouri 45 Cb
Jackson, N. Carolina 45 Jb
Jackson, Ohio 40 Ef
Jackson, Tennessee 45 Cc
Jackson, Wyoming 46 Bd
Jackson Bay, B.C. 39 Lk
Jackson Mts., Nevada 47 De
Jackson's Arm, Nfld. 33 Pd
Jacksonville, Florida 45 Ge
Jacksonville, Illinois 49 Mc
Jacksonville, N. Carolina 45 Jc
Jacksonville, Texas 49 Kg
Jacmel, Haiti 51 Ec
Jacobabad, Pakistan 88 Cc
Jacobina, Brazil 53 Jf
Jacobs, Ontario 37 Na
Jacques-Cartier, Mt., Quebec 32 Gd
Jacques-Cartier, R., Que. 35 Te
Jacques-Cartier Passage, Quebec 32 Hc
Jacquet River, N.B. 32 Gf
Jade Mines, Burma 89 Jc
Jadib, S. Yemen 93 Ff
Jaén, Spain 70 Dd
Jafarabad, India 88 Dd
Jaffna, Sri Lanka 88 Eg
Jagadhri, India 90 Ee
Jagdispur, India 91 Ec
Jagraon, India 90 De
Jaguarão, Brazil 54 Fd
Jaguari, Brazil 54 Fc
Jaguariaiva, Brazil 53 Hh
Jaguaruna, Brazil 54 Gc
Jahanabad, India 91 Ec
Jahangirabad, India 90 Ff
Jahra, Al, Kuwait 92 Ed
Jahrom, Iran 93 Fd
Jaicos, Brazil 53 Je
Jaipur, Assam, India 89 Jc
Jaipur, Rajasthan, India 88 Ec
Jais, India 91 Cb
Jaisalmer, India 88 Dc
Jajarm, Iran 93 Gb
Jajpur, India 89 Gd
Jakarta, Java 83 Em
Jäkkvik, Sweden 66 Gc
Jakobi, Estonia 67 Mg
Jakobshavn, Greenland 31 Od
Jalalabad, Afghanistan 90 Bc
Jalalpur, Faizabad, India 91 Db
Jalalpur, Pakistan 90 Dd
Jalalpur, Pirwala, Pak. 90 Bf
Jalapa Enríquez, Mexico 50 Ed
Jalasjärvi, Finland 66 Ke
Jalaun, India 91 Bb
Jaldak, Afghanistan 93 Jc
Jalgaon, India 88 Ed
Jalisco, Mexico 50 Dd
Jalor, India 88 Dc
Jalpaiguri, India 91 Gb
Jalq, Iran 93 Hd
Jaluit, Marshall Is. 102 Fg
Jam, Iran 93 Fd
Jamaica, West Indies 51 Dc
Jamaja, Estonia 67 Kg
Jamalabad, Iran 92 Eb
Jamalpur, Bangladesh 91 Hc
Jamalpur, Bihar, India 91 Fc
Jambon, Pt., Quebec 32 Fd
James, R., N.W.T. 38 Sb
James, R., Virginia 45 Hb
James Bay, Canada 31 Lg
Jamesburg, California 47 Cg
Jameson Is., N.W.T. 38 Sa
James R., S. Dakota 42 Gc
James Ranges, N. Terr. 56 Fd
James Ross I., Antarctica 104 Tc
James Ross Str., N.W.T. 38 Za
Jamestown, N. Dakota 46 Hb
Jamestown, New York 40 Gd
Jamestown, New York 44 Aa
Jamestown, St. Helena 96 Ah
Jamestown Res., N. Dakota 46 Hb
Jamiltepec, Mexico 50 Ed
Jammer Bugt, Denmark 67 Ch
Jammu and Kashmir, India 90 Dc
Jamnagar, India 88 Dd
Jampur, Pakistan 90 Bf
Jämsä, Finland 67 Lf
Jamshedpur, India 91 Fd
Jamui, India 91 Fc
Jamuna R., Bangladesh 91 Gc
Jamundi, Colombia 52 Bc
Jandaq, Iran 93 Fc
Jandiala, India 90 De
Janesville, Wisconsin 49 Na
Jangipur, India 91 Gc
Jani Khel, Pakistan 90 Bd
Janjira, India 88 De
Jan L., Saskatchewan 37 Pd
Jan Mayen, Arctic Ocean 78 Aa
Janos, Mexico 50 Ca
Jansath, India 90 Ef
Jansen, Saskatchewan 37 Ng
Jansenville, Cape Province 95 Cf
Januaria, Brazil 53 Jg
Janzé, France 72 Cc
Jaochow. See Boyang
Jaora, India 88 Ed
Japan, E. Asia 59 Ne
Japurá, Brazil 52 Dd
Japvo, India 89 Hc
Jaraguá, Brazil 53 Hg
Jaraguádo Sul, Brazil 54 Gc
Jarales, New Mexico 48 De
Jaramillo, Arg. 54 Cg
Jarandilla, Spain 70 Cb
Jardim do Serido, Brazil 53 Ke
Jardine Brook, N.B. 32 Ef
Jardines de la Reina, Cuba 51 Db
Jargalant. See Hovd
Jarji, Nigeria 98 Gf
Jarocin, Poland 69 Gc
Jaroměř, Czechoslovakia 69 Fc
Jaroslaw, Poland 69 Kc
Järpen, Sweden 66 Ee
Jarrow, Alberta 36 Ff
Jartai, China 84 Bc
Jarud Qi, China 82 Hb
Jarvie, Alberta 36 Dd
Jarvis, Ontario 34 Kk
Jarvis I., Pacific Ocean 102 Jh
Järvsö, Sweden 67 Gf
Jashpurnagar, India 91 Ed
Jask, Iran 93 Gd
Jasmin, Saskatchewan 37 Og
Jason I., Falkland Is. 54 Dh
Jasper, Alberta 39 Oj
Jasper, Florida 45 Fe
Jasper, Georgia, U.S.A. 45 Ec
Jasper, Ontario 35 Ph
Jasper, Texas 49 Lg
Jasper Nat. Park, Alberta 39 Oj
Jassy. See Iasi
Jastrowie, Poland 69 Gb
Jaswantnagar, India 91 Bb
Jaszberény, Hungary 69 He
Jataí, Brazil 53 Gg
Jath, India 88 Ee
Jativa, Spain 71 Ec
Jatobá, Brazil 53 Hd
Jaú, Brazil 53 Hh
Jauche, Belgium 64 Cd
Jauja, Peru 52 Bf
Jaumave, Mexico 50 Ec
Jaunpur, India 91 Dc
Java, Indonesia 83 Em
Javarí, Peru/Brazil 52 Ce
Javhlant. See Uliastay
Javier, Chile 54 Bg
Jawa, Nigeria 99 Hf
Jawalamukhi, India 90 Ee
Jawarah, Oman 93 Gf
Jawf, Al, Arabia 92 Cd
Jayapura, Irian Jaya 83 Ml
Jean Marie River, N.W.T. 38 Ne
Jebba, Nigeria 98 Fg
Jeble, Syria 94 Db
Jech Doab, Pakistan 90 Cd
Jedburgh, Saskatchewan 37 Pg
Jedburgh, Scotland 62 Fe
Jedede, Arabia 92 De
Jedway, B.C. 39 Hj
Jefferson, Georgia, U.S.A. 45 Fc
Jefferson, Oregon 36 Be
Jefferson, Wisconsin 49 Na
Jefferson, Mt., Oregon 47 Cc
Jefferson City, Missouri 49 Lc
Jeffersonville, Indiana 45 Ea
Jekabpils, Latvia 67 Lh
Jelgava, Latvia 67 Kh
Jellicoe, Ontario 34 Cc
Jelšava, Czechoslovakia 69 Jd
Jemeppe, Belgium 64 Cd
Jemseg, New Brunswick 32 Fh
Jena, East Germany 68 Dc
Jenin, Jordan 94 De
Jenipapo, Brazil 52 Fe
Jenner, Alberta 36 Fh
Jennings, Louisiana 49 Lg
Jennings, R., B.C. 38 Hf
Jenny Lind, I., N.W.T. 38 Xa
Jens Munk I., N.W.T. 31 Ld
Jeppo, Finland 66 Ke
Jerablus, Syria 94 Fa
Jerash, Jordan 94 De
Jeremie, Haiti 51 Ec
Jeremoabo, Brazil 53 Kf
Jerez de Garcia Salinas, Mexico 50 Dc
Jerez de la Frontera, Spain 70 Bd
Jericho, Jordan 94 Df
Jericho, Queensland 57 Jd
Jerome, Arizona 48 Ae
Jerome, Ontario 34 He
Jerruck, Pakistan 88 Cc
Jersey, Channel Is. 72 Bb
Jersey City, New Jersey 44 Cb
Jerseyshore, Pennsylvania 44 Bb
Jerusalem, Israel/Jordan 94 Df
Jervis Bay, Australia 57 Kg
Jervis Inlet, B.C. 39 Mk
Jervois Range, N. Terr. 57 Gd
Jessore, Bangladesh 91 Gd
Jesup, Georgia, U.S.A. 45 Ge
Jésus, Ile, Quebec 35 Rh
Jetait, Manitoba 37 Qb
Jetalsar, India 88 Dd
Jeypore, Orissa, India 89 Fe
Jezzin, Lebanon 94 Dd
Jhal, Pakistan 88 Cc
Jhalawar, India 88 Ed
Jhang Maghiana, Pakistan 90 Ce
Jhansi, India 91 Bc
Jhelum, Pakistan 90 Cd
Jhelum R., Pakistan 90 Cd
Jhunjhunu, India 90 Df
Jiamusi, China 82 Ka
Ji'an, China 85 Gj
Jiande, China 85 Jh
Jiangbei, China 85 Ch
Jiangdu, China 84 Jf
Jiange, China 84 Bf
Jiangling, China 85 Fg
Jiangmen, China 85 Fl
Jiangsu, China 84 Jf
Jiangxi, China 85 Gj
Jiangyin, China 84 Kg
Jian'ou, China 85 Jj
Jianping, China 84 Jb
Jianshui, China 82 Df
Jianyang, China 85 Bg
Jiao Xian, China 84 Kd
Jiaozhou Wan, China 84 Kd
Jiaozuo, China 84 Fe
Jiaupur, India 91 Db
Jiaxing, China 84 Kg
Jiayuguan, China 82 Cc
Jicaro, Nicaragua 51 Bd
Jičín, Czechoslovakia 68 Fc
Jidd, Iraq 92 Cc
Jiddah, Arabia 92 Cf
Jieshi, China 85 Gl
Jieyang, China 85 Hl
Jiggitai L., China 89 Ga
Jihlava, Czechoslovakia 69 Fd
Jildiah, Jebel, Arabia 92 Dd
Jilin, China 82 Jb
Jimena de la Frontera, Spain 70 Cd
Jiménez, Mexico 50 Db
Jimma, Ethiopia 97 Hc
Jim Thorpe, Pennsylvania 44 Cb
Jinan, China 82 Gc
Jinan, China 84 Hd
Jincheng, China 84 Fe
Jingdezhen, China 85 Hh
Jinggu, China 82 Df
Jinghai, China 84 Hc
Jingmen, China 85 Fg
Jing Shan, China 84 Fg
Jinhua, China 85 Jh
Jining, China 82 Gc
Jining, China 84 Fb
Jining, China 84 He
Jinjiang, China 85 Hk
Jinmen, Taiwan 85 Jk
Jinnah Barrage, Pakistan 90 Bd
Jinotega, Nicaragua 51 Bd
Jin Xian, China 84 Kc
Jinzhou, China 82 Hb
Jinzhou, China 84 Kb
Jipijapa, Ecuador 52 Ad
Jisr esh Shughur, Syria 94 Eb
Jiujiang, China 85 Hh
Jiul, Romania 76 Db
Ji Xian, China 84 Ge
Ji Xian, China 84 Gd
Ji Xian, China 84 Hb
Jiza, Jordan 94 Df
Jīzān, Arabia 92 Df
Joab L., Ontario 34 Ga
Joacaba, Brazil 54 Fc
João Pessoa, Brazil 53 Le
Jobrin, Ontario 34 Db
Jobson, Argentina 54 Dc
Jodhpur, India 88 Dc
Joe Batt's Arm, Nfld. 33 Sd
Joensuu, Finland 66 Ne
Jofane, Mozambique 95 Ed
Joffre, Mt., B.C. 39 Qk
Joggins, Nova Scotia 32 Hh
Jog L., Ontario 34 Eb
Jogues, Ontario 34 Gc
Jogyakarta, Java 83 Fm
Johannesburg, Transvaal 95 De
Johan Pen., N.W.T. 31 Mb
John C., Nova Scotia 32 Jh
John Martin Res., Colorado 48 Fc
John o'Groats, Scotland 62 Eb
John Redmond Res., Kansas 49 Kc
Johnsonburg, Pa. 44 Ab
Johnson City, Tennessee 45 Fb
Johnson Lake, Texas 49 Hg
Johnsons Crossing, Y.T. 38 Ge
Johnstone Str., B.C. 39 Kk
Johnston I., Pacific Ocean 102 Jf
Johnstown, New York 44 Ca
Johnstown, Pennsylvania 44 Ab
Johor Baharu, Pen. Malaysia 87 Cf
Joinville, Brazil 54 Gc
Joinville, France 72 Fb
Joinville I., Antarctica 104 Tc
Jokkmökk, Sweden 66 Hc
Joliet, Illinois 40 Be
Joliette, Quebec 35 Rf
Jolly L., N.W.T. 38 Rc
Jolo, Philippines 83 Hj
Jol Plateau, S. Yemen 92 Ef
Jonava, Lithuania 67 Lj
Jonesboro, Arkansas 49 Me
Jonesboro, Georgia, U.S.A. 45 Ed
Jonesboro, Illinois 45 Cb
Jonesboro, Louisiana 45 Ad
Jonesport, Maine 32 Ej
Jones Sd., N.W.T. 31 Lb
Jonglei, Sudan 97 Gc
Jönköping, Sweden 67 Fh
Jonquière, Quebec 35 Td
Jonuta, Mexico 50 Fd
Joplin, Missouri 49 Kd
Jordan, Minnesota 46 Lc
Jordan, Montana 46 Db
Jordan, W. Asia 92 Cc
Jordan, R., Israel/Jordan 94 De
Jordan, R., Utah 48 Bb
Jordan L., Nova Scotia 32 Gj
Jorhat, India 89 Hc
Jorje Montt, I., Chile 54 Bh
Jornada Del Meurto, New Mexico 48 Df
Joseph, L., Ontario 34 Lg
Joseph Bonaparte Gulf, W. Australia 56 Eb
Joseph L., Nfld. 31 Ng
Joseph Pt., Quebec 33 Kd
Jotun Fjell, Norway 67 Cf
Jotunheimen, Norway 60 Kc
Joussard, Alberta 36 Bc
Joux, L. de, Switzerland 65 Bb
Jowai, India 89 Hc
Joy, Mt., Y.T. 38 Gd
Juan de Fuca Strait, U.S.A./Can. 42 Bb
Juan Fernández, Pac. Oc. 103 Sl
Juan Stuven, I., Chile 54 Ag
Juárez, Argentina 54 Ee
Juàzeiro, Brazil 53 Je
Juba, Sudan 99 Mh
Jubbah, Arabia 92 Dd
Jubeil, Lebanon 94 Dc
Jubilee L., Newfoundland 33 Re
Juby, C., Morocco 98 Cc
Júcaro, Cuba 51 Db
Juchitán, Mexico 50 Ed
Jude I., Newfoundland 33 Sf
Judeidat el Wādī, Syria 94 Ed
Judenburg, Austria 68 Fe
Judique, Nova Scotia 33 Lh
Judith, Montana 46 Cb
Jugoslavia. See Yugoslavia
Juist, West Germany 68 Bb
Juiz de Fora, Brazil 53 Jh
Jukkasjärvi, Sweden 66 Jc
Julaca, Bolivia 52 Dh
Julesburg, Colorado 48 Fb
Juli, Peru 52 Dg
Juliaca, Peru 52 Cg
Julia Creek, Queensland 57 Hd
Julianehåb, Greenland 41 Pd
Julio de Castilhos, Brazil 54 Fc
Jullundur, India 90 De
Jumaymah, Iraq 92 Dd
Jumbo Mt., B.C. 39 Pk
Jumet, Belgium 64 Cd
Jumilla, Spain 71 Ec
Jumla, Nepal 91 Da
Junagadh, India 88 Dd
Junction City, Kansas 49 Jc
Jundah, Queensland 57 Hd
Jundiaí, Brazil 53 Hh
Juneau, Alaska 43 Zm
Junee, New South Wales 57 Jf
Jungfrau, Switzerland 65 Cb
Jungfraujoch, Switzerland 65 Cb
Juniata, Saskatchewan 36 Kp
Junín, Argentina 54 Dd
Junín, Argentina 54 Be
Junin, Peru 52 Bf
Juniper, New Brunswick 32 Eg
Juniper Mt., Oregon 47 Dd
Juniye, Lebanon 94 Dd
Junor, Saskatchewan 36 Ke
Junsele, Sweden 66 Ge
Jun Xian, China 84 Ef
Juo Järvi, Finland 66 Ne
Jupia, Brazil 53 Gh
Jupiter R., Quebec 32 Jd
Juquila, Mexico 50 Ed
Jura, France 72 Fc
Jura, Scotland 62 Dd
Jura, Mts., France/Switz. 72 Gc
Juradó, Colombia 52 Bb
Jurbarkas, Lithuania 67 Kj
Jurf ed Darawish, Jordan 94 Dg
Jüri, Estonia 67 Lg
Jurm, Afghanistan 93 Kb

Juruá, *Brazil* 52 Dd
Juruena, *Brazil* 52 Ff
Jurutí, *Brazil* 53 Fd
Jusiye, *Syria* 94 Ec
Jussy, *Switzerland* 65 Bb
Justice, *Manitoba* 37 Sh
Justo Daract, *Argentina* 54 Cd
Juticalpa, *Honduras* 51 Bd
Jutland. *See* Jylland
Juuka, *Finland* 66 Ne
Juwain, *Afghanistan* 93 Hc
Ju Xian, *China* 84 Je
Juxtlahuaco, *Mexico* 50 Ed
Jūymand, *Iran* 93 Gc
Jylland, *Denmark* 67 Ch
Jylland, Syd, *Denmark* 67 Cj
Jyväskylä, *Finland* 66 Le

K

K2, Mt., *Kashmir* 90 Ec
Kabajana, *Indonesia* 83 Hm
Kabala, *Sierra Leone* 98 Cg
Kabale, *Uganda* 97 Ge
Kabalega Falls, *Uganda* 97 Gd
Kabba, *Nigeria* 98 Gg
Kabetogama, L., *Minnesota* 46 La
Kabinakagami, R., *Ontario* 34 Fc
Kabinakagami L., *Ontario* 34 Fd
Kabinda, *Zaire* 96 Ef
Kabongo, *Zaire* 96 Ff
Kabosa I., *Burma* 87 Bd
Kābul, *Afghanistan* 93 Jc
Kabunda, *Zaire* 97 Fg
Kabwe, *Zambia* 95 Db
Kačanik, *Yugoslavia* 76 Cc
Kachiry, *Kazakhstan* 78 Gc
Kachkar, *U.S.S.R.* 81 Qc
Kachuga, *U.S.S.R.* 79 Kc
Kadaura, *India* 91 Bb
Kadiköy, *Turkey* 92 Aa
Kadiri, *India* 88 Ef
Kadiyevka, *Ukraine* 80 Lg
Kadoka, *S. Dakota* 46 Gd
Kadom, *U.S.S.R.* 81 Fc
Kadugli, *Sudan* 99 Lf
Kaduna, *Nigeria* 98 Gf
Kadur, *India* 88 Ef
Kadyi, *U.S.S.R.* 81 Fb
Kaegudeck L., *Nfld.* 33 Re
Kaesong, *Korea* 82 Jc
Kaf, *Arabia* 92 Cc
Kafakumba, *Zaire* 96 Ef
Kafanchan, *Nigeria* 98 Gg
Kafr Behum, *Syria* 94 Eb
Kafrun, *Syria* 94 Ec
Kafue Dam, *Zambia* 95 Dc
Kaga, *Japan* 86 Ef
Kagan, *Uzbekistan* 78 Fe
Kagawong, *Ontario* 34 Hg
Kagianagami L., *Ontario* 34 Cb
Kagiano L., *Ontario* 34 Dc
Kaglik L., *N.W.T.* 38 Ja
Kagoshima, *Japan* 86 Bj
Kagoshima wan, *Japan* 86 Aj
Kagul, *Moldavia* 80 Fj
Kahafa, *Arabia* 92 Dd
Kahama, *Tanzania* 97 Ge
Kahntah, *B.C.* 39 Nf
Kahnūj, *Iran* 93 Gd
Kahoka, *Missouri* 49 Lb
Kahror, *Pakistan* 90 Bf
Kahta, *Turkey* 92 Cb
Kahuta, *Pakistan* 90 Ce
Kaiama, *Nigeria* 98 Fg
Kaiapoi, *New Zealand* 55 De
Kaieteur Fall, *Guyana* 52 Eb
Kaifeng, *China* 84 Ge
Kaihu, *New Zealand* 55 Da
Kai-Kepuelen, *Indonesia* 83 Km
Kaikoura, *N.Z.* 55 De
Kaikoura Range, *N.Z.* 55 De
Kailas Ra. *See* Gangdisê Shan
Kaimana, *Irian Jaya* 83 Kl
Kaimanawa Mts., *N.Z.* 55 Ec
Kaimganj, *India* 91 Bb
Kaimur Range, *India* 91 Cc
Kaipara Harb., *N.Z.* 55 Eb
Kaira, *India* 88 Dd
Kairana, *India* 90 Ef
Kairouan, *Tunisia* 99 Ha
Kairovo, *U.S.S.R.* 81 Nc
Kaiserlautern, *W. Germany* 68 Bd
Kaiser Wilhelm II Land, *Antarctica* 104 Gc
Kaitangata, *N.Z.* 55 Bg
Kaithal, *India* 90 Ef
Kaiyuan, *China* 84 Ma
Kajaani, *Finland* 66 Md
Kajiado, *Kenya* 97 He
Kajiki, *Japan* 86 Bj
Kakabeka Falls, *Ontario* 37 Nb
Kakagi L., *Ontario* 36 Ja
Kakamari, *Uganda* 96 Gd
Kakamega, *Kenya* 97 Gd
Kakhk, *Iran* 93 Gc
Kakhovskoye Vdkhr., *Ukr.* 80 Jh
Kakia, *Botswana* 95 Cd
Kakisa L., *N.W.T.* 38 Pe
Kakori, *India* 91 Cb
Kaksha, *U.S.S.R.* 81 Ha
Kakwa, R., *Alberta* 39 Oh
Kalabagh, *Pakistan* 90 Bd
Kalabáka, *Greece* 77 Ce
Kalabo, *Zambia* 95 Cc
Kalabsha, *Egypt* 99 Md
Kalach, *U.S.S.R.* 81 Ee
Kaladar, *Ontario* 35 Nh
Kalahari, *Botswana* 95 Cd
Kalajoki, *Finland* 66 Kd
Kalak, *Iran* 93 Gd
Kalakan, *U.S.S.R.* 79 Lc
Kalakepen, *Sumatra* 83 Ck
Kalámai, *Greece* 77 Df
Kalamazoo, *Michigan* 40 Cd
Kalanaur, *India* 90 Ef
Kalannie, *W. Australia* 56 Cf
Kala Sarkari, *Afghanistan* 93 Jb
Kalat, *Pakistan* 88 Cc
Kalat-i-Ghilzai, *Afghanistan* 93 Jc
Kalaw, *Burma* 89 Jd
Kale, *Burma* 89 Hd
Kalediran, *Turkey* 92 Bb
Kaleet, R., *N.W.T.* 38 Zb
Kalémié, *Zaire* 97 Ff
Kalewa, *Burma* 89 Hd
Kalgan. *See* Zhangjiakou
Kalgoorlie, *W. Australia* 56 Df
Kalikino, *U.S.S.R.* 81 Md
Kalimnos, *Greece* 77 Ff
Kalingapatnam, *India* 89 Fe
Kalinin, *U.S.S.R.* 80 Jc
Kaliningrad, *U.S.S.R.* 67 Jj
Kalininsk, *U.S.S.R.* 81 Ge
Kalispell, *Montana* 42 Db
Kalisz, *Poland* 69 Hc
Kaliua, *Tanzania* 97 Gf
Kalix Älv, *Sweden* 66 Jc
Kalixfors, *Sweden* 66 Jc
Kalka, *India* 90 Ee
Kalkaska, *Michigan* 40 Dc
Kalkfeld, *Namibia* 95 Bd
Kalkfontein, *Botswana* 95 Cd
Kallaste, *Estonia* 67 Mg
Kallavesi, *Finland* 66 Me
Kalloni, *Greece* 77 Fe
Kallsjön, *Sweden* 66 Ee
Kalmar, *Sweden* 67 Fh
Kalmar Sund, *Sweden* 67 Gh
Kalmthout, *Belgium* 64 Cc
Kalmykovo, *Kazakhstan* 78 Ed
Kalna, *India* 91 Gd
Kalocsa, *Hungary* 69 He
Kalokhorio, *Cyprus* 94 Ab
Kalone Pk., *B.C.* 39 Kj
Kalpa, *India* 90 Fe
Kalpi, *India* 91 Bb
Kaltag, *Alaska* 43 Xl
Kaluga, *U.S.S.R* 80 Kd
Kalundborg, *Denmark* 67 Dj
Kalundu, *Zambia* 97 Fg
Kalutara, *Sri Lanka* 88 Eg
Kalvarija, *Lithuania* 67 Kj
Kalyan, *India* 88 Dd
Kalyazin, *U.S.S.R.* 80 Kc
Kama, *U.S.S.R.* 78 Eb
Kamaishi, *Japan* 86 Ge
Kamalampaka, *Tanzania* 97 Gf
Kamalia, *Pakistan* 90 Ce
Kaman, *India* 90 Eg
Kamarān, *Red Sea* 92 Df
Kamasin, *India* 91 Cc
Kamatsi L., *Saskatchewan* 37 Pb
Kamchatka, *U.S.S.R.* 79 Rc
Kamen, *U.S.S.R.* 78 Hc
Kamenets Podolskiy, *Ukr.* 80 Eg
Kamenskoye, *U.S.S.R.* 79 Rb
Kamensk Shakhtinskiy, *U.S.S.R.* 81 Ef
Kamensk Ural'skiy, *U.S.S.R.* 81 Qb
Kamet, *India* 88 Eb
Kami-iwami, *Japan* 86 Cg
Kamilukuak L., *N.W.T.* 38 Xd
Kamina, *Zaire* 96 Ef
Kaminak L., *N.W.T.* 30 Ke
Kaministikwia, *Ontario* 37 Nb
Kaminuriak L., *N.W.T.* 30 Ke
Kam Keut, *Laos* 87 Cc
Kamloops, *B.C.* 39 Nk
Kamloops L., *B.C.* 39 Nk
Kammon Tunnel, *Japan* 86 Bh
Kamnik, *Yugoslavia* 74 Eb
Kamouraska, *Quebec* 32 Cf
Kampala, *Uganda* 97 Gd
Kampen, *Netherlands* 64 Db
Kampot, *Kampuchea* 87 Cd
Kamptee, *India* 88 Ed
Kamsack, *Saskatchewan* 37 Qg
Kamuchawie L., *Sask.* 37 Pb
Kamyshin, *U.S.S.R.* 81 Ge
Kamyshlov, *U.S.S.R.* 81 Rb
Kanaaupscow, *Que.* 31 Mg
Kanab, *Utah* 48 Ad
Kananaskis Ls., *Alberta* 36 Bh
Kananga, *Zaire* 96 Ef
Kanazawa, *Japan* 86 Ef
Kanchanaburi, *Thailand* 87 Bd
Kancheepuram, *India* 88 Ef
Kandahar, *Afghanistan* 93 Jc
Kandahar, *Saskatchewan* 37 Ng
Kandalaksha, *U.S.S.R.* 78 Cb
Kandava, *Latvia* 67 Kh
Kandavu, *Fiji Is.* 102 Gj
Kandhla, *India* 90 Ef
Kandi, *India* 91 Gd
Kandla, *India* 93 Ke
Kandy, *Sri Lanka* 88 Fg
Kane, *Pennsylvania* 44 Ab
Kane Basin, *Greenland* 41 Qb
Kane Basin, *N.W.T.* 31 Mb
Kanev, *Ukraine* 80 Gg
Kangan, *Iran* 93 Fd
Kangar, *Pen. Malaysia* 87 Ce
Kangaroo I., *S. Australia* 57 Gg
Kangāvar, *Iran* 92 Ec
Kangbao, *China* 84 Gb
Kangchenjunga, *Nepal* 89 Gc
Kangeeak Pt., *N.W.T.* 31 Nd
Kangmar, *Kashmir* 88 Eb
Kango, *Gabon* 96 Dd
Kangra, *India* 90 Ed
Kangriboqe Feng, *China* 88 Fb
Kangsa, *Bangladesh* 89 Hc
Kani, *Burma* 89 Hd
Kaniama, *Zaire* 96 Ef
Kankakee, *Illinois* 40 Be
Kankan, *Guinea* 98 Df
Kanker, *India* 88 Fd
Kankesanturai, *Sri Lanka* 88 Eg
Kannauj, *India* 91 Bb
Kannus, *Finland* 66 Ke
Kano, *Nigeria* 98 Gf
Kanoya, *Japan* 86 Bj
Kanpūr, *India* 91 Cb
Kansas, *U.S.A.* 42 Gd
Kansas, R., *Kansas* 49 Jc
Kansas City, *Kansas* 49 Kc
Kansas City, *Missouri* 49 Kc
Kansk, *U.S.S.R.* 79 Jc
Kantali, *India* 91 Eb
Kantchari, *Upper Volta* 98 Ff
Kanturk, *Eire* 63 Bh
Kanuma, *Japan* 86 Ff
Kaohsiung, *Taiwan* 85 Kl
Kaolack, *Senegal* 98 Bf
Kaolan. *See* Lanzhou
Kaoma, *Zambia* 96 Eg
Kapaus, *Borneo (Kalimantan)* 83 Fk
Kapchagay, *Kazakhstan* 78 Gd
Kapfenberg, *Austria* 69 Fe
Kapiri Mposhi, *Zambia* 97 Fg
Kapiti I., *New Zealand* 55 Ed
Kapoeta, *Sudan* 99 Mh
Kaposvár, *Hungary* 76 Aa
Kapsabet, *Kenya* 97 Hd
Kapsukas, *Lithuania* 67 Kj
Kapurthala, *India* 90 De
Kapuskasing, *Ontario* 34 Hc
Kapuskasing, R., *Ontario* 34 Hd
Kar, *Iran* 92 Ec
Kara, *U.S.S.R.* 78 Fb
Kara Bogaz Gol, *Turkmen.* 78 Ed
Karabuk, *Turkey* 92 Ba
Karacabey, *Turkey* 92 Aa
Karaca Dagh, *Turkey* 92 Bb
Karachev, *U.S.S.R.* 80 Je
Karāchi, *Pakistan* 88 Cd
Karaganda, *Kazakhstan* 78 Gd
Karaginskiy Os., *U.S.S.R.* 79 Rc
Karaj, *Iran* 93 Fb
Karak, *China* 88 Eb
Karak, *Jordan* 94 Df
Kara Kalpakskaya, *Uzbek.* 78 Ed
Karakelong, *Indonesia* 83 Jk
Karakoram Range, *Kashmir* 90 Db
Kara Kum, *Turkmenistan* 78 Ee
Karaman, *Turkey* 92 Bb
Karamea, *New Zealand* 55 Dd
Karamea Bight, *N.Z.* 55 Dd
Karamsur Pass, *Pakistan* 90 Cb
Karasa, *U.S.S.R.* 81 Kc
Karasburg, *Namibia* 95 Be
Kara Sea, *U.S.S.R.* 78 Ga
Karasjok, *Norway* 66 Lb
Karatsu, *Japan* 86 Ah
Karaul, *U.S.S.R.* 78 Ha
Karauli, *India* 91 Ab
Karaurgan, *Turkey* 92 Da
Kardhitsa, *Greece* 77 Ce
Karelskaya, *A.S.S.R. (U.S.S.R.* 78 Cb
Karesuando, *Sweden* 66 Kb
Karganrud, *Iran* 92 Eb
Kargil, *Kashmir* 90 Ec
Kargopol, *U.S.S.R.* 80 La
Karhal, *India* 91 Bb
Kariba L., *Zimbabwe/Zambia* 95 Dc
Karibib, *Namibia* 95 Bd
Karikal, *India* 88 Ef
Karimata, *Indonesia* 83 El
Karin, *Somalia* 97 Kb
Karis, *Finland* 67 Kf
Kariz, *Iran* 93 Hc
Karkaralinsk, *U.S.S.R.* 78 Gd
Karkkila, *Finland* 67 Lf
Karla Marksa Pik, *Tadzhik.* 93 Kb
Karl-Marx-Stadt, *E. Germany* 68 Ec
Karlovac, *Yugoslavia* 74 Ec
Karlovy Vary, *Czech.* 68 Ec
Karlsborg, *Sweden* 67 Fg
Karlshamn, *Sweden* 67 Fh
Karlskrona, *Sweden* 67 Fh
Karlsruhe, *West Germany* 68 Cd
Karlstad, *Sweden* 67 Eg
Karmøy, *Norway* 67 Ag
Karnal, *India* 90 Ef
Karnataka, *India* 88 Ef
Karnes, *Texas* 48 Jh
Kärnten, *Austria* 68 Ee
Karona Fall, *Guyana* 52 Fc
Karora, *Sudan* 97 Ha
Karpáthos, *Greece* 77 Fg
Kárpathos Str., *Greece* 77 Fg
Karperón, *Greece* 77 Ce
Kars, *Turkey* 92 Da
Karsakpay, *Kazakhstan* 78 Fd
Karsakuwigamak, L., *Man.* 37 Sb
Kärsämäki, *Finland* 66 Le
Kärsava, *Latvia* 67 Mh
Karshi, *Uzbekistan* 78 Fe
Karstula, *Finland* 66 Le
Kartaly, *U.S.S.R.* 81 Qd
Kartarpur, *India* 90 De
Kartse, *Kashmir* 90 Ec
Karungi, *Sweden* 66 Kc
Karungu, *Kenya* 97 Ge
Karunki, *Finland* 66 Lc
Karur, *India* 88 Ef
Karviná, *Czechoslovakia* 69 Hd
Karwar, *India* 88 Df
Karymskoye, *U.S.S.R.* 79 Lc
Kasai R., *Zaire* 96 De
Kasama, *Zambia* 97 Gg
Kasane, *Botswana* 95 Dc
Kasanga, *Tanzania* 97 Gf
Kasauli, *India* 90 Ee
Kasba L., *N.W.T.* 38 We
Kasempa, *Zambia* 96 Fg
Kasenga, *Zaire* 97 Fg
Kasenga, *Zambia* 95 Dc
Kasganj, *India* 91 Bb
Kashabowie, *Ontario* 37 Mb
Kashan, *Iran* 93 Fc
Kashi, *China* 78 Ge
Kashira, *U.S.S.R.* 80 Ld
Kashishibog L., *Ontario* 37 Na
Kashiwazaki, *Japan* 86 Ff
Kāshmar, *Iran* 93 Gb
Kashmir, *N. India* 88 Eb
Kashmir. *See* Jammu and Kashmir
Kashmor, *Pakistan* 88 Cc
Kasimov, *U.S.S.R.* 81 Ec
Kaskinen, *Finland* 66 Je
Kas Kong, *Kampuchea* 87 Cd
Kaslo, *British Columbia* 39 Pl
Kasmere L., *Manitoba* 38 Xf
Kasongo, *Zaire* 96 Fe
Kásos, *Greece* 77 Fg
Kásos Str., *Crete* 77 Fg
Kaspichan, *Bulgaria* 76 Fc
Kassala, *Sudan* 97 Ha
Kassandra, *Greece* 77 Dd
Kassel, *West Germany* 68 Cc
Kassou, *Upper Volta* 98 Ef
Kastamonu, *Turkey* 92 Ba
Kastélli, *Crete* 77 Dg
Kastéllion, *Crete* 77 Eg
Kasterlee, *Belgium* 64 Cc
Kastoria, *Greece* 77 Cd
Kastrosikiá, *Greece* 77 Ce
Kasulu, *Tanzania* 97 Ge
Kasungu, *Malawi* 97 Gg
Kasur, *Pakistan* 90 De
Katákolon, *Greece* 77 Cf
Katanga. *See* Shaba
Katangli, *U.S.S.R.* 79 Pc
Katanning, *W. Australia* 56 Cf
Katav Ivanovsk, *U.S.S.R.* 81 Pc
Katepwa Beach, *Saskatchewan* 37 Oh
Katepwa Provincial Park, *Saskatchewan* 37 Oh
Katerini, *Greece* 77 Dd
Kates Needle, Mt., *B.C.* 39 Gg
Katha, *Burma* 89 Jd
Katherine, *N. Terr.* 56 Fb
Kathiawar, *India* 88 Dd
Kathmandu, *Nepal* 91 Eb
Kathryn, *Alberta* 36 Dg
Kathua, *Kashmir* 90 Dd
Katihar, *India* 91 Fc
Katimik L., *Manitoba* 37 Sf
Katmai Volcano, *Alaska* 43 Xm
Kato Akhaia, *Greece* 77 Ce
Káto Nevrokópion, *Greece* 76 Dd
Katoomba, *N.S.W.* 57 Kf
Katowice, *Poland* 69 Hc
Katrine, L., *Scotland* 62 Dd
Katrineholm, *Sweden* 67 Gg
Katsina, *Nigeria* 98 Gf
Kattawagami L., *Ontario* 34 Lc
Kattegat, *Sweden/Denmark* 67 Dh
Kattowitz. *See* Katowice
Katwa, *India* 91 Gd
Katwijk aan Zee, *Neth.* 64 Cb
Kauai, *Hawaiian Is.* 103 Ke
Kaufbeuren, *West Germany* 68 De
Kauhava, *Finland* 66 Ke
Kaukauna, *Wisconsin* 40 Bc
Kaunas, *Lithuania* 67 Kj
Kauriya, *India* 89 Fd
Kautokeino, *Norway* 66 Kb
Kavak, *Turkey* 92 Ca
Kavali, *India* 88 Ef
Kavála, *Greece* 77 Ed
Kavkaz, Bol'shoy & Maly, Mts., *U.S.S.R.* 78 Dd
Kaw, *Fr. Guiana* 53 Gc
Kawagama L., *Ontario* 35 Mg
Kawakawa, *New Zealand* 55 Ea
Kawambwa, *Zambia* 97 Ff
Kawanoe, *Japan* 86 Cg
Kawardha, *India* 91 Gd
Kawartha Lakes, *Ontario* 35 Mh
Kawasaki, *Japan* 86 Fg
Kaw City, *Oklahoma* 49 Jd
Kawene, *Ontario* 37 Lb
Kawhia, *New Zealand* 55 Ec
Kawich Range, *Nevada* 47 Eg
Kawinaw L., *Manitoba* 37 Sf
Kawkareik, *Burma* 89 Je
Kawnipi, L., *Ontario* 46 Ma
Kaw Res., *Oklahoma* 49 Jd
Kayah, *Burma* 89 Je
Kayes, *Mali* 98 Cf
Kay Pt., *Y.T.* 38 Da
Kayseri, *Turkey* 92 Cb
Kayshyadoris, *Lithuania* 67 Lj
Kaysville, *Utah* 48 Bb
Kayville, *Saskatchewan* 37 Mj
Kazabazua, *Quebec* 35 Pg
Kazach'ye, *U.S.S.R.* 79 Na
Kazakhskaya S.S.R. (Kazakhstan), *U.S.S.R.* 78 Fd
Kazalinsk, *Kazakhstan* 78 Fd
Kazan', *U.S.S.R.* 81 Jc
Kazan L., *Saskatchewan* 36 Jc
Kazanlŭk, *Bulgaria* 76 Ec
Kazan R., *N.W.T.* 31 Ke
Kazérun, *Iran* 93 Fd
Kazimoto, *Tanzania* 97 Hf
Kdyně, *Czechoslovakia* 68 Ed
Kéa, *Greece* 77 Ef
Kealey L., *Saskatchewan* 39 Th
Kearney, *Nebraska* 49 Hb
Kearney, *Ontario* 35 Lg
Keatley, *Saskatchewan* 36 Kf
Keban, *Turkey* 92 Cb
Kechika, R., *B.C.* 38 Kf
Kecskemét, *Hungary* 69 He
Kedainiai, *Lithuania* 67 Kj
Kedgwick & R., *N.B.* 32 Ef
Kediri, *Java* 83 Fm
Kedleston, *Saskatchewan* 37 Mh
Keefers, *B.C.* 39 Nk
Keele, R., *N.W.T.* 38 Kc
Keele Pk., *Y.T.* 38 Hd
Keeler, *Saskatchewan* 37 Mh
Keeley L., *Saskatchewan* 36 Jd
Keels, *Newfoundland* 33 Te
Keene, *New Hampshire* 44 Da
Keeseville, *New York* 40 Kc
Keetmanshoop, *Namibia* 95 Be
Keewatin, *Northwest Territories* 31 Ke
Keewatin, *Ontario* 36 Ha
Kefallinía, *Greece* 77 Ce
Kégashka, *Quebec* 33 Lc
Kégashka L., *Quebec* 33 Lc
Keg River, *Alberta* 39 Pg
Kegueur Terbi, *Libya* 99 Jd
Keila, *Estonia* 67 Lg
Keitele, *Finland* 66 Me
Keith, *Scotland* 62 Fc
Keith Arm, *N.W.T.* 38 Mc
Keithley Creek, *B.C.* 39 Nj
Kekertuk, *N.W.T.* 31 Nd
Kelan, *China* 84 Ec
Kelang, *Pen. Malaysia* 87 Cf
Kelcyre, *Albania* 77 Cd
Keller L., *N.W.T.* 38 Nd
Keller L., *Saskatchewan* 36 Lb
Kellett, C., *N.W.T.* 30 Gc
Kelliher, *Saskatchewan* 37 Og
Kelloselkä, *Finland* 66 Nc
Kelly L., *N.W.T.* 38 Kc
Kelme, *Lithuania* 67 Kj
Kelowna, *B.C.* 39 Ol
Kelp Hd., *B.C.* 39 Kk
Kelsey, *Manitoba* 37 Vb
Kelsey Bay, *B.C.* 39 Kk
Kelsey L., *Manitoba* 37 Qe
Kelso, *Saskatchewan* 37 Qj
Kelso, *Scotland* 62 Fe
Kelvington, *Saskatchewan* 37 Of
Kelvin I., *Ontario* 34 Bc
Kelwood, *Manitoba* 37 Sh
Ké Macina, *Mali* 98 Df
Kemano, *B.C.* 39 Kj
Kemerovo, *U.S.S.R.* 78 Hc
Kemi, *Finland* 66 Ld
Kemijärvi, *Finland* 66 Mc
Kemi Joki, *Finland* 66 Lc
Kemmerer, *Wyoming* 46 Be
Kemnay, *Manitoba* 37 Rj
Kemp, *Texas* 49 Jf
Kemp, L., *Texas* 49 Hf
Kempele, *Finland* 66 Ld
Kemp Ld., *Antarctica* 104 Ec
Kempsey, *N.S.W.* 57 Kf
Kempt, L., *Quebec* 35 Qe
Kempten, *West Germany* 68 De
Kemptville, *Ontario* 35 Pg
Kenabeek, *Ontario* 34 Le
Kenai Pen., *Alaska* 43 Xl
Kenaston, *Saskatchewan* 36 Lg
Kendal, *England* 63 Ff
Kendal, *Saskatchewan* 37 Oh
Kendall, *New York* 44 Aa
Kendall, C., *N.W.T.* 31 Le
Kendall, R., *N.W.T.* 38 Pb
Kendari, *Celebes (Sulawesi)* 83 Hl
Kendawangan, *Borneo (Kalimantan)* 83 Fl
Kenema, *Sierra Leone* 98 Cg
Kenge, *Zaire* 96 De
Keng-tung, *Burma* 89 Jd
Kenhardt, *Cape Province* 95 Ce
Kenitra, *Morocco* 98 Db
Kenmare, *Eire* 63 Aj
Kenmare, *N. Dakota* 46 Fa
Kennebec, *S. Dakota* 46 Hd
Kennebec R., *Maine* 32 Cj
Kennedy, *Nevada* 47 Ee
Kennedy, *Saskatchewan* 37 Ph
Kennedy, Mt., *Y.T.* 30 Fe
Kennedy Channel, *N.W.T./Greenland* 31 Na
Kennedy L., *Quebec* 33 Ob
Kennetcook, *Nova Scotia* 32 Jh
Kennett, *Missouri* 49 Md
Kenney Dam, *B.C.* 39 Lj
Kénogami, *Quebec* 35 Td
Kénogami, L., *Quebec* 35 Td
Kenogami, R., *Ontario* 34 Eb
Kenogami Lake, *Ontario* 34 Kd
Kenogamissi L., *Ontario* 34 Jd
Keno Hill, *Y.T.* 38 Fd
Kenora, *Ontario* 36 Ha
Kenosha, *Wisconsin* 40 Cd
Kensington, *P.E.I.* 32 Jg
Kent, *England* 63 Hj
Kent Bridge, *Ontario* 34 Hk
Kent I., *Maryland* 44 Bc
Kent Junction, *N.B.* 32 Gg
Kenton, *Manitoba* 37 Rj
Kent Pen., *N.W.T.* 38 Ua
Kentucky, *U.S.A.* 43 Jd
Kentucky L., *Tennessee* 49 Nd
Kentville, *Nova Scotia* 32 Hh
Kenville, *Manitoba* 37 Qg
Kenya, *East Africa* 97 Hd
Kenya, Mount, *Kenya* 97 He
Keokuk, *Iowa* 49 Mb
Keonjhar, *India* 89 Gd
Kepler Mts., *New Zealand* 55 Af
Keppel, *Falkland Is.* 54 Dh
Kerala, *India* 88 Ef
Kerang, *Victoria* 57 Hg
Kerava, *Finland* 67 Lf
Kerch, *U.S.S.R.* 80 Kj
Kerchoual, *Mali* 98 Fe
Kerema, *Papua New Guinea* 57 Ja
Keremeos, *B.C.* 39 Ol
Keren, *Ethiopia* 97 Ha
Kerguelen Is., *Indian Ocean* 100 Ej
Kericho, *Kenya* 97 He
Kerinci, *Sumatra* 83 Dl
Kerkenna Is., *Tunisia* 99 Hb
Kerki, *Turkmenistan* 78 Fe
Kérkira, *Greece* 77 Be
Kerkrade, *Netherlands* 64 Dd
Kermadec Is., *Pacific Ocean* 102 Gk
Kermān, *Iran* 93 Gc
Kermān Desert, *Iran* 93 Gd
Kermānshāh, *Iran* 92 Ec
Kerrobert, *Saskatchewan* 36 Hg
Kerry, *Eire* 63 Ah
Kerulen, *Mongolia* 82 Fa
Kerzers, *Switzerland* 65 Cb
Kesagami, R., *Ontario* 34 Kb
Kesagami L., *Ontario* 34 Kb
Kesariya, *India* 91 Eb
Kesteren, *Netherlands* 64 Dc
Kesteven, Parts of, *Lincs, England* 63 Gg
Kestilä, *Finland* 66 Md
Keswick, *England* 63 Ef
Keswick Ridge, *N.B.* 32 Fh
Keszthely, *Hungary* 69 Ge
Ketapang, *Borneo (Kalimantan)* 83 El
Ketchikan, *Alaska* 43 Zm
Kętrzyn, *Poland* 69 Ja
Kettering, *England* 63 Gh
Kettle I., *Quebec* 34 Dg
Kettlestone B., *Quebec* 31 Me
Keuka L., *New York* 44 Ba
Kewagama, *Quebec* 35 Md
Kewanee, *Illinois* 49 Nb
Kewaunee, *Wisconsin* 40 Cc
Keweenaw B., *Michigan* 40 Bb
Keweenaw Pen., *Wisconsin* 43 Jb
Keyes, *Manitoba* 37 Sh
Key Harbour, *Ontario* 34 Kg
Key Junction, *Ontario* 34 Kg
Key L., *Eire* 63 Bf
Key Largo, *Florida* 45 Gh
Keyser, *W. Virginia* 44 Ac
Keystown, *Saskatchewan* 37 Mh
Keysville, *Virginia* 45 Hb
Key West, *Florida* 45 Gh
Kezhma, *U.S.S.R.* 79 Kc
Khaapsalu, *Estonia* 67 Kg
Khabab, *Syria* 94 Ed
Khabarovsk, *U.S.S.R.* 79 Nd
Khadro, *Pakistan* 88 Cc
Khafs Maqran, *Arabia* 92 Ee
Khagaul, *India* 91 Ec
Khairabad, *India* 91 Cb
Khairpur, *Pakistan* 90 Cf
Khairpur, *Pakistan* 88 Cc
Khaiwan, *Yemen* 92 Df
Khajuri Kach, *Pakistan* 90 Ad
Khalki, *Greece* 77 Ff
Khalkidhiki, *Greece* 77 Dd
Khalkis, *Greece* 77 De
Khalturin, *U.S.S.R.* 81 Ja
Khaluf, *Arabia* 93 Ge
Khambat, *India* 88 Dd
Khambat, G. of, *India* 88 Dd
Khamgaon, *India* 88 Ed
Khamis Mushayt, *Arabia* 92 Df
Khamr, *Yemen* 92 Df
Khanabad, *Afghanistan* 93 Jb
Khān al Baghdādī, *Iraq* 92 Dc
Khanaqin, *Iraq* 92 Ec
Khandela, *India* 90 Dg
Khandwa, *India* 88 Ed
Khan-ez-Zebib, *Jordan* 94 Ef
Khanfar, *S. Yemen* 92 Eg
Khangarh, *Pakistan* 90 Bf
Khania, *Crete* 77 Dg
Khaniadhana, *India* 91 Bc
Khanka, Ozero, *U.S.S.R.* 79 Nd
Khanpur, *Pakistan* 90 Bf
Khan Sheikhun, *Syria* 94 Eb
Khanty Mansiysk, *U.S.S.R.* 78 Fb
Khan Yunis, *Egypt* 94 Cf
Khao Luang, *Thailand* 87 Be
Khapalu, *Kashmir* 90 Ec
Kharaghoda, *India* 88 Dd
Kharan, *Pakistan* 88 Cc
Kharar, *India* 91 Fd
Khar'kov, *Ukraine* 80 Kg
Kharmanli, *Bulgaria* 76 Ed
Kharovsk, *U.S.S.R.* 80 Mb
Kharsawan, *India* 91 Ed
Khartaksho, *Kashmir* 90 Ec
Khartoum, *Sudan* 99 Me
Khasfah, *Arabia* 93 Ff
Khash, *Afghanistan* 93 Hc
Khasi Hills, *India* 89 Hc
Khaskovo, *Bulgaria* 76 Ed
Khasmel Girba, *Sudan* 99 Nf
Khatanga, *U.S.S.R.* 79 Ka
Khatangskiy Guba, *U.S.S.R.* 79 La
Khaybar, *Arabia* 92 Df
Khemmarat, *Thailand* 87 Dc
Kheralu, *India* 88 Dd
Kheri, *India* 91 Cb
Kherson, *Ukraine* 80 Hh
Khetri, *India* 90 Df
Khilok, *U.S.S.R.* 79 Lc
Khinjan, *Afghanistan* 93 Jb
Khíos, *Greece* 77 Fe
Khisfin, *Syria* 94 De
Khiva, *Uzbekistan* 78 Fd
Khmel'nitskiy, *Ukraine* 80 Eg
Khmer Rep. *See* Kampuchea
Kholm, *U.S.S.R.* 80 Gc
Kholmsk, *U.S.S.R.* 79 Pd
Khomeyn, *Iran* 93 Fc
Khong, *Laos* 87 Dd
Khor, *U.S.S.R.* 79 Nd
Khóra Sfakíon, *Crete* 77 Eg
Khorramabad, *Iran* 92 Ec
Khorramshahr, *Iran* 92 Ec
Khosf, *Iran* 93 Gc
Khrisoúpolis, *Greece* 76 Ed
Khulm, *Afghanistan* 93 Jb
Khulna, *Bangladesh* 91 Gd
Khunsar, *Iran* 93 Fc
Khūr, *Iran* 93 Gc
Khurai, *India* 91 Bc
Khurja, *India* 90 Ef
Khurmah, Al, *Arabia* 92 De
Khushab, *Pakistan* 90 Cd
Khvaf, *Iran* 93 Hc
Khvalynsk, *U.S.S.R.* 81 Jd
Khvor, *Iran* 93 Fc
Khvoy, *Iran* 92 Db
Khyber Pass, *Pakistan* 90 Bc
Kiambi, *Zaire* 97 Ff
Kiamika, *Quebec* 35 Pf
Kiamika, Rés., *Quebec* 35 Pf
Kiangchow. *See* Jiangling
Kianto Jarvi, *Finland* 66 Nd
Kiao-chow B. *See* Jiaozhou Wan
Kiask L., *Manitoba* 37 Ub
Kibangula, *Zaire* 96 Fe
Kibombo, *Zaire* 96 Fe
Kibondo, *Tanzania* 97 Ge
Kičevo, *Yugoslavia* 76 Cd
Kichiginsk, *U.S.S.R.* 81 Qc
Kicking Horse Pass, *B.C.* 39 Pk
Kidal, *Mali* 98 Fe
Kidatu, *Tanzania* 97 Hf
Kidderminster, *England* 63 Fh
Kidnappers, C., *New Zealand* 55 Fc
Kiel, *West Germany* 68 Da
Kielce, *Poland* 69 Jc
Kieldrecht, *Belgium* 64 Cc
Kieler Bucht, *W. Germany* 68 Da
Kiel Kanal, *West Germany* 68 Ca
Kienning. *See* Jian'ou
Kiev. *See* Kiyev
Kiffa, *Mauritania* 98 Ce
Kigali, *Rwanda* 97 Ge
Kigoma, *Tanzania* 97 Fe
Kii suido, *Japan* 86 Dh
Kijabe, *Kenya* 97 He
Kikerk L., *N.W.T.* 38 Rb
Kikinda, *Yugoslavia* 76 Cb
Kikládhes, *Greece* 77 Ef
Kikori, *Papua New Guinea* 57 Ha
Kikuyu, *Kenya* 97 He
Kikwissi, L., *Quebec* 35 Mf
Kikwit, *Zaire* 96 Df
Kila Drosh, *Pakistan* 90 Bc
Kilbourn, *Wisconsin* 40 Bd
Kilburn, *New Brunswick* 32 Eg
Kilchu, *Korea* 82 Jb
Kildare, *Eire* 63 Cg
Kildare, C., *P.E.I.* 32 Jg
Kildonan, *B.C.* 39 Ll
Kilekale L., *N.W.T.* 38 Lb
Kilifi, *Kenya* 97 He
Kilimanjaro, *Tanzania* 97 He
Kilindini Harbour, *Kenya* 97 He
Kilkee, *Eire* 63 Ah
Kilkenny, *Eire* 63 Ch
Kilkieran B., *Eire* 63 Ag
Kilkis, *Greece* 76 Dd
Killala B., *Eire* 63 Af
Killala L., *Ontario* 34 Dc
Killaloe, *Eire* 63 Bh
Killaloe Station, *Ontario* 35 Ng
Killaly, *Saskatchewan* 37 Ph
Killam, *Alberta* 36 Ff
Killarney, *Eire* 63 Ah
Killarney, *Manitoba* 37 Sj
Killarney, *Ontario* 34 Jg
Killary Harb., *Eire* 63 Ag
Killdeer, *Saskatchewan* 36 Lj
Killin, *Scotland* 62 Ed
Killíni, *Greece* 77 Cf
Killybegs, *Eire* 63 Bf
Kilmarnock, *Scotland* 62 De
Kilosa, *Tanzania* 97 Hf
Kilrush, *Eire* 63 Ah
Kilwa Kivinje, *Tanzania* 97 Hf
Kilwinning, *Sask.* 36 Le
Kima, *Zaire* 96 Fe
Kimball, *S. Dakota* 46 Hd
Kimberley, *B.C.* 39 Ql
Kimberley, *Cape Province* 95 Ce
Kimberley, *Ontario* 34 Kh
Kimi, *Greece* 77 Ee
Kimito, *Finland* 67 Kf
Kimiwan L., *Alberta* 36 Ac
Kimolos, *Greece* 77 Ef
Kimvula, *Zaire* 96 Df
Kinabalu, *Sabah* 83 Gj
Kinbrace, *Scotland* 62 Eb
Kinbrook Island Provincial Park, *Alberta* 36 Fh
Kincaid, *Saskatchewan* 36 Kj
Kincardine, *Ontario* 34 Jh
Kincolith, *B.C.* 39 Jh
Kindat, *Burma* 89 Hd
Kindersley, *Saskatchewan* 36 Hg
Kindia, *Guinea* 98 Cf
Kindu, *Zaire* 96 Fe
Kinel', *U.S.S.R.* 81 Kd
Kinel'Cherkkassy, *U.S.S.R.* 81 Kd
Kineshma, *U.S.S.R.* 81 Fb
King and Queen, *Virginia* 45 Jb

Kingaroy, Queensland 57 Ke
King Christian I., N.W.T. 30 Jb
King Christian IX Land, Greenland 41 Nc
Kingcome Inlet, B.C. 39 Kk
King Edward VII Land, Antarctica 104 Nb
Kingfisher, Oklahoma 49 Je
King Frederick VIII Land, Greenland 41 Nb
King Frederick VI Land, Greenland 41 Pc
King George, Mt., B.C. 39 Qk
King George, Mt., Y.T. 38 De
King George I, I., South Shetlands 104 Tc
King George Is., N.W.T. 31 Mf
King George Is., Pacific Oc. 103 Lj
King George Sound, W. Aust. 56 Cg
King George VI Falls, Guyana 52 Eb
King George VI Sound, Antarctica 104 Sb
King George V Ld., Antarc. 104 Kc
Kinghorn, Ontario 34 Cc
King I., British Columbia 39 Kj
King I., Burma 89 Jf
King I., Tasmania 57 Hg
Kingisepp, U.S.S.R. 67 Ng
King Leopold & Queen Astrid Coast, Antarctica 104 Gc
King Leopold Range, W. Aust. 56 Ec
Kingman, Alberta 36 Ee
Kingman, Kansas 49 Hd
Kingsbridge, England 63 Ek
King's Canyon National Park, California 47 Dg
Kingscourt, Eire 63 Cg
King's Lynn, England 63 Hh
King Sound, W. Australia 56 Dc
Kings Pk., Utah 48 Bb
Kingsport, Nova Scotia 32 Hh
Kingsport, Tennessee 45 Fb
Kingston, Jamaica 51 Dc
Kingston, New York 44 Cb
Kingston, New Zealand 55 Bf
Kingston, Ontario 35 Oh
Kingston-on-Thames, Eng. 63 Gj
Kingstree, S. Carolina 45 Hd
Kingsville, Ontario 34 Hk
Kingtung, China 82 Df
Kingussie, Scotland 62 Ec
King William I., N.W.T. 38 Ya
King William Ld., Greenland 41 Nb
Kingwood, W. Virginia 40 Gf
Kinistino, Saskatchewan 37 Mf
Kinkora, P.E.I. 32 Jg
Kinleith, New Zealand 55 Ec
Kinley, Saskatchewan 36 Kf
Kinmount, Ontario 35 Mh
Kinnaird, B.C. 39 Pl
Kinoosao, Saskatchewan 37 Pa
Kinross, Scotland 62 Ed
Kinsale, Eire 63 Bj
Kinsale, Old Head of, Eire 63 Bj
Kinsella, Alberta 36 Fe
Kinshasa, Zaire 96 De
Kintap, Borneo (Kalimantan) 83 Gl
Kintyre, Scotland 62 De
Kintyre, Mull of, Scotland 62 De
Kinuso, Alberta 36 Bc
Kinyangiri, Tanzania 97 Ge
Kiosk, Ontario 35 Mf
Kiowa, Kansas 49 Hd
Kipahigan L., Man./Sask. 37 Qc
Kiparissia, Greece 77 Cf
Kiparissia, G. of, Greece 77 Cf
Kipawa, Quebec 35 Mf
Kipawa, L., Quebec 35 Mf
Kipini, Kenya 97 Je
Kipling, Saskatchewan 37 Ph
Kipp, Alberta 36 Ej
Kirá Panayiá. See Pelagos
Kirby's Corner, Ontario 34 Ff
Kirchberg, Switzerland 65 Ca
Kirensk, U.S.S.R. 79 Kc
Kirgizskaya S.S.R. (Kirghizia), U.S.S.R. 78 Gd
Kiri, Zaire 96 De
Kiribati, Pacific Ocean 102 Gh
Kirit, Somalia 97 Kc
Kiriwina. See Trobriand I.
Kirkağaç, Turkey 92 Ab
Kirkby Lonsdale, England 63 Ff
Kirkcaldy, Alberta 36 Dh
Kirkcaldy, Scotland 62 Ed
Kirkcudbright, Scot. 62 Ee
Kirkee, India 88 De
Kirkella, Manitoba 37 Qh
Kirkenes, Norway 66 Na
Kirkland Lake, Ontario 34 Kd
Kirksville, Missouri 49 Lb
Kirkūk, Iraq 92 Db
Kirkwall, Orkney 62 Fb
Kirov, U.S.S.R. 80 Jd
Kirov, U.S.S.R. 81 Ja
Kirovagrad, Ukraine 80 Hg
Kirovgrad, U.S.S.R. 81 Pb
Kirovsk, U.S.S.R. 78 Cb
Kirriemuir, Alberta 36 Gg
Kirriemuir, Scotland 62 Ed
Kirsanov, U.S.S.R. 81 Fd
Kirsehir, Turkey 92 Bb
Kirthar Ra., Pakistan 88 Cc
Kiruna, Sweden 66 Jc
Kisangani, Zaire 96 Fd
Kisbér, Hungary 69 He
Kisbey, Saskatchewan 37 Pj
Kishanganj, India 91 Gb
Kishangarh, India 88 Dc
Kishangarh, India 90 Bg
Kishi, Nigeria 98 Fg
Kishinev, Moldavia 80 Fh
Kishtwar, Kashmir 90 Dd
Kisii, Kenya 97 Ge
Kisiju, Tanzania 97 Hf
Kiska, I., Aleutian Is. 43 Um
Kiskittogisu L., Manitoba 37 Td
Kiskitto L., Manitoba 37 Td
Kiskunfélégyháza, Hungary 69 He
Kismayu. See Chisimaio
Kispest, Hungary 69 He
Kispiox, R., B.C. 39 Jh
Kissaraing I., Burma 89 Jf
Kissidougou, Guinea 98 Cg
Kississing L., Manitoba 37 Qc
Kisujszállás, Hungary 69 Je
Kisumu, Kenya 97 Ge
Kisvárda, Hungary 69 Kd
Kiswe, Syria 94 Ed
Kita, Mali 98 Df
Kitab, Uzbekistan 78 Fe
Kita Kyūshū, Japan 82 Kd
Kitale, Kenya 97 Hd
Kitchener, Ontario 34 Kj
Kitgum, Uganda 97 Gd
Kithira, Greece 77 Df
Kithirai Chan., Greece 77 Dg
Kithnos, Greece 77 Ef
Kitigan, Ontario 34 Hc
Kitimat, British Columbia 39 Jh
Kitimat Mill, B.C. 39 Jj
Kitscoty, Alberta 36 Ge
Kittanning, Pa. 44 Ab
Kittatinny Mts., New Jersey 44 Cb
Kittila, Finland 66 Lc
Kitui, Kenya 97 He
Kitwanga, B.C. 39 Kh
Kitzingen, W. Germany 68 Dd
Kiumbi, Zaire 96 Ff
Kiungchow. See Qiongshan
Kiungchow Str. See Qiongzhou Haixia
Kiuruvesi, Finland 66 Me
Kivi Järvi, Finland 66 Le
Kivu L., Zaire 97 Fe
Kivu Nat. Park, Zaire 97 Fe
Kiwai I., Papua New Guinea 57 Ha
Kiyev, Ukraine 80 Gf
Kiyiu L., Saskatchewan 36 Jg
Kiyma, Kazakhstan 78 Fc
Kizel, U.S.S.R. 78 Ec
Kizil Irmak, Turkey 92 Ba
Kizyl Arvat, Turkmenistan 78 Ee
Kizyl Jilga, Kashmir 88 Ea
Kjerringøy, Norway 66 Fc
Kladanj, Yugoslavia 76 Bb
Kladno, Czechoslovakia 68 Fc
Klagenfurt, Austria 68 Fe
Klaipeda, Lithuania 67 Jj
Klamath Falls, Oregon 47 Cd
Klamath Mts., California 47 Be
Klamath R., California 47 Be
Klamono, Irian Jaya 83 Kl
Klappan R., B.C. 39 Jg
Klar Alv, Sweden 66 Ef
Kleczkowski L., Quebec 32 Jc
Kleena Kleene, B.C. 39 Lk
Klemtu, B.C. 39 Jj
Klerksdorp, Transvaal 95 De
Kleszczele, Poland 69 Kb
Klimpfjall, Sweden 66 Fd
Klinaklini, R., B.C. 39 Lk
Klisura, Bulgaria 76 Ec
Kliuchi, U.S.S.R. 81 Gd
Ključ, Yugoslavia 74 Fc
Klock, Ontario 35 Mf
Klodawa, Poland 69 Hb
Klofta, Norway 67 Df
Klomnice, Poland 69 Hc
Klondike R., Y.T. 38 Dc
Kloosterzande, Netherlands 64 Cc
Klosters, Switzerland 65 Eb
Kluane, Yukon Territory 38 De
Kluane, L. & R., Y.T. 38 De
Kluane Nat. Park, Y.T. 38 De
Klundert, Netherlands 64 Cc
Klyuchevskaya Sopka, U.S.S.R. 79 Rc
Knee L., Saskatchewan 36 Kc
Knewstubb L., B.C. 39 Lj
Knight Inlet, B.C. 39 Kk
Knighton, Wales 63 Eh
Knin, Yugoslavia 74 Fc
Knob, C., W. Australia 56 Cf
Knockke, Belgium 64 Bc
Knockmealdown Mts., Eire 63 Bh
Knowlton, Quebec 35 Sg
Knox, Pennsylvania 44 Ab
Knox, C., B.C. 39 Gh
Knox Coast, Antarctica 104 Hc
Knoxville, Iowa 49 Lb
Knoxville, Tennessee 45 Fc
Knysna, Cape Province 95 Cf
Knyszyn, Poland 69 Kb
Koartac, Quebec 31 Ne
Kobarid, Yugoslavia 74 Db
Kobdo. See Hovd
Kōbe, Japan 86 Dg
København, Denmark 67 Dj
Koblenz, West Germany 68 Bc
Kobrin, Byelorussia 80 De
Kobroör, Indonesia 83 Km
Kočani, Yugoslavia 76 Dd
Kočevje, Yugoslavia 74 Ec
Ko Chang, Thailand 87 Cd
Kōchi, Japan 86 Ch
Koch I., N.W.T. 31 Md
Kochow. See Maoming
Kochumdek, U.S.S.R. 79 Jb
Kodiak, Alaska 43 Xm
Koekelare, Belgium 64 Ac
Koffiefontein, O.F.S. 95 De
Koforidua, Ghana 98 Eg
Kōfu, Japan 86 Fg
Køge B., Greenland 41 Nc
Kohat, Pakistan 90 Bd
Kohima, India 89 Hc
Koidern, Y.T. 30 Ee
Kojonup, W. Australia 56 Cf
Kokand, Uzbekistan 93 Ka
Kokanee Glacier Provincial Park, British Columbia 39 Pl
Kokchetav, Kazakhstan 78 Fc
Kokhtla Yarva, Estonia 67 Mg
Kokkola, Finland 66 Ke
Kokoda, Papua New Guinea 57 Ja
Kokomo, Indiana 40 Ce
Koko Nor. See Qinghai Hu
Kokpekty, Kazakhstan 78 Hd
Koksijde, Belgium 64 Ac
Koksoak, R., Quebec 31 Nf
Kokstad, Cape Province 95 Df
Kokura. See Kita Kyūshū
Ko Kut, Thailand 87 Cd
Kolar, India 88 Ef
Kolari, Finland 66 Kc
Kolberg. See Kolobrzeg
Koida, Senegal 98 Bf
Kolding, Denmark 67 Cj
Kole, Zaire 96 Fd
Kolguyev Ostrov, U.S.S.R. 78 Db
Kolhapur, India 88 De
Kolín, Czechoslovakia 68 Fc
Kolkas Rags, Latvia 67 Kh
Köln, West Germany 68 Bc
Kolno, Poland 69 Jb
Kolo, Poland 69 Hb
Kolo, Tanzania 97 He
Kolobrzeg, Poland 69 Fa
Kologriv, U.S.S.R. 81 Ga
Kolokani, Mali 98 Df
Kolomna, U.S.S.R. 80 Ld
Kolomyya, Ukraine 80 Dg
Kolosia, Kenya 97 Hd
Kolozsvár. See Cluj
Kolpakovskiy, U.S.S.R. 79 Qc
Kolpashevo, U.S.S.R. 78 Hc
Kol'skiy Poluostrov, pen., U.S.S.R. 78 Cb
Kolwezi, Zaire 96 Fg
Kolyma, U.S.S.R. 79 Qb
Kolymskiy, Khrebet, U.S.S.R 79 Qb
Komandorskiye Os., U.S.S.R. 79 Rc
Komariya, Sri Lanka 88 Fg
Komárno, Czechoslovakia 69 He
Komarno, Manitoba 37 Uh
Komatsu, Japan 86 Ef
Komi, A.S.S.R., U.S.S.R. 78 Eb
Kommunisma Pik, Tadzhikistan 78 Ge
Komoran, Irian Jaya 83 Lm
Komotini, Greece 76 Ed
Kompong Cham, Kampuchea 87 Dd
Kompong Chhnang, Kampuchea 87 Cd
Komsomolets Ostrov, U.S.S.R. 79 Ja
Komsomol'sk-nd-Amur, U.S.S.R. 79 Nc
Kondiaronk, L., Quebec 35 Of
Kondinskoe, U.S.S.R. 78 Fb
Kondoa, Tanzania 97 He
Kondratevo, U.S.S.R. 79 Jc
Kong, Ivory Coast 98 Eg
Kong Karls Land, Arctic Ocean 78 Ba
Kongor, Sudan 99 Mg
Kongsberg, Norway 67 Cg
Kongsmoen, Norway 66 Ed
Kongsvinger, Norway 67 Ef
Kongur Shan, China 90 Da
Königsberg. See Kaliningrad
Konispol, Albania 77 Ce
Konjic, Yugoslavia 76 Ac
Konkiep, Namibia 95 Be
Konotop, Ukraine 80 Hf
Konstantinovka, Ukraine 80 Jg
Konstantinovsk, U.S.S.R. 81 Eg
Konstanz, West Germany 68 Ce
Kontiomäki, Finland 66 Nd
Konya, Turkey 92 Bb
Konza, Kenya 97 He
Koostatak, Manitoba 37 Ug
Kootenay L., B.C. 39 Pl
Kootenay Nat. Park, B.C. 39 Pk
Kootenay R., B.C. 39 Pl
Kootwijk, Netherlands 64 Db
Kopervik, Norway 67 Ag
Kopeysk, U.S.S.R. 81 Qc
Köping, Sweden 67 Fg
Kopparberg, Sweden 67 Fg
Koppigen, Switzerland 65 Ca
Koprivnica, Yugoslavia 74 Fb
Kora, India 91 Cb
Korangi, Pakistan 93 Je
Korçë, Albania 77 Cd
Korçula, Yugoslavia 74 Fd
Kordofan, Northern, Sudan 97 Fa
Kordofan, Southern, Sudan 97 Fb
Korea, N., East Asia 82 Jb
Korea, S., East Asia 82 Jc
Korea B., Korea 82 Hc
Korea Kaikyo, Korea 82 Jd
Korinthia, Greece 77 Df
Kórinthos, Greece 77 Df
Kórinthos, G. of, Greece 77 De
Kormak, Ontario 34 He
Kormakiti, C., Cyprus 94 Ab
Kornat, Yugoslavia 74 Ed
Korneuburg, Austria 69 Gd
Korogwe, Tanzania 97 Hf
Körös, Hungary 76 Ca
Korosten, Ukraine 80 Ff
Koro Toro, Chad 99 Je
Korpo, Finland 67 Jf
Korsakov, U.S.S.R. 79 Pd
Korsnas, Finland 66 Je
Korsnes, Norway 66 Gb
Kortessem, Belgium 64 Dd
Kortgene, Netherlands 64 Bc
Korthpulë, Albania 76 Bd
Korti, Sudan 99 Me
Kortrijk, Belgium 64 Bd
Korwai, India 91 Bc
Koryakskiy Khrebet, U.S.S.R. 79 Rb
Kos, Greece 77 Ff
Kościerzyna, Poland 69 Ga
Kosciusko, Mississippi 49 Nf
Kosciusko, New South Wales 57 Jg
Kosha, Sudan 99 Md
Koshchagyl, Kazakhstan 78 Ed
Koshiki Rettō, Japan 86 Aj
Kosi, India 90 Eg
Košice, Czechoslovakia 69 Jd
Koskaecodde L., Nfld. 33 Rf
Koslan, U.S.S.R. 78 Db
Köslin. See Koszalin
Kosovo Metohija, Yugosl. 76 Cc
Kostajnica, Yugoslavia 74 Fc
Kosti, Sudan 99 Mf
Kostino, U.S.S.R. 78 Hb
Kostroma, U.S.S.R. 80 Mc
Koszalin, Poland 69 Ga
Kota, India 88 Ec
Kota Baharu, Pen. Malaysia 87 Ce
Kota Kinabalu, Sabah 83 Gj
Kotalpur, India 91 Fd
Kota Tinggi, Pen. Malaysia 87 Cf
Kotcho, R., B.C. 39 Nf
Kotcho L., B.C. 39 Nf
Kotehandpur, Bangladesh 91 Gd
Kotel, Bulgaria 76 Fc
Kotelnich, U.S.S.R. 81 Ja
Kotel'nyy, Ostrov, U.S.S.R. 79 Na
Köthen, East Germany 68 Dc
Kotido, Uganda 97 Gd
Kotka, Finland 67 Mf
Kot Kapura, India 90 De
Kot Kasim, India 90 Ef
Kotkhai, India 90 Ee
Kotlas, U.S.S.R. 78 Db
Kotli, Kashmir 90 Cd
Kotonkoro, Nigeria 98 Gf
Kotturu, India 88 Ef
Kotzebue Sound, Alaska 43 Wl
Kouango, Cent. Afr. Rep. 99 Kg
Koudougou, Upper Volta 98 Ef
Koulikoro, Mali 98 Df
Kourou, French Guiana 53 Gb
Koutiala, Mali 98 Df
Kouvola, Finland 67 Mf
Kovel, Ukraine 80 Df
Kovno. See Kaunas
Kovrov, U.S.S.R. 81 Eb
Kowkash, Ontario 34 Cb
Kowloon, China 85 Gl
Koxtag, China 90 Eb
Koyukuk, R., Alaska 43 Xl
Kozan, Turkey 92 Cb
Kozani, Greece 77 Cd
Kozhikode. See Calicut
Kra, Isthmus of, Thailand 87 Bd
Krabi, Thailand 87 Be
Kragerø, Norway 67 Cg
Kragujevac, Yugoslavia 76 Cb
Kraków, Poland 69 Hc
Kramatorsk, Ukraine 80 Kg
Kranj, Yugoslavia 74 Eb
Kranystaw, Poland 69 Kc
Krapina, Yugoslavia 74 Eb
Krasino, Novaya Zemlya 78 Ea
Krasnobród, Poland 69 Kc
Krasnodar, U.S.S.R. 78 Cd
Krasnograd, Ukraine 80 Jg
Krasnoufimsk, U.S.S.R. 81 Nb
Krasnovishersk, U.S.S.R. 78 Eb
Krasnovodsk, Turkmenistan 78 Ed
Krasnoyarsk, U.S.S.R. 79 Jc
Krasny Uzel, U.S.S.R. 81 Gc
Krasnyy Kholm, U.S.S.R. 80 Kb
Krasnyy Kut, U.S.S.R. 81 He
Krasnyy Yar, U.S.S.R. 81 Ge
Kratie, Kampuchea 87 Dd
Krefeld, West Germany 68 Bc
Kremenchug, Ukraine 80 Hg
Kremenchugskoye Vdkhr., Ukr. 80 Hg
Kremensk, U.S.S.R. 81 Ff
Krems, Austria 69 Fd
Kretinga, Lithuania 67 Jj
Kreuzlingen, Switzerland 65 Ea
Kribi, Cameroun 99 Gh
Krimml, Austria 68 Ee
Krishna, India 88 Ee
Krishnanagar, India 91 Gd
Krishnaraja Res., India 88 Ef
Kristiansand, Norway 67 Cg
Kristianstad, Sweden 67 Fh
Kristiansund, Norway 66 Be
Kristiinankaupunki, Finland 66 Je
Kristinehamn, Sweden 67 Fg
Kriti, Greece 77 Eg
Kriva Palanka, Yugoslavia 76 Dc
Krivoy Rog, Ukraine 80 Hh
Krizevči, Yugoslavia 74 Fb
Krk, Yugoslavia 74 Ec
Krnov, Czechoslovakia 69 Gc
Kroken, Norway 66 Fd
Kroměříž, Czechoslovakia 69 Gd
Kronau, Saskatchewan 37 Nh
Kronoby, Finland 66 Ke
Kronshtadt, U.S.S.R 80 Fa
Kroonstad, O.F.S. 95 De
Kropotkin, U.S.S.R. 78 Dd
Krotoszyn, Poland 69 Gc
Krško, Yugoslavia 74 Ec
Krugerdorf, Ontario 34 Le
Krugersdorp, Transvaal 95 De
Kruishoutem, Belgium 64 Bd
Krujë, Albania 76 Bd
Krumbach, West Germany 68 Dd
Krumlov, Czechoslovakia 68 Fd
Krung Thep. See Bangkok
Krupnik, Bulgaria 76 Dd
Krusenstern, C., N.W.T. 38 Ra
Krusevac, Yugoslavia 76 Cc
Kruševo, Yugoslavia 76 Cd
Krustpils, Latvia 67 Lh
Krydor, Saskatchewan 36 Kf
Krzyz, Poland 69 Gb
Ksabi, Algeria 98 Ec
Ksar El Boukhari, Algeria 98 Fa
Ksar-el-Kebir, Morocco 98 Db
Ktima, Cyprus 94 Ac
Kuala, Sumatra 83 Ck
Kuala Kangsar, Pen. Malaysia 87 Cf
Kuala Kelawang, Pen. Malaysia 87 Cf
Kuala Kerai, Pen. Malaysia 87 Ce
Kuala Lipis, Pen. Malaysia 87 Cf
Kuala Lumpur, Pen. Malaysia 87 Cf
Kuandang, Celebes (Sulawesi) 83 Hk
Kuangchow. See Guangzhou
Kuantan, Pen. Malaysia 83 Dk
Kub, Namibia 95 Bd
Kuchaman, India 88 Ec
Kuching, Sarawak 83 Fk
Kuchow. See Rongjiang
Kudat, Sabah 83 Gj
Kudymkar, U.S.S.R. 78 Ec
Kuei-chou. See Guizhou
Kuei-lin. See Guilin
Kugaluk, R., N.W.T. 38 Ha
Kugmallit B., N.W.T. 38 Ga
Kuhak, Iran 93 Hd
Kühbonān, Iran 93 Gc
Kuh-e-Bul, Iran 93 Fc
Kuh Furgan, Iran 93 Gd
Kuh-i-Dinar, Iran 93 Fc
Kuhmo, Finland 66 Nd
Kuhpayeh, Iran 93 Fc
Kuhsan, Afghanistan 93 Hc
Kuibis, Namibia 95 Be
Kuinre, Netherlands 64 Db
Kui Nua, Thailand 87 Bd
Kukatush, Ontario 34 Hd
Kukawa, Nigeria 99 Hf
Kukës, Albania 76 Cc
Kukong. See Chiukwan
Kukukus L., Ontario 36 La
Kulachi, Pakistan 90 Be
Kuldiga, Latvia 67 Kh
Kuldja. See Yining
Kuldo, B.C. 39 Kh
Kulgera, N. Terr. 57 Fe
Kulhakangri, China 89 Hc
Kulmbach, West Germany 68 Dc
Kulu, India 90 Ee
Kulunda, U.S.S.R. 78 Gc
Kumai, Borneo (Kalimantan) 83 Fl
Kumamoto, Japan 86 Bh
Kumara, New Zealand 55 Ce
Kumara, U.S.S.R. 79 Mc
Kumasi, Ghana 98 Eg
Kumbakonam, India 88 Ef
Kumher, India 91 Ab
Kumora, U.S.S.R. 79 Lc
Kumta, India 88 Df
Kunda, Estonia 67 Mg
Kunduz, Afghanistan 93 Jb
Kungchang. See Longxi
Kunghit I., B.C. 39 Hj
Kungnang, India 89 Hd
Kungrad, Uzbekistan 78 Ed
Kungur, U.S.S.R. 81 Nb
Kunlun Shan, China 58 He
Kunming, China 82 De
Kunsan, Korea 82 Jc
Kunwak, R., N.W.T. 38 Yd
Kuopio, Finland 66 Me
Kupang, Timor I. 83 Hn
Kupa R., Yugoslavia 74 Ec
Kupiškis, Lithuania 67 Lj
Kupyansk, Ukraine 80 Kg
Kuqa, China 78 Hd
Kure, Hawaiian Is. 102 He
Kure, Japan 86 Cg
Kureika, U.S.S.R. 78 Hb
Kurgan, U.S.S.R. 78 Fc
Kuria Muria Is., Arabian Sea 93 Gf
Kurigram, Bangladesh 91 Gc
Kuril'skiye Ostrova, U.S.S.R. 79 Pd
Kurnool, India 88 Ee
Kuroki, Saskatchewan 37 Og
Kurram, Pakistan 90 Bd
Kursk, U.S.S.R. 80 Kf
Kurskiy Zaliv, U.S.S.R. 67 Jj
Kurtalan, Turkey 92 Db
Kuru, Finland 67 Kf
Kuruman, Cape Province 95 Ce
Kurume, Japan 86 Bh
Kurunegala, Sri Lanka 88 Fg
Kurung, U.S.S.R. 79 Lb
Kusa, U.S.S.R. 81 Pc
Kusaie, Caroline Is. 102 Fg
Kusawa L. & R., Y.T. 38 Ee
Kushersk, U.S.S.R. 81 Ma
Kushiro, Japan 86 Jc
Kushk, Afghanistan 93 Hc
Kushka, Turkmenistan 78 Fe
Kushtia, Bangladesh 91 Gd
Kushva, U.S.S.R. 81 Pa
Kuskokwim B., Alaska 43 Wm
Kusma, Nepal 91 Da
Kustanay, Kazakhstan 78 Fc
Kütahya, Turkey 92 Ab
Kutai, Borneo (Kalimantan) 83 Gk
Kutaradja. See Banda Aceh
Kutch, India 88 Cd
Kutch, Rann of, India 88 Cd
Kutchian, Japan 86 Gc
Kutina, Yugoslavia 74 Fc
Kutno, Poland 69 Hb
Kutum, Sudan 99 Kf
Kuuk, R., N.W.T. 38 Ra
Kuusamo, Finland 66 Nd
Kuusjärvi, Finland 66 Ne
Kuwait, Persian G. 92 Ed
Kuybyshev, U.S.S.R. 81 Kd
Kuybyshev, U.S.S.R. 78 Gc
Kuybyshevskoye Vdkhr., U.S.S.R. 81 Jc
Kuytan, U.S.S.R. 79 Kc
Kuzhbal, U.S.S.R. 81 Ga
Kuzino, U.S.S.R. 81 Pb
Kuzmin, Yugoslavia 76 Bb
Kuznetsk, U.S.S.R. 81 Hd
Kuzovatovo, U.S.S.R. 81 Hd
Kvalöy, N., Norway 66 Ha
Kvalöy, S., Norway 66 Hb
Kvarken, Ostra, Sweden 66 Je
Kvarner, Yugoslavia 74 Ec
Kvarnerić, Yugosl. 74 Ec
Kvesmenes, Norway 66 Jb
Kwajalein, Marshall Is. 102 Fg
Kwakoegron, Surinam 53 Fb
Kwangchow. See Guangzhou
Kwangping. See Yongnian
Kwangsin. See Shangrao
Kwania L., Uganda 97 Gd
Kwataboahegan, R., Ont. 34 Ja
Kweichow. See Fengjie
Kweihwa. See Ziyun
Kweisui. See Hohhot
Kweiteh. See Shangqiu
Kwidzyń, Poland 69 Hb
Kwitao, Burma 89 Jc
Kwoka, Irian Jaya 83 Kl
Kyaikkami, Burma 89 Je
Kyakhta, U.S.S.R. 79 Kc
Kyancutta, S. Australia 57 Gf
Kyaukpadaung, Burma 89 Jd
Kyaukpyu, Burma 89 He
Kyaukse, Burma 89 Jd
Kyauktaw, Burma 89 Hd
Kyelang, India 90 Ed
Kyle, Saskatchewan 36 Jh
Kymi, Finland 67 Mf
Kynšperk, Czechoslovakia 68 Ec
Kynuna, Queensland 57 Hd
Kyoga L., Uganda 97 Gd
Kyōto, Japan 86 Dg
Kyrenia, Cyprus 94 Bb
Kyshtym, U.S.S.R. 81 Qc
Kythrea, Cyprus 94 Bb
Kyuquot, B.C. 39 Kk
Kyūshū, Japan 86 Bh
Kyustendil, Bulgaria 76 Dc
Kyusyur, U.S.S.R. 79 Ma
Kyzyl, U.S.S.R. 79 Jc
Kyzyl Kum, Uzbek 78 Fd
Kyzylsk, U.S.S.R. 81 Pd
Kzyl Orda, Kazakhstan 78 Fd

L

Laanila, Finland 66 Mb
La Asuncion, Margarita I., Venezuela 52 Ea
Laban, Jordan 94 Dg
La Banda, Argentina 54 Dc
Labang, Sarawak 83 Fk
Labé, Guinea 98 Cf
Labelle, Quebec 35 Qf
Laberge, L., Y.T. 38 Fe
La Biche, R., Y.T. 38 Le
Labouheyre, France 73 Cd
Laboulaye, Argentina 54 Dd
Labrador City, Nfld. 31 Ng
Labrea, Brazil 52 Ee
La Brea, Trinidad 52 Ea
Labrieville, Quebec 32 Cd
La Broquerie, Manitoba 36 Ea
Labuan, Sabah 83 Gj
Labuk B., Sabah 83 Gj
Labyrinth L., N.W.T. 38 Ue
Labytnangi, U.S.S.R. 58 Fb
Lac-à-Beauce, Quebec 35 Se
Lacadena, Saskatchewan 36 Jh
La Canoa, Venezuela 52 Eb
La Carlota, Argentina 54 Dd
La Carolina, Spain 70 Dc
Lac-au-Saumon, Quebec 32 Ee
Lac-aux-Brochets, Quebec 35 Se
Lac-aux-Sables, Quebec 35 Sf
Lac-Baker, N.B. 32 Df
Lac-Bouchette, Quebec 35 Sd
Laccadive Is., Indian Ocean 88 Df
Lac-Castagnier, Quebec 35 Nd
Lac-Chat, Quebec 35 Se
Lac-Drolet, Quebec 32 Bh
Lac-Édouard, Quebec 35 Se
La Ceiba, Venezuela 52 Cb
Lac-Etchemin, Quebec 32 Bg
Lac-Frontière, Quebec 32 Cg
Lac-Gatineau, Quebec 35 Pf
Lachen, Switzerland 65 Da
Lachine, Quebec 35 Rk
Lachine Canal, Quebec 35 Rk
Lachine Rapids, Quebec 35 Rk
Lachlan, R., N.S.W. 57 Jf
Lachmangarh, India 90 Dg
Lac-Humqui, Quebec 32 Ee
Lachute, Quebec 35 Qg
Lackawanna, New York 44 Aa
Lackawaxen, Pa. 44 Cb
Lac La Biche, Alberta 36 Ed
Lac La Ronge Provincial Park, Saskatchewan 37 Mc
Lac-Mégantic, Quebec 32 Bh
Lac Nominingue, Quebec 35 Pf
La Cocha, Argentina 54 Cc
Lacolle, Quebec 35 Rg
Lacombe, Alberta 36 Df
La Conception, Quebec 35 Qf
Laconia, New Hampshire 44 Ea
La Copelina, Argentina 54 Ce
Lacorne, Quebec 35 Nd
La Coruña, Spain 70 Aa
Lac-Rémi, Quebec 35 Pf
La Croche, Quebec 35 Se
La Croix, L., Minn./Ont. 36 Lb
La Crosse, Wisconsin 46 Md
La Cruz, Colombia 52 Bc
Lac-Saguay, Quebec 35 Pf
Lac Ste Anne, Alberta 36 Ce
Lac-Ste-Marie, Quebec 35 Pg
Lac-Ste-Thérèse, Ontario 34 Gc
Lac Vert, Saskatchewan 37 Nf
Ladakh Ra., China/Kashmir 88 Eb
Ladiz, Iran 93 Hd
Ladner, British Columbia 39 Hm
Ladoga L. See Ladozhskoye Oz.
La Dorada, Colombia 52 Cb
Ladozhskoye Ozero, U.S.S.R. 80 Ga
Ladwa, India 90 Ef
Lady Ann Str., N.W.T. 31 Lb
Lady Evelyn L., Ontario 34 Ke
Lady Franklin Pt., N.W.T. 38 Ra
Lady Newnes Ice Shelf, Antarctica 104 Lb
Lady Richardson, B., N.W.T. 38 Pa
Ladysmith, B.C. 39 Ml
Ladysmith, Natal 95 De
Ladysmith, Wisconsin 46 Mc
Lae, New Guinea 57 Ja
Laeken, Belgium 64 Cd
Laesó, I., Denmark 67 Dh
La Esperanza, Honduras 51 Bd
La Estrada, Spain 70 Aa
La Fayette, Georgia, U.S.A. 45 Ec
La Fayette, Indiana 40 Ce
Lafayette, Louisiana 45 Be
Laferté, Quebec 35 Md
Laflamme, R., Quebec 35 Nc
Lafleche, Saskatchewan 36 Lj
Laforce, Quebec 35 Me
Laforest, Ontario 34 Je
Lages, Brazil 53 Ke
Laggan L., Scotland 62 Ed
Laghouat, Algeria 98 Fb
Lagkor Co, China 89 Fb
Lagonegro, Italy 75 Ee
Lagos, Nigeria 98 Fg
Lagos, Portugal 70 Ad
Lagos de Moreno, Mexico 50 Dc
La Grande, Oregon 47 Dc
La Grange, Georgia, U.S.A. 45 Ed
Lagrange, Indiana 40 De
La Grange, Kentucky 45 Ea
La Grange, W. Australia 56 Dc
La Granja, Spain 70 Cb
La Guaira, Venezuela 52 Da
La Guardia, Argentina 54 Cc
La Guardia, Spain 70 Ab
Laguna, Brazil 54 Gc
Lagunas, Peru 52 Be
Lagunillas, Bolivia 52 Eg
Laharpur, India 91 Cb
La Have, Nova Scotia 32 Hj
La Have Is., Nova Scotia 32 Hj
Lahej, South Yemen 92 Dg
Lahijan, Iran 93 Fb
Laholm, Sweden 67 Eh
Lahore, Pakistan 90 De
Lahti, Finland 67 Lf
Lai, C., Vietnam 87 Dc
Laibach. See Ljubljana
Lai Chau, Vietnam 87 Cb
Laichow. See Ye Xian
Laingsburg, Cape Province 95 Cf
Laird, Saskatchewan 36 Lf
Lairet, R., Quebec 35 Rb
Lairg, Scotland 62 Eb
Laisamis, Kenya 97 Hd
Laishev, U.S.S.R. 81 Jc
Laives, Italy 65 Gb
Laja, L., Chile 54 Be
La Japonesa, Argentina 54 Ce
Lajes, Brazil 54 Fc
Lajord, Saskatchewan 37 Nh
La Junquera, Spain 71 Ga
La Junta, Colorado 48 Fd
Lakaträsk, Sweden 66 Jc
Lake Alma, Saskatchewan 37 Nj
Lake Andes, S. Dakota 46 Hd
Lake Butler, Florida 45 Fe
Lake Charles, Louisiana 49 Lg
Lake City, Florida 45 Fe
Lake City, Michigan 40 Dc
Lake Eliza, Alberta 36 Fe
Lake Erie, Ont./U.S.A. 34 Jk
Lakefield, Ontario 35 Mh
Lake Geneva, Wisconsin 40 Bd
Lake George, New York 44 Da
Lake Grace, W. Australia 56 Cf
Lake Harbour, N.W.T. 31 Ne
Lake Huron, Ont./U.S.A. 34 Gg
Lake King, W. Australia 56 Cf
Lakeland, Florida 45 Ff
Lake Lenore, Sask. 37 Nf
Lake Louise, Alberta 39 Pk

Lake Majella, *California* 47 Cg
Lake Nash, *N. Terr.* 57 Gd
Lake Ontario, *Ont./U.S.A.* 35 Mj
Lake Pleasant, *New York* 44 Ca
Lake Providence, *Louisiana* 49 Mf
Lake Pukaki, *New Zealand* 55 Cf
Lake River, *Ontario* 31 Lg
Lakeside, *Utah* 48 Ab
Lake Superior, *Ont./U.S.A.* 34 Ce
Lake Superior Provincial Park, *Ontario* 34 Fe
Lake Traverse, *Ontario* 35 Mg
Lake Valley, *Sask.* 36 Lh
Lakeview, *Minnesota* 46 Mb
Lakeview, *Oregon* 47 Cd
Lakewood, *New Jersey* 44 Cb
Lakewood, *New York* 44 Aa
Lakewood, *Ohio* 40 Fe
Lakhimpur, *India* 89 Hc
Lakhimpur, *India* 91 Cb
Lakki, *Pakistan* 90 Bd
Lakonía, *Greece* 77 Df
Lakonía, G. of, *Greece* 77 Df
Lakota, *Ivory Coast* 98 Dg
Lakota, *N. Dakota* 46 Ha
Lakse Fd., *Norway* 66 Ma
Lakselv, *Norway* 66 La
Lakshadweep, *Indian Oc.* 88 Df
Lala Musa, *Pakistan* 90 Dd
Lalbagh, *India* 91 Gc
Lalganj, *India* 91 Ec
La Libertad, *Ecuador* 52 Ad
La Libertad, *Guatemala* 50 Fd
La Libertad, *Nicaragua* 51 Bd
La Ligua, *Chile* 54 Bd
Lalin, *Spain* 70 Aa
Lalitpur, *India* 91 Bc
La Loche, *Saskatchewan* 39 Tg
La Loche, L., *Sask.* 36 Hb
La Loche West, *Sask.* 36 Hb
Lalyo, *Sudan* 99 Mh
La Maddalena, *Sardinia* 75 Be
La Malbaie, *Quebec* 32 Bf
Lamaline, *Newfoundland* 33 Rg
Lamar, *Colorado* 48 Fc
Lamar, *Missouri* 49 Kd
Lamastre, *France* 73 Fd
La Mauricie Parc, *Quebec* 35 Tf
Lambach, *Austria* 68 Ed
Lamballe, *France* 72 Bb
Lambayeque, *Peru* 52 Be
Lambert's Ld., *Greenland* 41 Mb
Lambertville, *New Jersey* 44 Cb
Lambeth, *Ontario* 34 Jk
Lámbia, *Greece* 77 Cf
Lambton, *Quebec* 35 Tg
Lambton, C., *N.W.T.* 38 Ma
Lamé, *Chad* 99 Hg
Lamégo, *Portugal* 70 Bb
Lamesa, *Texas* 48 Gf
Lamía, *Greece* 77 De
Lammermuir Hills, *Scotland* 62 Fe
Lamont, *Alberta* 36 Ee
Lamotrek, *Caroline Is.* 102 Dg
La Motte, *Quebec* 35 Md
La Moure, *N. Dakota* 46 Hb
Lampazos, *Mexico* 50 Db
Lampedusa, *Medit. Sea* 99 Ha
Lampeter, *Wales* 63 Eh
Lamphun, *Thailand* 87 Bc
Lampi, *Burma* 89 Jf
Lampman, *Saskatchewan* 37 Pj
Lamu, *Kenya* 97 Je
Lamud, *Peru* 52 Be
Lanark, *Ontario* 35 Og
Lanark, *Scotland* 62 Ee
Lancashire, *England* 63 Fg
Lancaster, *England* 63 Ff
Lancaster, *Missouri* 49 Lb
Lancaster, *New York* 44 Aa
Lancaster, *N.H.* 40 Lc
Lancaster, *Ontario* 35 Qg
Lancaster, *Pennsylvania* 44 Bb
Lancaster, *S. Carolina* 45 Gc
Lancaster, *Wisconsin* 40 Ad
Lancaster Sound, *N.W.T.* 31 Lc
Lancer, *Saskatchewan* 36 Jh
Landeck, *Austria* 68 De
Landen, *Belgium* 64 Dd
Lander, *Wyoming* 46 Cd
Landerneau, *France* 72 Ab
Landes, *France* 73 Cd
Landi Kotal, *Pakistan* 90 Bc
Landing L., *Manitoba* 37 Uc
Landis, *Saskatchewan* 36 Jf
Landon, *Sweden* 66 Fe
Landrienne, *Quebec* 35 Nd
Landsberg. *See* Gorzów Wielkopolski
Landsberg, *West Germany* 68 Dd
Land's End, *England* 63 Dk
Lands End, C., *N.W.T.* 30 Gb
Landshut, *West Germany* 68 Ed
Landskrona, *Sweden* 67 Ej
Lands Lokk Pt., *N.W.T.* 30 Ka
Lanfine, *Alberta* 36 Gg
Lang, *Saskatchewan* 37 Nj
Langaa, *Denmark* 67 Ch
Langadhas, *Greece* 77 Dd
Langana L., *Ethiopia* 97 Hc
Langara I., *B.C.* 39 Gh
Langbank, *Saskatchewan* 37 Ph
Langdon, *Alberta* 36 Dh
Langeac, *France* 73 Ed
Langeland, I., *Denmark* 67 Dj
Längelmavesi, *Finland* 67 Lf
Langenburg, *Sask.* 37 Qh
Langenthal, *Switzerland* 65 Ca
Langham, *Saskatchewan* 36 Lf
Langholm, *Scotland* 62 Fe
Lang Jökull, *Iceland* 66 Vm
Langkawi, *Pen. Malaysia* 87 Be
Langlade, *Quebec* 35 Pd
Langlade I., *Miquelon I.* 33 Qg
Langley, district, *B.C.* 39 Km
Langogne, *France* 73 Ed
Langon, *France* 73 Cd
Langøy, *Norway* 66 Fb
Langres, *France* 72 Fc
Langruth, *Manitoba* 37 Th
Langsa, *Sumatra* 83 Ck
Langsele, *Sweden* 66 Ge
Lang Son, *Vietnam* 87 Db
LangSuan, *Thailand* 87 Be
Langträsk, *Sweden* 66 Jd
Languedoc, *France* 73 Ee
Langzhong, *China* 84 Bg
Laniel, *Quebec* 35 Le
Lanigan, *Saskatchewan* 37 Mg
Lankao, *China* 84 Ge
Lanklaar, *Belgium* 64 Dc
Lankor Tso, *China* 89 Fb
Lannion, *France* 72 Bb
L'Annonciation, *Quebec* 35 Qf
Lanoraie, *Quebec* 35 Rg
Lansdale, *Pennsylvania* 44 Cb
Lansdowne, *Ontario* 35 Ph
Lansdowne House, *Ont.* 31 Lg
L'Anse-Amour, *Nfld.* 33 Qb
L'Anse-au-Loup, *Nfld.* 33 Qb
L'Anse-St-Jean, *Quebec* 32 Be
Lansing, *Michigan* 40 Dd
Lanusei, *Sardinia* 75 Bf
Lanzarote, *Canary Is.* 98 Cc
Lanzhou, *China* 84 Ad
Laoag, *Philippines* 83 Hg
Lao Bao, *Laos* 87 Dc
Lao Cai, *Vietnam* 87 Cb
Laon, *France* 72 Eb
La Oroya, *Peru* 52 Bf
Laos, *S.E. Asia* 87 Cc
Laoshan, *China* 84 Kd
Laotie Shan, *China* 84 Kc
Lapalisse, *France* 72 Ec
La Paragua, *Venezuela* 52 Eb
La Patrie, *Quebec* 35 Tg
La Paz, *Argentina* 54 Cd
La Paz, *Argentina* 54 Ed
La Paz, *Bolivia* 52 Dg
La Paz, *Honduras* 51 Bd
La Paz, *Mexico* 50 Bc
Lapchung L., *China* 89 Gb
Lapeer, *Michigan* 40 Ed
La Pelada, *Argentina* 54 Dd
La Pérade, *Quebec* 35 Sf
La Pérouse, *Manitoba* 37 Uc
La Pérouse, str., *U.S.S.R./Japan* 86 Gb
Lapinlahti, *Finland* 66 Me
Lapithos, *Cyprus* 94 Bb
La Plata, *Argentina* 54 Ed
La Pocatière, *Quebec* 32 Bf
La Porte, *Indiana* 40 Ce
Laporte, *Pennsylvania* 44 Bb
Laporte, *Saskatchewan* 36 Hg
La Porte City, *Iowa* 49 La
Lapovo, *Yugoslavia* 76 Cb
Lappa Järvi, *Finland* 66 Ke
Lappeenranta, *Finland* 67 Nf
Lappland, *N. Europe* 66 Jb
Lapptrask, *Sweden* 66 Kc
La Prairie, *Quebec* 35 Rg
La Prairie Basin, *Quebec* 35 Sk
Laprida, *Argentina* 54 De
Laptevykh Sea, *U.S.S.R.* 79 La
Łapy, *Poland* 69 Kb
La Quiaca, *Argentina* 54 Cb
Lar, *Iran* 93 Fd
Larache, *Morocco* 98 Da
Laragne, *France* 73 Fd
Laramate, *Peru* 52 Cf
Laramie, *Wyoming* 46 Ee
Laramie Mts., *Wyoming* 46 Dd
Laramie Pk., *Wyoming* 46 Ed
Laranjeiras, *Brazil* 53 Kf
La Rasse, *Switzerland* 65 Ba
Larder Lake, *Ontario* 35 Ld
L'Ardoise, *Nova Scotia* 33 Mh
Laredo, *Texas* 48 Hj
La Reine, *Quebec* 35 Ld
Largeau, *Chad* 96 Da
Largo, *New Mexico* 48 Dd
Largs, *Scotland* 62 De
Larino, *Italy* 75 Ee
La Rioja, *Argentina* 54 Cc
Larisa, *Greece* 77 De
La Rivière, *Manitoba* 37 Tj
Larkana, *Pakistan* 88 Cc
Larnaca, *Cyprus* 94 Bc
Larne, *N. Ireland* 63 Df
Larned, *Kansas* 49 Hc
La Robla, *Spain* 70 Ca
La Rochelle, *France* 72 Cc
La Roda, *Spain* 71 Dc
La Ronge & L., *Sask.* 37 Mc
Larrimah, *N. Terr.* 56 Fc
Larry's River, *Nova Scotia* 33 Lh
Lars Christensen Coast, *Antarctica* 104 Fc
Larson, *Ontario* 37 Na
Laruns, *France* 73 Ce
Larvik, *Norway* 67 Dg
Laryak, *U.S.S.R.* 78 Gb
La Salle, *Illinois* 49 Nb
La Salle, *Manitoba* 37 Uj
La Salle, *Ontario* 34 Gk
La Salle, *Quebec* 35 Rk
Las Animas, *Colorado* 48 Fc
Las Anod, *Somalia* 97 Kc
La Sarre, *Quebec* 35 Ld
Las Cejas, *Argentina* 54 Dc
La Scie, *Newfoundland* 33 Rd
Las Colorados, *Argentina* 54 Be
Las Cruces, *Mexico* 50 Cb
Las Cruces, *New Mexico* 48 Df
La Serena, *Chile* 54 Bc
Las Flores, *Argentina* 54 Ee
Lashburn, *Saskatchewan* 36 He
Las Heras, *Argentina* 54 Cg
Lashio, *Burma* 89 Jd
Lashkar, *India* 91 Bb
Lashkar Gah, *Afghanistan* 88 Bb
Lasíthi, *Crete* 77 Eg
Lasjerd, *Iran* 93 Fb
Las Khoreh, *Somalia* 97 Kb
Las Lajas, *Argentina* 54 Be
Las Lomitas, *Argentina* 54 Db
Las Palmas, *Canary Is.* 98 Bc
Las Pipinas, *Argentina* 54 Ee
Las Plumas, *Argentina* 54 Cf
Lasqueti I., *B.C.* 39 Ll
Lassen Peak, *California* 47 Ce
Lassen Vol. Nat. Park, *California* 47 Ce
L'Assomption, *Quebec* 35 Rg
Las Tablas, *Panama* 51 Ce
Last Mountain, range, *Saskatchewan* 37 Ng
Last Mountain L., *Sask.* 37 Mg
Lastovo, *Yugoslavia* 74 Fd
Las Vegas, *Nevada* 47 Fg
Las Vegas, *New Mexico* 48 Ee
Latacunga, *Ecuador* 52 Bd
Latakia, *Syria* 94 Db
Latchford, *Ontario* 34 Le
Latina, *Italy* 75 De
Latornell, *Alberta* 39 Oh
La Trève, L., *Quebec* 35 Pc
Latrobe, *Pennsylvania* 44 Ab
Latrun, *Jordan* 94 Cf
La Tuque, *Quebec* 35 Se
Latvia (Latviyskaya S.S.R.), *U.S.S.R.* 80 Dc
Lauchlan R., *N.W.T.* 38 Ta
Lauder, *Manitoba* 37 Rj
Laufen, *Switzerland* 65 Ca
Launay, *Quebec* 35 Md
Launceston, *England* 63 Ek
Launceston, *Tasmania* 57 Jh
Launggyang, *Burma* 89 Jc
La Unión, *Chile* 54 Bf
La Unión, *Mexico* 50 Dd
La Unión, *Salvador* 51 Bd
La Unión, *Spain* 71 Ed
Laura, *Queensland* 57 Hc
Laura, *Saskatchewan* 36 Kg
La Urbana, *Venezuela* 52 Db
Laurel, *Maryland* 44 Bc
Laurel, *Mississippi* 45 Ce
Laurel, *Montana* 46 Cc
Laurel, *Ontario* 34 Kj
Laurel Hill, *Pennsylvania* 44 Ab
Laurens, *S. Carolina* 45 Fc
Laurent, *Quebec* 40 Kb
Laurentides, *Quebec* 35 Rg
Laurentides, Parc prov. des, *Quebec* 35 Te
Lauria, *Italy* 75 Ee
Laurie I., *South Orkneys* 104 Tc
Laurie L., *Manitoba* 37 Pb
Laurier, *Manitoba* 37 Sh
Laurie River, *Manitoba* 37 Rb
Laurierville, *Quebec* 35 Tf
Laurinburg, *N. Carolina* 45 Hc
Lausanne, *Switzerland* 65 Bb
Lautaro, *Chile* 54 Be
Lauzon, *Quebec* 32 Ag
Lavacherie, *Belgium* 64 Dd
Laval, *France* 72 Cb
Laval, *Quebec* 35 Rg
Lavalle, *Argentina* 54 Cd
Lavalleja. *See* Minas
Lavamünd, *Austria* 68 Fe
Lavant Station, *Ontario* 35 Og
Lavardac, *France* 73 Dd
La Vega, *Dominican Rep.* 51 Ec
La Vela, *Venezuela* 52 Da
Laverton, *W. Australia* 56 De
Lavieille, L., *Ontario* 35 Mg
Lavina, *Montana* 46 Cb
Lavongai. *See* New Hanover
Lavos, *Portugal* 70 Ab
Lavoy, *Alberta* 36 Fe
Lavras, *Brazil* 53 Hh
Lavras, *Brazil* 54 Fd
Lavras da Mangabeira, *Brazil* 53 Ke
Lavrentiya, *U.S.S.R.* 79 Tb
Lávrion, *Greece* 77 Ef
Lawford Is., *N.W.T.* 38 Rb
Lawford L., *Manitoba* 37 Vd
Lawk Sawk, *Burma* 89 Jd
Lawlers, *W. Australia* 56 De
Lawn, *Newfoundland* 33 Rg
Lawra, *Ghana* 98 Ef
Lawrence, *Kansas* 49 Kc
Lawrence, *Massachusetts* 44 Ea
Lawrence, *New Zealand* 55 Bf
Lawrenceburg, *Tennessee* 45 Dc
Lawrence Station, *N.B.* 32 Eh
Lawrencetown, *N.S.* 32 Jj
Lawrenceville, *Illinois* 49 Oc
Lawson, *Saskatchewan* 36 Lh
Lawton, *Oklahoma* 49 He
Laysan I., *Hawaiian Is.* 102 He
Lazarevac, *Yugoslavia* 76 Cb
Lazio, *Italy* 75 Dd
Leach I., *Ontario* 34 Fe
Lead, *S. Dakota* 46 Fc
Leader, *Saskatchewan* 36 Hh
Leadville, *Colorado* 48 Dc
Leaf L., *Saskatchewan* 37 Pe
Leakesville, *Mississippi* 45 Ce
Leaksville, *N. Carolina* 45 Hb
Leamington, *Ontario* 34 Hk
Leamington Spa, Royal, *England* 63 Fh
Leamy L., *Quebec* 34 Dh
Learmonth, *W. Australia* 56 Bd
Leask, *Saskatchewan* 36 Le
Leavenworth, *Indiana* 45 Da
Leavenworth, *Kansas* 49 Kc
Łeba, *Poland* 69 Ga
Lebanon, *Kentucky* 45 Eb
Lebanon, *Missouri* 49 Ld
Lebanon, *New Hampshire* 44 Da
Lebanon, *Pennsylvania* 44 Bb
Lebanon, *S.W. Asia* 92 Cc
Lebel-sur-Quévillon, *Quebec* 35 Nc
Lebesby, *Norway* 66 Ma
Lebombo Mts., *S. Africa* 95 Ee
Le Borgne, *Haiti* 51 Ec
Lębork, *Poland* 69 Ga
Lebret, *Saskatchewan* 37 Oh
Lebu, *Chile* 54 Be
Lebwa, *Lebanon* 94 Ec
Lecce, *Italy* 75 Ge
Lecco, *Italy* 74 Bc
L'échourie, *Quebec* 32 Hd
Lectoure, *France* 73 De
Ledbury, *England* 63 Fh
Ledesma, *Argentina* 54 Db
Ledesma, *Spain* 70 Cb
Ledo, *India* 89 Jc
Leduc, *Alberta* 36 De
Leech L., *Saskatchewan* 37 Pg
Leeds, *England* 63 Fg
Leende, *Netherlands* 64 Dc
Lee R., *Eire* 63 Bj
Leerbeek, *Belgium* 64 Cd
Leerdam, *Netherlands* 64 Dc
Leesburg, *Virginia* 44 Bc
Leesville, *Louisiana* 49 Lg
Leesville, L., *Virginia* 45 Hb
Leeuwarden, *Netherlands* 64 Da
Leeuwin, C., *W. Australia* 56 Bf
Leeward Is., *West Indies* 51 Gc
Lefka, *Cyprus* 94 Ab
Lefkara, *Cyprus* 94 Bc
Lefkoniko, *Cyprus* 94 Bb
Lefroy, *Ontario* 35 Lh
Lefroy, L., *W. Australia* 56 Df
Leftrook L., *Manitoba* 37 Tb
Legal, *Alberta* 36 De
Légaré, L., *Quebec* 35 Rf
Legaspi, *Philippines* 83 Hh
Legges Tor, *Tasmania* 57 Jh
Leghorn. *See* Livorno
Le Gîte, *Quebec* 35 Td
Legnica, *Poland* 69 Gc
Legoff, L., *Quebec* 35 Oa
Leh, *Kashmir* 90 Ec
Le Havre, *France* 72 Db
Lehi, *Utah* 48 Bb
Lehututu, *Botswana* 95 Cd
Leiah, *Pakistan* 90 Be
Leicester, *England* 63 Gh
Leichhardt, R., *Queensland* 57 Gc
Leiden, *Netherlands* 64 Cb
Leigh Creek, *S. Australia* 57 Gf
Leighton Buzzard, *England* 63 Gj
Leignon, *Belgium* 64 Dd
Leimuiden, *Netherlands* 64 Cb
Leinan, *Saskatchewan* 36 Kh
Leinster, *Eire* 63 Cg
Leipzig, *East Germany* 68 Ec
Leipzig, *Saskatchewan* 36 Jf
Leisele, *Belgium* 64 Ad
Leitchfield, *Kentucky* 45 Db
Leith, *Scotland* 62 Ee
Leitrim, *Eire* 63 Bf
Leiyang, *China* 85 Fj
Leizhou Bandao, *China* 82 Ef
Leka, *Norway* 66 Dd
Leksands Noret, *Sweden* 67 Ff
Leksvik, *Norway* 66 De
Leland, *Michigan* 40 Dc
Leland, *Mississippi* 49 Mf
Leleque, *Argentina* 54 Bf
Le Maire, Estrecho de, *Arg.* 54 Dh
Léman, Lac, *Switzerland* 65 Bb
Le Mans, *France* 72 Db
Le Mars, *Iowa* 49 Ja
Lemberg, *Saskatchewan* 37 Oh
Lemberg. *See* L'vov
Lemieux, *Quebec* 35 Sf
Lemieux Is., *N.W.T.* 31 Ne
Lemnos. *See* Limnos
Lempriere, *B.C.* 39 Oj
Lemsford, *Saskatchewan* 36 Hh
Lemyethna, *Burma* 89 Je
Lena, *U.S.S.R.* 79 Mb
Leney, *Saskatchewan* 36 Kf
Leninabad, *Uzbekistan* 78 Fd
Leninakan, *Armenia* 78 Dd
Lenina Peak, *Kirghizia* 78 Ge
Leningrad, *U.S.S.R.* 80 Gb
Leninogorsk, *Kazakhstan* 78 Hc
Leninsk Kuznetskiy, *U.S.S.R.* 78 Hc
Lenk, *Switzerland* 65 Cb
Lennox, I., *Chile/Arg.* 54 Cj
Lennoxville, *Quebec* 35 Tg
Lenoir, *N. Carolina* 45 Gb
Lenore, *Manitoba* 37 Rj
Lenore L., *Saskatchewan* 37 Mf
Lens, *France* 72 Ea
Lensk. *See* Mukhtuya
Lent, *Netherlands* 64 Dc
Lentiira, *Finland* 66 Nd
Lenvik, *Norway* 66 Hb
Lenya, *Burma* 89 Jf
Lenz, *Switzerland* 65 Eb
Lenzerheide, *Switzerland* 65 Eb
Leoben, *Austria* 68 Fe
Leola, *S. Dakota* 46 Hc
Leominster, *England* 63 Fh
Leominster, *Massachusetts* 44 Ea
León, *France* 73 Ce
León, *Mexico* 50 Dc
León, *Nicaragua* 51 Bd
León, *Spain* 70 Ca
León, Monts. de, *Spain* 70 Ba
Leonforte, *Sicily* 75 Eg
Leonidhion, *Greece* 77 Df
Leonora, *W. Australia* 56 De
Leontevo, *U.S.S.R.* 80 Kb
Leopold II, L. *See* Mai Ndombe, L.
Leopoldsburg, *Belgium* 64 Dc
Leoville, *Saskatchewan* 36 Ke
Lephepe, *Botswana* 95 Dd
L'Épiphanie, *Quebec* 35 Rg
Lepontine, Alpi, *Switzerland/Italy* 65 Db
Lepreau, *New Brunswick* 32 Fh
Lepreau, Pt., *N.B.* 32 Fh
Lercara Friddi, *Sicily* 75 Dg
Lerdo, *Mexico* 50 Db
Lérida, *Spain* 71 Fb
Lerma, *Spain* 70 Da
Lermoos, *Austria* 68 De
Léros, *Greece* 77 Ff
Leross, *Saskatchewan* 37 Og
Le Roy, *New York* 44 Aa
Leroy, *Saskatchewan* 37 Ng
Lerwick, *Scotland* 62 Ja
Lesbos. *See* Lesvos
Les Éboulements, *Quebec* 32 Bf
Les Escoumins, *Quebec* 32 Ce
Les Étroits, *Quebec* 32 Df
Leshan, *China* 85 Ah
Leskovac, *Yugoslavia* 76 Cc
Leslie, *Saskatchewan* 37 Og
Leslieville, *Alberta* 36 Cf
Les Méchins, *Quebec* 32 Fe
Lesnoy, *U.S.S.R.* 78 Cb
Lesotho, *S.E. Africa* 95 De
Lesozavodsk, *U.S.S.R.* 79 Nd
Lesparre, *France* 73 Cd
Lesser Slave Lake, *Alta.* 36 Bc
Lesser Slave Lake Provincial Park, *Alta.* 36 Cc
Lesser Slave R., *Alberta* 36 Cc
Lessines, *Belgium* 64 Bd
Lestijärvi, *Finland* 66 Le
Lestock, *Saskatchewan* 37 Ng
Lesvos, *Greece* 77 Ee
Leszno, *Poland* 69 Gc
L'Étape, *Quebec* 35 Te
Letcher, *S. Dakota* 46 Hd
Letea, *Romania* 76 Gb
Letellier, *Manitoba* 37 Uj
Lethbridge, *Alberta* 36 Ej
Lethbridge, *Newfoundland* 33 Te
Leticia, *Colombia* 52 Cd
Leti Kep., *Indonesia* 83 Jm
Letpadan, *Burma* 89 Je
Letterkenny, *Eire* 62 Bf
Letur, *Spain* 71 Dc
Leucate, *France* 73 Ee
Leucite Hills, *Wyoming* 46 Ce
Leuk, *Switzerland* 65 Cb
Leuser, *Sumatra* 83 Ck
Leuven, *Belgium* 64 Cd
Leuze, *Belgium* 64 Bd
Levack, *Ontario* 34 Jf
Levádhia, *Greece* 77 De
Levanger, *Norway* 66 De
Leven L., *Scotland* 62 Ed
Levêque, C., *W. Australia* 56 Dc
Lever L., *N.W.T.* 38 Pc
Levice, *Czechoslovakia* 69 Hd
Levick, Mt., *Antarctica* 104 Lb
Levin, *New Zealand* 55 Ed
Lévis, *Quebec* 32 Ag
Lévis, Pte., *Quebec* 35 Tb
Levítha, *Greece* 77 Ff
Levkás, *Greece* 77 Ce
Levoča, *Czechoslovakia* 69 Jd
Lewes, *England* 63 Hk
Lewis, *Scotland* 62 Cb
Lewis, Butt of, *Scotland* 62 Cb
Lewisburg, *Pennsylvania* 40 He
Lewisburg, *Tennessee* 45 Dc
Lewisburg, *W. Virginia* 45 Gb
Lewis Hills, *Newfoundland* 33 Oe
Lewisporte, *Newfoundland* 33 Rd
Lewis Range, *Montana* 42 Db
Lewis Smith L., *Alabama* 45 Dc
Lewiston, *Idaho* 47 Eb
Lewiston, *Maine* 32 Bj
Lewiston, *Michigan* 40 Dc
Lewiston, *N. Carolina* 45 Jb
Lewistown, *Illinois* 40 Ae
Lewistown, *Montana* 46 Cb
Lewistown, *Pennsylvania* 44 Bb
Lewvan, *Saskatchewan* 37 Nh
Lexington, *Georgia, U.S.A.* 45 Fd
Lexington, *Kentucky* 45 Ea
Lexington, *Missouri* 49 Lc
Lexington, *N. Carolina* 45 Gc
Lexington, *Nebraska* 49 Hb
Lexington, *Tennessee* 45 Cc
Lexington, *Virginia* 45 Hb
Leydsdorp, *Transvaal* 95 Ed
Leyte, *Philippines* 83 Hh
Lezajsk, *Poland* 69 Kc
L'gov, *U.S.S.R.* 80 Jf
Lhasa, *China* 89 Hc
Lhasa He, *China* 89 Hc
Lhazê, *China* 89 Gc
Lhünzê, *China* 89 Hc
Liangchow. *See* Wuwei
Lianjiang, *China* 85 Jj
Lianping, *China* 85 Kf
Liant, C., *Thailand* 87 Cd
Lianyungang, *China* 84 Je
Liaocheng, *China* 84 Hd
Liaodong Wan, *China* 84 Kc
Liao He, *China* 82 Hb
Liaoning, *China* 84 Kb
Liaoyang, *China* 84 Lb
Liard, R., *N.W.T.* 38 Me
Liard Ra., *N.W.T.* 38 Me
Liard River, *B.C.* 38 Kf
Liari, *Pakistan* 88 Cc
Libby L., *N.W.T.* 38 Pa
Liberal, *Kansas* 48 Gd
Liberec, *Czechoslovakia* 68 Fc
Liberia, *Costa Rica* 51 Bd
Liberia, *West Africa* 98 Cg
Libertad, *Mexico* 50 Bb
Liberty, *Saskatchewan* 37 Mg
Libnan, Jebel, *Lebanon* 94 Dc
Libourne, *France* 73 Cd
Libreville, *Gabon* 96 Bd
Libya, *North Africa* 99 Hc
Licata, *Sicily* 75 Dg
Lichfield, *England* 63 Fh
Lichinga, *Mozambique* 95 Fb
Licking R., *Kentucky* 45 Ea
Lida, *Byelorussia* 80 De
Liddes, *Switzerland* 65 Cc
Lidköping, *Sweden* 67 Eg
Lido di Roma, *Italy* 75 De
Lidzbark, *Poland* 69 Ja
Liebenthal, *Saskatchewan* 36 Hh
Liechtenstein, *Europe* 65 Ea
Liège, *Belgium* 64 Dd
Liegnitz. *See* Legnica
Lieksa, *Finland* 66 Pe
Lienz, *Austria* 68 Ee
Liepāja, *Latvia* 67 Jh
Lier, *Belgium* 64 Cc
Lierneux, *Belgium* 64 Dd
Liestal, *Switzerland* 65 Ca
Lièvre, R. du, *Quebec* 35 Pg
Lièvres, I. aux, *Quebec* 32 Cf
Lifu, *Loyalty Is.* 102 Fk
Liguria, *Italy* 74 Bc
Ligurian Sea, *Italy* 74 Bd
Lijiang, *China* 82 De
Likasi, *Zaire* 96 Fg
Likely, *British Columbia* 39 Nj
Likimi, *Zaire* 96 Ed
Liling, *China* 85 Fj
Lilla Edet, *Sweden* 67 Eg
Lille, *Belgium* 64 Cc
Lille, *France* 72 Ea
Lillehammer, *Norway* 67 Df
Lillesand, *Norway* 67 Cg
Lillo, *Belgium* 64 Cc
Lillo, *Spain* 70 Dc
Lillooet, *B.C.* 39 Nk
Lillooet, R., *B.C.* 39 Mk
Lilongwe, *Malawi* 97 Gg
Lima, *Ohio* 40 De
Lima, *Peru* 52 Bf
Limache, *Chile* 54 Bd
Limassol, *Cyprus* 94 Bc
Limay, R., *Argentina* 54 Ce
Limay Mahuida, *Argentina* 54 Ce
Limbaži, *Latvia* 67 Lh
Limbe, *Malawi* 97 Hh
Limbourg, *Belgium* 64 Dd
Limburg, *Belgium* 64 Dd
Limburg, *West Germany* 68 Cc
Limchow. *See* Hepu
Limeira, *Brazil* 53 Hh
Limerick, *Saskatchewan* 36 Lj
Limerick (Luimneach), *Eire* 63 Bh
Limes, *Belgium* 64 De
Limestone, *Maine* 32 Eg
Limestone L., *Manitoba* 37 Wb
Limestone Pt., cape, *Man.* 37 Te
Lim Fjorden, *Denmark* 67 Ch
Limmavady, *N. Ireland* 62 Ce
Limmen, *Netherlands* 64 Cb
Limmen Bight, *N. Terr.* 57 Gb
Limni, *Greece* 77 De
Limnos, *Greece* 77 Ee
Limoges, *France* 72 Dd
Limoges, *Ontario* 35 Pg
Limon, *Colorado* 48 Fc
Limón, *Costa Rica* 51 Cd
Limousin, *France* 72 Dd
Limoux, *France* 73 Ee
Limpopo, *Mozamb.* 95 Ed
Linares, *Chile* 54 Be
Linares, *Mexico* 50 Ec
Linares, *Spain* 70 Dc
Lincang, *China* 82 Df
Linchwan. *See* Fuzhou
Lincoln, *Argentina* 54 Dd
Lincoln, *England* 63 Gg
Lincoln, *Illinois* 49 Nb
Lincoln, *Maine* 32 Dh
Lincoln, *Michigan* 40 Ec
Lincoln, *Nebraska* 49 Jb
Lincoln, *New Zealand* 55 De
Lincoln Sea, *Arctic Ocean* 41 Qa
Lincolnton, *N. Carolina* 45 Gc
Lincolnville, *Nova Scotia* 33 Lh
Lincoln Wolds, *England* 63 Gg
Lindau, *West Germany* 68 Ce
Lindbergh, *Alberta* 36 Ge
Lindeman Is., Mt., *Queensland* 57 Ke
Lindesnes, *Norway* 67 Bh
Lindi, *Tanzania* 97 Hf
Lindley, *Orange Free State* 95 De
Lindos, *Greece* 77 Gf
Lindsay, *Ontario* 35 Mh
Lindsey, *England* 63 Gg
Line Is., *Pacific Ocean* 103 Kg
Linfen, *China* 84 Ed
Lingayen, *Philippines* 83 Hg
Lingchuan, *China* 85 Ek
Lingen, *West Germany* 68 Bb
Lingga, *Riouw Arch.*, *Indonesia* 83 El
Lingley, *New Brunswick* 32 Fh
Lingling, *China* 85 Ej
Linguère, *Senegal* 98 Be
Ling Xian, *China* 85 Fj
Lingyun, *China* 85 Ck
Lingyun. *See* Lingyan
Linhai, *China* 85 Kh
Linhares, *Brazil* 53 Jg
Linhe, *China* 84 Cb
Linière, *Quebec* 32 Bg
Linkiang. *See* Qingjiang
Linköping, *Sweden* 67 Fg
Linkuva, *Lithuania* 67 Kh
Linn, *Missouri* 45 Ba
Linnhe L., *Scotland* 62 Dd
Linosa, *Medit. Sea* 75 Dh
Lins, *Brazil* 54 Gb
Lintan, *China* 84 Ae
Linth, *Switzerland* 65 Eb
Linthal, *Switzerland* 65 Db
Lintlaw, *Saskatchewan* 37 Of
Linton, *Quebec* 35 Se
Linxi, *China* 82 Gb
Linxia, *China* 84 Ae
Lin Xian, *China* 85 Fk
Linyi, *China* 82 Gc
Linyi, *China* 84 Je
Linz, *Austria* 68 Fd
Lion, G. du, *France* 73 Fe
Lions Head, *Ontario* 34 Jh
Lio Porgyul, *China* 88 Eb
Liouesso, *Congo* 96 Dd
Lipa, *Yugoslavia* 74 Fc
Lipari Is., *Italy* 75 Ef
Lipetsk, *U.S.S.R.* 80 Le
Liping, *China* 85 Dj
Lipkany, *Moldavia* 80 Eg
Lipovets, *Ukraine* 80 Fg
Lippstadt, *West Germany* 68 Cc
Lipsói, *Greece* 77 Ff
Lipton, *Saskatchewan* 37 Oh
Lira, *Uganda* 97 Gd
Lircay, *Peru* 52 Cf
Liria, *Spain* 71 Ec
Lisala, *Zaire* 96 Ed
Lisboa, *Portugal* 70 Ac
Lisbon. *See* Lisboa
Lisburn, *N. Ireland* 63 Cf
Lisburne C., *Alaska* 43 Wl
Liscannor B., *Eire* 63 Ah
Liscomb, *Nova Scotia* 33 Kh
Lisdoonvarna, *Eire* 63 Ag
Lishi, *China* 84 Ed
Lishui, *China* 85 Jh
Lisianski, *Hawaiian Is.* 102 He
Lisieux, *France* 72 Db
Lisieux, *Saskatchewan* 37 Mj
L'Isle, *Switzerland* 65 Bb
L'Islet, *Quebec* 32 Bf
L'Isle-Verte, *Quebec* 32 Ce
Lismore, *Eire* 63 Bh
Lismore, *Nova Scotia* 33 Kh
Lismore, *N.S.W.* 57 Ke
Listowel, *Eire* 63 Ah
Listowel, *Ontario* 34 Kj
Litchfield, *Illinois* 49 Nc
Litchfield, *Minnesota* 46 Kc
Lith, Al, *Arabia* 92 De
Lithgow, *N.S.W.* 57 Kf
Lithinon, C., *Crete* 77 Eg
Lithuania (Litovskaya S.S.R.), *U.S.S.R.* 80 Cd
Litoměřice, *Czechoslovakia* 68 Fc
Little Abitibi L., *Ontario* 34 Kc
Little Bay Islands, *Nfld.* 33 Rd
Little Bear L., *Sask.* 37 Nd
Little Beaver R., *Man.* 37 Va
Little Belt Mts., *Montana* 46 Bb
Little Bow Provincial Park, *Alberta* 36 Eh
Little Bow R., *Alberta* 36 Dh
Little Buffalo R., *N.W.T.* 38 Re
Little Bullhead, *Manitoba* 37 Vg
Little Burnt Bay, *Nfld.* 33 Rd
Little Current, *Ontario* 34 Jg
Little Current, R., *Ontario* 34 Db
Little Falls, *Minnesota* 46 Kc
Little Falls, *New York* 44 Ca
Little Fort, *B.C.* 39 Nk
Little Harbour Deep, *Nfld.* 33 Qc
Little Horn Mts., *Arizona* 47 Gj
Little Longlac, *Ontario* 34 Dc
Little Playgreen L., *Man.* 37 Ud
Little R., *Missouri* 45 Bb
Little River, *New Zealand* 55 De
Little Rock, *Arkansas* 45 Ac
Little Rocky Mts., *Montana* 46 Cb
Little Salmon L., *Y.T.* 38 Fd
Little Smoky, *Alberta* 39 Ph
Littleton, *Colorado* 48 Ec
Littleton, *New Hampshire* 40 Lc
Little Valley, *New York* 44 Aa
Liucheng, *China* 85 Dk
Liuheng Dao, *China* 85 Lh
Liupan Shan, *China* 84 Be
Liusvaara, *U.S.S.R.* 66 Pe
Liuzhou, *China* 85 Dk
Livelong, *Saskatchewan* 36 Je
Live Oak, *Florida* 45 Fe
Liverpool, *England* 63 Eg
Liverpool, *Nova Scotia* 32 Hj
Liverpool, *N.S.W.* 57 Kf
Liverpool, C., *N.W.T.* 31 Mc
Liverpool B., *N.W.T.* 38 Ha
Liverpool Coast, *Greenland* 41 Nb
Liverpool Range, *N.S.W.* 57 Jf
Livingston, *Alabama* 45 Cd
Livingston, *Guatemala* 51 Bc
Livingston, *Montana* 46 Bc
Livingston, *Tennessee* 45 Eb
Livingston, *Texas* 49 Kg
Livingston, L., *Texas* 49 Kg
Livingstone. *See* Maramba

Livingstone Creek, Y.T. 38 Fe
Livingstone Ra., Alberta 36 Ch
Livingston I., S. Shetlands 104 Sc
Livingstonia, Malawi 95 Eb
Livno, Yugoslavia 74 Fd
Livny, U.S.S.R. 80 Ke
Livo Joki, Finland 66 Md
Livorno, Italy 74 Cd
Livramento, Brazil 54 Ed
Liwale, Tanzania 97 Hf
Li Xian, China 85 Eh
Liyepaya, Latvia 67 Jh
Lizard Pt., England 63 Dl
Lizotte, Quebec 35 Sd
Ljubljana, Yugoslavia 74 Eb
Ljubuški, Yugoslavia 74 Fd
Ljungdalen, Sweden 66 Ee
Ljusdal, Sweden 67 Gf
Llandovery, Wales 63 Ej
Llandrindod Wells, Wales 63 Eh
Llandudno, Wales 63 Eg
Llanelli, Wales 63 Ej
Llanes, Spain 70 Ca
Llangollen, Wales 63 Eh
Llanguihue, L., Chile 54 Bf
Llano Estacado, N. Mex. 48 Fe
Llerena, Spain 70 Bc
Llico, Chile 54 Bd
Lloyd George, Mt., B.C. 39 Lg
Lloyd L., Saskatchewan 39 Tg
Lloydminster, Sask. 36 He
Lluchmayor, Balearic Is. 71 Gc
Llullaillaco, Chile/Arg. 54 Cb
Loango, Congo 96 Ce
Lobbes, Belgium 64 Cd
Loberia, Argentina 54 Ee
Lobito, Angola 96 Cg
Lobos, Argentina 54 Ee
Locarno, Switzerland 65 Db
Lochaber Mines, N.S. 33 Kh
Lochalsh, Ontario 34 Fd
Lochalsh, Kyle of, Scotland 62 Dc
Lochem, Netherlands 64 Eb
Lochinver, Scotland 62 Db
Lochnagar, Scotland 62 Ed
Lochristi, Belgium 64 Bc
Lochy L., Scotland 62 Dd
Lockeport, Nova Scotia 32 Gk
Lockerbie, Scotland 62 Ee
Locker Pt., N.W.T. 38 Qa
Lockhart, R., N.W.T. 38 Td
Lock Haven, Pennsylvania 44 Bb
Lockport, Manitoba 37 Uh
Lockport, New York 44 Aa
Lockwood, Saskatchewan 37 Ng
Locle, le, Switzerland 65 Ba
Loc Ninh, Vietnam 83 Eh
Lodeynoye Pole, U.S.S.R. 80 Ha
Lodhran, Pakistan 90 Bf
Lodi, Wisconsin 40 Bd
Lödingen, Norway 66 Fb
Lodwar, Kenya 97 Hd
Łódź, Poland 69 Hc
Loenen, Netherlands 64 Eb
Lofer, Austria 68 Ee
Lofoten, Is., Norway 66 Ec
Logan, Utah 48 Bb
Logan, Mt., Quebec 32 Fe
Logan, Mt., Y.T. 38 Ce
Logan L., Alberta 36 Fc
Logan Mts., Y.T./N.W.T. 38 Je
Logansport, Indiana 40 Ce
Logone, Cameroun/Chad 96 Cb
Logroño, Spain 71 Da
Lohardaga, India 91 Ed
Loharu, India 90 Df
Loikaw, Burma 89 Je
Loir, France 72 Cc
Loire, France 72 Dc
Loire, France 72 Ed
Loire-Atlantique, Fr. 72 Cc
Loiret, France 72 Ec
Loir-et-Cher, France 72 Dc
Loja, Ecuador 52 Bd
Loja, Spain 70 Cd
Lokeren, Belgium 64 Cc
Lokka, Finland 66 Mc
Løkken, Denmark 67 Ch
Løkken, Norway 66 Ce
Loko, Nigeria 98 Gg
Loks Land, N.W.T. 31 Ne
Lola, Angola 96 Cg
Lolland, Denmark 67 Dj
Lom, Bulgaria 76 Dc
Loman, Minnesota 46 La
Lomas, Peru 52 Cg
Lomas de Zamorah, Arg. 54 Ed
Lombard, Montana 46 Bb
Lombardy, Italy 74 Bc
Lomblem, Indonesia 83 Hm
Lombok, Indonesia 83 Gm
Lomé, Togo 98 Fg
Lomela, Zaire 96 Ee
Lomié, Cameroun 99 Hh
Lommel, Belgium 64 Dc
Lomond, Alberta 36 Eh
Lomond, Newfoundland 33 Pd
Lomond, Loch, N.S. 33 Mh
Lomond L., Scotland 62 Dd
Łomza, Poland 69 Kb
Loncoché, Chile 54 Be
Loncopué, Argentina 54 Be
Londesborough, Ontario 34 Jj
Londiani, Kenya 97 He
London, England 63 Gj
London, Ontario 34 Jk
Londonderry, N. Ire. 62 Cf
Londonderry, N.S. 32 Jh
Londonderry, C., W. Aust. 56 Eb
Londonderry, I., Chile 54 Bj
Lonely I., Ontario 34 Jg
Lone Rock, Sask. 36 He
Long B., S. Carolina 43 Le
Long Beach, California 47 Dj
Long Beach, New Jersey 44 Cc
Long Branch, New Jersey 44 Cb
Longchamps, Belgium 64 Dd
Long Cr., Saskatchewan 37 Oj
Longford, Eire 63 Bg
Long Harbour, Nfld. 33 Tf
Long I., New York 44 Db
Long I., Nova Scotia 32 Fj
Long I., N.W.T. 31 Mg
Long I., The Bahamas 51 Db
Long Island City, New York 44 Db
Long Island Sound, N.Y./Conn. 44 Db
Long L., Maine 32 Df
Long L., N. Dakota 46 Gb
Long L., New Brunswick 32 Ff
Long L., Ontario 34 Dc
Long L., Scotland 62 Dd
Longlac, Ontario 34 Dc
Longmont, Colorado 48 Eb
Longnan, China 85 Gk
Long Point, pen, Man. 37 Te
Long Point B., Ontario 34 Kk
Long Pond, Nfld. 33 Uf
Long Prairie, Minnesota 46 Kb
Long Pt., Ontario 34 Kk
Long Range Mts., Nfld. 33 Pd
Longreach, Queensland 57 Hd
Longs Pk., Colorado 42 Ec
Longs Pk., Colorado 48 Eb
Longtom L., N.W.T. 38 Pc
Longtown, England 62 Fe
Longué, France 72 Cc
Longue Pointe, Quebec 35 Th
Longueuil, Quebec 35 Rg
Longuyon, France 72 Fb
Longview, Alberta 36 Ch
Longview, Texas 49 Kf
Longview, Washington 47 Bb
Longwy, France 72 Fb
Longxi, China 84 Be
Long-Xuyen, Vietnam 87 Dd
Longyan, China 85 Hk
Lonneker, Netherlands 64 Eb
Lons-le-Saunier, France 72 Fc
Looc, Philippines 83 Hh
Looe, England 63 Ek
Lookout, C., N. Carolina 43 Le
Loolmalasin, Tanzania 97 He
Looma, Alberta 36 De
Loomis, Saskatchewan 36 Jj
Loon, Ontario 34 Bd
Loon, R., Alberta 39 Qg
Loon Bay, Newfoundland 33 Sd
Loon Lake, Saskatchewan 36 Hd
Loon R., Manitoba 37 Qb
Loop Hd., Eire 63 Ah
Loos, British Columbia 39 Nj
Lopez C., Gabon 96 Be
Lopik, Netherlands 64 Cc
Lop Nur, China 82 Bb
Lopphavet, Norway 66 Ja
Lorain, Ohio 40 Ee
Loralai, Pakistan 88 Cb
Lorca, Spain 71 Ed
Lord Howe I., Pacific Ocean 102 El
Lord Mayor B., N.W.T. 31 Kd
Lordsburg, New Mexico 48 Cf
Loreburn, Saskatchewan 36 Lg
Lorena, Brazil 53 Jh
Loreto, Brazil 53 He
Loreto, Mexico 50 Bb
Lorette, Manitoba 37 Vj
Loretteville, Quebec 35 Tf
Lorica, Colombia 52 Bb
Lorient, France 72 Bc
L'Orignal, Ontario 35 Qg
Lorlie, Saskatchewan 37 Oh
Lorn, Firth of, Scotland 62 Dd
Lörrach, West Germany 68 Be
Lorraine, France 72 Fb
Lorrainville, Quebec 35 Le
Los Andes, Chile 54 Bd
Los Angeles, California 47 Dh
Los Angeles, Chile 54 Be
Los Blancos, Argentina 54 Db
Lošinj, Yugoslavia 74 Ec
Los Menucos, Argentina 54 Cf
Los Pozos, Chile 54 Bc
Los Santos, Panama 51 Ce
Los Santos de Maimona, Spain 70 Bc
Lossiemouth, Scotland 62 Ec
Los Teques, Venezuela 52 Da
Los Tigres, Argentina 54 Dc
Los Vilos, Chile 54 Bd
Lot, France 73 Dd
Lot, R., France 73 Dd
Lota, Chile 54 Be
Lotbinière, Quebec 40 Lb
Lot-et-Garonne, Fr. 73 Dd
Lothian, Scotland 62 Ee
Lottigna, Switzerland 65 Db
Loubet Coast, Antarctica 104 Sc
Loudéac, France 72 Bb
Loudima, Congo 96 Ce
Loudon, Malawi 97 Gg
Loudon, Tennessee 45 Ec
Loudun, France 72 Dc
Louga, Senegal 98 Be
Loughborough, England 63 Gh
Loughborough I., Burma 89 Jf
Loughead, Alberta 36 Ff
Lougheed I., N.W.T. 30 Jb
Loughrea, Eire 63 Bg
Louhans, France 72 Fc
Louisa, Kentucky 45 Fa
Louisbourg, Nova Scotia 33 Nh
Louisburg, N. Carolina 45 Hb
Louisdale, Nova Scotia 33 Lh
Louise, L., Alberta 39 Pk
Louise Falls, N.W.T. 38 Pe
Louise I., B.C. 39 Hj
Louiseville, Quebec 35 Sf
Louisiade Arch., Papua New Guinea 57 Kb
Louisiana, U.S.A. 43 He
Louis Trichardt, Transvaal 95 Dd
Louisville, Colorado 48 Ec
Louisville, Kentucky 45 Ea
Louisville, Mississippi 45 Cd
Louis XIV, Pt. (C. Jones), Quebec 31 Mg
Loulé, Portugal 70 Ad
Loup, I. au, Quebec 33 Lf
Loup City, Nebraska 49 Hb
Loups, B. des, Quebec 33 Mc
Loups, L. des, Quebec 40 Gb
Lourdes, France 73 Ce
Lourdes, Newfoundland 33 Ne
Lourenço Marques. See Maputo
Louriçal, Portugal 70 Ab
Lourinhã, Portugal 70 Ac
Lousana, Alberta 36 Df
Louth, Eire 63 Cg
Louth, England 63 Hg
Louth, N.S.W. 57 Jf
Louvain. See Leuven
Louveigne, Belgium 64 Dd
Louviers, France 72 Db
Lövanger, Sweden 66 Jd
Love, Saskatchewan 37 Ne
Loveland, Colorado 46 Ee
Lovell, Wyoming 46 Cc
Loverna, Saskatchewan 36 Hg
Loviisa, Finland 67 Mf
Lovington, New Mexico 48 Ff
Lövlid, Sweden 66 Gd
Low, Quebec 35 Pg
Low, C., N.W.T. 31 Le
Lowa, Zaire 96 Fe
Low Bush River, Ontario 34 Kd
Lowell, Massachusetts 40 Ld
Lowell, Michigan 40 Dd
Lower Brule, S. Dakota 46 Hc
Lower Island Cove, Nfld. 33 Uf
Lower Laberge, Y.T. 38 Fe
Lower Neguac, N.B. 32 Gf
Lower Ohio, Nova Scotia 32 Gk
Lower Post, B.C. 38 Jf
Lower Savage Is., N.W.T. 31 Ne
Lower West Pubnico, N.S. 32 Gk
Lower Woods Harbour, N.S. 32 Gk
Lowestoft, England 63 Jh
Łowicz, Poland 69 Hb
Lowther I., N.W.T. 31 Kc
Lowville, New York 40 Jd
Loyalist, Alberta 36 Fg
Loyalty Is., Pacific Ocean 102 Fk
Lozère, France 73 Ed
Loznica, Yugoslavia 76 Bb
Lu'an, China 82 Gd
Luan. See Changzhi
Luanda, Angola 96 Cf
Luang Prabang, Laos 87 Cc
Luan He, China 84 Jb
Luanping, China 84 Hb
Luan Xian, China 84 Jc
Luarca, Spain 70 Ba
Luashi, Zaire 96 Eg
Lubaczów, Poland 69 Kc
Lubana, Latvia 67 Mh
Lubango, Angola 96 Cg
Lubartów, Poland 69 Kc
Lübben, East Germany 68 Ec
Lubbock, Texas 48 Gf
Lübeck, West Germany 68 Db
Lubefu, Zaire 96 Ee
Lubicon L., Alberta 36 Bb
Lubin, Poland 69 Gc
Lublin, Poland 69 Kc
Lubliniec, Poland 69 Hc
Lubuklinggau, Sumatra 83 Dl
Lubumbashi, Zaire 95 Db
Luc, le, France 73 Ge
Lucala, Angola 96 Df
Lucan, Ontario 34 Jj
Lucania. See Basilicata
Lucania Mt., Y.T. 38 Ce
Lucca, Italy 74 Cd
Lucea, Jamaica 51 Dc
Luce B., Scotland 63 Df
Lucena, Spain 70 Cd
Lučenec, Czechoslovakia 69 Hd
Lucera, Italy 75 Ee
Lucerne. See Luzern
Luceville, Quebec 32 De
Luchi, U.S.S.R. 81 Fb
Luchow. See Hefei
Lucie, L., Quebec 35 Mb
Lucinda, Pennsylvania 44 Ab
Luckau, East Germany 68 Ec
Luckenwalde, East Germany 68 Eb
Lucknow, India 91 Cb
Lucknow, Ontario 34 Jj
Lucky Lake, Sask. 36 Kh
Lucky Strike, Alberta 36 Fj
Luçon, France 72 Cc
Lüda, China 84 Kc
Luderitz, Namibia 95 Ae
Ludgate, Ontario 34 Kg
Ludhiana, India 90 De
Ludington, Michigan 40 Cc
Ludlow, England 63 Fh
Ludlow, New Brunswick 32 Fg
Ludvika, Sweden 67 Ff
Ludwigshafen, West Ger. 68 Cd
Ludwigslust, East Germany 68 Db
Ludza, Latvia 67 Mh
Luebo, Zaire 96 Ef
Luga, U.S.S.R. 80 Fb
Lugano, Switz. 65 Db
Lugo, Spain 70 Ba
Lugoj, Romania 76 Cb
Lugovay, Kazakhstan 78 Gd
Luhit, India 89 Jc
Luitpold Coast, Antarctica 104 Ab
Luján, Argentina 54 Ed
Luján, Argentina 54 Cd
Lukachek, U.S.S.R. 79 Nc
Lukovit, Bulgaria 76 Ec
Lukoyanov, U.S.S.R. 81 Gc
Lukula, Zaire 96 Cf
Luleå, Sweden 66 Kd
Lule Älv, Sweden 66 Jc
Lulong, China 84 Jc
Luluabourg. See Kananga
Lulu I., British Columbia 39 Hm
Lumberton, N. Carolina 45 Hc
Lumbres, France 72 Ea
Lummen, Belgium 64 Dd
Lumsden, Newfoundland 33 Td
Lumsden, New Zealand 55 Bf
Lumsden, Saskatchewan 37 Nh
Luna, Arkansas 45 Bd
Lund, Sweden 67 Ej
Lundar, Manitoba 37 Th
Lundbreck, Alberta 36 Cj
Lundy I., England 63 Dj
Lüneburg, West Germany 68 Db
Lunel, France 73 Fe
Lunenburg, Nova Scotia 32 Hj
Lunéville, France 72 Gb
Lungan. See Pingwu
Lungki. See Zhangzhou
Luni, India 88 Dc
Lunino, U.S.S.R. 81 Gd
Lunz, Austria 68 Fe
Luöbcker Bucht, Germany 68 Da
Luocheng, China 85 Dk
Luohe, China 84 Gf
Luoyang, China 84 Fe
Lupa Market, Tanzania 97 Hf
Łupków, Poland 69 Kd
Luputa, Zaire 96 Ef
Luque, Paraguay 54 Ec
Luray, Virginia 40 Gf
Lurgan, N. Ireland 63 Cf
Luribay, Bolivia 52 Dg
Lurøy, Norway 66 Ec
Lusaka, Zambia 95 Dc
Lusambo, Zaire 96 Ef
Luscar, Alberta 39 Pj
Luseland, Saskatchewan 36 Hf
Lushai Hills. See Mizo Hills
Lushes Bight, Nfld. 33 Rd
Lushnjë, Albania 77 Bd
Lü-shun. See Lüda
Lusk, Wyoming 46 Ed
Luso, Angola 96 Dg
Lussanvira, Brazil 53 Gh
Lut Desert, Iran 93 Gc
Lutembo, Angola 96 Eg
Luther, Michigan 40 Dc
Luton, England 63 Gj
Lutsen, Minnesota 40 Ab
Lutsk, Ukraine 80 Df
Luttre, Belgium 64 Cd
Luvia, Finland 67 Jf
Luwuk, Celebes (Sulawesi) 83 Hl
Luxembourg, Belg. 72 Fb
Luxembourg, N.-W. Europe 72 Gb
Luxeuil, France 72 Gc
Luxor, Egypt 99 Mc
Luzern, Switz. 65 Da
Luzhou, China 85 Bh
Luziânia, Brazil 53 Hg
Luzilândia, Brazil 53 Jd
Luzon, Philippines 83 Hg
Luzon Str., Philippines 82 Hf
Luzy, France 72 Ec
L'vov, Ukraine 80 Dg
Lyallpur, Pakistan 90 Ce
Lybster, Scotland 62 Eb
Lycksele, Sweden 66 Hd
Lydavėnai, Lithuania 67 Kj
Lydda, Israel 94 Cf
Lyddal, Manitoba 37 Tc
Lydenburg, Transvaal 95 Ee
Lydiatt, Manitoba 37 Vj
Lyell, Mt., California 47 Dg
Lyell I., British Columbia 39 Hj
Lyell Range, New Zealand 55 Dd
Lykens, Pennsylvania 44 Bb
Lyleton, Manitoba 37 Qj
Lymburn, Alberta 39 Oh
Lyme B., England 63 Fk
Lyme Regis, England 63 Fk
Lynchburg, Virginia 45 Hb
Lynden, Ontario 34 Kj
Lynn, Massachusetts 44 Ea
Lynn Lake, Manitoba 37 Qb
Lynton, England 63 Ej
Lynx L., N.W.T. 38 Ud
Lyon, France 72 Fd
Lyon, Montana 46 Bc
Lyonnais, France 72 Ed
Lyons, Georgia, U.S.A. 45 Fd
Lyons, Kansas 49 Hc
Lyons, New York 44 Ba
Lyons, R., W. Australia 56 Cd
Lys, Belgium/France 64 Bd
Łyse, Poland 69 Jb
Lysekil, Sweden 67 Dg
Lyss, Switzerland 65 Ca
Lyster, Quebec 35 Tf
Lysva, U.S.S.R. 81 Na
Lyttelton, New Zealand 55 De
Lytton, British Columbia 39 Nk
Lytton, Quebec 35 Of

M

Ma'an, Jordan 94 Dg
Maarheeze, Netherlands 64 Dc
Maarianhamina. See Mariehamn
Ma'arret en Numan, Syria 94 Eb
Maas, Netherlands 64 Dc
Maasbree, Netherlands 64 Ec
Maaseik, Belgium 64 Dc
Maassluis, Netherlands 64 Cc
Maastricht, Netherlands 64 Dd
Mabalane, Mozambique 95 Ed
Mabella, Ontario 37 Nb
Maberly, Ontario 35 Oh
Mabote, Mozambique 95 Ed
Mabou, Nova Scotia 33 Lg
Mabuki, Tanzania 97 Ge
McAdam, N.B. 32 Eh
Macaé, Brazil 53 Jh
Macaíba, Brazil 53 Ke
McAlester, Oklahoma 49 Ke
MacAlpine L., N.W.T. 38 Wb
Macamic, Quebec 35 Md
Macapá, Brazil 53 Gc
Macás, Ecuador 52 Bd
Macau, Brazil 53 Ke
Macau, S.E. Asia 85 Fl
Macauba, Brazil 53 Gf
McAuley, Manitoba 37 Qh
McBeth Pt., cape, Man. 37 Uf
McBride, B.C. 39 Nj
McCammon, Idaho 48 Aa
Maccan, Nova Scotia 32 Hh
McCann L., N.W.T. 38 Ue
McCauley I., B.C. 39 Hj
Macclesfield, England 63 Fg
Maccles L., Newfoundland 33 Se
McClure Str., N.W.T. 30 Hc
McComb, Mississippi 45 Be
McConnell Ra., N.W.T. 38 Mc
McConnellsburg, Pa. 44 Ac
McCook, Nebraska 48 Gb
McCord, Saskatchewan 36 Lj
McCreary, Manitoba 37 Sh
Macculloch, C., N.W.T. 31 Mc
McCusker R., Sask. 36 Jc
McDame, B.C. 38 Jf
Macdiarmid, Ontario 34 Bc
Macdonald, L., W. Aust. 56 Ed
Macdonnell Ranges, N. Terr. 56 Fd
McDouall Range, N. Terr. 57 Fc
Macdougall L., N.W.T. 30 Kd
Mace, Ontario 34 Ld
Maceió, Brazil 53 Ke
Macerata, Italy 74 Dd
McGee, Saskatchewan 36 Jg
McGill, Nevada 47 Ff
Macgillycuddy's Reeks, Eire 63 Aj
MacGregor, Manitoba 37 Tj
McGregor, Texas 49 Jg
McGregor L. (Res.), Alberta 36 Eh
McGregor R., B.C. 39 Nh
McGregor Range, Queensland 57 He
Mach, Pakistan 88 Cc
Machala, Ecuador 52 Bd
Macharetí, Bolivia 52 Eh
Machias, Maine 32 Ej
Machias Seal I., N.B. 32 Ej
Machilipatnam, India 88 Fe
Machiques, Venezuela 52 Ca
Machiwara, India 90 Ee
Macias Nguema. See Bioko
Măcin, Romania 76 Gb
McInnis, Ontario 34 Jc
McIntosh, Ontario 36 Ja
McIntosh, S. Dakota 46 Gc
McIntyre B., Ontario 34 Bc
McKague, Saskatchewan 37 Of
Mackay, Queensland 57 Jd
Mackay, L., W. Australia 56 Ed
MacKay L., N.W.T. 38 Sd
McKay L., Ontario 34 Dc
MacKay R., Alberta 39 Rg
McKeesport, Pennsylvania 44 Ab
Mackenzie, Guyana 52 Fb
Mackenzie, Ontario 34 Ad
McKenzie, Tennessee 45 Cb
Mackenzie, District of, N.W.T. 30 He
Mackenzie B., Y.T. 38 Ea
Mackenzie Bay, Antarctica 104 Fc
Mackenzie King I., N.W.T. 30 Hb
McKenzie L., Ontario 37 Mb
McKenzie L., Sask. 37 Pd
Mackenzie Mts., Y.T./N.W.T. 38 Fc
Mackenzie R., N.W.T. 38 Gb
MacKerracher L., Man. 37 Sa
Mackinac I., Michigan 40 Dc
Mackinaw, Michigan 40 Dc
McKinley, Mt., Alaska 43 Xl
McKirdy, Ontario 34 Bc
Macklin, Saskatchewan 36 Hf
McKnight L., Manitoba 37 Qb
McLaughlin, Alberta 36 Gf
McLaughlin R., Manitoba 37 Ue
McLean, Manitoba 37 Nh
McLean L., Saskatchewan 36 Hb
McLeansboro, Illinois 45 Ca
McLennan, Alberta 39 Ph
McLeod B., N.W.T. 38 Sd
McLeod Lake, B.C. 39 Mh
McLeod R., Alberta 36 Be
McLoughlin B., N.W.T. 38 Yb
Mac-Mahon, Algeria 98 Fc
McMahon, Saskatchewan 36 Kh
McMillan, L., New Mexico 48 Ef
Macmillan, R., Y.T. 38 Fd
McMinnville, Tennessee 45 Ec
McMorran, Saskatchewan 36 Jg
McMunn, Manitoba 36 Fa
McMurdo Sound, Antarctica 104 Lb
McMurphy, B.C. 39 Ok
McNary, Arizona 48 Ce
MacNutt, Saskatchewan 37 Qg
McNutt I., Nova Scotia 32 Gk
Macomb, Illinois 49 Mb
Macomer, Sardinia 75 Be
Macon, Belgium 64 Cd
Mâcon, France 72 Fc
Macon, Georgia, U.S.A. 45 Fd
Macon, Mississippi 45 Cd
Macon, Missouri 49 Lc
Macoun, Saskatchewan 37 Oj
Macoun L., Saskatchewan 39 Wg
McPherson, Kansas 49 Jc
Macpherson Range, Qnsld. 57 Ke
Macquarie, R., N.S.W. 57 Jf
Macquarie Harb., Tasmania 57 Jh
Macquarie I., Pacific Ocean 102 En
McQuesten, Y.T. 38 Ed
McQuesten, R., Y.T. 38 Ed
McRae, Georgia, U.S.A. 45 Fd
MacRae, Yukon Territory 38 Fe
Mac-Robertson Land, Antarctica 104 Fb
Macroom, Eire 63 Bj
Macrorie, Saskatchewan 36 Kg
McTaggart, Saskatchewan 37 Nj
McTavish, Manitoba 37 Uj
McTavish Arm, N.W.T. 38 Ob
MacTier, Ontario 34 Lg
Macuje, Colombia 52 Cc
Macusani, Peru 52 Cf
McVeigh, Manitoba 37 Qb
McVicar Arm, N.W.T. 38 Nc
McWatters, Quebec 35 Md
Madaba, Jordan 94 Df
Madain Salih, Arabia 92 Cd
Madame, I., Nova Scotia 33 Mh
Madan, Iran 93 Gb
Madaripur, Bangladesh 89 Hd
Madawaska, Ontario 35 Mg
Madawaska, R., Ontario 35 Ng
Madawaska R., Que./N.B. 32 Df
Madeira, Brazil 52 Ee
Madeira, Is., Atlantic Ocean 98 Bb
Madeleine, C. de la, Que. 32 Gd
Madeleine, Is. de la, Que. 32 Kf
Madge, L., Saskatchewan 37 Qg
Madgoul, Djibouti 97 Jb
Madhepur, India 91 Fb
Madhipura, India 91 Fc
Madhopur, India 90 Dd
Madhopur, Punjab, India 88 Ec
Madhubani, India 91 Fb
Madhupur, India 91 Fc
Madhya Pradesh, India 88 Ed
Madinat ash Sha'b, Yemen 92 Dg
Madingo-Kayes, Congo 96 Ce
Madison, Georgia, U.S.A. 45 Fd
Madison, Kansas 49 Jc
Madison, N. Carolina 45 Hb
Madison, Nebraska 49 Jb
Madison, New Jersey 44 Cb
Madison, Saskatchewan 36 Jg
Madison, S. Dakota 46 Jc
Madison, Wisconsin 49 Na
Madisonville, Kentucky 45 Db
Madoc, Ontario 35 Nh
Madona, Latvia 67 Mh
Madras, India 88 Ff
Madras, state. See Tamil Nadu
Madre, Laguna, Mexico 50 Ec
Madre, Laguna, Texas 48 Jj
Madre, Laguna, Texas 42 Ch
Madre, Sierra, Mexico 50 Cb
Madre, Sierra, Wyoming 46 De
Madre de Díos, Peru/Bolivia 52 Df
Madre de Díos, I., Chile 54 Ah
Madre del Sur, Sa., Mexico 50 Dd
Madrid, New Mexico 48 De
Madrid, Spain 70 Db
Madridejos, Spain 70 Dc
Madura, Indonesia 83 Fm
Madurai, India 88 Eg
Maebashi, Japan 86 Ff
Maestra, Sierra, Cuba 51 Db
Maevatanana, Madagascar 97 Nk
Mafeking, Cape Province 95 De
Mafeking, Manitoba 37 Qf
Mafeteng, Lesotho 95 De
Mafia I., Tanzania 97 Hf
Mafra, Portugal 70 Ac
Mafraq, Jordan 94 Ee
Magadan, U.S.S.R. 79 Qc
Magadi, Kenya 95 He
Magadi, L., Kenya 97 He
Magadino, Switzerland 65 Db
Magaguadavic L., N.B 32 Eh
Magallanes, Estrecho de, Chile 54 Bh
Magangué, Colombia 52 Cb
Magaz, Spain 70 Cb
Magburaka, Sierra Leone 98 Cg
Magdagachi, U.S.S.R. 79 Mc
Magdala, Ethiopia 97 Hb
Magdalena, Bolivia 52 Ef
Magdalena, Colombia 52 Cb
Magdalena, Mexico 50 Ba
Magdalena, New Mexico 48 De
Magdalena, B., Mexico 50 Bc
Magdalena, I., Chile 54 Bf
Magdeburg, East Germany 68 Db
Magellan, Str. of, Chile 54 Ch
Magerøya, Norway 66 Ma
Maggia, Switzerland 65 Db
Maggiore, L., Italy 74 Bb
Maghara, Gebel, Egypt 94 Bg
Magherafelt, N. Ireland 63 Cf
Maglaj, Yugoslavia 76 Bb
Maglie, Italy 75 Ge
Magnet, Manitoba 37 Sg
Magnetawan, Ontario 35 Lg
Magnetawan R., Ontario 40 Fc
Magnetic I., Queensland 57 Jc
Magnetic Pole, N., 30 Jc
Magnitogorsk, U.S.S.R. 81 Pd
Magnolia, Alabama 45 Dd
Magnolia, Arkansas 49 Lf
Magnolia, Mississippi 49 Mg
Magnolia, N. Carolina 45 Hc
Magog, Quebec 35 Sg
Magpie, Quebec 32 Hc
Magpie L., Quebec 32 Hb
Magpie R., Ontario 34 Fd
Magpie R., Quebec 32 Hc
Magpie R., Ouest, Quebec 32 Hb
Magrath, Alberta 36 Ej
Maguse River, N.W.T. 30 Ke
Magwe, Burma 89 Jd
Mahabad, Iran 92 Eb
Mahabaleshwar, India 88 De
Mahaban, India 90 Eg
Mahabharat Range, Nepal 91 Eb
Mahaddei Uen, Somalia 97 Kd
Mahadeo Hills, India 91 Ad
Mahail, Arabia 92 Df
Mahajamba, B. de, Madag. 97 Nk
Mahajan, India 90 Cf
Mahalapye, Botswana 95 Dd
Mahallat, Iran 93 Fc
Maham, India 90 Ef
Mahanadi, India 89 Fd
Mahanoro, Madagascar 97 Nk
Mahanoy City, Pennsylvania 44 Bb
Maharashtra, India 88 De
Mahbubnagar, India 88 Ee
Mahdia, Tunisia 99 Ha
Mahé, India 88 Ef
Mahendragiri, India 89 Fe
Maher, Ontario 34 Jc
Mahia Pen, New Zealand 55 Fc
Mahmed-Hussein-magala. See Shahsavar
Mahmudabad, India 91 Cb
Mahmudabad, Iran 93 Fb
Mahone Bay, Nova Scotia 32 Hj
Mahony L., N.W.T. 38 Lc
Mahuva, India 88 Dd
Maicasagi, R., Quebec 35 Oc
Maida, Yemen 92 Df
Maidan, Afghanistan 93 Jc
Maidstone, England 63 Hj
Maidstone, Saskatchewan 36 He
Maiduguri, Nigeria 99 Hf
Maienfeld, Switzerland 65 Ea
Maihar, India 91 Cc
Maikal Range, India 91 Cd
Maikop, U.S.S.R. 78 Dd
Maimana, Afghanistan 93 Hb
Main, West Germany 68 Cd
Main-à-Dieu, Nova Scotia 33 Nh
Main Barrier Range, N.S.W. 57 Hf
Main Brook, Newfoundland 33 Qb
Main Centre, Sask. 36 Kh
Main Channel, Ontario 34 Jg
Mai Ndombe, L., Zaire 96 De
Main Duck I., Ontario 35 Oj
Maine, France 72 Cb
Maine, U.S.A. 43 Nb
Maine-et-Loire, France 72 Cc
Maingkwan, Burma 89 Jc
Mainpuri, India 88 Ec
Mainz, West Germany 68 Cd
Maipo, Argentina 54 Cd
Maipú, Argentina 54 Ee
Maissin, Belgium 64 De
Mait, Somalia 97 Kb
Maitland, Nova Scotia 32 Jh
Maitland, N.S.W. 57 Kf
Maitland, L., W. Australia 56 De
Maitland Bridge, N.S. 32 Gj
Maitland Pt., N.W.T. 38 Ja
Maíz, Mexico 50 Ec
Maizuru, Japan 86 Dg
Majagual, Colombia 52 Cb
Majdanpek, Yugoslavia 76 Cb
Majitha, India 90 De
Majmaa, Arabia 92 Ed
Major, Saskatchewan 36 Hg
Majorca. See Mallorca
Majunga, Madagascar 97 Nk
Majuro, Marshall Is. 102 Gg
Makale, Ethiopia 97 Hb
Makalu, Nepal/China 91 Fb
Makanya, Tanzania 97 He
Makariev, U.S.S.R. 81 Fb
Makarvey, U.S.S.R. 81 Gb
Makassar, Celebes (Sulawesi) 83 Gm
Makassar Str., Indonesia 83 Gl
Makatea, Tuamotu Arch. 103 Lj
Makedhonia, Greece 77 Cd
Makemo, Tuamotu Arch. 103 Lj
Makeyevka, Ukraine 80 Kg
Makhach Kala, U.S.S.R. 78 Dd
Makikihi, New Zealand 55 Cf
Makinak, Manitoba 37 Sh
Makindu, Kenya 97 He
Makinson Inlet, N.W.T. 31 Mb
Makkah, Arabia 92 Ce
Makkinga, Netherlands 64 Eb
Makkovik, Nfld. 31 Of
Makla, Jebel el, Arabia 92 Cd
Makó, Hungary 76 Ca
Makokibatan L., Ontario 34 Ca
Makongolosi, Tanzania 97 Gf
Makorako, Mt., N. Zealand 55 Fc
Makram, Arabia 92 Ce
Makran Coast Ra., Pakistan 93 Hd
Makri, India 88 Fe

Maksamaa, *Finland* 66 Ke
Maku, *Iran* 92 Db
Makurdi, *Nigeria* 98 Gg
Makwa L., *Saskatchewan* 36 Hd
Makwiro, *Zimbabwe* 95 Ec
Malá, *Peru* 52 Bf
Malabang, *Philippines* 83 Hj
Malabar Coast, *India* 88 Df
Malabo, *Bioko* 96 Bd
Malabu, *Nigeria* 99 Hg
Malacca, Str. of, *Sumatra/Pen. Malaysia* 83 Dk
Malachi, *Ontario* 36 Ga
Malad City, *Idaho* 48 Aa
Maladeta, Mt., *Spain* 71 Fa
Málaga, *Spain* 70 Cd
Malagasy Rep., *Indian Oc.* 97 Nl
Malaita, *Solomon Is.* 102 Fh
Malakal, *Sudan* 99 Mg
Malakand, *Pakistan* 90 Bc
Malån, *Sweden* 66 Hd
Malang, *Java* 83 Fm
Malanje, *Angola* 96 Df
Mälaren, L., *Sweden* 67 Gg
Malargüe, *Argentina* 54 Ce
Malartic, *Quebec* 35 Md
Malartic, L., *Quebec* 35 Md
Malaspina Str., *B.C.* 39 Ll
Malathia, *Kenya* 97 He
Malatya, *Turkey* 92 Cb
Malaut, *India* 90 De
Malawi, *Central Africa* 97 Gg
Malayer, *Iran* 92 Ec
Malaysia, *S.E. Asia* 87 De
Malazgirt, *Turkey* 92 Db
Malbaie, B. de, *Quebec* 32 He
Malbaie, R., *Quebec* 32 Bf
Malbork, *Poland* 69 Ha
Malchow, *East Germany* 68 Eb
Malcolm R., *Y.T.* 38 Ca
Malda, *India* 91 Gc
Maldegem, *Belgium* 64 Bc
Malden, *Massachusetts* 44 Ea
Malden, *Missouri* 45 Bb
Malden, I., *Pacific Ocean* 103 Kh
Maldives, *Indian Ocean* 58 Gh
Maldon, *England* 63 Hj
Maldonado, *Uruguay* 54 Fd
Maléa, C., *Greece* 77 Df
Malé Karpaty, *Czech.* 69 Gd
Malekula, *Vanuatu* 102 Fj
Máleme, *Crete* 77 Dg
Maler Kotla, *India* 90 De
Malesherbes, *France* 72 Eb
Malheur L., *Oregon* 47 Dd
Mali, *West Africa* 98 Ee
Malignant Cove, *N.S.* 33 Kh
Malihabad, *India* 91 Cb
Malinau, *Borneo (Kalimantan)* 83 Gk
Malindi, *Kenya* 97 Je
Malines. *See* Mechelen 64 Cc
Malin Hd., *Eire* 62 Ce
Malkangiri, *India* 89 Fe
Malko Tŭrnovo, *Bulgaria* 76 Fd
Mallaig, *Alberta* 36 Fd
Mallaig, *Scotland* 62 Dc
Mallery L., *N.W.T.* 38 Yd
Mállia G., *Crete* 77 Eg
Mallorca, *Balearic Is.* 71 Gc
Mallorytown, *Ontario* 35 Ph
Mallow, *Eire* 63 Bh
Malmberget, *Sweden* 66 Jc
Malmédy, *Belgium* 64 Ed
Malmesbury, *England* 63 Fj
Malmö, *Sweden* 67 Ej
Malmyzh, *U.S.S.R.* 81 Kb
Maloja (Maloggia), *Switzerland* 65 Eb
Malombe L., *Malawi* 97 Hg
Malone, *New York* 40 Jc
Malone, *Ontario* 35 Nh
Malonga, *Zaire* 96 Eg
Malpeque B., *P.E.I.* 32 Jg
Malta, *Mediterranean Sea* 75 Eh
Malta, *Montana* 46 Da
Malta Chan., *Mediterranean Sea* 75 Eg
Malters, *Switzerland* 65 Da
Malton, *England* 63 Gf
Malton, airport, *Ontario* 35 Lj
Malung, *Sweden* 67 Ef
Malvaglia, *Switzerland* 65 Db
Malvan, *India* 88 De
Malvern, *Arkansas* 49 Le
Malvern Hills, *England* 63 Fh
Malvinas, Islas. *See* Falkland Is.
Mama, *U.S.S.R.* 79 Lc
Mamainse Point, *Ontario* 34 Fe
Mamantel, *Mexico* 50 Fd
Mambasa, *Zaire* 97 Fd
Mameigwess L., *Ontario* 36 La
Ma-Me-O Beach, *Alberta* 36 Df
Mammamattawa, *Ontario* 34 Fb
Mammoth Cave, *Kentucky* 45 Eb
Mammoth Cave Nat. Park, *Kentucky* 45 Db
Mamou, *Guinea* 98 Cf
Mampoko, *Zaire* 96 Dd
Mamuju, *Celebes (Sulawesi)* 83 Gl
Mamuno, *Botswana* 95 Cd
Man, *Ivory Coast* 98 Dg
Man, I. of, *British Isles* 63 Ef
Manacapuru, *Brazil* 52 Ed
Manacor, *Balearic Is.* 71 Gc
Manado, *Celebes (Sulawesi)* 83 Hk
Managua, *Nicaragua* 51 Bd
Managua L., *Nicaragua* 51 Bd
Manākhah, *Yemen* 92 Df
Manamah, *Bahrain* 93 Fd
Mananjary, *Madagascar* 97 Nl
Manantenina, *Madagascar* 97 Nl
Manapouri, *New Zealand* 55 Af
Manasquan, *New Jersey* 40 Je
Manassas, *Virginia* 40 Hf
Manaus, *Brazil* 52 Ed
Manawan L., *Sask.* 37 Oc
Mancelona, *Michigan* 40 Dc
Manche, *France* 72 Cb
Manchester, *England* 63 Fg
Manchester, *Iowa* 49 Ma
Manchester, *N.H.* 40 Ld
Manchester, *Tennessee* 45 Dc
Manchester, *Virginia* 45 Jb
Manchuria, *China* 82 Ha
Mancora, *Peru* 52 Ad
Manda, *Tanzania* 97 Gg
Mandal, *Norway* 67 Bg
Mandala Peak, *Irian Jaya* 83 Ml
Mandalay, *Burma* 89 Jd
Mandalgovĭ, *Mongolia* 82 Ea
Mandan, *N. Dakota* 46 Gb
Mandarin B., *China* 85 Em
Mandera, *Kenya* 97 Jd
Mandeville, *Louisiana* 45 Be
Mandi, *India* 90 Ee
Mandih, *Philippines* 83 Hj
Mandla, *India* 91 Cd
Mandritsara, *Madagascar* 97 Nk
Mandvi, *India* 88 Cd
Manfredonia, G. di, *Italy* 75 Fe
Manfuha, *Arabia* 92 Ee
Mangaia, *Cook Is.* 103 Kk
Mangaldai, *India* 89 Hc
Mangalme, *Chad* 99 Jf
Mangalore, *India* 88 Df
Mangareva, *Tuamotu Arch.* 103 Mk
Mangaweka, *New Zealand* 55 Ec
Mangfall Geb., *W. Germany* 68 De
Manglar Alto, *Ecuador* 52 Ad
Mangoche, *Malawi* 97 Hg
Mangonui, *New Zealand* 55 Da
Mangrol, *India* 88 Dd
Mangualde, *Portugal* 70 Bb
Mangueira, L. da, *Brazil* 54 Fd
Manhattan, *Kansas* 49 Jc
Manhuaçu, *Brazil* 53 Jh
Manic-Deux Dam, *Quebec* 32 Dd
Manicoré, *Brazil* 52 Ee
Manicouagan, Pén. de & R., *Quebec* 32 Dd
Manicouagan Rés., *Quebec* 32 Db
Manic-Trois Dam, *Quebec* 32 Dd
Manifold, C., *Queensland* 57 Kd
Manigotagan, *Manitoba* 37 Vg
Manigouche, *Quebec* 35 Sd
Manihi, *India* 91 Ec
Manihiki, *Pacific Ocean* 102 Jj
Manikarchar, *India* 91 Gc
Manikganj. *See* Dasara
Manikpur, *Bangladesh* 89 Hd
Manila, *Philippines* 83 Hh
Manipur, *India* 89 Hc
Manisa, *Turkey* 92 Ab
Manistee, *Michigan* 40 Cc
Manistee R., *Michigan* 40 Dc
Manistique, *Michigan* 40 Cb
Manitoba, *Canada*
Manitoba, L., *Manitoba* 37 Th
Manito L., *Saskatchewan* 36 Hf
Manitou, *Manitoba* 37 Tj
Manitou, L., *Quebec* 32 Gc
Manitou, R., *Quebec* 32 Gb
Manitou Beach, *Sask.* 37 Mg
Manitou Is., *Michigan* 40 Cc
Manitou L., *Ontario* 34 Jg
Manitou L., *Quebec* 32 Hc
Manitou L., Lower, *Ont.* 36 Ka
Manitou L., Upper, *Ont.* 36 Ja
Manitoulin I., *Ontario* 34 Hg
Manitouwadge, *Ontario* 34 Ec
Manitouwadge L., *Ontario* 34 Ec
Manitowaning, *Ontario* 34 Jg
Manitowik L., *Ontario* 34 Fd
Manitowoc, *Wisconsin* 40 Cc
Maniwaki, *Quebec* 35 Of
Maniyah, *Arabia* 92 Dc
Manizales, *Colombia* 52 Bb
Manja, *Madagascar* 97 Ml
Manjimup, *W. Australia* 56 Cf
Mankato, *Minnesota* 46 Lc
Mankheri, *India* 91 Ed
Mankota, *Saskatchewan* 36 Kj
Manlleu, *Spain* 71 Ga
Manmad, *India* 88 Dd
Mannar, *Sri Lanka* 88 Eg
Mannar, G. of, *India* 88 Eg
Mannargudi, *India* 88 Ef
Mannheim, *West Germany* 68 Cd
Manning, *Alberta* 39 Pg
Manning, *S. Carolina* 45 Gd
Manning Prov. Park, *B.C.* 39 Nl
Mannville, *Alberta* 36 Fe
Manoa, *Bolivia* 52 De
Manokwari, *Irian Jaya* 83 Kl
Manono, *Zaire* 96 Ff
Manor, *Saskatchewan* 37 Pj
Manosque, *France* 73 Fe
Manouane, *Quebec* 35 Qe
Manouane, R., *Quebec* 35 Qe
Manouane L. and R., *Que.* 32 Bc
Manouanis, L., *Quebec* 32 Bc
Manresa, *Spain* 71 Fb
Mansa, *Zambia* 95 Db
Manseau, *Quebec* 35 Sf
Mansehra, *Pakistan* 90 Cc
Mansel I., *N.W.T.* 31 Le
Mansfield, *England* 63 Gg
Mansfield, *Louisiana* 49 Lf
Mansfield, *Massachusetts* 40 Ld
Mansfield, *Ohio* 40 Ee
Mansfield, *Pennsylvania* 44 Bb
Mansfield, Mt., *Vermont* 40 Kc
Mansi, *Burma* 89 Jd
Mansilla de Las Mulas, *Spain* 70 Ca
Manson Creek, *B.C.* 39 Lh
Manta, *Ecuador* 52 Ad
Mantario, *Saskatchewan* 36 Hg
Manti, *Utah* 48 Bc
Mantova, *Italy* 74 Cc
Mantua. *See* Mantova
Manú, *Peru* 52 Cf
Manu'a, *Samoa* 102 Jj
Manuel Rodriguez, I., *Chile* 54 Bh
Manujan, *Iran* 93 Gd
Manukau, *New Zealand* 55 Eb
Manus, *Admiralty Is.* 102 Dh
Many, *Louisiana* 49 Lg
Manyberries, *Alberta* 36 Gj
Many Island L., *Alberta* 36 Gh
Manyoni, *Tanzania* 97 Gf
Manzala L., *Egypt* 99 Mb
Manzanares, *Spain* 70 Dc
Manzanillo, *Cuba* 51 Db
Manzanillo, *Mexico* 50 Dd
Manzanillo, Pta., *Panama* 51 De
Manzhouli, *China* 82 Ga
Mao, *Chad.* 99 Jf
Maoming, *China* 85 Em
Mapam Yumco, *China* 88 Fb
Mapia, *Pacific Ocean* 102 Cg
Mapimí, *Mexico* 50 Db
Maping. *See* Luizhou
Mapire, *Venezuela* 52 Eb
Maple Creek, *Sask.* 36 Hj
Maputo, *Mozambique* 95 Ee
Maqainama, *Arabia* 92 Ee
Maqatin, *S. Yemen* 92 Eg
Maqna, *Arabia* 92 Bd
Maquan He, *China* 89 Gc
Maquela do Zombo, *Angola* 96 Df
Maquereau, Pte. au, cape, *Quebec* 32 He
Maquinchao, *Argentina* 54 Cf
Maquoketa, *Iowa* 49 Ma
Mara, R., *N.W.T.* 38 Tb
Maraã, *Brazil* 52 Dd
Marabá, *Brazil* 53 He
Maracá, I. de, *Brazil* 53 Gc
Maracaçume, *Brazil* 53 Hd
Maracaibo, *Venezuela* 52 Ca
Maracaibo, L. de, *Venezuela* 52 Cb
Maracanã, *Brazil* 53 Hd
Maracay, *Venezuela* 52 Da
Marādah, *Libya* 99 Jc
Maradi, *Niger* 98 Gf
Maragheh, *Iran* 92 Eb
Maragogi, *Brazil* 53 Ke
Marakei, *Kiribati* 102 Gg
Maralinga, *S. Australia* 56 Ff
Maramba, *Zaire* 95 Dc
Maramures, *Romania* 69 Ke
Marand, *Iran* 92 Eb
Maranguape, *Brazil* 53 Kd
Marañón, R., *Peru* 52 Cd
Maraş, *Turkey* 92 Cb
Marathon, *Ontario* 34 Dd
Maraú, *Brazil* 53 Kf
Maravilha, *Brazil* 52 De
Marbella, *Spain* 70 Cd
Marble Bar, *W. Australia* 56 Cd
Marblehead, *Massachusetts* 44 Ea
Marbleton, *Quebec* 35 Tg
Marc, L., *Newfoundland* 32 Jd
Marceau, L., *Quebec* 32 Fb
Marcelin, *Saskatchewan* 36 Lf
Marcelino, *Brazil* 52 Dc
Marchand, *Manitoba* 36 Fa
Marche, Le, *Italy* 74 Dd
Marche en Famenne, *Belgium* 64 Dd
Marchena, *Spain* 70 Cd
Marchin, *Belgium* 64 Dd
Mar Chiquita, *Argentina* 54 Dd
Marcus I., *Pacific Ocean* 102 Ee
Marcy, Mt., *New York* 40 Kc
Mardan, *Pakistan* 90 Cc
Mar del Plata, *Argentina* 54 Ee
Mardin, *Turkey* 92 Db
Mardo, *Mozambique* 95 Ed
Mare, *Loyalty Is.* 102 Fk
Marechal Deodoro, *Brazil* 53 Ke
Maree, L., *Scotland* 62 Dc
Mareeba, *Queensland* 57 Jc
Marengo, *Saskatchewan* 36 Hg
Marengo, *Wisconsin* 40 Ab
Margaree Harbour, *N.S.* 33 Lg
Margaree Valley, *N.S.* 33 Lg
Margaret Bay, *B.C.* 39 Kk
Margaret L., *N.W.T.* 38 Pc
Margarita, *Venezuela* 52 Ea
Margarites, *Crete* 77 Eg
Margate, *England* 63 Hj
Margie, *Alberta* 39 Sh
Margo, *Saskatchewan* 37 Og
Marguerite, *B.C.* 39 Mj
Maria, *Quebec* 32 Fe
Marianao, *Cuba* 51 Cb
Marianas, Is., *Pacific Ocean* 102 Df
Marian L., *N.W.T.* 38 Pd
Marianna, *Arkansas* 45 Bc
Marianna, *Florida* 45 Ee
Mariánské Lázně, *Czech.* 68 Ed
Mariapolis, *Manitoba* 37 Tj
Marias, *Montana* 46 Bb
Marias R., *Montana* 42 Db
Marib, *Yemen* 92 Df
Maribor, *Yugoslavia* 74 Eb
Maricourt (Wakenham), *Que.* 31 Me
Maridi, *Sudan* 99 Lh
Marie Byrd Land, *Antarctica* 104 Pb
Mariefred, *Sweden* 67 Gg
Marie Galante, *Leeward Is.* 51 Gc
Mariehamn, *Finland* 67 Hf
Marie L., *Alberta* 36 Gd
Marienbad. *See* Mariánské Lázně
Mariënberg, *Netherlands* 64 Eb
Marienbourg, *Belgium* 64 Cd
Marienburg. *See* Malbork
Mariental, *Namibia* 95 Bd
Marienville, *Pennsylvania* 44 Ab
Mariestad, *Sweden* 67 Eg
Marietta, *Georgia, U.S.A.* 45 Ed
Marietta, *Ohio* 40 Ff
Marieville, *Quebec* 35 Rg
Mari Indus, *Pakistan* 90 Bd
Marine City, *Michigan* 40 Ed
Marinette, *Wisconsin* 40 Cc
Marinha Grande, *Portugal* 70 Ac
Marion, *Arkansas* 45 Bc
Marion, *Illinois* 45 Cb
Marion, *Indiana* 40 De
Marion, *Iowa* 49 Ma
Marion, *Kentucky* 45 Cb
Marion, *N. Carolina* 45 Fc
Marion, *N. Dakota* 46 Hb
Marion, *Ohio* 40 Ee
Marion, *Virginia* 45 Gb
Maritsa, *Bulgaria* 76 Ed
Mariyskaya A.S.S.R., *U.S.S.R.* 78 Dc
Märjamaa, *Estonia* 67 Lg
Marjorie L., *N.W.T.* 38 Yc
Markapur, *India* 88 Ee
Markdale, *Ontario* 34 Kh
Markelo, *Netherlands* 64 Eb
Marken, *Netherlands* 64 Db
Market Drayton, *England* 63 Fh
Market Harborough, *Eng.* 63 Gh
Markham, *Ontario* 35 Lj
Markham, L., *China* 89 Fa
Markham, Mt., *Antarctica* 104 Ka
Markham L., *N.W.T.* 38 Wd
Markinch, *Saskatchewan* 37 Nh
Markovo, *U.S.S.R.* 79 Sb
Marks, *U.S.S.R.* 81 He
Markstay, *Ontario* 34 Kf
Marlbank, *Ontario* 35 Nh
Marlboro, *Massachusetts* 44 Ea
Marlborough, *Guyana* 52 Fb
Marlette, *Michigan* 40 Ed
Marmagão, *Goa, India* 88 De
Marmande, *France* 73 Dd
Marmara, Sea of, *Turkey* 92 Aa
Marmaris, *Turkey* 92 Ab
Marmion L., *Ontario* 36 Lb
Marmora, *Ontario* 35 Nh
Marne, *France* 72 Fb
Maroua, *Cameroun* 99 Hf
Marouini, *Fr. Guiana* 53 Gc
Marquesas, Is., *Pacific Oc.* 103 Mh
Marquette, *Manitoba* 37 Uh
Marquette, *Michigan* 40 Cb
Marquina, *Spain* 71 Da
Marquis, *Saskatchewan* 37 Mh
Marrakech, *Morocco* 98 Db
Marree, *S. Australia* 57 Ge
Marsabit, *Kenya* 97 Hd
Marsala, *Sicily* 75 Dg
Marsden, *Saskatchewan* 36 Hf
Marseille, *France* 73 Fe
Marshall, *Illinois* 40 Cf
Marshall, *Michigan* 40 Dd
Marshall, *Minnesota* 46 Kc
Marshall, *Missouri* 49 Lc
Marshall, *Saskatchewan* 36 He
Marshall, *Texas* 49 Kf
Marshall Is., *Pacific Ocean* 102 Fg
Marshall L., *Ontario* 34 Cb
Marshalltown, *Iowa* 49 La
Marshfield, *Missouri* 49 Ld
Marshfield, *Wisconsin* 40 Ac
Marsh I., *Louisiana* 49 Mh
Mars Hill, *Maine* 32 Eg
Marsh L., *Y.T.* 38 Fe
Marstrand, *Sweden* 67 Dh
Martaban, *Burma* 89 Je
Martaban, G. of, *Burma* 89 Je
Martel, R. à la, *Quebec* 35 Pa
Martelange, *Belgium* 64 De
Martha's Vineyard, *Mass.* 44 Eb
Martigny-Ville, *Switzerland* 65 Cb
Martin, *Ontario* 37 La
Martin, *S. Dakota* 46 Gd
Martina, *Switzerland* 65 Fb
Martinborough, *N. Zealand* 55 Ed
Martinique, *Windward Is.* 51 Gd
Martin L., *Alabama* 45 Ed
Martinsburg, *W. Virginia* 44 Bc
Martinsville, *Virginia* 45 Hb
Marton, *New Zealand* 55 Ed
Martos, *Spain* 70 Dd
Martre, L. la, *N.W.T.* 38 Od
Maruf, *Afghanistan* 93 Jc
Marugame, *Japan* 86 Cg
Marum, *Netherlands* 64 Ea
Marutea, *Tuamotu Arch.* 103 Lj
Marvejols, *France* 73 Ed
Marwayne, *Alberta* 36 Ge
Mary, *Turkmenistan* 78 Fe
Maryborough, *Queensland* 57 Ke
Maryborough. *See* Portlaoise
Maryborough, *Victoria* 57 Hg
Marydale, *Cape Province* 95 Ce
Maryfield, *Saskatchewan* 37 Qj
Mary Frances L., *N.W.T.* 38 Ud
Mary Henry, Mt., *B.C.* 39 Lf
Mary Kathleen, *Queensland* 57 Hd
Mary L., *N.W.T.* 38 Wd
Maryland, *U.S.A.* 43 Ld
Maryport, *England* 63 Ef
Mary's Harbour, *Nfld.* 33 Ra
Marystown, *Newfoundland* 33 Rf
Marysville, *California* 42 Bd
Marysville, *Kansas* 49 Jc
Marysville, *New Brunswick* 32 Fh
Maryville, *Missouri* 49 Kb
Marzūq, *Libya* 99 Hc
Masaka, *Uganda* 97 Ge
Masasi, *Tanzania* 97 Hg
Masaya, *Nicaragua* 51 Bd
Masbate, *Philippines* 83 Hh
Mascara, *Algeria* 98 Fa
Masefield, *Saskatchewan* 36 Kj
Masères, L., *Quebec* 35 Pd
Maseru, *Lesotho* 95 De
Mashaki, *Afghanistan* 93 Jc
Masharbrum, Mt., *Kashmir* 90 Ec
Mashhad, *Iran* 93 Gb
Mashiz, *Iran* 93 Gc
Mashkel, Hamun-i-, *Pak.* 88 Bc
Mashkode, *Ontario* 34 Fe
Masi-Manimba, *Zaire* 96 De
Masindi, *Uganda* 97 Gd
Maşira, *Oman* 93 Ge
Maşirah, G. of, *Arabia* 93 Gf
Maşirah Channel, *Arabia* 93 Ge
Masjed Soleyman, *Iran* 92 Ec
Maskinongé, *Quebec* 35 Rf
Mask L., *Eire* 63 Ag
Masoala C., *Madagascar* 97 Pk
Mason, *Michigan* 40 Dd
Mason City, *Iowa* 49 La
Mason Creek, *B.C.* 39 Mg
Masöy, *Norway* 66 La
Massa, *Italy* 74 Cc
Massachusetts, *U.S.A.* 43 Mc
Massachusetts B., *Mass.* 44 Ea
Massafra, *Italy* 75 Fe
Massakori, *Chad* 99 Jf
Massangena, *Mozambique* 95 Ed
Massapê, *Brazil* 53 Jd
Massawa, *Ethiopia* 97 Ha
Massena, *New York* 40 Jc
Massénya, *Chad* 99 Jf
Masset, *British Columbia* 39 Gj
Masset Inlet, *B.C.* 39 Gj
Masseube, *France* 73 De
Massey, *Ontario* 34 Hf
Massillon, *Ohio* 40 Fe
Massinga, *Mozambique* 95 Fd
Masson, *Quebec* 35 Pg
Masterton, *New Zealand* 55 Ed
Mastuj, *Pakistan* 90 Cb
Mastung, *Pakistan* 88 Cc
Mastura, *Arabia* 92 Ce
Maşyaf, *Syria* 94 Eb
Mat, *India* 90 Eg
Mata Amarilla, *Argentina* 54 Bg
Matachewan, *Ontario* 34 Ke
Matador, *Saskatchewan* 36 Kh
Matadi, *Zaire* 96 Cf
Matagalpa, *Nicaragua* 51 Bd
Matagami, *Quebec* 35 Nc
Matagami, L., *Quebec* 35 Nc
Matagorda, B. and Pen., *Texas* 48 Jh
Matagorda, I., *Texas* 48 Jh
Matakana I., *New Zealand* 55 Fb
Matale, *Sri Lanka* 88 Fg
Matam, *Senegal* 98 Ce
Matamata, *N. Zealand* 55 Eb
Matamoros, *Mexico* 50 Eb
Matamoros, *Mexico* 50 Db
Matane & R., *Quebec* 32 Ee
Matanzas, *Cuba* 51 Cb
Matapédia, *Quebec* 32 Ff
Matapédia L. & R., *Que.* 32 Ee
Matapozuelos, *Spain* 70 Cb
Matara, *Sri Lanka* 88 Fg
Mataram, *Lombok I., Indon.* 83 Gm
Mataranka, *N. Terr.* 56 Fb
Mataró, *Spain* 71 Gb
Matatiele, *Cape Province* 95 Df
Matauale, *Brazil* 53 Gc
Mataura, *New Zealand* 55 Bg
Matawin, R., *Quebec* 35 Rf
Matchi-Manitou, L., *Que.* 35 Oe
Matehuala, *Mexico* 50 Dc
Matera, *Italy* 75 Fe
Mátészalka, *Hungary* 69 Ke
Mateur, *Tunisia* 99 Ga
Matfors, *Sweden* 66 Ge
Matheson, *Ontario* 34 Kd
Matheson Island, *Man.* 37 Vg
Mathura, *India* 88 Ec
Matiara, *India* 89 Gc
Matinenda L., *Ontario* 34 Gf
Matlock, *England* 63 Fg
Matna, *Sudan* 99 Nf
Mato Grosso, *Brazil* 52 Ff
Matonipi, L., *Quebec* 32 Cb
Matonipis, L., *Quebec* 32 Cb
Maţrah, *Oman* 93 Ge
Matruh, *Egypt* 99 Lb
Matsue, *Japan* 86 Cg
Matsumae, *Japan* 86 Gd
Matsumoto, *Japan* 86 Ff
Matsuyama, *Japan* 86 Ch
Mattagami Heights, *Ont.* 34 Jd
Mattagami L., *Ontario* 34 Je
Mattagami R., *Ontario* 34 Hb
Mattawa, *Ontario* 35 Mf
Matterhorn, *Switz./It.* 65 Cc
Matthew Town, *The Bahamas* 51 Eb
Mattice, *Ontario* 34 Gc
Mattoon, *Illinois* 49 Nc
Matty I., *N.W.T.* 38 Za
Matucana, *Peru* 52 Bf
Matun, *Afghanistan* 93 Jc
Matura, *Brazil* 52 Dd
Maturin, *Venezuela* 52 Eb
Matvaieva, *U.S.S.R.* 81 Nb
Mau, *India* 88 Ec
Mau Aimma, *India* 91 Cc
Maubeuge, *France* 72 Ea
Maubin, *Burma* 89 Je
Maubourguet, *France* 73 De
Maudaha, *India* 91 Cc
Maudheim, *Antarctica* 104 Bb
Maués, *Brazil* 53 Fd
Mauganj, *India* 91 Cc
Maui, *Hawaiian Is.* 103 Ke
Mauléon Licharre, *France* 73 Ce
Maunoir, L., *N.W.T.* 38 Lb
Maurawan, *India* 91 Cb
Maurice, L., *S. Australia* 56 Fe
Mauriceville, *N. Zealand* 55 Ed
Mauritania, *West Africa* 98 Cd
Mauritius, *Indian Ocean* 100 Df
Maurs, *France* 73 Ed
Mauston, *Wisconsin* 40 Ad
Mawdesley L., *Manitoba* 37 Rd
Mawer, *Saskatchewan* 36 Lh
Mawk Mai, *Burma* 89 Jd
Mawlaik, *Burma* 89 Hd
Mawson, *Antarctica* 104 Ec
Maxcanú, *Mexico* 50 Gc
Maxhamish L., *B.C.* 38 Mf
Maxixe, *Mozambique* 95 Fd
Maxstone, *Saskatchewan* 36 Lj
Maxton, *N. Carolina* 45 Hc
Maxville, *Ontario* 35 Qg
May, C., *New Jersey* 44 Cc
May, I. of, *Scotland* 62 Fd
Maya, I., *Indonesia* 83 El
Mayaguana, *The Bahamas* 51 Eb
Mayagüez, *Puerto Rico* 51 Fc
Mayari, *Cuba* 51 Db
Mayen, *West Germany* 68 Bc
Mayenne, *France* 72 Cb
Mayersville, *Mississippi* 49 Mf
Mayerthorpe, *Alberta* 39 Qj
Mayfair, *Saskatchewan* 36 Kf
Mayfield, *Kentucky* 45 Cb
Maymont, *Saskatchewan* 36 Kf
Maymyo, *Burma* 89 Jd
Maynooth, *Ontario* 35 Ng
Mayo, *Eire* 63 Ag
Mayo, *Yukon Territory* 38 Fd
Mayo L., *Yukon Territory* 38 Fd
Mays Landing, *New Jersey* 44 Cc
Mayson L., *Saskatchewan* 39 Ug
Maysville, *Kentucky* 45 Fa
Mayumba, *Gabon* 96 Ce
Mayūram, *India* 88 Ef
Mayville, *New York* 44 Aa
Maza, *Argentina* 54 De
Mazabuka, *Zambia* 95 Dc
Mazagão, *Brazil* 53 Gd
Mazamet, *France* 73 Ee
Mazán, *Argentina* 54 Cc
Mazán, *Peru* 52 Cd
Mazapil, *Mexico* 50 Dc
Mazara del Vallo, *Sicily* 75 Dg
Mazar-i-Sharif, *Afghanistan* 93 Jb
Mazarrado, *Argentina* 54 Cg
Mazarron, *Spain* 71 Ed
Mazatenango, *Guatemala* 50 Fe
Mazatlán, *Mexico* 50 Cc
Mažeikiai, *Lithuania* 67 Kh
Mazenod, *Saskatchewan* 36 Lj
Mazeppa, *Alberta* 36 Dh
Mazu Dao, *Taiwan* 85 Jj
Mazury, *Poland* 69 Jb
Mbabane, *Swaziland* 95 Ee
Mbala, *Zambia* 97 Gf
Mbale, *Uganda* 97 Gd
Mbamba Bay, *Kenya* 95 Fb
Mbandaka, *Zaire* 96 Dd
Mbanza Ngungu, *Zaire* 96 Cf
Mbarara, *Uganda* 97 Ge
Mbeya, *Tanzania* 97 Gf
Mbini, *Equat. Guinea* 96 Cd
Mbuji-Mayi, *Zaire* 96 Ef
M'Clintock, *Y.T.* 38 Fe
M'Clintock, C., *N.W.T.* 31 Ma
M'Clintock Channel, *N.W.T.* 30 Jc
M'Clintock Inlet, *N.W.T.* 31 Ma
Meacham, *Saskatchewan* 37 Mf
Mead, *Ontario* 34 Gc
Mead L., *Nevada* 47 Fg
Meadowbank, R., *N.W.T.* 38 Zc
Meadow Lake, *Sask.* 36 Jd
Meadow Lake Provincial Park, *Sask.* 36 Jd
Meadow Portage, *Man.* 37 Sg
Meadville, *Pennsylvania* 40 Fe
Meaford, *Ontario* 34 Kh
Meaghers Grant, *N.S.* 32 Jj
Mealy Mts., *Nfld.* 31 Og
Meander River, *Alberta* 39 Pf
Meath, *Eire* 63 Cg
Meath Park, *Sask.* 37 Me
Mécatina, I. du Gros, *Que.* 33 Oc
Mécatina, I. du Petit, *Que.* 33 Nc
Mécatina, R. du Petit, *Newfoundland/Quebec* 33 Nb
Mecca, *Arabia* 92 Ce
Mechanicville, *New York* 44 Da
Mechelen, *Belgium* 64 Cc
Mechelen, *Belgium* 64 Dd
Mecheria, *Algeria* 98 Eb
Medak, *India* 88 Ee
Medak, *Yugoslavia* 74 Ec
Medan, *Sumatra* 83 Ck
Médanos, *Argentina* 54 De
Medellín, *Colombia* 52 Bb
Medemblik, *Netherlands* 64 Db
Médenine, *Tunisia* 99 Hb
Meder, *Ethiopia* 97 Jb
Medford, *Oklahoma* 49 Jd
Medford, *Oregon* 47 Bd
Medford, *Wisconsin* 40 Ac
Medgidia, *Romania* 76 Gb
Media, *Pennsylvania* 44 Cc
Medias, *Romania* 76 Ea
Medicine Bow Pk., *Wyoming* 42 Ec
Medicine Bow Ra., *Wyoming/Colorado* 46 De
Medicine Hat, *Alberta* 36 Gh
Medicine R., *Alberta* 36 Cf
Medina, *Arabia* 92 Ce
Medina, *N. Dakota* 46 Hb
Medina, *New York* 44 Aa
Medina, *Ohio* 40 Fe
Medinaceli, *Spain* 71 Db
Medina del Campo, *Spain* 70 Cb
Medina de Rioseco, *Spain* 70 Cb
Medina Sidonia, *Spain* 70 Cd
Médine, *Mali* 98 Cf
Mediterranean Sea, *S. Europe* 61 Jj
Medora, *Manitoba* 37 Rj
Medora, *N. Dakota* 46 Fb
Medstead, *Saskatchewan* 36 Je
Meductic, *New Brunswick* 32 Eg
Medvezhegorsk, *U.S.S.R.* 78 Cb
Medvezhi Ova, *U.S.S.R.* 79 Ra
Medvezhiy Yar, *U.S.S.R.* 79 Ja
Meekatharra, *W. Australia* 56 Ce
Meerle, *Belgium* 64 Cc
Meerlo, *Netherlands* 64 Ec
Meersburg, *West Germany* 68 Ce
Meerssen, *Netherlands* 64 Dd
Meerut, *India* 90 Ef
Meeting Creek, *Alberta* 36 Ef
Meetoos, *Saskatchewan* 36 Ke
Meeuwen, *Belgium* 64 Dc
Mega, *Ethiopia* 97 Hd
Megalópolis, *Greece* 77 Df
Mégantic, L., *Quebec* 32 Bh
Mégara, *Greece* 77 De
Meghalaya, *India* 89 Hc
Mégiscane, *Quebec* 40 Ha
Mégiscane, L., *Quebec* 35 Pd
Mehar, *Pakistan* 88 Cc
Meherpur, *Bangladesh* 91 Gd
Mehndawal, *India* 91 Db
Meighen I., *N.W.T.* 31 Ka
Meikle, R., *Alberta* 39 Og
Meiktila, *Burma* 89 Jd
Meilleur Cr., *N.W.T.* 38 Le
Meiningen, *East Germany* 68 Dc
Meiringen, *Switzerland* 65 Db
Meissen, *East Germany* 68 Ec
Meitene, *Latvia* 67 Kh
Mei Xian, *China* 85 Hk
Mejillones, *Chile* 54 Bb
Mekatina, *Ontario* 34 Fe
Meknès, *Morocco* 98 Db
Mekong, *S.E. Asia* 87 Dd
Melaka, *Pen. Malaysia* 83 Dk
Melanesia, *Pacific Ocean* 102 Dg
Melaval, *Saskatchewan* 36 Lj
Melbourne, *Victoria* 57 Jg
Melbourne I., *N.W.T.* 38 Va
Melchett L., *Ontario* 34 Db
Meldrum Bay, *Ontario* 34 Gg
Melezes, R. aux, *Quebec* 37 Uh
Melfi, *Italy* 75 Ee
Melfort, *Saskatchewan* 37 Nf
Meligalá, *Greece* 77 Cf
Melilla, *Morocco* 98 Ea
Melipilla, *Chile* 54 Bd
Melita, *Manitoba* 37 Qj
Melitopol, *Ukraine* 80 Jh
Melk, *Austria* 68 Fd
Melle, *France* 72 Cc
Meller, *Belgium* 64 De
Mellingen, *Switzerland* 65 Da
Melo, *Uruguay* 54 Fd
Melona, *Israel* 94 De
Melreux, *Belgium* 64 Dd
Melrose, *Minnesota* 46 Kc
Melrose, *Nova Scotia* 33 Kh
Melton Mowbray, *England* 63 Gh
Melun, *France* 72 Eb
Melut, *Sudan* 99 Mf
Melville, *Saskatchewan* 37 Ph
Melville, C., *Queensland* 57 Hb
Melville, L., *Nfld.* 31 Og
Melville B., *Greenland* 41 Qb
Melville Hills, *N.W.T.* 38 Na
Melville I., *N. Terr.* 56 Fb
Melville I., *N.W.T.* 30 Hb
Melville Pen., *N.W.T.* 31 Ld
Melville Sd., *N.W.T.* 38 Ua
Melvin L., *Ireland* 63 Bf
Melvin L., *Manitoba* 37 Ra
Memba, *Mozambique* 97 Jg
Memba Bay, *Mozambique* 97 Jg
Membij, *Syria* 94 Fa
Memel. *See* Klaipeda
Memphis, *Tennessee* 45 Bc
Memphrémagog, L., *Quebec/Vermont* 35 Sg
Memramcook, *N.B.* 32 Hg
Mena, *Arkansas* 49 Ke
Menai Str., *Wales* 63 Eg
Ménaka, *Mali* 98 Fe
Ménascouagama, L., *Que.* 33 Lb
Menasha, *Wisconsin* 40 Bc
Mendak, *Arabia* 92 De
Mendawai, *Borneo (Kalimantan)* 83 Fl
Mende, *France* 73 Ed
Mendebo Mts., *Ethiopia* 97 Hc
Menderes, *Turkey* 92 Ab
Mendham, *Saskatchewan* 36 Hh
Mendip Hills, *England* 63 Fj
Mendocino, C., *California* 47 Ae
Mendota, *Illinois* 40 Be
Mendota, L., *Wisconsin* 40 Bd
Mendoza, *Argentina* 54 Cd
Mendrisio, *Switzerland* 65 Dc
Menen, *Belgium* 64 Bd
Menfi, *Sicily* 75 Dg

Meng Chainat, Thailand 87 Cc
Meng Fang, Thailand 87 Bc
Meng Phrae, Thailand 87 Bc
Meng Thoen, Thailand 87 Bc
Meng Uthen. See Ban tha U
Menindee, N.S.W. 57 Hf
Menominee, Michigan 40 Cc
Menomonie, Wisconsin 46 Mc
Menorca, Balearic Is. 71 Hb
Mentawai Is., Indonesia 59 Jj
Menton, France 73 Ge
Menyapa, Borneo (Kalimantan) 83 Gk
Menzelinsk, U.S.S.R. 81 Lc
Menzies, W. Australia 56 De
Me'ona, Israel 94 De
Meoqui, Mexico 50 Cb
Meota, Saskatchewan 36 Je
Meppel, Netherlands 64 Eb
Merabello G., Crete 77 Eg
Merano, Italy 74 Cb
Merasheen & I., Nfld. 33 Sf
Meratus Peg, Borneo (Kalimantan) 83 Gl
Merauke, Irian Jaya 83 Mm
Merca, Somalia 97 Jd
Mercara, India 88 Ef
Merced, California 47 Cg
Mercedario, Mt., Argentina 54 Bd
Mercedes, Argentina 54 Ec
Mercedes, Argentina 54 Ed
Mercedes, Bolivia 52 Df
Mercedes, Uruguay 54 Ed
Mercer, New Zealand 55 Eb
Mercer, Pennsylvania 40 Fe
Merchtem, Belgium 64 Cd
Mercier Dam, Quebec 35 Of
Mercoal, Alberta 39 Pj
Mercy, C., N.W.T. 31 Ne
Mercy B., N.W.T. 30 Gc
Meredith, Michigan 40 Dc
Meredith, C., Falkland Is. 54 Dh
Meredith, L., Texas 48 Ge
Meregh, Somalia 97 Kd
Mergentheim, Bad, W. Germany 68 Cd
Mergui, Burma 89 Jf
Mergui Arch., Burma 89 Jf
Merid, Saskatchewan 36 Hg
Mérida, Mexico 50 Gc
Mérida, Spain 70 Bc
Mérida, Venez. 52 Cb
Meriden, Connecticut 44 Db
Meridian, Mississippi 45 Cd
Merj Uyun, Lebanon 94 Dd
Merksplas, Belgium 64 Cc
Merlin, Ontario 34 Hk
Merowe, Sudan 99 Me
Merredin, W. Australia 56 Cf
Merrickville, Ontario 35 Ph
Merrill, Wisconsin 40 Bc
Merrimack R., N.H./Mass. 44 Ea
Merritt, British Columbia 39 Nk
Mersey R., England 63 Fg
Merseyside, England 63 Fg
Mersin, Turkey 92 Bb
Mersing, Pen. Malaysia 83 Dk
Mersrags, Latvia 67 Kh
Merta, India 88 Dc
Merthyr Tydfil, Wales 63 Ej
Mertola, Portugal 70 Bd
Meru, Kenya 97 Hd
Mervin, Saskatchewan 36 Je
Merzig, W. Germany 68 Bd
Mesa, Arizona 48 Bf
Mesabi Ra., Minnesota 46 Lb
Mésaconane, Pte., Quebec 35 La
Mesagne, Italy 75 Fe
Mesa L., N.W.T. 38 Qc
Mesará B., Crete 77 Eg
Mesa Verde Nat. Park, Colo. 42 Ed
Mesen, Belgium 64 Ad
Mesgouez, L., Quebec 35 Pa
Meshchovsk, U.S.S.R. 80 Jd
Meshghara, Lebanon 94 Dd
Mesilinka, R., B.C. 39 Lg
Meskene, Syria 94 Fa
Mesmiye, Syria 94 Ed
Mesocco, Switzerland 65 Eb
Mesolóngion, Greece 77 Ce
Mesplet, L., Quebec 35 Pd
Messancy, Belgium 64 De
Messina, Sicily 75 Ef
Messina, Str. di, Italy 75 Ef
Messines, Quebec 35 Pf
Messinía, Greece 77 Cf
Messinía, G. of, Greece 77 Df
Mesudiye, Turkey 92 Ca
Metagama, Ontario 34 Je
Meta L., Ontario 34 Cb
Metán, Argentina 54 Dc
Meta Pond, Newfoundland 33 Se
Meteghan, Nova Scotia 32 Fj
Meteghan Sta., N.S. 32 Fj
Méthana Pen., Greece 77 Df
Methil, Scotland 62 Ed
Methley, Manitoba 37 Sg
Methven, New Zealand 55 Ce
Metionga L., Ontario 37 Na
Metiskow, Alberta 36 Gf
Métis-sur-Mer, Quebec 32 De
Metkovic, Yugoslavia 76 Ac
Metlakatla, Alaska 43 Zm
Metlika, Yugoslavia 74 Ec
Metropolis, Illinois 49 Nd
Metropolitan, Michigan 40 Cb
Métsovon, Greece 77 Ce
Mettet, Belgium 64 Cd
Mettlen, Switzerland 65 Cb
Mettur Dam, India 88 Ef
Metulla, Israel 94 Dd
Metz, France 72 Gb
Meulebeke, Belgium 64 Bd
Meurthe-et-Moselle, France 72 Gb
Meuse, Belgium 64 Dd
Meuse, France 72 Fb
Mexcala & R., Mexico 50 Ed
Mexiana, I., Brazil 53 Hd
Mexicali, Mexico 50 Aa
Mexico, Cent. America 50 Dc
Mexico, Mexico 50 Ed
Mexico, New York 44 Ba
Mexico, Gulf of, Louisiana 49 Lh
Mexico B., New York 44 Ba
Meyadin, Syria 92 Db
Meybod, Iran 93 Fc
Meyersdale, Pennsylvania 44 Ac
Meymac, France 72 Ed
Meynypil'gyno, U.S.S.R. 79 Sb
Meyronne, Saskatchewan 36 Lj
Mèze, France 73 Ee
Mezen', U.S.S.R. 78 Db
Mézières, France 72 Fb
Mezöberény Békés, Hungary 69 Je
Mezökövesd, Hungary 69 Je
Mezötúr, Hungary 69 Je
Mezquitic, Mexico 50 Dc
Mgori, Tanzania 97 Ge
Mhow, India 88 Ed
Miahuatlan, Mexico 50 Ed
Miajadas, Spain 70 Cc
Miami, Arizona 48 Bf
Miami, Florida 45 Gh
Miami, Manitoba 37 Tj
Miami, Oklahoma 49 Kd
Miandowab, Iran 92 Eb
Miandrivazo, Madagascar 97 Nk
Mianeh, Iran 92 Eb
Miani, India 90 De
Miani, Pakistan 90 Cd
Mian Kalai, Pakistan 90 Bc
Mianwali, Pakistan 90 Bd
Mianyang, China 84 Bg
Mianyang, China 85 Fg
Miaodao Qundao, China 84 Kc
Miass, U.S.S.R. 81 Qc
Miastko, Poland 69 Ga
Mica Creek, B.C. 39 Oj
Mica Dam, B.C. 39 Oj
Micay, Colombia 52 Bc
Michel, British Columbia 39 Ql
Michel, Saskatchewan 36 Hb
Michichi, Alberta 36 Eg
Michigan, U.S.A. 43 Jb
Michigan, L., U.S.A./Can. 43 Jc
Michigan City, Indiana 40 Ce
Michipicoten, Ontario 34 Fe
Michipicoten B., Ontario 34 Ee
Michipicoten I., Ontario 34 Ee
Michipicoten River, Ontario 34 Fe
Michoacan, state, Mexico 50 Dd
Michurinsk, U.S.S.R. 81 Ed
Micronesia, Pacific Ocean 102 Df
Midale, Saskatchewan 37 Oj
Mid Canyon, Montana 46 Bb
Middelburg, Netherlands 64 Bc
Middelburg, Transvaal 95 De
Middelharnis, Netherlands 64 Cc
Middelkerke, Belgium 64 Ac
Middle Bay, Quebec 33 Pb
Middleboro, Massachusetts 44 Eb
Middlebro, Manitoba 36 Fa
Middleburg, New York 40 Jd
Middleburg, Pennsylvania 44 Bb
Middlebury, Vermont 40 Kd
Middle Lake, Sask. 37 Mf
Middlemarch, New Zealand 55 Cf
Middle Musquodoboit, Nova Scotia 32 Jh
Middleport, New York 44 Aa
Middle Ridge, Nfld. 33 Re
Middlesboro, Kentucky 45 Fb
Middlesbrough, England 63 Gf
Middleton, England 63 Ff
Middleton, Nova Scotia 32 Gj
Middletown, Connecticut 44 Db
Middletown, Delaware 40 Jf
Middletown, New York 44 Cb
Middletown, Ohio 40 Df
Middletown, Pennsylvania 44 Bb
Middlewood, Nova Scotia 32 Hj
Mid Glamorgan, Wales 63 Ej
Midhurst, Ontario 35 Lh
Midland, Michigan 40 Dd
Midland, Ontario 34 Lh
Midland, Texas 48 Fg
Midnapore, Alberta 36 Ch
Midnapore, India 91 Fd
Midway, British Columbia 39 Ol
Midway Is., Hawaiian Is. 102 He
Midwest, Wyoming 46 Dd
Midye, Turkey 92 Aa
Miécourt, Switzerland 65 Ca
Międzyrzec, Poland 69 Kc
Mier, Mexico 50 Eb
Mieres, Spain 70 Ca
Mifflintown, Pennsylvania 44 Bb
Mikado, Saskatchewan 37 Pg
Mikhailovgrad, Bulgaria 76 Dc
Mikhaylovka, U.S.S.R. 81 Fe
Mikkeli, Finland 67 Mf
Mikkwa R., Alberta 39 Qg
Mikonos, Greece 77 Ef
Milaca, Minnesota 46 Lc
Milan, Missouri 49 Lb
Milan, New Hampshire 40 Lc
Milan, Quebec 32 Ah
Milan. See Milano
Milan, Tennessee 49 Ne
Milano, Italy 74 Bc
Milas, Turkey 92 Ab
Milazzo, Sicily 75 Ef
Milbank, S. Dakota 46 Jc
Milden, Saskatchewan 36 Kg
Mildmay, Ontario 34 Jh
Mildred, Saskatchewan 36 Ke
Mildura, Victoria 57 Hf
Miléai, Greece 77 De
Miles, Queensland 57 Ke
Milesburg, Pennsylvania 44 Bb
Miles City, Montana 46 Eb
Milestone, Saskatchewan 37 Nj
Milford, Delaware 44 Cc
Milford, Massachusetts 44 Ea
Milford, Pennsylvania 44 Cb
Milford, Utah 47 Gf
Milford Haven, Wales 63 Dj
Milford Res., Kansas 49 Jc
Milford Sound, N. Zealand 55 Af
Milgun, W. Australia 56 Ce
Mili, Marshall Islands 102 Gg
Miliana, Algeria 98 Fa
Miljet, Yugoslavia 74 Fd
Milke Pass, Nepal 91 Fb
Milkovo, U.S.S.R. 79 Qc
Milk R., Montana 46 Da
Milk River, Alberta 36 Ej
Milk River Ridge, Alberta 36 Ej
Mill, Netherlands 64 Dc
Millau, France 73 Ed
Millbridge, Ontario 40 Hc
Millbrook, Ontario 35 Mh
Mille Lacs, L. des, Ontario 37 Mb
Mille Lacs L., Minnesota 46 Lb
Miller, S. Dakota 46 Hc
Millerovo, U.S.S.R. 81 Ef
Millersburg, Ohio 40 Ee
Miller's Flat, New Zealand 55 Bf
Millerton, New Brunswick 32 Gg
Millertown, Nfld. 33 Qe
Millertown Jct., Nfld. 33 Qd
Millet, Alberta 36 De
Mill I., Antarctica 104 Hc
Mill I., N.W.T. 31 Me
Millicent, Alberta 36 Fh
Millicent, S. Australia 57 Hg
Millinocket, Maine 32 Dh
Mills L., N.W.T. 38 Oe
Milltown, New Brunswick 32 Eh
Mill Village, Nova Scotia 32 Hj
Millville, New Brunswick 32 Eg
Millville, New Jersey 44 Cc
Milne B., Papua New Guinea 57 Kb
Milner Ridge, Manitoba 36 Fa
Milnet, Ontario 34 Kf
Milnor, N. Dakota 46 Jb
Milo, Alberta 36 Eh
Milo, Maine 32 Ch
Milos, Greece 77 Ef
Milparinka, N.S.W. 57 He
Milton, New Zealand 55 Bg
Milton, Nova Scotia 32 Hj
Milton, Ontario 34 Lj
Milton, Pennsylvania 44 Bb
Miltown Malbay, Eire 63 Ah
Milverton, Ontario 34 Kj
Milwaukee, Wisconsin 40 Cd
Mimika, Irian Jaya 83 Ll
Mina al Ahmadī, Kuwait 92 Ed
Minab, Iran 93 Gd
Minago R., Manitoba 37 Td
Minaki, Ontario 36 Ga
Minas, Uruguay 54 Ed
Minas Basin & Chan., N.S. 32 Hh
Minas de Riotinto, Spain 70 Bd
Minas Novas, Brazil 53 Jg
Minataree, Ontario 34 Bb
Minatitlán, Mexico 50 Fd
Minbu, Burma 89 Hd
Minburn, Alberta 36 Fe
Minch, Little, Scotland 62 Cc
Minch, North, Scotland 62 Cb
Mindanao, Philippines 83 Jj
Minden, Louisiana 49 Lf
Minden, Ontario 35 Mh
Minden, West Germany 68 Cb
Mindoro, Phil. 83 Hh
Mine Centre, Ontario 36 Kb
Mîneciu-Ungureni, Romania 76 Fb
Mine Head, Eire 63 Bj
Minehead, England 63 Ej
Mineola, New York 44 Db
Mineral Point, Wisconsin 40 Ad
Mineral Wells, Texas 49 Hf
Minga, Zambia 97 Gg
Mingan, Quebec 32 Hc
Mingan, Chenal de & Iles de, Quebec 32 Hc
Mingan, I. de, Quebec 32 Hc
Mingan, R., Quebec 32 Jc
Mingenew, W. Australia 56 Ce
Mingin, Burma 89 Hd
Mingkwang, China 84 Jf
Minglanilla, Spain 71 Ec
Mingoyo, Tanzania 97 Hg
Mingshui, China 82 Cb
Minhla, Burma 89 Je
Minicoy, India 88 Dg
Minilya, W. Australia 56 Bd
Miniota, Manitoba 37 Qh
Minipi L., Nfld. 33 La
Ministikwan L., Sask. 36 Hd
Minitonas, Manitoba 37 Qf
Minna, Nigeria 98 Gg
Minneapolis, Minnesota 46 Lc
Minnedosa, Manitoba 37 Sh
Minnesota, U.S.A. 42 Gb
Minnesota R., Minn. 42 Gc
Minnewanka, L., Alberta 36 Bg
Minnik, Syria 94 Fa
Minnipuka, Ontario 34 Gd
Minnitaki L., Ontario 36 Ka
Miño, Spain/Portugal 70 Aa
Minorca. See Menorca
Minot, N. Dakota 46 Ga
Minqin, China 84 Ac
Minqing, China 85 Jj
Min Shan, China 84 Af
Minsk, Byelorussia 80 Ee
Mińsk Mazowiecki, Poland 69 Jb
Minto, Manitoba 37 Rj
Minto, N. Dakota 46 Ja
Minto, New Brunswick 32 Fg
Minto, L., Quebec 31 Mf
Minto Head, N.W.T. 30 Jc
Minto Inlet, N.W.T. 38 Oa
Minton, Saskatchewan 37 Nj
Minusinsk, U.S.S.R. 79 Jc
Minya Konka. See Gongga Shan
Mio, Michigan 40 Dc
Miquelon, Quebec 35 Oc
Miquelon, I., 33 Qf
Mira, Nova Scotia 33 Ng
Miracema do Norte, Brazil 53 He
Mirador, Brazil 53 Je
Miraflores, Colombia 52 Cb
Miraj, India 88 De
Mirambeau, France 73 Cd
Miramichi B., N.B. 32 Gf
Miramichi R., Little S.W., N.B. 32 Fg
Miramichi R., Main S.W., N.B. 32 Fg
Miramichi R., N.W., N.B. 32 Ff
Miramont, France 73 Dd
Miram Shah, Pakistan 90 Bd
Miranda, Argentina 54 Ee
Miranda, Brazil 53 Fh
Miranda de Ebro, Spain 70 Da
Miranda do Corvo, Portugal 70 Ab
Miranda do Douro, Portugal 70 Bb
Mirande, France 73 De
Mirandela, Portugal 70 Bb
Mirandilla, Spain 70 Bc
Mirbat, Oman 93 Ff
Mirebeau, France 72 Dc
Miri, Sarawak 83 Fk
Mirim, L., Brazil 54 Fd
Miri Padam, India 89 Jc
Mirjaveh, Iran 93 Hd
Mirnoye, U.S.S.R. 78 Hb
Mirond L., Saskatchewan 37 Pc
Mirosi, Romania 76 Eb
Mirpur, Kashmir 90 Cd
Mirpur Khas, Pakistan 88 Cc
Mirror, Alberta 36 Df
Mirtoan Sea, Greece 77 Df
Mirtos, Crete 77 Eg
Mirzapur, India 91 Dc
Misaw L., Saskatchewan 38 Wf
Miscouche, P.E.I. 32 Jg
Miscou I., N.B. 32 Hf
Miscou Pt., N.B. 32 He
Mishibishu L., Ontario 34 Ed
Misis, Turkey 92 Cb
Miska, Arabia 92 De
Miskolc, Hungary 69 Jd
Misoöl, Irian Jaya 83 Kl
Misquah Hills, Minnesota 40 Ab
Misrātah, Libya 99 Jb
Missanabie, Ontario 34 Fd
Missinaibi L., Ontario 34 Gd
Missinaibi R., Ontario 34 Hb
Mission City, B.C. 39 Ml
Missisicabi, R., Quebec 35 La
Mississagi, R., Ontario 34 Gf
Mississauga, Ontario 40 Gd
Mississinewa Resr., Indiana 40 De
Mississippi, U.S.A. 43 He
Mississippi Delta, Louisiana 45 Cf
Mississippi L., Ontario 35 Og
Mississippi R., U.S.A. 49 Mg
Mississippi Sound, Mississippi 49 Ng
Missonga, Ontario 34 Hd
Missoula, Montana 47 Fb
Missouri, U.S.A. 43 Hd
Missouri Coteau, The, Sask. 36 Lh
Missouri R., U.S.A. 49 Mc
Missouri Valley, Iowa 49 Kb
Mistanipisipou, R., Quebec 33 Kb
Mistaouac, L., Quebec 35 Mc
Mistassibi, R., N.E., Que. 32 Ac
Mistassini, Quebec 35 Sd
Mistassini, L., Quebec 31 Mg
Mistatim, Saskatchewan 37 Of
Mistigougèche, L., Quebec 32 De
Mistretta, Sicily 75 Eg
Misurata. See Misrātah
Mitala Maria, Uganda 97 Gd
Mitchell, Ontario 34 Jj
Mitchell, Queensland 57 Je
Mitchell, S. Dakota 46 Hd
Mitchell, Mt., N. Carolina 45 Fc
Mitchell, R., Queensland 57 Hc
Mitchell River, Qnsld. 57 Hc
Mitchelstown, Eire 63 Bh
Mitchinamécus, Rés., Que. 35 Qe
Mithankot, Pakistan 90 Bf
Mithi, Pakistan 88 Cd
Mithimna, Greece 77 Fe
Mitilíni, Lesvos, Greece 77 Fe
Mitis, L., Quebec 32 Ee
Mitishto R., Manitoba 37 Sd
Mito, Japan 86 Gf
Mittelmark, East Germany 68 Eb
Mitú, Colombia 52 Dc
Mitumba Mts., Zaire 97 Fe
Mitzic, Gabon 96 Cd
Miyako, Japan 86 Ge
Miyazaki, Japan 86 Bj
Mizdah, Libya 99 Hb
Mizen Head, Eire 63 Aj
Mizhi, China 84 Ed
Mizil, Romania 76 Fb
Mizo Hills, India 89 Hd
Mizoram, India 89 Hd
Mizpah, Montana 46 Eb
Mizque, Bolivia 52 Dg
Mjölby, Sweden 67 Fg
Mjosa, L., Norway 67 Df
Mladá Boleslav, Czech. 68 Fc
Mlawa, Poland 69 Jb
Mo, Norway 66 Fc
Moab, Utah 48 Cc
Moak L., Manitoba 37 Uc
Moanda, Gabon 96 Ce
Mo Ångsåg, Sweden 66 He
Moapa, Nevada 47 Fg
Moba, Zaire 97 Ff
Mobay, Cent. African Rep. 96 Ed
Moberly, Missouri 49 Lc
Moberly Lake, B.C. 39 Nh
Mobert, Ontario 34 Ed
Mobile, Alabama 45 Ce
Mobridge, S. Dakota 46 Gc
Mobutu Sese Seko, L. See Albert, L.
Mocajuba, Brazil 53 Hd
Moçâmedes, Angola 96 Ch
Mocha, Yemen 92 Dg
Mocimboa da Praia, Mozambique 97 Jg
Mocksville, N. Carolina 45 Gc
Mocoa, Colombia 52 Bc
Mocorito, Mexico 50 Cb
Moctezuma, Mexico 50 Cb
Moctezuma, Mexico 50 Dc
Mocuba, Mozambique 95 Fc
Mocuburi, Mozambique 97 Hg
Modane, France 73 Gd
Modave, Belgium 64 Dd
Modena, Italy 74 Cc
Modesto, California 47 Cg
Modica, Sicily 75 Eg
Modjamboli, Zaire 96 Ed
Mo Duc, Vietnam 87 Dd
Modung, China 82 Ce
Moengo, Surinam 53 Gb
Moffat, Scotland 62 Ee
Mogadiscio, Somalia 97 Kd
Mogadouro, Portugal 70 Bb
Mogaung, Burma 89 Jc
Mogilev, Byelorussia 80 Ge
Mogilev Podol'skiy, Ukraine 80 Eg
Mogocha, U.S.S.R. 79 Lc
Mogochin, U.S.S.R. 78 Hc
Mogok, Burma 89 Jd
Mogollon Mesa, Arizona 48 Be
Mogollon Mts., New Mexico 48 Cf
Mogu, Ethiopia 97 Jd
Moguer, Spain 70 Bd
Mohacs, Hungary 76 Bb
Mohaka, R., New Zealand 55 Fc
Mohammedia, Algeria 98 Fa
Mohawk, New York 44 Ca
Mohéli I., Comoros 97 Jg
Mohoro, Tanzania 97 Hf
Moirang, India 89 Hd
Moisie & R., Quebec 32 Fc
Moissac, France 73 Dd
Mojave, California 47 Dh
Moji, Brazil 53 Hh
Mojikit L., Ontario 34 Bb
Moju, Brazil 53 Hd
Mokameh, India 91 Ec
Mokau, R., New Zealand 55 Ec
Mokolo, Cameroun 99 Hf
Mokpo, Korea 82 Jd
Moksha, U.S.S.R. 81 Gd
Mol, Belgium 64 Dc
Molanosa, Saskatchewan 37 Md
Moldava, Czechoslovakia 69 Jd
Moldavia, Romania 76 Fa
Moldavia (Moldavskaya S.S.R.), U.S.S.R. 80 Fh
Molde & Fd., Norway 66 Be
Moldova Nouă, Romania 76 Cb
Molepolole, Botswana 95 Dd
Môle St Nicolas, Haiti 51 Ec
Molfetta, Italy 75 Fe
Molina, Chile 54 Be
Molina, Spain 71 Eb
Molina, Spain 71 Ec
Moline, Illinois 49 Mb
Molino, Florida 45 De
Moliro, Zaire 97 Gf
Mollendo, Peru 52 Cg
Mollis, Switzerland 65 Ea
Mollösund, Sweden 67 Dg
Molndal, Sweden 67 Eh
Molotov. See Perm
Molotovsk. See Nolinsk
Molotovsk. See Severodvinsk
Molson, Manitoba 36 Ea
Molson L., Manitoba 37 Vd
Moluccas, Indonesia 83 Jl
Molucca Sea, Indonesia 83 Jk
Moma, Mozambique 97 Hh
Mombasa, Kenya 97 He
Mombetsu, Japan 86 Hb
Mombuey, Spain 70 Ba
Momchilgrad, Bulgaria 76 Ed
Momeik. See Mong-mit
Momignies, Belgium 64 Cd
Momotombo, Nicaragua 51 Bd
Mompós, Colombia 52 Cb
Møn, I., Denmark 67 Ej
Mona, Puerto Rico 51 Fc
Monach I., Scotland 62 Bc
Monaco, Mediterranean Sea 73 Ge
Monadhliath Mts., Scotland 62 Ec
Monå Fd., Finland 66 Ke
Monaghan, Eire 63 Cf
Monango, N. Dakota 46 Hb
Mona Passage, West Indies 51 Fc
Monarch, Alberta 36 Dj
Monarch Mt., B.C. 39 Lk
Monarch Pass, Colorado 42 Ed
Monashee Mts., B.C. 30 Hg
Monashee Provincial Park, B.C. 39 Ok
Monasterace Marina, Italy 75 Ff
Monastir, Sardinia 75 Bf
Monastir. See Bitola
Monastir, Tunisia 99 Ha
Moncão, Portugal 70 Aa
Mönchengladbach, W. Ger. 68 Bc
Monchique, Portugal 70 Ad
Monclova, Mexico 50 Db
Moncton, New Brunswick 32 Hg
Mondoñedo, Spain 70 Ba
Mondovi, Wisconsin 46 Mc
Monduli, Tanzania 97 He
Monemvasia, Greece 77 Df
Monessen, Pennsylvania 44 Ab
Monet, Quebec 35 Pd
Monetny, U.S.S.R. 81 Qb
Monett, Missouri 49 Ld
Moneva, Spain 71 Eb
Monforte, Portugal 70 Bc
Monga, Zaire 96 Ed
Mongalla, Sudan 99 Mg
Mong Cai, Vietnam 85 Cm
Monger, L., W. Australia 56 Ce
Möng-Hsu, Burma 89 Jd
Monghyr, India 91 Fc
Möng Kung, Burma 89 Jd
Mong Mit, Burma 89 Jd
Mongo, Chad 99 Jf
Mongolia, E. Asia 59 Jd
Mongolia, Inner, China 59 Kd
Mongonu, Nigeria 99 Hf
Mongoumba, Cent. Afr. Rep. 99 Jh
Möng Pai, Burma 89 Je
Möng Pan, Burma 89 Jd
Möng Pawn, Burma 89 Jd
Möng-Sit, Burma 89 Jd
Mongu, Zambia 95 Cc
Mong Yai, Burma 89 Jd
Monitor, Alberta 36 Gg
Monkey Bay, Malawi 95 Eb
Monkira, Queensland 57 Hd
Monkton, Ontario 34 Kj
Monmouth, Illinois 49 Mb
Monmouth, Wales 63 Fj
Monmouth, Mt., B.C. 39 Mk
Monnikendam, Netherlands 64 Db
Mono L., California 47 Df
Monomoy I., Mass. 44 Eb
Monopoli, Italy 75 Fe
Monóvar, Spain 71 Ec
Monreal del Campo, Spain 71 Eb
Monroe, Louisiana 43 He
Monroe, Michigan 40 Ee
Monroe, N. Carolina 45 Gc
Monroe, Wisconsin 49 Na
Monroeville, Alabama 45 De
Monrovia, Liberia 98 Cg
Mons, Belgium 64 Bd
Monsanto, Portugal 70 Bb
Monserrato, Sardinia 75 Bf
Monson, Massachusetts 44 Da
Monster, Netherlands 64 Cb
Mönsterås, Sweden 67 Gh
Mont, Belgium 64 Dd
Montague, Michigan 40 Cd
Montague, P.E.I. 32 Kg
Montagu I., S. Sandwich Is. 104 Ad
Montalbán, Spain 71 Eb
Montana, U.S.A. 42 Db
Montánchez, Spain 70 Bc
Mont-Apica, Quebec 35 Te
Montargis, France 72 Ec
Montauban, France 73 Dd
Montbard, France 72 Fc
Montblanch, Spain 71 Fb
Montbrison, France 72 Fd
Montcevelles, L., Quebec 33 Mb
Montclair, New Jersey 44 Cb
Montcornet, France 72 Fb
Mont-de-Marsan, France 73 Ce
Montdidier, France 72 Eb
Mont Dore, le, France 72 Ed
Monte Alegre, Brazil 53 Gd
Monte Alegre, Brazil 53 Hg
Montebello, Quebec 35 Qg
Monte Carlo, Monaco 73 Ge
Monte Carmelo, Brazil 53 Hg
Monte Caseros, Argentina 54 Ed
Monte Comán, Argentina 54 Cd
Monte Cristi, Dom. Republic 51 Ec
Montecristo, Italy 74 Cd
Montefrío, Spain 70 Cd
Montego Bay, Jamaica 51 Dc
Montélimar, France 73 Fd
Montello, Wisconsin 40 Bd
Montemorelos, Mexico 50 Eb
Montenegro, Yugoslavia 76 Bc
Montereau, France 72 Eb
Monterey, California 47 Cg
Monterey, Virginia 45 Ha
Monterey, B. of, California 47 Cg
Montería, Colombia 52 Bb
Montero, Bolivia 52 Eg
Monteros, Argentina 54 Cc
Monterrey, Mexico 50 Db
Monte Sant' Angelo, Italy 75 Ee
Montes Claros, Brazil 53 Jg
Montevideo, Minnesota 46 Kc
Montevideo, Uruguay 54 Ed
Monte Vista, Colorado 48 Dd
Montezuma, Georgia, U.S.A. 45 Fd
Montfort-sur-Meu, France 72 Bb
Montgomery, Alabama 45 Dd
Montgomery, Missouri 49 Mc
Montgomery, Wales 63 Eh
Monthey, Switzerland 65 Bb
Monticello, Arkansas 49 Mf
Monticello, Georgia, U.S.A. 45 Fd
Monticello, New York 40 Je
Monticello, Utah 48 Cd
Montijo, B. de, Panama 51 Ce
Montilla, Spain 70 Cd
Mont-Joli, Quebec 32 Ed
Mont Laurier, Quebec 40 Jb
Mont-Laurier, Quebec 35 Pf
Mont-Louis, Quebec 32 Gd
Montluçon, France 72 Ec
Montmagny, Quebec 32 Bg
Montmartre, Sask. 37 Oh
Montmédy, France 72 Fb
Montmirail, France 72 Eb
Montmorency, Quebec 32 Ag
Montmorency, R., Quebec 32 Af
Montmorency Falls, Quebec 32 Ag
Mont-Orford, Parc prov. du, Quebec 35 Sg
Montoro, Spain 70 Cc
Montoursville, Pennsylvania 44 Bb
Montpelier, Idaho 48 Ba
Montpelier, Vermont 40 Kc
Montpellier, France 73 Ee
Montpellier, Quebec 35 Pg
Montréal, Quebec 35 Rg
Montreal, R., Ontario 34 Ke
Montréal-Est, Quebec 35 Th
Montreal Falls, Ontario 34 Fe
Montreal I., Ontario 34 Fe
Montreal Lake, Sask. 37 Md
Montreal L. & R., Sask. 37 Md
Montréal-Nord, Quebec 35 Rh
Montréal-Ouest, Quebec 35 Rk
Montreal R., Ontario 34 Fe
Montreal River, Ontario 35 Le
Montreal River Harbour, Ontario 34 Fe
Montréjeau, France 73 De
Montreuil, France 72 Da
Montreuil Bellay, France 72 Cc
Montreux, Switzerland 65 Bb
Montrose, Colorado 48 Dc
Montrose, Pennsylvania 44 Bb
Montrose, Scotland 62 Fd
Monts, Pte. des, Quebec 31 Nh
Mont-Saint-Michel, Fr. 72 Cb
Montserrat, Leeward Is. 51 Gc
Mont-Tremblant, Quebec 35 Qf
Mont-Tremblant, Parc Prov. Au, Quebec 35 Qf
Monywa, Burma 89 Jd
Monza, Italy 74 Bc
Monze, Zambia 95 Dc
Monzón, Spain 71 Fb
Moonbeam, Ontario 34 Hc
Moora, W. Australia 56 Cf
Moorcroft, Wyoming 46 Ec
Moore, L., W. Australia 56 Ce
Moorefield, W. Virginia 44 Ac
Moore's Mills, N.B. 32 Eh
Moorfoot Hills, Scotland 62 Ee
Moorhead, Minnesota 46 Jb
Moor Lake, Ontario 35 Nf
Moorsel, Belgium 64 Cd
Moorslede, Belgium 64 Bd
Moose Factory, Ontario 34 Ka
Moosehead L., Maine 32 Ch
Moose Hill, Ontario 37 Nb
Moosehorn, Manitoba 37 Tg
Moose I., Manitoba 37 Ug
Moose Jaw, Saskatchwan 37 Mh
Moose Jaw R., Sask. 37 Nh
Moose Lake, Manitoba 37 Re
Moose Mt. Prov. Park, Sask. 37 Pj
Moose Nose L., Manitoba 37 Wb
Moose R., Ontario 34 Jb
Moose River, Ontario 34 Jb
Moosic Mts., Pennsylvania 44 Cb
Moosomin, Saskatchewan 37 Qh
Moosonee, Ontario 34 Ka
Mopti, Mali 98 Ef
Moquegua, Peru 52 Cg
Mora, Cameroun 99 Hf
Mora, Minnesota 46 Lc
Mora, Portugal 70 Ac
Mora, Spain 70 Dc
Mora, Sweden 66 Ff
Moradabad, India 91 Ba
Mora de Rubielos, Spain 71 Eb
Moraine L., N.W.T. 38 Vc
Moramanga, Madagascar 97 Nk
Morano Calabro, Italy 75 Ff
Morar, India 91 Bb
Morar L., Scotland 62 Dd
Morat. See Murten
Moratalla, Spain 71 Ec
Morava, Czechoslovakia 69 Gd
Morava R., Yugoslavia 76 Cb
Moravska Trebova, Czech. 69 Gd
Morawhanna, Guyana 52 Fb
Moray Firth, Scotland 62 Ec
Morbihan, France 72 Bc
Morden, Manitoba 37 Tj
Morden, Nova Scotia 32 Hh
Mordova, U.S.S.R. 81 Ed
Mordovskaya A.S.S.R., U.S.S.R. 78 Dc
Moreau R., S. Dakota 42 Fb
Morecambe, England 63 Ff
Moreda, Spain 70 Dd
Moree, N.S.W. 57 Je
Moreira, Brazil 52 Ed
Mörel, Switzerland 65 Db
Morelia, Mexico 50 Dd
Morella, Spain 71 Eb
Morelos, Mexico 50 Db
Morelos, Mexico 50 Cb
Morelos, Mexico 50 Ed
Morena, Sierra, Spain 70 Cc
Morenci, Arizona 48 Cf

Morere, *New Zealand* 55 Fc
Moresby I., *B.C.* 39 Gj
Moreton B., *Queensland* 57 Ke
Morez, *France* 72 Gc
Morgan, *S. Australia* 57 Gf
Morgan City, *Louisiana* 49 Mh
Morganton, *N. Carolina* 45 Gc
Morgat, *France* 72 Ab
Morges, *Switzerland* 65 Bb
Morgins, *Switzerland* 65 Bb
Morhiban, Lde, *Quebec* 32 Kb
Moriani, *India* 89 Hc
Morice L., *B.C.* 39 Kh
Morin Creek, *Sask.* 36 Jd
Morinville, *Alberta* 36 De
Morioka, *Japan* 86 Ge
Morisset, *Quebec* 32 Bg
Morlaix, *France* 72 Bb
Morley, *Alberta* 36 Cg
Morley River, *Y.T.* 38 Ge
Mornington, *Chile* 54 Ag
Morobe, *Papua New Guinea* 57 Ja
Morocco, *N.W. Africa* 98 Db
Moro G., *Philippines* 83 Hj
Morogoro, *Tanzania* 97 Hf
Morokweng, *Cape Province* 95 Ce
Morón, *Cuba* 51 Db
Morona, *Ecuador* 52 Bd
Morondava, *Madagascar* 97 Ml
Morón de la Frontera, *Spain* 70 Cd
Morotai, *Indonesia* 83 Jk
Moroto, *Uganda* 97 Gd
Morpeth, *England* 62 Fe
Morpeth, *Ontario* 34 Jk
Morphou, *Cyprus* 94 Ab
Morrillton, *Arkansas* 49 Le
Morrin, *Alberta* 36 Eg
Morrinhos, *Brazil* 53 Hg
Morrinsville, *New Zealand* 55 Eb
Morris, *Illinois* 49 Nb
Morris, *Manitoba* 37 Uj
Morris, *Minnesota* 46 Kc
Morrisburg, *Ontario* 35 Ph
Morris Jesup C., *Arctic Oc.* 41 Na
Morrison, *Illinois* 40 Be
Morristown, *New Jersey* 44 Cb
Morristown, *Tennessee* 43 Kd
Morrisville, *New York* 40 Jd
Morrosquillo, G. de, *Colomb.* 52 Bb
Mors, *Denmark* 67 Ch
Morse, *Saskatchewan* 36 Kh
Morshansk, *U.S.S.R.* 81 Ed
Morson, *Ontario* 36 Ha
Mort, L. du, *N.W.T.* 38 Sd
Mortagne, *France* 72 Db
Mortágua, *Portugal* 70 Ab
Mortain, *France* 72 Cb
Mortlach, *Saskatchewan* 37 Lh
Morven, *New Zealand* 55 Cf
Morven, *Queensland* 57 Je
Morvi, *India* 88 Dd
Moscow, *Idaho* 47 Eb
Moscow. *See* Moskva
Moselle, R., *France* 72 Gb
Moser River, *Nova Scotia* 32 Kj
Mosgiel, *New Zealand* 55 Cf
Mosher, *Ontario* 34 Fd
Moshupa, *Botswana* 95 Dd
Mosjøen, *Norway* 66 Ed
Moskenesöy, *Norway* 66 Ec
Moskva, *U.S.S.R.* 80 Kd
Mosonmagyarovar, *Hungary* 69 Ge
Mosquera, *Colombia* 52 Bc
Mosquito L., *N.W.T.* 38 Wd
Moss, *Norway* 67 Dg
Mossâmedes. *See* Moçâmedes
Mossbank, *Saskatchewan* 36 Mj
Mossburn, *New Zealand* 55 Bf
Mossel Bay, *Cape Province* 95 Cf
Mossendjo, *Congo* 96 Ce
Moss L., *Manitoba* 37 Ta
Mossoro, *Brazil* 53 Ke
Mossuma, *Angola* 96 Eg
Mossy Pt., *Manitoba* 37 Uf
Mossy R., *Saskatchewan* 37 Od
Most, *Czechoslovakia* 68 Ec
Mostaganem, *Algeria* 98 Fa
Mostar, *Yugoslavia* 76 Ac
Mostardas, *Brazil* 54 Fd
Mostoos Hills, *Sask.* 39 Th
Mosul, *Iraq* 92 Db
Mota del Marqués, *Spain* 70 Cb
Motala, *Sweden* 67 Fg
Motatan, *Venezuela* 52 Cb
Motherwell, *Scotland* 62 Ee
Môtier, *Switzerland* 65 Cb
Môtiers, *Switzerland* 65 Bb
Motihari, *India* 91 Eb
Motôt, *Switzerland* 65 Cb
Motril, *Spain* 70 Dd
Mott, *N. Dakota* 46 Fb
Motueka, *New Zealand* 55 Dd
Motul, *Mexico* 50 Gc
Mouchalagane, R., *Quebec* 32 Ca
Moudhros, *Greece* 77 Ee
Moudon, *Switzerland* 65 Bb
Mouila, *Gabon* 96 Ce
Mould Bay, *N.W.T.* 30 Hb
Moulin-Caron, *Quebec* 35 Md
Moulins, *France* 72 Ec
Moulmein, *Burma* 89 Je
Moulouya, *Morocco* 98 Eb
Moulton, *Alabama* 45 Dd
Mound City, *Illinois* 45 Cb
Mountain, R., *N.W.T.* 38 Jc
Mountain Grove, *Missouri* 45 Ab
Mountain Home, *Arkansas* 45 Ab
Mountain Park, *Alberta* 39 Pj
Mountain Sheep Bluffs, *Montana* 46 Eb
Mountain View, *Alberta* 36 Dj
Mountain View, *Arkansas* 45 Ac
Mount Assiniboine Prov. Park, *Alberta* 36 Bh
Mount Ayr, *Iowa* 49 Kb
Mount Bellew, *Eire* 63 Bg
Mount Brydges, *Ontario* 34 Jk
Mount Carmel, *Illinois* 45 Da
Mount Carmel, *Nfld.* 33 Tf
Mount Carmel, *Pennsylvania* 44 Bb
Mount Carroll, *Illinois* 40 Bd
Mount Clemens, *Michigan* 40 Ed
Mount Desert I., *Maine* 32 Dj
Mount Dutton, *S. Australia* 57 Ge
Mount Forest, *Ontario* 34 Kj
Mount Gambier, *S. Australia* 57 Hg
Mount Holly, *New Jersey* 44 Cc
Mount Jewett, *Pennsylvania* 44 Ab
Mount Lofty Range, *S. Australia* 57 Gf
Mount Magnet, *W. Australia* 56 Ce
Mount Morgan, *Queensland* 57 Kd
Mount Morris, *New York* 44 Ba
Mount Olive, *Mississippi* 49 Ng
Mount Olive, *N. Carolina* 45 Hc
Mount Pleasant, *Iowa* 49 Mb
Mount Pleasant, *Michigan* 40 Dd
Mount Pleasant, *Pa.* 44 Ab
Mount Pleasant, *Tennessee* 49 Oe
Mount Pleasant, *Texas* 49 Kf
Mount Pleasant, *Utah* 48 Bc
Mount Revelstoke Nat. Park, *British Columbia* 39 Ok
Mount Royal, *Quebec* 35 Rj
Mounts B., *England* 63 Dk
Mount Sterling, *Kentucky* 45 Fa
Mount Stewart, *Prince Edward I.* 32 Kg
Mount Uniacke, *N.S.* 32 Jj
Mount Union, *Pennsylvania* 44 Bb
Mount Vernon, *Illinois* 45 Ca
Mount Vernon, *Indiana* 49 Pd
Mount Vernon, *Kentucky* 45 Eb
Mount Vernon, *Virginia* 40 Hf
Mount Vernon, *W. Australia* 56 Cd
Moura, *Brazil* 52 Ed
Moura, *Portugal* 70 Bc
Mourão, *Portugal* 70 Bc
Mourne Mts., *N. Ireland* 63 Cf
Moussoro, *Chad* 99 Jf
Moutier, *Switzerland* 65 Ca
Moutohora, *New Zealand* 55 Fc
Mouton I., *Nova Scotia* 32 Hk
Moutons, Baie-des-, *Quebec* 33 Oc
Moyale, *Kenya* 97 Hd
Moyie, *British Columbia* 39 Ql
Moyobamba, *Peru* 52 Be
Mozambique, *East Africa* 97 Hg
Mozambique, *Mozambique* 97 Jh
Mozhabong L., *Ontario* 34 Hf
Mozhga, *U.S.S.R.* 81 Lb
Mozyr, *Byelorussia* 80 Fe
Mpanda, *Tanzania* 97 Gf
Mporokoso, *Zambia* 97 Gf
Mstislavl, *Byelorussia* 80 Gd
Mtakuja, *Tanzania* 97 Gf
Mtito Andei, *Kenya* 97 He
Mtoko, *Zimbabwe* 95 Ec
Mtsensk, *U.S.S.R.* 80 Ke
Mu, *Burma* 89 Jd
Muádhdham, el, *Arabia* 92 Cd
Muang Chaiya, *Thailand* 87 Be
Muang Nan, *Thailand* 87 Cc
Muang Phitsanulok, *Thailand* 87 Cc
Muang Ubon, *Thailand* 87 Cc
Mubarraz, Al, *Arabia* 92 Ed
Mubende, *Uganda* 97 Gd
Muchinga Mts., *Zambia* 97 Gg
Mucuri, *Brazil* 53 Kg
Mudanya, *Turkey* 92 Aa
Mudawwara, *Jordan* 94 Dh
Mud B., *British Columbia* 39 Jm
Muddus Järvi, *Finland* 66 Mb
Muddy L., *Saskatchewan* 36 Hf
Mudgee, *New S. Wales* 57 Jf
Mudhnib, *Arabia* 92 Dd
Mudjatik, R., *Sask.* 39 Ug
Mud L., *Minnesota* 46 Ka
Mueda, *Mozambique* 97 Hg
Muenster, *Saskatchewan* 37 Nf
Mufu Shan, *China* 85 Gh
Muggendorf, *West Germany* 68 Dd
Mugía, *Spain* 70 Aa
Muğla, *Turkey* 92 Ab
Muglad, *Sudan* 99 Lf
Muhamdi, *India* 91 Cb
Muhammadgarh, *India* 91 Bd
Muharraq, *Persian Gulf* 93 Fd
Mühldorf, *West Germany* 68 Ed
Mühlehorn, *Switzerland* 65 Ea
Muhu, *Estonia* 67 Kg
Mui Bai Bung, *Vietnam* 87 Ce
Muinak, *Uzbekistan* 78 Ed
Muine Bheag, *Eire* 63 Ch
Mukdahan, *Thailand* 87 Cc
Mukhtuya, *U.S.S.R.* 79 Lb
Mukhu Väin, *Estonia* 66 Kg
Muktinath, *Nepal* 91 Da
Muktsar, *India* 90 De
Mukutawa R., *Manitoba* 37 Ue
Mula, *Spain* 71 Ec
Mulanje, Mt., *Malawi* 97 Hh
Mulchen, *Chile* 54 Be
Mulege, *Mexico* 50 Bb
Mulgrave, *Nova Scotia* 33 Lh
Mülhausen, *East Germany* 68 Dc
Mülheim, *West Germany* 68 Bc
Mulhouse, *France* 72 Gc
Mulki, *India* 88 Df
Mullaittivu, *Sri Lanka* 88 Fg
Muller Geb., *Borneo (Kalimantan)* 83 Fk
Mullet L., *Michigan* 40 Dc
Mullewa, *W. Australia* 56 Ce
Müllheim, *Switzerland* 65 Ea
Mull I., *Scotland* 62 Dd
Mullingar, *Eire* 63 Cg
Multan, *Pakistan* 90 Be
Multia, *Finland* 66 Le
Mulvihill, *Manitoba* 37 Th
Mumbondo, *Angola* 96 Cg
Mumbwa, *Zambia* 96 Fg
Muna, *Indonesia* 83 Hm
München, *West Germany* 68 Dd
Muncho Lake, *B.C.* 39 Lf
Muncho Lake Prov. Park, *British Columbia* 39 Lf
Muncie, *Indiana* 40 De
Mundare, *Alberta* 36 Ee
Mundiwindi, *W. Australia* 56 Dd
Mundo Novo, *Brazil* 53 Jf
Mundrabilla, *W. Australia* 56 Ef
Munfordville, *Kentucky* 45 Eb
Mungari, *Mozambique* 95 Ec
Munich. *See* München
Muniesa, *Spain* 71 Eb
Munising, *Michigan* 40 Cb
Munk, *Manitoba* 37 Wc
Munkfors, *Sweden* 67 Eg
Münnerstadt, *W. Germany* 68 Dc
Muñoz Gamero, *Chile* 54 Bh
Munroe, *Louisiana* 49 Lf
Munson, *Alberta* 36 Eg
Munster, *Eire* 63 Ah
Münster, *Switzerland* 65 Db
Munster, *Switzerland* 65 Fb
Münster, *West Germany* 68 Bc
Muntok, *Bangka, Indon.* 83 El
Muonio, R., *Swed./Finland* 66 Kc
Muonionalusta, *Sweden* 66 Kc
Muotathal, *Switzerland* 65 Db
Muping, *China* 84 Kd
Murakami, *Japan* 86 Fe
Muranga, *Kenya* 97 He
Murat, *Turkey* 92 Db
Murat Dagh, *Turkey* 92 Ab
Murça, *Portugal* 70 Bb
Murcheh Khvort, *Iran* 93 Fc
Murchison, *New Zealand* 55 Dd
Murchison, R., *W. Australia* 56 Ce
Murchison Falls. *See* Kabalega Falls
Murchison Mts., *N.Z.* 55 Af
Murcia, *Spain* 71 Ed
Murdo, *S.Dakota* 46 Gd
Murdochville, *Quebec* 32 Ge
Muresul (Maros), *Rom.* 76 Ca
Murfreesboro, *Tennessee* 45 Dc
Murgon, *Queensland* 57 Ke
Muri, *Switzerland* 65 Da
Muriaé, *Brazil* 53 Jh
Murias de Paredes, *Spain* 70 Ba
Muriel L., *Alberta* 36 Gd
Murillo, *Ontario* 37 Ob
Müritz See, *East Germany* 68 Eb
Murmansk, *U.S.S.R.* 78 Cb
Murom, *U.S.S.R.* 81 Fc
Muroran, *Japan* 86 Gc
Muroroa, *Tuamotu Arch.* 103 Mk
Muros, *Spain* 70 Aa
Murphy, *N. Carolina* 45 Ec
Murphysboro, *Illinois* 45 Cb
Murray, *Kentucky* 49 Nd
Murray, *Utah* 42 Dc
Murray, R., *N.S.W./S. Australia* 57 Jg
Murray Bridge, *S. Australia* 57 Gg
Murray Harbour, *P.E.I.* 32 Kg
Murray Head, *P.E.I.* 32 Kh
Murray Pt., *N.W.T.* 38 Sa
Murray R., *B.C.* 39 Nh
Murray River, *P.E.I.* 32 Kh
Murree, *Pakistan* 90 Cd
Mürren, *Switzerland* 65 Cb
Murrumbidgee, R., *N.S.W.* 57 Jf
Mursan, *India* 90 Eg
Murshidabad, *India* 91 Gc
Murten, *Switzerland* 65 Cb
Murtle L., *B.C.* 39 Oj
Murwara, *India* 91 Cd
Muryo, *Java* 83 Fm
Muş, *Turkey* 92 Db
Musa Qala, *Afghanistan* 93 Hc
Muscat, *Oman* 93 Ge
Muscatine, *Iowa* 49 Mb
Muscat & Oman. *See* Oman
Musemir, *South Yemen* 92 Dg
Musgrave, *Queensland* 57 Hb
Musgrave Range, *S. Aust./Northern Territory* 56 Fe
Musgravetown, *Nfld.* 33 Te
Mushie, *Zaire* 96 De
Muskeg, R., *N.W.T.* 38 Me
Muskeget Chan., *Mass.* 44 Eb
Muskeg L., *Ontario* 37 Na
Muskegon, *Michigan* 40 Cd
Muskegon R., *Michigan* 40 Dd
Muskogee, *Oklahoma* 49 Ke
Muskoka, L., *Ontario* 35 Lg
Muskwa, *British Columbia* 39 Mf
Muskwa L., *Alberta* 36 Cb
Muskwa R., *Alberta* 36 Cb
Musmar, *Sudan* 99 Ne
Musoma, *Tanzania* 97 Ge
Musquanousse, L., *Quebec* 33 Lc
Musquaro, *Quebec* 33 Lc
Musquaro, L., *Quebec* 33 Lc
Musquash, *New Brunswick* 32 Fh
Musquodoboit, Harbour, *N.S.* 32 Jj
Mussau, *Pacific Ocean* 102 Dh
Mussidan, *France* 73 Dd
Mustahil, *Ethiopia* 97 Jc
Mustajidda, *Arabia* 92 Dd
Mustang, *Nepal* 91 Da
Mustang I., *Texas* 48 Jj
Musters, *Argentina* 54 Cg
Muswellbrook, *N.S.W.* 57 Kf
Mut, *Egypt* 99 Lc
Mut, *Turkey* 92 Bb
Mutanda, *Zambia* 96 Fg
Mutoray, *U.S.S.R.* 79 Kb
Mutsu wan, *Japan* 86 Gd
Mutton I., *Eire* 63 Ah
Mutumbo, *Angola* 96 Dg
Mutupet, *India* 88 Ef
Muwale, *Tanzania* 97 Gf
Muy, le, *France* 73 Ge
Muya. *See* Naruta
Muya, *U.S.S.R.* 79 Lc
Muy Muy, *Nicaragua* 51 Bd
Muzaffarabad, *Kashmir* 90 Cc
Muzaffargarh, *Pakistan* 90 Be
Muzaffarnagar, *India* 90 Ef
Muzaffarpur, *India* 91 Eb
Muzhi, *U.S.S.R.* 78 Fb
Múzquiz, *Mexico* 50 Db
Muztag, *China* 89 Ga
Muztagata, *China* 90 Da
Mwanza, *Tanzania* 97 Ge
Mweelrea, *Eire* 63 Ag
Mweru L., *Zaire* 97 Ff
Mwinilunga, *Zambia* 96 Eg
Myadaung, *Burma* 89 Jd
Myanaung, *Burma* 89 Je
Myaungmya, *Burma* 89 Je
Myebon, *Burma* 89 Hd
Myingyan, *Burma* 89 Jd
Myinmolettkat, *Burma* 89 Jf
Myitkyina, *Burma* 89 Jc
Myjava, *Czechoslovakia* 69 Gd
Mymensingh, *Bangladesh* 89 Hd
Myohaung, *Burma* 89 Hd
Myrdal, *Norway* 67 Bf
Myrnam, *Alberta* 36 Fe
Myrtle, *Manitoba* 37 Uj
Myrtle, *Ontario* 35 Mh
Myslowice, *Poland* 69 Hc
Mysore. *See* Karnataka
Mystery L., *Manitoba* 37 Uc
Mystic, *S. Dakota* 46 Fc
My Tho, *Vietnam* 83 Eh
Myzakyula, *Estonia* 67 Lg
Mziha, *Tanzania* 97 Hf
Mzimba, *Malawi* 97 Gg

N

Naantali, *Finland* 67 Kf
Naarden, *Netherlands* 64 Db
Naas, *Eire* 63 Cg
Nabadwip, *India* 91 Gd
Nabatiya, *Lebanon* 94 Dd
Nabberu, L., *W. Australia* 56 De
Nabha, *India* 90 Ee
Nabisipi, R., *Quebec* 33 Kc
Nablus, *Jordan* 94 De
Nacaome, *Honduras* 51 Bd
Nacimiento, *Mexico* 50 Db
Nacmine, *Alberta* 36 Eg
Naco, *Arizona* 48 Cg
Nacogdoches, *Texas* 49 Kg
Nacozari de Garcia, *Mexico* 50 Ca
Nadiad, *India* 88 Dd
Naerøy, *Norway* 66 Dd
Naestved, *Denmark* 67 Dj
Nafels, *Switzerland* 65 Ea
Naft, *Iran* 92 Ec
Nafud, An, *Arabia* 92 Cd
Naga, *Philippines* 83 Hh
Naga, *South Yemen* 92 Eg
Nagagami, *Ontario* 34 Fc
Nagagami, R., *Ontario* 34 Fc
Nagagami L., *Ontario* 34 Ec
Nagagamisis L., *Ontario* 34 Fc
Nagagamisis Prov. Park, *Ontario* 34 Fc
Naga Hills, *India* 89 Hc
Nagalama, *Uganda* 97 Gd
Nagaland, *India* 87 Aa
Nagano, *Japan* 86 Ff
Nagaoka, *Japan* 86 Ff
Nagapattinam, *India* 88 Ef
Nagar, *India* 90 Ed
Nagar Karnul, *India* 88 Ee
Nagar Parkar, *India* 88 Dd
Nagasaki, *Japan* 86 Ah
Nagaur, *India* 88 Dc
Nagda, *India* 88 Ed
Nagercoil, *India* 88 Eg
Nagha Kalat, *Pakistan* 88 Cc
Nagina, *India* 91 Ba
Nagir, *Kashmir* 90 Db
Nagoya, *Japan* 86 Eg
Nagpur, *India* 88 Ed
Nagu, *Finland* 67 Jf
Nagykanizsa, *Hungary* 69 Ge
Naha, *Japan* 86 Mp
Nahael Niyeu, *Argentina* 54 Cf
Nahan, *India* 90 Ee
Nahanni Butte, *N.W.T.* 38 Me
Nahanni Nat. Park, *Y.T.* 38 Le
Nahanni R., North, *N.W.T.* 38 Ld
Nahanni R., South, *N.W.T.* 38 Ke
Nahanni Ra., *N.W.T.* 38 Me
Nahariya, *Israel* 94 Dd
Nahavand, *Iran* 92 Ec
Naica, *Mexico* 50 Cb
Naicam, *Saskatchewan* 37 Nf
Naifar, *Iraq* 92 Ec
Naihati, *India* 91 Gd
Na'in, *Iran* 93 Fc
Nain, *Newfoundland* 31 Nf
Naini Tal, *India* 91 Ba
Nairn, *Ontario* 34 Jf
Nairn, *Scotland* 62 Ec
Nairobi, *Kenya* 97 He
Naismith, *Montana* 46 Ba
Naivasha, *Kenya* 97 He
Naivasha, L., *Kenya* 95 He
Najd, *Arabia* 92 Dd
Najera, *Spain* 71 Da
Najibabad, *India* 91 Ba
Najin, *Korea* 82 Kb
Najrān, *Arabia* 92 Df
Nakajo, *Japan* 86 Fe
Nakatsu, *Japan* 86 Bh
Nakfa, *Ethiopia* 97 Ha
Nakhichevan, *U.S.S.R.* 78 De
Nakhla, *Arabia* 93 Fe
Nakhon Pathom, *Thailand* 87 Cd
Nakhon Phanom, *Thailand* 87 Cc
Nakhon Ratchasima, *Thailand* 87 Cd
Nakhon Sawan, *Thailand* 87 Cc
Nakhon Si Thammarat, *Thailand* 87 Be
Nakina, *British Columbia* 38 Gf
Nakina, *Ontario* 34 Db
Nakina, R., *B.C.* 38 Gf
Nakl Mubarak, *Arabia* 92 Ce
Nakodar, *India* 90 De
Nakuru, *Kenya* 97 He
Nakusp, *British Columbia* 39 Pk
Nalagarh, *India* 90 Ee
Nalgonda, *India* 88 Ee
Nallamalai Hills, *India* 88 Ee
Nalut, *Libya* 99 Hb
Namaka, *Alberta* 36 Dh
Namangan, *Uzbekistan* 78 Gd
Namasagali, *Uganda* 97 Gd
Nambala, *Zambia* 96 Fh
Namcha Barwa, *China* 89 Jc
Nam Dinh, *Vietnam* 87 Db
Nametail, *Mozambique* 97 Hh
Namew L., *Saskatchewan* 37 Pd
Namhoi. *See* Foshan
Namib, *Namibia* 95 Ad
Namibia, *Africa* 95 Bd
Namlea, *Indonesia* 83 Jl
Namling, *China* 89 Gc
Namonuito, *Caroline Is.* 102 Eg
Namorona, *Madagascar* 97 Nl
Nampa, *Alberta* 39 Pg
Nampa, *Idaho* 47 Ed
Nampula, *Mozambique* 97 Hh
Namsen R., *Norway* 66 Ed
Namsos, *Norway* 66 Dd
Namsvatnet, *Norway* 66 Ed
Namtsy, *U.S.S.R.* 79 Mb
Namtu, *Burma* 89 Jd
Namu, *British Columbia* 39 Kk
Namur, *Belgium* 64 Cd
Namur, *Quebec* 35 Qg
Namur L., *Alberta* 39 Rg
Namutoni, *Namibia* 95 Bc
Namwala, *Zambia* 95 Dc
Nanaimo, *B.C.* 39 Ml
Nana Kru, *Liberia* 98 Dh
Nanan. *See* Dayu
Nanao, *Japan* 86 Ef
Nanchang, *China* 85 Gh
Nancheng, *China* 85 Hj
Nancheng. *See* Hanzhong
Nanchong, *China* 84 Cg
Nancy, *France* 72 Gb
Nanda Devi, *India* 88 Eb
Nandan, *China* 85 Ck
Nanded, *India* 88 Ee
Nanga Parbat, *Kashmir* 90 Dc
Nanjangud, *India* 88 Ef
Nanjing, *China* 84 Jf
Nannine, *W. Australia* 56 Ce
Nanning, *China* 85 Dl
Nanortalik, *Greenland* 41 Pd
Nanpara, *India* 91 Cb
Nanping, *China* 85 Jj
Nanripo, *Mozambique* 97 Hg
Nansen Sound, *N.W.T.* 31 Ka
Nantais, L., *Quebec* 31 Me
Nantes, *France* 72 Cc
Nantes, *Quebec* 32 Ah
Nanticoke, *Ontario* 34 Kk
Nanticoke, *Pennsylvania* 44 Bb
Nanton, *Alberta* 36 Dh
Nantong, *China* 84 Kf
Nantucket, *Massachusetts* 40 Le
Nantucket I., *Massachusetts* 44 Eb
Nantucket Sound, *Mass.* 44 Eb
Nanuque, *Brazil* 53 Jg
Nanxiong, *China* 85 Gk
Nanyang, *China* 84 Ff
Nanyō, *Japan* 86 Ge
Nanyuki, *Kenya* 97 Hd
Naococane L., *Quebec* 31 Mg
Naoetsu, *Japan* 86 Ff
Napa, *California* 47 Bf
Napadogan, *N.B.* 32 Fg
Napanee, *Ontario* 35 Oh
Napas, *U.S.S.R.* 78 Hc
Napétipi, R., *Quebec* 33 Ob
Napier, *New Zealand* 55 Fc
Napierville, *Quebec* 35 Rg
Napinka, *Manitoba* 37 Rj
Naples. *See* Napoli
Napoleon, *N. Dakota* 46 Hb
Napoli, *Italy* 75 Ee
Napoli, G. di, *Italy* 75 De
Naqb Ashtar, *Jordan* 94 Dg
Nara, *Japan* 86 Dg
Nara, *Mali* 98 De
Naracoorte, *S. Australia* 57 Hg
Narathiwat, *Thailand* 87 Ce
Narayanganj, *Bangladesh* 89 Hd
Narbonne, *France* 73 Ee
Nares Ld., *Greenland* 41 Pa
Nares Str., *Canada/Greenland* 31 Mb
Nari, *Pakistan* 88 Cc
Narino, *Colombia* 52 Bc
Narken, *Sweden* 66 Kc
Narmada, *India* 88 Dd
Narnaul, *India* 90 Df
Narok, *Kenya* 97 He
Narovchat, *U.S.S.R.* 81 Fd
Narowal, *Pakistan* 90 Dd
Narrabri, *N.S.W.* 57 Jf
Narragansett B., *Rhode I.* 44 Eb
Narranderra, *N.S.W.* 57 Jf
Narrogin, *W. Australia* 56 Cf
Narsimhapur, *India* 91 Bd
Narsinghgarh, *India* 91 Bd
Naruta, *Japan* 86 Dg
Narva, *Estonia* 67 Ng
Narva Laht, *Estonia* 67 Mg
Narvik, *Norway* 66 Gb
Narwar, *India* 91 Ac
Naryan Mar, *U.S.S.R.* 78 Eb
Narykary, *U.S.S.R.* 78 Fb
Narym, *U.S.S.R.* 78 Hc
Naryn, *Kirghizia* 78 Gd
Naseby, *New Zealand* 55 Cf
Nash Creek, *N.B.* 32 Ff
Nashua, *N.H.* 44 Ea
Nashville, *Arkansas* 49 Lf
Nashville, *Illinois* 45 Ca
Nashville, *N. Carolina* 45 Jc
Nashville, *Tennessee* 45 Db
Nashwaaksis, *N.B.* 32 Fg
Nasian, *Ivory Coast* 98 Eg
Nasi Järvi, *Finland* 67 Kf
Nasik, *India* 88 Dd
Nasirabad, *India* 88 Dc
Nassau, *Pacific Ocean* 102 Jj
Nassau, *The Bahamas* 51 Da
Nassau, B. de, *Chile* 54 Cj
Nasser, L., *Egypt* 99 Md
Nässjö, *Sweden* 67 Fh
Nass R., *British Columbia* 39 Jh
Natapoka Is., *N.W.T.* 31 Mf
Nata, *Panama* 51 Ce
Natal, *Brazil* 53 Ke
Natal, *British Columbia* 36 Cj
Natal, *South Africa* 95 Ee
Natal, *Sumatra* 83 Ck
Natanes Plat., *Arizona* 48 Cf
Natashquan, *Quebec* 33 Lc
Natashquan R., *Nfld./Que.* 32 Ka
Natchez, *Mississippi* 45 Be
National City, *California* 47 Ej
Nation R., *B.C.* 39 Lh
Natiscotec, B., *Quebec* 33 Kd
Natividade, *Brazil* 53 Hf
Natron L., *Tanzania* 97 He
Nattavaara, *Sweden* 66 Jc
Naudville, *Quebec* 56 Bf
Naujoji Vilnia, *Lithuania* 35 Td
Naukhas, *Namibia* 67 Lj
Naumburg, *West Germany* 95 Bd
Naur, *Jordan* 68 Dc
Nauru, *Pacific Ocean* 94 Df
Naushahra, *Kashmir* 102 Fh
Naushahro, *Pakistan* 90 Dd
Naushki, *U.S.S.R.* 88 Cc
Nauta, *Peru* 79 Kc
Nautla, *Mexico* 52 Cd
Nauvoo, *Illinois* 51 Ab
Nava del Rey, *Spain* 49 Mb
Navajo, Mt., *Utah* 70 Cb
Navajo Res., *New Mexico* 48 Bd
Navalcarnero, *Spain* 48 Dd
Navalmoral, *Spain* 70 Cb
Navan, *Eire* 70 Cc
Navarino, *Chile* 63 Cg
Navarre, *France* 54 Cj
Navojoa, *Mexico* 73 Ce
Navplion, *Greece* 50 Cb
Navrongo, *Ghana* 77 Df
Navsari, *India* 98 Ef
Nawa, *Syria* 88 Dd
Nawab Basoda, *India* 94 Ee
Nawabganj, *India* 91 Bd
Nawabganj, *India* 91 Cb
Nawada, *India* 91 Db
Nawahganj, *India* 91 Ec
Nawai, *India* 91 Ba
Nawalgarh, *India* 88 Ec
Náxos, *Greece* 80 Dg
Nayakhan, *U.S.S.R.* 77 Ef
Nayarit, *Mexico* 79 Qb
Nayarit, Sa. de, *Mexico* 50 Cc
Nay Band, *Iran* 50 Dc
Nayfah, *Arabia* 93 Fd
Nayoro, *Japan* 93 Ff
Nazaré da Mata, *Brazil* 86 Hb
Nazaret, *Ethiopia* 53 Ke
97 Hc
Nazareth, *Israel* 94 De
Nazas, *Mexico* 50 Db
Nazca, *Peru* 52 Cf
Naze, The. *See* Lindesnes
Nazilli, *Turkey* 92 Ab
Nazimovo, *U.S.S.R.* 79 Jc
Nazko, *British Columbia* 39 Mj
Nazko, R., *B.C.* 39 Mj
Nazwa, *Oman* 93 Ge
Ncheu, *Malawi* 97 Gg
Ndala, *Tanzania* 97 Ge
Ndeni, *Santa Cruz Is.* 102 Fj
N'Djamena, *Chad* 99 Jf
Ndjolé, *Gabon* 96 Ce
Ndola, *Zambia* 97 Fg
Neagh L., *N. Ireland* 63 Cf
Neápolis, *Crete* 77 Eg
Near Is., *Aleutian Islands* 43 Um
Neath, *Wales* 63 Ej
Nebikon, *Switzerland* 65 Ca
Nebit-Dag, *Turkmenistan* 78 Ee
Nebo, Mt., *Utah* 48 Bc
Nebraska, *U.S.A.* 42 Fc
Nebraska City, *Nebraska* 49 Kb
Necedah, *Wisconsin* 40 Ac
Nechako, R., *B.C.* 39 Lj
Neckar, *West Germany* 68 Cd
Necochea, *Argentina* 54 Ee
Nedelec, *Quebec* 35 Le
Nederweert, *Netherlands* 64 Dc
Nêdong, *China* 89 Hc
Neede, *Netherlands* 64 Eb
Needles, *California* 47 Fh
Needles, The, *Arizona* 47 Fh
Needles, The, *England* 63 Fk
Neelin, *Manitoba* 37 Sj
Neenah, *Wisconsin* 40 Bc
Neepawa, *Manitoba* 37 Sh
Neergaard L., *N.W.T.* 31 Lc
Neerpelt, *Belgium* 64 Dc
Negaunee, *Michigan* 40 Cb
Negombo, *Sri Lanka* 88 Eg
Negrais, C., *Burma* 89 He
Negra Pt., *Philippines* 83 Hg
Negritos, *Peru* 52 Ad
Negro, R., *Argentina* 54 De
Negro, R., *Brazil* 52 Ed
Negro, R., *Uruguay* 54 Ed
Negros, *Philippines* 83 Hj
Negru Vodă, *Romania* 76 Gc
Nehbandān, *Iran* 93 Hc
Neidpath, *Saskatchewan* 36 Kh
Neijiang, *China* 85 Bh
Neilburg, *Saskatchewan* 36 Hf
Neil's Harbour, *N.S.* 33 Mg
Neilsville, *Wisconsin* 40 Ac
Neiva, *Colombia* 52 Bc
Neksø, *Bornholm, Den.* 67 Fj
Nelkan, *U.S.S.R.* 79 Nc
Nellore, *India* 88 Ff
Nelma, *U.S.S.R.* 79 Nd
Nelson, *B.C.* 39 Pl
Nelson, *New Zealand* 55 Dd
Nelson, R., *Manitoba* 30 Kf
Nelson Forks, *B.C.* 38 Mf
Nelson Head, *N.W.T.* 38 Ma
Nelson House, *Manitoba* 37 Tc
Néma, *Mauritania* 98 De
Neman, *U.S.S.R.* 67 Kj
Nemegos, *Ontario* 34 Ge
Nemegosenda L., *Ontario* 34 Gd
Nemeiben L., *Sask.* 37 Mc
Némiscachinque, L., *Quebec* 40 Jb
Némiscau, *Quebec* 31 Mg
Némiscau, L., *Quebec* 35 Oa
Nemours, *France* 72 Eb
Nemunas, R., *Lithuania* 67 Kj
Nemuro, *Japan* 86 Jc
Nemuro wan, *Japan* 86 Jc
Nenagh, *Eire* 63 Bh
Nendeln, *Liechtenstein* 65 Ea
Nene R., *England* 63 Gh
Nen Jiang, *China* 82 Ha
Nenjiang, *China* 82 Ja
Neodesha, *Kansas* 49 Kd
Neópolis, *Brazil* 53 Kf
Neosho, *Missouri* 49 Kd
Nepa, *U.S.S.R.* 79 Kc
Nepal, *S. Asia* 89 Fc
Nepalganj, *Nepal* 91 Ca
Nephi, *Utah* 48 Bc
Nephton, *Ontario* 35 Nh
Nepisiguit Bay, *N.B.* 32 Gf
Nepisiguit R., *N.B.* 32 Ff
Neptune, *Saskatchewan* 37 Nj
Nérac, *France* 73 Dd
Nerchinsk, *U.S.S.R.* 79 Lc
Neringa, *Lithuania* 80 Bd
Nerpio, *Spain* 71 Dc
Nes, *U.S.S.R.* 78 Db
Nesle, L., *Quebec* 33 Nc
Nesna, *Norway* 66 Ec
Ness City, *Kansas* 49 Hc
Nesselrode, Mt., *B.C.* 38 Ff
Nesset, *Norway* 66 Ce
Ness L., *Scotland* 62 Ec
Nesslau, *Switzerland* 65 Ea
Nesthorn, *Switzerland* 65 Cb
Nestor Falls, *Ontario* 36 Ha
Nestorville, *Ontario* 34 Gf
Nesttun, *Norway* 67 Af
Netanya, *Israel* 94 Ce
Netherhill, *Saskatchewan* 36 Hg
Netherlands, *W. Europe* 60 Je
Nettetal, *W. Germany* 68 Bc
Nettilling L., *N.W.T.* 31 Md
Nettuno, *Italy* 75 De
Neubrandenburg, *E. Ger.* 68 Eb
Neuburg, *West Germany* 68 Dd
Neuchâtel, *Switzerland* 65 Ba
Neuchâtel, L. de, *Switz.* 65 Bb
Neudorf, *Saskatchewan* 37 Ph
Neufchâteau, *Belgium* 64 De
Neufchâteau, *France* 72 Fb
Neufchâtel, *France* 72 Db
Neufelden, *Austria* 68 Ed
Neuhausen, *Switzerland* 65 Da
Neumünster, *W. Germany* 68 Ca
Neunkirch, *Switzerland* 65 Da
Neuquén, *Argentina* 54 Ce
Neuse R., *N. Carolina* 45 Jc
Neusiedler See, *Austria* 69 Ge
Neuss, *West Germany* 68 Bc
Neustadt, *West Germany* 68 Da
Neustettin. *See* Szczecinek
Neustrelitz, *East Germany* 68 Eb
Neu Ulm, *West Germany* 68 Dd
Neuveville, *Switzerland* 65 Ca
Nevada, *Iowa* 49 La
Nevada, *Missouri* 49 Kd
Nevada, *U.S.A.* 42 Cd
Nevis, *Cuba* 51 Db

Nevada, Sierra, *California* 42 Bd
Nevada, Sierra, *Spain* 70 Dd
Nevel, *U.S.S.R.* 80 Fc
Nevel'sk, *U.S.S.R.* 79 Pd
Nevers, *France* 72 Ec
Nevesinje, *Yugoslavia* 76 Bc
Neveyezhkino, *U.S.S.R.* 81 Ge
Neville, *Saskatchewan* 36 Kj
Nevis, *Alberta* 36 Df
Nevis, *Leeward Islands* 51 Gc
Nevşehir, *Turkey* 92 Bb
Nevyansk, *U.S.S.R.* 81 Qb
New Albany, *Indiana* 45 Ea
New Albany, *Mississippi* 45 Cc
New Albany, *Nova Scotia* 32 Gj
New Amsterdam, *Guyana* 53 Fb
Newark, *Delaware* 44 Cc
Newark, *England* 63 Gg
Newark, *New Jersey* 44 Cb
Newark, *Ohio* 40 Ee
Newaygo, *Michigan* 40 Dd
New Bedford, *Mass.* 44 Eb
New Bern, *N. Carolina* 45 Jc
Newbern, *Tennessee* 45 Cb
Newberry, *Michigan* 40 Db
Newberry, *S. Carolina* 45 Gc
New Bloomfield, *Pa.* 44 Bb
Newboro, *Ontario* 35 Oh
New Brigden, *Alberta* 36 Gg
New Britain, *Bismarck Arch.* 102 Dh
New Britain, *Connecticut* 44 Db
Newbrook, *Alberta* 36 Ed
New Brunswick, *Canada* 31 Nh
New Brunswick, *New Jersey* 44 Cb
Newburgh, *New York* 44 Cb
Newburgh, *Ontario* 35 Oh
New Burnt Cove, *Nfld.* 33 Te
Newbury, *England* 63 Gj
Newburyport, *Mass.* 44 Ea
New Caledonia, *Pacific Oc.* 102 Fk
New Carlisle, *Quebec* 32 Gf
Newcastle, *Delaware* 40 Jf
Newcastle, *Natal* 95 De
Newcastle, *N.B.* 32 Gf
New Castle, *New Jersey* 44 Cc
Newcastle, *N. Ireland* 63 Cf
Newcastle, *N.S.W.* 57 Kf
Newcastle, *Ontario* 35 Mj
New Castle, *Pennsylvania* 40 Fe
Newcastle, *Wyoming* 46 Ed
Newcastle Bridge, *N.B.* 32 Fg
Newcastle Emlyn, *Wales* 63 Dh
Newcastle Mine, *Alberta* 36 Eg
Newcastle-under-Lyme, *Eng.* 63 Fg
Newcastle upon Tyne, *England* 62 Fe
Newcastle Waters, *N. Terr.* 57 Fc
Newchwang. *See* Yingkou
New City, *New York* 44 Cb
Newdale, *Manitoba* 37 Rh
New Dayton, *Alberta* 36 Ej
New Denmark, *N.B.* 32 Eg
Newell, L. (Res.), *Alberta* 36 Eh
New England Range, *N.S.W.* 57 Kf
Newfane, *Vermont* 44 Da
New Fish Creek, *Alberta* 39 Ph
New Forest, *England* 63 Fk
Newfoundland, *Canada* 31 Nf
Newfoundland, I. of, *Canada* 31 Oh
New Galloway, *Scotland* 62 Ee
Newgate, *B.C.* 36 Bj
New Georgia, *Solomon Is.* 102 Eh
New Germany, *Nova Scotia* 32 Hj
New Glasgow, *Nova Scotia* 32 Kh
New Guinea, *Pacific Ocean* 59 Pj
New Hamburg, *Ontario* 34 Kj
New Hampshire, *U.S.A.* 43 Mc
New Hampton, *Iowa* 49 La
New Hanover, *Bismarck Arch.* 102 Dh
New Haven, *Connecticut* 40 Ke
Newhaven, *England* 63 Hk
New Haven, *Missouri* 45 Ba
New Hazelton, *B.C.* 39 Kh
New Hebrides. *See* Vanuatu
New Hope Res., *N. Carolina* 45 Hc
New Iberia, *Louisiana* 49 Mh
New Ireland, *Bismarck Arch.* 102 Eh
New Jersey, *U.S.A.* 43 Mc
New Lisbon, *Wisconsin* 40 Ad
New Liskeard, *Ontario* 35 Le
New London, *Connecticut* 44 Db
New London, *Wisconsin* 40 Bc
New Madrid, *Missouri* 49 Nd
Newman, *W. Australia* 56 Cd
Newmans Cove, *Nfld.* 33 Te
Newmarket, *Eire* 63 Bh
Newmarket, *England* 63 Hh
Newmarket, *Ontario* 35 Lh
New Mexico, *U.S.A.* 42 Ee
New Norfolk, *Tasmania* 57 Jh
New Norway, *Alberta* 36 Ef
New Orleans, *Louisiana* 49 Mh
New Osgoode, *Sask.* 37 Of
New Plymouth, *N. Zealand* 55 Ec
Newport, *Arkansas* 45 Bc
Newport, *I. of W., England* 63 Gk
Newport, *Kentucky* 40 Df
Newport, *New Hampshire* 44 Da
Newport, *Quebec* 32 He
Newport, *Rhode Island* 40 Lc
Newport, *Vermont* 40 Kc
Newport, *Wales* 63 Fj
Newport News, *Virginia* 43 Ld
New Providence, *The Bahamas* 51 Db
Newquay, *England* 63 Dk
New Richmond, *Quebec* 32 Ge
New Richmond, *Wisconsin* 46 Lc
New Rochelle, *New York* 44 Db
New Rockford, *N. Dakota* 46 Hb
New Ross, *Eire* 63 Ch
Newry, *N. Ireland* 63 Cf
New Salem, *N. Dakota* 46 Gb
New Siberian Islands. *See* Novosibirskiye Ostrova
New South Wales, *Australia* 57 Jf
Newton, *Iowa* 49 Lb
Newton, *Kansas* 49 Jc
Newton, *Massachusetts* 44 Ea
Newton, *New Jersey* 44 Cb
Newton Abbot, *England* 63 Ek
Newton Stewart, *Scotland* 63 Ef
Newtown, *Nfld.* 33 Td
Newtown, *Wales* 63 Eh
Newtownards, *N. Ireland* 63 Df
Newtownstewart, *N. Ireland* 63 Cf
New Ulm, *Minnesota* 46 Kc
New Waterford, *N.S.* 33 Mg
New Westminster, *B.C.* 39 Ml
New World I., *Nfld.* 33 Sd
New York, *New York* 40 Ke
New York, *U.S.A.* 43 Mc
New Zealand, 55
Neya, *U.S.S.R.* 81 Ha
Neyriz, *Iran* 93 Fd
Neyshābūr, *Iran* 93 Gb
Nezhin, *Ukraine* 80 Gf
Ngangla Ringco, *China* 89 Fb
Nganglong Kangri, *China* 88 Fb
N'Gaoundéré, *Cameroun* 99 Hg
Ngapara, *New Zealand* 55 Cf
Ngaruawahia, *New Zealand* 55 Eb
Ngatik, *Caroline Islands* 102 Eg
Ngauruhoe, Mt., *N.Z.* 55 Ec
Ngong, *Kenya* 97 He
Ngoring Hu, *China* 82 Cd
N'guigmi, *Niger* 99 Hf
Ngulu, *Pacific Ocean* 102 Cg
Ngwasi, *Tanzania* 97 Hf
Nha Trang, *Vietnam* 87 Dd
Nhill, *Victoria* 57 Hg
Niafounké, *Mali* 98 Ee
Niagara, *Ontario* 40 Gd
Niagara Falls, *New York* 40 Gd
Niagara Falls, *Ontario* 35 Lj
Niagara-on-the-Lake, *Ont.* 35 Lj
Niagara R., *Ont./N.Y.* 35 Mj
Niah, *Sarawak* 83 Fk
Niamey, *Niger* 98 Ff
Nia Nia, *Zaire* 97 Fd
Niapa, *Borneo (Kalimantan)* 83 Gk
Nias, *Indonesia* 83 Ck
Nicaragua, *Cent. Amer.* 51 Bd
Nicaragua, L. de, *Nicaragua* 51 Bd
Nicastro, *Italy* 75 Ff
Nice, *France* 73 Ge
Nichicun L., *Quebec* 31 Mg
Nicholson, *Ontario* 34 Ge
Nicholson L., *N.W.T.* 38 Wd
Nickel Lake, *Ontario* 36 Jb
Nicman, *Quebec* 32 Gc
Nicobar Is., *Indian Ocean* 89 Hg
Nicola, *British Columbia* 39 Nk
Nicolet, *Quebec* 35 Sf
Nicosia, *Cyprus* 94 Bd
Nicoya, *Costa Rica* 51 Bd
Nictau, *New Brunswick* 32 Ef
Nictaux Falls, *Nova Scotia* 32 Gj
Nidau, *Switzerland* 65 Ca
Nidzica, *Poland* 69 Jb
Niedere Tauern, *Austria* 68 Ee
Niedersachsen, *W. Germany* 68 Cb
Niellé, *Ivory Coast* 98 Df
Nieuw Amsterdam, *Surinam* 53 Fb
Nieuwendijk, *Netherlands* 64 Cc
Nieuwersluis, *Netherlands* 64 Cb
Nieuwkerke, *Belgium* 64 Ad
Nieuwkoop, *Netherlands* 64 Cb
Nieuw Nickerie, *Surinam* 53 Fb
Nieuwpoort, *Belgium* 64 Ac
Nieuwpoort, *Netherlands* 64 Cc
Nieves, *Mexico* 50 Dc
Nièvre, *France* 72 Ec
Nigadoo, *New Brunswick* 32 Gf
Nigde, *Turkey* 92 Bb
Niger, *West Africa* 98 Ge
Niger, *West Africa* 98 Ff
Nigeria, *West Africa* 98 Gg
Nighasan, *India* 91 Ca
Night Hawk L., *Ontario* 34 Kd
Nigula, *Estonia* 67 Mg
Niigata, *Japan* 86 Ff
Niihau, *Hawaiian Is.* 102 Je
Nijil, *Jordan* 94 Dg
Nijkerk, *Netherlands* 64 Db
Nijmegen, *Netherlands* 64 Dc
Nikaria. *See* Ikaria
Nikiforos, *Greece* 76 Ed
Nikitinka, *U.S.S.R.* 80 Hd
Nikki, *Benin* 98 Fg
Nikko Nat. Park, *Japan* 86 Ff
Nikolayev, *Ukraine* 80 Gh
Nikolayevsk, *U.S.S.R.* 81 Ge
Nikolayevsk-na-Amure, *U.S.S.R.* 79 Pc
Nikolo-Kozel'sk, *Ukraine* 80 Hh
Nikol'skaya Pestrovka, *U.S.S.R.* 81 Gd
Nikol'sk-Berezovka, *U.S.S.R.* 81 Mb
Nikopol, *Ukraine* 80 Jh
Niksar, *Turkey* 92 Ca
Nikšić, *Yugoslavia* 76 Bc
Nila, *Indonesia* 83 Jm
Nile, *Sudan* 97 Ga
Nile, R., *North Africa* 99 Me
Niles, *Michigan* 40 Ce
Nilgaut, L., *Quebec* 35 Nf
Nilgiri, *India* 89 Gd
Nilgiri Hills, *India* 88 Ef
Nilphamari, *Bangladesh* 91 Gc
Nîmes, *France* 73 Fe
Nimgiri, *India* 89 Fe
Nine de Julio, *Argentina* 54 De
Ninette, *Manitoba* 37 Sj
Nineveh, *Iraq* 92 Db
Ning'an, *China* 82 Jb
Ningbo, *China* 85 Kh
Ninghai, *China* 85 Kh
Ninghsien. *See* Ningbo
Ningkwo. *See* Xuancheng
Ning-sia. *See* Yinchuan
Ningwu, *China* 84 Fc
Ningxiang, *China* 85 Fh
Ninh Binh, *Vietnam* 87 Db
Ninove, *Belgium* 64 Cd
Niobrara R., *Nebraska* 42 Fc
Nioro, *Mali* 98 De
Niort, *France* 72 Cc
Nios. *See* Ios
Nipawin, *Saskatchewan* 37 Ne
Nipawin Prov. Park, *Sask.* 37 Nd
Nipe, B. de, *Cuba* 51 Db
Nipigon, *Ontario* 34 Bc
Nipigon, L. & R., *Ontario* 34 Bc
Nipigon B., *Ontario* 34 Cd
Nipin R., *Saskatchewan* 36 Hc
Nipisi R., *Alberta* 36 Cc
Nipissing, L., *Ontario* 35 Lf
Nipissing Jct., *Ontario* 35 Lf
Nipissis L. & R., *Quebec* 32 Fc
Nipisso L., *Quebec* 32 Gc
Niquelândia, *Brazil* 53 Hf
Nirmal, *India* 88 Ee
Nis, *Yugoslavia* 76 Cc
Nischu, *Kashmir* 88 Eb
Nisiros, *Greece* 77 Ff
Nisling, R., *Y.T.* 38 Dd
Nissan, *Solomon Islands* 102 Eh
Nissi, *Estonia* 67 Lg
Nisutlin, R., *Y.T.* 38 Ge
Niterói, *Brazil* 53 Jh
Nith R., *Scotland* 62 Ee
Nitra, *Czechoslovakia* 69 Hd
Nitrianské Pravno, *Czech.* 69 Hd
Niue, *Cook Islands* 102 Jj
Niugini. *See* Papua New Guinea
Niut, *Borneo (Kalimantan)* 83 Ek
Nivala, *Finland* 66 Le
Nivelles, *Belgium* 64 Cd
Nivernais, *France* 72 Ec
Niverville, *Manitoba* 37 Uj
Nizamabad, *India* 88 Ee
Nizampatnam, *India* 88 Fe
Nizhne Udinsk, *U.S.S.R.* 79 Jc
Nizhniy Lomov, *U.S.S.R.* 81 Fd
Nizhniy Tagil, *U.S.S.R.* 81 Pb
Nizhnyaya Pesha, *U.S.S.R.* 78 Db
Nizké Tatry, *Czechoslovakia* 69 Hd
Nizzana, *Israel* 94 Cg
Njombe, *Tanzania* 97 Gf
Nkhota-Kota, *Malawi* 97 Gg
Nkonde, *Tanzania* 97 Gf
N'Kongsamba, *Cameroun* 99 Gh
Nmai, *Burma* 89 Jc
Noagarh, *India* 89 Fd
Noakhali, *Bangladesh* 89 Hd
Noanama, *Colombia* 52 Bc
Noatak R., *Alaska* 43 Wl
Nobel, *Ontario* 34 Kg
Nobleford, *Alberta* 36 Dj
Nocera, *Italy* 75 Ee
Nochixtlán, *Mexico* 50 Ed
Noel Paul's Brook, *Nfld.* 33 Qe
Noelville, *Ontario* 34 Kf
Noemfoor, *New Guinea* 83 Kl
Noerbø, *Norway* 67 Ag
Nogales, *Arizona* 48 Bg
Nogaro, *France* 73 Ce
Nogent-le-Rotrou, *France* 72 Db
Nogent-sur-Seine, *France* 72 Eb
Noginsk, *U.S.S.R.* 80 Ld
Nohar, *India* 90 Df
Noire, R., *Quebec* 35 Nf
Noirmoutier, I. de, *France* 72 Bc
Nokhtuysk, *U.S.S.R.* 79 Lc
Nokomis, *Saskatchewan* 37 Ng
Nokomis L., *Saskatchewan* 39 Wg
Nola, *Cent. Afr. Rep.* 96 Dd
Nola, *Italy* 75 Ee
Nolalu, *Ontario* 37 Nb
Nolinsk, *U.S.S.R.* 81 Jb
Nome, *Alaska* 43 Wl
Nomoi, *Caroline Is.* 102 Eg
Nonacho L., *N.W.T.* 38 Te
Nonancourt, *France* 72 Db
Nong-han, *Thailand* 87 Cc
Nong Khai, *Thailand* 87 Cc
Nongoma, *Natal* 95 Ee
Nonno, *Ethiopia* 97 Hc
Nonoava, *Mexico* 50 Cb
Nonouti, *Kiribati* 102 Gh
Nõo, *Estonia* 67 Mg
Noonkanbah, *W. Australia* 56 Dc
Noordeloos, *Netherlands* 64 Cc
Noordwolde, *Netherlands* 64 Eb
Nootka I., *B.C.* 39 Kl
Nootka & Sd., *B.C.* 39 Kl
Nora, *Saskatchewan* 37 Of
Nora, *Sweden* 67 Fg
Noranda, *Quebec* 35 Ld
Nord, *France* 72 Ea
Nord Cap. *See* Horn, C.
Norddal, *Norway* 66 Be
Nordegg R., *Alberta* 36 Bf
Nordenshelda, Arkh., *U.S.S.R.* 79 Ja
Nordenskiold, R., *Y.T.* 38 Ee
Nordhausen, *East Germany* 68 Dc
Nordkapp, *Norway* 66 La
Nordkinn Halvöya, *Norway* 66 Ma
Nördlingen, *West Germany* 68 Dd
Nordost Rundingen, *Greenland* 41 Ma
Nordreisa, *Norway* 66 Jb
Nordrhein-Westfalen, *Ger.* 68 Bc
Nord Slesvig. *See* Jylland, S.
Nordstrand, *W. Ger.* 68 Ca
Nordvik, *U.S.S.R.* 79 La
Nore, *Norway* 67 Cf
Norembego, *Ontario* 34 Kd
Nore R., *Eire* 63 Ch
Norfolk, *England* 63 Hh
Norfolk, *Nebraska* 49 Ja
Norfolk, *Pacific Ocean* 102 Fk
Norfolk, *Virginia* 45 Jb
Norfolk Res., *Arkansas* 49 Ld
Norheimsund, *Norway* 67 Bf
Norily, *U.S.S.R.* 78 Hb
Norman, *Oklahoma* 49 Je
Norman, Ft., *N.W.T.* 30 Ge
Norman, L., *N. Carolina* 45 Gc
Normanby I., *Papua New Guinea* 57 Ka
Normandie, *France* 72 Cb
Normandin, *Quebec* 35 Sd
Normanton, *Queensland* 57 Hc
Norman Wells, *N.W.T.* 38 Kc
Normétal, *Quebec* 35 Ld
Norquay, *Saskatchewan* 37 Pg
Norquin, *Argentina* 54 Be
Norquiñco, *Argentina* 54 Bf
Norris, L., *Tennessee* 45 Eb
Norris Arm, *Nfld.* 33 Rd
Norristown, *Pennsylvania* 44 Cb
Norrköping, *Sweden* 67 Gg
Norrsundet, *Sweden* 67 Gf
Norrtalje, *Sweden* 67 Hg
Norseman, *W. Australia* 56 Df
Norsholm, *Sweden* 67 Fg
North, C., *Antarctica* 104 Lb
North Adams, *Mass.* 44 Da
Northallerton, *England* 63 Gf
Northam, *W. Australia* 56 Cf
Northampton, *Eng.* 63 Gh
Northampton, *Mass.* 44 Da
Northampton, *W. Australia* 56 Be
North Aulatsivik I., *Nfld.* 31 Nf
North Battleford, *Sask.* 36 Jf
North Bay, *Newfoundland* 33 Of
North Bay, *Ontario* 35 Lf
North Bend, *Oregon* 47 Ad
North Berwick, *Scotland* 62 Fd
North Borneo. *See* Sabah
North Branch, *Ontario* 36 Ha
North Branch Renous R., *N.B.* 32 Fg
Northbridge, *Massachusetts* 44 Ea
Northbrook, *Ontario* 35 Nh
North C., *New Zealand* 55 Da
North Cape, *P.E.I.* 32 Hf
North Caribou L., *Ontario* 31 Lg
North Carolina, *U.S.A.* 43 Kd
North Chan., *Ontario* 34 Gf
North Chan., *Scot./N. Ire.* 62 De
North Creek, *New York* 40 Jd
North Dakota, *U.S.A.* 42 Fb
North Downs, *England* 63 Hj
North-East Foreland, *Greenland* 41 Ma
Northeast Pt., *Nfld.* 33 Ra
Northern Bight, *Nfld.* 33 Se
Northern Circars, *India* 88 Fe
Northern Head, *N.B.* 32 Fj
Northern Ireland, *Br. Isles* 63 Cf
Northern Light L., *Ont.* 37 Mb
Northern Territory, *Aust.* 56 Fc
Northfield, *Minnesota* 46 Lc
North French, R., *Ontario* 34 Jb
Northgate, *Saskatchewan* 37 Pj
North Head, *N.B.* 32 Fj
North Head, *Nfld.* 33 Od
North I., *New Zealand* 55 Dc
North Kent I., *N.W.T.* 31 Lb
North Knife L., *Man.* 37 Va
North Land. *See* Severnaya Zemlya
North Little Rock, *Ark.* 43 He
North McIntyre, *Ontario* 37 Ob
North Magnetawan, *Ontario* 34 Kg
North Magnetic Pole, 30 Jc
North Moose L., *Manitoba* 37 Rd
North Platte, *Nebraska* 48 Gb
North Platte R., *Neb.* 42 Fc
North Pole, *Arctic Ocean* 41 a
Northport, *Nova Scotia* 32 Jh
North Riding, *England* 63 Ff
North River Bridge, *N.S.* 33 Mg
North Ronaldsay, *Orkney* 62 Fa
North Rustico, *P.E.I.* 32 Jg
North Sea, *W. Europe* 60 Gd
North Star, *Alberta* 39 Pg
North Sydney, *N.S.* 33 Mg
North Thompson R., *B.C.* 39 Nk
North Tonawanda, *N.Y.* 44 Aa
North Truchas Pk., *New Mexico* 48 Ed
Northumberland, *Eng.* 62 Fe
Northumberland, *Pa.* 44 Bb
Northumberland Str., *N.S.* 32 Jg
North Vancouver, *B.C.* 39 Ml
North Vermilion, *Alberta* 39 Pf
Northville, *New York* 40 Jd
North Wabasca L., *Alberta* 36 Db
North West C., *W. Aust.* 56 Bd
North West Frontier Province, *Pakistan* 88 Db
Northwest Gander R., *Nfld.* 33 Re
North West River, *Nfld.* 31 Ng
Northwest Territories, *Canada* 30 Hd
Northwood, *Iowa* 49 La
North York, *Ontario* 34 Cj
North Yorkshire, *Eng.* 63 Ff
Norton, *Kansas* 49 Hc
Norton, *New Brunswick* 32 Gh
Norton Sound, *Alaska* 43 Wl
Norvegia, Kapp, *Antarctica* 104 Bb
Norwalk, *Connecticut* 44 Db
Norwalk, *Ohio* 40 Ee
Norway, *Michigan* 40 Cc
Norway, *North-West Europe* 60 Kc
Norway House, *Manitoba* 37 Ue
Norwegian B., *N.W.T.* 31 Kb
Norwich, *Connecticut* 44 Db
Norwich, *England* 63 Hh
Norwich, *New York* 44 Ca
Norwich, *Ontario* 34 Kk
Norwood, *Massachusetts* 44 Ea
Norwood, *New York* 40 Jc
Norwood, *Ontario* 35 Mh
Nose L., *N.W.T.* 38 Tc
Noshiro, *Japan* 86 Fd
Nossegem, *Belgium* 64 Cd
Nossi Bé, I., *Madagascar* 97 Nj
Notikewin, R., *Alberta* 39 Og
Noto, *Sicily* 75 Eg
Notodden, *Norway* 67 Cg
Noto Hanto, *Japan* 86 Ef
Notre Dame, *N.B.* 32 Hg
Notre-Dame, Les Monts, *Que.* 32 Fe
Notre Dame B., *Nfld.* 33 Rd
Notre-Dame-de-la-Doré, *Que.* 35 Sd
Notre-Dame-de-la-Salette, *Quebec* 35 Pg
Notre Dame de Lourdes, *Manitoba* 37 Tj
Notre-Dame-des-Bois, *Que.* 32 Bh
Notre-Dame-du-Lac, *Que.* 32 Cf
Notre-Dame-du-Laus, *Quebec* 35 Pf
Nottawasaga B., *Ontario* 34 Kh
Nottaway R., *Quebec* 35 Mb
Nottingham, *England* 63 Gh
Nottingham I., *N.W.T.* 31 Me
Nottingham Island, *N.W.T.* 31 Me
Nottinghamshire, *England* 63 Gh
Nouadhibou, *Mauritania* 98 Bd
Nouakchott, *Mauritania* 98 Be
Nouveau-Quebec, Cratère du, *Quebec* 31 Me
Nouvel, Lac, *Quebec* 32 Dc
Nouvelle, *Quebec* 32 Fe
Nouvelle France, C. de (C. Weggs), *Quebec* 31 Me
Nova Bečej, *Yugoslavia* 76 Cb
Nova Chaves, *Angola* 96 Eg
Nova Cruz, *Brazil* 53 Ke
Nova Freixo. *See* Cuamba
Nova Gaia, *Angola* 96 Dg
Nova Iorque, *Brazil* 53 Je
Nova Lisboa. *See* Huambo
Novara, *Italy* 74 Bc
Nova Scotia, *Canada* 31 Nj
Nova Sofala, *Mozambique* 95 Ed
Nova Venecia, *Brazil* 53 Jg
Novaya Sibir, Ostrov, *U.S.S.R.* 79 Qa
Novaya Zemlya, *U.S.S.R.* 78 Ea
Nové Zámky, *Czech.* 69 He
Novgorod, *U.S.S.R.* 80 Gb
Novi, *Yugoslavia* 74 Ec
Novi Ligure, *Italy* 74 Bc
Novi Pazar, *Bulgaria* 76 Fc
Novi Pazar, *Yugoslavia* 76 Cc
Novi Sad, *Yugoslavia* 76 Bb
Novocherkassk, *U.S.S.R.* 81 Eg
Novokazalinsk, *Kazakh.* 78 Fd
Novokuznetsk, *U.S.S.R.* 78 Hc
Novo Mesto, *Yugoslavia* 74 Ec
Novo Moskovsk, *Ukraine* 80 Jg
Novomoskovsk, *U.S.S.R.* 80 Ld
Novo Redondo, *Angola* 96 Cg
Novorossiysk, *U.S.S.R.* 78 Cd
Novoshakhtinsk, *U.S.S.R.* 81 Dg
Novosibirsk, *U.S.S.R.* 78 Hc
Novosibirskiye Ostrova, *U.S.S.R.* 79 Na
Novska, *Yugoslavia* 74 Fc
Nový Jičín, *Czechoslovakia* 69 Hd
Novyy Port, *U.S.S.R.* 78 Gb
Nowgong, *India* 89 Hc
Nowleye L., *N.W.T.* 38 Xd
Nowra, *N.S.W.* 57 Kf
Nowshera, *Pakistan* 90 Cc
Nowy Sącz, *Poland* 69 Jd
Nowy Targ, *Poland* 69 Jd
Nowy Tomyśl, *Poland* 69 Gb
Noya, *Spain* 70 Aa
Noyrot, L., *Quebec* 33 Ob
Nozay, *France* 72 Cc
Nsanje, *Malawi* 95 Fc
Nuanetsi, *Zimbabwe* 95 Ed
Nueces R., *Texas* 48 Hh
Nueltin L., *N.W.T.* 30 Ke
Nueva, I., *Chile/Arg.* 54 Cj
Nueva Imperial, *Chile* 54 Be
Nuevo, G., *Argentina* 54 Df
Nuevo Laredo, *Mexico* 50 Eb
Nuevo Leon, *Mexico* 50 Db
Nuevo Rocafuerte, *Ecuador* 52 Bd
Nûgssuaq pen., *Greenland* 41 Pb
Nuits St Georges, *France* 72 Fc
Nuku Hiva, *Marquêsas Is.* 103 Lh
Nukuoro, *Caroline Is.* 102 Eg
Nukus, *Uzbekistan* 78 Ed
Nules, *Spain* 71 Ec
Nullagine, *W. Australia* 56 Dd
Nullarbor, *S. Australia* 56 Ff
Nullarbor Plain, *S.W. Aust.* 56 Ef
Numata, *Japan* 86 Ff
Numazu, *Japan* 86 Fg
Nunchía, *Colombia* 52 Cb
Nunivak I., *Alaska* 43 Wl
Nuoro, *Sardinia* 75 Be
Nuquí, *Colombia* 52 Bb
Nur-Gal, *Afghanistan* 90 Bc
Nurmes, *Finland* 66 Ne
Nürnberg, *West Germany* 68 Dd
Nurpur, *India* 90 Dd
Nurri, *Sardinia* 75 Bf
Nusaybin, *Turkey* 92 Db
Nushki, *Pakistan* 88 Cc
Nutak, *Newfoundland* 31 Nf
Nut L., *Saskatchewan* 37 Of
Nut Mountain, *Sask.* 37 Of
Nut Mountain, ra., *Sask.* 37 Pf
Nutrias, *Venezuela* 52 Db
Nuwara Eliya, *Sri Lanka* 88 Fg
Nyada, *Sweden* 66 Ge
Nyåker, *Sweden* 66 He
Nyala, *Sudan* 99 Kf
Nyalikungu, *Tanzania* 97 Ge
Nyamlell, *Sudan* 99 Lg
Nyandoma, *U.S.S.R.* 78 Db
Nyantakara, *Tanzania* 97 Ge
Nyanza, *Rwanda* 97 Fe
Nyarling, R., *N.W.T.* 38 Qe
Nyasa, L. (L. Malawi), *Malawi* 97 Gg
Nyazepetrovsk, *U.S.S.R.* 81 Pb
Nyda, *U.S.S.R.* 78 Gb
Nyeri, *Kenya* 97 He
Nyhammar, *Sweden* 67 Ff
Nyíregyháza, *Hungary* 69 Je
Nyköbing, *Denmark* 67 Ch
Nykóbing, *Denmark* 67 Dj
Nyköping, *Sweden* 67 Gg
Nylstroom, *Transvaal* 95 Dd
Nymagee, *N.S.W.* 57 Jf
Nyngan, *N.S.W.* 57 Jf
Nyon, *Switzerland* 65 Bb
Nyonga, *Tanzania* 97 Gf
Nyons, *France* 73 Fd
Nysa, *Poland* 69 Gc
Nysted, *Denmark* 67 Dj
Nyurba, *U.S.S.R.* 79 Lb
Nyuya, *U.S.S.R.* 79 Lb
Nzega, *Tanzania* 97 Ge

O

Oacoma, *S. Dakota* 46 Hd
Oahe Res., *S. Dakota* 46 Gc
Oahu, *Hawaiian Is.* 103 Ke
Oakan, *Japan* 86 Jc
Oak Bay, *N.B.* 32 Eh
Oakburn, *Manitoba* 37 Rh
Oakes, *N. Dakota* 46 Hb
Oakham, *England* 63 Gh
Oak L., *Manitoba* 37 Rj
Oak Lake, *Manitoba* 37 Rj
Oakland, *California* 47 Bg
Oakland, *Maryland* 40 Gf
Oakley, *Kansas* 48 Gc
Oakner, *Manitoba* 37 Rh
Oak Point, *Manitoba* 37 Th
Oak Ridge, *Tennessee* 43 Kd
Oak River, *Manitoba* 37 Rh
Oakville, *Manitoba* 37 Tj
Oakville, *Ontario* 35 Lj
Oamaru, *New Zealand* 55 Cf
Oates Land, *Antarctica* 104 Kc
Oaxaca, *Mexico* 50 Ed
Ob', R., *U.S.S.R.* 78 Fb
Oba, *Ontario* 34 Fc
Oba, L., *Ontario* 34 Fd
Obakamiga L., *Ontario* 34 Ec
Obama, *Japan* 86 Dg
Oban, *New Zealand* 55 Bg
Oban, *Saskatchewan* 36 Jf
Oban, *Scotland* 62 Dd
Obatanga Prov. Park, *Ontario* 34 Ed
Obbia, *Somalia* 97 Kc
Obed, *Alberta* 39 Pj
Obeh, *Afghanistan* 93 Hc
Oberammergau, *W. Ger.* 68 De
Oberhausen, *W. Germany* 68 Bc
Oberlin, *Kansas* 48 Gc
Oberriet, *Switzerland* 65 Ea
Oberwald, *Switzerland* 65 Db
Obi, *Indonesia* 83 Jl
Obidos, *Brazil* 53 Fd
Obidos, *Portugal* 70 Ac
Obihiro, *Japan* 86 Hc
Obo, *Cent. Afr. Rep.* 99 Lg
Obock, *Djibouti* 97 Jb
Obonga L., *Ontario* 37 Oa
Oborona, *U.S.S.R.* 81 Ed
Obrayera, *Nicaragua* 51 Cd
Obre L., *N.W.T.* 38 We
O'Brien, *Ontario* 34 Ke
Observatory Inlet, *B.C.* 39 Jh
Obskaya Guba, *U.S.S.R.* 78 Gb
Ocala, *Florida* 45 Ff
Ocampo, *Mexico* 50 Ec
Ocana, *Colombia* 52 Cb
Ocana, *Spain* 70 Dc
Occidental, Cord., *Colombia* 52 Bc
Oceana, *W. Virginia* 45 Gb
Ocean City, *New Jersey* 44 Cc
Ocean Falls, *B.C.* 39 Kj
Ocean I. *See* Barnaba
Ochil Hills, *Scotland* 62 Ed
Ochre River, *Manitoba* 37 Sg
Ocland, *Romania* 76 Ea
Ocoa, B. de, *Dom. Rep.* 51 Ec
Ocona, *Peru* 52 Cg
Oconto, *Wisconsin* 40 Cc
Ocos, *Guatemala* 50 Fe
Ocotal, *Nicaragua* 51 Bd
Ocumare, *Venezuela* 52 Da
Oda, *Ghana* 98 Eg
Oda, *Japan* 86 Cg
Odate, *Japan* 86 Gd
Odawara, *Japan* 86 Fg
Odemira, *Portugal* 70 Ad
Ödemiş, *Turkey* 92 Ab
Odense, *Denmark* 67 Dj
Oder, *East Germany* 68 Fb
Odessa, *Ontario* 35 Oh
Odessa, *Saskatchewan* 37 Oh
Odessa, *Texas* 48 Fg
Odessa, *Ukraine* 80 Gh
Odhill, *Manitoba* 37 Tc
Odienné, *Ivory Coast* 98 Dg
Odoorn, *Netherlands* 64 Eb
Odorhei, *Romania* 76 Ea
Odra, *Poland* 68 Fb
Odzala, *Congo* 96 Cd
Oedelem, *Belgium* 64 Bc
Oeiras, *Brazil* 53 Je
Oelwein, *Iowa* 49 Ma
Of, *Turkey* 92 Da
Offaly, *Eire* 63 Bg
Offenbach, *West Germany* 68 Cc
Ogahalla, *Ontario* 34 Eb
Ogaki, *Japan* 86 Eg
Ogallala, *Nebraska* 48 Gb
Ogascanane, L., *Quebec* 35 Me
Ogden, *Nova Scotia* 33 Lh
Ogden, *Utah* 48 Ab
Ogden, Mt., *B.C./Alaska* 39 Gf
Ogdensburg, *New York* 40 Jc
Ogema, *Saskatchewan* 37 Nj
Ogidaki, *Ontario* 34 Ff
Ogilvie Mts., *Y.T.* 38 Dc
Ogoja, *Nigeria* 98 Gg
Ogoki, *Ontario* 31 Lg
Ogoki L., *Ontario* 34 Cb
Ogoki R., *Ontario* 34 Db
Ogoki Res., *Ontario* 34 Bb
Ogr, *Sudan* 99 Lf
Ogulin, *Yugoslavia* 74 Ec
Ogwashi Uku, *Nigeria* 96 Bc
Ohakune, *New Zealand* 55 Ec
Ohaton, *Alberta* 36 Ef
Ohau, L., *New Zealand* 55 Bf
Ohey, *Belgium* 64 Dd
O'Higgins, Mt., *Chile* 54 Bg
Ohio, *U.S.A.* 43 Kc
Ohio R., *U.S.A.* 49 Nd
Ohrid, *Yugoslavia* 76 Cd
Ohridsko Jezero, *Yugosl.* 76 Cd
Ohura, *New Zealand* 55 Ec
Oiapoque, *Brazil* 53 Gc
Oignies, *Belgium* 64 Cd
Oil City, *Pennsylvania* 44 Ab
Oil Springs, *Ontario* 34 Hk
Oirschot, *Netherlands* 64 Dc
Oise, *France* 72 Eb
Oita, *Japan* 86 Bh
Oiticica, *Brazil* 53 Je
Ojinaga, *Mexico* 50 Db
Ojiya, *Japan* 86 Ff
Ojocaliente, *Mexico* 50 Dc
Ojo de Agua, *Argentina* 54 Dc
Ojo del Toro, Pico, *Cuba* 51 Dc
Ojos del Salado, *Chile/Arg.* 54 Cc
Oka, *Quebec* 35 Qg
Oka, *U.S.S.R.* 81 Fc
Okahandja, *Namibia* 95 Bd
Okak Is., *Newfoundland* 31 Nf
Okanagan Centre, *B.C.* 39 Ok
Okanagan Falls, *B.C.* 39 Ol
Okanagan L., *B.C.* 39 Ok
Okanagan Landing, *B.C.* 39 Ok
Okanogan R., *Washington* 42 Cb
Okaukuejo, *Namibia* 95 Bc
Okavango, *Angola* 95 Bc
Okayama, *Japan* 86 Cg
Okeechobee, L., *Florida* 45 Gg
Okehampton, *England* 63 Ek
Okha, *U.S.S.R.* 79 Pc
Okhansk, *U.S.S.R.* 81 Mb
Okhotsk, *U.S.S.R.* 79 Pc
Okhotsk, Sea of, *U.S.S.R.* 79 Pc
Okinawa gunto, *Japan* 86 Mp
Oki shoto, *Japan* 86 Cf
Oklahoma, *U.S.A.* 42 Gd
Oklahoma City, *Oklahoma* 49 Je
Okmulgee, *Oklahoma* 49 Ke
Okolona, *Mississippi* 45 Cc
Okotoks, *Alberta* 36 Dh
Oktyabr'sk, *U.S.S.R.* 81 Nf
Oktyabr'skiy, *U.S.S.R.* 80 Fe
Oktyabrskoy Revolyutsii, Os., *U.S.S.R.* 79 Ja
Okučani, *Yugoslavia* 74 Fc
Okuru, *New Zealand* 55 Be
Okushiri, *Japan* 86 Fc
Olaine, *Latvia* 67 Kh
Olanchito, *Honduras* 51 Bc
Öland, *Sweden* 67 Gh
Olasan, *Ethiopia* 97 Kc
Olavarría, *Argentina* 54 De
Oława, *Poland* 69 Gc
Olbia, *Sardinia* 75 Be
Olcott, *New York* 44 Aa
Oldcastle, *Eire* 63 Cg
Old Crow, *Y.T.* 38 Cb
Old Crow R., *Y.T.* 38 Ca
Oldenburg, *East Germany* 68 Da
Oldenburg, *West Germany* 68 Cb
Oldenzaal, *Netherlands* 64 Eb
Old Forge, *Pennsylvania* 44 Cb
Oldham, *England* 63 Fg
Old Hogem, *B.C.* 39 Lh
Oldman R., *Alberta* 39 Ql
Old Orchard Beach, *Maine* 44 Ea
Old Perlican, *Nfld.* 33 Te
Olds, *Alberta* 36 Cg
Old Town, *Maine* 32 Dj
Old Wives & L., *Sask.* 37 Mh
Olean, *New York* 44 Aa
O'Leary, *P.E.I.* 32 Hg
Olecko, *Poland* 69 Ka
Olekminsk, *U.S.S.R.* 79 Mb
Olenek, *U.S.S.R.* 79 Lb

Olenek, U.S.S.R. 79 Ma
Olenekskiy Zaliv, U.S.S.R. 79 Ma
Oléron, I. d', France 72 Cd
Olga, U.S.S.R. 79 Nd
Olga, L., Quebec 35 Nc
Olimbos, Greece 77 Dd
Oliva de Jerez, Spain 70 Bc
Olivares, Spain 71 Dc
Olivares, Cerro de, Arg. 54 Cd
Oliveira dos Brejinhos, Brazil 53 Jf
Olivenza, Spain 70 Bc
Oliver, British Columbia 39 Ol
Olivone, Switzerland 65 Db
Ollague, Bolivia 52 Dh
Ollague, Chile 52 Dh
Olmedo, Spain 70 Cb
Olney, Illinois 49 Nc
Olomane, R., Quebec 33 Mc
Olomouc, Czechoslovakia 69 Gd
Olot, Spain 71 Ga
Olovyannaya, U.S.S.R. 79 Lc
Olpe, West Germany 68 Bc
Olst, Netherlands 64 Eb
Olsztyn, Poland 69 Jb
Olten, Switzerland 65 Ca
Oltu, Turkey 92 Da
Oltul, Romania 76 Eb
Olvera, Spain 70 Cd
Olympia, Greece 77 Cf
Olympia, Washington 47 Bb
Olympic Nat. Park, Wash. 42 Bb
Olympus. See Olimbos
Olympus, Mt., Washington 42 Bb
Olyutorskiy Zaliv, U.S.S.R. 79 Rb
Omagh, N. Ireland 63 Cf
Omaguas, Peru 52 Cd
Omaha, Nebraska 49 Kb
Oman, Persian Gulf 93 Ge
Oman, G. of, Arabia/Iran 93 Ge
Omarama, N. Zealand 55 Bf
Omaruru, Namibia 95 Bd
Ombabika B., Ontario 34 Bb
Ombombo, Namibia 95 Ac
Omdurman, Sudan 99 Me
Omemee, Ontario 35 Mh
Omer, Michigan 40 Ec
Ometepec, Mexico 50 Ed
Omineca, R., B.C. 39 Lh
Omineca Mts., B.C. 39 Kg
Ommanney B., N.W.T. 30 Jc
Ommen, Netherlands 64 Eb
Omoa, Honduras 51 Bc
Omsk, U.S.S.R. 78 Gc
Omuta, Japan 86 Bh
Omutninsk, U.S.S.R. 81 La
Onakawana, Ontario 34 Jb
Onakwahegan, R., Ont. 34 Ja
Onaman L., Ontario 34 Cb
Onaping L., Ontario 34 Je
Onatchiway L., Quebec 32 Ad
Onawa, Iowa 49 Ja
Onaway, Michigan 40 Dc
Öndör Haan, Mongolia 82 Fa
Onega, U.S.S.R. 78 Cb
Onehunga, New Zealand 55 Eb
Oneida, New York 44 Ca
Oneida L., New York 44 Ca
O'Neill, Nebraska 49 Ha
Oneonta, New York 44 Ca
One Sided Lake, Ontario 36 Ja
Onezhskoye Oz., U.S.S.R. 78 Cb
Ongole, India 88 Fe
Ongudai, U.S.S.R. 78 Hc
Onion Lake, Sask. 36 He
Onistagane L., Quebec 32 Ac
Onitsha, Nigeria 98 Gg
Onjüül, Mongolia 82 Ea
Onoto, Venezuela 52 Db
Onotoa, Kiribati 102 Gh
Onoway, Alberta 36 Ce
Onslow, W. Australia 56 Bd
Onslow B., N. Carolina 43 Le
Ontaratue R., N.W.T. 38 Hb
Ontario, Canada 31 Kg
Ontario, L., U.S.A./Can. 43 Lc
Onteniente, Spain 71 Ec
Ontiñena, Spain 71 Fb
Oodnadatta, S. Australia 57 Ge
Ooldea, S. Australia 56 Ff
Oostburg, Netherlands 64 Bc
Oostende, Belgium 64 Ac
Oostende. See Ostende
Oosterschelde, Netherlands 64 Bc
Oosterwolde, Netherlands 64 Eb
Oosthuizen, Netherlands 64 Db
Oostkamp, Belgium 64 Bc
Oostmalle, Belgium 64 Cc
Oostvoorne, Netherlands 64 Cc
Ootacamund, India 88 Ef
Ootsa L., B.C. 39 Lj
Opachuanau L., Manitoba 37 Sb
Opal, Alberta 36 De
Opala, U.S.S.R. 79 Qc
Opari, Sudan 99 Mh
Opasatika, Ontario 34 Hc
Opasatika L., Ontario 34 Gc
Opasatika R., Ontario 34 Hc
Opastica L., Quebec 40 Ga
Opataca, L., Quebec 35 Qb
Opatija, Yugoslavia 74 Ec
Opava, Czechoslovakia 69 Gd
Opawica, L. & R., Quebec 35 Pc
Opelousas, Louisiana 49 Lg
Opemisca, L., Quebec 35 Qb
Opeongo L., Ontario 35 Mg
Ophir, Pen. Malaysia 87 Cf
Ophoven, Belgium 64 Dc
Opochka, U.S.S.R. 80 Fc
Opocopa, L., Quebec 32 Fa
Opodepe, Mexico 50 Ba
Opole, Poland 69 Gc
Oporto. See Porto
Opotiki, New Zealand 55 Fc
Oppa wan, Japan 86 Ge
Optic Lake, Manitoba 37 Qd
Opunake, New Zealand 55 Dc
Oputo, Mexico 50 Cb
Oradea, Romania 76 Ca
Orai, India 91 Bc
Oran, Algeria 98 Ea
Orange, France 73 Fd
Orange, Massachusetts 44 Da
Orange, South Africa 95 Be
Orange, Texas 49 Lg
Orange, Virginia 45 Ha
Orangeburg, S. Carolina 45 Gd
Orange City, Iowa 49 Ja
Orangedale, Nova Scotia 33 Lh
Orange Free State, South Africa 95 De
Orangeville, Ontario 34 Kj
Oranje Geb., Surinam 53 Fc
Oras, Philippines 83 Jh
Orăștie, Romania 76 Db
Oravita, Romania 76 Cb
Oravská Magura, Czech. 69 Hd
Orbe, Switzerland 65 Bb
Orcera, Spain 71 Dc
Orchha, India 91 Bc
Ord, Mt., W. Australia 56 Ec
Ordale, Saskatchewan 36 Le
Ordenes, Spain 70 Aa
Ord River, W. Australia 56 Ec
Ordu, Turkey 92 Ca
Ordzhonikidze, U.S.S.R. 78 Dd
Örebro, Sweden 67 Fg
Oregon, Illinois 49 Na
Oregon, U.S.A. 42 Bc
Oregon City, Oregon 47 Bc
Öregrund, Sweden 67 Hf
Orekhovo Zuyevo, U.S.S.R. 80 Ld
Orel, U.S.S.R. 80 Ke
Orellana, Peru 52 Be
Orellana, Spain 70 Cc
Orellana, Emb. de, Spain 70 Cc
Orenburg, U.S.S.R. 81 Me
Orense, Spain 70 Ba
Orepuki, New Zealand 55 Ag
Öresund, Denmark/Sweden 67 Ej
Organa, Spain 71 Fa
Orgaz, Spain 70 Dc
Orhon, Mongolia 82 Da
Oriental, Cord., Colombia 52 Cb
Oriental, Cord., Peru 52 Be
Orient Bay, Ontario 34 Bc
Orihuela, Spain 71 Ec
Orillia, Ontario 35 Lh
Orinoco, Venezuela 52 Eb
Orion, Alberta 36 Gj
Orissa, India 89 Fd
Oristano, Sardinia 75 Bf
Orivesi, Finland 66 Ne
Oriximiná, Brazil 53 Fd
Orizaba, Mexico 50 Ed
Orizare, Bulgaria 76 Fc
Orizona, Brazil 53 Hg
Orkanger, Norway 66 Ce
Orkney, Saskatchewan 36 Kj
Orkney Is., Scotland 62 Fb
Ørland, Norway 66 Ce
Orlando, Florida 45 Gf
Orléanais, France 72 Dc
Orléans, France 72 Dc
Orléans, I. d', Quebec 32 Ag
Orman, Syria 94 Ee
Ormara, Pakistan 88 Bc
Ormiston, Saskatchewan 37 Mj
Ormondville, New Zealand 55 Fd
Ormsby, Ontario 35 Nh
Ormstown, Quebec 35 Rg
Ornach, Pakistan 88 Bc
Orne, France 72 Cb
Örnsköldsvik, Sweden 66 He
Orochen, U.S.S.R. 79 Mc
Orocué, Colombia 52 Cc
Oroluk, Caroline Islands 102 Eg
Oromocto & L., N.B. 32 Fh
Orono, Maine 32 Dj
Orono, Ontario 35 Mj
Orontes, Syria 92 Cb
Orosei, G. di, Sardinia 75 Be
Orosi, Vol., Costa Rica 51 Bd
Orr L., Manitoba 37 Ub
Orsa, Sweden 67 Ff
Orsha, Byelorussia 80 Gd
Orsières, Switzerland 65 Cb
Orsk, U.S.S.R. 81 Pe
Orşova, Romania 76 Db
Ortegal, C., Spain 70 Ba
Orthez, France 73 Ce
Ortiz, Mexico 50 Cb
Ortiz, Venezuela 52 Db
Orugueira, Spain 70 Ba
Orulgan Khrebet, U.S.S.R. 79 Mb
Oruro, Bolivia 52 Dg
Orust, Sweden 67 Dg
Oryekhovo, U.S.S.R. 80 Gd
Osa, U.S.S.R. 81 Mb
Osage, Iowa 49 La
Osage, Saskatchewan 37 Oj
Osage City, Kansas 49 Kc
Osaka, Japan 86 Dg
Osakis, Minnesota 46 Kc
Osawatomie, Kansas 49 Kc
Osborne, Kansas 49 Hc
Oscar II Coast, Antarctica 104 Tc
Osceola, Arkansas 45 Cc
Osceola, Iowa 49 Lb
Oschiri, Sardinia 75 Be
Oscoda, Michigan 40 Ec
Osen, Norway 66 Dd
Osgoode, Ontario 35 Pg
Osh, Kirghizia 78 Gd
Oshawa, Ontario 35 Mj
Oshikango, Namibia 95 Bc
O shima, Japan 86 Fg
Oshkosh, Wisconsin 40 Bc
Oshnoviyeh, Iran 92 Eb
Osijek, Yugoslavia 76 Bb
Osilo, Sardinia 75 Be
Osipenko, U.S.S.R. 79 Nc
Osipovichi, Byelorussia 80 Fe
Oskaloosa, Iowa 49 Lb
Oskarshamn, Sweden 67 Gh
Oskélanéo, Quebec 35 Pd
Osler, Saskatchewan 36 Lf
Oslo, Norway 67 Dg
Oslo Fd., Norway 67 Dg
Osmanabad, India 88 Ee
Osmancik, Turkey 92 Ba
Osnabrück, West Germany 68 Cb
Osorio, Brazil 54 Fc
Osorno, Chile 54 Bf
Osorno, Spain 70 Ca
Osowiec, Poland 69 Kb
Osoyoos, B.C. 39 Ol
Ospika, R., B.C. 39 Mg
Oss, Netherlands 64 Dc
Osseo, Ontario 34 Ke
Ossining, New York 44 Db
Ostaboningue, L., Que. 35 Me
Östavall, Sweden 66 Fe
Österreich, Nieder, Austria 69 Fd
Österreich, Ober, Austria 68 Fd
Östersund, Sweden 66 Fe
Östhammar, Sweden 67 Hf
Ostrava, Czechoslovakia 69 Hd
Ostroda, Poland 69 Hb
Ostroleka, Poland 69 Jb
Ostrom, Ontario 34 Je
Ostrov, Romania 76 Gb
Ostrov, U.S.S.R. 80 Fc
Ostrovno, U.S.S.R. 79 Rb
Ostrowiec, Poland 69 Jc
Ostrów Mazowiecka, Poland 69 Jb
Ostuni, Italy 75 Fe
Östvagöy, Norway 66 Fb
O'Sullivan L., Ontario 34 Cb
O'Sullivan L., Quebec 35 Pe
Ösumi Kaikyō, Japan 86 Bj
Ösumi Shotō, Japan 86 Bj
Osuna, Spain 70 Cd
Oswego, New York 44 Ba
Oswestry, England 63 Eh
Otago Peninsula, N.Z. 55 Cf
Otaki, New Zealand 55 Ed
Otaru, Japan 86 Gc
Otavalo, Ecuador 52 Bc
Otepää, Estonia 67 Mg
Otherside R., Sask. 38 Uf
Othris, Greece 77 De
Otira, New Zealand 55 Ce
Otish Mts., Quebec 31 Mg
Otjiwarongo, Namibia 95 Bd
Otoçac, Yugoslavia 74 Ec
Otoineppu, Japan 86 Hb
Otorohanga, New Zealand 55 Ec
Otosquen, Saskatchewan 37 Pe
Otradnyy, U.S.S.R. 81 Kd
Otranto, Str. of, It./Albania 77 Bd
Otsego, L., New York 44 Ca
Otsu, Japan 86 Dg
Ottawa, Illinois 49 Nb
Ottawa, Kansas 49 Kc
Ottawa, Ontario 35 Pg
Ottawa International Airport, Ontario 35 Pg
Ottawa Is., N.W.T. 31 Lf
Ottawa R., Que./Ont. 35 Mf
Otter I., Ontario 34 Dd
Otter L., Saskatchewan 37 Nc
Otter Lake, Ontario 34 Lg
Otter Lake, Quebec 35 Og
Otterlo, Netherlands 64 Db
Otterøy, Norway 66 Be
Otthon, Saskatchewan 37 Pg
Ottignies, Belgium 64 Cd
Otting, West Germany 68 Ed
Otto Fd., N.W.T. 31 La
Ottumwa, Iowa 49 Lb
Otukamamoan L., Ontario 36 Kb
Otus, U.S.S.R. 80 Jj
Otway, B., Chile 54 Bh
Otway, C., Victoria 57 Hg
Otwock, Poland 69 Jb
Ötz, Austria 68 De
Ötztaler Alpen, Italy/Austria 74 Cb
Ouachita Mts., Arkansas 43 He
Ouachita R., Arkansas 49 Lf
Ouagadougou, Upper Volta 98 Ef
Ouagama, L., Quebec 35 Pc
Ouahigouya, Upper Volta 98 Ef
Ouahran. See Oran
Ouareau, L., Quebec 35 Qf
Ouargla, Algeria 98 Gb
Oubangui, Congo 96 Dd
Ouddorp, Netherlands 64 Bc
Oudekapelle, Belgium 64 Ac
Oudemirdum, Netherlands 64 Db
Oudenaarde, Belgium 64 Bd
Oudenbosch, Netherlands 64 Cc
Oudtshoorn, Cape Province 95 Cf
Ouessant, I. d', France 72 Ab
Ouezzane, Morocco 98 Db
Ouidah, Benin 98 Fg
Ouimet, Ontario 37 Pa
Oujda, Morocco 98 Eb
Oulu, Finland 66 Ld
Oulu Järvi, Finland 66 Md
Oulu Joki, Finland 66 Md
Oum Chalouba, Chad 99 Ke
Ounas Joki, Finland 66 Lc
Ouricuri, Brazil 53 Je
Ourinhos, Brazil 53 Hh
Ouro Preto, Brazil 53 Jh
Ours, C. de l', Quebec 33 Kd
Ouse R., England 63 Gf
Ouse R., England 63 Hh
Outaouais, R. des (Ottawa River), Ontario/Quebec 35 Mf
Outardes, R. aux, Que. 32 Dd
Outardes Quatre Dam, Quebec 32 Dd
Outardes Trois Dam, Quebec 32 Dd
Outjo, Namibia 95 Bd
Outlook, Saskatchewan 36 Kg
Outremont, Quebec 35 Sj
Ouyen, Victoria 57 Hg
Ovalle, Chile 54 Bd
Ovar, Portugal 70 Ab
Overflakkee, Netherlands 64 Cc
Overflowing R., Man./Sask. 37 Qe
Overflowing River, Man. 37 Qe
Overijssel, Neth. 64 Eb
Överkalix, Sweden 66 Kc
Övermark, Finland 66 Je
Overpelt, Belgium 64 Dc
Övertornea, Sweden 66 Kc
Oviedo, Spain 70 Ca
Ovruch, Ukraine 80 Ff
Owaka, New Zealand 55 Bg
Owasco L., New York 44 Ba
Owatonna, Minnesota 46 Lc
Owego, New York 44 Ba
Owen, Wisconsin 40 Ac
Owen Falls, Uganda 97 Gd
Owen I., Burma 89 Jf
Owensboro, Kentucky 45 Db
Owen Sd., Ontario 34 Kh
Owens L., California 47 Eg
Owen Sound, Ontario 34 Kh
Owen Stanley Range, Papua New Guinea 57 Ja
Owensville, Indiana 45 Da
Owenton, Kentucky 45 Ea
Owerri, Nigeria 98 Gg
Owikeno L., B.C. 39 Kk
Owl Creek Mts., Wyoming 46 Cd
Owlseye, Alberta 36 Fd
Owo, Nigeria 98 Gg
Owosso, Michigan 40 Dd
Owyhee R., Oregon 47 Ed
Oxbow, Saskatchewan 37 Pj
Oxdrift, Ontario 36 Ja
Oxford, England 63 Gj
Oxford, Maryland 40 Hf
Oxford, Mississippi 45 Cc
Oxford, N. Carolina 45 Hb
Oxford, New York 40 Jd
Oxford, Nova Scotia 32 Jh
Oxford House, Manitoba 37 Wd
Oxford L., Manitoba 37 Wd
Oxfordshire, England 63 Gj
Oxley's Pk., N.S.W. 57 Jf
Oyem, Gabon 96 Cd
Oyen, Alberta 36 Gg
Oymyakon, U.S.S.R. 79 Pb
Oyo, Nigeria 98 Fg
Oyster B., Tasmania 57 Jh
Ozark Mts., Ark./Mo. 49 Ke
Ozark Plat., Missouri 43 Hd
Ozarks, L. of the, Missouri 45 Aa
Ozd, Hungary 69 Jd
Ozerki, U.S.S.R. 81 Gd
Ozhogino, U.S.S.R. 79 Pb
Ozieri, Sardinia 75 Be
Ozun, Romania 76 Eb

P

Paan, Burma 89 Je
Paarl, Cape Province 95 Bf
Pabaži, Latvia 67 Lh
Pabianice, Poland 69 Hc
Pabna, Bangladesh 91 Gd
Pabos, Quebec 32 He
Pacaraima, Sa., Brazil 52 Ec
Pacasmayo, Peru 52 Be
Pachbhadra, India 88 Dc
Pachen, China 82 Bd
Pachow. See Bazhong
Pachuca, Mexico 50 Ec
Pacific, Missouri 45 Ba
Paços, Portugal 70 Ab
Pacquet, Newfoundland 33 Pd
Padam, Kashmir 90 Ed
Padang, Sumatra 83 Dl
Padangsidempuan, Indon. 87 Bf
Paddle Prairie, Alberta 39 Pg
Paddle R., Alberta 36 Cd
Paddockwood, Sask. 37 Me
Paderborn, West Germany 68 Cc
Padilla, Bolivia 52 Eg
Padlei, N.W.T. 30 Ke
Padloping Island, N.W.T. 31 Nd
Padoue, Quebec 32 Ee
Padova, Italy 74 Cc
Padrauna, India 91 Eb
Padre I., Texas 48 Jj
Padstow, England 63 Dk
Padua. See Padova
Paducah, Kentucky 45 Cb
Padul, Spain 70 Dd
Paeroa, New Zealand 55 Eb
Pafuri, Mozambique 95 Ed
Pagai Kep., Indonesia 83 Dl
Pagalu I., Gulf of Guinea 96 Be
Pagan, Burma 89 Hd
Pagan, Mariana Is. 102 Df
Pagasaí, G. of, Greece 77 De
Pagato R., Saskatchewan 37 Pb
Pago, Yugoslavia 74 Ec
Pagosa Springs, Colorado 48 Dd
Pagwachuan, Ontario 34 Dc
Pagwachuan, R., Ontario 34 Ec
Pagwa River, Ontario 34 Eb
Paharpur, Pakistan 90 Bd
Pahiatua, New Zealand 55 Ed
Pahlavi Dezh, Iran 93 Fb
Pahsien. See Chongqing
Paignton, England 63 Ek
Paijanne, L., Finland 67 Lf
Paikü Co, China 89 Gc
Pailani, India 91 Cc
Paimpol, France 72 Bb
Paincourt, Ontario 34 Hk
Painted Desert, Arizona 42 Dd
Paint L., Manitoba 37 Tc
Paintsville, Kentucky 45 Fb
Paisley, Ontario 34 Jh
Paisley, Scotland 62 Ee
Paita, Peru 52 Ae
Paiz do Vinho, Portugal 70 Bb
Pajakumbuh, Sumatra 83 Dl
Pajala, Sweden 66 Kc
Pajares, Spain 70 Ca
Pajde, Estonia 67 Lg
Pakashkan L., Ontario 37 Na
Pakaur, India 91 Fc
Pak Chan, Burma 89 Jf
Pakenham, Ontario 35 Og
Pakistan, South Asia 88 Cc
PakLay, Laos 87 Cc
Pakokku, Burma 89 Jd
Pakowki L., Alberta 36 Fj
Pakpattan, Pakistan 90 Ce
Pakrac, Yugoslavia 74 Fc
Paks, Hungary 69 He
Pakse, Laos 87 Dc
Pakwach, Uganda 97 Gd
Pakwash L., Manitoba 37 Sd
Palafrugell, Spain 71 Gb
Palaiokhóra, Crete 77 Dg
Palamau, India 91 Ed
Palamcottah, India 88 Eg
Palamós, Spain 71 Gb
Palamuse, Estonia 67 Mg
Palana, U.S.S.R. 79 Rc
Palangkaraja, Indonesia 83 Fl
Palanpur, India 88 Dd
Palapye Road, Botswana 95 Dd
Palatka, Florida 45 Gf
Palau Is., Pacific Ocean 83 Kj
Palaw, Burma 87 Bd
Palawan, Philippines 83 Gj
Paldiski, Estonia 67 Lg
Palembang, Sumatra 83 Dl
Palena, Chile 54 Bf
Palencia, Spain 70 Ca
Palenque, Mexico 50 Fd
Paleokhorio, Cyprus 94 Bc
Palermo, Argentina 54 Db
Palermo, N. Dakota 46 Fa
Palermo, Ontario 34 Lj
Palermo, Sicily 75 Df
Palestina, Chile 54 Cb
Palestine, Texas 49 Kg
Paletwa, Burma 89 Hd
Palghat, India 88 Ef
Palgrave Pt., Namibia 95 Ad
Palhoca, Brazil 54 Gc
Pali, India 88 Dc
Palien, Thailand 87 Be
Palime, Togo 98 Fg
Palisade, Nevada 47 Ee
Paliseul, Belgium 64 De
Palizada, Mexico 50 Fd
Palkot, India 91 Ed
Palk Str., India 88 Eg
Palliser B., New Zealand 55 Ed
Palma, Balearic Is. 71 Gc
Palma, Mozambique 97 Jg
Palma, La, Canary Is. 98 Bc
Palmares do Sul, Brazil 54 Fd
Palmas, Brazil 54 Fc
Palmas, B., Mexico 50 Cc
Palmas, G. di, Sardinia 75 Bf
Palmas C., Liberia 98 Dh
Palm Beach, Florida 45 Gg
Palm Beach, West, Florida 43 Kf
Palmeira, Brazil 54 Fc
Palmer, Saskatchewan 36 Lj
Palmer Arch., Antarctica 104 Sc
Palmerston, N.Z. 55 Cf
Palmerston, Ontario 34 Kj
Palmerston I., Cook Islands 102 Jj
Palmerston North, N.Z. 55 Ed
Palm I., Queensland 57 Jc
Palmira, Colombia 52 Bc
Palms, Michigan 40 Ed
Palmyra, Missouri 49 Mc
Palmyra, Syria 92 Cc
Palmyra I., Pacific Ocean 102 Jg
Palni Hills, India 88 Ef
Paloh, Borneo (Kalimantan) 83 Ek
Paloich, Sudan 99 Mf
Palo Santo, Argentina 54 Ec
Palpa, Nepal 91 Db
Palu, Turkey 92 Db
Palwal, India 90 Ef
Pamban Chan., India 88 Eg
Pambrun, Saskatchewan 36 Kj
Pamekasan, Indonesia 83 Fm
Pamiers, France 73 De
Pamir, U.S.S.R. 78 Ge
Pamlico Sound, N. Carolina 45 Jc
Pamouscachiou, L., Quebec 32 Ad
Pampa, Texas 48 Ge
Pampas, Peru 52 Cf
Pamplona, Colombia 52 Cb
Pamplona, Spain 71 Ea
Pana, Illinois 49 Nc
Panache, L., Ontario 34 Jf
Panagyurishte, Bulgaria 76 Ec
Panaji, Goa, India 88 De
Panama, Central America 51 De
Panama, G. of, Panama 51 De
Panama Canal, Central America 51 Gb
Panama City, Florida 45 Ee
Panarea, Italy 75 Ef
Panay, Philippines 83 Hh
Pančevo, Yugoslavia 76 Cb
Panciu, Romania 76 Fb
Pandan, Philippines 83 Hh
Pan de Azucar, Chile 54 Bc
Pandharpur, India 88 Ee
Pando, Uruguay 54 Ed
Pandora, Costa Rica 51 Ce
Panevezys, Lithuania 67 Lj
Panfilov, Kazakhstan 78 Hd
Panfilovo, U.S.S.R. 81 Fe
Pangala, Congo 96 Ce
Pangman, Saskatchewan 37 Nj
Pangnirtung, N.W.T. 31 Nd
Panguitch, Utah 48 Ad
Pania Mutombo, Zaire 96 Ef
Panipat, India 90 Ef
Panjim. See Panaji
Panjnad R., Pakistan 90 Bf
Pannerden, Netherlands 64 Ec
Panruti, India 88 Ef
Panshanaw, Burma 89 Je
Pantar, Indonesia 83 Hm
Pantelleria, Medit. Sea 75 Dg
Panuke Lake, N.S. 32 Hj
Pão de Açúcar, Brazil 53 Ke
Paoking. See Shaoyang
Paola, Italy 75 Ff
Paola, Kansas 49 Kc
Paoli, Indiana 45 Da
Paoning. See Langzhong
Papakura, New Zealand 55 Eb
Papantla, Mexico 50 Ec
Papa Stour I., Scotland 62 Ha
Papa Westray I., Orkney Is. 62 Fa
Papenburg, West Germany 68 Bb
Papendrecht, Netherlands 64 Cc
Paphos, Cyprus 94 Ac
Papineauville, Quebec 35 Pg
Paposo, Chile 54 Bc
Papua, Papua New Guinea 57 Ha
Papua, G. of, Papua New Guinea 57 Ha
Papua New Guinea, Pacific Ocean 59 Pj
Papun, Burma 89 Je
Pará. See Belém
Paraburdoo, W. Australia 56 Cd
Paracatú, Brazil 53 Hg
Paracel Is., South China Sea 87 Ec
Parachinar, Pakistan 90 Bd
Paracin, Yugoslavia 76 Cc
Paracurú, Brazil 53 Kd
Paradis, Quebec 35 Od
Paradise Hill, Sask. 36 He
Paradise Valley, Alberta 36 Ge
Paragould, Arkansas 49 Md
Paraguari, Paraguay 54 Ec
Paraguay, Arg. 54 Ec
Paraguay, S. America 54 Eb
Parakou, Benin 98 Fg
Paramaribo, Surinam 53 Fb
Paramé, L., Quebec 33 Ob
Paramonga, Peru 52 Bf
Paramoshir, U.S.S.R. 79 Qc
Paraná, Argentina 54 Ec
Paraná, Argentina 54 Dd
Paranã, Brazil 53 Hf
Paranaguá, Brazil 54 Gc
Paranáiba, Brazil 53 Gg
Parang, Philippines 83 Hj
Paranga, Uganda 97 Gd
Parapóla, Greece 77 Df
Paratinga, Brazil 53 Jf
Parbati, India 88 Ed
Parbhani, India 88 Ee
Parchim, East Germany 68 Db
Parc prov. du Mont-Orford, Quebec 35 Sg
Pardubice, Czechoslovakia 69 Fc
Parecis, Sierra dos, Brazil 52 Ef
Parent, Quebec 35 Qe
Parent, L., Quebec 35 Od
Pareora, New Zealand 55 Cf
Pariaguan, Venezuela 52 Eb
Parika, Guyana 52 Fb
Parinari, Peru 52 Cd
Parintins, Brazil 53 Fd
Paris, France 72 Eb
Paris, Illinois 40 Cf
Paris, Kentucky 45 Ea
Paris, Ontario 34 Kj
Paris, Tennessee 49 Nd
Paris, Texas 49 Kf
Parisienne, I., Ontario 34 Ff
Parita, B. de, Panama 51 Ce
Pariz, Iran 93 Gd
Park, Iran 93 Hd
Parkbeg, Saskatchewan 36 Lh
Parker, S. Dakota 46 Jd
Parker Dam, Arizona 42 De
Parkersburg, W. Virginia 40 Ff
Parkerview, Saskatchewan 37 Og
Parkes, N.S.W. 57 Jf
Park Falls, Wisconsin 40 Ac
Parkhill, Ontario 34 Jj
Park Lake Prov. Park, Alta. 36 Ej
Parkland, Alberta 36 Dh
Parkman, Saskatchewan 37 Qj
Park Ra., Colorado 48 Db
Park Ra., Wyoming 42 Ec
Park Rapids, Minnesota 46 Kb
Parkside, Saskatchewan 36 Le
Parkston, S. Dakota 46 Jd
Parma, Italy 74 Cc
Parmele, N. Carolina 45 Jc
Parnagua, Brazil 53 Jf
Parnaíba, Brazil 53 Jd
Parnaíba, Brazil 53 Jd
Parnon, Greece 77 Df
Pärnu, Estonia 67 Lg
Paro, Bhutan 91 Gb
Paron, India 88 Ed
Parowan, Utah 47 Gg
Parral, Chile 54 Be
Parral, Hidalgo del, Mexico 50 Cb
Parramatta, N.S.W. 57 Kf
Parras, Mexico 50 Db
Parrsboro, Nova Scotia 32 Hh
Parry, Saskatchewan 37 Nj
Parry, C., Greenland 31 Mb
Parry, C., N.W.T. 38 La
Parry B., N.W.T. 31 Ld
Parry I., Ontario 34 Kg
Parry Pen., N.W.T. 38 La
Parry Sd., Ontario 34 Kg
Parry Sound, Ontario 34 Kg
Parsa, India 91 Ec
Parsons, Kansas 49 Kd
Parsons, West Virginia 44 Ac
Parsons L., N.W.T. 38 Ga
Parson's Pond, Nfld. 33 Pc
Partabgarh, India 88 Dd
Partabpur, India 91 Dd
Parthenay, France 72 Cc
Partinico, Sicily 75 Df
Partizansk, U.S.S.R. 79 Nd
Partridge, R, Ontario 34 Kb
Partridgeberry Hills, Nfld. 33 Re
Partridge Breast L., Man. 37 Ua
Paryang, China 89 Fb
Pas, The, Manitoba 37 Qe
Pasadena, California 47 Dh
Pasargadae, Iran 93 Fc
Pasawng, Burma 89 Je
Pascagoula, Miss. 49 Ng
Pascalis, Quebec 35 Nd
Pascopee, Ontario 34 Ab
Pas-de-Calais, France 72 Ea
Pasfield L., Saskatchewan 39 Vf
Paskuh, Iran 93 Hd
Pasley, C., W. Australia 56 Df
Pasni, Pakistan 88 Bc
Paso de Indios, Arg. 54 Cf
Paso de los Libres, Arg. 54 Ec
Paso de los Toros, Uruguay 54 Ed
Paso Limay, Argentina 54 Bf
Paso Robles, California 47 Ch
Paspébiac, Quebec 32 Ge
Pasqua, Saskatchewan 37 Mh
Pasquia Hills, Sask. 37 Oe
Pasquia R., Man./Sask. 37 Qe
Pasrur, Pakistan 90 Dd
Passaic, New Jersey 44 Cb
Passau, West Germany 68 Ed
Passendale, Belgium 64 Bd
Passero C., Sicily 75 Eg
Pass Lake, Ontario 34 Bd
Passo Fundo, Brazil 54 Fc
Passos, Brazil 53 Hh
Pasteur, L., Quebec 32 Fc
Pasto, Colombia 52 Bc
Pastrana, Spain 70 Db
Pasvik Elv, Norway 66 Nb
Paswegin, Saskatchewan 37 Of
Pásztó, Hungary 69 He
Patan, India 88 Dd
Patan, India 88 De
Patan, Nepal 91 Eb
Pataudi, India 90 Ef
Pataz, Peru 52 Be
Patchogue, New York 44 Db
Patea, New Zealand 55 Ec
Paternò, Sicily 75 Eg
Paterson, New Jersey 44 Cb
Pathankot, India 90 Dd
Pathari, India 91 Bd
Pathfinder Res., Wyoming 46 Dd
Pathlow, Saskatchewan 37 Nf
Patiala, India 90 Ee
Patkai Hills, Burma 89 Jc
Pat Mayse Res., Texas 49 Kf
Pátmos, I., Greece 77 Ff
Patna, India 89 Gc
Patna, India 91 Ec
Patos, Brazil 53 Ke
Patos, L. dos, Brazil 54 Fd
Patos de Minas, Brazil 53 Hg
Patquia, Argentina 54 Cd
Pátrai, Greece 77 Ce
Pátrai, G. of, Greece 77 Ce
Patras. See Pátrai
Patrasayar, India 91 Fd
Patricia, Alberta 36 Fh
Patricio Lynch, Chile 54 Ag
Patrocinio, Brazil 53 Hg
Pattani, Thailand 87 Ce
Patten, Maine 32 Dh
Patterson, Louisiana 45 Bf
Patterson, Mt., Y.T. 38 Fc
Patti, Sicily 75 Ef
Pattullo, Mt., B.C. 39 Jg
Patuanak, Saskatchewan 39 Uh
Patutahi, New Zealand 55 Fc
Patzcuaro, Mexico 50 Dd
Pau, France 73 Ce
Pau d'Arco, Brazil 53 He
Pau dos Ferros, Brazil 53 Ke
Paugan Falls, Quebec 35 Og
Paulatuk, N.W.T. 38 Ma
Paul I., Newfoundland 31 Nf
Paulistana, Brazil 53 Je
Paul's Valley, Oklahoma 49 Je
Paungde, Burma 89 Je
Pauni, India 88 Ed
Pautrask, Sweden 66 Gd
Pavia, Italy 74 Bc
Pavilion, B.C. 39 Nk
Pāvilosta, Latvia 67 Jh
Pavlodar, Kazakhstan 78 Gc
Pavlograd, Ukraine 80 Jg

Pavlovka, *U.S.S.R.* 81 Fe
Pavlovo, *U.S.S.R.* 81 Fc
Pavlovsk, *U.S.S.R.* 81 Ee
Pavlovski, *U.S.S.R.* 80 Ld
Pawnee City, *Nebraska* 49 Jb
Paw Paw, *Michigan* 40 Dd
Pawtucket, *Rhode Island* 44 Eb
Paxoi, *Greece* 77 Ce
Paxton, *Illinois* 49 Nb
Payerne, *Switzerland* 65 Bb
Pay-Khoy, Khrebet, *U.S.S.R.* 78 Fb
Payne, L., *Quebec* 31 Mf
Payne's Find, *W. Australia* 56 Ce
Paynesville, *Minnesota* 46 Kc
Paynton, *Saskatchewan* 36 Je
Paysandú, *Uruguay* 54 Ed
Payson, *Utah* 48 Bb
Paz, *Salvador* 51 Ad
Pazardzhik, *Bulgaria* 76 Ec
Peace R., *Alberta* 39 Qf
Peace River, *Alberta* 39 Pg
Peachland, *B.C.* 39 Ol
Peacock Sound, *Antarctica* 104 Qb
Peak, The, *England* 63 Fg
Peak Hill, *W. Australia* 56 Ce
Peale, Mt., *Utah* 48 Cc
Pearce, *Alberta* 36 Dj
Pearl, *Ontario* 34 Bd
Pearl Harbor, *Hawaiian Is.* 103 Ke
Pearl R., *Mississippi* 49 Ng
Pearsall, *Texas* 49 Hh
Pearson L., *Manitoba* 37 Ub
Peary Channel, *N.W.T.* 30 Jb
Peary Ld., *Greenland* 41 Na
Pebane, *Mozambique* 97 Hh
Pebas, *Peru* 52 Cd
Pebble I., *Falkland Islands* 54 Eh
Pébo, *Cent. Afr. Rep.* 99 Jg
Peć, *Yugoslavia* 76 Cc
Pechenga, *U.S.S.R.* 78 Cb
Pechora, *U.S.S.R.* 78 Eb
Pecos, *New Mexico* 48 Ee
Pecos, *Texas* 48 Fg
Pecos R., *Texas* 42 Fe
Pecos R., *Texas/New Mexico* 48 Fg
Pécs, *Hungary* 76 Ba
Pedernales, *Venezuela* 52 Eb
Pedhoulas, *Cyprus* 94 Ac
Pedregal, *Panama* 51 Ce
Pedro, Pt., *Sri Lanka* 88 Fg
Pedro Afonso, *Brazil* 53 He
Pedro Azul, *Brazil* 53 Jg
Pedro Juan Caballero, *Paraguay* 54 Eb
Pedroll, *Brazil* 53 Jd
Pedro Luro, *Argentina* 54 De
Peebles, *Saskatchewan* 37 Ph
Peebles, *Scotland* 62 Ee
Peekskill, *New York* 44 Db
Peel, *New Brunswick* 32 Eg
Peel, R., *Y.T.* 38 Fb
Peel Pt., *N.W.T.* 30 Hc
Peel Sound, *N.W.T.* 30 Kc
Peenemünde, *E. Germany* 68 Ea
Peerless L., *Alberta* 39 Qg
Peers, *Alberta* 39 Qj
Peetri, *Estonia* 67 Lg
Pegasus B., *New Zealand* 55 De
Pegu, *Burma* 89 Je
Pegu Yoma, *Burma* 89 Je
Pehowa, *India* 90 Ef
Pehuajó, *Argentina* 54 De
Peineta, *Chile* 54 Bh
Peipus, L. *See* Chudskoye, Oz
Peixe, *Brazil* 53 Hf
Pekan, *Pen. Malaysia* 87 Cf
Pekanbaru, *Sumatra* 83 Dk
Pekin, *Illinois* 49 Nb
Peking. *See* Beijing
Pekisko, *Alberta* 39 Rk
Pelagie Is., *Medit. Sea* 99 Ha
Pélagos, *Greece* 77 De
Peleduy, *U.S.S.R.* 79 Lc
Pelee I. & Pt., *Ontario* 34 Hk
Peleng, *Indonesia* 83 Hl
Pelican B., *Manitoba* 37 Rf
Pelican L., *Alberta* 36 Dc
Pelican L., *Manitoba* 37 Sj
Pelican L., *Manitoba* 37 Rf
Pelican L., *Saskatchewan* 37 Oc
Pelican Mtn., *Alberta* 36 Dc
Pelican Narrows, *Sask.* 37 Pc
Pelican Portage, *Alberta* 36 Ec
Pelican Rapids, *Manitoba* 37 Rf
Peljesac, *Yugoslavia* 74 Fd
Pelkosenniemi, *Finland* 66 Mc
Pella, *Greece* 77 Cd
Pella, *Iowa* 49 Lb
Pellatt L., *N.W.T.* 38 Tc
Pellegrini, *Argentina* 54 De
Pelletier L., *Manitoba* 37 Ub
Pellworm, *West Germany* 68 Ca
Pelly, *Saskatchewan* 37 Qg
Pelly, R., *Y.T.* 38 Hd
Pelly Bay, *N.W.T.* 31 Ld
Pelly Crossing, *Y.T.* 38 Ed
Pelly I., *N.W.T.* 38 Fa
Pelly L., *N.W.T.* 38 Xc
Pelly Mts., *Y.T.* 38 Ge
Pelly Pt., *N.W.T.* 38 Xa
Peloncillo Range, *Arizona* 48 Cf
Pelopónnisos, *Greece* 77 Cf
Pelotas, *Brazil* 54 Fd
Pemba, *Mozambique* 97 Jg
Pemba Is., *East Africa* 97 Hf
Pemberton, *B.C.* 39 Mk
Pembina Mt., ra., *Man.* 37 Tj
Pembina Oil Fields & R., *Alberta* 36 Be
Pembroke, *Ontario* 35 Ng
Pembroke, *Wales* 63 Dj
Pembroke, C., *Falkland Is.* 54 Eh
Penafiel, *Portugal* 70 Ab
Peñafiel, *Spain* 70 Cb
Penalva, *Brazil* 53 Jd
Penambo Ra., *Sarawak* 83 Fk
Peña Negra, Sa. de, *Spain* 70 Ba
Penang. *See* Pinang
Penápolis, *Brazil* 53 Gh
Peñaranda de Bracamonte, *Spain* 70 Cb
Peñarroya, *Spain* 70 Cc
Penas, G. de, *Chile* 54 Bg
Pendembu, *Sierra Leone* 98 Cg
Pendleton, *Arkansas* 45 Bd
Pendleton, *Oregon* 47 Dc
Pendleton Mt., *B.C.* 38 Jf
Pend Oreille, L., *Idaho* 42 Cb
Penedo, *Brazil* 53 Kf
Penedono, *Portugal* 70 Bb
Penetanguishene, *Ontario* 34 Lh
Penggaram, *Pen. Malaysia* 87 Cf
Penglai, *China* 84 Kd
Pengpu, *China* 82 Gd
Penhalonga, *Zimbabwe* 95 Ec
Penhold, *Alberta* 36 Df
Penhurst, *Ontario* 34 Fc
Peniche, *Portugal* 70 Ac
Peninsular Malaysia, *Malaysia* 83 Dk
Peñiscola, *Spain* 71 Fb
Penn, *N. Dakota* 46 Ha
Penn, *Saskatchewan* 36 Ke
Pennant, *Saskatchewan* 36 Jh
Pennant Pt., *Nova Scotia* 32 Jj
Pennfield, *New Brunswick* 32 Fh
Pennine, Alpi, *Switzerland* 65 Cb
Pennine Chain, *England* 63 Ff
Penns Grove, *New Jersey* 44 Cc
Pennsylvania, *U.S.A.* 43 Lc
Penn Yan, *New York* 44 Ba
Penny B., *N.W.T.* 38 Pa
Penny Ice Cap, *N.W.T.* 31 Nd
Penobscot, B., *Maine* 32 Dj
Penobsquis, *N.B.* 32 Gh
Penong, *S. Australia* 56 Ff
Penonome, *Panama* 51 Ce
Penrhyn, *Pacific Ocean* 103 Kh
Penrith, *England* 63 Ff
Pensacola, *Florida* 45 De
Pense, *Saskatchewan* 37 Nh
Pentecôte, L., *Quebec* 32 Ed
Penticton, *B.C.* 39 Ol
Pentland Firth, *Scotland* 62 Eb
Pentland Hills, *Scotland* 62 Ee
Pentwater, *Michigan* 40 Cd
Penylan L., *N.W.T.* 38 Ue
Penza, *U.S.S.R.* 81 Gd
Penzance, *England* 63 Dk
Penzance, *Saskatchewan* 37 Mg
Penzhino, *U.S.S.R.* 79 Rb
Penzhinskaya Guba, *U.S.S.R.* 79 Rb
Peoria, *Illinois* 49 Nb
Peperga, *Netherlands* 64 Eb
Pepinster, *Belgium* 64 Dd
Peqin, *Albania* 76 Bd
Perai, *Pen. Malaysia* 87 Ce
Peralta, *Spain* 71 Ea
Percé, *Quebec* 32 He
Percy L., *Ontario* 34 Db
Perdido, Mte., *Spain* 71 Fa
Perdu, L., *Quebec* 32 Bc
Perdue, *Saskatchewan* 36 Kf
Pereira, *Colombia* 52 Bc
Perelló, *Spain* 71 Fb
Perez, *Chile* 54 Cc
Pergamino, *Argentina* 54 Dd
Perho, *Finland* 66 Le
Péribonca, *Quebec* 35 Td
Péribonca L., *Quebec* 32 Ac
Péribonca R., *Quebec* 32 Ad
Perico, *Argentina* 54 Cb
Périgueux, *France* 73 Dd
Perija, Sa. de, *Venezuela* 52 Ca
Perim, *Red Sea* 92 Dg
Peristéra, *Greece* 77 Ee
Perlas, *Nic.* 51 Cd
Perlas, Arch. de las, *Pan.* 51 De
Perm', *U.S.S.R.* 81 Nb
Pernambuco. *See* Recife
Pernik, *Bulgaria* 76 Dc
Péronne, *France* 72 Eb
Péronnes, *Belgium* 64 Cd
Perpignan, *France* 73 Ee
Perrot I., *Quebec* 40 Jc
Perry, *Iowa* 49 Kb
Perry, *New York* 44 Aa
Perry, *Oklahoma* 49 Jd
Perry, *Ontario* 34 Fe
Perry Island, *N.W.T.* 30 Jd
Perry R., *N.W.T.* 38 Xb
Perry Res., *Kansas* 49 Kc
Perryvale, *Alberta* 36 Dd
Perryville, *Missouri* 45 Cb
Persepolis, *Iran* 93 Fd
Pershing, *Quebec* 35 Od
Persia. *See* Iran
Persian Gulf, *Arabia* 92 Ed
Perth, *New Brunswick* 32 Eg
Perth, *Ontario* 35 Oh
Perth, *Scotland* 62 Ed
Perth, *W. Australia* 56 Cf
Perth Amboy, *New Jersey* 44 Cb
Peru, *Indiana* 40 Ce
Peru, *South America* 52 Cf
Perugia, *Italy* 74 Dd
Peruibe, *Brazil* 53 Hh
Péruwelz, *Belgium* 64 Bd
Pervijze, *Belgium* 64 Ac
Pervomaysk, *Ukraine* 80 Gg
Perwez, *Belgium* 64 Cd
Pesaro, *Italy* 74 Dd
Pescadores, Is. *See* Penghu Liedao
Pescara, *Italy* 74 Ed
Peschici, *Italy* 75 Fe
Peshawar, *Pakistan* 90 Bc
Peshtigo R., *Wisconsin* 40 Bc
Pêso do Régua, *Portugal* 70 Bb
Pesqueira, *Brazil* 53 Ke
Pestravka, *U.S.S.R.* 81 Jd
Petah Tiqwa, *Israel* 94 Ce
Petalioí, *Greece* 77 Ef
Petalioí, G. of, *Greece* 77 Ef
Petaluma, *California* 47 Bf
Petawaga, L., *Quebec* 35 Pf
Petawawa, *Ontario* 35 Ng
Peterbell, *Ontario* 34 Gd
Peterborough, *England* 63 Gh
Peterborough, *Ontario* 35 Mh
Peterborough, *S. Australia* 57 Gf
Peterhead, *Scotland* 62 Fc
Peter I, I., *Antarctica* 104 Rc
Petermann Fd., *Greenland* 41 Pa
Petermann Pk., *Greenland* 41 Nb
Petermann Range, *W. Aust.* 56 Ee
Peter Pond L., *Sask.* 36 Hb
Peter Richards, C., *Northwest Territories* 38 Oa
Petersburg, *Alaska* 43 Zm
Petersburg, *Virginia* 45 Jb
Petersfield, *Manitoba* 37 Uh
Peterview, *Nfld.* 33 Rd
Petit Bois I., *Alabama* 49 Ng
Petitcodiac, *N.B.* 32 Gh
Petite Baleine, R., *Quebec* 31 Mf
Petite-Matane, *Quebec* 32 Ee
Petite-Rivière, *Quebec* 32 Bf
Petite Rivière Bridge, *Nova Scotia* 32 Hj
Petit-Étang, *N.S.* 33 Mg
Petite-Vallée, *Quebec* 32 Hd
Petit Jardin, *Newfoundland* 33 Ne
Petit lac Manicouagan, *Quebec* 32 Eb
Petitot, R., *B.C.* 38 Nf
Petit-Rocher, *N.B.* 32 Gf
Peto, *Mexico* 50 Gc
Petone, *New Zealand* 55 Ed
Petorca, *Chile* 54 Bd
Petoskey, *Michigan* 40 Dc
Petra, *Jordan* 94 Dg
Petra Velikogo Zaliv, *U.S.S.R.* 79 Nd
Petre, Pt., *Ontario* 35 Nj
Petrich, *Bulgaria* 76 Dd
Petrified Forest Nat. Mon., *Arizona* 48 Ce
Petrinja, *Yugoslavia* 74 Fc
Petrodvorets, *U.S.S.R.* 80 Fb
Petrolândia, *Brazil* 53 Ke
Petrolia, *Ontario* 34 Hk
Petrolina, *Brazil* 53 Je
Petropavlovsk, *Kazakhstan* 78 Fc
Petropavlovsk, *U.S.S.R.* 79 Qc
Petrópolis, *Brazil* 53 Jh
Petrovac, *Yugoslavia* 76 Cb
Petrovsk, *U.S.S.R.* 79 Kc
Petrovsk, *U.S.S.R.* 81 Nd
Petrovsk, *U.S.S.R.* 81 Gd
Petrozavodsk, *U.S.S.R.* 78 Cb
Petsamo. *See* Pechenga
Petty Harbour, *Nfld.* 33 Uf
Pevek, *U.S.S.R.* 79 Sb
Pézenas, *France* 73 Ee
Pforzheim, *W. Germany* 68 Cd
Phagwara, *India* 90 De
Phalodi, *India* 88 Dc
Phanom Dang Raek, *Thailand* 87 Cd
Phan Rang, *Vietnam* 87 Dd
Phan-Thiet, *Vietnam* 87 Dd
Phaphund, *India* 91 Bb
Phatthalung, *Thailand* 87 Be
Phelps L., *Saskatchewan* 38 Wf
Phenix City, *Alabama* 45 Ed
Phet Buri, *Thailand* 87 Bd
Philadelphia, *Pennsylvania* 40 Je
Philip, *S. Dakota* 46 Gc
Philip Edward I., *Ontario* 40 Fc
Philippeville, *Belgium* 64 Cd
Philippi, *West Virginia* 40 Ff
Philippi, L., *Queensland* 57 Gd
Philippines, Is., *S.E. Asia* 83 Hh
Philippopolis. *See* Plovdiv
Philipsburg, *Quebec* 35 Rg
Phillaur, *India* 90 De
Phillip Edward I., *Ontario* 40 Fc
Phillips, *Maine* 32 Bj
Phillips, *Wisconsin* 40 Ac
Phillipsburg, *Kansas* 49 Hc
Phillipsburg, *New Jersey* 44 Cb
Phillips Inlet, *N.W.T.* 31 La
Philomena, *Alberta* 39 Sh
Philpots Island, *N.W.T.* 31 Mc
Phimai, *Thailand* 87 Cc
Phippen, *Saskatchewan* 36 Jf
Phnom-Penh, *Kampuchea* 87 Cd
Phoenix, *Arizona* 48 Af
Phoenix I., *Phoenix Is.* 102 Hh
Phoenix Is., *Pacific Ocean* 102 Hh
Phoenixville, *Pennsylvania* 44 Cb
Phou San, *Laos* 87 Cc
Phu Dien Mat, *Vietnam* 87 Dc
Phuket, *Thailand* 83 Cj
Phulji, *Pakistan* 88 Cc
Phulpur, *India* 91 Dc
Phu Qui, *Vietnam* 87 Dc
Phu-Quoc, *Vietnam* 87 Cd
Piacenza, *Italy* 74 Bc
Pianosa, *Italy* 74 Cd
Piapot, *Saskatchewan* 36 Hj
Pias, *Portugal* 70 Bc
Piashti, L., *Quebec* 32 Kc
Piatra Neamţ, *Romania* 76 Fa
Piazza Armerina, *Sicily* 75 Eg
Piazzi, I., *Chile* 54 Bh
Pibroch, *Alberta* 36 Dd
Piccadilly, *Newfoundland* 33 Oe
Pichanal, *Argentina* 54 Db
Picher, *Oklahoma* 49 Kd
Pichilemu, *Chile* 54 Bd
Pickardville, *Alberta* 36 Dd
Pickens, *Mississippi* 45 Cd
Pickerel, *Ontario* 34 Kg
Pickerel L., *Ontario* 36 Lb
Pickerel River, *Ontario* 34 Kf
Pickering, *England* 63 Gf
Pickle Lake, *Ontario* 31 Kg
Pickwick L., *Tenn./Alabama* 49 Ne
Picouadie, L., *Quebec* 32 Bb
Pic R., *Ontario* 34 Dc
Picton, *New South Wales* 57 Kf
Picton, *New Zealand* 55 Dd
Picton, *Ontario* 35 Nj
Pictou & I., *Nova Scotia* 32 Kh
Picture Butte, *Alberta* 36 Ej
Picún Leufú, *Argentina* 54 Ce
Pidark, *Pakistan* 88 Bc
Piedad, La, *Mexico* 50 Dc
Piedmont, *S. Carolina* 45 Fc
Piedmont, *S. Dakota* 46 Fc
Piedrahita, *Spain* 70 Cb
Piedras Negras, *Mexico* 50 Db
Piedras Sola, *Uruguay* 54 Ed
Pie I., *Ontario* 37 Ob
Pieksämäki, *Finland* 66 Me
Pielinen, *Finland* 66 Ne
Piemonte, *Italy* 74 Ac
Pierre, *S. Dakota* 46 Gc
Pierre L., *Ontario* 34 Kc
Pierreville, *Quebec* 35 Sf
Pierson, *Manitoba* 37 Qj
Pietarsaari, *Finland* 66 Ke
Pietermaritzburg, *Natal* 95 Ee
Pietersburg, *Transvaal* 95 Dd
Pigeon B., *Ontario* 34 Hk
Pigeon L., *Alberta* 36 De
Pigeon L., *Ontario* 35 Mh
Pigeon R., *Manitoba* 37 Vf
Pigeon River, *Ontario* 37 Nb
Piggott, *Arkansas* 49 Md
Pigüé, *Argentina* 54 De
Pihtipudas, *Finland* 66 Le
Pikangikum L., *Ontario* 30 Kg
Pikes Pk., *Colorado* 48 Ec
Pikeville, *Kentucky* 45 Fb
Pikwitonei, *Manitoba* 37 Uc
Pila, *Argentina* 54 Ee
Pila, *Poland* 69 Gb
Pilāni, *India* 90 Df
Pilao Arcado, *Brazil* 53 Jf
Pilar, *Argentina* 54 Dd
Pilar, *Paraguay* 54 Ec
Pilar, C., *Chile* 54 Bh
Pilcaniyeu, *Argentina* 54 Bf
Pilger, *Saskatchewan* 37 Mf
Pilibhit, *India* 91 Ba
Pilley's I., *Newfoundland* 33 Rd
Pílos, *Greece* 77 Cf
Pilot Butte, *Sask.* 37 Nh
Pilot Knob, *Missouri* 45 Bb
Pilot L., *N.W.T.* 38 Se
Pilot Mound, *Manitoba* 37 Tj
Pilsen. *See* Plzeň
Piltene, *Latvia* 67 Jh
Pimentel, *Peru* 52 Be
Pina, *Spain* 71 Eb
Pinaki, *Tuamotu Arch.* 103 Mj
Pinaleno Range, *Arizona* 48 Bf
Pinang, *Pen. Malaysia* 87 Ce
Pinang. *See* George Town
Pinarbasi, *Turkey* 92 Cb
Pinar del Río, *Cuba* 51 Cb
Pincher, *Alberta* 36 Dj
Pincher Creek, *Alberta* 36 Dj
Pinchi, *British Columbia* 39 Lh
Pinckneyville, *Illinois* 45 Ca
Pind Dadan Khan, *Pakistan* 90 Cd
Pindhos, *Greece* 77 Ce
Pindi Gheb, *Pakistan* 90 Cd
Pine, C., *Newfoundland* 33 Tg
Pine Bluff, *Arkansas* 45 Ac
Pinebluff L., *Saskatchewan* 37 Pd
Pine City, *Minnesota* 46 Lc
Pine Cr., *Alberta* 36 Dd
Pine Creek, *N. Terr.* 56 Fb
Pinedale, *Alberta* 39 Pj
Pinedale, *Wyoming* 46 Cd
Pinehouse L., *Sask.* 36 Lc
Pinehurst, *N. Carolina* 45 Hc
Pinehurst L., *Alberta* 36 Fd
Pine I., *Florida* 45 Fg
Pine Mts., *Kentucky* 45 Fb
Pineola, *N. Carolina* 45 Gb
Pine Point, *N.W.T.* 38 Qe
Pine Portage, *Ontario* 34 Bc
Pine Pt., *N.W.T.* 38 Qe
Pine R., *British Columbia* 39 Nh
Pine River, *Manitoba* 37 Rg
Pine River, *Minnesota* 46 Kb
Pine River, *Saskatchewan* 36 Kc
Pinery Prov. Pk., *Ontario* 34 Hj
Pines, L. of the, *Texas* 49 Kf
Pinetown, *Natal* 95 Ee
Pineville, *Kentucky* 45 Fb
Pineville, *Missouri* 49 Kd
Pineville, *W. Virginia* 45 Gb
Pinewood, *Ontario* 36 Hb
Piney, *Manitoba* 36 Fa
Piney Buttes, *Montana* 46 Db
Ping, *Thailand* 87 Bc
Pingdingshan, *China* 84 Ff
Pingelap, *Caroline Is.* 102 Fg
Pingelly, *W. Australia* 56 Cf
Pingjiang, *China* 85 Fh
Pingle, *China* 85 Ek
Pingliang, *China* 84 Ce
Pingquan, *China* 84 Jb
Pingrup, *W. Australia* 56 Cf
Pingtan Dao, *China* 85 Jk
Pingwu, *China* 84 Bf
Pingxiang, *China* 85 Cl
Pingyang. *See* Linfen
Pingyao, *China* 84 Fd
Pingyuan, *China* 84 Hd
Pingyüanchow. *See* Zhijin
Pinhel, *Portugal* 70 Bb
Pini, *Indonesia* 83 Ck
Pinjarra, *W. Australia* 56 Bf
Pinkham, *Saskatchewan* 36 Hg
Pink Mountain, *B.C.* 39 Mg
Pinnaroo, *S. Australia* 57 Hg
Pinos, *Mexico* 50 Dc
Pinos, I. de, *Cuba* 51 Cb
Pinos, Mt., *California* 47 Dh
Pinrang, *Celebes (Sulawesi)* 83 Gl
Pins, Pte. aux, *Ontario* 34 Jk
Pinsk, *Byelorussia* 80 Ee
Pintados, *Chile* 54 Cb
Pinto, *Argentina* 54 Dc
Pinto Butte, pk., *Sask.* 36 Kj
Pinware R. & B., *Nfld.* 33 Qb
Pioner Ostrov, *U.S.S.R.* 79 Ja
Piotrków, *Poland* 69 Hc
Pipar, *India* 88 Dc
Pipestone, *Manitoba* 37 Rj
Pipestone, *Minnesota* 42 Gc
Pipestone Creek, *Manitoba/Sask.* 37 Qj
Pipmuacan Rés., *Quebec* 32 Bd
Pipli, *India* 89 Gd
Piqua, *Ohio* 40 De
Piracuruca, *Brazil* 53 Jd
Piraeus. *See* Piraiévs
Piraiévs, *Greece* 77 Df
Piramide, *Chile* 54 Bg
Piranhas, *Brazil* 53 Ke
Pirapora, *Brazil* 53 Jg
Piratini, *Brazil* 54 Fd
Piraube L., *Quebec* 32 Ac
Piray, *Argentina* 54 Fc
Pirgos, *Crete* 77 Eg
Pirgos, *Greece* 77 Cf
Pirgos, *Greece* 77 Df
Pirin Planina, *Bulgaria* 76 Dd
Piripiri, *Brazil* 53 Jd
Piritu, *Venezuela* 52 Ea
Pirmasens, *West Germany* 68 Bd
Pirna, *East Germany* 68 Ec
Pirot, *Yugoslavia* 76 Dc
Pir Panjal Ra., *Kashmir* 90 Dd
Pisa, *Italy* 74 Cd
Pisagua, *Chile* 54 Ba
Pisco, *Peru* 52 Bf
Písek, *Czechoslovakia* 68 Fd
Pishin, *Iran* 93 Hd
Pishin, *Pakistan* 88 Bc
Pisticci, *Italy* 75 Fe
Pistolet B., *Nfld.* 33 Rb
Pitaga, *Nfld.* 32 Ga
Pitangui, *Brazil* 53 Jg
Pitcairn I., *Pacific Ocean* 103 Mk
Piteå, *Sweden* 66 Jd
Pite Älv, *Sweden* 66 Hd
Piterka, *U.S.S.R.* 81 He
Piteşti, *Romania* 76 Eb
Pithiviers, *France* 72 Eb
Pithoria, *India* 91 Bc
Pitlochry, *Scotland* 62 Ed
Pitok, R, *N.W.T.* 38 Xb
Pitt I., *British Columbia* 39 Hj
Pitt R., *British Columbia* 39 Jl
Pitt R., *California* 47 Ce
Pittsboro, *N. Carolina* 45 Hc
Pittsburg, *Kansas* 43 Hd
Pittsburgh, *Pennsylvania* 40 Ge
Pittsfield, *Illinois* 49 Mc
Pittsfield, *Maine* 32 Cj
Pittsfield, *Massachusetts* 40 Kd
Pittston, *Pennsylvania* 44 Cb
Piua-Petri, *Romania* 76 Fb
Piura, *Peru* 52 Ae
Pivabiska, R., *Ontario* 34 Gb
Piza, *Latvia* 67 Jh
Piz Sardona, *Switzerland* 65 Eb
Placentia, *Newfoundland* 33 Tf
Placentia B., *Nfld.* 33 Sf
Placer Guadalupe, *Mexico* 50 Cb
Plainfield, *New Jersey* 40 Je
Plainview, *Nebraska* 49 Ja
Plainview, *Texas* 48 Ge
Plainwell, *Michigan* 40 Dd
Pláka B., *Crete* 77 Eg
Plakoti C., *Cyprus* 94 Cb
Plamondon, *Alberta* 36 Ed
Planá, *Czechoslovakia* 68 Ed
Planaltina, *Brazil* 53 Hg
Planina, *Yugoslavia* 74 Ec
Plantagenet, *Ontario* 35 Qg
Plant City, *Florida* 45 Gf
Plasencia, *Spain* 70 Bb
Plaški, *Yugoslavia* 74 Ec
Plassen, *Norway* 67 Ef
Plaster Rock, *N.B.* 32 Eg
Plastun, *U.S.S.R.* 79 Nd
Plata, R. de la, *Argentina* 54 Ed
Platamón, *Greece* 77 Dd
Plate, I., *Quebec* 33 Oc
Plate Cove, *Nfld.* 33 Te
Platí, *Greece* 77 Dd
Plato, *Saskatchewan* 36 Jg
Platres, *Cyprus* 94 Ac
Platte, North, *Nebraska* 42 Fc
Platte R., *Nebraska* 49 Hb
Platteville, *Wisconsin* 49 Ma
Platt Nat. Park, *Oklahoma* 42 Ge
Plattsburg, *Missouri* 49 Kc
Plattsburg, *New York* 40 Kc
Plattsmouth, *Nebraska* 49 Kb
Plauen, *East Germany* 68 Ec
Plav, *Yugoslavia* 76 Bc
Plavnica, *Yugoslavia* 76 Bc
Playas, *Ecuador* 52 Ad
Playas L., *New Mexico* 42 Ee
Playgreen L., *Manitoba* 37 Te
Plaza Huincul, *Argentina* 54 Ce
Pleasantdale, *Sask.* 37 Nf
Pleasant Grove, *Utah* 48 Bb
Pleasant Mt., *N.B.* 32 Fh
Pleasant Point, *Manitoba* 37 Sj
Pleasantville, *New Jersey* 44 Cc
Pledger L., *Ontario* 34 Gb
Pleiku, *Vietnam* 83 Eh
Plenty, *Saskatchewan* 36 Jg
Plenty, B. of, *New Zealand* 55 Fb
Plentywood, *Montana* 46 Ea
Plessisville, *Quebec* 35 Tf
Plétipi, L., *Quebec* 32 Bb
Plettenberg B., *Cape Prov.* 95 Cf
Pleven, *Bulgaria* 76 Ec
Pljevlja, *Yugoslavia* 76 Bc
Płock, *Poland* 69 Hb
Ploeşti, *Romania* 76 Fb
Plomarion, *Greece* 77 Fe
Plomosa Mts., *Arizona* 47 Gj
Plön, *West Germany* 68 Da
Plonge, L. la, *Sask.* 36 Kc
Płońsk, *Poland* 69 Jb
Plovdiv, *Bulgaria* 76 Ec
Plumas, *Manitoba* 37 Sh
Plum Coulée, *Manitoba* 37 Uj
Plumtree, *Zimbabwe* 95 Dd
Plunkett, *Saskatchewan* 37 Mg
Plymouth, *England* 63 Ek
Plymouth, *Indiana* 40 Ce
Plymouth, *Massachusetts* 40 Le
Plymouth, *N. Carolina* 45 Jc
Plymouth, *New Hampshire* 40 Ld
Plymouth, *Pennsylvania* 44 Cb
Plymouth, *Wisconsin* 40 Bd
Plympton, *Nova Scotia* 32 Gj
Plynlimon, *Wales* 63 Eh
Plzeň, *Czechoslovakia* 68 Ed
Pobedy, Pik, *China* 78 Hd
Pobla de Segur, *Spain* 71 Fa
Pocahontas, *Arkansas* 45 Bb
Pocahontas, *Virginia* 45 Gb
Pocatello, *Idaho* 47 Gd
Pochinki, *U.S.S.R.* 81 Gc
Pochutla, *Mexico* 50 Ed
Podkagernoye, *U.S.S.R.* 79 Rb
Podkamennaya Tunguska, *U.S.S.R.* 78 Hd
Podlubovo, *U.S.S.R.* 81 Mc
Podolsk, *U.S.S.R.* 80 Kd
Pogamasing, *Ontario* 34 Jf
Poincaré, L., *Quebec* 33 Ob
Pointe-à-Maurier, *Quebec* 33 Nc
Pointe-à-Pitre, *Guadeloupe* 51 Gc
Pointe au Baril Station, *Ont.* 34 Kg
Pointe-au-Pic, *Quebec* 32 Bf
Pointe-aux-Anglais, *Que.* 32 Ed
Pointe-aux-Trembles, *Que.* 35 Rg
Pointe-Bleue, *Quebec* 35 Sd
Pointe-Claire, *Quebec* 35 Rg
Pointe de l'Ouest, *Que.* 32 Hd
Pointe-du-Chêne, *N.B.* 32 Hg
Pointe du Renard, *Que.* 33 Ld
Pointe du Sud-Ouest, *Que.* 32 Jd
Point Edward, *Ontario* 34 Hj
Pointe Ouest, *Miquelon I.* 33 Qg
Pointe-Verte, *N.B.* 32 Gf
Point L., *N.W.T.* 38 Rc
Point Leamington, *Nfld.* 33 Rd
Point Pelee Nat. Park, *Ont.* 34 Hk
Point Prim, *P.E.I.* 32 Jg
Point Tupper, *N.S.* 33 Lh
Poisson Blanc, L., *Quebec* 35 Pf
Poitiers, *France* 72 Dc
Poitou, *France* 72 Cc
Poix, *France* 72 Db
Pokaakku, *Pacific Ocean* 102 Ff
Pokhara, *Nepal* 91 Da
Pokka, *Finland* 66 Lb
Pokrovsk, *U.S.S.R.* 81 Fd
Pokrovskoe, *U.S.S.R.* 79 Mb
Pokrovskoye, *U.S.S.R.* 81 Dg
Pola de Laviana, *Spain* 70 Ca
Poland, *Europe* 60 Mf
Polesk, *U.S.S.R.* 67 Jj
Polevskoi, *U.S.S.R.* 81 Qb
Polgahawela, *Sri Lanka* 88 Fg
Polgar, *Hungary* 69 Je
Poli, *Cameroun* 99 Hg
Políaigos, *Greece* 77 Ef
Policastro, G. di, *Italy* 75 Ef
Poligny, *France* 72 Fc
Polillo, *Philippines* 83 Hh
Pólinos. *See* Políaigos
Polis, *Cyprus* 94 Ab
Pollensa, *Balearic Islands* 71 Gc
Pollockville, *Alberta* 36 Fg
Polotsk, *Byelorussia* 80 Fd
Polson, *Montana* 47 Fb
Poltava, *Ukraine* 80 Jg
Poltimore, *Quebec* 35 Pg
Põltsamaa, *Estonia* 67 Mg
Poluostrov Buzachi, *Kazakh.* 78 Ed
Põlva, *Estonia* 67 Mg
Polwarth, *Saskatchewan* 36 Le
Polynesia, *Pacific Ocean* 102 Jk
Pomań, *Argentina* 54 Cc
Pombal, *Brazil* 53 Ke
Pombal, *Portugal* 70 Ac
Pombetsu, *Japan* 86 Hc
Pommersche Bucht, *E. Germany* 68 Fa
Pomorie, *Bulgaria* 76 Fc
Pomos, Pt., *Cyprus* 94 Ab
Pompey's Pillar, *Montana* 46 Dc
Pomquet, *Nova Scotia* 33 Lh
Ponape, *Caroline Islands* 102 Eg
Ponass L., *Saskatchewan* 37 Of
Ponca City, *Oklahoma* 49 Jd
Ponce, *Puerto Rico* 51 Fc
Poncheville, L., *Quebec* 35 Ob
Pondicherry, *India* 88 Ef
Pond Inlet, *N.W.T.* 31 Mc
Ponferrada, *Spain* 70 Ba
Pong Qu, *China* 89 Gc
Ponoka, *Alberta* 36 Df
Ponoy, *U.S.S.R.* 78 Db
Pons, *France* 72 Cd
Pons, *Spain* 71 Fb
Ponta Grossa, *Brazil* 54 Fc
Pont-Audemer, *France* 72 Db
Pontax, R., *Quebec* 35 Ma
Pontbriand B., *Quebec* 32 Kc
Pontchartrain, L., *Louisiana* 49 Mg
Pontchâteau, *France* 72 Bc
Pont d'Ain, *France* 72 Fc
Ponte, *Switzerland* 65 Eb
Ponte da Barca, *Portugal* 70 Ab
Ponte de Sôr, *Portugal* 70 Ac
Ponteix, *Saskatchewan* 36 Kj
Ponte Nova, *Brazil* 53 Jh
Pontevedra, *Spain* 70 Aa
Pontiac, *Illinois* 49 Nb
Pontiac, *Michigan* 40 Ed
Pontianak, *Borneo (Kalimantan)* 83 El
Pontivy, *France* 72 Bb
Pont-Lafrance, *N.B.* 32 Hf
Pontoise, *France* 72 Eb
Ponton, *Manitoba* 37 Sd
Pontotoc, *Mississippi* 45 Cc
Pontresina, *Switzerland* 65 Eb
Pontrilas, *Saskatchewan* 37 Ne
Pont-Rouge, *Quebec* 35 Tf
Ponts, le, *Switzerland* 65 Bb
Pontypool, *Ontario* 35 Mh
Pontypool, *Wales* 63 Ej
Pontypridd, *Wales* 63 Ej
Ponza, *Italy* 75 De
Poole, *England* 63 Fk
Poona, *India* 88 De
Pooncarie, *N.S.W.* 57 Hf
Poopo, *Bolivia* 52 Dg
Poopo, L., *Bolivia* 52 Dg
Popa, *Burma* 89 Jd
Popayán, *Colombia* 52 Bc
Poperinge, *Belgium* 64 Ad
Poplar, *Montana* 46 Ea
Poplar Bluff, *Missouri* 45 Bb
Poplarfield, *Manitoba* 37 Uh
Poplar Point, *Manitoba* 37 Uh
Poplar Pt., *Manitoba* 37 Uf
Poplar R., *Manitoba* 37 Uf
Poplarville, *Mississippi* 45 Ce
Popocatapetl, *Mexico* 50 Ed
Popokabaka, *Zaire* 96 Df
Popovača, *Yugoslavia* 74 Fc
Poppel, *Belgium* 64 Dc
Porahat, *India* 91 Ed
Porbandar, *India* 88 Cd
Porcher I., *B.C.* 39 Hj
Porcupine Hills, *Alberta* 36 Ch
Porcupine Hills, *Manitoba/Sask.* 37 Qf
Porcupine Plain, *Sask.* 37 Of
Porcupine R., *Y.T.* 38 Db
Poreč, *Yugoslavia* 74 Dc
Pori, *Finland* 67 Jf
Porirua, *New Zealand* 55 Ed
Porjus, *Sweden* 66 Hc
Porkhov, *U.S.S.R.* 80 Fc
Porkkala, *Finland* 67 Lg
Porlamar, *Margarita I., Venezuela* 52 Ea
Pornic, *France* 72 Bc
Poronaysk, *U.S.S.R.* 79 Pd
Póros, *Greece* 77 Df
Porquis Junction, *Ontario* 34 Kd
Porsanger Fd., *Norway* 66 La
Porsanger Halvøya, *Norway* 66 La
Porsgrund, *Norway* 67 Cg
Portachuelo, *Bolivia* 52 Eg
Porta Cordon, *Venezuela* 52 Ca
Port Adelaide, *S. Australia* 57 Gf
Portadown, *N. Ireland* 63 Cf
Portage, *P.E.I.* 32 Hg
Portage, *Wisconsin* 40 Bd
Portage I., *N.B.* 32 Gf
Portage la Prairie, *Man.* 37 Tj
Portageville, *New York* 44 Aa
Portal, *N. Dakota* 46 Fa
Port Alberni, *B.C.* 39 Ll
Port Albert, *Ontario* 34 Jj
Portalegre, *Portugal* 70 Bc
Portales, *New Mexico* 48 Fe
Port-Alfred, *Quebec* 32 Be
Port Alice, *B.C.* 39 Kk
Port Allen, *Louisiana* 45 Be
Port Antonio, *Jamaica* 51 Dc
Portarlington, *Eire* 63 Cg
Port Arthur, *Texas* 49 Lh
Port Augusta, *S. Australia* 57 Gf
Port au Port & B., *Nfld.* 33 Oe
Port au Port Pen., *Nfld.* 33 Ne
Port-au-Prince, *Haiti* 51 Ec
Port Blair, *Andaman Islands* 89 Hf
Port Blandford, *Nfld.* 33 Se
Port Bruce, *Ontario* 34 Kk
Port Burwell, *Ontario* 34 Kk
Port Carling, *Ontario* 35 Lg
Port-Cartier, *Quebec* 32 Fc
Port-Cartier-Ouest, *Quebec* 32 Fc
Port Chalmers, *N. Zealand* 55 Cf

Port Chester, New York 44 Db
Port Clements, B.C. 39 Gj
Port Clinton, Ohio 40 Ee
Port Colborne, Ontario 35 Lk
Port Coquitlam, B.C. 39 Ml
Port Cornwallis, Andaman Islands 89 Hf
Port Credit, Ontario 35 Lj
Port Dalhousie, Ontario 35 Lj
Port-Daniel, Quebec 32 He
Port Darwin, Falkland Is. 54 Eh
Port de Paix, Haiti 51 Eb
Port Dickson, Pen. Malaysia 87 Cf
Port Douglas, Queensland 57 Jc
Port Dover, Ontario 34 Kk
Port Dufferin, Nova Scotia 33 Kj
Port Edward, B.C. 39 Hh
Portel, Brazil 53 Gd
Port Elgin, New Brunswick 32 Hg
Port Elgin, Ontario 34 Jh
Port Elizabeth, Cape Prov. 95 Df
Port Ellen, Scotland 62 Ce
Porter L., N.W.T. 38 Ue
Porter L., Saskatchewan 39 Ug
Porter Landing, B.C. 39 Hf
Port Felix, Nova Scotia 33 Lh
Port-Francqui. See Ilebo
Port George, Nova Scotia 32 Gj
Port Gibson, Mississippi 49 Mg
Port Greville, Nova Scotia 32 Hh
Port Harcourt, Nigeria 98 Gh
Port Hardy, B.C. 39 Kk
Port Hastings, N.S. 33 Lh
Port Hawkesbury, N.S. 33 Lh
Port Hedland, W. Australia 56 Cd
Porthmadog, Wales 63 Eh
Port Hood, N.S. 33 Lh
Port Hope, Michigan 40 Ed
Port Hope, Ontario 35 Mj
Port Hope Simpson, Newfoundland 33 Qa
Port Huron, Michigan 40 Ed
Portimão, Portugal 70 Ad
Port Jackson, N.S.W. 57 Kf
Port Jervis, New York 44 Cb
Port Kembla, N.S.W. 57 Kf
Portland, Arkansas 45 Bd
Portland, Maine 32 Bk
Portland, Ontario 35 Oh
Portland, Oregon 47 Bc
Portland, Victoria 57 Hg
Portland Bill, England 63 Fk
Portland Can., Alaska/B.C. 39 Hh
Portland Creek Pond, Nfld. 33 Pc
Portland Inlet, B.C. 39 Hh
Portland Point, Jamaica 51 Dc
Port Laoise, Eire 63 Cg
Port Lavaca, Texas 48 Jh
Port Lincoln, S. Australia 57 Gf
Port Loko, Sierra Leone 98 Cg
Port Loring, Ontario 34 Lg
Port McNicoll, Ontario 34 Lh
Port Macquarie, N.S.W. 57 Kf
Port Maitland, Nova Scotia 32 Fk
Port Maitland, Ontario 35 Lk
Port Manvers Run, Nfld. 31 Nf
Port Medway, Nova Scotia 32 Hj
Port-Menier, Quebec 32 Hd
Port Moody, B.C. 39 Ml
Port Moody, B.C. 39 Jl
Port Moresby, Papua New Guinea 57 Ja
Port Morien, N.S. 33 Ng
Port Mouton, Nova Scotia 32 Hk
Portneuf, Quebec 35 Tf
Portneuf, L., Quebec 32 Bd
Portneuf, R., Quebec 32 Ce
Portneuf-sur-Mer, Que. 32 Ce
Port Nolloth, Cape Prov. 95 Be
Port Norris, New Jersey 40 Jf
Port-Nouveau-Québec (George River), Quebec 31 Nf
Porto, Portugal 70 Ab
Porto Acre, Brazil 52 De
Pôrto Alegre, Brazil 54 Fd
Porto Alexandre, Angola 95 Ac
Porto Arroia, Mozambique 97 Gg
Portobello, Panama 51 De
Porto Botte, Sardinia 75 Bf
Porto Camargo, Brazil 53 Gh
Porto d'Ascoli, Italy 74 Dd
Porto de Mos, Brazil 53 Gd
Porto de Moz, Portugal 70 Ac
Porto Empedocle, Sicily 75 Dg
Porto Esperança, Brazil 53 Fg
Porto Espiridião, Brazil 52 Fg
Porto Franco, Brazil 53 He
Port of Spain, Trinidad 52 Ea
Port Okha, India 88 Cd
Portola, California 47 Cf
Pôrto Lucena, Brazil 54 Fc
Porto Mendes, Brazil 53 Gh
Porto Nacional, Brazil 53 Hf
Porto Novo, Benin 98 Fg
Porto Novo, India 88 Ef
Port Ontario, New York 44 Ba
Pôrto Seguro, Brazil 53 Kg
Porto Torres, Sardinia 75 Be
Porto Vecchio, Corsica 75 Be
Porto Vêlho, Brazil 52 Ee
Portoviejo, Ecuador 52 Ad
Portpatrick, Scotland 63 Df
Port Pegasus, New Zealand 55 Ag
Port Perry, Ontario 35 Mh
Port Phillip B., Victoria 57 Hg
Port Pirie, S. Australia 57 Gf
Port Pleasant, New Jersey 40 Je
Portree, Scotland 62 Cc
Portreeve, Saskatchewan 36 Jh
Port Renfrew, B.C. 39 Ll
Port Rexton, Nfld. 33 Te
Port Rowan, Ontario 34 Kk
Port Royal, Jamaica 51 Dc
Port Royal, S. Carolina 45 Gd
Port Royal Nat. Hist. Park, Nova Scotia 32 Gj
Portrush, N. Ireland 62 Ce
Port Safaga, Egypt 99 Mc
Port Said, Egypt 99 Mb
Port Saint Johns, Cape Prov. 95 Df
Port Saunders, Nfld. 33 Pc
Port Shepstone, Natal 95 Ef
Port Simpson, B.C. 39 Hh
Portsmouth, England 63 Gk
Portsmouth, Ohio 40 Ef
Portsmouth, Virginia 45 Jb
Port Stanley, Ontario 34 Jk
Port Sudan, Sudan 99 Ne
Port Tampa City, Florida 45 Fg
Port Taufiq, Egypt 99 Mc
Portugal, W. Europe 61 Ej
Portugal Cove, Nfld. 33 Uf
Portugalia, Angola 96 Ef
Portuguese Guinea. See Guinea-Bissau
Portumna, Eire 63 Bg
Port Union, Nfld. 33 Te
Port-Vendres, France 73 Ee
Port Victoria, Kenya 97 Gd
Port Washington, Wisconsin 40 Cd
Port Weld, Pen. Malaysia 87 Cf
Port Weller, Ontario 40 Gd
Port Williams, N.S. 32 Hh
Poru Tso, China 89 Fb
Porvenir, Chile 54 Bh
Porvoo, Finland 67 Lf
Posadas, Argentina 54 Ec
Posadowsky D., Antarctica 104 Gc
Poschiavo, Switzerland 65 Fb
Posen. See Poznan
Poshkokagan L., Ontario 37 Oa
Posht-e-Badam, Iran 93 Gc
Poso, Celebes (Sulawesi) 83 Hl
Poso Danau, Celebes (Sulawesi) 83 Gl
Possession, Antarctica 104 Lb
Possum Kingdom L., Texas 49 Hf
Post, Texas 48 Gf
Poste-de-la-Baleine, Que. 31 Mf
Poste M. Cortier, Algeria 98 Fd
Poste Weygand, Algeria 98 Fd
Posušje, Yugoslavia 74 Fd
Potapovo, U.S.S.R. 78 Hb
Potchefstroom, Transvaal 95 De
Poteau, Oklahoma 49 Ke
Potemkino, U.S.S.R. 81 Ge
Potenza, Italy 75 Ee
Poti, Georgia, U.S.S.R. 78 Dd
Potiskum, Nigeria 99 Hf
Potomac R., Maryland/W. Virginia 44 Ac
Potosí, Bolivia 52 Dg
Potosi, Missouri 45 Bb
Potrerillos, Chile 54 Cc
Potsdam, East Germany 68 Eb
Potter, Ontario 34 Kd
Pottstown, Pennsylvania 40 Je
Pottsville, Pennsylvania 40 He
Pouce Coupé, B.C. 39 Nh
Pouch Cove, Nfld. 33 Uf
Poughkeepsie, New York 40 Ke
Poulin-de-Courval, L., Que. 32 Be
Pouso Alegre, Brazil 53 Ff
Pouso Alegre, Brazil 53 Hh
Poutrincourt, L., Quebec 35 Qc
Povenets, U.S.S.R. 78 Cb
Poverty B., New Zealand 55 Gc
Povoa de Varzim, Portugal 70 Ab
Povorino, U.S.S.R. 81 Fe
Povungnituk, Quebec 31 Mf
Povungnituk, R., Quebec 31 Me
Powassan, Ontario 35 Lf
Powder R., Montana 42 Eb
Powder River Ra., Montana 46 Ec
Powderville, Montana 46 Ec
Powell, Lake, Utah 42 Dd
Powell Creek, N. Terr. 57 Fc
Powell L., B.C. 39 Lk
Powell Mts., Pa./Va. 45 Fb
Powell River, B.C. 39 Ll
Powys, Wales 63 Eh
Poyang
Poza de la Sal, Spain 70 Da
Požarevac, Yugoslavia 76 Cb
Požega, Yugoslavia 76 Ab
Poznan, Poland 69 Gb
Pozo Almonte, Chile 54 Cb
Pozoblanco, Spain 70 Cc
Prachin Buri, Thailand 87 Cd
Prado, Brazil 53 Kg
Praga, Poland 69 Jb
Prague. See Praha
Praha, Czechoslovakia 68 Fc
Praid, Romania 76 Ea
Prainha, Brazil 52 Ee
Prainha, Brazil 53 Gd
Prairie, Queensland 57 Hd
Prairie du Chien, Wisconsin 49 Ma
Prairie du Sac, Wisconsin 40 Bd
Prairie River, Sask. 37 Pf
Prairies, L. des, Quebec 32 Bc
Prairies, R. des, Quebec 35 Rj
Pratapgarth, India 91 Cc
Prathet, Thailand 87 Cd
Prato, Italy 74 Cd
Pratt, Kansas 49 Hd
Pratt, Manitoba 37 Tj
Pratt City, Alabama 45 Dd
Pravia, Spain 70 Ba
Preeceville, Saskatchewan 37 Pg
Pregolya, R., U.S.S.R. 67 Jj
Preissac, Quebec 35 Md
Preissac L., Quebec 35 Md
Prelate, Saskatchewan 36 Hh
Premio, Quebec 32 Gb
Prenay, Lithuania 67 Kj
Prendergast, Saskatchewan 36 Jd
Prentice, Wisconsin 40 Ac
Prerov, Czechoslovakia 69 Gd
Prescott, Arizona 47 Gh
Prescott, Ontario 35 Ph
Presidente Hermes, Brazil 52 Ef
President R. Saénz-Pena, Argentina 54 Dc
Prešov, Czechoslovakia 69 Jd
Prespansko Jezero, L., Albania 77 Cd
Presque Isle, Maine 32 Dg
Presqu'ile Prov. Pk., Ontario 35 Nj
Press, Quebec 35 Od
Pressburg. See Bratislava
Press L., Ontario 36 La
Přeštice, Czechoslovakia 68 Ed
Preston, England 63 Fg
Preston, Idaho 48 Ba
Preston, Minnesota 46 Ld
Prestwick, Scotland 62 De
Pretoria, Transvaal 95 De
Pretty Boy L., Maryland 44 Bc
Pribilof Is., Bering Sea 43 Vm
Příbram, Czechoslovakia 68 Fd
Price, Quebec 32 De
Price, Utah 48 Bc
Price I., British Columbia 39 Jj
Price R., Utah 48 Bc
Priego, Spain 70 Cd
Prieska, Cape Province 95 Ce
Prignitz, East Germany 68 Db
Prijedor, Yugoslavia 74 Fc
Prijepolje, Yugoslavia 76 Bc
Prilep, Yugoslavia 76 Cd
Priluki, Ukraine 80 Hf
Primate, Saskatchewan 36 Hf
Primrose, R., Y.T. 38 Fe
Primrose L., Sask. 36 Hd
Prince, Saskatchewan 36 Jf
Prince Albert, Cape Prov. 95 Cf
Prince Albert, Sask. 37 Me
Prince Albert Mts., Antarc. 104 Lb
Prince Albert Nat. Park, Sask. 36 Ld
Prince Albert Pen., N.W.T. 30 Hc
Prince Albert Sd., N.W.T. 38 Pa
Prince Alfred C., N.W.T. 30 Gc
Prince Charles I., N.W.T. 31 Md
Prince Edward B., Ontario 35 Oj
Prince Edward Is., Indian Oc. 100 Bj
Prince Edward Island, Canada 31 Nh
Prince Edward Island National Park, P.E.I. 32 Jg
Prince Edward Pt., Ontario 35 Oj
Prince George, B.C. 39 Mj
Prince Gustaf Adolf Sea, Northwest Territories 30 Jb
Prince Harald Ld., Antarc. 104 Db
Prince of Wales, C., Alaska 43 Wl
Prince of Wales I., Alaska 30 Ff
Prince of Wales I., N.W.T. 30 Jc
Prince of Wales I., Qnsld. 57 Hb
Prince of Wales Strait, N.W.T. 30 Hc
Prince Patrick I., N.W.T. 30 Hb
Prince Regent Inlet, N.W.T. 31 Kc
Prince Rupert, B.C. 39 Hh
Princes Lake, Ontario 40 Gc
Princess Astrid Ld., Antarc. 104 Cb
Princess Charlotte B., Queensland 57 Hb
Princess Elizabeth Land, Antarctica 104 Fb
Princess Ragnhild Ld., Antarctica 104 Db
Princess Royal I., B.C. 39 Jj
Princeton, B.C. 39 Nl
Princeton, Illinois 49 Nb
Princeton, Indiana 45 Da
Princeton, Kentucky 49 Od
Princeton, Wisconsin 40 Bd
Princeville, Quebec 35 Tf
Prince William Sound, Alaska 43 Yl
Principe Chan., B.C. 39 Jj
Principe da Beira, Brazil 52 Ef
Príncipe I., G. of Guinea 96 Bd
Pringles, Argentina 54 Df
Prins Karls Forland, Arctic Ocean 78 Aa
Prinsta, B., Quebec 33 Ld
Prinzapolca, Nicaragua 51 Cd
Pripet Marshes, Byelorussia 80 Ee
Pripyat', Byelorussia 80 Ff
Pristina, Yugoslavia 76 Cc
Pritzwalk, East Germany 68 Eb
Privolnoye, U.S.S.R. 81 He
Prizren, Yugoslavia 76 Cc
Prizzi, Sicily 75 Dg
Procter, British Columbia 39 Pl
Progreso, Mexico 50 Gc
Prokop'yevsk, U.S.S.R. 78 Hc
Prokuplje, Yugoslavia 76 Cc
Proliv Longa, U.S.S.R. 79 Sb
Prome, Burma 89 Je
Prophet, R., B.C. 39 Mf
Prophet River, B.C. 39 Mf
Propria, Brazil 53 Kf
Proserpine, Queensland 57 Jd
Prospector, Manitoba 37 Qe
Provence, France 73 Fe
Providence, Kentucky 45 Db
Providence, Rhode Island 40 Le
Providence Bay, Ontario 34 Hg
Providence I., Indian Ocean 100 De
Provins, France 72 Eb
Provo, Utah 48 Bb
Provost, Alberta 36 Gf
Prozor, Yugoslavia 74 Fd
Prudentopolis, Brazil 54 Fc
Prudhoe Bay, Alaska 43 Yk
Prudhoe Ld., Greenland 41 Qb
Prud'homme, Sask. 37 Mf
Prüm, West Germany 68 Bc
Prut, U.S.S.R. 80 Fj
Przasnysz, Poland 69 Jb
Przemyśl, Poland 69 Kd
Przhevalsk, Kirghizia 78 Gd
Psará, Greece 77 Ee
Pskov, U.S.S.R. 80 Fc
Pskovskoye Oz., U.S.S.R. 80 Fb
Ptuj, Yugoslavia 74 Eb
Puán, Argentina 54 De
Pubnico, Nova Scotia 32 Gk
Pucacuro, Peru 52 Bd
Pucallpa, Peru 52 Ce
Puchezh, U.S.S.R. 81 Fb
Puchow. See Yongji
Puck, Poland 69 Ha
Pudasjärvi, Finland 66 Md
Pudukkottai, India 88 Ef
Puebla, Mexico 50 Ed
Puebla Bonito, New Mexico 42 Ed
Puebla de Alcocer, Spain 70 Cc
Puebla de Sanabria, Spain 70 Ba
Puebla de Trives, Spain 70 Ba
Pueblo, Colorado 48 Ec
Pueblo Hundido, Chile 54 Cc
Puelches, Argentina 54 Ce
Puente Aréas, Spain 70 Aa
Puente Caldelas, Spain 70 Aa
Puentedeume, Spain 70 Aa
Pu'er, China 82 Df
Puerco, R., New Mexico 48 De
Puerto Aisen, Chile 54 Bg
Puerto Armuelles, Panama 52 Ab
Puerto Asis, Colombia 52 Bc
Puerto Ayacucho, Venez. 52 Db
Puerto Barrios, Guatemala 50 Gd
Puerto Bermudez, Peru 52 Cf
Puerto Berrío, Colombia 52 Cb
Puerto Cabello, Venezuela 52 Da
Puerto Cabezas, Nicaragua 51 Cd
Puerto Carreño, Colombia 52 Db
Puerto Carrizal, Chile 54 Bc
Puerto Casado, Paraguay 54 Eb
Puerto Chicama, Peru 52 Be
Puerto Coig, Argentina 54 Ch
Puerto Colombia, Colombia 52 Ca
Puerto Córdoba, Colombia 52 Dd
Puerto Cortés, Honduras 51 Bc
Puerto Cumarebo, Venez. 52 Da
Puerto de S. Maria, Spain 70 Bd
Puerto Eten, Peru 52 Be
Puerto Grether, Bolivia 52 Eg
Puerto Harberton, Arg. 54 Ch
Puerto Heath, Bolivia 52 Df
Puerto La Cruz, Venezuela 52 Ea
Puerto Leguizamo, Colombia 52 Cd
Puertollano, Spain 70 Cc
Puerto Lobos, Argentina 54 Cf
Puerto Madryn, Argentina 54 Cf
Puerto Maldonado, Peru 52 Df
Puerto Montt, Chile 54 Bf
Puerto Morelos, Mexico 50 Gc
Puerto Natales, Chile 54 Bh
Puerto Nuevo, Colombia 52 Db
Puerto Pirámides, Arg. 54 Df
Puerto Plata, Dom. Rep. 51 Ec
Puerto Princesa, Philippines 83 Gj
Puerto Quellen, Chile 54 Bf
Puerto Quijarro, Bolivia 52 Fg
Puerto Rico, W. Indies 51 Fc
Puerto Saavedra, Chile 54 Be
Puerto Suarez, Bolivia 53 Fg
Puerto Sucre, Bolivia 52 Df
Puerto Varas, Chile 54 Bf
Puerto Victoria, Peru 52 Ce
Puerto Villamizar, Colombia 52 Cb
Puerto Visser, Argentina 54 Cg
Puerto Wilches, Colombia 52 Cb
Pueyrredón, L., Argentina 54 Bg
Pugachev, U.S.S.R. 81 Jd
Pugal, India 90 Cf
Puget, France 73 Ge
Puget Sound, Washington 42 Bb
Puglia, Italy 75 Fe
Pugwash, N.S. 32 Jh
Pugwash Junction, N.S. 32 Jh
Pühalepa, Estonia 67 Kg
Puigcerdá, Spain 71 Fa
Puimro, Brazil 53 Gc
Pukaki, L., New Zealand 55 Cf
Pukapuka, Pacific Ocean 102 Jj
Pukapuka, Tuamotu Arch. 103 Mj
Pukaskwa Nat. Park, Ontario 40 Da
Pukatawagan & L., Man. 37 Qc
Pukchong, Korea 82 Jb
Pukekohe, New Zealand 55 Eb
Pula, Yugoslavia 74 Dc
Pulacayo, Bolivia 52 Dh
Pulandian Wan, China 84 Kc
Pulap, Caroline Islands 102 Dg
Pulaski, New York 40 Hd
Pulaski, Tennessee 45 Dc
Pulaski, Virginia 45 Gb
Pulicat, India 88 Ff
Pulkkila, Finland 66 Ld
Pultneyville, New York 44 Ba
Puma, Tanzania 97 Ge
Puma Yumco, China 89 Hc
Puná, Ecuador 52 Ad
Puncak Jaya, Mt., Indonesia 83 Ll
Punch, Kashmir 90 Dd
Punchaw, B.C. 39 Mj
Pundri, India 90 Ef
Punjab, India 90 De
Punjab, Pakistan 88 Db
Punnichy, Saskatchewan 37 Ng
Puno, Peru 52 Cg
Punta Alta, Argentina 54 De
Punta Arenas, Chile 54 Bh
Punta Colorado, Chile 54 Bc
Punta del Faro, Sicily 75 Ef
Punta de Pedras, Brazil 53 Hd
Punta Gorda, Belize 51 Bc
Puntarenas, Costa Rica 51 Ce
Puntudo, Argentina 54 Cg
Punxsutawney, Pennsylvania 44 Ab
Puolanka, Finland 66 Md
Puquio, Peru 52 Cf
Puquios, Chile 54 Cc
Purang Chaka, China 89 Fb
Purcell Mts., B.C. 39 Pk
Purgatoire R., Colorado 48 Fd
Puri, India 89 Ge
Purificación, Colombia 52 Cc
Purna, India 88 Ee
Purnea, India 91 Fc
Purple Springs, Alberta 36 Fj
Pursat, Kampuchea 87 Cd
Purulia, India 91 Fd
Purus, Brazil 52 De
Purvis, Mississippi 45 Ce
Purwa, India 91 Cb
Pusan, Korea 82 Jc
Pusht-e-Kuh, Iran 92 Ec
Pushthrough, Nfld. 33 Qf
Pusticamica, L., Quebec 35 Oc
Putao, Burma 89 Jc
Putao. See Fort Hertz
Putaruru, New Zealand 55 Ec
Putbus, East Germany 68 Ea
Putian, China 85 Jk
Putignano, Italy 75 Fe
Putnam, Connecticut 44 Eb
Putnok, Hungary 69 Jd
Putorana, Gory, U.S.S.R. 79 Jb
Puttalam, Sri Lanka 88 Eg
Putte, Belgium 64 Cc
Putte, Netherlands 64 Cc
Putten, Netherlands 64 Db
Putumayo, Colombia 52 Cd
Putussibau, Borneo (Kalimantan) 83 Fk
Puula Vesi, Finland 67 Mf
Puurs, Belgium 64 Cc
Puy, le, France 73 Ed
Puyallup, Washington 47 Bb
Puy-de-Dôme, France 72 Ed
Pyapon, Burma 89 Je
Pyatistennoye, U.S.S.R. 79 Rb
Pyhä Järvi, Finland 66 Le
Pyhä Järvi, Finland 67 Kf
Pyhäntä, Finland 66 Md
Pyinmana, Burma 89 Je
Pyŏngyang, N. Korea 82 Jc
Pyramid L., Nevada 47 De
Pyramid Pk., California 47 Cf
Pyrénées, Mts., France/Sp. 71 Ea
Pyrénées Atlantiques, France 73 Gd
Pyrénées-Orientales, France 73 Ee
Pyrzyce, Poland 68 Fb
Pythonga, L., Quebec 35 Of
Pyu, Burma 89 Je
Pyzdry, Poland 69 Gb

Q

Qabatiya, Israel 94 De
Qafar, Arabia 92 Dd
Qaiya, Arabia 92 Ee
Qala Bist., Afghanistan 93 Hc
Qal'at al Akhdar, Arabia 92 Cd
Qal'at Bīshah, Arabia 92 De
Qal'at ed Dab'a, Jordan 94 Ef
Qal'at el Marqah, Syria 94 Db
Qalat es Sālihīya, Syria 92 Dc
Qal'at Uneiza, Jordan 94 Dg
Qalqiliya, Jordan 94 Ce
Qamar B., S. Yemen 93 Ff
Qamdo, China 82 Cd
Qara, Egypt 99 Lc
Qarachuk, Syria 92 Db
Qardaha, Syria 94 Eb
Qartaba, Lebanon 94 Dc
Qasab, United Arab Emirates 93 Gd
Qasim, Arabia 92 Dd
Qasr Amij, Iraq 92 Dc
Qasr el Azraq, Jordan 94 Ef
Qasr e Qand, Iran 93 Hd
Qasr ibn Aliya, Arabia 92 Dd
Qasr-i-Shīrīn, Iran 92 Ec
Qa'taba, Yemen 92 Dg
Qatana, Syria 94 Ed
Qatar, Persian Gulf 93 Fd
Qatīf, Al, Arabia 92 Ed
Qayen, Iran 93 Gc
Qazvīin, Iran 93 Fb
Qena, Egypt 99 Mc
Qeshm, Iran 93 Gd
Qeys, Iran 93 Fd
Qeziot, Israel 94 Cg
Qilian Shan, China 82 Cc
Qingdao, China 84 Kd
Qinghai Hu, China 82 Dc
Qingjiang, China 84 Jf
Qingjiang, China 85 Gh
Qingliang Jiang, China 84 Hd
Qing Xian, China 84 Hc
Qingyang, China 84 Cd
Qingyuan, China 85 Fl
Qinhuangdao, China 84 Jc
Qin Ling Shan, China 84 Ed
Qinyang, China 84 Fe
Qiongshan, Hainan, China 85 En
Qiongzhou Haixia, China 85 Dm
Qiqihar, China 82 Ha
Qishan, China 84 Ce
Qishran, Arabia 92 Ce
Qom, Iran 93 Fc
Qotur, Iran 92 Db
Qoz Bal'Air, Arabia 92 Df
Quabbin Res., Mass. 44 Da
Quaco Hd., N.B. 32 Gh
Quakenbrück, W. Germany 68 Bb
Quang Tri, Vietnam 83 Eg
Quantz L., Ontario 34 Ea
Quanzhou, China 85 Jk
Quanzhou, China 85 Ej
Qu'Appelle, Sask. 37 Oh
Qu'Appelle R., Sask. 37 Ph
Qu'Appelle River Dam, Sask. 36 Lg
Quaraí, Brazil 54 Ed
Quarryville, N.B. 32 Gg
Quatre Bras, Belgium 64 Cd
Quatsino, B.C. 39 Kk
Qubeiyat, Lebanon 94 Ec
Quchan, Iran 93 Gb
Québec, Canada 31 Mg
Québec, Quebec 32 Ag
Québec City Airport, Quebec 35 Tf
Queen, C., N.W.T. 31 Me
Queen Alexandra Range, Antarctica 104 Ka
Queen Anne, Maryland 44 Cc
Queen Bess, Mt., B.C. 39 Lk
Queen Charlotte, B.C. 39 Gj
Queen Charlotte Bay, Falkland Islands 54 Dh
Queen Charlotte Is., B.C. 39 Gj
Queen Charlotte Sound, B.C. 30 Gg
Queen Charlotte Str., B.C. 39 Kk
Queen Elizabeth Is., N.W.T. 30 Ja
Queen Mary Land, Antarctica 104 Gc
Queen Maud G., N.W.T. 38 Wa
Queen Maud Ld., Antarc. 104 Cb
Queen Maud Range, Antarc. 104 Pa
Queen's Chan., N. Terr. 56 Eb
Queensland, Australia 57 Hd
Queensport, Nova Scotia 33 Lh
Queenstown, Alberta 36 Eh
Queenstown, Cape Province 95 Df
Queenstown, New Zealand 55 Bf
Queenstown, Tasmania 57 Jh
Queimadas, Brazil 53 Kf
Quelimane, Mozambique 95 Fc
Quemu Quemú, Argentina 54 De
Quénonisca, L., Quebec 35 Ob
Quequén, Argentina 54 Ee
Querétaro, Mexico 50 Dc
Quesnel, B.C. 39 Mj
Quesnel L., B.C. 39 Nj
Quetico, Ontario 37 Mb
Quetico L., Ontario 36 Lb
Quetico Prov. Park, Ont. 36 Lb
Quetta, Pakistan 88 Cb
Quévillon, L., Quebec 35 Oc
Quezaltenango, Guatemala 50 Fe
Quezon City, Philippines 83 Hh
Quibdo, Colombia 52 Bb
Quibell, Ontario 36 Ja
Quiberon B. de, France 72 Bc
Quiet L., Y.T. 38 Ge
Quiévrain, Belgium 64 Bd
Quigley, Alberta 36 Gb
Quilá, Mexico 50 Cc
Quilca, Peru 52 Cg
Quilino, Argentina 54 Dd
Quillabamba, Peru 52 Cf
Quillan, France 73 Ee
Quill Lake, Saskatchewan 37 Nf
Quill Ls., Saskatchewan 37 Ng
Quillota, Chile 54 Bd
Quilon, India 88 Eg
Quilpie, Queensland 57 He
Quimper, France 72 Ab
Quimperlé, France 72 Bc
Quince Mil, Peru 52 Cf
Quincy, Illinois 49 Mc
Quincy, Massachusetts 40 Ld
Quines, Argentina 54 Cd
Quiney, Michigan 40 De
Quinnimont, W. Virginia 45 Gb
Quintana de la Serena, Sp. 70 Cc
Quintanar de la Orden, Sp. 70 Dc
Quintana Roo, Mexico 50 Gd
Quinton, Saskatchewan 37 Ng
Quipapa, Brazil 53 Ke
Quiriquire, Venezuela 52 Ea
Quirke L., Ontario 34 Hf
Quiroga, Spain 70 Ba
Quissanga, Mozambique 97 Jg
Quissico, Mozambique 95 Ed
Quitapa, Angola 96 Dg
Quito, Ecuador 52 Bd
Quixadá, Brazil 53 Kd
Quixeramobim, Brazil 53 Ke
Quixinge, Angola 96 Cf
Qujing, China 85 Ak
Qunsuliye, Arabia 92 De
Quorn, Ontario 37 Ma
Quorn, S. Australia 57 Gf
Qurah, Arabia 92 Dd
Quryat, Oman 93 Ge
Qus, Egypt 99 Mc
Qusayir, S. Yemen 93 Ff
Quseir, Egypt 99 Mc
Qusuriya, Arabia 92 De
Quteifa, Syria 94 Ed
Qu Xian, China 85 Jh
Quyon, Quebec 35 Og

R

Raahe, Finland 66 Ld
Raanes Pen., N.W.T. 31 Lb
Raasay, Scotland 62 Cc
Rab, Yugoslavia 74 Ec
Raba, Sumbawa I., Indonesia 83 Gm
Rabast, C. de, Quebec 32 Hd
Rabat, Morocco 98 Db
Rabat Karim, Iran 93 Fb
Rabbit, R., B.C. 38 Kf
Rabbit Lake, Sask. 36 Ke
Rabbitskin, R., N.W.T. 38 Ne
Rabigh, Arabia 92 Ce
Race, The, Conn./New York 44 Db
Rach Gia, Vietnam 87 Dd
Racibórz, Poland 69 Hc
Racine, Wisconsin 40 Cd
Racine-de-Bouleau, R. de la, Quebec 32 Da
Racine L., Ontario 34 Gd
Rada, Yemen 92 Dg
Radak Chain, Marshall Is. 102 Gf
Rădăuti, Romania 80 Dh
Radford, Virginia 45 Gb
Radhanpur, India 88 Dd
Radhwa, Jebel, Arabia 92 Ce
Radisson, Saskatchewan 36 Kf
Radium Hot Springs, B.C. 39 Pk
Radnevo, Bulgaria 76 Ec
Radom, Poland 69 Jc
Radomir, Bulgaria 76 Dc
Radomsko, Poland 69 Hc
Radstadt, Austria 68 Ee
Radviliskis, Lithuania 67 Kj
Radville, Saskatchewan 37 Nj
Radway, Alberta 36 Ed
Radzyń Podlaski, Poland 69 Kc
Rae, N.W.T. 38 Qd
Rae, Mt., Alberta 36 Ch
Rae, R., N.W.T. 38 Pa
Rae Bareli, India 91 Cb
Rae Isthmus, N.W.T. 31 Ld
Rae L., N.W.T. 30 He
Raeside, L., W. Australia 56 De
Raetihi, New Zealand 55 Ec
Rafaela, Argentina 54 Dd
Rafah, Egypt 94 Cf
Rafsanjan, Iran 93 Gc
Rafter, Manitoba 37 Qc
Raga, Sudan 99 Lg
Raghugarh, India 91 Ac
Raghunathpur, India 91 Fd
Raglan, New Zealand 55 Eb
Raglan Range, New Zealand 55 De
Raguba, Libya 99 Jc
Ragunda, Sweden 66 Ge
Ragusa, Sicily 75 Eg
Rahaeng. See Tak
Raiatea, Society Islands 103 Kj
Raichur, India 88 Ee
Raida, S. Yemen 92 Eg
Raiganj, India 91 Gc
Raikot, India 90 De
Raingarh, India 90 Ee
Rainier, Mt., Washington 47 Cb
Rainy L., Ontario/Minn. 31 Kh
Rainy River, Ontario 36 Hb
Raipur, India 88 Fd
Raith, Ontario 37 Na
Raivavae, Tubuai Is. 103 Lk
Raiwind, Pakistan 90 De
Rajahmundry, India 88 Fe
Rajakhera, India 91 Bb
Rajang, Sarawak 83 Fk
Rajanpur, Pakistan 90 Bf
Rajapalaiyam, India 88 Eg
Rajasthan, India 88 Dc
Rajgarh, India 90 Df
Rajkot, India 88 Dd
Rajmahal, India 91 Fc
Rajmahal Hills, India 91 Ec
Rajura, India 88 Ee
Rakahanga, Pacific Oc. 102 Jh
Rakaposhi, Mt., Kashmir 90 Db
Raka Zangbo, China 89 Gc
Rakvere, Estonia 67 Mg
Raleigh, N. Carolina 43 Ld
Raleigh, Nfld. 33 Rb
Raleigh B., N. Carolina 45 Jc
Raley, Alberta 36 Dj
Ralik Chain, Marshall Is. 102 Fg
Ram, Jordan 94 Dh
Ram, R., N.W.T. 38 Me
Rama, Ethiopia 97 Jb
Rama, Israel 94 De
Rama, Saskatchewan 37 Pg
Ramallah, Jordan 94 Df
Ramallo, Argentina 54 Dd
Ramanthapuran, India 88 Eg
Rambouillet, France 72 Db
Ramea Is., Newfoundland 33 Pf
Rameswaram, India 88 Eg
Ramgarh, India 90 Df
Ramgarh, India 91 Cd
Ramgarh, India 91 Ed
Ram Hormuz, Iran 92 Ec
Ramkola, India 91 Dd
Ramla, Israel 94 Cf
Ramnagar, India 91 Cd
Ramnagar, Kashmir 90 Dd
Ramore, Ontario 34 Kd
Ramotswa, Botswana 95 Dd
Rampart House, Y.T. 38 Cb
Ramparts, R., N.W.T. 38 Hb
Rampur, India 89 Fd
Rampur, India 90 Ee
Rampur, India 91 Ba
Rampur Boalia, Bangladesh 91 Gc
Ramree, Burma 89 He
Ramsele, Sweden 66 Ge
Ramsey, Isle of Man 63 Ef
Ramsey, Ontario 34 He
Ramsey I., Wales 63 Dj
Ramsey L., Ontario 34 He
Ramsgate, England 63 Hj
Ramsjö, Sweden 67 Fe
Ramskapelle, Belgium 64 Ac
Ramtha, Jordan 94 Ee

Ramtok, India 88 Ed
Ranaghat, India 91 Gd
Rancagua, Chile 54 Bd
Rance, Belgium 64 Cd
Ranch, Alberta 36 Dc
Rancheria, Y.T. 38 He
Rancheria, R., Y.T. 38 He
Rancheria, R. Lit., B.C. 38 Hf
Ranchi, India 91 Ed
Randazzo, Sicily 75 Eg
Randers, Denmark 67 Dh
Randolph, Vermont 40 Kd
Random I., Nfld. 33 Te
Randsfjord, Norway 66 Df
Ranenburg, U.S.S.R. 81 Ed
Ran Fd., Norway 66 Ec
Ranfurly, Alberta 36 Fe
Ranfurly, New Zealand 55 Cf
Rangamati, Bangladesh 89 Hd
Rangeley, Maine 32 Bj
Ranger, Texas 42 Ge
Ranger L., Ontario 34 Gf
Rangiora, New Zealand 55 De
Rangitaiki, R., N.Z. 55 Fc
Rangitikei, R., N.Z. 55 Ed
Rangitoto Range, N.Z. 55 Ec
Rangoon, Burma 89 Je
Rania, India 90 Df
Ranibennur, India 88 Ef
Raniganj, India 91 Fd
Raniganj, India 91 Fc
Ranikhet, India 91 Ba
Rankin Inlet, N.W.T. 31 Ke
Rannoch L., Scotland 62 Ed
Ranoke, Ontario 34 Jb
Rantauparapap, Sumatra 83 Ck
Rantekombola, Celebes (Sulawesi) 83 Gh
Rantsila, Finland 66 Ld
Ranua, Finland 66 Md
Rapa, Austral Islands 103 Lk
Rapadama, Upper Volta 98 Ef
Raper, C., N.W.T. 31 Nd
Rapid City, Manitoba 37 Rh
Rapid City, S. Dakota 46 Fc
Rapide-Blanc, Quebec 35 Se
Rapide-Deux, Quebec 35 Me
Rapides-des-Cèdres, Que. 31 Mh
Rapides-des-Joachims, Que. 35 Nf
Rapide-Sept, Quebec 35 Me
Rapid View, Sask. 36 Jd
Rapla, Estonia 67 Lg
Rappahannock R., Virginia 45 Ja
Rapperswil, Switzerland 65 Da
Raqqa, Syria 92 Cb
Rarotonga, Cook Islands 103 Kk
Ras al Had, Oman 93 Ge
Ras al Khaymah, United Arab Emirates 93 Gd
Ras Dashan, Ethiopia 97 Hb
Rashad, Sudan 99 Mf
Rashadiya, Jordan 94 Dg
Rasheiya., Lebanon 94 Dd
Rashid, Egypt 99 Mb
Rashm, Iran 93 Fb
Rasht, Iran 92 Eb
Raška, Yugoslavia 76 Cc
Ras Lanuf, Libya 99 Jb
Rason, L., W. Australia 56 De
Rasova, Romania 76 Fb
Rasskazovo, U.S.S.R. 81 Ed
Rasulnagar, Pakistan 90 Cd
Ratangarh, India 90 Df
Ratchaburi, Thailand 87 Bd
Rathburn Res., Iowa 49 Lb
Rathlin I., N. Ireland 62 Ce
Rath Luirc, Eire 63 Bh
Rathwell, Manitoba 37 Tj
Ratibor. See Racibórz
Ratikon, Switz./Austria 65 Ea
Rat L., Manitoba 37 Sb
Ratnagiri, India 88 De
Ratner, Saskatchewan 37 Ne
Raton, New Mexico 48 Ed
Raton, New Mexico 42 Fd
Rat Rapids, Ontario 31 Kg
Rat River, N.W.T. 38 Re
Rattlesnake Ra., Wyoming 46 Dd
Rattling Brook, Nfld. 33 Qd
Rättvik, Sweden 67 Ff
Ratz, Mt., B.C. 39 Gg
Rauch, Argentina 54 Ee
Raukumara Range, N.Z. 55 Fc
Rauma, Finland 67 Jf
Rautas, Sweden 66 Hb
Rautavaara, Finland 66 Ne
Rautio, Finland 66 Ld
Ravar, Iran 93 Gc
Ravendal, Saskatchewan 37 Oe
Ravenna, Italy 74 Dc
Ravenscrag, Saskatchewan 36 Hj
Ravensworth, Ontario 35 Lg
Ravi R., Pakistan 90 De
Rawaidha, Arabia 92 Dd
Rawalpindi, Pakistan 90 Cd
Rawalpindi L., N.W.T. 38 Qc
Rawandiz, Iraq 92 Db
Rawatsar, India 90 Df
Rawdon, Quebec 35 Rf
Rawene, New Zealand 55 Da
Rawlinna, W. Australia 56 Ef
Rawlins, Wyoming 46 De
Rawson, Argentina 54 Cf
Raya, Borneo (Kalimantan) 83 Fl
Rayadrug, India 88 Ef
Raymond, Alberta 36 Ej
Raymondville, Texas 48 Jj
Raymore, Saskatchewan 37 Ng
Rayón, Mexico 50 Bb
Rays Hill, Pennsylvania 44 Ac
Razan, Iran 92 Eb
Razelm L., Romania 76 Gb
Razgrad, Bulgaria 76 Fc
Razmak, Pakistan 90 Ad
Ré, I. de, France 72 Cc
Reader L., Manitoba 37 Qe
Reading, England 63 Gj
Reading, Pennsylvania 40 Je
Readlyn, Saskatchewan 37 Mj
Real, Cord., Bolivia 52 Dg
Real, Cord., Ecuador 52 Bd
Real Castillo, Mexico 50 Aa
Realico, Argentina 54 De
Realp, Switzerland 65 Db
Reata, Mexico 50 Db
Rebecca L., N.W.T. 38 Pc
Rebun, Japan 86 Gb
Recalada, Chile 54 Ah
Recalde, Argentina 54 De
Recherche Arch., W. Aust. 56 Df
Rechna Doab, Pakistan 90 Ce
Recht, Belgium 64 Ed
Recife, Brazil 53 Le
Reconquista, Argentina 54 Ec
Recontre East, Nfld. 33 Rf
Recreio, Brazil 53 Fe
Redbank, New Jersey 44 Cb
Red Bay, Newfoundland 33 Qb
Red Bay, Ontario 34 Jh
Redberry L., Sask. 36 Kf
Red Bluff Res., New Mexico/Texas 48 Fg
Redby, Minnesota 46 Kb
Redcliff, Alberta 36 Gh
Red Deer, Alberta 36 Df
Red Deer L., Manitoba 37 Qf
Red Deer R., Alberta 36 Eg
Red Deer R., Sask. 37 Pf
Red Des., Wyoming 46 Cd
Redding, California 47 Be
Reddit, Ontario 36 Ha
Redfield, Arkansas 45 Ac
Redfield, S. Dakota 46 Hc
Red I., Newfoundland 33 Sf
Rédics, Hungary 69 Ge
Red Indian L., Nfld. 33 Pe
Redknife, R., N.W.T. 38 Oe
Red L., Minnesota 46 Ka
Red Lake, Ontario 30 Kg
Redlands, California 47 Eh
Red Lodge, Montana 46 Cc
Red Lodge Prov. Park, Alta. 36 Cg
Red Oak, Iowa 49 Kb
Redon, France 72 Bc
Redondela, Spain 70 Aa
Red Pass, B.C. 39 Oj
Red Pheasant, Sask. 36 Jf
Red R., British Columbia 38 Jf
Red R., Man./N. Dakota 30 Kh
Red R., Minnesota/N. Dakota/Canada 42 Gb
Red R. See Song-koi
Red R., U.S.A. 49 Lg
Red Rapids, N.B. 32 Eg
Red Rock, Ontario 34 Bd
Red Rock, L., Iowa 49 Lb
Redrock L., N.W.T. 38 Qc
Redruth, Michigan 40 Bb
Red Sea, Africa 58 Cf
Red Sea, Sudan 97 Ha
Redstone, R., N.W.T. 38 Kd
Redstone, R., Ontario 34 Jd
Redvers, Saskatchewan 37 Qj
Redwater, Alberta 36 De
Redwater, Ontario 35 Lf
Red Willow, Alberta 36 Ef
Red Wing, Minnesota 46 Lc
Redwood Falls, Minnesota 46 Kc
Reed City, Michigan 40 Dd
Reed L., Manitoba 37 Rd
Reedsburg, Wisconsin 40 Ad
Reefton, New Zealand 55 Ce
Ree L., Eire 63 Bg
Reelfoot, L., Tennessee 45 Cb
Reesor, Ontario 34 Gc
Refresco, Chile 54 Cc
Regan, Ontario 34 Ed
Regencia, Brazil 53 Kg
Regensburg, West Germany 68 Ed
Regent, Manitoba 37 Rj
Reggan, Algeria 98 Fc
Reggio di Calabria, Italy 75 Ef
Reggio nell'Emilia, Italy 74 Cc
Reghin, Romania 76 Ea
Regina, Saskatchewan 37 Nh
Regina Beach, Sask. 37 Nh
Registro do Araguaia, Brazil 53 Gg
Rehoboth, Namibia 95 Bd
Rehovot, Israel 94 Cf
Reichenbach, W. Germany 68 Ec
Reidsville, N. Carolina 45 Hb
Reigate, England 63 Gj
Reigi, Estonia 67 Kg
Reims, France 72 Fb
Reina Adelaide, Arch. de la, Chile 54 Bh
Reindeer I., Manitoba 37 Uf
Reindeer L., Man./Sask. 30 Jf
Reindeer L., Sask. 39 Wg
Reindeer R., Sask. 39 Wh
Reinosa, Spain 70 Ca
Reitan, Norway 66 De
Reitz, Orange Free State 95 De
Rekinniki, U.S.S.R. 79 Rb
Reliance, N.W.T. 38 Td
Remansão, Brazil 53 Hd
Remanso, Brazil 53 Je
Rembang, Java 83 Fm
Remedios, Cuba 51 Db
Remedios, Panama 51 Ce
Remeshk, Iran 93 Gd
Remic Rapids, Que./Ont. 34 Ch
Rémigny, Quebec 35 Le
Rémigny, L., Quebec 35 Le
Remiremont, France 72 Gb
Remoulins, France 73 Fe
Remscheid, West Germany 68 Bc
Remüs, Switzerland 65 Fb
Rena, Norway 67 Df
Renaix. See Ronse
Renca, Argentina 54 Cd
Rencontre East, Nfld. 33 Rf
Rendsburg, West Germany 68 Ca
Reneault, Quebec 35 Ld
Renews, Newfoundland 33 Ug
Renfrew, Ontario 35 Og
Rengat, Sumatra 83 Dl
Renigunta, India 88 Ef
Renison, Ontario 34 Jb
Renk, Sudan 99 Mf
Renkum, Netherlands 64 Dc
Renmark, S. Australia 57 Hf
Rennell, Solomon Islands 102 Fj
Rennes, France 72 Cb
Rennie, Manitoba 36 Fa
Rennie L., N.W.T. 38 Ve
Reno, Nevada 47 Df
Renous, New Brunswick 32 Gg
Renovo, Pennsylvania 40 He
Renown, Saskatchewan 37 Mg
Renqiu, China 84 Hc
Rensselaer, New York 40 Kd
Renswoude, Netherlands 64 Db
Renville, Minnesota 46 Kc
Renwer, Manitoba 37 Rf
Reo, Flores I., Indonesia 83 Hm
Réole, la, France 73 Cd
Rep. of South Africa, Afr. 95 Ce
Republican R., Nebraska 49 Hb
Repulse B., Queensland 57 Jd
Repulse Bay, N.W.T. 31 Ld
Requena, Peru 52 Ce
Requena, Spain 71 Ec
Reserve, Saskatchewan 37 Pf
Resistencia, Argentina 54 Ec
Reşiţa, Romania 76 Cb
Resolute, N.W.T. 30 Kc
Resolution I., New Zealand 55 Af
Resolution Island, N.W.T. 31 Ne
Resolution L., Quebec 31 Nf
Restigouche, Quebec 32 Fe
Restigouche R., N.B. 32 Ef
Reston, Manitoba 37 Qj
Restoule, Ontario 35 Lf
Rethel, France 72 Fb
Réthimnon, Crete 77 Eg
Retie, Belgium 64 Dc
Retlaw, Alberta 36 Eh
Réunion, Indian Ocean 100 Dg
Reusel, Netherlands 64 Dc
Reutlingen, West Germany 68 Cd
Reutte, Austria 68 De
Revda, U.S.S.R. 81 Qb
Revelstoke, B.C. 39 Ok
Revenue, Saskatchewan 36 Jf
Revilla Gigedo Is., Mexico 50 Bd
Revivim, Israel 94 Cf
Rewa, India 91 Cc
Reward, Saskatchewan 36 Hf
Rewari, India 90 Ef
Rexton, New Brunswick 32 Hg
Rey, I. del, Panama 51 De
Reydharfjord, Iceland 66 Zm
Reyes, Mexico 50 Dd
Reykjavik, Iceland 66 Um
Reykjavik, Manitoba 37 Tg
Reynaud, Saskatchewan 37 Mf
Reynolds, Manitoba 36 Fa
Reynosa, Mexico 50 Eb
Rezā'īyeh, Iran 92 Db
Rēzekne, Latvia 67 Mh
Rheden, Netherlands 64 Eb
Rhein, Germany 68 Bc
Rhein, Saskatchewan 37 Pg
Rheine, West Germany 68 Bb
Rheinland-Pfalz, W. Ger. 68 Bc
Rhenen, Netherlands 64 Dc
Rheydt, West Germany 68 Bc
Rhinelander, Wisconsin 40 Bc
Rhine R. See Rhein
Rhode Island, U.S.A. 44 Eb
Rhodesia. See Zimbabwe
Rhodes (Rodhos), Greece 77 Gf
Rhondda, Wales 63 Ej
Rhône, France 72 Fd
Rhön Gebirge, West Germany 68 Cc
Rhyl, Wales 63 Eg
Riaño, Spain 70 Ca
Riau, Kep., Indonesia 83 Dk
Riaza, Spain 70 Db
Ribadeo, Spain 70 Ba
Ribadesella, Spain 70 Ca
Ribble R., England 63 Fg
Ribe, Denmark 67 Cj
Ribeirão Prêto, Brazil 53 Hh
Ribera, Sicily 75 Dg
Riberalta, Bolivia 52 Df
Rib Lake, Ontario 35 Le
Ribstone, Alberta 36 Gf
Ribstone Cr., Alberta 36 Ff
Rice L., Ontario 34 He
Rice L., Ontario 35 Mh
Rice Lake, Wisconsin 46 Mc
Riceton, Saskatchewan 37 Nh
Richard, Saskatchewan 36 Kf
Richard Collinson Inlet, N.W.T. 30 Hc
Richards C., Arctic Ocean 41 Ra
Richards I., N.W.T. 38 Fa
Richards Landing, Ontario 34 Ff
Richardson, Sask. 37 Nh
Richardson, R., N.W.T. 38 Pb
Richardson I., N.W.T. 38 Oc
Richardson Is., N.W.T. 38 Sa
Richardson Mts., N.Z. 55 Bf
Richardson Mts., Y.T./N.W.T. 38 Ea
Richardson R., Alberta 39 Sf
Richardton, N. Dakota 46 Fb
Richdale, Alberta 36 Fg
Riche, Pt., Nfld. 33 Pc
Richelieu, R., Quebec 35 Rg
Richey, Montana 46 Eb
Richfield, Utah 47 Gf
Richibucto, N.B. 32 Hg
Rich Lake, Alberta 36 Fd
Richland, Missouri 45 Ab
Richland, Washington 47 Db
Richland Center, Wisconsin 40 Ad
Richlea, Saskatchewan 36 Jg
Richmond, California 47 Bg
Richmond, Cape Province 95 Cf
Richmond, Indiana 40 Df
Richmond, Kentucky 45 Eb
Richmond, New York 40 Je
Richmond, New Zealand 55 Dd
Richmond, Ontario 35 Pg
Richmond, P.E.I. 32 Hg
Richmond, Quebec 35 Sg
Richmond, Queensland 57 Hd
Richmond, Utah 48 Bb
Richmond, Virginia 45 Jb
Richmond, district, B.C. 39 Gm
Richmond Hill, Ontario 35 Lj
Richmound, Saskatchewan 36 Hh
Richwood, Minnesota 46 Kb
Richwood, W. Virginia 45 Ga
Ricla, Spain 71 Eb
Riddes, Switzerland 65 Cb
Rideau, R., Ontario 35 Pg
Rideau Can., Ontario 35 Ph
Rideau L., Ontario 35 Oh
Ridge, R., Ontario 34 Fb
Ridgedale, Saskatchewan 37 Ne
Ridgetown, Ontario 34 Jk
Ridgeville, Manitoba 37 Vj
Ridgway, Pennsylvania 40 Ge
Ridi, Nepal 91 Db
Riding Mt., ra., Manitoba 37 Rh
Riding Mt. Nat. Park, Man. 37 Rh
Ridout, Ontario 40 Eb
Ridpath, Saskatchewan 36 Jg
Riesa, East Germany 68 Ec
Rietavas, Lithuania 67 Jj
Rieti, Italy 74 Dd
Rifle, Colorado 48 Dc
Riga, Latvia 67 Lh
Riga, G. of, Latvia 67 Kh
Rigan, Iran 93 Gd
Rigaud, Quebec 35 Qg
Rigi Mati, Iran 93 Gd
Rigolet, Newfoundland 31 Og
Rig-Rig, Chad 99 Hf
Rijeka, Yugoslavia 74 Ec
Rijswijk, Netherlands 64 Cb
Rimatara, Tubuai Is. 103 Kk
Rimbey, Alberta 36 Cf
Rimini, Italy 74 Dc
Rîmnicu Sărat, Romania 76 Fb
Rîmnicu Vîlcea, Romania 76 Eb
Rimouski & R., Quebec 32 De
Rincon, New Mexico 42 Ee
Rindal, Norway 66 Ce
Ringelspitz, Switz. 65 Eb
Ringkøbing, Denmark 67 Ch
Ringvassøy I., Norway 66 Hb
Rinihue, Chile 54 Be
Rinjani, Mt., Indonesia 59 Lj
Riobamba, Ecuador 52 Bd
Rio Bonito, Brazil 53 Jh
Rio Branco, Brazil 54 Gc
Rio Branco, Brazil 52 De
Rio Branco, Uruguay 54 Fd
Rio Bravo del Norte, Mexico/U.S.A. 50 Ca
Rio Bueno, Chile 54 Bf
Rio Chico, Argentina 54 Cg
Rio Chico, Venezuela 52 Da
Rio Colorado, Argentina 54 De
Rio Conchos, Mexico 48 Eh
Rio Cuarto, Argentina 54 Dd
Rio de Janeiro, Brazil 53 Jh
Rio de Oro, Mauritania 98 Bd
Rio do Sul, Brazil 54 Gc
Rio Gallegos, Arg. 54 Ch
Rio Grande, Brazil 54 Fd
Río Grande, Mexico 50 Dc
Rio Grande, Mexico/Texas/New Mexico 48 Eg
Rio Grande, Mexico/U.S.A. 50 Db
Rio Grande City, Texas 48 Hj
Riohacha, Colombia 52 Ca
Rio Hondo, Argentina 54 Dc
Rio Muerto, Argentina 54 Dc
Rio Mulatos, Bolivia 52 Dg
Rio Negro, Brazil 54 Gc
Rionero in Vulture, Italy 75 Ee
Rio Pardo, Brazil 53 Gh
Riou L., Saskatchewan 38 Uf
Rio Verde, Brazil 53 Gg
Rio Verde, Ecuador 52 Bc
Rioverde, Mexico 50 Ec
Rioz, France 72 Gc
Ripats, Sweden 66 Jc
Ripault, L., Quebec 32 Kb
Ripley, California 47 Fj
Ripley, Mississippi 45 Cc
Ripley, New York 44 Aa
Ripley, Ontario 34 Jh
Ripley, Tennessee 45 Cc
Ripley, West Virginia 40 Ff
Ripon, England 63 Ff
Ripon, Quebec 35 Pg
Ripon, Wisconsin 40 Bd
Risafe, Syria 92 Cb
Risalpur, Pakistan 90 Cc
Risbäck, Sweden 66 Jc
Rishiri, Japan 86 Gb
Rishon-le-Zion, Israel 94 Cf
Risør, Norway 67 Cg
Ristijärvi, Finland 66 Nd
Ritch I., N.W.T. 38 Ob
Ritchie's Arch., Andaman Islands 89 Hf
Rivadavia, Argentina 54 Db
Rivas, Nicaragua 51 Bd
Rivera, Argentina 54 De
Rivera, Uruguay 54 Ed
River Denys, N.S. 33 Lh
Riverhead, Newfoundland 33 Tg
Riverhead, New York 40 Ke
River Hébert, N.S. 32 Hh
Riverhurst, Saskatchewan 36 Lh
River John, Nova Scotia 32 Jh
Rivero, Chile 54 Bg
River of Ponds, Nfld. 33 Pc
Riverport, Nova Scotia 32 Hj
Rivers, Manitoba 37 Rh
Rivers, L. of the, Sask. 37 Mj
Riversdale, New Zealand 55 Bf
Riverside, California 47 Ej
Riverside, Ontario 34 Hk
Rivers Inlet, B.C. 39 Kk
Riverton, Manitoba 37 Uh
Riverton, New Zealand 55 Bg
Riverton, Wyoming 46 Cd
River Valley, Ontario 34 Kf
Riviera di Levante, Italy 74 Bc
Riviera di Ponente, Italy 74 Ad
Rivière-à-Claude, Que. 32 Gd
Rivière-à-la-Loutre, Que. 32 Jd
Rivière-à-Pierre, Quebec 35 Sf
Rivière-au-Renard, Que. 32 He
Rivière-aux-Graines, Que. 32 Gd
Rivière-aux-Rats, Quebec 35 Se
Rivière-Bleue, Quebec 32 Cf
Rivière-de-la-Chaloupe, Quebec 32 Kd
Rivière-des-Prairies, Quebec 35 Sh
Rivière-du-Loup, Quebec 32 Cf
Rivière-du-Milieu, Quebec 35 Se
Rivière-Héva, Quebec 35 Md
Rivière-la-Madeleine, Que. 32 Gd
Rivière-Matawin, Que. 35 Rf
Rivière-Ouelle, Quebec 32 Cf
Rivière-Pentecôte, Que. 32 Ed
Rivière-Pigou, Quebec 32 Gc
Rivière-St-Jean, Quebec 32 Hc
Rivière-Verte, N.B. 32 Df
Rivière-Verte, Quebec 32 Cf
Riyadh, Arabia 92 Ee
Riyaq, Lebanon 94 Ed
Rize, Turkey 92 Da
Rizokarpaso, Cyprus 94 Cb
Rizzuto C., Italy 75 Ff
Roa, Spain 70 Db
Roanne, France 72 Fc
Roanoke, Alabama 45 Ed
Roanoke, Virginia 45 Hb
Roanoke R., N. Carolina 45 Hb
Roaringwater B., Eire 63 Aj
Roatán, I., Honduras 51 Bc
Robat Thana, Pakistan 88 Bc
Robe Noire, L. de la, Quebec 32 Kc
Roberts, Montana 46 Cc
Robertsfors, Sweden 66 Jd
Robertsganj, India 91 Dc
Robert S. Kerr L., Okla. 49 Ke
Robertson, L., Quebec 33 Nb
Robertsonville, Quebec 35 Tf
Robertsport, Liberia 98 Cg
Robertville, N.B. 32 Gf
Roberval, Quebec 35 Sd
Robeson Ch., Arctic Ocean 41 Qa
Robeson Chan., Arctic Ocean 31 Na
Robinson, Illinois 49 Oc
Robinson, Y.T. 38 Fe
Robinson Crusoe, Chile 103 Tl
Robinsonville, N.B. 32 Ff
Roblin, Manitoba 37 Qg
Robore, Bolivia 52 Fg
Robsart, Saskatchewan 36 Hj
Robson, Mt., B.C. 39 Oj
Robstown, Texas 48 Jj
Roca, la, Spain 70 Bc
Rocanville, Saskatchewan 37 Qh
Rocha, Uruguay 54 Fd
Rochdale, England 63 Fg
Rochebaucourt, Quebec 35 Nd
Rochefort, Belgium 64 Dd
Rochefort, France 72 Cd
Roche Percée, Sask. 37 Pj
Rocher, L., Quebec 35 Ob
Rocher Noir, Quebec 33 Nc
Rocher Peril, Quebec 33 Pb
Rocher River, N.W.T. 38 Re
Rochers, R. aux, Quebec 32 Ec
Rochers aux Oiseaux Lt. Ho., Quebec 33 Lf
Rochester, Alberta 36 Dd
Rochester, England 63 Hj
Rochester, Michigan 40 Ed
Rochester, Minnesota 46 Lc
Rochester, New Hampshire 40 Ld
Rochester, New York 40 Hd
Roche-sur-Yon, la, France 72 Cc
Rochfort Bridge, Alberta 36 Be
Rock, R., Y.T. 38 Eb
Rock, R., Y.T. 38 Ke
Rockall, Atlantic Ocean 60 Dd
Rock Bay, B.C. 39 Lk
Rockcliffe Park, Ontario 34 Dh
Rockefeller Plateau, Antarctica 104 Pb
Rockford, Illinois 40 Bd
Rockglen, Saskatchewan 37 Mj
Rockhampton, Queensland 57 Kd
Rockhaven, Sask. 36 Jf
Rock Hill, S. Carolina 45 Gc
Rockingham, N. Carolina 45 Hc
Rock Island, Illinois 40 Ae
Rock Island, Quebec 35 Sg
Rockland, Maine 32 Cj
Rockland, Massachusetts 44 Ea
Rockland, Ontario 35 Pg
Rocknest L., N.W.T. 38 Qc
Rockport, Indiana 45 Db
Rockport, Missouri 49 Kb
Rock Pt., New Zealand 55 Dd
Rock Springs, Wyoming 46 Ce
Rockstone, Guyana 52 Fb
Rockville, Maryland 44 Bc
Rockwell City, Iowa 49 Ka
Rockwood, Ontario 34 Kj
Rockwood, Tennessee 45 Ec
Rockyford, Alberta 36 Dg
Rockyford, Colorado 48 Fc
Rocky Island L., Ontario 34 Hf
Rocky L., Manitoba 37 Qd
Rocky Mount, N. Carolina 45 Jc
Rockymount, Virginia 45 Hb
Rocky Mountain House, Alta. 36 Cf
Rocky Mountain Nat. Park, Colorado 42 Ec
Rocky Mts., N. America 42 Db
Rocroi, France 72 Fb
Rødby, Denmark 67 Dj
Rodchevo, U.S.S.R. 79 Qb
Roddickton, Nfld. 33 Qc
Rodez, France 73 Ed
Rodhopi, Greece 76 Ed
Ródhos, Greece 77 Gf
Rodkhan, Pakistan 88 Bc
Rodney, Mississippi 45 Be
Rodney, Ontario 34 Jk
Rodopi Planina, Bulg./Greece 76 Dd
Rodosto. See Tekirdag
Rodriguez, I., Indian Ocean 100 Ef
Roebourne, W. Australia 56 Cd
Roermond, Netherlands 64 Dc
Roesbrugge, Belgium 64 Ad
Roeselare, Belgium 64 Bd
Roes Welcome Sound, N.W.T. 31 Le
Roeulx, Belgium 64 Cd
Rogachev, Byelorussia 80 Ge
Roger, L., Quebec 35 Me
Rogers, Mt., B.C. 39 Pk
Rogers City, Michigan 40 Ec
Rogersville, N.B. 32 Gg
Rogersville, Tennessee 45 Fb
Rogliano, Corsica 73 Kh
Rohault, L., Quebec 35 Qc
Rohri, Pakistan 88 Cc
Rohtak, India 90 Ef
Roi Et, Thailand 87 Cc
Roisin, Belgium 64 Bd
Rojas, Argentina 54 Dd
Rokeby, Saskatchewan 37 Pg
Rokiškis, Lithuania 67 Lj
Roland, Manitoba 37 Uj
Rolde, Netherlands 64 Eb
Rolla, British Columbia 39 Nh
Rolla, Missouri 45 Bb
Rolle, Switzerland 65 Bb
Rollet, Quebec 35 Le
Rolphton, Ontario 35 Nf
Rolsvøy, Norway 66 Ka
Roma, Indonesia 83 Jm
Roma, Italy 75 De
Roma, Queensland 57 Je
Roma, Sweden 67 Hh
Romaine, R., Quebec 32 Jb
Roman, Romania 76 Fa
Romania, Cent. Europe 61 Pg
Romans, France 73 Fd
Romanshorn, Switzerland 65 Ea
Romanzof, C., Alaska 43 Wl
Rome, Georgia, U.S.A. 45 Ec
Rome, New York 40 Jd
Rome, Italy. See Roma
Romerée, Belgium 64 Cd
Romford, England 63 Hj
Romney, West Virginia 40 Gf
Romny, Ukraine 80 Hf
Rømø I., Denmark 67 Cj
Romont, Switzerland 65 Bb
Romsdalshorn, Norway 66 Be
Ron, Vietnam 87 Dc
Ronda, Kashmir 90 Dc
Ronda, Spain 70 Cd
Rondeau Prov. Park, Ont. 34 Jk
Rondônia, Brazil 52 Ef
Ronehamn, Sweden 67 Hh
Ronge, Lac la, Sask. 37 Mc
Rongjiang, China 85 Dk
Rønne, Bornholm, Den. 67 Fj
Ronneby, Sweden 67 Fh
Ronne Entrance, Antarctica 104 Sb
Ronne Ice Shelf, Antarctica 104 Sb
Ronse, Belgium 64 Bd
Ronse's Point, New York 40 Kc
Roosendaal, Netherlands 64 Cc
Roosevelt, I., Antarctica 104 Mb
Roosevelt, Mt., B.C. 39 Lf
Rooseveltown, New York 40 Jc
Root, R., N.W.T. 38 Ld
Roper, R., N. Terr. 57 Fb
Roquefort, France 73 Cd
Roquemaure, Quebec 35 Ld
Rorey L., N.W.T. 38 Jb
Rori, India 90 Df
Rorketon, Manitoba 37 Sg
Røros, Norway 66 De
Rorschach, Switzerland 65 Ea
Rosa, la, Switzerland 65 Fb
Rosa, Monte, Switz./Italy 65 Cc
Rosablanche, Switz. 65 Cb
Rosaire, Quebec 32 Bg
Rosalind, Alberta 36 Ef
Rosario, Argentina 54 Dd
Rosario, Brazil 53 Jd
Rosario, Chile 54 Bb
Rosario, Mexico 50 Cc
Rosario, Mexico 50 Aa
Rosario, Paraguay 54 Eb
Rosario de la Frontera, Argentina 54 Dc
Rosario de Lerma, Argentina 54 Cb
Rosario del Tala, Arg. 54 Ed
Rosario Oeste, Brazil 53 Ff
Rosas, Spain 71 Ga
Rosas, Golfo de, Spain 71 Ga
Roscommon, Eire 63 Bg
Roscommon, Michigan 40 Dc
Roscrea, Eire 63 Bh
Roseau, Minnesota 46 Ka
Rose Blanche, Nfld. 33 Of
Rosebud, Alberta 36 Eg
Rosebud, S. Dakota 46 Gd
Rosebud R., Alberta 36 Dg
Roseburg, Oregon 47 Bd
Rosedale, Alberta 36 Eg
Rosedale, Mississippi 45 Bd
Rose I., Samoa 102 Jj
Rose Lynn, Alberta 36 Fg
Rosemary, Alberta 36 Eh
Roseneath, Ontario 35 Mh
Rosenheim, West Germany 68 Ee
Rose Pt., B.C. 39 Hh
Roseray, Saskatchewan 36 Jh
Rosetown, Saskatchewan 36 Kg
Rosetta. See Rashid
Rose Valley, Sask. 37 Of
Rosevear, Alberta 36 Ae
Rosiers, C. des, Quebec 32 He
Rosignano Marittimo, Italy 74 Cd
Rosignol, Guyana 52 Fb
Roslavl, U.S.S.R. 80 He
Rosport, Luxembourg 64 Ee
Ross, England 63 Fj
Ross, New Zealand 55 Ce
Ross, R., Y.T. 38 Hd
Rossa, Switzerland 65 Eb
Rossano, Italy 75 Ff
Ross Barnet Res., Mississippi 45 Cd
Rossburn, Manitoba 37 Rh
Rosseau, Ontario 35 Lg
Rosseau L., Ontario 40 Gc
Rossel I., Papua New Guinea 57 Kb
Rossendale, Manitoba 37 Tj
Ross I., Antarctica 104 Lb
Ross I., Burma 89 Jf
Ross I., Manitoba 37 Ud
Ross Ice Shelf, Antarctica 104 Ma
Rossignol, Belgium 64 De
Rossignol, L., N.S. 32 Gj
Rossland, B.C. 39 Pl
Rosslare, Eire 63 Ch
Rosslyn, Virginia 44 Bc
Rossport, Ontario 34 Cd
Ross River, Y.T. 38 Gd
Ross Sea, Antarctica 104 Mb
Rossvatnet, Norway 66 Fd
Rossway, Nova Scotia 32 Gj
Rosswood, B.C. 39 Jh
Rosta, Norway 66 Hb
Rosthern, Saskatchewan 36 Lf
Rostock, E. Germany 68 Ea
Rostov, U.S.S.R. 80 Lc
Rostov, U.S.S.R. 81 Dg
Roswell, New Mexico 48 Ef
Roswell, New Mexico 42 Fe
Rota, Mariana Islands 102 Df
Rothenburg, W. Germany 68 Dd
Rotherham, England 63 Gg
Rothesay, New Brunswick 32 Gh
Rothesay, Scotland 62 De
Roti, Indonesia 83 Hn
Rotorua, New Zealand 55 Fc
Rotterdam, Netherlands 64 Cc
Rotuma, Fiji 102 Gj
Roubaix, France 72 Ea
Rouen, France 72 Db
Rõuge, Estonia 67 Mh
Rouleau, Saskatchewan 37 Nh
Roulers. See Roeselare
Roulier, Quebec 35 Le
Round Harbour, Nfld. 33 Rd
Round Hill, Alberta 36 Ee
Round Pond, Nfld. 33 Re
Roundrock L., N.W.T. 39 Rc
Roundup, Montana 46 Cb
Rounthwaite, Manitoba 37 Sj
Roura, Fr. Guiana 53 Gc
Rous, Pen., Chile 54 Cj
Rousay I., Orkney 62 Ea
Rousseau, S. Dakota 46 Gc
Roussillon, France 73 Ee
Routhierville, Quebec 32 Ee
Rouveen, Netherlands 64 Eb
Rouvray, L., Quebec 32 Bd
Rouyn, Quebec 35 Md
Rouyn, Quebec 40 Ga
Rovaniemi, Finland 66 Lc
Roveredo, Switzerland 65 Eb
Rovigo, Italy 74 Cc
Rovinari, Romania 76 Db
Rovno, Ukraine 80 Ef
Rovnoye, U.S.S.R. 81 Ge
Rovuma, Mozambique 97 Hg
Rowan L., Ontario 36 Ja
Rowley, Alberta 36 Eg
Rowley I., N.W.T. 31 Md
Roxas, Philippines 83 Hh
Roxburgh, New Zealand 55 Bf
Roxbury, New York 44 Ca
Roxton Falls, Quebec 35 Sg
Roy, L., Quebec 32 Cd

Royal, Mt., *Ontario* 34 Bc
Royal Canal, *Eire* 63 Cg
Royale, I., *Michigan* 40 Bb
Royal Geographical Society Is., *Northwest Territories* 38 Xa
Royalties, *Alberta* 36 Ch
Royan, *France* 72 Cd
Rozet, *Wyoming* 46 Ec
Rožňava, *Czechoslovakia* 69 Jd
Rtishchevo, *U.S.S.R.* 81 Fd
Ruahine Range, *New Zealand* 55 Fc
Ruapehu, Mt., *New Zealand* 55 Ec
Ruawai, *New Zealand* 55 Eb
Rubtsovsk, *U.S.S.R.* 78 Hc
Ruby, *Alaska* 43 Xl
Rudauli, *India* 91 Cb
Rudbar, *Afghanistan* 93 Hc
Ruddell, *Saskatchewan* 36 Kf
Ruddervoorde, *Belgium* 64 Bc
Rudkøbing, *Denmark* 67 Dj
Rudnaya Pristan', *U.S.S.R.* 79 Nd
Rudolf L., *Kenya* 97 Hd
Ruel, *Ontario* 34 Je
Ruffec, *France* 72 Dc
Rufino, *Argentina* 54 Dd
Rufus L., *N.W.T.* 38 Ja
Rugao, *China* 84 Kf
Rugby, *England* 63 Gh
Rugby, *N. Dakota* 46 Ha
Rügen, *E. Germany* 68 Ea
Rui'an, *China* 85 Kj
Rui Barbosa, *Brazil* 53 Jf
Rujiena, *Latvia* 67 Lh
Rukumkot, *Nepal* 91 Da
Rukwa, L., *Tanzania* 97 Gf
Rum, I., *Scotland* 62 Cd
Rumbek, *Sudan* 99 Lg
Rumburk, *Czechoslovakia* 68 Fc
Rum Cay, *The Bahamas* 51 Eb
Rumegies, *France* 64 Bd
Rumigny, *France* 64 Ce
Rumillies, *Belgium* 64 Bd
Rum Jungle, *N. Terr.* 56 Fb
Rumoi, *Japan* 86 Gc
Rumsey, *Alberta* 36 Eg
Rumuruti, *Kenya* 97 Hd
Runan, *China* 84 Gf
Runanga, *New Zealand* 55 Ce
Rungwa, *Tanzania* 97 Gf
Rungwe, *Tanzania* 97 Gf
Runnymede, *Saskatchewan* 37 Qg
Ruo Shui, *China* 82 Db
Rupar, *India* 90 Ee
Rupbas, *India* 91 Ab
Rupert, *Idaho* 48 Aa
Rupert B., *Quebec* 35 La
Rupert R. de, *Quebec* 35 Ma
Rurrenabaque, *Bolivia* 52 Df
Rurutu, *Tubuai Islands* 103 Kk
Rusape, *Zimbabwe* 95 Ec
Ruse, *Bulgaria* 76 Ec
Ruseifa, *Jordan* 94 Ee
Rusele, *Sweden* 66 Hd
Rush Lake, *Saskatchewan* 36 Kh
Rusne, R., *Lithuania* 67 Jj
Russas, *Brazil* 53 Kd
Russell, *Kansas* 49 Hc
Russell, *Manitoba* 37 Qh
Russell, *New Zealand* 55 Ea
Russell, *Ontario* 35 Pg
Russell I., *N.W.T.* 30 Kc
Russellkonda, *India* 89 Fe
Russell L., *Manitoba* 37 Qb
Russell L., *N.W.T.* 38 Qd
Russell L., *Saskatchewan* 39 Vg
Russellville, *Alabama* 49 Oe
Russellville, *Kentucky* 45 Db
Russian Soviet Federated Socialist Rep., *U.S.S.R.* 78
Russkoye Ust'ye, *U.S.S.R.* 79 Pa
Russo, *Switzerland* 65 Db
Rustak, *Afghanistan* 93 Jb
Rustburg, *Virginia* 45 Hb
Ruston, *Louisiana* 49 Lf
Rutbah, *Iraq* 92 Dc
Rutherfordton, *N. Carolina* 45 Gc
Rutherglen, *Ontario* 35 Lf
Ruthi, *Switzerland* 65 Ea
Ruthilda, *Saskatchewan* 36 Jg
Ruthin, *Wales* 63 Eg
Rutland, *Vermont* 40 Kd
Rutland I., *Andaman Is.* 89 Hf
Rutland Station, *Sask.* 36 Hf
Rutledge L., *N.W.T.* 38 Se
Rutog, *China* 88 Eb
Rutter, *Ontario* 34 Kf
Ruurlo, *Netherlands* 64 Eb
Ruweiba, *Sudan* 99 Le
Ruwenzori, *Uganda* 97 Gd
Ružomberok, *Czechoslovakia* 69 Hd
Rvazhsk, *U.S.S.R.* 80 Me
Rwanda, *Central Africa* 97 Fe
Ryan, L., *Scotland* 62 Df
Ryazan', *U.S.S.R.* 80 Ld
Rybachiy, Pol., *U.S.S.R.* 78 Cb
Rybinsk, *U.S.S.R.* 80 Lb
Rybinskoye Res., *U.S.S.R.* 80 Lb
Rybnoye, *U.S.S.R.* 79 Ka
Rycroft, *Alberta* 39 Oh
Rydal Bank, *Ontario* 34 Gf
Ryde, *I. of W., England* 63 Gk
Rye, *England* 63 Hk
Rye Patch Res., *Nevada* 47 De
Ryerson, *Saskatchewan* 37 Qj
Ryland, *Ontario* 34 Gc
Ryley, *Alberta* 36 Ee
Rýmařov, *Czechoslovakia* 69 Gd
Rypin, *Poland* 69 Hb
Ryūkyū Retto, Is., *Japan* 82 Hf
Rzeszów, *Poland* 69 Jc
Rzhev, *U.S.S.R.* 80 Jc

S

Saalfeld, *E. Germany* 68 Dc
Saanen, *Switzerland* 65 Cb
Saarbrücken, *W. Germany* 68 Bd
Saaremaa, Ostrov, *Lith.* 67 Kg
Saari Selkä, *Finland* 66 Nb
Saarland, *Europe* 68 Bd
Saarlouis, *W. Germany* 68 Bd
Saas Grund, *Switzerland* 65 Cb
Saavedra, *Argentina* 54 De
Sabac, *Yugoslavia* 76 Bb
Sabadell, *Spain* 71 Gb
Sabah, *Malaysia* 83 Gj
Sabalan, *Iran* 92 Eb
Sabalgarh, *India* 88 Ec
Sabana, Arch. de, *Cuba* 51 Cb
Sabanalarga, *Colombia* 52 Ca
Sabancuy, *Mexico* 50 Fd
Sab Biyar, *Syria* 94 Fd
Sabha, *Jordan* 94 Ee
Sabhah, *Libya* 99 Hc
Sabile, *Latvia* 67 Kh
Sabiñánigo, *Spain* 71 Ea
Sabinas, *Mexico* 50 Db
Sabine, *Antarctica* 104 Lb
Sabine, *Texas* 49 Lh
Sabine, *Texas* 43 Hf
Sabine R., *Texas* 49 Lg
Sablé, *France* 72 Cc
Sable, C., *Florida* 43 Kf
Sable I., *Nova Scotia* 33 Nk
Sable Island Bank, *N.S.* 33 Mk
Sable River, *Nova Scotia* 32 Gk
Sables, R. aux, *Ontario* 34 Gf
Sables d'Olonne, les, *France* 72 Cc
Sabrina Coast, *Antarctica* 104 Hc
Sabzevar, *Iran* 93 Gb
Sacaca, *Bolivia* 52 Dg
Sacandaga Res., *New York* 44 Ca
Sac City, *Iowa* 49 Ka
Sacedon, *Spain* 71 Db
Sachigo, R., *Ontario* 31 Kg
Sachs Harbour, *N.W.T.* 30 Gc
Sackets Harbor, *New York* 40 Hd
Sackville, *New Brunswick* 32 Hh
Saco, *Maine* 32 Bk
Saco, *Montana* 46 Da
Sacramento, *Brazil* 53 Hg
Sacramento, *California* 47 Cf
Sacramento Mts., *N. Mex.* 48 Ef
Sacramento R., *California* 47 Cf
Sacré-Coeur, *Quebec* 32 De
Sacré-Coeur-Saguenay, *Que.* 32 Ce
Sa'da, *Yemen* 92 Df
Sádaba, *Spain* 71 Ea
Sadabad, *India* 91 Bb
Sá da Bandeira, *Angola* 96 Cg
Sadad, *Syria* 94 Ec
Sa. da Ibiapaba, *Brazil* 53 Jd
Sa. de S. Luis, *Arg.* 54 Cd
Sadhaura, *India* 90 Ee
Sadiya, *India* 89 Jc
Sa 'diya, Jebel, *Arabia* 92 De
Sado, *Japan* 86 Fe
Sadra, *India* 88 Dd
Saeki, *Japan* 86 Bh
Safad, *Israel* 94 Ed
Safaniya, *Arabia* 92 Ed
Safed Koh Range, *Afghan./Pakistan* 90 Bc
Safi, *Morocco* 98 Db
Safi, *Syria* 94 Df
Safidabeh, *Iran* 93 Hc
Safita, *Syria* 94 Ec
Safranbolu, *Turkey* 92 Ba
Saga, *China* 89 Gc
Saga, *Japan* 86 Bh
Sagaing, *Burma* 89 Jd
Sagami wan, *Japan* 86 Fg
Saganaga L., *Ontario* 37 Mb
Saganash L., *Ontario* 34 Hc
Sagar, *India* 91 Bd
Sagar I., *India* 91 Ge
Sagauli, *India* 91 Eb
Saginaw, *Michigan* 40 Dd
Saginaw B., *Michigan* 40 Ed
Saglek B., *Newfoundland* 31 Nf
Saglouc, *Quebec* 31 Me
Sagone, G. de, *Corsica* 73 Gd
Sagres, *Portugal* 70 Ad
Sagua la Grande, *Cuba* 51 Cb
Saguenay, R., *Quebec* 32 Be
Saguia el Hamra, *Morocco* 98 Cc
Sagunto, *Spain* 71 Ec
Sahand, *Iran* 92 Eb
Sahara, *Africa* 98
Sahara, *India* 88 Dc
Saharanpur, *India* 90 Ef
Saharien Atlas, Mts., *Algeria* 98 Fb
Sahaswan, *India* 91 Ba
Sahiadriparvat Ra., *India* 88 Ed
Sahibganj, *India* 91 Fc
Sahiwal, *Pakistan* 90 Ce
Sahm, *Oman* 93 Ge
Sahuaripa, *Mexico* 50 Cb
Sahuayo, *Mexico* 50 Dc
Sahugún, *Spain* 70 Ca
Šahy, *Czechoslovakia* 69 Hd
Sahyadri Mts., *India* 88 De
Saibai, I., *Qnsld.* 57 Ha
Saida, *Lebanon* 94 Dd
Saidabad, *Iran* 93 Gd
Saidapet, *India* 88 Ff
Said Bundas, *Sudan* 99 Kg
Saidpur, *India* 91 Dc
Saignelégier, *Switzerland* 65 Ba
Saigon, *Vietnam* 87 Dd
Sailana, *India* 88 Dd
Saimaa, L., *Finland* 67 Mf
Saimaa Kanal, *Fin./U.S.S.R.* 67 Nf
Saimbeyli, *Turkey* 92 Cb
St Abbs Head, *Scotland* 62 Fe
St Affrique, *France* 73 Ee
St-Agapitville, *Quebec* 35 Tf
St Agrève, *France* 73 Fd
St Albans, *England* 63 Gj
St Alban's, *Nfld.* 33 Rf
St-Albans, *Vermont* 40 Kc
St Albert, *Alberta* 36 De
St-Alexandre, *Quebec* 32 Cf
St-Alexis-des-Monts, *Quebec* 35 Rf
St-Ambroise, *Quebec* 35 Td
St Amour, *France* 72 Fc
St-Anaclet, *Quebec* 32 De
St André C., *Madagascar* 97 Mk
St-André-Est, *Quebec* 35 Qg
St Andrew's, *N.B.* 32 Eh
St Andrews, *New Zealand* 55 Cf
St Andrew's, *Nfld.* 33 Nf
St Andrews, *Scotland* 62 Fd
St Andrew's Chan., *N.S.* 33 Mg
St Anns, *Nova Scotia* 33 Mg
St Anns B., *N.S.* 33 Mg
St Anns Bay, *Jamaica* 51 Dc
St Anthony, *Idaho* 42 Dc
St Anthony, *Nfld.* 33 Rb
St Antönien, *Switzerland* 65 Eb
St-Antonin, *Quebec* 32 Cf
St Antonis, *Netherlands* 64 Dc
St-Arsène, *Quebec* 32 Cf
St-Athanase, *Quebec* 32 Cf
St-Aubert, *Quebec* 32 Bf
St-Augustin, B. de, *Quebec* 33 Ob
St-Augustin, R., *Quebec* 33 Ob
St Augustine, *Florida* 45 Gf
St Augustine B. de, *Madagascar* 97 Ml
St-Augustin Nord-Ouest, R., *Quebec* 33 Nb
St-Augustin-Saguenay, *Que.* 33 Ob
St Austell, *England* 63 Dk
St-Barnabé, *Quebec* 35 Sf
St-Barthélémi, *Quebec* 35 Rf
St Barthélemy, *Leeward Is.* 51 Gc
St Béat, *France* 73 De
St Benedict, *Sask.* 37 Mf
St-Benoit-Labre, *Quebec* 32 Bg
St-Bernard, *Quebec* 35 Tf
St Bernard, Gd., *Switzerland/Italy* 74 Ac
St Bernard, I., *Quebec* 35 Qk
St Boniface, *Manitoba* 37 Uj
St Boswells, *Sask.* 36 Lh
St Brendan's, *Nfld.* 33 Te
St Bride, Mt., *Alberta* 36 Bg
St Bride's, *Nfld.* 33 Sg
St Bride's B., *Wales* 63 Dj
St Brieuc, *France* 72 Bb
St Brieux, *Sask.* 37 Nf
St Calais, *France* 72 Dc
St-Camille-de-Bellechasse, *Quebec* 32 Bg
St-Casimir, *Quebec* 35 Sf
St Catharines, *Ontario* 35 Lj
St-Catherine Lock, *Que.* 35 Sk
St-Césaire, *Quebec* 35 Rg
St Chamond, *France* 72 Fd
St Charles, *Michigan* 40 Dd
St-Charles, *Quebec* 32 Bg
St-Charles R., *Quebec* 35 Rb
St Chély d'Apcher, *France* 73 Ed
St Christopher, *Leeward Islands* 51 Gc
St Clair, *Michigan* 40 Ed
St Clair, L., *Ont./Mich.* 34 Hk
St Clair R., *Ont./Mich.* 34 Hj
St Claude, *Manitoba* 37 Tj
St-Clément, *Quebec* 32 Cf
St Cloud, *Minnesota* 46 Kc
St-Coeur-de-Marie, *Que.* 35 Td
St-Côme, *Quebec* 35 Rf
St Croix, *N.B.* 32 Eh
St Croix, *West Indies* 51 Gc
St Croix, R., *Wisconsin* 43 Hb
St Croix R., *Maine/N.B.* 32 Eh
St-Cyprien, *Quebec* 32 Df
St-Cyr, L., *Quebec* 35 Pd
St-Cyrille, *Quebec* 35 Sg
St Cyr Lake, *Sask.* 36 Jd
St-Damien-de-Buckland, *Que.* 32 Bg
St-David, *Que.* 35 Tc
St David's, *Newfoundland* 33 Oe
St Davids Head, *Wales* 63 Dj
St Denis, *France* 72 Eb
St-Denis, *Quebec* 32 Cf
St-Denis, *Quebec* 35 Rg
St di Nova Siri, *Italy* 75 Fe
St Dizier, *France* 72 Fb
St-Dominique-du-Rosaire, *Que.* 35 Md
St-Donat, *Quebec* 35 Qf
Ste-Adèle, *Quebec* 35 Qg
Ste-Agathe, *Manitoba* 37 Uj
Ste Agathe-des-Monts, *Que.* 35 Qf
Ste Anne, *Manitoba* 37 Ea
Ste-Anne, L., *Alberta* 39 Qj
Ste-Anne, L., *Quebec* 32 Ec
Ste-Anne, R., *Quebec* 32 Bf
Ste-Anne-de-Beaupré, *Que.* 32 Bf
Ste-Anne-des-Monts, *Que.* 32 Fd
Ste-Anne-du-Lac, *Que.* 35 Pf
Ste Bárbara, *Venezuela* 52 Eb
Ste-Blandine, *Quebec* 32 De
Ste-Cécile-de-Whitton, *Que.* 32 Bh
Ste-Clothilde-de-Horton, *Que.* 35 Sg
Ste Croix, *Switzerland* 65 Bb
Ste-émilie-de-l'énergie, *Que.* 35 Rf
Ste-Famille, *Quebec* 32 Bg
Ste-Famille-d'Aumond, *Que.* 35 Pf
Ste-Félicité, *Quebec* 32 Ee
Ste-Florence, *Quebec* 32 Ee
Ste-Foy, *Quebec* 35 Rc
Ste Genevieve, *Missouri* 45 Bb
Ste-Genevieve B., *Nfld.* 33 Pb
Ste-Germaine-Station, *Que.* 32 Bg
Ste-Hélène, *Quebec* 32 Cf
Ste Hélène, I., *Quebec* 35 Sj
Ste-Hénédine, *Quebec* 32 Bg
Ste-Justine, *Quebec* 40 Lb
St Elias Mt., *Alaska* 43 Yl
St Elias Mts., *Y.T./Alaska* 38 Ce
St-Éloi, *Quebec* 32 Ce
Ste-Louise, *Quebec* 32 Bf
Ste-Lucie, *Quebec* 35 Qf
Ste-Marguerite, B., *Que.* 32 Fd
Ste-Marguerite, R., *Que.* 32 Fc
Ste-Marguerite, R., *Que.* 32 Be
Ste-Marie, *Quebec* 32 Ag
Ste-Marie, Is., *Quebec* 33 Nc
Ste-Marie, Récifs, *Quebec* 33 Nc
Ste Marie C., *Madagascar* 97 Nm
Ste Marie I., *Madagascar* 97 Nk
Ste-Marthe-de-Gaspé, *Que.* 32 Fd
Ste-Perpétue, *Quebec* 32 Cf
Ste-Pétronille, *Quebec* 35 Ub
St-Éphrem-de-Beauce, *Que.* 32 Bg
St-Epiphane, *Quebec* 32 Cf
Ste-Rose-du-Dégelis, *Que.* 32 Df
Ste Rose du Lac, *Man.* 37 Sg
Saintes, *France* 72 Cd
Ste-Thècle, *Quebec* 35 Sf
Ste-Thérèse, *Quebec* 35 Rg
Ste Thérèse L., L., *N.W.T.* 38 Nc
St Étienne, *France* 72 Fd
St-Eugène, *Quebec* 32 Bf
St-Eugène-de-Chazel, *Que.* 35 Md
St-Eusèbe, *Quebec* 32 Df
St-Eustache, *Quebec* 35 Rg
St Eustatius, *Leeward Is.* 51 Gc
Ste-Véronique, *Quebec* 35 Qf
St-Fabien, *Quebec* 32 De
St Fargeau, *France* 72 Ec
St-Félicien, *Quebec* 35 Sd
St-Félix-de-Valois, *Que.* 35 Rf
St Fintan's, *Nfld.* 33 Oe
St-Flavien, *Quebec* 35 Tf
St Florent, *Corsica* 74 Bd
St Florentin, *France* 72 Eb
St Flour, *France* 73 Ed
St-Fortunat, *Quebec* 35 Tg
St Francis, *Maine* 32 Dd
St Francis, C., *Nfld.* 33 Uf
St Franciscus B., *Namibia* 95 Ae
St Francis R., *Arkansas* 45 Bc
St-François, L., *Quebec* 35 Qg
St-François, L., *Quebec* 32 Ah
St-François, R., *Quebec* 40 Kc
St-François, R., *Quebec* 35 Sf
St Fulgent, *France* 72 Cc
St-Gabriel, *Quebec* 35 Rf
St Gallen, *Switz.* 65 Ea
St Gaudens, *France* 73 De
St-Gédéon, *Quebec* 35 Td
St-Gédéon, *Quebec* 32 Bh
St George, *N.B.* 32 Fh
St George, C., *Nfld.* 33 Ne
St George I., *Bering Sea* 43 Vm
St Georges, *Fr. Guiana* 53 Gc
St George's, *Nfld.* 33 Oe
St-Georges, *Quebec* 32 Bg
St-Georges, *Quebec* 32 He
St George's B., *Nfld.* 33 Ne
St Georges B., *N.S.* 33 Lh
St George's Chan., *Ireland/Wales* 63 Cj
St Gérard, *Belgium* 64 Cd
St-Gérard, *Quebec* 35 Tg
St Germain, *France* 72 Eb
St-Gervais, *Quebec* 32 Bg
St Gheorghe I., *Romania* 76 Gb
St Ghislain, *Belgium* 64 Bd
St Gilgen, *Austria* 68 Ee
St Gilles, *Belgium* 64 Cc
St Gilles, *France* 73 Fe
St-Gillies, *Quebec* 35 Tf
St Gillis-Waas, *Belgium* 64 Cc
St Gingolph, *Switzerland* 65 Bb
St Girons, *France* 73 De
St-Godefroi, *Quebec* 32 Ge
St Gotthard, *Switz.* 65 Db
St Gregor, *Saskatchewan* 37 Nf
St Gregory, Mt., *Nfld.* 33 Od
St Guénolé, *France* 72 Ac
St-Guillaume, *Quebec* 35 Sg
St Helena, *Atlantic Ocean* 101 Kk
St Helena B., *Cape Province* 95 Bf
St Helens, *England* 63 Eg
St Helens, Mt., *Washington* 47 Bb
St-Hélier, *Quebec* 32 Hd
St-Henri, *Quebec* 32 Ag
St-Herménégilde, *Que.* 35 Tg
St-Honoré, *Quebec* 32 Cf
St-Honoré, *Quebec* 32 Ae
St Hubert, *Belgium* 64 Dd
St-Hyacinthe, *Quebec* 35 Sg
St Ignace, *Michigan* 40 Dc
St-Ignace-du-Lac, *Quebec* 35 Rf
St Ignace I., *Ontario* 34 Cd
St Imier, *Switzerland* 65 Ba
St-Irénée, *Quebec* 32 Bf
St-Isidore, *Quebec* 35 Le
St-Isidore-d'Auckland, *Que.* 35 Tg
St Ives, *England* 63 Dk
St Jacques, *N.B.* 32 Df
St-Jacques, *Quebec* 35 Rf
St James, *Minnesota* 46 Kd
St James, C., *B.C.* 39 Hd
St Jan, *Belgium* 64 Ad
St-Janvier, *Quebec* 35 Ld
St Jean, *France* 72 Gd
St-Jean, *Quebec* 35 Rg
St-Jean, L., *Quebec* 35 Sd
St-Jean, R., *Quebec* 32 Fd
St Jean Baptiste, *Man.* 37 Uj
St Jean d'Angély, *France* 72 Cd
St-Jean-de-Dieu, *Quebec* 32 Ce
St Jean de Luz, *France* 73 Ce
St-Jean-de-Matha, *Que.* 35 Rf
St-Jean-Port-Joli, *Quebec* 32 Bf
St-Jérôme, *Quebec* 35 Td
St-Jérôme, *Quebec* 35 Qg
St-Joachim, *Quebec* 32 Bf
St-Joachim-de-Courval, *Que.* 35 Sg
Saint John, *N.B.* 32 Gh
St John B. & I., *Nfld.* 33 Pc
Saint John R., *Me./N.B.* 32 Eg
St Johns, *Arizona* 48 Ce
St John's, *Michigan* 40 Dd
St John's, *Newfoundland* 33 Uf
St Johnsbury, *Vermont* 40 Kc
St John's I., *Red Sea* 92 Ce
St Johns R., *Florida* 45 Ge
St Joris-Winge, *Belgium* 64 Cd
St Joseph, *Louisiana* 45 Be
St Joseph, *Michigan* 40 Cd
St Joseph, *Missouri* 49 Kc
St Joseph, L., *Ontario* 31 Kg
St-Joseph-de-Beauce, *Que.* 32 Bg
St Joseph I., *Ontario* 34 Gf
St Joseph I., *Texas* 48 Jj
St Joseph's, *Nfld.* 33 Tf
St-Jovite, *Quebec* 35 Qf
St Kilda, I., *Scotland* 62 Bc
St Kitts, *Leeward Is.* 51 Gc
St Kitts. *See* St. Christopher I.
St-Lambert, *Quebec* 35 Rg
St-Lambert-de-Lauzon, *Que.* 35 Tf
St Laurent, *Fr. Guiana* 53 Gb
St Laurent, *Manitoba* 37 Uh
St-Laurent, *Quebec* 35 Rj
St-Laurent, Fleuve, *Quebec* 35 Ue
St Lawrence, *Nfld.* 33 Rg
St Lawrence, *Queensland* 57 Jd
St Lawrence, C., *N.S.* 33 Mf
St Lawrence, G. of, 32 Kf
St Lawrence I., *Alaska* 43 Vl
St Lawrence I., *Bering Sea* 43 Vl
St Lawrence Islands Nat. Pk., *Ontario* 35 Oh
St Lawrence River, 35 Ue
St Lawrence Seaway, *N. America* 40 Jc
St Lazare, *Manitoba* 37 Qh
St Léger, *Belgium* 64 De
St Lenaarts, *Belgium* 64 Cc
St Léonard, *France* 72 Dd
St-Léonard, *N.B.* 32 Ef
St-Léonard, *Quebec* 35 Sh
St-Léonard-d'Aston, *Que.* 35 Sf
St-Léon-de-Chicoutimi, *Que.* 32 Ae
St-Léon-de-Standon, *Que.* 32 Bg
St-Léon-le-Grand, *Quebec* 32 Ee
St Lewis R., *Nfld.* 33 Pa
St-Liboire, *Quebec* 35 Sg
St Lô, *France* 72 Cb
St Louis, *Mauritania* 98 Be
St Louis, *Michigan* 40 Dd
St Louis, *Missouri* 45 Ba
St Louis, *Prince Edward I.* 32 Hg
St Louis, *Saskatchewan* 37 Mf
St-Louis, L., *Quebec* 35 Rg
St-Louis-de-Kent, *N.B.* 32 Hg
St-Louis-du-Ha-Ha, *Que.* 32 Df
St Lucia, *Windward Is.* 51 Gd
St Lucia C., *Natal* 95 Ee
St Lucia L., *Natal* 95 Ee
St-Ludger, *Quebec* 32 Bh
St Luke's I., *Burma* 89 Jf
St Lunaire B., *Nfld.* 33 Rb
St Maartensdijk, *Neth.* 64 Cc
St Magnus B., *Shetland* 62 Ha
St Maixent, *France* 72 Cc
St-Malachie, *Quebec* 32 Bg
St Malo, *France* 72 Bb
St Marc, *Haiti* 51 Ec
St-Marc-des-Carrières, *Que.* 35 Sf
St-Marcel, *Quebec* 32 Bg
St Mard, *Belgium* 64 De
St Margaret B., *Nfld.* 33 Pb
St Margarets B., *N.S.* 32 Jj
St Marks, *Florida* 45 Ee
St Martin, *Leeward Is.* 51 Gc
St Martin, L., *Manitoba* 37 Tg
St Martins, *N.B.* 32 Gh
St Mary, Mt., *B.C.* 39 Pl
St Mary Is., *India* 88 Df
St Mary Pk., *S. Australia* 57 Gf
St Mary Res., *Alberta* 36 Dj
St Mary's, *Nfld.* 33 Tg
St Marys, *Ontario* 34 Jj
St Marys, *Pennsylvania* 44 Ab
St Marys, *Tasmania* 57 Jh
St Mary's B., *Nfld.* 33 Tg
St Marys B., *Nova Scotia* 32 Fj
St Mary's C., *Nfld.* 33 Sg
St Mary's L., *Scotland* 62 Ee
St Mary's R., *Nova Scotia* 33 Kh
St Mary's R., *Ont./Mich.* 34 Ff
St-Mathieu, *Quebec* 32 De
St-Mathieu, *Quebec* 35 Md
St Matthew I., *Alaska* 43 Vl
St Matthew I., *Bering Sea* 43 Vm
St Matthew's I., *Burma* 89 Jg
St Maurice, *Switzerland* 65 Cb
St-Maurice, R., *Quebec* 35 Re
St-Maxime, *Quebec* 32 Bg
St Maximin, *France* 73 Fe
St Meen, *France* 72 Bb
St Michael, *Alaska* 43 Wl
St Michaels, *Maryland* 40 Hf
St-Michel, *Quebec* 35 Rj
St-Michel-des-Saints, *Que.* 35 Rf
St Moritz, *Switzerland* 65 Eb
St Nazaire, *France* 72 Bc
St Nicolaasga, *Netherlands* 64 Db
St Niklaas, *Belgium* 64 Cc
St Niklaus, *Switzerland* 65 Cb
St Norbert, *Manitoba* 37 Uj
St Odiliënberg, *Netherlands* 64 Ec
St Omer, *France* 72 Ea
St-Omer, *Quebec* 32 Fe
Saintonge, *France* 72 Cd
St-Ours, *Quebec* 35 Rg
St-Pacôme, *Quebec* 32 Cf
St-Pamphile, *Quebec* 32 Cg
St-Pascal, *Quebec* 32 Cf
St-Patrice, L., *Quebec* 35 Nf
St Paul, *Alberta* 36 Fd
St Paul, *Minnesota* 46 Lc
St Paul, I., *Indian Ocean* 100 Fh
Saint-Paul, R., *Quebec* 33 Pb
St Paul de Fenouillet, *France* 73 Ee
St-Paul-de-la-Croix, *Quebec* 32 Cf
St-Paul-de-Montminy, *Que.* 32 Bg
St-Paul-du-Nord, *Quebec* 32 Ce
St Paul I., *Bering Sea* 43 Vm
St Paul I., *Nova Scotia* 33 Mf
St-Paulin, *Quebec* 35 Rf
St Pauls Inlet, *Nfld.* 33 Pd
St Peter, *Minnesota* 46 Lc
Saint Peter Bay, *Nfld.* 33 Ra
St Peters, *Nova Scotia* 33 Mh
St Peters, *Prince Edward I.* 32 Kg
St Petersburg, *Florida* 45 Fg
St Petersburg, *Pennsylvania* 44 Ab
St-Philémon, *Quebec* 32 Bg
St Philipsland, *Netherlands* 64 Cc
St-Pie, *Quebec* 35 Sg
St Pierre, *Manitoba* 36 Ea
St Pierre, *Martinique, W.I.* 51 Gd
St-Pierre, *Quebec* 35 Rk
St-Pierre, L., *Quebec* 35 Sf
St Pierre & I., 33 Qg
St Pierre & Miquelon, 33 Pg
St-Pierre-Montmagny, *Que.* 40 Lb
St Pol, *France* 72 Ea
St Pölten, *Austria* 69 Fd
St Pons, *France* 73 Ee
St Pourçain, *France* 72 Ec
St-Prime, *Quebec* 35 Sd
St Quentin, *France* 72 Eb
St Quentin, *N.B.* 32 Ef
St-Raphaël, *Quebec* 32 Bg
St-Raymond, *Quebec* 35 Tf
St-Rémi, *Quebec* 35 Rg
St-Robert, *Quebec* 35 Rg
St-Romain, *Quebec* 32 Ah
St-Romauld-d'Etchemin, *Quebec* 32 Ag
St-Sauveur-des-Monts, *Que.* 35 Qg
St Sébastien C., *Madagascar* 97 Nj
St Sernin-sur-Rance, *France* 73 Ee
St Servan, *France* 72 Bb
St Sever, *France* 73 Ce
St Shotts, *Nfld.* 33 Tg
St-Siméon, *Quebec* 32 Bf
St-Simon, *Quebec* 32 Ce
St Stephen, *N.B.* 32 Eh
St-Sylvestre, *Quebec* 35 Tf
St-Théophile, *Quebec* 32 Bh
St Thomas, *Ontario* 34 Jk
St Thomas, *Virgin Is.* 51 Gc
St-Tite, *Quebec* 35 Sf
St-Tite-des-Caps, *Quebec* 32 Bf
St Trond. *See* St Truiden
St Tropez, *France* 73 Ge
St Truiden, *Belgium* 64 Dd
St-Ulric, *Quebec* 32 Ee
St-Urbain, *Quebec* 32 Bf
St Valéry, *France* 72 Da
St Valéry-en-Caux, *France* 72 Db
St-Vallier, *Quebec* 32 Bg
St Veit, *Austria* 68 Fe
St-Victor, *Quebec* 32 Bg
St Vincent, *Windward Is.* 51 Gd
St Vincent, G., *S. Australia* 57 Gg
St Vincent C., *Madagascar* 97 Ml
St-Vincent-de-Paul, *Que.* 35 Rh
St Vincent's, *Nfld.* 33 Tg
St Vith, *Belgium* 64 Ed
St Walburg, *Sask.* 36 He
St Williams, *Ontario* 34 Kk
St Xavier, *Montana* 46 Dc
St-Yvon, *Quebec* 32 Hd
Saipan, *Mariana Is.* 102 Df
Saivomuotka, *Sweden* 66 Kb
Saiyidwala, *Pakistan* 90 Ce
Sajama, *Bolivia* 52 Dg
Sakai, *Japan* 86 Dg
Sakai-Minato, *Japan* 86 Cg
Sakakah, *Arabia* 92 Dd
Sakakawea L., *N. Dakota* 46 Fb
Sakami, L., *Quebec* 31 Mg
Sakania, *Zaire* 97 Fg
Sakarya, *Turkey* 92 Bb
Sakata, *Japan* 86 Fe
Sakesar, *Pakistan* 90 Cd
Sakha, *Arabia* 92 De
Sakhalin, *U.S.S.R.* 79 Pc
Sakhalinskiy Zaliv, *U.S.S.R.* 79 Pc
Saki, *U.S.S.R.* 80 Hj
Sakiai, *Lithuania* 67 Kj
Sakishima Shotō, Is., *Japan* 86 Kk
Sakti, *India* 91 Db
Sakylä, *Finland* 67 Kf
Šala, *Czechoslovakia* 69 Gd
Sala, *Sweden* 67 Gg
Salaberry-de-Valleyfield, *Que.* 35 Qg
Salacgriva, *Latvia* 67 Lh
Sala Consilina, *Italy* 75 Ee
Salada, L., *Mexico* 50 Aa
Salado, *Argentina* 54 Dc
Salado, R., *Texas* 48 Hj
Salaga, *Ghana* 98 Eg
Salala, *Oman* 93 Ff
Salama, *Guatemala* 50 Fd
Salamanca, *Mexico* 50 Dc
Salamanca, *New York* 40 Gd
Salamanca, *Spain* 70 Cb
Salamaua, *New Guinea* 57 Ja
Salamina, *Colombia* 52 Bb
Salamís, *Greece* 77 Df
Salangen, *Norway* 66 Gb
Salas, *Spain* 70 Ba
Salas de los Infantes, *Spain* 70 Da
Salaverry, *Peru* 52 Be
Salayar, *Indonesia* 83 Hm
Sala-y-gomez, *Pacific Oc.* 103 Qk
Salbris, *France* 72 Ec
Saldana, *Spain* 70 Ca
Saldus, *Latvia* 67 Kh
Sale, *Victoria* 57 Jg
Salekhard, *U.S.S.R.* 78 Fb
Salem, *Illinois* 49 Nc
Salem, *India* 88 Ef
Salem, *Massachusetts* 40 Ld
Salem, *Missouri* 45 Bb
Salem, *New Jersey* 40 Jf
Salem, *Oregon* 47 Bc
Salem, *Virginia* 45 Gb
Salemi, *Sicily* 75 Dg
Sälen, *Sweden* 67 Ef
Salerno, *Italy* 75 Ee
Salerno, G. di., *Italy* 75 Ee
Salford, *England* 63 Fg
Salgueiro, *Brazil* 53 Ke
Salida, *Colorado* 48 Dc
Salina, *Italy* 75 Ef
Salina, *Kansas* 49 Jc
Salina, *Utah* 48 Bc
Salina Cruz, *Mexico* 50 Ed
Salinas, *California* 47 Cg
Salinas, *Ecuador* 52 Ad
Salinas, *Mexico* 50 Dc
Salinas, *Mexico* 50 Db
Salinas Pk., *New Mexico* 48 Df
Salinas R., *California* 47 Cg
Saline R., *Kansas* 42 Gd
Salinitas, *Chile* 54 Cc
Salinópolis, *Brazil* 53 Hd
Salins, *France* 72 Fc
Salisbury, *England* 63 Fj
Salisbury, *Maryland* 43 Kd
Salisbury, *N. Carolina* 45 Gc
Salisbury, *New Brunswick* 32 Gg
Salisbury, *Zimbabwe* 95 Ec
Salisbury, L. *See* Bisina, L.
Salisbury I., *N.W.T.* 31 Me
Salisbury Plain, *England* 63 Fj
Salkhad, *Syria* 94 Ee
Sallisaw, *Oklahoma* 49 Ke
Sallyana, *Nepal* 91 Da
Salmas, *Iran* 92 Db
Salmo, *British Columbia* 39 Pl
Salmon, R., *B.C.* 39 Mh
Salmon Arm, *B.C.* 39 Ok
Salmon Bay, *Quebec* 33 Pb
Salmon Gums, *W. Australia* 56 Df
Salmon R., *Idaho* 47 Fc
Salmon R., *New Brunswick* 32 Gg
Salmon River Mts., *Idaho* 47 Fc
Salo, *Finland* 67 Kf
Salon, *France* 73 Fe
Salon, *India* 91 Cb
Salonica. *See* Thessaloniki
Salonta, *Romania* 76 Ca
Salop, *England* 63 Fh
Salqin, *Syria* 94 Ea
Salsette I., *India* 88 De
Salta, *Argentina* 54 Cb
Saltcoats, *Saskatchewan* 37 Pg
Saltdal, *Norway* 66 Fc
Saltee, Is., *Eire* 63 Ch
Salt Fd., *Norway* 66 Fc
Saltillo, *Mexico* 50 Db
Salt L., *Utah* 48 Ac
Salt L., *W. Australia* 56 Bd
Salt Lake City, *Utah* 48 Bb
Salt Ls., *W. Australia* 56 Ee
Salto, *Argentina* 54 Dd
Salto, *Uruguay* 54 Ed
Salto da Divisa, *Brazil* 53 Kg
Salton Sea, *California* 47 Fj
Salt R., *Arizona* 48 Bf
Salt Ra., *Pakistan* 88 Db
Salt River, *N.W.T.* 38 Re
Saltrou, *Haiti* 51 Ec
Salt Sulphur Springs, *W. Virginia* 45 Gb
Saltville, *Virginia* 45 Gb
Saluda, *Virginia* 45 Jb
Salûm & G. of, *Egypt* 99 Lb
Salur, *India* 89 Fe
Salut, Is du, *Fr. Guiana* 53 Gb
Saluzzo, *Italy* 74 Ac
Salvador, *Brazil* 53 Kf
Salvador, *Saskatchewan* 36 Hf
Salvador, El, *Central America* 51 Bd
Salvador, L., *Louisiana* 49 Mh
Salvage, *Newfoundland* 33 Te
Salvaterra, *Portugal* 70 Ac
Salvatierra, *Mexico* 50 Dc
Salvus, *British Columbia* 39 Jh
Salzburg, *Austria* 68 Ee
Salzgitter, *W. Germany* 68 Db
Salzwedel, *E. Germany* 68 Db
Samalut, *Egypt* 99 Mc
Samanã, *Dom. Rep.* 51 Fc
Samangan, *Afghanistan* 93 Jb
Samar, *Philippines* 83 Jh
Samarai, *Papua New Guinea* 57 Kb

Samarinda, Borneo (Kalimantan) 83 Gl
Samarkand, Uzbekistan 78 Fe
Samarra Balad, Iraq 92 Dc
Samastipur, India 91 Ec
Sambalpur, India 89 Fd
Sambava, Madagascar 97 Pj
Sambeek, Netherlands 64 Dc
Sambhal, India 91 Ba
Sambhar L., India 88 Dc
Sambor, Ukraine 80 Cg
Samborombón, B., Arg. 54 Ee
Sambre, Belgium 64 Cd
Samedan, Switzerland 65 Eb
Samira, Arabia 92 Dd
Sam Neau, Laos 87 Cb
Samoa, Pacific Ocean 102 Hj
Samoa. See Western Samoa and American Samoa
Samokov, Bulgaria 76 Dc
Samorogouan, Upper Volta 98 Ef
Samos, Greece 77 Ff
Samothrace. See Samothráki
Samothráki, Greece 77 Ed
Sampacho, Arg. 54 Dd
Sampit, Borneo (Kalimantan) 83 Fl
Sam Rayburn Res., Texas 49 Kg
Samrée, Belgium 64 Dd
Samsang, China 89 Fb
Samsat, Turkey 92 Cb
Samsö, I., Denmark 67 Dj
Samsu, Korea 82 Jb
Samsun, Turkey 92 Ca
Samthar, India 91 Bc
San, Mali 98 Ef
San'ā, Yemen 92 Df
Sanam, Jebel, Iraq 92 Ec
San Ambrosio, Pacific Oc. 103 Tk
Sanana, Moluccas 83 Jl
Sanandaj, Iran 92 Eb
San Andres Mts., New Mex. 48 Df
San Angelo, Texas 48 Gg
San Antioco, Sardinia 75 Bf
San Antonio, Chile 54 Bd
San Antonio, Chile 54 Cb
San Antonio, Mexico 50 Cc
San Antonio, Texas 49 Hh
San Antonio, C., Argentina 54 Ee
San Antonio, C., Cuba 51 Cb
San Antonio Oeste, Arg. 54 Df
San Antonio Pk., New Mex. 48 Dd
San Antonio R. and B., Texas 48 Jh
Sanaraipo, Venezuela 52 Db
San Bartolomeu de Messines, Portugal 70 Ad
San Benedetto del Tronto, Italy 74 Dd
San Benito, Texas 48 Jj
San Benito Is., Mexico 50 Ab
San Bernardino, California 47 Eh
San Bernardino Range, Cal. 47 Fj
San Bernardo, Chile 54 Bd
San Blas, Argentina 54 Df
San Blas, Mexico 50 Cb
San Blas, Mexico 50 Cc
San Blas, C., Florida 43 Jf
San Blas, G. de, Panama 51 De
San Borja, Mexico 50 Bb
Sanborn, N. Dakota 46 Hb
San Carlos, Amazonas, Venez. 52 Dc
San Carlos, Argentina 54 Cc
San Carlos, Argentina 54 Cd
San Carlos, Chile 54 Be
San Carlos, Cojedes, Venez. 52 Db
San Carlos, Mexico 50 Ec
San Carlos, Nicaragua 51 Cd
San Carlos Córdoba, Arg. 54 Cd
San Carlos de Bariloche, Argentina 54 Bf
San Carlos del Zulia, Venez. 52 Cb
San Carlos L., Arizona 48 Bf
Sanchez, Dominican Rep. 51 Fc
San Clemente, Spain 71 Dc
San Cosme, Paraguay 54 Ec
San Cristóbal, Argentina 54 Dd
San Cristobal, Galápagos I. 103 Sh
San Cristóbal, Mexico 50 Fd
San Cristobal, Solomon Is. 102 Fj
San Cristóbal, Venezuela 52 Cb
Sancti Spiritus, Cuba 51 Db
Sanctuary, Saskatchewan 36 Jh
Sand, Norway 67 Bg
Sandakan, Sabah 83 Gj
Sanday I., Orkney 62 Fa
Sandbank L., Ontario 34 Ha
Sandefjord, Norway 67 Dg
Sanders, Arizona 48 Ce
Sandfly L., Sask. 36 Lc
Sandgate, Queensland 57 Ke
Sand Hills, Great, Sask. 36 Hh
Sand Hills, Middle, Alberta 36 Gh
Sandhornøy, Norway 66 Ec
Sandia, Peru 52 Df
San Diego, California 47 Ej
San Diego, Texas 48 Hj
San Diego, C., Argentina 54 Ch
San Diego de Cabrutica, Venezuela 52 Eb
Sandikli, Turkey 92 Bb
Sandila, India 91 Cb
Sandilands, Manitoba 36 Fa
San Dimas, Mexico 50 Cc
Sand L., Ontario 36 Ha
Sand L., Big, Manitoba 37 Sa
Sand L., Little, Manitoba 37 Ta
Sand Lake, Ontario 34 Fe
Sandnes, Norway 67 Ag
Sandoa, Zaire 96 Ef
San Domingos, Portugal 70 Bd
Sandoway, Burma 89 He
Sandpoint, Idaho 42 Cb
Sand Point L., Minnesota 36 Kb
Sand R., Alberta 36 Fd
Sandspit, B.C. 39 Hj
Sandstone, Minnesota 46 Lb
Sandstone, W. Australia 56 Ce
Sandtop, C., Quebec 33 Ld
Sandträsk, Sweden 66 Jc
Sandusky, Michigan 40 Ed
Sandusky, Ohio 40 Ee
Sandvig, Bornholm, Den. 67 Fj
Sandwich B., Nfld. 31 Og
Sandwith, Saskatchewan 36 Je
Sandybeach L., Ontario 36 Ka
Sandy C., Queensland 57 Kd
Sandy Creek, Quebec 35 Og
Sandy L., Newfoundland 33 Qd
Sandy L., Ontario 30 Kg
Sandy Lake, Manitoba 37 Rh
Sandy Lake, Saskatchewan 39 Ug
Sandy Narrows, Sask. 37 Oc
San Esteban de Gormaz, Spain 70 Db
San Felipe, Chile 54 Bd
San Felipe, Guatemala 50 Fe
San Felipe, Mexico 50 Ba
San Felipe, Mexico 50 Fd
San Felipe, Venezuela 52 Da
San Feliú de Guixols, Spain 71 Gb
San Feliu de Llobregat, Spain 71 Fb
San Félix, Venezuela 52 Eb
San Félix, I., Pacific Ocean 103 Sk
San Fernando, Chile 54 Bd
San Fernando, Mexico 50 Ab
San Fernando, Mexico 50 Ec
San Fernando, Philippines 83 Hg
San Fernando, Trinidad 52 Ea
San Fernando de Apure, Venezuela 52 Db
San Fernando de Atabapo, Venezuela 52 Dc
Sanford, Florida 45 Gf
Sanford, Maine 32 Bk
Sanford, Manitoba 37 Uj
Sanford, N. Carolina 45 Hc
Sanford, Mt., Alaska 43 Yl
San Francisco, Argentina 54 Dd
San Francisco, California 47 Bg
San Francisco de Maconis, Dominican Rep. 51 Ec
San Francisco Mts., Arizona 48 Be
Sangareddipet, India 88 Ee
Sanger, N. Dakota 46 Gb
San German, Costa Rica 51 Fc
Sanggau, Borneo (Kalimantan) 83 Fk
Sangihe Kep., Indonesia 83 Jk
San Giovanni in Fiore, Italy 75 Ff
Sangkulirang, Borneo (Kalimantan) 83 Gk
Sangla, Pakistan 90 Ce
Sangre de Cristo Mts., Colorado/New Mexico 48 Ed
Sangre Grande, Trinidad 52 Ea
Sangrur, India 90 De
Sangudo, Alberta 36 Ce
Sanguin, Liberia 98 Dg
San Ignacio, Bolivia 52 Eg
San Ignacio, Mexico 50 Cc
San Ignacio, Mexico 50 Bb
San Ignacio, Paraguay 54 Ec
San Javier, Argentina 54 Ed
San Javier, Bolivia 52 Eg
San Javier, Chile 54 Be
San João, Portugal 70 Bb
San Joaquim, Bolivia 52 Ef
San Jorge, G., Argentina 54 Cg
San Jose, California 47 Cg
San José, Costa Rica 51 Ce
San José, Guatemala 50 Fe
San José, Uruguay 54 Ed
San José, G., Argentina 54 Df
San José, I., Mexico 50 Bb
San José Carpizo, Mexico 50 Fd
San José de Amacuro, Venezuela 52 Eb
San José de Chiquitos, Bolivia 52 Eg
San José de Feliciano, Arg. 54 Ed
San José del Cabo, Mexico 50 Cc
San José del Gulaviare, Colombia 52 Cc
San José de Ocune, Colombia 52 Cc
San Juan, Argentina 54 Cd
San Juan, Bolivia 52 Fg
San Juan, Peru 52 Bg
San Juan, Puerto Rico 51 Cd
San Juan, C., Argentina 54 Dh
San Juan, R., Mexico 50 Ed
San Juan, R., Nicaragua 51 Cd
San Juan de Camarones, Mexico 50 Cb
San Juan de Guadalupe, Mexico 50 Dc
San Juan del Norte, Nic. 51 Cd
San Juan de los Cayos, Venezuela 52 Da
San Juan de los Lagos, Mexico 50 Dc
San Juan del Rio, Mexico 50 Ec
San Juan del Sur, Nicaragua 51 Bd
San Juan Mts., Colorado 48 Dd
San Juan R., Utah/New Mexico 48 Bd
San Julian, Argentina 54 Cg
San Justo, Argentina 54 Dd
San Lázaro, C., Mexico 50 Bc
San Leandro, California 47 Bg
San Lorenzo, Argentina 54 Dd
San Lorenzo, Ecuador 52 Bc
San Lorenzo, Honduras 51 Bd
San Lorenzo, Mexico 50 Ba
San Lorenzo, Peru 52 Df
San Lorenzo del Escorial, Spain 70 Cb
San Lorenzo Is., Mexico 50 Bb
Sanlucar la Mayor, Spain 70 Bd
San Lucas, Bolivia 52 Dh
San Lucas, C., Mexico 50 Cc
San Luis, Argentina 54 Ec
San Luis, Cuba 51 Db
San Luis de la Paz, Mexico 50 Dc
San Luis Obispo, California 47 Ch
San Luis Potosi, Mexico 50 Dc
Sanluri, Sardinia 75 Bf
San Marcos, Colombia 52 Bb
San Marino, Italy 74 Dd
San Martin, Argentina 54 Bf
San Martin, Colombia 52 Cc
San Martin, L., Chile/Arg. 54 Bg
San Martin de los Andes, Argentina 54 Bf
San Martín de Valdeiglesias, Spain 70 Cb
San Martinho, Portugal 70 Ac
San Mateo, Florida 45 Gf
San Mateo, Spain 71 Fb
San Mateo Pk., New Mexico 48 Df
San Matias, Bolivia 52 Fg
San Matias, G., Argentina 54 Df
Sanmaur, Quebec 35 Re
San Maura. See Levkás
Sanmenxia, China 84 Ee
San Miguel, Bolivia 52 Eg
San Miguel, Mexico 50 Dc
San Miguel, Peru 52 Cf
San Miguel, Salvador 51 Bd
San Miguel, B. de, Panama 51 De
San Miguel, I. del Rey, Panama 51 De
San Miguel, R., Bolivia 52 Eg
San Miguel de Huachi, Bolivia 52 Dg
San Miguel de Tucuman, Argentina 54 Cc
San Miguel I., California 47 Ch
Sanming, China 85 Hj
Sanming, China 85 Hj
San Nicolás, Argentina 54 Dd
San Pablo, Bolivia 52 Dh
San Pablo, C., Argentina 54 Ch
San Pedro, Argentina 54 Ed
San Pedro, Belize 51 Bc
San Pedro, California 47 Dj
San Pedro, Ivory Coast 98 Dh
San Pedro, Mexico 50 Db
San Pedro, Paraguay 54 Eb
San Pedro Channel, California 47 Dj
San Pedro de Arimena, Colombia 52 Cc
San Pedro del Gallo, Mexico 50 Db
San Pedro de Lloc, Peru 52 Be
San Pedro de Macorís, Dominican Rep. 51 Fc
San Pedro do Sul, Portugal 70 Ab
San Pedro R., Arizona 48 Bf
San Pedro Sula, Honduras 51 Bc
San Pietro, Sardinia 75 Bf
San Quintín, Mexico 50 Aa
San Rafael, Argentina 54 Cd
San Rafael, California 47 Bg
San Rafael, New Mexico 42 Ed
San Ramón, Peru 52 Bf
San Remo, Italy 74 Ad
San Roque, Argentina 54 Ec
San Salvador, Salvador 51 Bd
San Salvador, The Bahamas 51 Eb
San Salvador de Jujuy, Argentina 54 Cb
Sansanne Mango, Togo 98 Ff
San Sebastián, Arg. 54 Ch
San Sebastián, Spain 71 Da
San Severo, Italy 75 Ee
Sanshui, China 85 Fl
Sans Souci, Ontario 40 Fc
Santa, Peru 52 Be
Santa Ana, Bolivia 52 Df
Santa Ana, Bolivia 52 Fg
Santa Ana, California 47 Ej
Santa Ana, Ecuador 52 Ad
Santa Ana, Mexico 50 Ba
Santa Ana, Salvador 51 Bd
Santa Barbara, California 47 Dh
Santa Barbara, Honduras 51 Bd
Santa Barbara Channel, Cal. 47 Ch
Santa Catalina, Chile 54 Cc
Santa Catalina, I., Mexico 50 Bb
Santa Catalina I., California 47 Dj
Santa Catarina, Mexico 50 Cc
Santa Catarina, I., Brazil 54 Gc
Santa Clara, Brazil 52 Dd
Santa Clara, Cuba 51 Cb
Santa Clara, Sa., Mexico 50 Bb
Santa Coloma de Farnes, Spain 71 Gb
Santa Cruz, Argentina 54 Ch
Santa Cruz, Bolivia 52 Eg
Santa Cruz, California 47 Bg
Santa Cruz, Chile 54 Bd
Santa Cruz, Mexico 50 Ba
Santa Cruz, Peru 52 Be
Santa Cruz, Philippines 83 Hh
Santa Cruz, R., Argentina 54 Bh
Santa Cruz Channel, Cal. 47 Dj
Santa Cruz de la Zarza, Spain 70 Dc
Santa Cruz del Sur, Cuba 51 Db
Santa Cruz de Tenerife, Canary Is. 98 Bc
Santa Cruz Is., Pacific Ocean 102 Fj
Santa Elena, Ecuador 52 Ad
Santa Eufemia, G. di, Italy 75 Ff
Santa Fé, Argentina 54 Dd
Santa Fé, Cuba 51 Cb
Santa Fe, New Mexico 48 Ee
Santa Fe, New Mexico 42 Ed
Santa Filomena, Brazil 53 He
Santa Helena, Brazil 53 Fe
Santa Helena, Brazil 53 Hd
Santa Helena, Brazil 54 Fb
Santai, China 84 Bg
Santa Inés, B., Mexico 50 Bb
Santa Ines, I., Chile 54 Bh
Santa Isabel, Argentina 54 Ce
Santa Isabel. See Malabo
Santa Isabel, Solomon Islands 102 Eh
Santa Lucia, Cuba 51 Db
Santa Margarita, I., Mexico 50 Bc
Santa Maria, Argentina 54 Cc
Santa Maria, Brazil 54 Fc
Santa Maria, California 47 Ch
Santa María, Mexico 50 Cb
Santa Maria, I., Atlantic Oc. 98 Bb
Santa Maria, I., Chile 54 Be
Santa Maria, Mt., Argentina 54 Ce
Santa María del Rio, Mex. 50 Dc
Santa Maria di Leuca C., Italy 75 Gf
Santa Maria la Real de Nieva, Spain 70 Cb
Santa Marta, Colombia 52 Ca
Santa Monica, California 47 Dh
Santa Monica B., California 47 Dj
Santander, Colombia 52 Bc
Santander, Spain 70 Da
Santa Paula, California 47 Dh
Santa Quiteria, Brazil 53 Jd
Santarem, Brazil 53 Gd
Santarem, Portugal 70 Ac
Santa Rita, Brazil 53 Fe
Santa Rita, Venezuela 52 Ca
Santa Rosa, Argentina 54 Cd
Santa Rosa, Argentina 54 Cd
Santa Rosa, Bolivia 52 Eg
Santa Rosa, Brazil 54 Fc
Santa Rosa, California 47 Bf
Santa Rosa, Honduras 51 Bd
Santa Rosa, New Mexico 48 Ee
Santa Rosa de Toay, Argentina 54 De
Santa Rosa I., California 47 Cj
Santa Rosalia, Mexico 50 Bb
Santa Sylvina, Argentina 54 Dc
Santa Vitoria do Palmar, Brazil 54 Fd
Santee R., S. Carolina 43 Ke
Santiago, Brazil 54 Fc
Santiago, Chile 54 Bd
Santiago, Dominican Rep. 51 Ec
Santiago, Mexico 50 Cc
Santiago, Mexico 50 Cc
Santiago, Panama 51 Ce
Santiago, Cerro, Panama 51 Ce
Santiago, Sa. de, Bolivia 52 Fg
Santiago de Compostela, Spain 70 Aa
Santiago de Cuba, Cuba 51 Dc
Santiago del Estero, Arg. 54 Dc
Santiago Mts., Texas 48 Fh
Santiago Papasquiaro, Mexico 50 Cc
Santillana, Spain 70 Ca
Santipur, India 91 Gd
Santis, Switzerland 65 Ea
Santo Angelo, Brazil 54 Fc
Santo Antônio, Brazil 52 Ef
Santo Antonio, Brazil 53 Gd
Santo Antonio do Zaire, Angola 96 Cf
Santo Corazón, Bolivia 52 Fg
Santo Domingo, Cuba 51 Cb
Santo Domingo, Dom. Rep. 51 Fc
Santo Domingo, Mexico 50 Aa
Santoríni. See Thira
Santos, Brazil 53 Hh
Santo Tomás, Mexico 50 Aa
Santo Tomás, Peru 52 Cf
Santo Tomé, Argentina 54 Ec
San Urbano, Argentina 54 Dd
San Valentin, Chile 54 Bg
San Vicente, Salvador 51 Bd
San Vicente del Caguán, Colombia 52 Cc
San Vito C., Italy 75 Fe
São Antonio do Içá, Brazil 52 Dd
São Bento do Norte, Brazil 53 Ke
São Borja, Brazil 54 Ec
São Carlos, Brazil 53 Hh
São Cristovão, Brazil 53 Kf
São Domingos, Brazil 53 Hf
São Félix, Brazil 53 Ge
São Francisco, Brazil 53 Ke
São Francisco, Brazil 53 Jg
São Francisco, Brazil 53 Je
São Francisco do Sul, Brazil 54 Gc
Sao Hill, Tanzania 97 Hf
São Jeronimo, Brazil 53 Gh
São Jeronimo, Brazil 54 Fc
São Joao da Barra, Brazil 53 Jh
São Joao da Boa Vista, Brazil 53 Hh
São Joao del Rei, Brazil 53 Jh
São João do Araguaya, Brazil 53 He
São João do Piau, Brazil 53 Je
São Joaquim, Brazil 52 Dc
São José, Brazil 52 Dd
São José, Brazil 54 Gc
São José, Brazil 54 Ed
São José do Mipibu, Brazil 53 Ke
São José do Rio Prêto, Brazil 53 Hh
São Lourenço, Brazil 53 Fg
São Luis, Brazil 53 Jd
São Luis, I. de, Brazil 53 Jd
São Luiz Gonzaga, Brazil 54 Fc
São Martinho, Brazil 53 Fe
São Mateus, Brazil 53 Kg
São Mateus do Sul, Brazil 54 Fc
São Miguel, Atlantic Oc. 98 Ba
Saona, Dominican Rep. 51 Fc
Saône, France 72 Fc
Saône-et-Loire, France 72 Fc
São Paulo, Brazil 53 Hh
São Paulo de Olivença, Brazil 52 Dd
São Raimundo Nonato, Brazil 53 Je
São Romão, Brazil 52 De
São Salvador, Angola 96 Cf
São Sebastião, Brazil 53 Hh
São Sebastião, Brazil 52 Ee
São Tomé, G. of Guinea 96 Bd
Saouayane, Pte., Quebec 35 La
São Vicente, Brazil 53 Hh
Sapiéntza, Greece 77 Cf
Saposoa, Peru 52 Be
Sapotnica, Yugoslavia 76 Cd
Sapporo, Japan 86 Gc
Sapri, Italy 75 Ee
Sapulpa, Oklahoma 49 Je
Saqqez, Iran 92 Eb
Saragossa. See Zaragoza
Saraguro, Ecuador 52 Bd
Saraikela, India 91 Ed
Sarajevo, Yugoslavia 76 Bc
Sarala, U.S.S.R. 78 Hc
Saranac Lake, New York 40 Jc
Sarandí del Yi, Uruguay 54 Ed
Sarangarh, India 89 Fd
Saransk, U.S.S.R. 81 Gc
Sarapul, U.S.S.R. 81 Lb
Sarasota, Florida 45 Fg
Saratoga, Wyoming 46 De
Saratoga L., New York 44 Da
Saratoga Springs, New York 44 Da
Saratov, U.S.S.R. 81 Ge
Saravane, Laos 87 Dc
Sarawak, Malaysia 83 Fk
Sarbaz, Iran 93 Hd
Sárbogárd, Hungary 69 He
Sarco, Chile 54 Bc
Sardalas, Libya 99 Hc
Sardarshahr, India 90 Df
Sardegna, Italy 75 Be
Sardhana, India 90 Ef
Sardinia. See Sardegna
Sardis, Mississippi 45 Cc
Sardoal, Portugal 70 Ac
Sareks Nat. Park, Sweden 66 Gc
Sargans, Switzerland 65 Ea
Sarh, Chad 96 Dc
Sāri, Iran 93 Fb
Sarikamis, Turkey 92 Da
Sarina, Queensland 57 Jd
Sariñena, Spain 71 Eb
Sar-i-Pul, Afghanistan 93 Jb
Sar-i-pul, Iran 92 Ec
Sarir, Libya 99 Kc
Sark, Channel Islands 72 Bb
Sarkad, Hungary 69 Je
Sarlat, France 73 Dd
Sarles, N. Dakota 46 Ha
Sarmi, Irian Jaya 83 Ll
Sarmiento, Argentina 54 Cg
Sarmiento, Chile 54 Bh
Sarna, Sweden 67 Ef
Sarnen, Switzerland 65 Db
Sarnia, Ontario 34 Hk
Sarno, Italy 75 Ee
Saronic G., Greece 77 Df
Saronno, Italy 74 Bc
Sarpsborg, Norway 67 Dg
Sarrebourg, France 72 Gb
Sarreguemines, France 72 Gb
Sarre-Union, France 72 Gb
Sarria, Spain 70 Ba
Sart, Belgium 64 Dd
Sartene, Corsica 75 Be
Sarthe R., France 72 Dc
Sarufutsu, Japan 86 Hb
Sarvar, Hungary 69 Ge
Sasa Baneh, Ethiopia 97 Jc
Sasaram, India 91 Ec
Sascumica, L., Quebec 35 Nb
Sasebo, Japan 86 Ah
Saskatchewan, Canada 30 Jg
Saskatchewan R., N., Alberta/Sask. 36 Kf
Saskatchewan R., S., Sask. 36 Jh
Saskatoon, Sask. 36 Lf
Saskeram L., Manitoba 37 Qe
Saskylakh, U.S.S.R. 79 La
Sasovo, U.S.S.R. 81 Ec
Sassandra, Ivory Coast 98 Dh
Sassari, Sardinia 75 Be
Sassnitz, East Germany 68 Ea
Sass R., N.W.T. 38 Re
Sastre, Argentina 54 Dd
Sas-van-Gent, Netherlands 64 Bc
Satadougou, Mali 98 Cf
Satara, India 88 De
Satellite B., N.W.T. 30 Hb
Säter, Sweden 67 Ff
Satevo, Mexico 50 Cb
Satka, U.S.S.R. 81 Pc
Satkhira, Bangladesh 91 Gd
Sátoraljaujhely, Hungary 69 Jd
Satpura Ra., India 88 Dd
Satu Mare, Romania 69 Ke
Satun, Thailand 87 Ce
Sauda, Norway 67 Bg
Saudhárkrókur, Iceland 66 Wm
Saudi Arabia, S.W. Asia 92
Saugeen, R., Ontario 34 Jh
Saugerties, New York 40 Kd
Saugstad, Mt., B.C. 39 Kj
Sauk Center, Minnesota 46 Kc
Sauk Rapids, Minnesota 46 Kc
Saulieu, France 72 Fc
Saulnierville, Nova Scotia 32 Fj
Sault-au-Mouton, Quebec 32 Ce
Sault aux Cochon, R. du, Quebec 32 Ce
Sault Ste Marie, Michigan 40 Db
Sault Ste Marie, Ontario 34 Ff
Saumons, R. aux, Quebec 32 Kd
Saumur, France 72 Cc
Saumur, L., Quebec 32 Kb
Saunders, Alberta 36 Bf
Saunders, S. Sandwich Is. 104 Ad
Sauterelles, L. aux, Que. 32 Jb
Sauvagesse, L. de la, Que. 33 Lc
Sava, Yugoslavia 76 Bb
Savai'i, Western Samoa 102 Hj
Savane R., Quebec 32 Ab
Savanna, Illinois 40 Ad
Savannah, Georgia, U.S.A. 45 Gd
Savannah, Missouri 49 Kc
Savannah R., Ga./S.C. 43 Ke
Savannakhet, Laos 87 Cc
Savanna la Mar, Jamaica 51 Dc
Savant Lake, Ontario 37 Ma
Savantvadi, India 88 De
Savanur, India 88 Ef
Savé, Benin 98 Fg
Save, Mozambique 95 Ed
Saveh, Iran 93 Fb
Savenay, France 72 Cc
Savoff, Ontario 34 Fc
Savoie, France 72 Gd
Savona, British Columbia 39 Nk
Savona, Italy 74 Bc
Savonlinna, Finland 66 Nf
Savu Sea, Indonesia 83 Hm
Sawatch Mts., Colorado 48 Dc
Sawbill, Manitoba 37 Qa
Sawdy, Alberta 36 Dd
Sawmill Bay, N.W.T. 38 Oc
Sawqirah B., Oman 93 Gf
Sawyerville, Quebec 35 Tg
Saxnäs, Sweden 66 Fd
Saxton, Pennsylvania 44 Ab
Saya, Syria 94 Db
Sayabec, Quebec 32 Ee
Saya Buri. See Pak-lay
Sayán, Peru 52 Bf
Sayan, Vostochnyy, U.S.S.R. 79 Jc
Sayan, Zapadnyy, U.S.S.R. 79 Jc
Sayhut, South Yemen 93 Ff
Saynshand, Mongolia 82 Fa
Sayre, Oklahoma 49 He
Sayre, Pennsylvania 44 Bb
Sayula, Mexico 50 Dd
Sayward, B.C. 39 Lk
Saywun, South Yemen 92 Ef
Scafell Pike, England 63 Ef
Scalea, Italy 75 Ef
Scandia, Alberta 36 Eh
Scânteia, Romania 76 Fa
Scanterbury, Manitoba 37 Vh
Scanzano, Italy 75 Fe
Scapa, Alberta 36 Fg
Scapa Flow, Orkney, Scot. 62 Eb
Scarborough, England 63 Gf
Scarborough, Ontario 34 Ej
Scarborough Bluffs, Ont. 34 Ek
Scărisoara, Romania 76 Da
Scarth, Manitoba 37 Rj
Scatarie I., Nova Scotia 33 Ng
Sceptre, Saskatchewan 36 Hh
Schafer, N. Dakota 46 Fb
Schaffhausen, Switzerland 65 Da
Schefferville, Quebec 31 Ng
Schelde, Ooster, Netherlands 64 Bc
Schenectady, New York 40 Jd
Scherpenheuvel, Belgium 64 Cd
Scheveningen, Netherlands 64 Cb
Schiedam, Netherlands 64 Cc
Schiermonnikoog, Neth. 64 Ea
Schiphol, Netherlands 64 Cb
Schleins, Switzerland 65 Fb
Schleswig, West Germany 68 Ca
Schleswig-Holstein, W. Ger. 68 Ca
Schneidemühl. See Pila
Schoharie, New York 44 Ca
Schönbuhl, Switzerland 65 Ca
Schönebeck, East Germany 68 Dc
Schongau, West Germany 68 De
Schoonhoven, Netherlands 64 Cc
Schötz, Switzerland 65 Da
Schouwen I., Netherlands 64 Bc
Schreiber, Ontario 34 Cd
Schuler, Alberta 36 Gh
Schull, Eire 63 Aj
Schultz L., N.W.T. 30 Ke
Schumacher, Ontario 34 Jd
Schüpfheim, Switzerland 65 Db
Schuyler, Nebraska 49 Jb
Schwabach, West Germany 68 Dd
Schwägalp, Switzerland 65 Ea
Schwandorf, West Germany 68 Ed
Schwaner Geb., Borneo (Kalimantan) 83 Fl
Schwarzhorn, Switz. 65 Cb
Schwarzwald, W. Germany 68 Cd
Schwedt, East Germany 68 Fb
Schweidnitz. See Swidnica
Schweinfurt, W. Germany 68 Dc
Schwerin, East Germany 68 Db
Schwyz, Switz. 65 Da
Sciacca, Sicily 75 Dg
Scilly, Is. of, England 63 Cl
Scituate, Massachusetts 44 Ea
Sclater, Manitoba 37 Rg
Scobey, Montana 46 Ea
Scollard, Alberta 36 Eg
Scoresby Ld., Greenland 41 Nb
Scoresby Sd., Greenland 41 Nb
Scotch Bay, Manitoba 37 Th
Scotia, Ontario 35 Lg
Scotia Bay, B.C. 38 Gf
Scotia Sea, Antarctica 104 Td
Scotland, Great Britain 62 Dc
Scotland, S. Dakota 46 Jd
Scotsburn, Nova Scotia 32 Kh
Scotsguard, Saskatchewan 36 Jj
Scotstown, Quebec 35 Tg
Scotsville, Nova Scotia 33 Lg
Scott, Saskatchewan 36 Jf
Scott, C., B.C. 39 Jk
Scott, Mt., Oregon 42 Bc
Scott City, Kansas 48 Gc
Scott I., Antarctica 104 Mc
Scott Inlet, N.W.T. 31 Mc
Scott Is., B.C. 39 Jk
Scott L., Sask./N.W.T. 38 Uf
Scotts Bluff, Nebraska 48 Fb
Scottsdale, Tasmania 57 Jh
Scout Lake, Sask. 37 Mj
Scranton, Pennsylvania 40 Je
Scudder, Ontario 34 Hk
Scugog, L., Ontario 35 Mh
Scuol (Schuls), Switzerland 65 Fb
Scutari. See Shkodër
Scutari. See Üsküdar
Seaford, Delaware 40 Jf
Seaforth, Ontario 34 Jj
Seager Wheeler L., Sask. 37 Od
Seahorse Pt., N.W.T. 31 Le
Sea I., British Columbia 39 Gl
Sea Isle City, New Jersey 40 Jf
Seal, R., Manitoba 30 Kf
Seal Bight, Nfld. 33 Ra
Seal Cove, N.B. 32 Fj
Seal Cove, Newfoundland 33 Qd
Sea Lion Is., Falkland Is. 54 Eh
Seal L., N.W.T. 38 Tc
Searchmont, Ontario 34 Ff
Searcy, Arkansas 49 Me
Searston, Newfoundland 33 Nf
Seattle, Washington 47 Bb
Seattle, Mt., Y.T./Alaska 38 De
Seba Beach, Alberta 36 Ce
Sebago L., Maine 32 Bk
Sebastian Vizcaino, B. de, Mexico 50 Bb
Sebenico. See Šibenik
Sebewaing, Michigan 40 Ed
Sebin Karahisar, Turkey 92 Ca
Séchelles, L., Quebec 32 Ca
Sechelt, British Columbia 39 Ml
Sečovce, Czechoslovakia 69 Jd
Secretan, Saskatchewan 36 Lh
Secretary I., New Zealand 55 Af
Secunderabad, India 88 Ee
Seda, Lithuania 67 Kh
Sedalia, Alberta 36 Gg
Sedalia, Missouri 49 Lc
Sedan, France 72 Fb
Sedano, Spain 70 Da
Seddon, New Zealand 55 Ed
Seddonville, New Zealand 55 Cd
Sedgewick, Alberta 36 Ff
Sedhiou, Senegal 98 Bf
Sedley, Saskatchewan 37 Oh
Sedom, Israel 94 Df
Sedrun, Switzerland 65 Db
Seebe, Alberta 36 Cg
Seeheim, Namibia 95 Be
Seeleys Bay, Ontario 35 Oh
Seelisberg, Switzerland 65 Db
Sées, France 72 Db
Seewis, Switzerland 65 Eb
Sefrou, Morocco 98 Eb
Sefton, New Zealand 55 De
Sefton, Mt., New Zealand 55 Ce
Segorbe, Spain 71 Ec
Ségou, Mali 98 Df
Segovia, Spain 70 Cb
Segovia, R., Nicaragua 51 Cd
Séguela, Ivory Coast 98 Dg
Sehkuheh, Iran 93 Hc
Sehwan, Pakistan 88 Cc
Seignelay, R., Quebec 32 Ca
Seiland, Norway 66 Ka
Seinäjoki, Finland 66 Ke
Seine, France 72 Db
Seine-et-Marne, France 72 Eb
Seine Maritime, France 72 Db
Seitler, U.S.S.R. 80 Jj
Sekenke, Tanzania 97 Ge
Seki, Japan 86 Eg
Sekondi, Ghana 98 Eg
Selby, England 63 Gg
Selby, S. Dakota 46 Gc
Seldom, Newfoundland 33 Sd
Selemiya, Syria 94 Fb
Selenge, Mong./U.S.S.R. 79 Kd
Selima Oasis, Sudan 99 Ld
Selinsgrove, Pennsylvania 44 Bb
Selkirk, Manitoba 37 Vh
Selkirk, Ontario 34 Lk
Selkirk, Scotland 62 Fe
Selkirk (Horse) I., Manitoba 37 Te
Selkirk Mts., B.C./Montana 30 Hg
Selle, Sa. de la, Haiti 51 Ec
Selles, France 72 Dc
Selma, Alabama 45 Dd
Selma, N. Carolina 45 Hc
Selous, Mt., Y.T. 38 Gd
Selva, Argentina 54 Dc
Selwyn, Queensland 57 Hd
Selwyn L., N.W.T. 38 Ve
Selwyn Mts., Y.T. 38 Fd
Selwyn Range, Queensland 57 Gd
Sem, Norway 67 Dg
Semans, Saskatchewan 37 Ng
Semarang, Java 83 Fm
Seminoe Res., Wyoming 42 Ec

Seminoe Res., *Wyoming* 46 Dd
Seminole, L., *Georgia, U.S.A.* 45 Ee
Semipalatinsk, *Kazakhstan* 78 Hc
Semnan, *Iran* 93 Fb
Senador Pompeu, *Brazil* 53 Ke
Sena Madureira, *Brazil* 52 De
Senate, *Saskatchewan* 36 Hj
Senatobia, *Mississippi* 45 Cc
Sendai, *Japan* 86 Ge
Seneca Falls, *New York* 44 Ba
Seneca L., *New York* 40 Hd
Sénégal, *West Africa* 98 Bf
Sénégal, *West Africa* 98 Ce
Senev, *Michigan* 40 Cb
Senga Hill, *Zambia* 97 Gf
Sengilei, *U.S.S.R.* 81 Jd
Senhor do Bonfim, *Brazil* 53 Jf
Senise, *Italy* 75 Fe
Senj, *Yugoslavia* 74 Ec
Senja, *Norway* 66 Gb
Senlac, *Saskatchewan* 36 Hf
Senneterre, *Quebec* 35 Nd
Sens, *France* 72 Eb
Senta, *Yugoslavia* 76 Cb
Sentinel Pk., *B.C.* 39 Nh
Sentinel Range, *Antarctica* 104 Rb
Seondha, *India* 91 Bb
Seoni, *India* 91 Bd
Seoni-Malwa, *India* 91 Ad
Seoul. *See* Sŏul
Separation Pt., *New Zealand* 55 Dd
Sępólno, *Poland* 69 Gb
Sept-Iles, *Quebec* 32 Fc
Sept Milles, L. des, *Quebec* 32 Ab
Sepulveda, *Spain* 70 Db
Sequeros, *Spain* 70 Bb
Sequoia Nat. Park, *Cal.* 47 Dg
Serai, *Syria* 94 Db
Serakhs, *Turkmenistan* 78 Fe
Seram, *Indonesia* 83 Jl
Serampur, *India* 91 Gd
Serbia, *Yugoslavia* 76 Cc
Serdobsk, *U.S.S.R.* 81 Gd
Sergach, *U.S.S.R.* 81 Gc
Serginskaya, *U.S.S.R.* 78 Fb
Sergiyevsk, *U.S.S.R.* 81 Kc
Serifos, *Greece* 77 Ef
Sermata, *Indonesia* 83 Jm
Serov, *U.S.S.R.* 78 Fc
Serowe, *Botswana* 95 Dd
Serpa, *Portugal* 70 Bd
Serpent, R. au, *Quebec* 32 Ad
Serpins, *Portugal* 70 Ab
Serpukhov, *U.S.S.R.* 80 Kd
Sérrai, *Greece* 76 Dd
Serra San Bruno, *Italy* 75 Ff
Serrezuela, *Argentina* 54 Cd
Sertã, *Portugal* 70 Ac
Sertânia, *Brazil* 53 Ke
Sertig, *Switzerland* 65 Eb
Sérvia, *Greece* 77 Dd
Seseganaga L., *Ontario* 37 Na
Sesekinika, *Ontario* 34 Kd
Sesheke, *Zambia* 95 Cc
Sète, *France* 73 Ee
Sete Lagoas, *Brazil* 53 Jg
Setif, *Algeria* 98 Ga
Settee L., *Manitoba* 37 Ua
Setting L., *Manitoba* 37 Tc
Setúbal, *Portugal* 70 Ac
Seul, Lac, *Ontario* 31 Kg
Sevan, Ozero, *Armenia* 78 Dd
Sevastopol', *U.S.S.R.* 80 Hj
Sevelen, *Switzerland* 65 Ea
Seven Islands. *See* Sept Iles C
Seven Persons, *Alberta* 36 Gj
Seventy Mile House, *B.C.* 39 Nk
Severac-le-Château, *France* 73 Ed
Severn, R., *Ontario* 31 Lf
Severnaya Dvina, R., *U.S.S.R.* 78 Db
Severnaya Zemlya, *U.S.S.R.* 79 Ka
Severn R., *England/Wales* 63 Fj
Severodvinsk, *U.S.S.R.* 78 Cb
Sevier Bridge Res., *Utah* 48 Bc
Sevier L., *Utah* 47 Gf
Sevier R., *Utah* 48 Ac
Sevilla, *Spain* 70 Cd
Seville. *See* Sevilla
Seward, *Alaska* 43 Ym
Seward Glacier, *Y.T./Alaska* 38 Ce
Seward Pen., *Alaska* 43 Wl
Sexsmith, *Alberta* 39 Oh
Seybaplaya, *Mexico* 50 Fd
Seychelles, *Indian Ocean* 100 De
Seydhisfjördhur, *Iceland* 66 Za
Seyhan, *Turkey* 92 Cb
Seymchan, *U.S.S.R.* 79 Qb
Seymour, *Indiana* 40 Df
Seymour, L., *B.C.* 39 Hk
Seymour Creek, *B.C.* 39 Hk
Seyne, *France* 73 Gd
Sézanne, *France* 72 Eb
Sfakiá. *See* Khóra Sfakíon
Sfax, *Tunisia* 99 Hb
Sfintu Gheorghe, *Romania* 76 Eb
Sfira, *Syria* 94 Fa
's Gravenhage, *Netherlands* 64 Cb
's Gravenzande, *Netherlands* 64 Cb
Shaanxi, *China* 84 De
Shaba, *Zaire* 96 Eg
Shabaqua, *Ontario* 37 Nb
Shache (Yarkant), *China* 90 Ea
Shackleton, *Antarctica* 104 Ab
Shackleton, *Saskatchewan* 36 Jh
Shadegan, *Iran* 92 Ec
Shadehill Res., *S. Dakota* 46 Fc
Shadrinsk, *U.S.S.R.* 81 Rb
Shadwan, *Egypt* 99 Mc
Shaftesbury, *England* 63 Fj
Shag Rocks, *Atlantic Ocean* 104 Td
Shahabad, *India* 90 Ee
Shahabad, *India* 91 Cb
Shahba, *Syria* 94 Ee
Shahbandar, *Pakistan* 88 Cd
Shahdād, *Iran* 93 Gc
Shahdadkot, *Pakistan* 88 Cc
Shahdara, *India* 90 Ef
Shahdheri, *Pakistan* 90 Dd
Shahdol, *India* 91 Cd
Shahganj, *India* 91 Db
Shahin Dezh, *Iran* 92 Eb
Shahjahanpur, *India* 91 Bb
Shahjui, *Afghanistan* 93 Jc
Shahpur, *Pakistan* 90 Cd
Shāhpūr. *See* Salmas
Shahpura, *India* 88 Dc
Shahrakht, *Iran* 93 Gc
Shahr-e-Babak, *Iran* 93 Gc
Shahreza, *Iran* 93 Fc
Shahr-i-Zabul. *See* Zābol
Shāhrūd. *See* Emamrūd
Shahsavar, *Iran* 93 Fb
Shakespeare I., *Ontario* 34 Bc
Shakhty, *U.S.S.R.* 81 Eg
Shakopee, *Minnesota* 46 Lc
Shakubetsueki, *Japan* 86 Hc
Shala L., *Ethiopia* 97 Hc
Shalalth, *British Columbia* 39 Mk
Shallow B., *N.W.T.* 38 Fa
Shallow Lake, *Ontario* 34 Jh
Shamil, *Iran* 93 Gd
Shammar, Jabal, *Arabia* 92 Dd
Shamokin, *Pennsylvania* 40 He
Shamrock, *Saskatchewan* 36 Lh
Shandong, *China* 84 Hd
Shandong Bandao, *China* 82 Hc
Shanghai, *China* 84 Kg
Shangqiu, *China* 84 Ge
Shangrao, *China* 85 Hh
Shangtu, *China* 84 Fb
Shangyou, *China* 85 Gk
Shannah, *Arabia* 93 Ff
Shannon, *Eire* 63 Bh
Shannon, *New Zealand* 55 Ed
Shannon, I., *Greenland* 41 Mb
Shannon R., *Eire* 63 Bg
Shantarskiye Os., *U.S.S.R.* 79 Nc
Shantou, *China* 85 Hl
Shanxi, *China* 84 Ec
Shaoguan, *China* 85 Fk
Shaowu, *China* 85 Hj
Shaoxing, *China* 85 Kg
Shaoyang, *China* 85 Ej
Shapinsay, *Orkney Is.* 62 Fa
Shaqa, *Arabia* 92 Df
Shaqra, *Arabia* 92 Ed
Sharakpur, *Pakistan* 90 De
Sharbot Lake, *Ontario* 35 Oh
Sharjah, *United Arab Emirates* 93 Gd
Shark B., *W. Australia* 56 Be
Sharon, *Pennsylvania* 40 Fe
Sharpe, L., *S. Dakota* 46 Gc
Sharqi, Jeb. esh., *Leb./Syria* 94 Ec
Sharr, Jebel el, *Arabia* 92 Cd
Sharya, *U.S.S.R.* 81 Ga
Shashi, *Botswana* 95 Dd
Shashi, *China* 85 Fg
Shasta, *California* 47 Be
Shasta, Mt., *California* 47 Be
Shasta L., *California* 47 Ce
Shatra, Ash, *Iraq* 92 Ec
Shatt'o-al-Arab, *Iraq* 92 Ec
Shaubek, *Jordan* 94 Dg
Shaunavon, *Saskatchewan* 36 Jj
Shawenaga, *Ontario* 34 Kf
Shawano, *Wisconsin* 40 Bc
Shawbridge, *Quebec* 35 Rg
Shawinigan, *Quebec* 35 Sf
Shawnee, *Oklahoma* 49 Je
Shawneetown, *Illinois* 45 Cb
Shawville, *Quebec* 35 Og
Sha Xian, *China* 85 Hj
Shay Gap, *W. Australia* 56 Dd
Shaykh 'Uthman, *S. Yemen* 92 Eg
Shchors, *Ukraine* 80 Gf
Shchuchinsk, *Kazakhstan* 78 Gc
Shebandowan L., *Ont.* 37 Mb
Sheboygan, *Wisconsin* 40 Cd
Shedden, *Ontario* 34 Jk
Shediac, *New Brunswick* 32 Hg
Sheelin L., *Eire* 63 Cg
Sheenboro, *Quebec* 35 Ng
Sheenjik R., *Alaska* 38 Ac
Sheep Cr., *Alberta* 39 Oj
Sheep Haven, *Eire* 62 Be
Sheerness, *Alberta* 36 Fg
Sheerness, *England* 63 Hj
Sheet Harbour, *N.S.* 32 Kj
Sheffield, *Alabama* 49 Oe
Sheffield, *England* 63 Gg
Sheffield, *New Zealand* 55 Ce
Sheguindah, *Ontario* 34 Jg
Sheho, *Saskatchewan* 37 Og
Sheikh, Jeb. esh, *Syria* 94 Dd
Sheikh Miskin, *Syria* 94 Ee
Sheik Seraq, *Syria* 94 Fd
Shekak, R., *Ontario* 34 Fc
Shekha, *South Yemen* 92 Ef
Shekhupura, *Pakistan* 90 Ce
Shelburne, *Nova Scotia* 32 Gk
Shelburne, *Ontario* 34 Kh
Shelby, *Michigan* 40 Cd
Shelby, *Montana* 46 Ba
Shelby, *N. Carolina* 45 Gc
Shelbyville, *Illinois* 49 Nc
Shelbyville, *Kentucky* 45 Ea
Shelbyville, *Tennessee* 45 Dc
Shelbyville, L., *Illinois* 45 Ca
Sheldon, *Iowa* 49 Ka
Sheldon Mt., *Y.T.* 38 Hd
Sheldrake, *Quebec* 32 Hc
Shelikhova, Zaliv, *U.S.S.R.* 79 Qc
Shellbrook, *Sask.* 36 Le
Shell Lake, *Saskatchewan* 36 Ke
Shellmouth, *Manitoba* 37 Qh
Shelter I., *New York* 44 Db
Shenandoah, *Iowa* 49 Kb
Shenandoah, *Pennsylvania* 44 Bb
Shenandoah Junction, *W. Va.* 44 Bc
Shenandoah Nat. Park, *Va.* 43 Ld
Shenandoah R., *Virginia* 44 Bc
Shenchow. *See* Yüanling
Shendam, *Nigeria* 99 Gg
Shendi, *Sudan* 99 Me
Shëngjin, *Albania* 76 Bd
Shenkursk, *U.S.S.R.* 78 Db
Shenyang, *China* 82 Hb
Shenyang, *China* 84 Lb
Sheopur, *India* 88 Ec
Shepard, *Alberta* 36 Dg
Shepetovka, *Ukraine* 80 Ef
Sheppard Peak, *B.C.* 39 Gg
Shepparton, *Victoria* 57 Jg
Sherada, *Ethiopia* 97 Hc
Sherard, C., *N.W.T.* 31 Lc
Sherard Osborn Fd., *Greenland* 41 Pa
Sherbro I., *Sierra Leone* 98 Cg
Sherbrooke, *Nova Scotia* 33 Kh
Sherbrooke, *Quebec* 35 Tg
Sherbrooke L., *N.S.* 32 Hj
Sheridan, *Wyoming* 46 Dc
Sheridan, C., *N.W.T.* 31 Na
Sheridan, Mt., *Wyoming* 46 Bc
Sherman, *Texas* 49 Jf
Sherman Basin, *N.W.T.* 38 Zb
Sherman Res., *Nebraska* 46 He
Sherpur, *Bangladesh* 91 Gc
Sherridon, *Manitoba* 37 Qc
's Hertogenbosch, *Neth.* 64 Dc
Sherwood L., *N.W.T.* 38 We
Sheslay, *British Columbia* 39 Hf
Sheslay, R., *B.C.* 39 Hf
Shetland Is, *Scotland* 62 Ja
Shevaroy Hills, *India* 88 Ef
She Xian, *China* 85 Jh
Sheyenne, *N. Dakota* 46 Hb
Shiant Is., *Scotland* 62 Cc
Shibam, *South Yemen* 92 Ef
Shibarghan, *Afghanistan* 93 Jb
Shibata, *Japan* 86 Ff
Shibetsu, *Japan* 86 Jc
Shibin el Kom, *Egypt* 99 Mb
Shibushi wan, *Japan* 86 Bj
Shidao, *China* 84 Ld
Shiel L., *Scotland* 62 Dd
Shigawake, *Quebec* 32 He
Shihnan. *See* Enshi
Shihpao Shan, *China* 82 Ee
Shijiazhuang, *China* 84 Gc
Shikag L., *Ontario* 37 Ma
Shikarpur, *Pakistan* 88 Cc
Shikohabad, *India* 91 Bb
Shikoku, *Japan* 86 Ch
Shilka, *U.S.S.R.* 79 Lc
Shillelagh, *Eire* 63 Ch
Shillington, *Ontario* 34 Kd
Shillong, *India* 89 Hc
Shiloh, *Tennessee* 45 Cc
Shilong, *China* 85 Fl
Shimoga, *India* 88 Ef
Shimo jima, *Japan* 86 Ah
Shimoni, *Kenya* 97 He
Shimonoseki, *Japan* 86 Bg
Shindand, *Afghanistan* 93 Hc
Shinghar, *Pakistan* 90 Ae
Shingshal, *Kashmir* 90 Db
Shingu, *Japan* 86 Dh
Shining Tree, *Ontario* 34 Je
Shinjo, *Japan* 86 Gf
Shin L., *Scotland* 62 Eb
Shinshar, *Syria* 94 Ec
Shinyanga, *Tanzania* 97 Ge
Ship Cove, *Newfoundland* 33 Sf
Shipman, *Saskatchewan* 37 Ne
Shippegan & I., *N.B.* 32 Hf
Shipshaw, R., *Quebec* 35 Td
Shipshaw Dam, *Quebec* 35 Td
Shiqian, *China* 85 Dj
Shīrāz, *Iran* 93 Fd
Shireza, *Pakistan* 88 Cc
Shirley, *Montana* 46 Eb
Shiroishi, *Japan* 86 Gf
Shishou, *China* 85 Fh
Shisur, *Arabia* 93 Ff
Shiuhing. *See* Zhaoqing
Shivpuri, *India* 91 Ac
Shiyan, *China* 84 Ef
Shizugawa, *Japan* 86 Ge
Shizuishan, *China* 84 Cc
Shizuoka, *Japan* 86 Fg
Shklov, *Byelorussia* 80 Gd
Shkodër, *Albania* 76 Bc
Shoal Harbour, *Nfld.* 33 Se
Shoal L., *Ontario* 36 Ga
Shoal Lake, *Manitoba* 37 Rh
Shoal Ls., *Manitoba* 37 Uh
Shoe Cove, *Newfoundland* 33 Rd
Sholapur, *India* 88 Ee
Shorkot, *Pakistan* 90 Ce
Short, *Missouri* 45 Bb
Shortdale, *Manitoba* 37 Rg
Short Mts., *West Virginia* 44 Ac
Short Pine Hills, *S. Dakota* 46 Fc
Shoshone Falls, *Idaho* 42 Dc
Shoshone Mts., *Wyoming* 46 Cc
Shoshone Res., *Wyoming* 42 Ec
Shouldice, *Alberta* 36 Eh
Shovo Tso, *China* 89 Fb
Shreveport, *Louisiana* 49 Lf
Shrewsbury, *England* 63 Fh
Shrewsbury, *Ontario* 40 Fd
Shtora, *Lebanon* 94 Dd
Shubenacadie, *Nova Scotia* 32 Jh
Shubenacadie L., *N.S.* 32 Jj
Shubuta, *Mississippi* 45 Ce
Shufu, *China* 90 Da
Shujaabad, *Pakistan* 90 Bf
Shumagin Is., *Alaska* 43 Xm
Shumen, *Bulgaria* 76 Fc
Shumerlya, *U.S.S.R.* 81 Hc
Shunking. *See* Nanchong
Shunteh. *See* Xingtai
Shuqra, *South Yemen* 92 Eg
Shurab, *Iran* 93 Gc
Shurma, *Arabia* 92 De
Shuru Tso, *China* 89 Gb
Shusf, *Iran* 93 Hc
Shushal, *Kashmir* 88 Eb
Shūshtar, *Iran* 92 Ec
Shuswap L., *B.C.* 39 Ok
Shuya, *U.S.S.R.* 91 Eb
Shuyang, *China* 84 Je
Shwebo, *Burma* 89 Jd
Shwedaung, *Burma* 89 Je
Shwegyin, *Burma* 89 Je
Shweli, *Burma* 89 Jd
Sialkot, *Pakistan* 90 Dd
Siam. *See* Thailand
Siam, G. of. *See* Thailand, G. of
Siargao, *Philippines* 83 Jj
Siaton, *Philippines* 83 Hj
Šiauliai, *Lithuania* 67 Kj
Sīb, *Oman* 93 Ge
Sibbald, *Alberta* 36 Gg
Sibenik, *Yugoslavia* 74 Ed
Siberia, *U.S.S.R.* 59
Siberut, *Indonesia* 83 Cl
Sibi, *Pakistan* 88 Cc
Sibiu, *Romania* 76 Eb
Sibley Prov. Park, *Ont.* 34 Bd
Sibolga, *Sumatra* 83 Ck
Sibsagar, *India* 89 Hc
Sibu, *Sarawak* 83 Fk
Sicasica, *Bolivia* 52 Dg
Sichuan, *China* 84 Ag
Sicie C., *France* 73 Fe
Sicilia, *Italy* 75 Dg
Sicilian Chan., *Medit. Sea* 75 Cg
Sicily. *See* Sicilia
Sickle L., *Manitoba* 37 Rb
Sicuani, *Peru* 52 Cf
Sid, *Yugoslavia* 76 Bb
Siderno Marina, *Italy* 75 Ff
Sidewood, *Saskatchewan* 36 Hh
Sidhout, *India* 88 Ef
Sidi Barrani, *Egypt* 99 Lb
Sidi bel Abbès, *Algeria* 98 Ea
Sidi Ifni, *Morocco* 98 Cc
Sid L., *N.W.T.* 38 Vd
Sidlaw Hills, *Scotland* 62 Ed
Sidnaw, *Michigan* 40 Bb
Sidney, *British Columbia* 39 Ml
Sidney, *Manitoba* 37 Sj
Sidney, *Montana* 46 Eb
Sidney, *Nebraska* 48 Fb
Sidney, *New York* 40 Jd
Sidon, *Lebanon* 94 Dd
Siedlce, *Poland* 69 Kb
Siegen, *West Germany* 68 Cc
Siem Reap, *Kampuchea* 87 Cd
Siena, *Italy* 74 Cd
Sieradz, *Poland* 69 Hc
Siero, *Spain* 70 Ca
Sierra Colorada, *Argentina* 54 Cf
Sierra Grande, *Argentina* 54 Cf
Sierra Leone, *W. Afr.* 98 Cg
Sierra Madre Occidental, *Mexico* 50 Cb
Sierra Madre Oriental, *Mex.* 50 Ec
Sierra Mojada, *Mexico* 50 Db
Sierra Rosada, *Argentina* 54 Cf
Sifnos, *Greece* 77 Ef
Sifton, *Manitoba* 37 Rg
Sifton Pass, *B.C.* 39 Kg
Sigean, *France* 73 Ee
Sighet, *Romania* 69 Ke
Sighisoara, *Romania* 76 Ea
Siglufjördhur, *Iceland* 66 Wl
Sigmaringen, *West Germany* 68 Cd
Sigourney, *Iowa* 49 Lb
Sigsig, *Ecuador* 52 Bd
Sigüenza, *Spain* 70 Db
Siguiri, *Guinea* 98 Df
Sigulda, *Latvia* 67 Lh
Sihanoukville, *Kampuchea* 87 Cd
Sihl See, *Switzerland* 65 Da
Siilinjärvi, *Finland* 66 Me
Sikandarabad, *India* 90 Ef
Sikandra Rao, *India* 91 Bb
Sikanni Chief R., *B.C.* 39 Mg
Sikar, *India* 90 Dg
Sikasso, *Mali* 98 Df
Siking. *See* Xi'an
Sikinos, *Greece* 77 Ef
Sikkim, *India* 91 Gb
Siktyakh, *U.S.S.R.* 79 Ma
Sila, La, *Italy* 75 Ff
Silairsk, *U.S.S.R.* 81 Nd
Silao, *Mexico* 50 Dc
Silchar, *India* 89 Hd
Silenen, *Switzerland* 65 Db
Silenrieux, *Belgium* 64 Cd
Silesia, *Montana* 46 Cc
Silgarhi-Doti, *Nepal* 91 Ca
Silifke, *Turkey* 92 Bb
Silistra, *Bulgaria* 76 Fb
Siljan, L., *Sweden* 67 Ff
Silkeborg, *Denmark* 67 Ch
Sillery, *Quebec* 35 Rc
Silloth, *England* 62 Ef
Sils, *Switzerland* 65 Eb
Silsby L., *Manitoba* 37 Wc
Silton, *Saskatchewan* 37 Nh
Silvânia, *Brazil* 53 Hg
Silvaplana, *Switzerland* 65 Eb
Silva Porto, *Angola* 96 Dg
Silver City, *New Mexico* 48 Cf
Silvercreek, *New York* 40 Gd
Silver Heights, *Alberta* 36 Ff
Silver Islet, *Ontario* 34 Bd
Silver L., *Oregon* 47 Cd
Silver Mt., pk., *Nfld.* 33 Pd
Silver Star Prov. Park, *B.C.* 39 Ok
Silverthrone Mt., *B.C.* 39 Kk
Silverton, *Colorado* 48 Dd
Silves, *Brazil* 52 Fd
Silves, *Portugal* 70 Ad
Silvretta, *Austria/Switz.* 68 Ce
Simao, *China* 82 Df
Simard, L., *Quebec* 35 Me
Simcoe, *Ontario* 34 Kk
Simcoe, L., *Ontario* 40 Gc
Simcoe, L., *Ontario* 35 Lh
Simeulue, *Indonesia* 83 Ck
Simferopol, *U.S.S.R.* 80 Jj
Simi, *Greece* 77 Ff
Simla, *India* 90 Ee
Simleul Silvaniei, *Romania* 69 Ke
Simmie, *Saskatchewan* 36 Jj
Simmons, *Quebec* 34 Bh
Simo, *Finland* 66 Ld
Simola, *Finland* 67 Nf
Simon, L., *Quebec* 35 Pg
Simonette, R., *Alberta* 39 Oh
Simonhouse, *Manitoba* 37 Qd
Simoom Sound, *B.C.* 39 Kk
Simpelveld, *Netherlands* 64 Dd
Simplon, *Switz.* 65 Db
Simpson, *Chile* 54 Bg
Simpson, *Saskatchewan* 37 Mg
Simpson, Fort, *N.W.T.* 30 Ge
Simpson B., *N.W.T.* 38 Qa
Simpson Desert, *Australia* 57 Ge
Simpson I., *Ontario* 34 Cd
Simpson Is., *N.W.T.* 38 Re
Simpson L., *N.W.T.* 38 Ka
Simpson Pen., *N.W.T.* 31 Ld
Simpson Str., *N.W.T.* 38 Ya
Simuna, *Estonia* 67 Mg
Sinai, *Egypt* 99 Mc
Sinaloa, *Mexico* 50 Cb
Sinaloa, Rio, *Mexico* 50 Cb
Sinamaica, *Venezuela* 52 Ca
Sinan, *China* 85 Dj
Sinbo, *Burma* 89 Jd
Sind, *Pakistan* 88 Cc
Sindel, *Bulgaria* 76 Fc
Sindhuli Garhi, *Nepal* 91 Eb
Sind Sagar Doab, *Pakistan* 90 Be
Sines, *Portugal* 70 Ad
Singa, *Sudan* 99 Mf
Singapore, *S.E. Asia* 87 Cf
Singaraja, *Bali, Indon.* 83 Gm
Singen, *West Germany* 68 Ce
Singhana, *India* 90 Df
Singida, *Tanzania* 97 Ge
Singitic G., *Greece* 77 Dd
Singkawang, *Borneo (Kalimantan)* 83 Ek
Singkep, *Riouw Arch., Indonesia* 83 Dl
Singora. *See* Songkhla
Siniscola, *Sardinia* 75 Be
Sinj, *Yugoslavia* 74 Fd
Sinjar, *Iraq* 92 Db
Sinjil, *Jordan* 94 De
Sinnamary, *Fr. Guiana* 53 Gb
Sinoe L., *Romania* 76 Gb
Sinoia, *Zimbabwe* 95 Ec
Sinop, *Turkey* 92 Ca
Sintaluta, *Manitoba* 37 Oh
Sinton, *Texas* 48 Jh
Sintra, *Portugal* 70 Ac
Sinuiju, *Korea* 82 Hb
Sion, *Switzerland* 65 Cb
Sioux City, *Iowa* 49 Ja
Sioux Falls, *S. Dakota* 46 Jd
Sioux Lookout, *Ontario* 36 La
Siparia, *Trinidad* 52 Ea
Sipiwesk, *Manitoba* 37 Uc
Sipiwesk L., *Manitoba* 37 Uc
Sipolilo, *Zimbabwe* 95 Ec
Sipora, *Indonesia* 83 Cl
Siquisique, *Venezuela* 52 Da
Sira, *India* 88 Ef
Sira. *See* Siros
Siracusa, *Sicily* 75 Eg
Sirajganj, *Bangladesh* 91 Gc
Sir Alexander, Mt., *B.C.* 39 Nj
Sir Douglas, Mt., *Alta./B.C.* 36 Bh
Sir Edward Pellew Group, *N. Territory* 57 Gc
Siretul, *Romania* 76 Fa
Sirhind, *India* 90 Ee
Siri, *Ethiopia* 97 Hc
Sir James MacBrien, Mt., *Northwest Territories* 38 Jd
Sirjan, *Iran* 93 Gd
Sirna, *Greece* 77 Ff
Sironcha, *India* 88 Fe
Sironj, *India* 88 Ed
Síros, *Greece* 77 Ef
Sirsa, *India* 90 Df
Sir Sanford, Mt., *B.C.* 39 Pk
Sirsi, *India* 88 Df
Sirsi, *India* 91 Ba
Sirte, G. of, *Libya* 99 Jb
Sir Wilfrid Laurier, Mt., *B.C.* 39 Oj
Sisak, *Yugoslavia* 74 Fc
Sisaket, *Thailand* 87 Cc
Sisal, *Mexico* 50 Fc
Sisha Pangma, *Nepal/China* 89 Gc
Sisib L., *Manitoba* 37 Sf
Sisipuk L., *Man./Sask.* 37 Qc
Sisophon, *Kampuchea* 87 Cd
Sisson Branch Res., *N.B.* 32 Ef
Sisteron, *France* 73 Fd
Sitamarhi, *India* 91 Eb
Sitamau, *India* 88 Ed
Sitapur, *India* 91 Cb
Sithonia, *Greece* 77 Dd
Sitia, *Crete* 77 Fg
Sitidgi L., *N.W.T.* 38 Ga
Sitka, *Alaska* 43 Zm
Sitpur, *Pakistan* 90 Bf
Sittang, *Burma* 89 Je
Sittard, *Netherlands* 64 Dd
Sivand, *Iran* 93 Fc
Sivas, *Turkey* 92 Cb
Siverek, *Turkey* 92 Cb
Sivrihisar, *Turkey* 92 Bb
Sivry, *Belgium* 64 Cd
Siwa, *Egypt* 99 Lc
Siwalik Hills, *India* 88 Eb
Siwan, *India* 91 Eb
Sixteen, *Montana* 46 Bb
Sixtymile, *Y.T.* 38 Cc
Sjaelland, *Denmark* 67 Dj
Sjötorp, *Sweden* 67 Eg
Skadarsko Jezero, *Yugoslavia/Albania* 76 Bc
Skagafjord, *Iceland* 66 Wl
Skagen, *Denmark* 67 Dh
Skagerrak, *Norway/Denmark* 67 Bh
Skagway, *Alaska* 43 Zm
Skaneateles, L., *New York* 44 Ba
Skara, *Sweden* 67 Eg
Skardu, *Kashmir* 90 Dc
Skarnes, *Norway* 67 Df
Skarzysko-Kamienna, *Poland* 69 Jc
Skead, *Ontario* 34 Kf
Skeena, R., *B.C.* 39 Jh
Skeena Crossing, *B.C.* 39 Kh
Skeena Mts., *B.C.* 39 Jg
Skegness, *England* 63 Hg
Skellefte, *Sweden* 66 Jd
Skellefte Älv, *Sweden* 66 Hd
Skiathos, *Greece* 77 De
Skibbereen, *Eire* 63 Aj
Skidegate, *B.C.* 39 Gj
Skien, *Norway* 67 Cg
Skierniewice, *Poland* 69 Jc
Skiff, *Alberta* 36 Fj
Skiftet Kihti, *Finland* 67 Jf
Skikda, *Algeria* 73 Qh
Skipton, *England* 63 Fg
Skíros, *Greece* 77 Ee
Skive, *Denmark* 67 Ch
Skofja Loka, *Yugoslavia* 74 Eb
Skoghall, *Sweden* 67 Eg
Skookumchuk, *B.C.* 39 Ql
Skópelos, *Greece* 77 De
Skopin, *U.S.S.R.* 80 Le
Skopje, *Yugoslavia* 76 Cd
Skövde, *Sweden* 67 Eg
Skovorodino, *U.S.S.R.* 79 Mc
Skowhegan, *Maine* 32 Cj
Skownan, *Manitoba* 37 Sg
Skradin, *Yugoslavia* 74 Ed
Skrunda, *Latvia* 67 Kh
Skudeshavn, *Norway* 67 Ag
Skuodas, *Lithuania* 67 Jh
Skye, I., *Scotland* 62 Cc
Slagelse, *Denmark* 67 Dj
Slamet, Mt., *Java* 83 Em
Slaney R., *Eire* 63 Ch
Slate Is., *Ontario* 34 Dd
Slatina, *Romania* 76 Eb
Slatina, *Yugoslavia* 76 Ab
Slatington, *Pennsylvania* 44 Cb
Slave L., Great, *N.W.T.* 38 Qe
Slave L., Lesser, *Alberta* 36 Bc
Slave Lake, *Alberta* 36 Cc
Slăveni, *Romania* 76 Eb
Slave Pt., *N.W.T.* 38 Qe
Slave R., *N.W.T.* 38 Re
Slavgorod, *U.S.S.R.* 78 Gc
Slavonia, *Yugoslavia* 76 Ab
Slavyansk, *Ukraine* 80 Kg
Slea Head, *Eire* 63 Ah
Sleat, Sound of, *Scotland* 62 Dc
Sled L., *Saskatchewan* 36 Kd
Sleeper Is., *N.W.T.* 31 Lf
Sleidinge, *Belgium* 64 Bc
Slide Mt., *New York* 40 Jd
Sliedrecht, *Netherlands* 64 Cc
Slieve Aughty, *Eire* 63 Bg
Slieve Bloom, *Eire* 63 Bg
Slieve Mish, *Eire* 63 Ah
Sligo, *Eire* 63 Bf
Sligo B., *Eire* 63 Bf
Slite, *Sweden* 67 Hh
Sliven, *Bulgaria* 76 Fc
Slobodskoy, *U.S.S.R.* 81 Ka
Slocan, *British Columbia* 39 Pl
Slocan L., *B.C.* 39 Pl
Sloka, *Latvia* 80 Cc
Sloko, R., *B.C.* 38 Gf
Slonim, *Byelorussia* 80 De
Sloten, *Netherlands* 64 Db
Slough, *England* 63 Gj
Slovakia, *Czechoslovakia* 69 Hd
Slovenija, *Yugoslavia* 74 Ec
Slovensko, *Czechoslovakia* 69 Hd
Sluis, *Netherlands* 64 Bc
Sluiskil, *Netherlands* 64 Bc
Slunj, *Yugoslavia* 74 Ec
Slupsk, *Poland* 69 Ga
Slussfors, *Sweden* 66 Gd
Slutsk, *Byelorussia* 80 Ee
Slyne Head, *Eire* 63 Ag
Slyudyanka, *U.S.S.R.* 79 Kc
Small L., *Manitoba* 37 Ua
Smallwood Reservoir, *Nfld.* 31 Ng
Smart L., *N.W.T.* 38 Ud
Smeaton, *Saskatchewan* 36 Ne
Smethport, *Pennsylvania* 44 Ab
Smiley, *Saskatchewan* 36 Hg
Smiltene, *Latvia* 67 Lh
Smith, *Alberta* 36 Cc
Smith, C., *Quebec* 31 Me
Smith Arm, bay, *N.W.T.* 38 Mb
Smith B., *N.W.T.* 31 Mb
Smithers, *B.C.* 39 Kh
Smithfield, *N. Carolina* 45 Hc
Smithfield, *Utah* 48 Bb
Smithfield, *Virginia* 45 Jb
Smith I., *N.W.T.* 31 Me
Smith I., *South Shetlands* 104 Sc
Smithland, *Kentucky* 45 Cb
Smith Mountain Lake, *Virginia* 45 Hb
Smith Pt., *Nova Scotia* 32 Jh
Smith River, *B.C.* 38 Kf
Smith Sd., *N.W.T.* 31 Mb
Smiths Falls, *Ontario* 35 Oh
Smithton, *Tasmania* 57 Hh
Smoking Hills, *N.W.T.* 38 Ka
Smoky, C., *Nova Scotia* 33 Mg
Smoky, R., *Alberta* 39 Ph
Smoky Falls, *Ontario* 34 Hb
Smoky Hill R., *Kansas* 42 Fd
Smoky Lake, *Alberta* 36 Ed
Smoky R., Lit., *Alberta* 39 Ph
Smøla I., *Norway* 66 Be
Smolensk, *U.S.S.R.* 80 Hd
Smooth Rock Falls, *Ont.* 34 Jc
Smoothrock L., *Ontario* 34 Ab
Smoothstone L., *Sask.* 36 Ld
Smoothstone R., *Sask.* 36 Lc
Smyrna. *See* Izmir
Snaefell, *Isle of Man* 63 Df
Snag, *Yukon Territory* 38 Cd
Snake, R., *Y.T.* 38 Gc
Snake R., *Washington/Idaho* 47 Db
Snake River Canyon, *Idaho* 47 Ec
Snare, L., *Saskatchewan* 39 Uf
Snare L., *N.W.T.* 38 Qc
Snare River, *N.W.T.* 38 Pd
Snares, Is., *New Zealand* 55 Ah
Snåsa, *Norway* 66 Ed
Snåsa Vatn, *Norway* 66 Dd
Sneek, *Netherlands* 64 Da
Sneem, *Eire* 63 Aj
Sneeuw Gebergte, *Irian Jaya* 83 Ll
Snipe L., *Alberta* 36 Ac
Snizort L., *Scotland* 62 Cc
Snøhetta, Mt., *Norway* 66 Ce
Snowbird L., *N.W.T.* 38 We
Snowden, *Saskatchewan* 37 Ne
Snowdon, *Wales* 63 Eg
Snowdrift, *N.W.T.* 38 Sd
Snowdrift, R., *N.W.T.* 38 Sd
Snow Flake, *Arizona* 48 Be
Snowflake, *Manitoba* 37 Tj
Snow Lake, *Manitoba* 37 Sd
Snow Road Station, *Ont.* 35 Oh
Snow Water L., *Nevada* 42 Dc
Snowy Mts., *Vict./N.S.W.* 57 Jg
Snyder, *Texas* 48 Gf
Soasiu, *Moluccas, Indon.* 83 Jk
Soazza, *Switzerland* 65 Eb
Sobakin, *U.S.S.R.* 81 Jd
Sobrado, *Brazil* 53 Ge
Sobral, *Brazil* 53 Jd
Sobrance, *Czechoslovakia* 69 Kd
Sobraon, *India* 90 De
Social Circle, *Georgia, U.S.A.* 45 Fd
Society Is., *Pacific Ocean* 103 Kj
Socorro, *Colombia* 52 Cb
Socorro, *New Mexico* 42 Ee
Socorro, *New Mexico* 48 De
Socorro, I., *Mexico* 50 Bd
Socotra, *Indian Ocean* 97 Lb
Soda Creek, *B.C.* 39 Mj
Sodankylä, *Finland* 66 Mc
Soda Springs, *Idaho* 48 Ba
Söderfors, *Sweden* 67 Gf
Söderhamn, *Sweden* 67 Gf
Söderköping, *Sweden* 67 Gg
Södertälje, *Sweden* 67 Gg
Sodiri, *Sudan* 99 Lf
Sodus, *New York* 44 Ba
Sodus Pt., *New York* 44 Ba
Soepiori, *Irian Jaya* 83 Ll
Soest, *Netherlands* 64 Db
Soest, *West Germany* 68 Cc
Soeurs, I. des, *Quebec* 35 Sk
Sofiya, *Bulgaria* 76 Dc
Sogamosa, *Colombia* 52 Cb
Sogndal, *Norway* 67 Bg
Sognefjord, *Norway* 67 Af
Sögüt, *Turkey* 92 Ba
Sohâg, *Egypt* 99 Mc
Sohan R., *Pakistan* 90 Cd
Sohawal, *India* 91 Cc
Soheb, *S. Yemen* 92 Eg
Sohna, *India* 90 Ef
Soignies, *Belgium* 64 Cd
Soissons, *France* 72 Eb
Sok, *Turkey* 92 Ab
Sok Karmalinsk, *U.S.S.R.* 81 Lc
Sokodé, *Togo* 98 Fg
Sokol, *U.S.S.R.* 80 Mb
Sokolo, *Mali* 98 Df
Sokota, *Ethiopia* 97 Hb
Sokoto, *Nigeria* 98 Ff
Solai, *Kenya* 97 Hd
Solbad Hall, *Austria* 68 De
Soledad, *Venezuela* 52 Eb
Soledade, *Brazil* 52 De
Solent, The, *England* 63 Gk
Solenzara, *Corsica* 75 Be

Solikamsk, *U.S.S.R.* 78 Ec
Sol Iletsk, *U.S.S.R.* 78 Ec
Solimões. *See* Amazonas
Solingen, *West Germany* 68 Bc
Solleftea, *Sweden* 66 Ge
Solok, *Sumatra* 83 Dl
Solomon Is., *Pacific Ocean* 102 Eh
Solomon R., *Kansas* 42 Gd
Solon, *India* 90 Ee
Solothurn, *Switzerland* 65 Ca
Solsona, *Spain* 71 Fb
Soltaniyeh, *Iran* 92 Eb
Soltau, *West Germany* 68 Cb
Solund, *Norway* 67 Af
Solway, *Minnesota* 46 Kb
Solway Firth, *Eng./Scot.* 62 Ef
Solwezi, *Zambia* 96 Fg
Soma, *Turkey* 92 Ab
Somalia, *E. Africa* 97 Jd
Sombor, *Yugoslavia* 76 Bb
Sombra, *Ontario* 34 Hk
Sombreiro Chan., *Nicobar Is.* 89 Hg
Sombrerete, *Mexico* 50 Dc
Sombrero, *Leeward Is.* 51 Gc
Somcuța Mare, *Romania* 69 Ke
Someren, *Netherlands* 64 Dc
Somerset, *England* 63 Ej
Somerset, *Manitoba* 37 Tj
Somerset, *Pennsylvania* 40 Ge
Somerset, *Queensland* 57 Hb
Somerset I., *N.W.T.* 31 Kc
Somerset Res., *Vermont* 44 Da
Somerville, *New Jersey* 44 Cb
Somerville, *Tennessee* 45 Cc
Somme, *Belgium* 64 Dd
Somme, *France* 72 Da
Somme, *France* 72 Eb
Sommières, *France* 73 Fe
Somoto, *Nicaragua* 51 Bd
Somovit, *Bulgaria* 76 Ec
Somzée, *Belgium* 64 Cd
Sonamukhi, *India* 91 Fd
Sonbarsa, *India* 91 Fc
Sónderborg, *Denmark* 67 Cj
Sonepat, *India* 90 Ef
Song Cau, *Vietnam* 87 Dd
Songea, *Tanzania* 97 Hg
Songhua, *China* 82 Ha
Songhua Hu, *China* 82 Jb
Songjiang, *China* 84 Kg
Songkhla, *Thailand* 87 Ce
Sonhat, *India* 91 Dd
Sonid Youqi, *China* 82 Fb
Sonkajärvi, *Finland* 66 Me
Sonkovo, *U.S.S.R.* 80 Kc
Sonmiani, *Pakistan* 88 Cc
Sonneberg, *East Germany* 68 Dc
Sonningdale, *Sask.* 36 Kf
Sonogno, *Switzerland* 65 Db
Sonora, *Mexico* 50 Bb
Sonora, *Nova Scotia* 33 Lh
Sonoyta, *Mexico* 50 Ba
Sonpur, *India* 89 Fd
Sonpur, *India* 91 Ec
Son R., *India* 91 Ec
Sonsón, *Colombia* 52 Bb
Soo Canals, *Ont./Mich.* 31 Lh
Sooke, *British Columbia* 39 Ml
Soping. *See* Youyu
Soppero, *Sweden* 66 Jb
Sopron, *Hungary* 74 Fb
Sop's Arm, *Newfoundland* 33 Pd
Sopur, *Kashmir* 90 Dc
Sora, *Italy* 75 De
Sorata, *Bolivia* 52 Dg
Sorbas, *Spain* 71 Dd
Sorel, *Quebec* 35 Rf
Sorell, *Tasmania* 57 Jh
Sörenberg, *Switzerland* 65 Db
Sörfold, *Norway* 66 Fc
Sorgono, *Sardinia* 75 Be
Soria, *Spain* 71 Db
Soriano, *Uruguay* 54 Ed
Sornico, *Switzerland* 65 Db
Sorocaba, *Brazil* 53 Hh
Soroka, *U.S.S.R.* 81 Ld
Soroki, *Moldavia* 80 Fg
Sorol, *Caroline Is.* 102 Cg
Soron, *India* 91 Bb
Sorong, *Irian Jaya* 83 Kl
Sororoca, *Brazil* 52 Ec
Soroti, *Uganda* 97 Gd
Söroy, *Norway* 66 Ka
Sorrento, *B.C.* 39 Ok
Sorrento, *Italy* 75 Ee
Sorsele, *Sweden* 66 Gd
Sortavala, *Karelia* 66 Pf
Soscumica, L., *Quebec* 35 Nb
Sosnovka, *U.S.S.R.* 81 Ed
Sosnovo Ozerskoye, *U.S.S.R.* 79 Lc
Sosnowiec, *Poland* 69 Hc
Sosva, *U.S.S.R.* 78 Fc
Soto la Marina, *Mexico* 50 Ec
Sotra, *Norway* 67 Af
Sotuta, *Mexico* 50 Gc
Souanke, *Congo* 96 Cd
Soudan, *N. Terr.* 57 Gd
Souflíon, *Greece* 76 Fd
Souillac, *France* 73 Dd
Sŏul, *S. Korea* 82 Jc
Soulanges Can., *Quebec* 35 Qg
Sounding L., *Alberta* 36 Gf
Soure, *Brazil* 53 Hd
Soure, *Portugal* 70 Ab
Sour El Ghozlane, *Algeria* 98 Fa
Souris, *Manitoba* 37 Rj
Souris, *P.E.I.* 33 Kg
Souris R., *Sask./N. Dak.* 30 Jh
Sousa, *Brazil* 53 Ke
Sousel, *Brazil* 53 Gd
Sousse, *Tunisia* 99 Ha
Souterraine, la, *France* 72 Dc
South Africa, Rep. of, *Africa* 95 Ce
Southampton, *England* 63 Fk
Southampton, *New York* 40 Ke
Southampton, *N.S.* 33 Jh
Southampton, *Ontario* 34 Jh
Southampton C., *N.W.T.* 31 Le
Southampton I., *N.W.T.* 31 Le
South Aulatsivik I., *Nfld.* 31 Nf
South Australia, *Australia* 56 Fe
South B., *Ontario* 34 Jg
South Baymouth, *Ontario* 34 Hg
South Bend, *Indiana* 40 Ce
South Bend, *Washington* 47 Bb
South Boston, *Virginia* 45 Hb
Southbridge, *Massachusetts* 44 Da
Southbridge, *New Zealand* 55 De
South Brook, *Nfld.* 33 Qd
South Brookfield, *N.S.* 32 Hj
South Carolina, *U.S.A.* 43 Ke
South China Sea. *See* Nan Hai
South Dakota, *U.S.A.* 42 Fc
South Downs, *England* 63 Gk
South-East C., *Tasmania* 57 Jh
Southend, *England* 63 Hj
Southend, *Saskatchewan* 39 Wg
Southern Alps, *New Zealand* 55 Be
Southern Cross, *W. Aust.* 56 Cf
Southern Harbour, *Nfld.* 33 Sf
Southern Ocean, *Antarctica* 104 Cc
Southey, *Saskatchewan* 37 Nh
South Fork, *Sask.* 36 Jj
South Georgia, I., *Atlantic Ocean* 104 Ad
South Glamorgan, *Wales* 63 Ej
South Hadley Falls, *Massachusetts* 44 Da
South Harbour, *N.S.* 33 Mg
South Haven, *Michigan* 40 Cd
South Heart R., *Alberta* 36 Ac
South Henik L., *N.W.T.* 30 Ke
South I., *New Zealand* 55 Be
South Indian Lake, *Man.* 37 Tb
South Jacksonville, *Florida* 45 Ge
South Junction, *Manitoba* 36 Fa
South Lochaber, *N.S.* 33 Kh
South Magnetic Pole, 104 Jc
South Milwaukee, *Wisconsin* 40 Cd
South Moose L., *Manitoba* 37 Re
South Nelson, *N.B.* 32 Gg
South Orkneys, Is., *Atlantic Ocean* 104 Tc
South Paris, *Maine* 32 Bj
South Pittsburg, *Tennessee* 45 Ec
South Point, *Newfoundland* 33 Rb
South Polar Plateau, *Antarctica* 104 Ma
South Pole, *Antarctica* 104 a
South Porcupine, *Ontario* 34 Jd
Southport, *England* 63 Eg
Southport, *Nfld.* 33 Tf
Southport, *Queensland* 57 Ke
South River, *New Jersey* 44 Cb
South River, *Ontario* 35 Lg
South Ronaldsay, *Orkney* 62 Fb
South Sandwich, Is., *Atlantic Ocean* 104 Ad
South Saskatchewan River Dam, *Saskatchewan* 36 Lg
South Seal R., *Manitoba* 37 Sa
South Shetlands Is., *Antarctica* 104 Tc
South Shields, *England* 62 Gf
South Slocan, *B.C.* 39 Pl
South-West Africa. *See* Namibia
South-West C., *Tasmania* 57 Jh
South Westminster, *B.C.* 39 Jl
Southwold, *England* 63 Jh
South Yemen, *S.W. Asia* 92 Eg
South Yorkshire, *Eng.* 63 Gg
Souzel, *Portugal* 70 Bc
Sovereign, *Saskatchewan* 36 Kg
Sovetsk, *U.S.S.R.* 67 Jj
Sovetskaya Gavan, *U.S.S.R.* 79 Pd
Sovietsk, *U.S.S.R.* 81 Jb
Sowden L., *Ontario* 37 Ma
Soweto, *Transvaal* 95 Ll
Soya, *Japan* 86 Gb
Soya Kaikyo, *Japan* 86 Gb
Soya Misaki, *Japan* 86 Hb
Soyopa, *Mexico* 50 Cb
Spa, *Belgium* 64 Dd
Spain, *W. Europe* 61 Fh
Spalato. *See* Split
Spalding, *England* 63 Gh
Spalding, *Saskatchewan* 37 Nf
Spandau, *W. Berlin, W. Germany* 68 Eb
Spaniard's Bay, *Nfld.* 33 Tf
Spanish, *Ontario* 34 Hf
Spanish Fork, *Utah* 48 Bb
Spanish R., *Ontario* 34 Jf
Spanish Town, *Jamaica* 51 Dc
Sparks, *Nevada* 47 Df
Sparta, *Illinois* 45 Ca
Sparta, *N. Carolina* 45 Gb
Sparta. *See* Sparti
Sparta, *Wisconsin* 40 Ad
Spartanburg, *S. Carolina* 45 Gc
Sparti, *Greece* 77 Df
Spartivento C., *Italy* 75 Fg
Spassk Dal'niy, *U.S.S.R.* 82 Kb
Spassk-Ryazanskiy, *U.S.S.R.* 81 Ec
Spearhill, *Manitoba* 37 Tg
Spedden, *Alberta* 36 Fd
Speers, *Saskatchewan* 36 Kf
Spence Bay, *N.W.T.* 31 Kd
Spencer, *Iowa* 49 Ka
Spencer, *S. Dakota* 46 Jd
Spencer G., *S. Australia* 57 Gf
Spences Bridge, *B.C.* 39 Nk
Spenser Mts., *New Zealand* 55 De
Sperling, *Manitoba* 37 Uj
Sperrin Mts., *N. Ireland* 63 Cf
Spétsai, *Greece* 77 Df
Speyer, *West Germany* 68 Cd
Spey R., *Scotland* 62 Ec
Spezand, *Pakistan* 88 Cc
Spezia, La, *Italy* 74 Bc
Sphinx, *Montana* 46 Bc
Spinazzola, *Italy* 75 Fe
Spiringen, *Switzerland* 65 Db
Spirit Lake, *Iowa* 49 Ka
Spirit River, *Alberta* 39 Oh
Spiritwood, *Sask.* 36 Le
Spiro, *Oklahoma* 49 Ke
Spitsbergen, *Arctic Ocean* 78 Aa
Spittal, *Austria* 68 Ee
Split, *Yugoslavia* 74 Fd
Split, C., *Nova Scotia* 32 Hh
Split L., *Manitoba* 37 Vb
Split Lake, *Manitoba* 37 Vb
Splügen, *Switzerland* 65 Eb
Splügen Pass, *Switz./Italy* 65 Eb
Spofford, *Texas* 48 Gh
Spokane, *Washington* 47 Eb
Spoleto, *Italy* 74 Dd
Spondin, *Alberta* 36 Fg
Spontin, *Belgium* 64 Cd
Sporádhes, *Aegean Sea* 77 Ff
Sporádhes, Voriai, *Aegean Sea* 77 Ee
Spotsylvania, *Virginia* 45 Ja
Spragge, *Ontario* 34 Hf
Sprague, *Manitoba* 36 Fa
Spree, *Germany* 68 Eb
Spremberg, *East Germany* 68 Fc
Sprimont, *Belgium* 64 Dd
Springbok, *Cape Province* 95 Be
Springburn, *Alberta* 39 Ph
Springburn, *N. Zealand* 55 Ce
Spring City, *Tennessee* 45 Ec
Spring Coulee, *Alberta* 36 Dj
Springdale, *Arkansas* 49 Kd
Springdale, *Montana* 46 Bc
Springdale, *Newfoundland* 33 Qd
Springer, *New Mexico* 48 Ed
Springer, Mt., *Quebec* 35 Qc
Springerville, *Arizona* 48 Ce
Springfield, *Colorado* 48 Fd
Springfield, *Georgia, U.S.A.* 45 Gd
Springfield, *Illinois* 40 Bf
Springfield, *Massachusetts* 40 Kd
Springfield, *Missouri* 49 Ld
Springfield, *N.B.* 32 Gh
Springfield, *Nova Scotia* 32 Hj
Springfield, *Ohio* 40 Ef
Springfield, *Ontario* 34 Jk
Springfield, *Vermont* 44 Da
Springfontein, *O.F.S.* 95 Df
Springhill, *Nova Scotia* 32 Jh
Spring Hope, *N. Carolina* 45 Hc
Spring Place, *Georgia, U.S.A.* 45 Ec
Springside, *Saskatchewan* 37 Pg
Springsure, *Queensland* 57 Jd
Spring Valley, *Sask.* 37 Mj
Springville, *New York* 40 Gd
Springville, *Utah* 48 Bb
Springwater, *Sask.* 36 Jg
Spruce Brook, *Nfld.* 33 Oe
Sprucedale, *Ontario* 35 Lg
Spruce Knob, *W. Virginia* 44 Ac
Spruce Lake, *Sask.* 36 He
Spruce Woods Prov. Park, *Manitoba* 37 Sj
Spruga, *Switzerland* 65 Db
Spurfield, *Alberta* 36 Cc
Spy Hill, *Saskatchewan* 37 Qh
Squamish, *B.C.* 39 Ml
Squatteck, *Quebec* 32 Df
Squillace, G. di, *Italy* 75 Ff
Srebrenica, *Yugoslavia* 76 Bb
Sredinnyy, Khrebet, *U.S.S.R.* 79 Rc
Srednekolymsk, *U.S.S.R.* 79 Qb
Sredne Sibirskoye Ploskogor'ye, *U.S.S.R.* 79 Kb
Srem, *Poland* 69 Gb
Srepok, *Kampuchea* 87 Dd
Sretensk, *U.S.S.R.* 79 Lc
Srikakulam, *India* 89 Fe
Sri Lanka, *S. Asia* 88 Eg
Sri Madhopur, *India* 90 Dg
Srinagar, *Kashmir* 90 Dc
Srirangapatna, *India* 88 Ef
Srivilliputtur, *India* 88 Eg
Srnetica, *Yugoslavia* 74 Fc
Sroda, *Poland* 69 Gb
Stackpool, *Ontario* 34 Je
Stadacona, *Quebec* 40 Kb
Staden, *Belgium* 64 Ad
Staffa I., *Scotland* 62 Cd
Stafford, *England* 63 Fh
Stafford, *Kansas* 49 Hd
Stafford, *Virginia* 45 Ja
Stagg L., *N.W.T.* 38 Qd
Stalin Mt., *B.C.* 39 Lf
Stalwart, *Saskatchewan* 37 Mg
Stambaugh, *Michigan* 40 Bb
Stamford, *Connecticut* 40 Ke
Stanberry, *Missouri* 49 Kb
Stanchik, *U.S.S.R.* 79 Qa
Standard, *Alberta* 36 Eg
Standerton, *Transvaal* 95 De
Standish, *Michigan* 40 Dd
Stange, *Norway* 67 Df
Stanislav. *See* Ivano-Frankovsk
Stanley, *Falkland Is.* 54 Eh
Stanley, *New Brunswick* 32 Fg
Stanley Falls. *See* Boyoma Falls
Stanley Mission, *Sask.* 37 Nc
Stanleyville. *See* Kisangani
Stanmore, *Alberta* 36 Fg
Stann Creek, *Belize* 51 Bc
Stanovoy Khrebet, *U.S.S.R.* 79 Mc
Stans, *Switzerland* 65 Db
Stansmore Ra., *W. Australia* 56 Ed
Stanthorpe, *Queensland* 57 Ke
Stanton, *Michigan* 40 Dd
Stanton, *N. Dakota* 46 Gb
Staphorst, *Netherlands* 64 Eb
Staples, *Minnesota* 46 Kb
Stapylton B., *N.W.T.* 38 Pa
Starachowice, *Poland* 69 Jc
Stara Planina, *Bulgaria* 76 Ec
Staraya Russa, *U.S.S.R.* 80 Gc
Stara Zagora, *Bulgaria* 76 Ec
Starbuck, *Manitoba* 37 Uj
Starbuck, I., *Pacific Ocean* 103 Kh
Star City, *Arkansas* 45 Bd
Star City, *Saskatchewan* 37 Nf
Stargard, *Poland* 68 Fb
Starkville, *Mississippi* 49 Nf
Starkweather, *N. Dakota* 46 Ha
Star'obelsk, *Ukraine* 80 Lg
Starodub, *U.S.S.R.* 80 He
Starogard, *Poland* 69 Hb
Staro Konstantinov, *Ukraine* 80 Eg
Staryy Oskol, *U.S.S.R.* 80 Kf
Staten I., *New York* 44 Cb
Staten I. *See* Estados, I.
Statesville, *N. Carolina* 45 Gc
Stattlandet, *Norway* 66 Ae
Staunton, *Virginia* 45 Ha
Stavanger, *Norway* 67 Ag
Stave L., *B.C.* 39 Ml
Stavelot, *Belgium* 64 Dd
Stavely, *Alberta* 36 Dh
Stavenisse, *Netherlands* 64 Cc
Staveren, *Netherlands* 64 Db
Stavern, *Norway* 67 Dg
Stavropol, *U.S.S.R.* 78 Dd
Stayner, *Ontario* 34 Kh
Stebark, *Poland* 69 Jb
Steckborn, *Switzerland* 65 Da
Steele, *N. Dakota* 46 Hb
Steele, Mt., *Y.T.* 38 Ce
Steel L., *Ontario* 34 Dc
Steel R., *Ontario* 34 Dd
Steelton, *Pennsylvania* 44 Bb
Steelville, *Missouri* 49 Mc
Steenbergen, *Netherlands* 64 Cc
Steenkool, *Irian Jaya* 83 Kl
Steen R., *Alberta* 38 Pf
Steensel, *Netherlands* 64 Dc
Steenwijk, *Netherlands* 64 Eb
Steephill L., *Sask.* 37 Oc
Steep Rock, *Manitoba* 37 Tg
Steep Rock Lake, *Ont.* 36 La
Stefanie L., *Ethiopia* 97 Hd
Stefansson I., *N.W.T.* 30 Jc
Steiermark, *Austria* 68 Fe
Stein, *Switzerland* 65 Da
Steinbach, *Manitoba* 37 Vj
Steinkjer, *Norway* 66 De
Stekene, *Belgium* 64 Cc
Stellarton, *Nova Scotia* 32 Kh
Stenay, *France* 72 Fb
Stendal, *East Germany* 68 Db
Stenen, *Saskatchewan* 37 Pg
Stenträsk, *Sweden* 66 Hc
Stephenson, *Michigan* 40 Cc
Stephenville, *Nfld.* 33 Oe
Stephenville Crossing, *Nfld.* 33 Oe
Stepnoy. *See* Elista
Stepnyak, *Kazakhstan* 78 Gc
Sterea, *Greece* 77 Ce
Sterlet L., *N.W.T.* 38 Tc
Sterling, *Colorado* 48 Fb
Sterling, *Illinois* 49 Nb
Sterling Res., *Colorado* 48 Fb
Sterlitamak, *U.S.S.R.* 81 Md
Sternberk, *Czechoslovakia* 69 Gd
Sterrebeek, *Belgium* 64 Cd
Stettin. *See* Szczecin
Stettler, *Alberta* 36 Ef
Steubenville, *Ohio* 40 Fe
Stevens, *Ontario* 34 Ec
Stevenson L., *Manitoba* 37 We
Stevens Point, *Wisconsin* 40 Bc
Steveston, *B.C.* 39 Gm
Stewart, *British Columbia* 39 Jh
Stewart, *Chile* 54 Bh
Stewart, R., *Y.T.* 38 Dd
Stewart Crossing, *Y.T.* 38 Ed
Stewart Is., *New Zealand* 55 Ag
Stewart Sound, *Andaman Is.* 89 Hf
Stewart Valley, *Sask.* 36 Kh
Stewiacke, *Nova Scotia* 32 Jh
Steyr, *Austria* 68 Fd
Stia, *Italy* 74 Cd
Stikine, R., *B.C.* 39 Hg
Stikine Ras., *B.C.* 38 Hf
Stillwater, *Minnesota* 46 Lc
Stillwater, *Oklahoma* 49 Jd
Stimlje, *Yugoslavia* 76 Cc
Stirling, *Alberta* 36 Ej
Stirling, *Ontario* 35 Nh
Stirling, *Scotland* 62 Ed
Stirling Range, *W. Australia* 56 Cf
Stjernöy, *Norway* 66 Ka
Stockholm, *Saskatchewan* 37 Ph
Stockholm, *Sweden* 67 Hg
Stockport, *England* 63 Fg
Stockton, *California* 47 Cg
Stockton, *Kansas* 49 Hc
Stockton, *Manitoba* 37 Sj
Stockton Res., *Missouri* 49 Ld
Stoke-on-Trent, *England* 63 Fg
Stokes Bay, *Ontario* 34 Jg
Stolbovaya, *U.S.S.R.* 79 Qb
Stolp. *See* Slupsk
Ston, *Yugoslavia* 74 Fd
Stonecliffe, *Ontario* 35 Mf
Stoneham, *Quebec* 32 Ag
Stonehaven, *Scotland* 62 Fd
Stone Mountain Prov. Park, *British Columbia* 39 Lf
Stoner, *British Columbia* 39 Mj
Stonewall, *Manitoba* 37 Uh
Stoney Beach, *Sask.* 37 Mh
Stoney Creek, *Ontario* 35 Lj
Stony Mountain, *Manitoba* 37 Uh
Stony Plain, *Alberta* 36 De
Stony Rapids, *Sask.* 38 Vf
Stora Lulevatten, *Sweden* 66 Hc
Stora Sjöfallets Nat. Park, *Sweden* 66 Gc
Storavan, *Sweden* 66 Hd
Stord, I., *Norway* 67 Ag
Støren, *Norway* 66 De
Storforshei, *Norway* 66 Fc
Stor I., *N.W.T.* 31 Lb
Storkerson B., *N.W.T.* 30 Gc
Storlien, *Sweden* 66 De
Storm Lake, *Iowa* 49 Ka
Stormy L., *Ontario* 36 Ka
Stornoway, *Saskatchewan* 37 Pg
Stornoway, *Scotland* 62 Cb
Stor Sjön, *Sweden* 66 Fe
Storsund, *Sweden* 66 Jd
Storthoaks, *Saskatchewan* 37 Qj
Storuman, *Sweden* 66 Gd
Storvik, *Sweden* 67 Gf
Stoughton, *Saskatchewan* 37 Oj
Stowmarket, *England* 63 Hh
Strabane, *N. Ireland* 63 Cf
Strachan, *Quebec* 40 Ja
Strachan, Mt., *B.C.* 39 Gk
Strachan I., *Papua New Guinea* 57 Ha
Strahan, *Tasmania* 57 Hh
Stralsund, *East Germany* 68 Ea
Stramproij, *Netherlands* 64 Dc
Strand, *Norway* 67 Bg
Stranda, *Norway* 66 Be
Strangford L., *N. Ireland* 63 Df
Strangways Springs, *S. Australia* 57 Ge
Stranraer, *Saskatchewan* 36 Jg
Stranraer, *Scotland* 63 Df
Strasbourg, *France* 72 Gb
Strasbourg, *Sask.* 37 Ng
Strasburg, *Virginia* 44 Ac
Stråssa, *Sweden* 67 Fg
Stratford, *Connecticut* 44 Db
Stratford, *Michigan* 40 Dc
Stratford, *New Zealand* 55 Ec
Stratford, *Ontario* 34 Jj
Stratford Centre, *Quebec* 32 Ah
Stratford-upon-Avon, *England* 63 Fh
Strathclair, *Manitoba* 37 Rh
Strathclyde, *Scot.* 62 Dd
Strathcona Prov. Park, *B.C.* 39 Ll
Strathlorne, *Nova Scotia* 33 Lg
Strathmore, *Alberta* 36 Dg
Strathnaver, *B.C.* 39 Mj
Strathroy, *Ontario* 34 Jk
Straubing, *West Germany* 68 Ed
Štrbské Pleso, *Czech.* 69 Jd
Streaky B., *S. Australia* 57 Ff
Streamstown, *Alberta* 36 Ge
Streator, *Illinois* 49 Nb
Strelka, *U.S.S.R.* 79 Jc
Strelka, *U.S.S.R.* 79 Qb
Strelka Chunya, *U.S.S.R.* 79 Kb
Strenči, *Latvia* 67 Lh
Stříbro, *Czechoslovakia* 68 Ed
Strickland, *Ontario* 34 Jc
Strijbeek, *Netherlands* 64 Cc
Strijen, *Netherlands* 64 Cc
Strimón, G. of, *Greece* 77 Ed
Stromboli, *Italy* 75 Ef
Strome, *Alberta* 36 Ef
Stromeferry, *Scotland* 62 Dc
Stromness, *Orkney* 62 Eb
Strömsberg, *Sweden* 67 Gf
Strömsbruk, *Sweden* 67 Gf
Strömstad, *Sweden* 67 Dg
Strömsund, *Sweden* 66 Fe
Ströms Vattudäl, *Sweden* 66 Fd
Strömtorp, *Sweden* 67 Fg
Strongfield, *Sask.* 36 Lg
Strongoli, *Italy* 75 Ff
Stronsay I., *Orkney* 62 Fa
Stroud, *England* 63 Fj
Stroudsburg, *Pennsylvania* 44 Cb
Struga, *Yugoslavia* 76 Cd
Struma, *Bulg./Greece* 76 Dd
Strumica, *Yugoslavia* 76 Dd
Stryy, *Ukraine* 80 Cg
Strzelin, *Poland* 69 Gc
Stuart, *Florida* 45 Gg
Stuart, *Virginia* 45 Gb
Stuart Highway, *N.Terr.* 57 Fc
Stuart L. & R., *B.C.* 39 Lh
Stuart Range, *S. Australia* 57 Fe
Stugun, *Sweden* 66 Fe
Stung Treng, *Kampuchea* 87 Dd
Stupendous Mt., *B.C.* 39 Kj
Sturgeon, R., *Ontario* 34 Kf
Sturgeon B., *Manitoba* 37 Uf
Sturgeon Bay, *Wisconsin* 40 Cc
Sturgeon Falls, *Ontario* 34 Lf
Sturgeon L., *Alberta* 39 Ph
Sturgeon L., *Ontario* 37 Lb
Sturgeon L., *Ontario* 37 Ma
Sturgeon L., *Ontario* 35 Mh
Sturgeon Landing, *Sask.* 37 Qd
Sturgeon R., *Alberta* 36 Ce
Sturgeon R., *Sask.* 36 Le
Sturgis, *Saskatchewan* 37 Pg
Sturgis, *S. Dakota* 46 Fc
Sturt Desert, *S. Aust./Queensland* 57 He
Stuttgart, *Arkansas* 45 Bc
Stuttgart, *West Germany* 68 Cd
Suakin, *Sudan* 99 Ne
Suaqui, *Mexico* 50 Cb
Subh, Jebel, *Arabia* 92 Ce
Subotica, *Yugoslavia* 76 Ba
Success, *Saskatchewan* 36 Jh
Sucha, *Poland* 69 Hd
Sucre, *Bolivia* 52 Dg
Sud, Pointe, *Quebec* 33 Kd
Sudan, *Africa* 99 Lf
Sudbury, *England* 63 Hh
Sudbury, *Ontario* 34 Jf
Suddie, *Guyana* 52 Fb
Sudety, Mts., *Czech.* 69 Fc
Sud-Ouest, C. du, *Que.* 33 Kf
Suez, *Egypt* 99 Mc
Suez, Gulf of, *Egypt* 99 Mc
Suez Canal, *Egypt* 99 Mb
Sufeina, *Arabia* 92 De
Suffield, *Alberta* 36 Fh
Suffolk, *England* 63 Hh
Suffolk, *Virginia* 45 Jb
Suggi L., *Saskatchewan* 37 Pd
Suggsville, *Alabama* 45 De
Suḩār, *Oman* 93 Ge
Suhl, *East Germany* 68 Dc
Suide, *China* 84 Ed
Suifu. *See* Yibin
Suihua, *China* 82 Ja
Suining, *China* 84 Hf
Suipacha, *Bolivia* 52 Dh
Sujangarh, *India* 90 Dg
Sujanpur, *India* 90 Ee
Sujanpur, *India* 90 Dd
Sujica, *Yugoslavia* 74 Fd
Sukadana, *Borneo (Kalimantan)* 83 El
Sukarnapura. *See* Japura
Sukarno, Peak. *See* Puncak Jaja
Sukhumi, *Georgia, U.S.S.R.* 78 Dd
Sukkur, *Pakistan* 88 Cc
Sukumo, *Japan* 86 Ch
Sukunka, R., *B.C.* 39 Nh
Sulaiman Ra., *Pakistan* 88 Db
Sulawesi. *See* Celebes
Sulaymānīya, *Iraq* 92 Eb
Suldal, *Sweden* 67 Bg
Sulęcin, *Poland* 68 Fb
Sulgen, *Switzerland* 65 Ea
Sulina, *Romania* 76 Gb
Sulitelma, Mt., *Norway* 66 Gc
Sullana, *Peru* 52 Ad
Sullivan, *Illinois* 49 Nc
Sullivan, *Indiana* 49 Oc
Sullivan, *Missouri* 45 Ba
Sullivan Bay, *B.C.* 39 Kk
Sullivan L., *Alberta* 36 Ff
Sulmona, *Italy* 75 Dd
Sulphur, *Oklahoma* 49 Je
Sulphur, *Y.T.* 30 Fe
Sulphur Springs, *Texas* 49 Kf
Sultan, *Ontario* 34 He
Sultan Dagh, *Turkey* 92 Bb
Sultan Hamud, *Kenya* 97 He
Sultanpur, *India* 90 De
Sultanpur, *India* 91 Db
Sulu Arch., *Philippines* 83 Hj
Sulu Kep., *Indonesia* 83 Jl
Sulu Sea, *Philippines* 83 Gj
Sumagawa, *Japan* 86 Hc
Sumatra, *Indonesia* 83 Ck
Sumba, *Indonesia* 83 Gm
Sumbawa, *Indonesia* 83 Gm
Sümber, *Mongolia* 82 Ea
Sumburgh Head, *Shetland Is.* 62 Jb
Sümeg, *Hungary* 69 Ge
Sumiswald, *Switzerland* 65 Ca
Summerford, *Nfld.* 33 Sd
Summerland, *B.C.* 39 Ol
Summerside, *P.E.I.* 32 Jg
Summerville, *Nfld.* 33 Te
Summit, *Ontario* 34 Fe
Summit, *S. Dakota* 46 Jc
Summit Lake, *B.C.* 39 Mh
Sumperk, *Czechoslovakia* 69 Gd
Sumprabum, *Burma* 89 Jc
Sumter, *S. Carolina* 45 Gd
Sumy, *Ukraine* 80 Jf
Suna, *Tanzania* 97 Gf
Sunapee L., *New Hampshire* 44 Da
Sunart L., *Scotland* 62 Dd
Sunbury, *Pennsylvania* 40 He
Suncho Corral, *Argentina* 54 Dc
Sunchow. *See* Quiping
Suncook, *New Hampshire* 40 Ld
Sunda, Selat, *Indonesia* 83 Dm
Sundance, *Wyoming* 46 Ec
Sundargarh, *India* 91 Ed
Sundarnagar, *India* 90 Ee
Sunderland, *England* 62 Gf
Sunderland, *Ontario* 35 Lh
Sundown, *Manitoba* 36 Fa
Sundre, *Alberta* 36 Cg
Sundridge, *Ontario* 35 Lg
Sundsvall, *Sweden* 66 Ge
Sungei Petani, *Pen. Malaysia* 87 Ce
Sunndalsøra, *Norway* 66 Ce
Sunnybrae, *Nova Scotia* 32 Kh
Sunnybrook, *Alberta* 36 Ce
Sunnynook, *Alberta* 36 Fg
Sunnyside, *Newfoundland* 33 Tf
Sunnyside, *Utah* 48 Bc
Sunnyslope, *Alberta* 36 Dg
Sunset House, *Alberta* 39 Ph
Sunstrum, *Ontario* 36 Ka
Suntar, *U.S.S.R.* 79 Lb
Sunyani, *Ghana* 98 Eg
Suomi, *Ontario* 37 Mb
Suō nada, *Japan* 86 Bh
Suonenjoki, *Finland* 66 Me
Supaul, *India* 91 Fb
Superb, *Saskatchewan* 36 Hg
Superior, *Nebraska* 49 Hb
Superior, *Wisconsin* 46 Lb
Superior, L., *U.S.A./Can.* 43 Jb
Suq ash Shuyukh, *Iraq* 92 Ec
Suqian, *China* 84 Jf
Sūr, *Oman* 93 Ge
Sūr. *See* Tyre
Sura, *U.S.S.R.* 81 Hc
Surab, *Pakistan* 88 Cc
Surabaya, *Java* 83 Fm
Surakarta, *Java* 83 Fm
Suran, *Syria* 94 Eb
Surapur, *India* 88 Ee
Surat, *India* 88 Dd
Suratgarh, *India* 90 Df
Surat Thani, *Thailand* 87 Be
Surendranagar, *India* 88 Dd
Surf Inlet, *B.C.* 39 Jj
Surgères, *France* 72 Cc
Surgut, *U.S.S.R.* 78 Gb
Suri, *India* 91 Fd
Surigao, *Philippines* 83 Jj
Surin, *Thailand* 87 Cd
Surinam, *S. America* 53 Fc
Suriname, *Surinam* 53 Fc
Suriya, *S. Yemen* 92 Eg
Surprise, *B.C.* 38 Gf
Surprise, L., *Quebec* 35 Pc
Surprise L., *B.C.* 38 Gf
Surrey, *England* 63 Gj
Surrey, district, *B.C.* 39 Jm
Sursee, *Switzerland* 65 Da
Sursk, *Ukraine* 80 Jg
Surt, *Libya* 99 Jb
Surtsey, I., *Iceland* 66 Vn
Surud Ad, *Somalia* 97 Kb
Süs, *Switzerland* 65 Fb
Susa, *Iran* 92 Ec
Susak, *Yugoslavia* 74 Ec
Susquehanna, *Pa.* 40 Hf
Sussex, *New Brunswick* 32 Gh
Susteren, *Netherlands* 64 Dc
Sustut Pk., *B.C.* 39 Kg
Sutherland, *Cape Province* 95 Cf
Suting. *See* Daxian
Sutlej R., *Pakistan* 90 Ce
Sutton, *Ontario* 35 Lh
Sutton, *Quebec* 35 Sg
Sutton Bay, *Ontario* 35 Le
Suure Jaani, *Estonia* 67 Lg
Suvavesi, *Finland* 66 Ne
Suvorov, *Pacific Ocean* 102 Jj
Suwair, *Arabia* 92 Dc
Suwałki, *Poland* 69 Ka
Suwannee L., *Manitoba* 37 Rb
Suweilih, *Jordan* 94 De
Suzhou, *China* 84 Kg
Svalbard, *Arctic Ocean* 78 Aa
Svanstein, *Sweden* 66 Kc
Svappavaara, *Sweden* 66 Jc
Svärholt, Halvöy, *Norway* 66 La
Svartenhuk Pen., *Greenland* 41 Pb
Svartisen, *Norway* 66 Ec
Svartvik, *Sweden* 66 Ge
Švekšna, *Lithuania* 67 Jj
Svendborg, *Denmark* 67 Dj
Sverdlovsk, *U.S.S.R.* 81 Qb
Sverdrup, Os., *U.S.S.R.* 78 Ga
Sverdrup Channel, *N.W.T.* 30 Ka
Sverdrup Is., *N.W.T.* 30 Jb
Svetogorsk, *U.S.S.R.* 67 Nf
Svetozarevo, *Yugoslavia* 76 Cc
Svishtov, *Bulgaria* 76 Ec
Svitavy, *Czechoslovakia* 69 Gd
Svīyazhsk, *U.S.S.R.* 81 Jc
Svobodnyy, *U.S.S.R.* 79 Mc
Svolvaer, *Norway* 66 Fb
Swabi, *Pakistan* 90 Cc
Swakopmund, *Namibia* 95 Ad
Swalwell, *Alberta* 36 Dg
Swan, R., *W. Australia* 56 Cf
Swan Hill, *Victoria* 57 Hg
Swan Hills, *Alberta* 36 Bd
Swan L., *B.C.* 39 Jh
Swan L., *Manitoba* 37 Rf
Swan Lake, *Manitoba* 37 Tj
Swan Plain, *Saskatchewan* 37 Qf
Swan R., *Alberta* 36 Bc
Swan R., *Manitoba* 37 Qf
Swan River, *Manitoba* 37 Qf
Swansea, *Tasmania* 57 Jh
Swansea, *Wales* 63 Ej
Swanson, *Saskatchewan* 36 Kg
Swanton, *Vermont* 40 Kc
Swarzewo, *Poland* 69 Ha
Swastika, *Ontario* 34 Kd
Swat, *Pakistan* 90 Cc
Swatow. *See* Shantou
Swaziland, *S. Africa* 95 Ee
Sweden, *N.-W. Europe* 60 Lc
Sweet Grass Hills, *Montana* 46 Ba
Sweetwater, *Texas* 48 Gf
Swellendam, *Cape Province* 95 Cf
Świdnica, *Poland* 69 Gc
Świetochlowice, *Poland* 69 Hc
Swift, R., *B.C.* 38 Hf
Swift Current, *Nfld.* 33 Sf
Swift Current, *Sask.* 36 Kh
Swiftcurrent Cr., *Sask.* 36 Jh
Swift River, *Y.T.* 38 He
Swilly L., *Eire* 62 Be
Swindon, *England* 63 Fj

Swinemünde. See Swinoujście
Swinoujście, Poland 68 Fb
Switzerland, Central Europe 61 Jg
Swords, Eire 63 Cg
Syas'stroy, U.S.S.R. 80 Ha
Sycamore, Illinois 40 Bd
Sydenham, Ontario 35 Oh
Sydney, New South Wales 57 Kf
Sydney, Nova Scotia 33 Mg
Sydney Mines, N.S. 33 Mg
Syktyvkar, U.S.S.R. 78 Eb
Sylhet, Bangladesh 89 Hd
Sylt, I., West Germany 67 Cj
Sylte, Norway 66 Be
Sylvania, Saskatchewan 37 Nf
Sylvan Lake, Alberta 36 Cf
Sylvester, Mt., Nfld. 33 Re
Sylvia, Mt., B.C. 39 Lf
Syracuse, Kansas 48 Gd
Syracuse, New York 44 Ba
Syracuse. See Siracusa
Syr Dar 'ya, Kazakhstan 78 Fd
Syria, W. Asia 92 Cb
Syrian Desert, Iraq 92 Cc
Sysert, U.S.S.R. 81 Qb
Syurkum, U.S.S.R. 79 Pc
Syzran, U.S.S.R. 81 Jd
Szarvas, Hungary 69 Je
Szczecin, Poland 68 Fb
Szczecinek, Poland 69 Gb
Szczecinski, Zal., Ger./Pol. 68 Fb
Szczytno, Poland 69 Jb
Szeged, Hungary 76 Ca
Székesfehérvár, Hungary 69 He
Szekszard, Hungary 76 Ba
Szeming. See Xiamen
Szentes, Hungary 69 Je
Szolnok, Hungary 69 Je
Szombathely, Hungary 74 Fb
Szprotawa, Poland 69 Fc
Szreńsk, Poland 69 Jb

T

Taba, Arabia 92 Dd
Tabas, Iran 93 Gc
Tabas, Iran 93 Hc
Tabasara, Sierra de, Panama 51 Ce
Tabasco, Mexico 50 Fd
Tabatière, La, Quebec 33 Nc
Tabatinga, Brazil 52 Dd
Tabelbala, Algeria 98 Ec
Taber, Alberta 36 Ej
Taber Prov. Park, Alta. 36 Ej
Table Mt., Cape Province 95 Bf
Table Mt., Newfoundland 33 Nf
Taboleiro, Brazil 52 Fe
Tábor, Czechoslovakia 68 Fd
Tabora, Tanzania 97 Ge
Tabou, Ivory Coast 98 Dh
Tabrīz, Iran 92 Eb
Tabuk, Arabia 92 Cd
Tabusintac R., N.B. 32 Gf
Tabut, South Yemen 93 Ff
Tacámbaro, Mexico 50 Dd
Tacheng, China 78 Hd
Tacloban, Philippines 83 Hh
Tacna, Peru 52 Cg
Tacoma, Washington 47 Bb
Taconic Mts., N.Y./Mass. 44 Da
Taco Pozo, Argentina 54 Dc
Tacuarembó, Uruguay 54 Ed
Tadenet L., N.W.T. 38 La
Tadjoura & G. of, Djibouti 97 Jb
Tadoussac, Quebec 32 Ce
Tadzhikskaya S.S.R. (Tadzhikistan), U.S.S.R. 78 Fe
Taegu, Korea 82 Jc
Taejŏn, Korea 82 Jc
Tafalla, Spain 71 Ea
Taff R., Wales 63 Ej
Tafila, Jordan 94 Dg
Taft, Iran 93 Fc
Taftville, Connecticut 44 Db
Taganrog, U.S.S.R. 80 Lh
Tagawa, Japan 86 Bh
Taga Zong, Bhutan 89 Hc
Tagish L., B.C. 38 Ff
Taguá, Brazil 53 Jf
Tagula, Papua New Guinea 57 Kb
Tagus, N. Dakota 46 Ga
Tagus, R. See Tajo
Tahakopa, New Zealand 55 Bg
Tahat, Algeria 98 Gd
Tahi, R., B.C. 38 Gf
Tahiryuak L., N.W.T. 38 Ra
Tahiti, Society Islands 103 Kj
Tahltan, B.C. 39 Hf
Tahoe, L., California 47 Cf
Tahoe L., N.W.T. 38 Ta
Tahora, New Zealand 55 Ec
Tahoua, Niger 98 Gf
Tahta, Egypt 99 Mc
Tahtsa Reach, B.C. 39 Kj
Tahuna, Indonesia 83 Jk
Tai'an, China 84 Hd
Taibus Qi, China 84 Gb
Taichow. See Linhai
Taichung, Taiwan 85 Kk
Taieri, R., New Zealand 55 Cf
Taigu, China 84 Fd
Taihang Shan, China 84 Fd
Taihape, New Zealand 55 Ec
Tai Hu, China 84 Kg
Tainan, Taiwan 85 Kl
Taipale, Finland 66 Ne
Taipei, Taiwan 85 Kk
Taiping, Pen. Malaysia 87 Cf
Taipingchuan, China 82 Hb
Taipinghs. See Wanyuan
Taira, Japan 86 Gf
Tairadate, Japan 86 Gd
Taishan, China 85 Fl
Taishun, China 85 Jj
Taitao, Pen. de, Chile 54 Bg
Taiwan, S.E. Asia 85 Kl
Taiwan Haixia, China 85 Jk
Taiwara, Afghanistan 93 Hc
Taixing, China 84 Kf
Taiyetos, Greece 77 Df
Taiyiba, Jordan 94 Dg
Taiyuan, China 84 Fd
Taizhou, China 84 Jf
Ta'izz, Yemen 92 Dg
Tajarhi, Libya 99 Hd
Tajo, R., (Tejo), Spain/Portugal 70 Bc
Tajrish, Iran 93 Fb
Tajumulco, Guatemala 50 Fd
Tak, Thailand 87 Bc
Takagi, Japan 86 Ge
Takahashi, Japan 86 Cg
Takaka, New Zealand 55 Dd
Takamatsu, Japan 86 Dg
Takaoka, Japan 86 Ef
Takapuna, New Zealand 55 Eb
Takasaki, Japan 86 Ff
Takaungu, Kenya 97 He
Takayama, Japan 86 Ef
Takefu, Japan 86 Eg
Takhini, R., N.W.T. 38 Fe
Takhta Bazar, Turkmen. 78 Fe
Takht-i-Sulaiman, Pakistan 90 Be
Takijuq L., N.W.T. 38 Rb
Takingeun, Sumatra 83 Ck
Takipy, Manitoba 37 Qc
Takla L., B.C. 39 Lh
Takla Landing, B.C. 39 Lh
Taklimakan Shamo, China 78 He
Takoradi, Ghana 98 Eh
Taku, British Columbia 38 Gf
Taku, R., B.C. 38 Gf
Takua Pa, Thailand 87 Be
Taku Arm, L., Y.T. 38 Fe
Talagang, Pakistan 90 Cd
Talaimannar, Sri Lanka 88 Eg
Talara, Peru 52 Ad
Talasski Ala Tau, Kirghizia 78 Gd
Talavera de la Reina, Spain 70 Cc
Talbot Inlet, N.W.T. 31 Mb
Talbot L., Manitoba 37 Sd
Talca, Chile 54 Be
Talcahuano, Chile 54 Be
Taldy Kurgan, Kazakhstan 78 Gd
Taliabu, Indonesia 83 Hl
Talien. See Lüda
Taliwang, Sumbawa I., Indonesia 83 Gm
Talladega, Alabama 45 Dd
Tallahassee, Florida 45 Ee
Tallinn, Estonia 67 Lg
Tall Pines, Saskatchewan 37 Pf
Tallulah, Louisiana 49 Mf
Tallulah Falls, Georgia, U.S.A. 45 Fc
Talmage, Saskatchewan 37 Oj
Talmenka, U.S.S.R. 78 Hc
Talsi, Latvia 67 Kh
Taltal, Chile 54 Bc
Taltson River, N.W.T. 38 Se
Tamale, Ghana 98 Eg
Tamanrasset, Algeria 98 Gd
Tamaqua, Pennsylvania 44 Cb
Tamarite de Litera, Spain 71 Fb
Tamási, Hungary 69 He
Tamatave, Madagascar 97 Nk
Tamaulipas, Mexico 50 Ec
Tamaya, Chile 54 Bd
Tambacounda, Senegal 98 Cf
Tambo, Queensland 57 Jd
Tambo de Mora, Peru 52 Bf
Tambohorano, Madag. 97 Mk
Tamboril, Brazil 53 Jd
Tambov, U.S.S.R. 81 Ed
Tambura, Sudan 99 Lg
Tame, Colombia 52 Cb
Tamel Aiken, Argentina 54 Bg
Tamiahua, Mexico 50 Ec
Tamil Nadu, India 88 Ef
Tamins, Switzerland 65 Eb
Tamluk, India 91 Fd
Tammisaari, Finland 67 Kg
Tammu, Burma 89 Hd
Tampa, Florida 43 Kf
Tampere, Finland 67 Kf
Tampico, Mexico 50 Ec
Tamrah, Arabia 92 Ee
Tamsagbulag, Mongolia 82 Ga
Tamsalu, Estonia 67 Mg
Tamworth, N.S.W. 57 Kf
Tamworth, Ontario 35 Oh
Tana, Vanuatu 102 Fj
Tana, R., Norway 66 Mb
Tanabe, Japan 86 Dh
Tanabu. See Mutsu
Tana Fd., Norway 66 Na
Tanaga I., Aleutian Is. 43 Vm
Tanah Merah, Pen. Malaysia 87 Ce
Tana L., Ethiopia 97 Hb
Tanami, N. Terr. 56 Ec
Tanana, Alaska 43 Xl
Tanana, R., Alaska 43 Yl
Tananarive. See Antananarivo
Tancheng, China 84 Je
Tanda, India 91 Db
Tanda Urmar, India 90 De
Tandil, Argentina 54 Ee
Taneatua, New Zealand 55 Fc
Tanega shima, Japan 86 Bj
Tanegashima kaikyo, Japan 86 Bj
Tanen-taung-gyi, Thailand/Burma 87 Bc
Tanga, Tanzania 97 Hf
Tanganyika, L., Congo 97 Ff
Tangen, Norway 67 Df
Tanger, Morocco 98 Da
Tangermünde, E. Germany 68 Db
Tangier, Nova Scotia 32 Kj
Tangier. See Tanger
Tangier Grand L., N.S. 32 Kj
Tangshan, China 84 Jc
Tanguy, U.S.S.R. 79 Kc
Tanimbar Kep., Indonesia 83 Km
Tanjung, Java, Indonesia 83 Em
Tanjungpandan, Indonesia 83 El
Tanjungpinang, Indonesia 87 Cf
Tanjungredeb, Borneo (Kalimantan) 83 Gk
Tanjungselor, Borneo (Kalimantan) 83 Gk
Tank, Pakistan 88 Db
Tankapirtti, Finland 66 Mb
Tankse, Kashmir 88 Eb
Tännäs, Sweden 66 Ee
Tannenberg. See Stebark
Tannin, Ontario 37 Ma
Tanta, Egypt 99 Mb
Tantallon, Sakatchewan 37 Qh
Tanzania, E. Africa 97 Gf
Tanzilla, R., B.C. 39 Hf
Tao, Burma 89 Hd
Taochow. See Lintan
Taormina, Sicily 75 Eg
Taos, New Mexico 48 Ed
Tapa, Estonia 67 Lg
Tapachula, Mexico 50 Fe
Tapah, Pen. Malaysia 87 Cf
Tapajós, Brazil 53 Fd
Tapalquen, Argentina 54 De
Tapan, Sumatra 83 Dl
Tapanui, New Zealand 55 Bg
Tapauá, Brazil 52 Ee
Taplejung, Nepal 91 Fb
Tappahannock, Virginia 45 Jb
Tapti, India 88 Ed
Tapuaenuku, Mt., N.Z. 55 Dd
Taqah, Oman 93 Ff
Taquara, Brazil 54 Fc
Taquaretinga, Brazil 53 Ke
Tara, Ontario 34 Jh
Tara, U.S.S.R. 78 Gc
Tarābulus al Gharb. See Tripoli
Taradale, New Zealand 55 Fc
Tarakan, Borneo (Kalimantan) 83 Gk
Tarakli, Turkey 92 Ba
Taranagar, India 90 Df
Taranaki Bight, N., N.Z. 55 Dc
Taranaki Bight, S., N.Z. 55 Dc
Tarancón, Spain 70 Db
Taranto, Italy 75 Fe
Taranto, G. di, Italy 75 Ff
Tarapoto, Peru 52 Be
Taraqua, Brazil 52 Dd
Tararua Range, New Zealand 55 Ed
Tarascon, France 73 De
Tarasp, Switzerland 65 Fb
Tarata, Peru 52 Cg
Tarauaca, Brazil 52 Ce
Tarawa, Kiribati 102 Gg
Tarawera, New Zealand 55 Fc
Tarazona, Spain 71 Eb
Tarazona de la Mancha, Spain 71 Ec
Tarbagatai Khrebet, Kazakhstan 78 Hd
Tarbat Ness, Scotland 62 Ec
Tarbela Dam, Pakistan 90 Cc
Tarbert, Scotland 62 De
Tarbert, Scotland 62 Cc
Tarbes, France 73 De
Tarboro, N. Carolina 45 Jc
Tarcoola, S. Australia 57 Ff
Taree, New South Wales 57 Kf
Tärendö, Sweden 66 Kc
Tarija, Bolivia 52 Eh
Tarim, Arabia 92 Ef
Tarko Sale, U.S.S.R. 78 Gb
Tarlac, Philippines 83 Hg
Tarma, Peru 52 Bf
Tarn, France 73 Ee
Tärna, Sweden 66 Fd
Tarn-et-Garonne, Fr. 73 Dd
Tarnobrzeg, Poland 69 Jc
Tarnopol, Saskatchewan 37 Mf
Tarnów, Poland 69 Jc
Tarnowskie Gory, Poland 69 Hc
Tarn Taran, India 90 De
Tarom, Iran 93 Gd
Taroom, Queensland 57 Je
Taroudant, Morocco 98 Db
Tarragona, Spain 71 Fb
Tarrega, Spain 71 Fb
Tarsus, Turkey 92 Bb
Tartagal, Argentina 52 Eh
Tartas, France 73 Ce
Tartu, Estonia 67 Mg
Tartus, Syria 94 Dc
Tarzwell, Ontario 34 Kd
Taschereau, Quebec 35 Md
Taseko, Mt., B.C. 39 Mk
Taseko, R., B.C. 39 Mk
Taseyevo, U.S.S.R. 79 Jc
Tashkent, Uzbekistan 78 Fd
Tashota, Ontario 34 Cb
Tasil, Syria 94 De
Taskan, U.S.S.R. 79 Qb
Tasman, Mt., New Zealand 55 Ce
Tasman B., New Zealand 55 Dd
Tasmania, Aust. 57 Jh
Tasman Mts., New Zealand 55 Dd
Tast, L. du, Quebec 35 Na
Tata, Hungary 69 He
Tatakoto, Tuamotu Arch. 103 Mj
Tatamagouche, N.S. 32 Jh
Tatarsk, U.S.S.R. 78 Gc
Tatarskaya A.S.S.R., U.S.S.R. 78 Ec
Tatarskiy Proliv, U.S.S.R. 79 Pd
Tate, Saskatchewan 37 Ng
Tathlina L., N.W.T. 38 Pe
Tathlith, Arabia 92 Df
Tatla L., British Columbia 39 Lk
Tatlayoko Lake, B.C. 39 Lk
Tatlow, Mt., B.C. 39 Mk
Tatnam, C., Manitoba 31 Kf
Tatranská Lomnica, Czechoslovakia 69 Jd
Tatry, Poland/Czech. 69 Hd
Tatshenshini, R., B.C. 38 Ef
Tatta, Pakistan 88 Cd
Tatuhí, Brazil 53 Hh
Tatu R., China 82 Dd
Tatvar, Turkey 92 Db
Tauá, Brazil 53 Je
Tauapeçaçú, Brazil 52 Ed
Taubate, Brazil 53 Hh
Taumarunui, New Zealand 55 Ec
Taungdwingyi, Burma 89 Jd
Taung-gyi, Burma 89 Je
Taungup, Burma 89 He
Taunton, England 63 Ek
Taunton, Massachusetts 40 Le
Taunus, W. Germany 68 Cc
Taupo, New Zealand 55 Fc
Taurage, Lithuania 67 Kj
Tauranga, New Zealand 55 Fb
Taureau, Rés., Quebec 35 Rf
Tauste, Spain 71 Eb
Tauysk, U.S.S.R. 79 Pc
Tavda, U.S.S.R. 78 Fc
Taverne, Switzerland 65 Db
Taverner B., N.W.T. 31 Md
Tavistock, England 63 Ek
Tavistock, Ontario 34 Kj
Tavolara, Sardinia 75 Be
Tavoy, Burma 89 Jf
Tavoy I., Burma 89 Jf
Tavsanli, Turkey 92 Ab
Tawang, India 89 Hc
Tawas City, Michigan 40 Ec
Tawatinaw & R., Alberta 36 Dd
Tawau, Sabah 83 Gk
Tawitawi, Philippines 83 Hj
Taxco, Mexico 50 Ed
Taxkorgan, China 90 Db
Tay, Firth of, Scotland 62 Ed
Tayan, Borneo (Kalimantan) 83 Fl
Tayga, U.S.S.R. 78 Hc
Tay L., Scotland 62 Ed
Taylor, British Columbia 39 Ng
Taylor, Mt., New Mexico 48 De
Taylor I., N.W.T. 38 Xa
Taylorsville, Alabama 45 Dc
Taylorsville, N. Carolina 45 Gc
Taymā', Arabia 92 Cd
Taymouth, N.B. 32 Fg
Taymyr, Ozero, U.S.S.R. 79 Ka
Tayshet, U.S.S.R. 79 Jc
Tayshir, Mongolia 82 Ca
Tayside, Scotland 62 Ed
Taytay, Philippines 83 Gh
Taza, Morocco 98 Eb
Tazewell, Virginia 45 Gb
Tazin L. & R., Sask. 38 Tf
Tazovskaya G., U.S.S.R. 78 Gb
Tazovskoye, U.S.S.R. 78 Gb
Tbilisi, Georgia, U.S.S.R. 78 Dd
Tchad. See Chad
Tchad, L. See Chad, L.
Tchaourou, Benin 98 Fg
Tczew, Poland 69 Ha
Te Anau, New Zealand 55 Af
Teano Range, W. Australia 56 Cd
Teapa, Mexico 50 Fd
Te Aroha, New Zealand 55 Eb
Tea Tree, N. Terr. 57 Fd
Te Awamutu, New Zealand 55 Ec
Tebesjuak L., N.W.T. 38 Yd
Teboursouk, Tunisia 99 Ga
Tecamachalco, Mexico 50 Ed
Tecka, Argentina 54 Bf
Tecolutla, Mexico 50 Ec
Tecpan, Mexico 50 Dd
Tecumseh, Michigan 40 Ed
Tecumseh, Ontario 34 Hk
Tedzhen, Turkmenistan 78 Fe
Tees, Alberta 36 Df
Tees R., England 63 Gf
Teeswater, Ontario 34 Jj
Tegucigalpa, Honduras 51 Bd
Tehek L., N.W.T. 30 Kd
Tehrān, Iran 93 Fb
Tehri, India 88 Eb
Tehuacán, Mexico 50 Ed
Tehuantepec, Mexico 50 Ed
Tehuantepec, G. of, Mexico 50 Ed
Tehuantepec, Isthmus of, Mexico 50 Ed
Teian. See Anlu
Teifi R., Wales 63 Eh
Teign R., England 63 Ek
Tejo R., (Tajo), Portugal/Spain 70 Bc
Tekapo, L., New Zealand 55 Ce
Te Karaka, New Zealand 55 Fc
Tekari, India 91 Ec
Tekirdag, Turkey 92 Aa
Te Kuiti, New Zealand 55 Ec
Tela, Honduras 51 Bc
Telanaipura, Indonesia 83 Dl
Tel Aviv-Yafo, Israel 94 Ce
Telegraph Creek, B.C. 39 Hg
Telen, Argentina 54 Ce
Telkalakh, Syria 94 Ec
Telkwa, British Columbia 39 Kh
Tell Bise, Syria 94 Ec
Tellicherry, India 88 Ef
Tellier, Quebec 32 Fc
Telok Anson, Pen. Malaysia 87 Cf
Teloloapan, Mexico 50 Ed
Telpos-iz, U.S.S.R. 78 Eb
Telsen, Argentina 54 Cf
Telshyay, Lithuania 67 Kj
Telukbetung, Sumatra 83 Em
Teluk Cendrawasih, Irian Jaya 83 Ll
Tembeling, Pen. Malaysia 87 Cf
Temblador, Venezuela 52 Eb
Temir, Kazakhstan 78 Ed
Temirtau, U.S.S.R. 78 Hc
Témiscamie L., Quebec 32 Ab
Témiscamie R., Quebec 32 Ab
Témiscaming, Quebec 35 Lf
Témiscouata, L., Quebec 32 Df
Temnikov, U.S.S.R. 81 Fc
Temosachic, Mexico 50 Cb
Tempe, Arizona 48 Bf
Tempio, Sardinia 75 Be
Temple, Texas 49 Jg
Temse, Belgium 64 Cc
Temta, U.S.S.R. 81 Gb
Temuco, Chile 54 Be
Temuka, New Zealand 55 Cf
Tenanzingo, Mexico 50 Ed
Tenasserim, Burma 89 Jf
Tenasserim R., Burma 89 Jf
Tenby, Wales 63 Dj
Tenby Bay, Ontario 34 Gf
Ten Degree Channel, Andaman Islands 89 Hg
Tenerife, I., Canary Is. 98 Bc
Ténès, Algeria 98 Fa
Tengchow. See Penglai
Tengiz, Oz., Kazakhstan 78 Fc
Tenke, Zaire 96 Fg
Tenkiller Ferry Res., Okla. 49 Ke
Ten Mile L., Nfld. 33 Qb
Tennant Creek, N. Terr. 57 Fc
Tennessee, U.S.A. 43 Jd
Tennessee Pass, Colorado 42 Ed
Tennessee R., Kentucky 45 Cc
Tennessee R., Tenn./Alabama 43 Jd
Tenterfield, N.S.W. 57 Ke
Ten Thousand Is., Florida 43 Kf
Ten Thousand Smokes, Val. of, Alaska 43 Xm
Tent L., N.W.T. 38 Td
Teocaltiche, Mexico 50 Dc
Téophilo Otôni, Brazil 53 Jg
Tepatitlán, Mexico 50 Dc
Tepehuanes, Mexico 50 Cb
Tepelene, Albania 77 Cd
Tepic, Mexico 50 Dc
Teramo, Italy 74 Dd
Ter Apel, Netherlands 64 Eb
Terban, Jebel, Arabia 92 Df
Terborg, Netherlands 64 Ec
Terence, Manitoba 37 Rj
Terence Bay, Nova Scotia 32 Jj
Teresina, Brazil 53 Je
Teressa, Nicobar Is. 89 Hg
Terezín, Czechoslovakia 68 Fc
Teri, Pakistan 90 Bd
Termez, Uzbekistan 78 Fe
Termini Imerese, Sicily 75 Df
Termoli, Italy 75 Ed
Ternate, Halmahera, Indon. 83 Jk
Terneuzen, Netherlands 64 Bc
Terni, Italy 74 Dd
Ternopol, Ukraine 80 Dg
Terpniya, Zal, U.S.S.R. 79 Pd
Terrace, B.C. 39 Jh
Terrace Bay, Ontario 34 Cd
Terracina, Italy 75 De
Terralba, Sardinia 75 Bf
Terra Nova & R., Nfld. 33 Se
Terra Santa, Brazil 53 Fd
Terre Adélie, Antarctica 104 Kc
Terrebonne, Quebec 35 Rg
Terrebonne B., Louisiana 49 Mh
Terre Haute, Indiana 40 Cf
Terrel, Texas 49 Jf
Terrenceville, Nfld. 33 Sf
Terror, Mt., Antarctica 104 Lb
Terry, Montana 46 Eb
Terschelling, Netherlands 64 Da
Teruel, Spain 71 Eb
Tervola, Finland 66 Lc
Tervuren, Belgium 64 Cd
Tésécau, L., Quebec 35 Pa
Teshekpuk L., Alaska 30 Dc
Teshio, Japan 86 Hb
Teslin, Yukon Territory 38 Ge
Teslin, R., Y.T./B.C. 38 Fe
Teslin L., Y.T./B.C. 38 Ge
Tessaoua, Niger 98 Gf
Tessenderlo, Belgium 64 Dc
Tessier, Saskatchewan 36 Kg
Tetachuck L., B.C. 39 Lj
Tetagouche R., N.B. 32 Ff
Tetas, Pta., Chile 54 Bb
Tete, Mozambique 95 Ec
Tête-à-la-Baleine, Que. 33 Nc
Tete Jaune Cache, B.C. 39 Oj
Teton Ra., Wyoming 46 Bd
Tetouan, Morocco 98 Da
Tetyushi, U.S.S.R. 81 Jc
Teulada, Sardinia 75 Bf
Teulada C., Sardinia 75 Bf
Teulon, Manitoba 37 Uh
Teutoburger Wald, W. Ger. 68 Bb
Tevere. See Tiber
Teviot R., Scotland 62 Fe
Tevriz, U.S.S.R. 78 Gc
Te Waewae B., N. Zealand 55 Ag
Texada I., B.C. 39 Ll
Texarkana, Arkansas 49 Kf
Texas, U.S.A. 42 Fe
Texcoco, Mexico 50 Ed
Texel, Netherlands 64 Ca
Texoma, L., Oklahoma 49 Je
Tezpur, India 89 Hc
Thadiq, Arabia 92 Ed
Thailand, S.E. Asia 87 Cc
Thailand, G. of, S.E. Asia 83 Dh
Thakhek, Laos 87 Cc
Thal, Pakistan 90 Bd
Thalkirch, Switzerland 65 Eb
Thames, New Zealand 55 Eb
Thames, Firth of, N.Z. 55 Eb
Thames, R., Ontario 34 Hk
Thamesford, Ontario 34 Jj
Thames R., Connecticut 44 Db
Thames R., England 63 Hj
Thamesville, Ontario 34 Jk
Thana, India 88 De
Thanesar, India 90 Ef
Thanh Hoa, Vietnam 87 Dc
Thanjavur, India 88 Ef
Thann, France 72 Gc
Thar, India 88 Dc
Thargomindah, Qnsld. 57 He
Tharrawaddy, Burma 89 Je
Tharsis, Spain 70 Bd
Thásos, Greece 77 Ed
Thásos Strait, Greece 77 Ed
Thatcher, Arizona 48 Cf
Thaton, Burma 89 Je
Thaungdut, Burma 89 Hd
Thayer, Missouri 45 Bb
Thayetmyo, Burma 89 He
Thazi, Burma 89 Jd
Thedford, Ontario 34 Jj
Thekulthili L., N.W.T. 38 Te
Thelon, R., N.W.T. 38 Wc
Théodat, L., Quebec 35 Ob
Theodore, Queensland 57 Ke
Theodore, Saskatchewan 37 Pg
Theodore Roosevelt L., Arizona 48 Bf
Therien, Alberta 36 Fd
Thérmai, G. of, Greece 77 Dd
Thermiá. See Kithnos
Thermopolis, Wyoming 46 Cd
Thesiger B., N.W.T. 38 La
Thesprotía, Greece 77 Ce
Thessalía, Greece 77 Ce
Thessalon, Ontario 34 Gf
Thessaloníki, Greece 77 Dd
Thetford, England 63 Hh
Thetford Mines, Quebec 35 Tf
Theux, Belgium 64 Dd
Thibodaux, Louisiana 49 Mh
Thicket Portage, Man. 37 Uc
Thickwood Hills, Alberta 36 Eb
Thief River Falls, Minnesota 46 Ja
Thielsen, Mt., Oregon 47 Bd
Thiers, France 72 Ed
Thiès, Senegal 98 Bf
Thimbu, Bhutan 89 Gc
Thingvalla vatn, Iceland 66 Vm
Thio, Ethiopia 97 Jb
Thionville, France 72 Gb
Thíra, Greece 77 Ef
Thirsk, England 63 Gf
Thisted, Denmark 67 Ch
Thistilfjord, Iceland 66 Yl
Thistle L., N.W.T. 38 Tc
Thityabin, Burma 89 Hd
Thiviers, France 72 Dd
Thjórsá, R., Iceland 66 Wm
Thoa R., N.W.T. 38 Te
Tholen, Netherlands 64 Cc
Thomas Hubbard, C., N.W.T. 31 Ka
Thomaston, Georgia, U.S.A. 45 Ed
Thomastown, Eire 63 Ch
Thomasville, Georgia, U.S.A. 45 Fe
Thompson, Manitoba 37 Uc
Thompson Lake, N.W.T. 38 Rd
Thompson Landing, N.W.T. 38 Sd
Thompsonville, Connecticut 44 Db
Thomson, R., Queensland 57 Hd
Thomson Ville, Michigan 40 Cc
Thonokied L., N.W.T. 38 Tc
Thorburn, Nova Scotia 33 Kh
Thorhild, Alberta 36 Dd
Thorn. See Torun
Thornbury, Ontario 34 Kh
Thornhill, Scotland 62 Ee
Thorold, Ontario 35 Lj
Thorsby, Alberta 36 Ce
Thorshavn, Faeröe Is. 60 Fc
Thórshöfn, Iceland 66 Yl
Thorsteinson, L., Man. 37 Ua
Thouars, France 72 Cc
Thousand Is., Ont./N.Y. 35 Ph
Thousand Lake Mt., Utah 48 Bc
Thraki, Dhitiki, Greece 76 Ed
Three Hills, Alberta 36 Dg
Three Kings Is., N.Z. 55 Da
Threepoint L., Manitoba 37 Tc
Three Points C., Ghana 98 Eh
Three Rivers, Michigan 40 Cd
Three Rivers, Quebec. See Trois Rivières
Three Rock Cove, Nfld. 33 Ne
Throssel Range, W. Australia 56 Dd
Thubun Ls., N.W.T. 38 Se
Thueyts, France 73 Fd
Thuin, Belgium 64 Cd
Thule, Greenland 31 Nb
Thule Air Base. See Dundas
Thule I., South, S. Sandwich Is. 104 Ad
Thun, Switzerland 65 Cb
Thunder B., Michigan 40 Ec
Thunder Bay, Ontario 37 Ob
Thunderbird, L., Oklahoma 49 Je
Thunder House Falls, Ont. 34 Gb
Thuner See, Switzerland 65 Cb
Thur, Switzerland 65 Da
Thurgau, Switz. 65 Da
Thüringer Wald, Germany 68 Dc
Thurles, Eire 63 Bh
Thursday I., Queensland 57 Hb
Thurso, Quebec 35 Pg
Thurso, Scotland 62 Eb
Thusis, Switzerland 65 Eb
Thutade L., B.C. 39 Kg
Tianjin, China 84 Hc
Tian Shan, Central Asia 78 Gd
Tianshui, China 84 Be
Tiaret, Algeria 98 Fa
Tiassale, Ivory Coast 98 Dg
Tibati, Cameroun 99 Hg
Tiber, Italy 74 Dd
Tiberias, Israel 94 De
Tibet, China 58 He
Tiblemont, Quebec 35 Nd
Tiburon, Haiti 51 Ec
Tiburón I., Mexico 50 Bb
Tichborne, Ontario 35 Oh
Tichfield, Saskatchewan 36 Kg
Ticino, Switzerland 65 Db
Ticonderoga, New York 40 Kd
Ticul, Mexico 50 Gc
Tide Head, N.B. 32 Ff
Tide L., Alberta 36 Fh
Tidjikja, Mauritania 98 Ce
Tidnish, Nova Scotia 32 Jh
Tiébissou, Ivory Coast 98 Dg
Tiefencastel, Switzerland 65 Eb
Tieh-ling, China 84 La
Tiel, Netherlands 64 Dc
Tielt, Belgium 64 Bc
Tien-ching. See Tianjin
Tienen, Belgium 64 Cd
Tiensha Pass, China 84 Ce
Tiermas, Spain 71 Ea
Tierra del Fuego, Chile/Argentina 54 Ch
Tiffin, Ohio 40 Ee
Tifton, Georgia, U.S.A. 45 Fe
Tigănesti, Romania 76 Fb
Tighina. See Bendery
Tigil, U.S.S.R. 79 Qc
Tignish, P.E.I. 32 Hg
Tigris, Iraq 92 Ec
Tijoca, Brazil 53 Hd
Tijuana, Mexico 42 Ce
Tika, Quebec 32 Gc
Tikhvin, U.S.S.R. 80 Hb
Tikrit, Iraq 92 Dc
Tiksi, U.S.S.R. 79 Ma
Tilburg, Netherlands 64 Dc
Tilbury, England 63 Hj
Tilbury, Ontario 34 Hk
Tilbury I., B.C. 39 Hm
Tilcara, Argentina 54 Cb
Tîles, Greece 77 Ff
Tilichiki, U.S.S.R. 79 Rb
Tillamook, Oregon 47 Bc
Tillanchang I., Nicobar Islands 89 Hg
Tilley, Alberta 36 Fh
Tillsonburg, Ontario 34 Kk
Tilsit. See Sovetsk
Tilston, Manitoba 37 Qj
Tilting, Newfoundland 33 Sd
Timagami, Ontario 34 Le
Timagami, L., Ontario 34 Kf
Timanski Kryazh, U.S.S.R. 78 Eb
Timaru, New Zealand 55 Cf
Timbalier B., Louisiana 49 Mh
Timber L., S. Dakota 46 Gc
Timbuktu. See Tombouctou
Timiskaming, L., Que./Ont. 35 Le
Timisoara, Romania 76 Cb
Timmins, Ontario 34 Jd
Timor, Indonesia 83 Jm
Timor Sea, Australia & Indonesia 83 Hn
Timote, Argentina 54 De
Tinaca Pt., Philippines 83 Jj
Tindouf, Algeria 98 Dc
Tineo, Spain 70 Ba
Tingchow. See Changting
Tingo Maria, Peru 52 Be
Tingri, China 89 Gc
Tingwick, Quebec 35 Tg
Tingyuanting. See Zhenba
Tinian, Mariana Is. 102 Df
Tinkhannock, Pennsylvania 44 Cb
Tinnevelly. See Tirunelveli
Tinogasta, Argentina 54 Cc
Tinos, Greece 77 Ef
Tinsukia, India 89 Jc
Tintigny, Belgium 64 De
Tintina, Argentina 54 Dc
Tinwald, New Zealand 55 Ce
Tioman Pulau, Pen. Malaysia 87 Cf
Tionaga, Ontario 34 Hd
Tionesta, Pennsylvania 44 Ab
Tipperary, Eire 63 Bh
Tipton, Iowa 49 Mb
Tip Top Mtn., Ontario 34 Dd
Tiracambú, Sa. do, Brazil 53 Hd
Tiran, Arabia 92 Bd
Tiranë, Albania 76 Bd
Tiraspol', Moldavia 80 Fh
Tire, Turkey 92 Ab
Tireboli, Turkey 92 Ca
Tiree I., Scotland 62 Cd
Tîrgoviste, Romania 76 Eb
Tîrgu Jiu, Romania 76 Db
Tîrgu Lăpuş, Romania 69 Ke

Tîrgu Mures, *Romania* 76 Ea
Tîrgu Ocna, *Romania* 76 Fa
Tirich Mir, *Pakistan* 90 Bb
Tirlemont. *See* Tienen
Tirlyanski, *U.S.S.R.* 81 Pc
Tirnavos, *Greece* 77 De
Tirol, *Austria* 68 De
Tiruchchendur, *India* 88 Eg
Tiruchirapalli, *India* 88 Ef
Tirunelveli, *India* 88 Eg
Tirupati, *India* 88 Ef
Tiruvannamalai, *India* 88 Ef
Tisa, *Yugoslavia* 76 Cb
Tisdale, *Saskatchewan* 37 Nf
Tisiye, *Syria* 94 Ee
Tisza, *Hungary* 69 Je
Titalyah, *Bangladesh* 91 Gb
Titicaca, *Bolivia/Peru* 52 Dg
Titisee, *West Germany* 68 Ce
Titograd, *Yugoslavia* 76 Bc
Titovo Uzice, *Yugoslavia* 76 Bc
Titov-Veles, *Yugoslavia* 76 Cd
Titu, *Romania* 76 Eb
Titusville, *Pennsylvania* 40 Ge
Tiverton, *England* 63 Ek
Tiverton, *Nova Scotia* 32 Fj
Tiverton, *Ontario* 34 Jh
Tiwi, *Oman* 93 Ge
Tixkokob, *Mexico* 50 Gc
Tixtla, *Mexico* 50 Ed
Tizimín, *Mexico* 50 Gc
Tizi Ouzou, *Algeria* 98 Fa
Tjalang. *See* Calang
Tjilatjap. *See* Cilatjap
Tjirebon. *See* Cirebon
Tjörn, I., *Sweden* 67 Dg
Tlacotalpan, *Mexico* 50 Ed
Tlaltenango, *Mexico* 50 Dc
Tlapa, *Mexico* 50 Ed
Tlaxcala, *Mexico* 50 Ed
Tlaxiaco, *Mexico* 50 Ed
Tlell, *British Columbia* 39 Hj
Tlemcen, *Algeria* 98 Eb
Tmassah, *Libya* 99 Jc
Toad R., *British Columbia* 39 Lf
Toay, *Argentina* 54 De
Toba, *Japan* 86 Eg
Toba, Donau, *Sumatra* 83 Ck
Tobago, *Windward Is.* 51 Gd
Toba Inlet, *B.C.* 39 Lk
Tobarra, *Spain* 71 Ec
Tobel, *Switzerland* 65 Ea
Tobelo, *Halmahera, Indonesia* 83 Jk
Tobermory, *Ontario* 34 Jg
Tobermory, *Scotland* 62 Cd
Tobin L., *Saskatchewan* 37 Oe
Tobique R., *N.B.* 32 Ef
Toboali, *Bangka, Indonesia* 83 El
Tobol, *U.S.S.R.* 81 Rd
Toboli, *Celebes (Sulawesi)* 83 Hl
Tobol'sk, *U.S.S.R.* 78 Fc
Tobruk. *See* Tubruq
Tocantinópolis, *Brazil* 53 He
Toccoa, *Georgia, U.S.A.* 45 Fc
Tocina, *Spain* 70 Cd
Toco, *Chile* 54 Cb
Tocopilla, *Chile* 54 Bb
Todd Mt., *New Brunswick* 32 Fg
Todenyang, *Kenya* 97 Hd
Todos Santos, *Mexico* 50 Bc
Todos Santos, B., *Mexico* 50 Aa
Tofield, *Alberta* 36 Ee
Tofino, *British Columbia* 39 Ll
Togara kaikyo, *Japan* 86 Aj
Togo, *Saskatchewan* 37 Qg
Togo, *West Africa* 98 Fg
Togtoh, *China* 84 Eb
To Huping Tso, *China* 89 Fb
Tojo, *Japan* 86 Cg
Tokachi dake, *Japan* 86 Hc
Tokanui, *New Zealand* 55 Bg
Tokar, *Sudan* 97 Ha
Tokara Gunto, *Japan* 86 Nn
Tokat, *Turkey* 92 Ca
Tokelau Is., *Pacific Ocean* 102 Hh
Tokmak, *Kirghizia* 78 Gd
Toko, *New Zealand* 55 Ec
Tokomaru, *New Zealand* 55 Gc
Tokushima, *Japan* 86 Dg
Tokuyama, *Japan* 86 Bg
Tōkyō, *Japan* 86 Fg
Tolaga Bay, *New Zealand* 55 Gc
Tolbukhin, *Bulgaria* 76 Fc
Toledo, *Chile* 54 Bc
Toledo, *Ohio* 40 Ee
Toledo, *Spain* 70 Cc
Toledo, Mtes. de, *Spain* 70 Cc
Toledo Bend Res., *Texas/Louisiana* 49 Lg
Tolmin, *Yugoslavia* 74 Db
Tolo, Teluk, *Celebes (Sulawesi)* 83 Hl
Tolstad, *Alberta* 39 Oh
Toluca, *Mexico* 50 Ed
Toluca, *Montana* 46 Dc
Tol'yatti, *U.S.S.R.* 78 Dc
Tölz, Bad, *West Germany* 68 De
Tomah, *Wisconsin* 40 Ac
Tomahawk, *Wisconsin* 40 Bc
Tomar, *Portugal* 70 Ac
Tomari, *U.S.S.R.* 79 Pd
Tomaszów Mazowiecki, *Poland* 69 Jc
Tombigbee R., *Alabama* 43 Je
Tombouctou, *Mali* 98 Ee
Tombstone Mtn., *Y.T.* 38 Dc
Tomé, *Chile* 54 Be
Tomiko, *Ontario* 35 Lf
Tomini, Teluk, *Celebes (Sulawesi)* 83 Hl
Tomkinson Range, *W. Aust.* 56 Ee
Tommot, *U.S.S.R.* 79 Mc
Tompkins, *Saskatchewan* 36 Jh
Tom Price, *W. Australia* 56 Cd
Tomsk, *U.S.S.R.* 78 Hc
Tom's River, *New Jersey* 40 Jf
Tonalá, *Mexico* 50 Fd
Tonawanda, *New York* 44 Aa
Tónder, *Denmark* 67 Cj
Tondern, *Ontario* 34 Ec
Tondi, *India* 88 Eg
Tonga, *Pacific Ocean* 102 Hk
Tonga, *Sudan* 99 Mg
Tongcheng, *China* 85 Fh
Tongchuan, *China* 84 De
Tongeren, *Belgium* 64 Dd
Tongguan, *China* 84 Ee
Tonghe, *China* 82 Ja
Tonghua, *China* 82 Jb
Tongking, G. of. *See* Beibu Wan
Tongling, *China* 84 Hg
Tongobory, *Madagascar* 97 Ml
Tongoy, *Chile* 54 Bd
Tongren, *China* 85 Dj
Tongres. *See* Tongeren
Tongue, *Scotland* 62 Eb
Tongue R., *Montana* 42 Eb
Tong Xian, *China* 84 Hc
Tonhil, *Mongolia* 82 Ba
Tonichi, *Mexico* 50 Cb
Tonk, *India* 88 Ec
Tonkin, *Vietnam* 87 Cb
Tonkova, *U.S.S.R.* 78 Hb
Tonle Sap, *Kampuchea* 87 Cd
Tonneins, *France* 73 Dd
Tonnerre, *France* 72 Fc
Tonopah, *Nevada* 47 Ef
Tönsberg, *Norway* 67 Dg
Tooele, *Utah* 47 Ge
Toowoomba, *Queensland* 57 Ke
Topeka, *Kansas* 49 Kc
Topland, *Alberta* 36 Bd
Topley Landing, *B.C.* 39 Kh
Topoľčany, *Czechoslovakia* 69 Hd
Topolobampo, *Mexico* 50 Cb
Top Oz, *Karelia/Finland* 78 Cb
Tor B., *Nova Scotia* 33 Lh
Torbat-e-Heydariyeh, *Iran* 93 Gb
Torbat-e-Jam, *Iran* 93 Hb
Torbay, *Newfoundland* 33 Uf
Torez, *U.S.S.R.* 80 Lh
Torhout, *Belgium* 64 Bc
Tori, *India* 91 Ed
Toriñana, C., *Spain* 70 Aa
Torino, *Italy* 74 Ac
Torit, *Sudan* 99 Mh
Tor Khama, *Pakistan* 90 Bc
Torma, *Estonia* 67 Mg
Tornado Mt., pk., *Alta./B.C.* 36 Cj
Torne Älv, *Sweden* 66 Kc
Torneträsk, *Sweden* 66 Hb
Torngat Mts., *Nfld.* 31 Nf
Tornio, *Finland* 66 Ld
Tornquist, *Argentina* 54 De
Torn Träsk, *Sweden* 66 Hb
Törökszentmiklós, *Hungary* 69 Je
Toroni, G. of, *Greece* 77 Dd
Toronto, *Ontario* 35 Lj
Toronto, *S. Dakota* 46 Jc
Toronto Harb., *Ontario* 34 Dk
Toronto Island Airport, *Ontario* 34 Dk
Tororo, *Uganda* 97 Gd
Toros Dağlari, *Turkey* 92 Bb
Torquay, *England* 63 Ek
Torquay, *Saskatchewan* 37 Oj
Torrance, *Ontario* 35 Lh
Torre Annunziata, *Italy* 75 Ee
Torreblanca, *Spain* 71 Fb
Torre del Greco, *Italy* 75 Ee
Torrelaguna, *Spain* 70 Db
Torrelapaja, *Spain* 71 Eb
Torrelavega, *Spain* 70 Da
Torrens, L., *S. Australia* 57 Gf
Torrente, *Spain* 71 Ec
Torreon, *Mexico* 50 Db
Torres, *Mexico* 50 Bb
Torres Is., *Pacific Ocean* 102 Fj
Torres Novas, *Portugal* 70 Ac
Torres Str., *Queensland* 57 Hb
Torres Vedras, *Portugal* 70 Ac
Torrevieja, *Spain* 71 Ed
Torridon L., *Scotland* 62 Dc
Torrijos, *Spain* 70 Cc
Torrington, *Alberta* 36 Dg
Torrington, *Connecticut* 44 Db
Torrington, *Wyoming* 46 Ed
Torrox, *Spain* 70 Dd
Torsby, *Sweden* 67 Ef
Tort, L. Le, *Quebec* 33 Mb
Tortola, *Virgin Is.* 51 Gc
Tortorici, *Sicily* 75 Ef
Tortosa, *Spain* 71 Fb
Tortue, I., *Haiti* 51 Eb
Tortuga I., *Mexico* 50 Bb
Torud, *Iran* 93 Gb
Toruń, *Poland* 69 Hb
Tõrva, *Estonia* 67 Mh
Tory, I., *Eire* 62 Be
Tory Hill, *Ontario* 35 Mh
Torzhok, *U.S.S.R.* 80 Jc
Tosa wan, *Japan* 86 Ch
Toscana, *Italy* 74 Cd
Tosco-Emiliano, Appennino, *Italy* 74 Cc
Tossa, *Spain* 71 Gb
Tostado, *Argentina* 54 Dc
Totana, *Spain* 71 Ed
Totma, *U.S.S.R.* 78 Dc
Totnes, *England* 63 Ek
Totonicapan, *Guatemala* 50 Fd
Totsk, *U.S.S.R.* 81 Ld
Tottenham, *Ontario* 34 Lh
Tottori, *Japan* 86 Dg
Totzke, *Saskatchewan* 37 Mf
Touba, *Ivory Coast* 98 Dg
Toubkal, *Morocco* 98 Db
Touchwood Hills, *Sask.* 37 Ng
Touggourt, *Algeria* 98 Gb
Toul, *France* 72 Fb
Toulnustouc R., *Quebec* 32 Ec
Toulon, *France* 73 Fe
Toulouse, *France* 73 De
Toungoo, *Burma* 89 Je
Touquet, le, *France* 72 Da
Touraine, *France* 72 Dc
Tourakom, *Laos* 89 Ke
Tourbis L., *Quebec* 40 Jb
Tourcoing, *France* 72 Ea
Tour-du-Pin, la, *France* 72 Fd
Tourgis L., *N.W.T.* 38 Uc
Tournai, *Belgium* 64 Bd
Tournon, *France* 73 Fd
Tournus, *France* 72 Fc
Tours, *France* 72 Dc
Tourville, *Quebec* 32 Bf
Toutes Aides, *Manitoba* 37 Sg
Touwsrivier, *Cape Province* 95 Cf
Towanda, *Pennsylvania* 44 Bb
Towari, *Celebes (Sulawesi)* 83 Hl
Tower City, *N. Dakota* 46 Jb
Townsend, *Montana* 46 Bb
Townsville, *Queensland* 57 Jc
Towson, *Maryland* 44 Bc
Towuti Danau, *Celebes (Sulawesi)* 83 Hl
Towy R., *Wales* 63 Ej
Toyah L., *Texas* 48 Fg
Toyama, *Japan* 86 Ef
Tozeur, *Tunisia* 99 Gb
Trabzon, *Turkey* 92 Ca
Tracadie, *New Brunswick* 32 Hf
Tracadie, *Nova Scotia* 33 Lh
Tracy, *Minnesota* 46 Kc
Tracy, *New Brunswick* 32 Fh
Trade L., *Saskatchewan* 37 Oc
Traer, *Iowa* 49 La
Traiguen, *Chile* 54 Be
Traiguen, I., *Chile* 54 Bg
Trail, *British Columbia* 39 Pl
Trainor L., *N.W.T.* 38 Ne
Trairi, *Brazil* 53 Kd
Tralee, *Eire* 63 Ah
Tramore, *Eire* 63 Ch
Tramping Lake, *Sask.* 36 Jf
Tranås, *Sweden* 67 Fg
Trancas, *Argentina* 54 Cc
Trancoso, *Portugal* 70 Bb
Trang, *Thailand* 87 Be
Trangan, *Indonesia* 83 Km
Tranquebar, *India* 88 Ef
Transcona, *Manitoba* 37 Vj
Transkei, *S. Africa* 95 Df
Transvaal, *S. Africa* 95 Dd
Transylvania, *Romania* 76 Da
Transylvanian Alps. *See* Carpatii Meridionali
Trapani, *Sicily* 75 Df
Traralgon, *Victoria* 57 Jg
Trasimeno, L., *Italy* 74 Dd
Trasparga, *Spain* 70 Ba
Traunstein, *West Germany* 68 Ee
Travaillant L., *N.W.T.* 38 Hb
Travers, *Alberta* 36 Eh
Traversay Is., *Atlantic Ocean* 104 Ad
Traverse, B., *Michigan* 40 Dc
Traverse City, *Michigan* 40 Dc
Travis, L., *Texas* 49 Jg
Třebíč, *Czechoslovakia* 69 Fd
Trebinje, *Yugoslavia* 76 Bc
Trebizond. *See* Trabzon
Tregarva, *Saskatchewan* 37 Nh
Treherne, *Manitoba* 37 Tj
Treinta-y-Tres, *Uruguay* 54 Fd
Trelew, *Argentina* 54 Cf
Trelleborg, *Sweden* 67 Ej
Tremadog B., *Wales* 63 Eh
Trembleur L., *B.C.* 39 Lh
Tremiti Is., *Italy* 74 Ed
Tremp, *Spain* 71 Fa
Trenche, R., *Quebec* 35 Se
Trenčín, *Czechoslovakia* 69 Hd
Trenel, *Argentina* 54 De
Trenque Lauquén, *Argentina* 54 De
Trent. *See* Trento
Trent Can., *Ontario* 35 Lh
Trentino-Alto Adige, *Italy* 74 Cb
Trento, *Italy* 74 Cb
Trenton, *Georgia, U.S.A.* 45 Ec
Trenton, *Michigan* 40 Ed
Trenton, *Missouri* 49 Lb
Trenton, *New Jersey* 44 Cb
Trenton, *Nova Scotia* 32 Kh
Trenton, *Ontario* 35 Nh
Trenton, *Tennessee* 45 Cc
Trent R., *England* 63 Gg
Trepassey & B., *Nfld.* 33 Tg
Tréport, le, *France* 72 Da
Treptow L., *Ontario* 34 Cc
Tres Arroyos, *Argentina* 54 De
Tres Lomas, *Argentina* 54 De
Tres Marías, Is., *Mexico* 50 Cc
Tres Montes, Pen., *Chile* 54 Ag
Três Rio, *Brazil* 53 Jh
Tres Virgenes, Las, *Mexico* 50 Bb
Trève, L. la, *Quebec* 35 Pc
Trèves. *See* Trier
Treviso, *Italy* 74 Dc
Triana, *Spain* 70 Bd
Triangle, *Alberta* 39 Ph
Tribune, *Saskatchewan* 37 Oj
Tricase, *Italy* 75 Gf
Trichinopoly. *See* Tiruchirapalli
Trichur, *India* 88 Ef
Trier, *West Germany* 68 Bd
Trieste, *Italy* 74 Dc
Trikeri Str., *Greece* 77 De
Trikkala, *Greece* 77 Ce
Trikomo, *Cyprus* 94 Bb
Trilsbeck L., *Ontario* 34 Fb
Trim, *Eire* 63 Cg
Trincomalee, *Sri Lanka* 88 Fg
Tring-Jonction, *Quebec* 32 Bg
Trinidad, *Bolivia* 52 Ef
Trinidad, *Colorado* 48 Ed
Trinidad, *Cuba* 51 Db
Trinidad, *Uruguay* 54 Ed
Trinidad, *West Indies* 52 Ea
Trinidad, I., *Argentina* 54 De
Trinidade, *Atlantic Ocean* 101 Hl
Trinity, *Newfoundland* 33 Se
Trinity, *Texas* 49 Kg
Trinity B., *Newfoundland* 33 Te
Trinity Pen., *Antarctica* 104 Tc
Trinity R., *Texas* 49 Kg
Trionto C., *Italy* 75 Ff
Tripoli, *Lebanon* 94 Dc
Tripoli, *Libya* 99 Hb
Tripolis, *Greece* 77 Df
Tripolitania, *Libya* 99 Hc
Tripura, *India* 89 Hd
Triquet, L., *Quebec* 33 Ob
Tristan da Cunha, *Atl. Oc.* 101 Jm
Triunfo, El, *Mexico* 50 Bc
Trivandrum, *India* 88 Eg
Trn, *Bulgaria* 76 Dc
Trnava, *Czechoslovakia* 69 Gd
Trobriand Is., *Papua New Guinea* 57 Ka
Trochu, *Alberta* 36 Dg
Trogir, *Yugoslavia* 74 Fd
Troilus, L., *Quebec* 35 Qb
Trois-Pistoles, *Quebec* 32 Ce
Trois Ponts, *Belgium* 64 Dd
Trois-Rivières, *Quebec* 35 Sf
Troitsk, *U.S.S.R.* 81 Fc
Troitsk, *U.S.S.R* 81 Qc
Troitsko Pechorsk, *U.S.S.R.* 78 Eb
Trollhättan, *Sweden* 67 Eg
Trollheimen, *Norway* 66 Ce
Tromen, *Argentina* 54 Be
Tromsø, *Norway* 66 Hb
Trondheim & Fd., *Norway* 66 De
Troödos, *Cyprus* 94 Ac
Troon, *Scotland* 62 De
Tropea, *Italy* 75 Ef
Trosa, *Sweden* 67 Gg
Trossachs, *Saskatchewan* 37 Nj
Trousers L., *N.B.* 32 Ff
Trout, R., *B.C.* 39 Lf
Trout Creek, *Ontario* 35 Lg
Trout L., *B.C.* 39 Pk
Trout L., *N.W.T.* 38 Ne
Trout Lake, *Michigan* 40 Db
Trout R., *Alberta* 36 Cb
Trout R., *N.W.T.* 38 Ne
Trout River, *Newfoundland* 33 Od
Troy, *New York* 40 Kd
Troy, *Turkey* 92 Ab
Troyes, *France* 72 Fb
Truax, *Saskatchewan* 37 Nj
Trubia, *Spain* 70 Ba
Truer Ra., *N. Terr.* 56 Fd
Truite, L. à la, *Quebec* 35 Me
Trujillo, *Honduras* 51 Bc
Trujillo, *Peru* 52 Be
Trujillo, *Spain* 70 Cc
Trujillo, *Venezuela* 52 Cb
Truk, *Caroline Is.* 102 Eg
Trumbull, Mt., *Arizona* 47 Gg
Truns, *Switzerland* 65 Db
Truro, *England* 63 Dk
Truro, *Nova Scotia* 32 Jh
Trutch, *British Columbia* 39 Mg
Trutch Cr., *B.C.* 39 Mg
Trutnov, *Czechoslovakia* 69 Fc
Tryavna, *Bulgaria* 76 Ec
Trzebnica, *Poland* 69 Gc
Tržič, *Yugoslavia* 74 Eb
Tsabong, *Botswana* 95 Ce
Tsahura, *S. Yemen* 92 Eg
Tsamkong. *See* Zhanjiang
Tsangbe, *Bhutan* 91 Gb
Tsangwu. *See* Wuzhou
Tsaochow. *See* Heze
Tsau, *Botswana* 95 Cd
Tsawwassen, *B.C.* 39 Gm
Tschenstochau. *See* Czestochowa
Tschida, L., *N. Dakota* 46 Fb
Tschiertschen, *Switzerland* 65 Eb
Tsehchow. *See* Jincheng
Tselinograd, *Kazakhstan* 78 Gc
Tses, *Namibia* 95 Be
Tsetserleg, *Mongolia* 79 Kd
Tshikapa, *Zaire* 96 Ef
Tsimlyanskoye Vdkhr., *U.S.S.R.* 81 Ff
Tsinchow. *See* Tianshui
Tsingchow. *See* Yidu
Tsing Hai. *See* Qinghai Hu
Tsingyuan. *See* Baoding
Tsitsutl Pk., *B.C.* 39 Lj
Tsivory, *Madagascar* 97 Nl
Tsivylsk, *U.S.S.R.* 81 Hc
Tso Morari L., *Kashmir* 90 Fd
Tso-motre-tung, L., *China* 89 Gc
Tsu, *Japan* 86 Eg
Tsugaru-Kaikyō, *Japan* 86 Gd
Tsugitaka, mt. *See* Tsukao Shan
Tsukao Shan, *Taiwan* 82 Hf
Tsuruga, *Japan* 86 Eg
Tsuruoka, *Japan* 86 Fe
Tsuyama, *Japan* 86 Dg
Tua, *Portugal* 70 Bb
Tua, *Zaire* 96 De
Tuakau, *New Zealand* 55 Eb
Tuamarino, *New Zealand* 55 Dd
Tuamotu Arch, *Pacific Oc.* 103 Mj
Tuao, *Philippines* 83 Hg
Tuapse, *U.S.S.R* 78 Cd
Tuatapere, *New Zealand* 55 Ag
Tuba, *U.S.S.R.* 79 Jc
Tubarão, *Brazil* 54 Gc
Tubas, *Jordan* 94 De
Tubeiq, Jeb. el, *Jordan* 94 Fh
Tuberose, *Saskatchewan* 36 Jh
Tübingen, *West Germany* 68 Cd
Tubize, *Belgium* 64 Cd
Tubruq, *Libya* 99 Kb
Tubuai, *Tubuai Is.* 103 Lk
Tucacas, *Venezuela* 52 Da
Tuchodi, R., *B.C.* 39 Lf
Tuckernuck I., *Mass.* 44 Eb
Tuckerton, *New Jersey* 40 Jf
Tucson, *Arizona* 48 Bf
Tucson Range, *Arizona* 48 Bf
Tucumcari, *New Mexico* 42 Fd
Tucumcari, *New Mexico* 48 Fe
Tucupare, *Brazil* 53 Fe
Tucupita, *Venezuela* 52 Eb
Tucuruí, *Brazil* 53 Hd
Tudela, *Spain* 71 Ea
Tufi, *Papua New Guinea* 57 Ja
Tug, *Turkey* 92 Db
Tugaske, *Saskatchewan* 36 Lh
Tuguegarao, *Philippines* 83 Hg
Tugur, *U.S.S.R.* 79 Nc
Tuktoyaktuk, *N.W.T.* 38 Ga
Tukums, *Latvia* 67 Kh
Tula, *Mexico* 50 Ec
Tula, *U.S.S.R* 80 Kd
Tulagi, *Solomon Islands* 102 Eh
Tulameen, *B.C.* 39 Nl
Tulancingo, *Mexico* 50 Ec
Tularosa, *New Mexico* 42 Ee
Tularosa, *New Mexico* 48 Ef
Tularosa Basin, *New Mexico* 48 Df
Tulcán, *Ecuador* 52 Bc
Tulcea, *Romania* 76 Gb
Tulchin, *Ukraine* 80 Fg
Tulear, *Madagascar* 97 Ml
Tulemalu L., *N.W.T.* 38 Yd
Tuli, *Zimbabwe* 95 Dd
Tulkarm, *Jordan* 94 De
Tullahoma, *Tennessee* 45 Dc
Tullamore, *Eire* 63 Cg
Tulle, *France* 73 Dd
Tulsa, *Oklahoma* 49 Kd
Tulsequah, *B.C.* 39 Gf
Tulua, *Colombia* 52 Bc
Tulun, *U.S.S.R.* 79 Kc
Tumaco, *Colomb.* 52 Bc
Tumany, *U.S.S.R.* 79 Qb
Tumatumari, *Guyana* 52 Fb
Tumbes, *Peru* 52 Ad
Tumd Zuoqi, *China* 84 Eb
Tumkur, *India* 88 Ef
Tumlong, *India* 91 Gb
Tummel R., *Scotland* 62 Ed
Tummo, *Libya* 99 Hd
Tumu, *Ghana* 98 Ef
Tumucumaque, Sierra, *Brazil* 53 Gc
Tumupasa, *Bolivia* 52 Df
Tunas de Zaza, *Cuba* 51 Db
Tunbridge Wells, Royal, *England* 63 Hj
Tundla, *India* 88 Ec
Tunduru, *Tanzania* 97 Hg
Tungchang. *See* Liaocheng
Tungchow. *See* Dali
Tungchwan. *See* Dongchuan
Tungchwan. *See* Santai
Tungliao, *China* 82 Hb
Tungshan. *See* Xuzhou
Tunguska, *U.S.S.R.* 79 Jb
Tuni, *India* 89 Fe
Tunica, *Mississippi* 45 Bc
Tunis, *Tunisia* 99 Ha
Tunisia, *N. Africa* 99 Gb
Tunja, *Colombia* 52 Cb
Tunnel Dam, *Ontario* 34 Gf
Tunnsjø, *Norway* 66 Ed
Tunungayualok I., *Nfld.* 31 Nf
Tunuyan, *Argentina* 54 Cd
Tunxi, *China* 85 Jh
Tuoy Khaya, *U.S.S.R.* 79 Lb
Tuparoa, *New Zealand* 55 Gb
Tupelo, *Mississippi* 45 Cc
Tupilco, *Mexico* 50 Fd
Tupinambaranas, *Brazil* 52 Fd
Tupiza, *Bolivia* 52 Dh
Tupper, *British Columbia* 39 Nh
Tupper Lake, *New York* 40 Jc
Tupungato, *Chile/Arg.* 54 Cd
Túquerres, *Colombia* 52 Bc
Tura, *India* 89 Hc
Tura, *U.S.S.R.* 79 Jb
Turabah, *Arabia* 92 Dd
Turan, *Iran* 93 Gb
Turbo, *Colombia* 52 Bb
Turda, *Romania* 76 Da
Tureia, *Tuamotu Arch.* 103 Mk
Turgay, *Kazakhstan* 78 Fd
Turgen Uul, *Mongolia* 79 Jd
Turgeon, R., *Quebec* 35 Lc
Turgutlu, *Turkey* 92 Ab
Türi, *Estonia* 67 Lg
Turiaçu, *Brazil* 53 Hd
Turiamo, *Venezuela* 52 Da
Turin, *Alberta* 36 Ej
Turin. *See* Torino
Turkana, Lake, *Kenya* 97 Hd
Turkestan, *Kazakh* 78 Fd
Turkey, *Europe/Asia* 58 Be
Turkmenskaya S.S.R., (Turkmenistan), *U.S.S.R.* 78 Ed
Turks Is., *The Bahamas* 51 Eb
Turku, *Finland* 67 Kf
Turnagain, R., *B.C.* 39 Jf
Turnberry, *Manitoba* 37 Qe
Turnbull, *Manitoba* 37 Sd
Turneffe Is., *Belize* 51 Bc
Turner Valley, *Alberta* 36 Ch
Turnhout, *Belgium* 64 Cc
Turnor L., *Saskatchewan* 39 Tg
Turnu Măgurele, *Romania* 76 Ec
Turnu Severin, *Romania* 76 Db
Turpan, *China* 82 Ab
Turquino, Pico de, *Cuba* 51 Dc
Turrialba, *Costa Rica* 51 Ce
Turtkul, *Uzbekistan* 78 Fd
Turtle Cove, *N.B.* 32 Hh
Turtleford, *Saskatchewan* 36 Je
Turtle L., *Saskatchewan* 36 Je
Turtle Mountain Prov. Park, *Manitoba* 37 Rj
Turtle Mts., *N. Dakota* 46 Ga
Turukhansk, *U.S.S.R.* 78 Hb
Turzovka, *Czechoslovakia* 69 Hd
Tus, *Iran* 93 Gb
Tuscaloosa, *Alabama* 45 Dd
Tuscarora Mts., *Pa.* 44 Bb
Tuscola, *Illinois* 40 Bf
Tuscumbia, *Alabama* 45 Dc
Tuscumbia, *Missouri* 45 Aa
Tusket, *Nova Scotia* 32 Gk
Tuticorin, *India* 88 Eg
Tuttlingen, *West Germany* 68 Ce
Tutuila, *Samoa* 102 Hj
Tuvalu, *Pacific Ocean* 102 Gh
Tuwairifa, *Arabia* 92 Ee
Tuxpan, *Mexico* 50 Cc
Tuxpan, *Mexico* 50 Ec
Tuxtepec, *Mexico* 50 Ed
Tuxtla, Vol. de, *Mexico* 50 Ed
Tuxtla Gutiérrez, *Mexico* 50 Fd
Túy, *Spain* 70 Aa
Tuya L., *British Columbia* 38 Hf
Tuyen-Quang, *Vietnam* 87 Db
Tuy-hoa, *Vietnam* 87 Dd
Tuz Gölu, *Turkey* 92 Bb
Tuzla, *Yugoslavia* 76 Bb
Tväran, *Sweden* 66 Jd
Tvurditsa, *Bulgaria* 76 Ec
Twante, *Burma* 89 Je
Tweed, *Ontario* 35 Nh
Tweed, R., *Scotland* 62 Fe
Tweedie, *Alberta* 36 Fd
Tweedsmuir Hills, *Scotland* 62 Ee
Tweedsmuir Provincial Park, *British Columbia* 39 Kj
Twelve Mile L., *Sask.* 36 Lj
Twenty-five de Mayo, *Arg.* 54 De
Twenty-five de Mayo, *Arg.* 54 Ce
Twillingate, *Newfoundland* 33 Sd
Twin Buttes, *Montana* 46 Ea
Twin City, *Ontario* 37 Ob
Twin Falls, *Idaho* 47 Fd
Twin L., N., *Nfld.* 33 Qd
Twin L., S., *Nfld.* 33 Rd
Twitya, R., *N.W.T.* 38 Jc
Two Creeks, *Manitoba* 37 Rh
Two Harbors, *Minnesota* 46 Mb
Two Hills, *Alberta* 36 Fe
Two Rivers, *Wisconsin* 40 Cc
Two Rivers, The, *Sask.* 39 Wh
Two Rivers Res., *N. Mex.* 48 Ef
Tygda, *U.S.S.R.* 79 Mc
Tyler, *Texas* 49 Kf
Tyndall, *Manitoba* 37 Vh
Tyndall, Mt., *New Zealand* 55 Ce
Tyndinskiy, *U.S.S.R.* 79 Mc
Tynemouth, *England* 62 Ge
Tyne R., *England* 62 Ff
Tyner, *Saskatchewan* 36 Jg
Tyne Valley, *P.E.I.* 32 Jg
Tyne & Wear, *England* 62 Fe
Tynset, *Norway* 66 De
Tyre (Sûr), *Lebanon* 94 Dd
Tyrone, *N. Ireland* 63 Cf
Tyrone, *Pennsylvania* 44 Ab
Tyrrell L., *N.W.T.* 38 Vd
Tyrrhenian Sea, *Italy* 75 Ce
Tyubelyakh, *U.S.S.R.* 79 Pb
Tyumen, *U.S.S.R.* 78 Fc
Tyvan, *Saskatchewan* 37 Oh
Tywyn, *Wales* 63 Eh

U

Uaupés, *Brazil* 52 Dc
Ubá, *Brazil* 53 Jh
Ubari. *See* Awbari
Uberaba, *Brazil* 53 Hg
Uberlândia, *Brazil* 53 Hg
Überlingen, *West Germany* 68 Ce
Ubon Ratchathani, *Thailand* 87 Cc
Ubundu, *Zaire* 96 Fe
Ucayali, *Peru* 52 Ce
Uch, *Pakistan* 90 Bf
Uchiura wan, *Japan* 86 Gc
Uchiza, *Peru* 52 Be
Uckermark, *E. Germany* 68 Eb
Ucluelet, *B.C.* 39 Ll
Udaipur, *India* 88 Dd
Uddevalla, *Sweden* 67 Dg
Udd Jaur, *Sweden* 66 Gd
Uden, *Netherlands* 64 Dc
Udine, *Italy* 74 Db
Udon Thani, *Thailand* 87 Cc
Udskaya Guba, *U.S.S.R.* 79 Nc
Udzha. *See* Bor Yuryakh
Uelen, *U.S.S.R.* 79 Tb
Ueno, *Japan* 86 Eg
Ufa, *U.S.S.R.* 81 Mc
Uganda, *E. Africa* 97 Gd
Uherské Hradiště, *Czech.* 69 Gd
Uhlman L., *Manitoba* 37 Tb
Ui Failghe, *Eire* 63 Bg
Uinta Mts., *Utah* 42 Dc
Uist, North, *Scotland* 62 Cc
Uist, South, *Scotland* 62 Cc
Uitenhage, *Cape Province* 95 Df
Uitgeest, *Netherlands* 64 Cb
Ujhani, *India* 91 Bb
Újpest, *Hungary* 69 He
Ukerewe Is., *Tanzania* 97 Ge
Ukhta, *U.S.S.R.* 78 Eb
Ukiah, *California* 47 Bf
Ukmerge, *Lithuania* 67 Lj
Ukraine (Ukrainskaya S.S.R.), *U.S.S.R.* 80 Eg
Ulaanbaatar, *Mongolia* 82 Ea
Ulan, *China* 82 Cc
Ulan, *Mongolia* 79 Jd
Ulan Ude, *U.S.S.R.* 79 Kc
Ulcinj, *Yugoslavia* 76 Bd
Uliastay, *Mongolia* 82 Ca
Ulithi, *Pacific Ocean* 102 Cf
Ullapool, *Scotland* 62 Dc
Ullared, *Sweden* 67 Eh
Ulldecona, *Spain* 71 Fb
Ullswater L., *England* 63 Ff
Ullung Do, *Sea of Japan* 86 Bf
Ulm, *West Germany* 68 Cd
Ulster, *N. Ire.* 63 Bf
Ulua, *Honduras* 51 Bc
Ulukişla, *Turkey* 92 Bb
Ulverston, *England* 63 Ef
Ul'yanovsk, *U.S.S.R.* 81 Jc
Ülzen, *West Germany* 68 Db
Uman, *Ukraine* 80 Gg
Umanak Fd., *Greenland* 41 Pb
Umarkot, *Pakistan* 88 Cc
Umbria, *Italy* 74 Dd
Umea, *Sweden* 66 Je
Umfreville, *Ontario* 36 La
Umk al-Qaiwain, *U.A.E.* 93 Gd
Umm el Qulban, *Arabia* 92 Dd
Umm Kuteira, *Sudan* 99 Lf
Umm Lej, *Arabia* 92 Cd
Umm Qasr, *Iraq* 92 Ec
Umm Ruwaba, *Sudan* 99 Mf
Umnak I., *Aleutian Is.* 43 Wm
Umtali, *Zimbabwe* 95 Ec
Umtata, *Cape Province* 95 Df
Umvuma, *Zimbabwe* 95 Ec
Una, *India* 90 Ee
Una, *Yugoslavia* 74 Fc
Unadilla, *New York* 44 Ca
Unalakleet, *Alaska* 43 Wl
Unalaska, *Aleutian Is.* 43 Wm
Unayzah, *Arabia* 92 Dd
Uncastillo, *Spain* 71 Ea
Uncía, *Bolivia* 52 Dg
Uncompahgre Plat., *Colo.* 48 Cc
Undzhul. *See* Onjül
Ungava B., *Quebec* 31 Nf
União, *Brazil* 53 Jd
União da Vitoria, *Brazil* 54 Fc
Uniejów, *Poland* 69 Hc
Unimak I., *Aleutian Is.* 43 Wm
Unión, *Argentina* 54 Ce
Union, *Missouri* 45 Ba
Union, *S. Carolina* 45 Gc
Union City, *Tennessee* 45 Cb
Union of Soviet Socialist Republics, *Europe/Asia* 58
Union Point, *Manitoba* 37 Uj
Uniontown, *Kentucky* 45 Db
Uniontown, *Pennsylvania* 44 Ac
Unionville, *Missouri* 49 Lb
Unionville, *Nevada* 47 De
United Arab Emirates, *Persian Gulf* 93 Fe
United Kingdom of Great Britain and N. Ireland, 62
United States of America, 42
United States Ra., *N.W.T.* 31 La
Unity, *Saskatchewan* 36 Hf
Unnao, *India* 91 Cb
Unst, *Shetland, Scotland* 62 Ja
Unterwalden, *Switz.* 65 Db
Unwin, *Saskatchewan* 36 Hf
Unzha, *U.S.S.R.* 81 Ga
Uozu, *Japan* 86 Ef
Upata, *Venezuela* 52 Eb
Upemba L., *Zaire* 96 Ff
Upernavik, *Greenland* 41 Pb
Upington, *Cape Province* 95 Ce
Upolu, *Western Samoa* 102 Hj
Upper Blackville, *N.B.* 32 Gg
Upper Duck I., *Ontario* 34 Eh
Upper Humber R., *Nfld.* 33 Pd
Upper Kent, *N.B.* 32 Ef
Upper Laberge, *Y.T.* 38 Fe
Upper Liard, *Y.T.* 38 Je
Upper Marlboro, *Maryland* 44 Bc
Upper Musquodoboit, *N.S.* 32 Kh
Upper Nile, *Sudan* 97 Gc
Upper Roslyn L., *Ontario* 34 Cc
Upper Saint John R., *Me./N.B.* 32 Df
Upper Sandusky, *Ohio* 40 Ee
Upper Stewiacke, *N.S.* 32 Jh
Upper Vaughan, *N.S.* 32 Hj
Upper Volta, *W. Africa* 98 Ef
Uppsala, *Sweden* 67 Gg
Upsala, *Ontario* 37 Ma
Upsalquitch & R., *N.B.* 32 Ff
Ur, *Iraq* 92 Ec
Uracoa, *Venezuela* 52 Eb
Urakawa, *Japan* 86 Hc
Ural, *Kazakh* 78 Ec
Ural'sk, *Kazakhstan* 78 Ec
Ural'skiy Khrebet, *U.S.S.R.* 78 Ec
Urandangi, *Queensland* 57 Gd

Uranium City, Sask. 38 Tf
Urapunga, N. Terr. 57 Fb
Ura Tyube, Tadzhikistan 78 Fe
Urawa, Japan 86 Fg
Urbakh, U.S.S.R. 81 He
Urcos, Peru 52 Cf
Urda, Kazakhstan 78 Dd
Urdzhar, Kazakhstan 78 Hd
Ure R., England 63 Ff
Ures, Mexico 50 Bb
Urfa, Turkey 92 Cb
Urgench, Uzbekistan 78 Fd
Urgun, Afghanistan 93 Jc
Uri, Switzerland 65 Db
Uribe, Colombia 52 Cc
Uribia, Colombia 52 Ca
Urnäsch, Switzerland 65 Ea
Urquhart L., N.W.T. 38 Ga
Urtazymsk, U.S.S.R. 81 Pd
Urtein, Mongolia 82 Ga
Urt Moron, China 82 Bc
Uruapan, Mexico 50 Dd
Urubamba, Peru 52 Cf
Urubupungo, Brazil 54 Fb
Urucará, Brazil 52 Fd
Urucuia, Brazil 53 Hg
Uruguaiana, Brazil 54 Ec
Uruguay, S. America 54 Ed
Uruguay, R., Uruguay 54 Ed
Urumes Sughra, Syria 94 Ea
ürümqi, China 78 Hd
Uruquí, Brazil 53 Je
Urussanga, Brazil 54 Gc
Urville, T. d', Irian Jaya 83 Ll
Uryupinsk, U.S.S.R. 81 Fe
Urzhum, U.S.S.R. 81 Kb
Urziceni, Romania 76 Fb
Usak, Turkey 92 Ab
Usakos, Namibia 95 Bd
Usborne, Mt., Falkland Is. 54 Eh
Usedom, East Germany 68 Ea
Ushant I. See Ouessant, I. d'
Ushirombo, Tanzania 97 Ge
Ush Tobe, Kazakhstan 78 Gd
Ushuaia, Argentina 54 Ch
Uska, India 91 Db
Uskedal, Norway 67 Ag
Uskub. See Skopje
Uskudar, Turkey 92 Aa
Usole Siberskoye, U.S.S.R. 79 Kc
Uspenskiy, Kazakhstan 79 Gd
Usquil, Peru 52 Be
Ussel, France 72 Ed
Ussuri, U.S.S.R./China 79 Nd
Ussuriysk, U.S.S.R. 79 Nd
Ust Aldan, U.S.S.R. 79 Mb
Ust Amginskoye, U.S.S.R. 79 Nb
Ust Belaya, U.S.S.R. 79 Sb
Ust Chaun, U.S.S.R. 79 Sb
Uster, Switzerland 65 Da
Ust'-Ilimsk, U.S.S.R. 79 Kc
ústí nad Labem, Czech. 68 Fc
Ust'-Ishim, U.S.S.R. 78 Gc
Ust Kamenogorsk, Kazakh. 78 Hc
Ust Kamo, U.S.S.R. 79 Jb
Ust Khayryuzovo, U.S.S.R. 79 Qc
Ust Kut, U.S.S.R. 79 Kc
Ust Maya, U.S.S.R. 79 Nb
Ust' Port, U.S.S.R. 78 Hb
Ust Sopochnoye, U.S.S.R. 79 Qc
Ust Tsilma, U.S.S.R. 78 Eb
Ust Uda, U.S.S.R. 79 Kc
Ust Usa, U.S.S.R. 78 Eb
Ust'-Uyskoye, U.S.S.R. 81 Rc
Ustyurt, Kazakhstan 78 Ed
Ustyuzhna, U.S.S.R. 80 Kb
Usumacinta, R., Mexico 50 Fd
Utah, U.S.A. 42 Dd
Utah L., Utah 42 Dc
Utajarvi, Finland 66 Md
Utena, Lithuania 67 Lj
Utete, Tanzania 97 Hf
Uthal, Pakistan 88 Cc
Utiariti, Brazil 52 Ff
Utica, New York 40 jd
Utiel, Spain 71 Ec
Utik L., Manitoba 37 Vc
Utikuma L., Alberta 36 Bc
Utraula, India 91 Db
Utrecht, Natal 95 Ee
Utrecht, Neth. 64 Db
Utrera, Spain 70 Cd
Utrillas, Spain 71 Eb
Utsjoki, Finland 66 Mb
Utsunomiya, Japan 86 Ff
Uttaradit, Thailand 87 Cc
Uttar Pradesh, India 88 Ec
Uusikaarlepyy, Finland 66 Ke
Uusikaupunki, Finland 67 Jf
Uvac, Yugoslavia 76 Bc
Uvat, U.S.S.R. 78 Fc
Uvea, Loyalty Islands 102 Fk
Uvira, Zaire 97 Fe
Uvs Nuur, L., Mongolia 79 Jc
Uxbridge, Massachusetts 44 Ea
Uxbridge, Ontario 35 Lh
Uxmal, Mexico 50 Gc
Uyu Chaung, Burma 89 Jc
Uyuni, Bolivia 52 Dh
Uzbekskaya S.S.R., (Uzbekistan), U.S.S.R. 78 Fd
Uzdin, Yugoslavia 76 Cb
Uzgen, Kirghizia 78 Gd
Uzhgorod, Ukraine 80 Cg
Uzyansk, U.S.S.R. 81 Nd

V

Vaal, S. Africa 95 De
Vaalwater, Transvaal 95 Dd
Vaasä, Finland 66 Je
Vác, Hungary 69 He
Vache, I. La, Haiti 51 Ec
Vadodara, India 88 Dd
Vadsø, Norway 66 Na
Vaduz, Liechtenstein 65 Ea
Vaeröy, Norway 66 Ec
Vags Fd., Norway 66 Gb
Váh, Czechoslovakia 69 Gd
Vaila I., Shetland 62 Ha
Vairowal, India 90 De
Valais, Switzerland 65 Cb
Val-Barrette, Quebec 35 Pf
Val-Brilliant, Quebec 32 Ee
Valcheta, Argentina 54 Cf
Valcourt, Quebec 35 Sg
Valday, U.S.S.R. 80 Hc
Valday Hills, U.S.S.R. 80 Hc
Valdecanas, Emb. de, Spain 70 Cc
Valdepeñas, Spain 70 Dc
Valderredible, Spain 70 Da
Valderrobres, Spain 71 Fb
Valdés, Argentina 54 Df
Val-des-Bois, Quebec 35 Pg
Valdez, Alaska 43 Yl
Valdivia, Chile 54 Be
Val-d'Oise, France 72 Db
Val-d'Or, Quebec 35 Nd
Valdosta, Georgia, U.S.A. 45 Fe
Valea-lui-Mihai, Romania 69 Ke
Valença, Brazil 53 Kf
Valença, Brazil 53 Je
Valençay, France 72 Dc
Valence, France 73 Fd
Valencia, Spain 71 Ec
Valencia, Venezuela 52 Da
Valencia, G. of, Spain 71 Fc
Valencia, I., Eire 63 Aj
Valencia, L. de, Venezuela 51 Fd
Valencia de Alcántara, Spain 70 Bc
Valencia de Don Juan, Spain 70 Ca
Valenciennes, France 72 Ea
Văleni de Munte, Romania 76 Fb
Valentine, Nebraska 48 Ga
Valera, Venezuela 52 Cb
Valga, Estonia 67 Mh
Val Gagné, Ontario 34 Kd
Valjala, Estonia 67 Kg
Valjevo, Yugoslavia 76 Bb
Valkeakoshi, Finland 67 Lf
Valkenburg, Netherlands 64 Dd
Valladolid, Mexico 50 Gc
Valladolid, Spain 70 Cb
Val-Laflamme, Quebec 35 Nd
Valldemosa, Balearic Is. 71 Gc
Valle-D'Aosta, Italy 74 Ac
Valle de La Pascua, Venezuela 52 Db
Valle de Santiago, Mexico 50 Dc
Valledupar, Colombia 52 Ca
Vallée-Jonction, Quebec 32 Bg
Vallejo, California 47 Bf
Vallenar, Chile 54 Bc
Valletta, Malta 75 Eh
Valley, Nova Scotia 32 Jh
Valley Centre, Sask. 36 Kg
Valley City, N. Dakota 46 Jb
Valleyfield, Salaberry-de-, Quebec 35 Qg
Valleyview, Alberta 39 Ph
Vallgrund, Finland 66 Je
Vallorbe, Switzerland 65 Bb
Val Marie, Saskatchewan 36 Kj
Valmaseda, Spain 70 Da
Valmiera, Latvia 67 Lh
Valognes, France 72 Cb
Valona. See Vlorë
Valor, Saskatchewan 36 Lj
Valoria la Buena, Spain 70 Cb
Valparaiso, Chile 54 Bd
Valparaiso, Indiana 49 Ob
Valparaiso, Mexico 50 Dc
Valparaiso, Saskatchewan 37 Nf
Val-Piché, Quebec 35 Nd
Val-Racine, Quebec 32 Ah
Vals Platz, Switzerland 65 Eb
Valtimo, Finland 66 Ne
Valverde de Júcar, Spain 71 Dc
Valverde del Camino, Spain 70 Bd
Vana Vändra, Estonia 67 Lg
Vanavara, U.S.S.R. 79 Kb
Van Bruyssel, Quebec 35 Se
Van Buren, Arkansas 43 Hd
Van Buren, Maine 32 Ef
Van Buren, Missouri 45 Bb
Vancouver, B.C. 39 Ml
Vancouver, Washington 47 Bc
Vancouver, Mt., Y.T. 30 Fe
Vancouver Harbour, B.C. 39 Gl
Vancouver I., B.C. 39 Kk
Vandalia, Illinois 49 Nc
Vandekerckhove L., Man. 37 Qa
Vanderhoof, B.C. 39 Mh
Van Diemen, C., N. Terr. 56 Fb
Van Diemen G., N. Terr. 56 Fb
Vandry, Quebec 35 Re
Vanegas, Mexico 50 Dc
Vänern, L., Sweden 67 Eg
Vänersborg, Sweden 67 Eg
Vangaindrano, Madagascar 97 Nl
Van & Gölu, Turkey 92 Db
Vanguard, Saskatchewan 36 Kj
Van Horn Mts., Texas 48 Eg
Vanier, Ontario 34 Dh
Vanier, Quebec 35 Rb
Vankarem, U.S.S.R. 79 Tb
Vankleek Hill, Ontario 35 Qg
Vanndale, Arkansas 45 Bc
Vannes, France 72 Bc
Vannøy, Norway 66 Ha
Van Rhyns Dorp, Cape Prov. 95 Bf
Vanscoy, Saskatchewan 36 Lf
Vansittart I., N.W.T. 31 Ld
Vantage, Saskatchewan 37 Lj
Vanua Levu, Fiji 102 Gj
Var, France 73 Ge
Varanasi, India 91 Dc
Varanger Fd., Norway 66 Pb
Varanger Halvøya, Norway 66 Na
Varaždin, Yugoslavia 74 Fb
Varberg, Sweden 67 Eh
Vardar, Greece 76 Dd
Vardø, Norway 66 Pa
Varese, Italy 74 Bc
Varkaus, Finland 66 Me
Varna, Bulgaria 76 Fc
Varnavin, U.S.S.R. 81 Gb
Värtsilä, Finland 66 Pe
Vasknarva, Estonia 67 Mg
Vassar, Manitoba 36 Fa
Vassar, Michigan 40 Ed
Vastanfors, Sweden 67 Fg
Västeras, Sweden 67 Gg
Väster Dal Alv, Sweden 67 Ef
Västervik, Sweden 67 Gh
Vasvár, Hungary 69 Ge
Vatican City, Italy 75 De
Vaticano C., Italy 75 Ef
Vatna Jökull, Iceland 66 Xm
Vatomandry, Madagascar 97 Nk
Vättern, L., Sweden 67 Fg
Vättis, Switzerland 65 Eb
Vaucluse, France 73 Fd
Vaud, Switzerland 65 Bb
Vaughn, New Mexico 48 Ee
Vauxhall, Alberta 36 Eh
Vawn, Saskatchewan 36 Je
Växjö, Sweden 67 Fh
Vaygach Ostrov, U.S.S.R. 78 Fa
Vedia, Argentina 54 Dd
Vedrin, Belgium 64 Cd
Veenendaal, Netherlands 64 Db
Veere, Netherlands 64 Bc
Vega & Fd., Norway 66 Dd
Veghel, Netherlands 64 Dc
Vegorrítis, Greece 77 Cd
Vegreville, Alberta 36 Ee
Vein L., Ontario 34 Dc
Vejle, Denmark 67 Cj
Vela, Argentina 54 Ee
Velaines, Belgium 64 Bd
Velebit Planina, Yugoslavia 74 Ec
Velestinon, Greece 77 De
Vélez Rubio, Spain 71 Dd
Velikiye Luki, U.S.S.R. 80 Gc
Velikiy Ustyug, U.S.S.R. 78 Db
Veliko Tŭrnovo, Bulgaria 76 Ec
Velizh, U.S.S.R. 80 Gd
Velletri, Italy 75 De
Vellore, India 88 Ef
Velp, Netherlands 64 Db
Velsen, Netherlands 64 Cb
Velsk, U.S.S.R. 80 Na
Venado, Mexico 50 Dc
Venado Tuerto, Argentina 54 Dd
Vendée, France 72 Cc
Vendôme, France 72 Dc
Veneto, Italy 74 Cc
Venezia, Italy 74 Dc
Venezia, Golfo di, Italy 74 Dc
Venezuela, S. America 52 Db
Venezuela, G. de, Venezuela 52 Ca
Vengurla, India 88 De
Venice, Alberta 36 Ed
Venice. See Venezia
Venlo, Netherlands 64 Ec
Venn, Saskatchewan 37 Mg
Venosta, Quebec 35 Og
Venraij, Netherlands 64 Dc
Ventotene, Italy 75 De
Ventspils, Latvia 67 Jh
Ventura, California 47 Dh
Vera, Spain 71 Ed
Veracruz, Mexico 50 Ed
Veramin, Iran 93 Fb
Veraval, India 88 Dd
Verbania, Italy 65 Dc
Vercelli, Italy 74 Bc
Verchères, Quebec 35 Rg
Verde C. See Vert C.
Verde R., Arizona 48 Bf
Verdigris L., Alberta 36 Fj
Verdun, France 72 Fb
Verdun, Quebec 35 Sk
Veregin, Saskatchewan 37 Pg
Vérendrye, Parc prov. de la, Quebec 35 Ne
Vereshchagino, U.S.S.R. 78 Hb
Vereshchagino, U.S.S.R. 81 Ma
Vereya, U.S.S.R. 81 Cc
Verga C., Guinea 98 Cf
Vergara, Uruguay 54 Fd
Vergennes, Vermont 40 Kc
Verín, Spain 70 Bb
Verkhneimbatskoye, U.S.S.R. 78 Hb
Verkhne Ural'sk, U.S.S.R. 81 Pd
Verkhnevilyuysk, U.S.S.R. 79 Mb
Verkhoturye, U.S.S.R. 78 Fc
Verkhoyansk, U.S.S.R. 79 Nb
Verkhoyanskiy Khr., U.S.S.R. 79 Mb
Verlo, Saskatchewan 36 Jh
Vermilion B., Louisiana 49 Lh
Vermilion Bay, Ontario 36 Ja
Vermilion Chutes, Alberta 39 Qf
Vermilion L., Ontario 36 Ka
Vermilion & R., Alberta 36 Ge
Vermillion, S. Dakota 46 Jd
Vermillon, R., Quebec 35 Re
Vermont, U.S.A. 43 Mc
Vernal, Utah 48 Cb
Verner, Ontario 34 Kf
Verneuil, France 72 Db
Vernon, British Columbia 39 Ok
Vernon, Texas 49 He
Vernon Bridge, P.E.I. 32 Kg
Veroia, Greece 77 Dd
Verona, Italy 74 Cc
Verona, Ontario 35 Oh
Verrières, les, Switzerland 65 Bb
Versailles, France 72 Eb
Versam, Switzerland 65 Eb
Vert C., Senegal 98 Bf
Verte, B., N.S./N.B. 32 Jg
Verte, L'Isle-, Quebec 32 Ce
Verte, Pte., Quebec 32 He
Verton, L., Quebec 33 Nb
Vertrijk, Belgium 64 Cd
Verviers, Belgium 64 Dd
Vervins, France 72 Eb
Verwood, Saskatchewan 37 Mj
Vesanto, Finland 66 Me
Vesoul, France 72 Gc
Vessem, Netherlands 64 Dc
Vesta. See Pandora
Vesteralen, Is., Norway 66 Fb
Vestfjorden, Norway 66 Ec
Vest Vagöy, Norway 66 Eb
Vesyegonsk, U.S.S.R. 80 Kb
Veszprem, Hungary 69 Ge
Veteran, Alberta 36 Ff
Vetluga, U.S.S.R. 81 Gb
Veurne, Belgium 64 Ac
Vevey, Switzerland 65 Bb
Vex, Switzerland 65 Cb
Veys, Iran 92 Ec
Viacha, Bolivia 52 Dg
Viana, Brazil 53 Jd
Vibank, Saskatchewan 37 Oh
Viborg, Denmark 67 Ch
Vibo Valentia, Italy 75 Ff
Vicenza, Italy 74 Cc
Viceroy, Saskatchewan 37 Mj
Vich, Spain 71 Gb
Vichuquen, Chile 54 Bd
Vichy, France 72 Ec
Vicksburg, Mississippi 45 Bd
Viçosa, Brazil 53 Jd
Victor Harbour, S. Aust. 57 Gg
Victoria, Argentina 54 Dd
Victoria, Australia 57 Hg
Victoria, B.C. 39 Ml
Victoria, Hong Kong 82 Ff
Victoria, Newfoundland 33 Tf
Victoria, Texas 49 Jh
Victoria, L., Quebec 35 Ne
Victoria, Mt., Burma 89 Hd
Victoria, Mt., Papua New Guinea 57 Ja
Victoria, R., N. Terr. 56 Fc
Victoria Beach, Manitoba 37 Vh
Victoria Falls, Zimbabwe 95 Dc
Victoria Harbour, Ontario 35 Lh
Victoria I., N.W.T. 30 Hc
Victoria L., Uganda 97 Ge
Victoria Land, Antarctica 104 Lb
Victoria Point, Burma 89 Jf
Victoria R., Nfld. 33 Pe
Victoria River Downs, N. Territory 56 Ec
Victoria Str., N.W.T. 38 Xa
Victoriaville, Quebec 35 Tf
Victoria West, Cape Prov. 95 Cf
Victorica, Argentina 54 Ce
Vicuña, Chile 54 Bd
Vicuña Mackenna, Argentina 54 Dd
Vidago, Portugal 70 Bb
Vidin, Bulgaria 76 Db
Vidisha, India 91 Ad
Vidora, Saskatchewan 36 Hj
Viedma, Argentina 54 Df
Viedma, Argentina 54 Bg
Vienna. See Wien
Vienne, France 72 Dc
Vienne, France 72 Fd
Vientiane, Laos 87 Cc
Vieques, I. de, West Indies 51 Fc
Vierlingsbeek, Netherlands 64 Ec
Vierwaldstätter See, Switz. 65 Da
Vierzon Ville, France 72 Ec
Viesīte, Latvia 67 Lh
Vietnam, S.E. Asia 87 Dc
Vieux-Fort, Quebec 33 Ob
Vieux Poste, Pte. du, Quebec 33 Kc
Vif, France 73 Fd
Vigan, Philippines 83 Hg
Vigan, le, France 73 Ee
Vigia, Brazil 53 Hd
Vigía Chico, Mexico 50 Gd
Vigo, Spain 70 Aa
Vigrestad, Norway 67 Ag
Vihanti, Finland 66 Ld
Vijayanagar, India 88 Ee
Vijayawada, India 88 Fe
Vijosë, Albania 77 Bd
Vikaviskis, Lithuania 67 Kj
Viking, Alberta 36 Fe
Vikna, Norway 66 Dd
Vila Arriaga, Angola 96 Cg
Vila Gamito, Mozambique 97 Gg
Vila Machado, Mozambique 95 Ec
Vila Manica, Mozambique 95 Ec
Vilanculos, Mozambique 95 Fd
Vilāne, Latvia 67 Mh
Vila Nova de Cerveira, Port. 70 Ab
Vila Nova de Famalicão, Portugal 70 Ab
Vila Nova de Malaca, Timor I., Indonesia 83 Jm
Vila Pery, Mozambique 95 Ec
Vila Real, Portugal 70 Bb
Vilar Formoso, Portugal 70 Bb
Vila Velha de Rodao, Port. 70 Bc
Vila Viçosa, Portugal 70 Bc
Vilcheka, Zemlya, Arctic Ocean 78 Fa
Vilhelmina, Sweden 66 Gd
Vilhena, Brazil 52 Ef
Viljandi, Estonia 67 Lg
Villa Bella, Bolivia 52 Df
Villablino, Spain 70 Ba
Villacañas, Spain 70 Dc
Villacarriedo, Spain 70 Da
Villach, Austria 68 Ee
Villa Constitución, Arg. 54 Dd
Villa del Rosario, Argentina 54 Dd
Villa Dolores, Argentina 54 Cd
Villafranca, Spain 71 Ea
Villafranca del Cid, Spain 71 Eb
Villafranca del Panadés, Spain 71 Fb
Villaguay, Argentina 54 Ed
Villa Guillermina, Argentina 54 Ec
Villahermosa, Mexico 50 Fd
Villa Hidalgo, Mexico 50 Db
Villa Ingavi, Bolivia 52 Eh
Villa Iris, Argentina 54 De
Villajoyosa, Spain 71 Ec
Villalba, Spain 70 Ba
Villaldama, Mexico 50 Db
Villalón de Campos, Spain 70 Ca
Villalonga, Argentina 54 De
Villalpando, Spain 70 Cb
Villa Maria, Argentina 54 Dd
Villa Mercedes, Argentina 54 Cd
Villa Montes, Bolivia 52 Eh
Villa Murtinho, Brazil 52 Df
Villanueva de Córdoba, Spain 70 Cc
Villanueva de la Serena, Spain 70 Cc
Villanueva de los Infantes, Spain 70 Dc
Villanueva -y-Geltrú, Spain 71 Fb
Villaodrid, Spain 70 Ba
Villaputzu, Sardinia 75 Bf
Villarcayo, Spain 70 Da
Villarreal, Spain 71 Ec
Villarrica, Chile 54 Be
Villarrica, Paraguay 54 Ec
Villarrobledo, Spain 71 Dc
Villa Unión, Argentina 54 Cc
Villavicencio, Colombia 52 Cc
Villaviciosa, Spain 70 Ca
Villa Viejo, Colombia 52 Bc
Villazón, Bolivia 52 Dh
Villefort, France 73 Ed
Villefranche-de-Rouergue, France 73 Dd
Ville-Marie, Quebec 35 Le
Villemontel, Quebec 35 Md
Villena, Spain 71 Ec
Villeneuve-sur-Lot, France 73 Dd
Villeroy, Quebec 35 Tf
Villeurbanne, France 72 Fd
Villingen, West Germany 68 Cd
Villisca, Iowa 49 Kb
Villupuram, India 88 Ef
Vilna, Alberta 36 Fd
Vilnius, Lithuania 67 Lj
Vilvoorde, Belgium 64 Cd
Vilyuysk, U.S.S.R. 79 Mb
Vimioso, Portugal 70 Bb
Vimperk, Czechoslovakia 68 Ed
Viña del Mar, Chile 54 Bd
Vinaroz, Spain 71 Fb
Vincennes, Indiana 40 Cf
Vincente de la Barquera, Spain 70 Ca
Vinces, Ecuador 52 Bd
Vinchiaturo, Italy 75 Ee
Vindelalven R., Sweden 66 Hd
Vindhya Ra., India 88 Ed
Vineland, New Jersey 44 Cc
Vineyard Sound, Mass. 44 Eb
Vinga, Romania 76 Cb
Vingt-Deuxième Mille, L. du, Quebec 32 Jc
Vinh, Vietnam 87 Dc
Vinh Loi, Vietnam 87 Dd
Vinita, Oklahoma 49 Kd
Vinkovci, Yugoslavia 76 Bb
Vinnitsa, Ukraine 80 Fg
Vinson Massif, Antarctica 104 Rb
Vinton, Iowa 49 La
Violet Grove, Alberta 36 Ce
Viranşehir, Turkey 92 Cb
Virden, Manitoba 37 Rj
Virginia, Minnesota 46 Kb
Virginia, U.S.A. 43 Ld
Virginia City, Montana 46 Bc
Virginia Falls, N.W.T. 38 Ke
Virginiatown, Ontario 35 Ld
Virgin Is., West Indies 51 Gc
Viroqua, Wisconsin 40 Ad
Virovitica, Yugoslavia 76 Ab
Virpazar, Yugoslavia 76 Bc
Virtsalmi, Finland 66 Me
Virton, Belgium 64 De
Virtsu, Estonia 67 Kg
Viru, Peru 52 Be
Vis, Yugoslavia 74 Fd
Visakhapatnam, India 89 Fe
Visalia, California 47 Dg
Visby, Gotland, Sweden 67 Hh
Viscount, Saskatchewan 37 Mg
Viscount Melville Sound, Northwest Territories 30 Jc
Visé, Belgium 64 Dd
Viseu, Brazil 53 Hd
Viseu, Portugal 70 Bb
Vishoek, S. Africa 95 Gj
Viški, Latvia 67 Mh
Viso, Mte., Italy 74 Ac
Visoko, Yugoslavia 76 Bc
Visp, Switzerland 65 Cb
Vista Alegre, Brazil 52 Ec
Vistula R. See Wislá
Vitebsk, Byelorussia 80 Gd
Viterbo, Italy 74 Dd
Vitigudino, Spain 70 Bb
Viti Levu, Fiji 102 Gj
Vitim, R., U.S.S.R. 79 Lc
Vitória, Brazil 53 Jh
Vitoria, Spain 71 Da
Vitoria do Mearim, Brazil 53 Jd
Vitré, L. De, Quebec 33 Nb
Vitry-le-François, France 72 Fb
Vittangi, Sweden 66 Jc
Vitteaux, France 72 Fc
Vittoria, Ontario 34 Kk
Vittoria, Sicily 75 Eg
Viver, Spain 71 Ec
Vivero, Spain 70 Ba
Vivi, U.S.S.R. 79 Jb
Vivorata, Argentina 54 Ee
Vizianagram, India 89 Fe
Vizirul, Romania 76 Fb
Vizovice, Czechoslovakia 69 Gd
Vizzini, Sicily 75 Eg
Vlaanderen, Oost, Belgium 64 Bd
Vlaanderen, West, Belgium 64 Bd
Vlaardingen, Netherlands 64 Cc
Vladimir, U.S.S.R. 80 Mc
Vladimirovka, U.S.S.R. 81 Hf
Vladivostok, U.S.S.R. 79 Nd
Vlieland, Netherlands 64 Ca
Vlissingen, Netherlands 64 Bc
Vlorë, Albania 77 Bd
Vltava, Czechoslovakia 68 Fc
Voghera, Italy 74 Bc
Vohemar, Madagascar 97 Pj
Võhma, Estonia 67 Lg
Voi, Kenya 97 He
Voiotía, Greece 77 De
Voiron, France 72 Fd
Voitsberg, Austria 68 Fe
Voiviis, Greece 77 De
Vojvodina, Yugoslavia 76 Bb
Volga, U.S.S.R. 78 Dd
Volgograd, U.S.S.R. 81 Gf
Volissos, Greece 77 Ee
Volkhov, U.S.S.R. 80 Gb
Vollenhove, Netherlands 64 Db
Volochanka, U.S.S.R. 79 Ja
Volochisk, Ukraine 80 Eg
Vologda, U.S.S.R. 80 Lb
Volokolamsk, U.S.S.R. 80 Jc
Vólos, Greece 77 De
Volovets, Ukraine 80 Cg
Volozhin, Byelorussia 80 Ed
Volsk, U.S.S.R. 81 Hd
Volta. See Upper Volta
Volta, L., Ghana 98 Eg
Voltveti, Estonia 67 Lg
Vonda, Saskatchewan 36 Lf
Vonêche, Belgium 64 Cd
Voorburg, Netherlands 64 Cb
Voorschoten, Netherlands 64 Cb
Voorst, Netherlands 64 Eb
Voorthuizen, Netherlands 64 Db
Vopnafjordhur, Iceland 66 Ym
Vorab, Switzerland 65 Eb
Vorarlberg, Austria 68 Ce
Vorauen, Switzerland 65 Da
Vorkuta, U.S.S.R. 78 Fb
Vormsi, I., Estonia 67 Kg
Voronezh, U.S.S.R. 80 Lf
Voroshilovgrad, Ukraine 80 Lg
Vosges, France 72 Gb
Voss, Norway 67 Bf
Vostok I., Pacific Ocean 103 Kj
Votkinsk, U.S.S.R. 81 Lb
Vouvry, Switzerland 65 Bb
Vouziers, France 72 Fb
Voxna, Sweden 66 Gf
Voyampolka, U.S.S.R. 79 Qc
Voznesensk, Ukraine 80 Gh
Vrangelya Ostrov, U.S.S.R. 79 Sa
Vranje, Yugoslavia 76 Cc
Vranov, Czechoslovakia 69 Jd
Vratsa, Bulgaria 76 Dc
Vrbas, Yugoslavia 76 Bb
Vrchovina Českomoravska, Czechoslovakia 69 Fd
Vredefort, O.F.S. 95 De
Vrin, Switzerland 65 Eb
Vrindavan, India 91 Ab
Vroomshoop, Netherlands 64 Eb
Vršac, Yugoslavia 76 Cb
Vrútky, Czechoslovakia 69 Hd
Vryburg, Cape Province 95 Ce
Vučitrn, Yugoslavia 76 Cc
Vukovar, Yugoslavia 76 Bb
Vulcan, Alberta 36 Dh
Vulcano, Italy 75 Ef
Vulpera, Switzerland 65 Fb
Vuolijoki, Finland 66 Md
Vurbitsa, Bulgaria 76 Fc
Vyatka, R., U.S.S.R. 78 Dc
Vyazemskiy, U.S.S.R. 79 Nd
Vyazma, U.S.S.R. 80 Jd
Vyazniki, U.S.S.R. 81 Fb
Vyborg, U.S.S.R. 80 Fa
Vyrtsyarv Oz., Estonia 67 Mg
Vyru, Estonia 67 Mh
Vyshniy Volochek, U.S.S.R. 80 Jc
Vyškov, Czechoslovakia 69 Gd
Vytegra, U.S.S.R. 80 Ka

W

Wa, Ghana 98 Ef
Waalwijk, Netherlands 64 Dc
Wababimiga L., Ontario 34 Db
Wabamun & L., Alberta 36 Ce
Wabana, Newfoundland 33 Uf
Wabano, R., Quebec 35 Rd
Wabasca, Alberta 36 Dc
Wabasca, R., Alberta 39 Qg
Wabasca L., North, Alta. 36 Db
Wabasca L., South, Alta. 36 Dc
Wabash R., Indiana 49 Oc
Wabatongushi L., Ontario 34 Fd
Wabigoon & L., Ontario 36 Ka
Wabinosh L., Ontario 37 Na
Waboose Dam, Ontario 34 Cb
Wabos, Ontario 34 Ff
Wabowden, Manitoba 37 Td
Wabra, Arabia 92 Ed
Wabuda, I., New Guinea 57 Ha
Wabu Hu, China 84 Hf
Wabush, Newfoundland 31 Ng
W.A.C. Bennett Dam, B.C. 30 Gf
Waco, Quebec 32 Gb
Waco, Texas 49 Jg
Wacouno, R., Quebec 32 Gb
Wad, Pakistan 88 Cc
Waddenzee, Netherlands 64 Da
Waddington Mt., B.C. 39 Lk
Wadena, Minnesota 46 Kb
Wadena, Saskatchewan 37 Og
Wadesboro, N. Carolina 45 Gc
Wad Hamid, Sudan 99 Me
Wadham Is., Nfld. 33 Td
Wadhams, B.C. 39 Kk
Wadi-es-Sir, Jordan 94 Df
Wadi Gemal I., Egypt 99 Nd
Wadi Halfa, Sudan 99 Md
Wadi Musa, Jordan 94 Dg
Wad Medani, Sudan 99 Mf
Wafi, Arabia 92 De
Wafra, Arabia 92 Ed
Wagaming, Ontario 34 Bb
Wageningen, Netherlands 64 Dc
Wager B., N.W.T 31 Ld
Wagga Wagga, N.S.W. 57 Jg
Wagin, W. Australia 56 Cf
Wagoner, Oklahoma 49 Ke
Wahoo, Nebraska 49 Jb
Wahpeton, N. Dakota 30 Kh
Waiau, New Zealand 55 Dh
Waichow. See Huizhou
Waigeo, Irian Jaya 83 Kl
Waiheke I., New Zealand 55 Eb
Waihi, New Zealand 55 Eb
Waikaia, New Zealand 55 Bf
Waikare Moana, N.Z. 55 Fc
Waikari, New Zealand 55 De
Waikato, R., New Zealand 55 Ec
Waikouaiti, New Zealand 55 Cf
Waimakariri, R., N.Z. 55 De
Waimate, New Zealand 55 Cf
Waimes, Belgium 64 Ed
Wainganga, India 88 Ed
Waingapu, Sumba I., Indonesia 83 Hm
Wainwright, Alaska 43 Xk
Wainwright, Alberta 36 Gf
Waipara, New Zealand 55 De
Waipawa, New Zealand 55 Fc
Waipukurau, New Zealand 55 Fd
Wairarapa, L., New Zealand 55 Ed
Wairau, R., New Zealand 55 Dd
Wairoa, R., New Zealand 55 Fc
Waitara, New Zealand 55 Ec
Waitomo, New Zealand 55 Ec
Waitville, Saskatchewan 37 Mf
Waiuku, New Zealand 55 Eb
Wajir, Kenya 97 Jd
Wakamatsu. See Aizuwakamatsu
Wakami L., Ontario 34 He
Wakasa wan, Japan 86 Dg
Wakatipu, L, N.Z. 55 Bf
Wakaw, Saskatchewan 37 Mf
Wakayama, Japan 86 Dg
Wakba. See El Jafr
Wakefield, England 63 Gg
Wakefield, Quebec 35 Og
Wake I., Pacific Ocean 102 Ff
Wakomata L., Ontario 34 Gf
Wakopa, Manitoba 37 Sj
Wakrah., Qatar, Persian Gulf 93 Fd
Wakwayowkastic, R., Ont. 34 Kb
Walachia, Romania 76 Eb
Wałbrzych, Poland 69 Gc
Walcheren, Netherlands 64 Bc
Walcott, B.C. 39 Kh
Walcott, L., Idaho 47 Gd
Wald, Switzerland 65 Da
Waldeck, Saskatchewan 36 Kh
Waldheim, Saskatchewan 36 Lf
Waldia, Ethiopia 97 Hb
Waldo, British Columbia 36 Bj
Waldoboro, Maine 32 Cj
Waldport, Oregon 47 Ac
Waldron, Saskatchewan 37 Ph
Walen See, Switzerland 65 Ea
Walenstadt, Switzerland 65 Ea
Wales, Great Britain 63 Eh
Wales I., N.W.T. 31 Ld
Walgett, N.S.W. 57 Jf
Walgreen Coast, Antarctica 104 Qb
Walhalla, S. Carolina 45 Fc
Walker, Minnesota 46 Kb
Walker, L., Quebec 32 Ec
Walker B., N.W.T. 38 Oa
Walker L., Manitoba 37 Vd
Walker L., Nevada 47 Df
Walkerton, Ontario 34 Jh
Wallace, Idaho 47 Fb
Wallace, Nova Scotia 32 Jh
Wallace, Ontario 35 Mg
Wallaceburg, Ontario 34 Hk
Wallace Mt., Alberta 36 Bc
Wallacetown, Ontario 34 Jk
Wallaroo, S. Australia 57 Gf
Wallaston, Mt., N. Terr. 56 Fc
Walla-Walla, Washington 47 Db

Wallenpaupack, L., *Pa.* 44 Cb
Wallowa Mts., *Oregon* 47 Ec
Walmsley L., *N.W.T.* 38 Td
Walnut Cove, *N. Carolina* 45 Gb
Walsall, *England* 63 Fh
Walsenburg, *Colorado* 48 Ed
Walsh, *Alberta* 36 Gj
Walsh, *Queensland* 57 Hc
Walsh, Mt., *Y.T.* 38 De
Walsoorden, *Netherlands* 64 Cc
Walterboro, *S. Carolina* 45 Gd
Waltham, *Massachusetts* 44 Ea
Waltham, *Quebec* 40 Hc
Waltham Station, *Quebec* 35 Og
Walton, *New York* 44 Ca
Walton, *Nova Scotia* 32 Jh
Walton, *Ontario* 34 Jj
Walvis Bay, *Namibia* 95 Ad
Walwale, *Ghana* 98 Ef
Wamba, *Zaire* 97 Fd
Wamel, *Netherlands* 64 Dc
Wampsville, *New York* 40 Jd
Wana, *Pakistan* 90 Ad
Wanaaring, *N.S.W.* 57 He
Wanaka, *New Zealand* 55 Bf
Wanapitei L., *Ontario* 34 Kf
Wandering River, *Alberta* 36 Ec
Wandiwash, *India* 88 Ef
Wandoan, *Queensland* 57 Je
Wandre, *Belgium* 64 Dd
Wandsbek, *W. Germany* 68 Db
Wanganui, *N.Z.* 55 Ec
Wangaratta, *Victoria* 57 Jg
Wangolodougou, *Ivory Coast* 98 Dg
Wankie, *Zimbabwe* 95 Dc
Wanless, *Manitoba* 37 Qd
Wanning, *Hainan, China* 85 En
Wanup, *Ontario* 34 Kf
Wanxian, *China* 84 Dg
Wanxien, *China* 82 Ed
Wanyuan, *China* 84 Df
Wapawekka Hills, *Sask.* 37 Nd
Wapawekka L., *Sask.* 37 Nd
Wapella, *Saskatchewan* 37 Ph
Wapello, *Iowa* 49 Mb
Wapikaimaski L., *Ontario* 37 Na
Wapisu L., *Manitoba* 37 Sc
Wapiti, R., *Alberta* 39 Oh
Wappapello Res., *Missouri* 49 Md
Wapus L., *Saskatchewan* 37 Pb
Wapustagamau, L., *Quebec* 33 Ob
Warandab, *Ethiopia* 97 Jc
Warangal, *India* 88 Ee
Warburg, *Alberta* 36 Ce
Wardair, *Ethiopia* 97 Kc
Warden, *Alberta* 36 Ef
Wardha, *India* 88 Ed
Ward Hunt I., *N.W.T.* 31 Ma
Wardlow, *Alberta* 36 Fh
Wardner, *B.C.* 39 Ql
Ware, *British Columbia* 39 Lg
Waremme, *Belgium* 64 Dd
Waren, *East Germany* 68 Eb
Warka, *Poland* 69 Jc
Warkworth, *Ontario* 35 Nh
Warmbad, *Namibia* 95 Be
Warmbad, *Transvaal* 95 Dd
Warm Bay Hotsprings, *B.C.* 38 Gf
Warneford, *Ontario* 34 Bc
Warnemünde, *E. Germany* 68 Ea
Warner, *Alberta* 36 Ej
Warner Valley, *Oregon* 47 Dd
Warneton, *Belgium* 64 Ad
Warora, *India* 88 Ed
Warragul, *Victoria* 57 Jg
Warren, *Arkansas* 45 Ad
Warren, *Illinois* 40 Bd
Warren, *Minnesota* 46 Ja
Warren, *Ohio* 40 Fe
Warren, *Ontario* 34 Kf
Warren, *Pennsylvania* 44 Ab
Warrender, C., *N.W.T.* 31 Lc
Warren Landing, *Man.* 37 Ue
Warrenpoint, *N. Ireland* 63 Cf
Warren Pt., *N.W.T.* 38 Ga
Warrensburg, *Missouri* 49 Lc
Warrenton, *N. Carolina* 45 Hb
Warrenton, *Virginia* 44 Bc
Warri, *Nigeria* 98 Gg
Warrington, *England* 63 Fg
Warrnambool, *Victoria* 57 Hg
Warroad, *Minnesota* 46 Ka
Warsaw, *Indiana* 40 De
Warsaw, *N. Carolina* 45 Hc
Warsaw, *New York* 44 Aa
Warsaw. *See* Warszawa
Warspite, *Alberta* 36 Ed
Warszawa, *Poland* 69 Jb
Warta, *Poland* 69 Hb
Warta, *Poland* 69 Hc
Wartburg, *Tennessee* 45 Eb
Wartime, *Saskatchewan* 36 Jg
Warwick, *England* 63 Fh
Warwick, *Quebec* 35 Tg
Warwick, *Queensland* 57 Ke
Warwick, *Rhode Island* 44 Eb
Wasa, *British Columbia* 39 Ql
Wasaga Beach, *Ontario* 34 Kh
Wasatch Mts., *Utah* 48 Bc
Waseca, *Minnesota* 46 Lc
Waseca, *Saskatchewan* 36 He
Wasekamio L., *Sask.* 39 Tg
Wasen, *Switzerland* 65 Ca
Wash, The, *England* 63 Hh
Washago, *Ontario* 35 Lh
Washakie Needles, *Wyo.* 46 Cd
Washaw B., *Manitoba* 37 Vg
Washburn, *Wisconsin* 46 Mb
Washburn L., *N.W.T.* 38 Ua
Washington, *Dist. of Columb.* 40 Hf
Washington, *Indiana* 49 Oc
Washington, *Iowa* 49 Mb
Washington, *Missouri* 45 Ba
Washington, *N. Carolina* 45 Jc
Washington, *New Jersey* 44 Cb
Washington, *Ohio* 40 Ef
Washington, *Pennsylvania* 40 Fe
Washington, *U.S.A.* 42 Bb
Washington, *Virginia* 44 Ac
Washington I., *Pacific Ocean* 102 Jg
Washington Ld., *Greenland* 41 Qa
Washir, *Afghanistan* 93 Hc
Washuk, *Pakistan* 88 Bc
Wasing, *Ontario* 35 Lf
Waskada, *Manitoba* 37 Rj
Waskaiowaka L., *Man.* 37 Vb
Waskatenau, *Alberta* 36 Ed
Waskesiu Lake, *Sask.* 36 Le
Wasmes, *Belgium* 64 Bd
Wassen, *Switzerland* 65 Db
Waswanipi, R., *Quebec* 35 Oc
Waswanipi & L., *Quebec* 35 Oc
Watabeag L., *Ontario* 34 Kd
Watcomb, *Ontario* 36 La
Waterbury, *Connecticut* 44 Db
Waterdown, *Ontario* 34 Lj
Waterford, *Ontario* 34 Kk
Waterford Harb., *Eire* 63 Ch
Waterford (Port Láirge), *Eire* 63 Ch
Waterhen L., *Manitoba* 37 Sf
Waterhen L., *Sask.* 36 Jd
Waterloo, *Belgium* 64 Cd
Waterloo, *Illinois* 45 Ba
Waterloo, *Iowa* 49 La
Waterloo, *Ontario* 34 Kj
Waterloo, *Ontario* 40 Fd
Waterloo, *Quebec* 35 Sg
Waterton Lakes Nat. Park, *Alberta* 36 Dj
Watertown, *New York* 40 Jd
Watertown, *S. Dakota* 46 Jc
Watertown, *Wisconsin* 40 Bd
Waterville, *Maine* 32 Cj
Waterville, *Nova Scotia* 32 Hh
Waterville, *Quebec* 35 Tg
Watervliet, *New York* 44 Da
Watford, *England* 63 Gj
Watford, *Ontario* 34 Jk
Watford City, *N. Dakota* 46 Fb
Watino, *Alberta* 39 Ph
Watkins Glen, *New York* 44 Ba
Watling I., *The Bahamas* 51 Eb
Watonga, *Oklahoma* 49 He
Watou, *Belgium* 64 Ad
Watrous, *Saskatchewan* 37 Mg
Watsa, *Zaire* 97 Fd
Watseka, *Illinois* 49 Cb
Watson, *Saskatchewan* 37 Nf
Watson, *Utah* 46 Cf
Watson Lake, *Y.T.* 38 Je
Watsonville, *California* 47 Cg
Watt Mt., *Alberta* 39 Pf
Watts Bar L., *Tennessee* 45 Ec
Wattsville, *Alabama* 45 Dd
Wau, *New Guinea* 57 Ja
Wau, *Sudan* 99 Lg
Waubamik, *Ontario* 34 Lg
Waubaushene, *Ontario* 34 Lh
Wauchope, *N. Terr.* 57 Fd
Wauchope, *Saskatchewan* 37 Qj
Wauchula, *Florida* 45 Gg
Waugh, *Manitoba* 36 Ga
Waukegan, *Illinois* 40 Cd
Waukesha, *Wisconsin* 40 Bd
Waupaca, *Wisconsin* 40 Bc
Waupun, *Wisconsin* 40 Bd
Waurika, *Oklahoma* 49 Je
Wausau, *Wisconsin* 40 Bc
Wautoma, *Wisconsin* 40 Bc
Wauwatosa, *Wisconsin* 40 Bd
Wave Hill, *N. Terr.* 56 Fc
Waveney R., *England* 63 Hh
Waverley, *Iowa* 49 La
Waverley, *Nova Scotia* 32 Jj
Waverly, *New York* 44 Ba
Waverly, *Ohio* 40 Ef
Wavre, *Belgium* 64 Cd
Wavy L., *Alberta* 36 Ef
Wawagosic, R., *Quebec* 35 Mc
Wawaitin Falls, *Ontario* 34 Jd
Wawa (Jamestown), *Ontario* 40 Da
Wawal Kabir, *Libya* 99 Jc
Wawanesa, *Manitoba* 37 Sj
Wawota, *Saskatchewan* 37 Pj
Waxahachie, *Texas* 49 Jf
Waycross, *Georgia, U.S.A.* 45 Fe
Wayne, *Alberta* 36 Eg
Wayne, *W. Virginia* 45 Fa
Waynesboro, *Georgia, U.S.A.* 45 Gd
Waynesboro, *Pennsylvania* 44 Bc
Waynesburg, *Pennsylvania* 40 Ff
Waynesville, *N. Carolina* 45 Fc
Waynoka, *Oklahoma* 49 Hd
Wazirabad, *Pakistan* 90 Dd
Wazirstan, *Pakistan* 90 Ad
Weald, The, *England* 63 Hj
Wear R., *England* 63 Ff
Weatherford, *Texas* 49 Jf
Weatherly, *Pennsylvania* 44 Cb
Weaver L., *Manitoba* 37 Vf
Webb, *Saskatchewan* 36 Jh
Webb City, *Missouri* 49 Kd
Webbwood, *Ontario* 34 Hf
Webster, *S. Dakota* 46 Jc
Webster City, *Iowa* 49 La
Webster Springs, *W. Virginia* 45 Ga
Wechelderzande, *Belgium* 64 Cc
Weda, Teluk, *Halmahera, Indon.* 83 Jk
Weddell I., *Falkland Islands* 54 Dh
Weddell Sea, *Antarctica* 104 Ac
Wedge Mt., *B.C.* 39 Mk
Wedgeport, *Nova Scotia* 32 Fk
Weed, *California* 47 Be
Weedon-Centre, *Quebec* 35 Tg
Weedsport, *New York* 44 Ba
Weekes, *Saskatchewan* 37 Pf
Weeping Water, *Nebraska* 49 Jb
Weert, *Netherlands* 64 Dc
Weesen, *Switzerland* 65 Ea
Weesp, *Netherlands* 64 Db
Weichang, *China* 84 Jb
Weichang, *China* 84 Hb
Weiden, *West Germany* 68 Ed
Weifang, *China* 84 Jd
Weihai, *China* 84 Ld
Wei He, *China* 82 Ed
Weihwei. *See* Ji Xian
Weimar, *East Germany* 68 Dc
Weinfelden, *Switzerland* 65 Ea
Weir, *Quebec* 35 Qg
Weirdale, *Saskatchewan* 37 Me
Weiser, *Idaho* 47 Ec
Weishan Hu, *China* 84 He
Weissenfels, *East Germany* 68 Dc
Weisshorn, *Switzerland* 65 Cb
Weissmies, *Switzerland* 65 Db
Weisstannen, *Switzerland* 65 Ea
Weitzel L., *Saskatchewan* 39 Ug
Wejh. *See* Al Wajh
Wekusko & L., *Manitoba* 37 Sd
Welch, *W. Virginia* 45 Gb
Weldon, *N. Carolina* 45 Jb
Weldon, *Saskatchewan* 37 Mf
Welford, *Queensland* 57 He
Welland, *Ontario* 35 Lk
Welland Can., *Ontario* 35 Lk
Wellesley Is., *Queensland* 57 Gc
Wellesley L., *Y.T.* 38 Dd
Wellin, *Belgium* 64 Dd
Wellingborough, *England* 63 Gh
Wellington, *Kansas* 49 Jd
Wellington, *Newfoundland* 33 Se
Wellington, *New Zealand* 55 Ed
Wellington, *Nova Scotia* 32 Jj
Wellington, *Ontario* 35 Nj
Wellington, *P.E.I.* 32 Hg
Wellington, I., *Chile* 54 Bg
Wellington B., *N.W.T.* 38 Ua
Wellington B., *Ontario* 35 Nj
Wellington Chan., *N.W.T.* 31 Kb
Wells, *British Columbia* 30 Gg
Wells, *England* 63 Fj
Wells, *England* 63 Hh
Wells, *Nevada* 47 Fe
Wellsboro, *Pennsylvania* 44 Bb
Wells Gray Provincial Park, *British Columbia* 39 Nj
Wells L., *Manitoba* 37 Ra
Wellsville, *Missouri* 49 Mc
Wellsville, *New York* 44 Ba
Wellwood, *Manitoba* 37 Sh
Wels, *Austria* 68 Ed
Welsford, *New Bunswick* 32 Fh
Welshpool, *N.B.* 32 Fj
Welshpool, *Wales* 63 Eh
Welwyn, *Saskatchewan* 37 Qh
Wema, *Zaire* 96 Ee
Wembley, *Alberta* 39 Oh
Wembo Nyama, *Zaire* 96 Ee
Wenatchee, *Washington* 47 Cb
Wenebegon L., *Ontario* 34 Ge
Wenman I. *See* Wolf I.
Wenshan, *China* 85 Bl
Wentworth Centre, *N.S.* 32 Jh
Wenxi, *China* 84 Ee
Wenzhou, *China* 85 Kh
Wernecke Mts., *Y.T.* 38 Fc
Wernham L., *Manitoba* 37 Ub
Wernhout, *Netherlands* 64 Cc
Wervershoof, *Netherlands* 64 Db
Wervik, *Belgium* 64 Bd
Wesel, *West Germany* 68 Bc
Wesenberg, *East Germany* 68 Eb
Weser, *West Germany* 68 Cb
Weslemkoon L., *Ontario* 35 Nh
Wesleyville, *Newfoundland* 33 Td
Wessel Is., *N. Terr.* 57 Gb
Wesson, *Mississippi* 45 Be
West Allis, *Wisconsin* 40 Bd
West B., *Louisiana* 49 Nh
West Barra, *Shetlands* 62 Ja
West Bend, *Saskatchewan* 37 Og
West Bend, *Wisconsin* 40 Bd
West Bengal, *India* 89 Gd
Westbourne, *Manitoba* 37 Th
West Branch, *Michigan* 40 Dc
Westbridge, *B.C.* 39 Ol
West Bromwich, *England* 63 Fh
Westbrook, *Maine* 32 Bk
West Chester, *Pennsylvania* 44 Cc
West Dover, *N.S.* 32 Jj
Westende, *Belgium* 64 Ac
Westerham, *Saskatchewan* 36 Hh
Westerlo, *Belgium* 64 Cc
Westerly, *Rhode Island* 44 Eb
Western Australia, *Australia* 56 Dd
Western Head, *N.S.* 33 Hk
Western Is., *Ontario* 34 Kg
Western R., *N.W.T.* 38 Ub
Western Sahara, *Morocco* 98 Cc
Western Samoa, *Pacific Ocean* 102 Hj
Westerschelde, *Netherlands* 64 Bc
Westerwald, *W. Ger.* 68 Cc
Westfield, *Massachusetts* 40 Kd
Westfield, *New York* 44 Aa
Westfield, *Pennsylvania* 44 Bb
West Frankfort, *Illinois* 45 Cb
West Glamorgan, *Wales* 63 Ej
Westham I., *B.C.* 39 Gm
West Indies, *Caribbean Sea* 101 Cg
West Kabenung L., *Ont.* 34 Ed
Westkapelle, *Netherlands* 64 Bc
Westlock, *Alberta* 36 Dd
West Lorne, *Ontario* 34 Jk
West Malaysia. *See* Peninsular Malaysia
Westmeath, *Eire* 63 Cg
Westmeath, *Ontario* 35 Og
West Midlands, *Eng.* 63 Fh
Westminster, *Maryland* 44 Bc
Westmount, *Quebec* 35 Sj
West Nicholson, *Zimbabwe* 95 Dd
Weston, *Sabah* 83 Gj
Weston, *West Virginia* 40 Ff
Weston-super-Mare, *Eng.* 63 Fj
West Pakistan. *See* Pakistan
West Palm Beach, *Florida* 43 Lf
Westplains, *Missouri* 45 Bb
West Point, *Arkansas* 45 Bc
West Point, *Georgia, U.S.A.* 45 Ed
West Point, *Mississippi* 45 Cd
Westpoint, *Nebraska* 49 Jb
West Point, *New York* 44 Db
West Point, *Virginia* 45 Jb
Westport, *Eire* 63 Ag
Westport, *Newfoundland* 33 Qd
Westport, *New Zealand* 55 Cd
Westport, *Ontario* 35 Oh
West Prairie R., *Alberta* 36 Ac
West Pt., *Nova Scotia* 33 Mk
West Pt., *P.E.I.* 32 Hg
West Pubnico, *N.S.* 32 Gk
Westray, *Manitoba* 37 Qe
Westray I., *Orkney* 62 Ea
Westree, *Ontario* 34 Je
West Road R., *B.C.* 39 Lj
West St. Modeste, *Nfld.* 33 Qb
West Sussex, *England* 63 Gk
West Union, *Iowa* 49 Ma
West Vancouver, *B.C.* 39 Gl
Westview, *B.C.* 39 Ll
Westville, *Nova Scotia* 32 Kh
West Virginia, *U.S.A.* 43 Kd
Westwoud, *Netherlands* 64 Db
West Yorkshire, *Eng.* 63 Fg
Wetar, *Indonesia* 83 Jm
Wetaskiwin, *Alberta* 36 Df
Wetetnagami, R., *Quebec* 35 Oc
Wetterhorn, *Switzerland* 65 Db
Wetumpka, *Alabama* 45 Dd
Wewoka, *Oklahoma* 49 Je
Wexford, *Eire* 63 Ch
Weyakwin L., *Sask.* 36 Ld
Weyburn, *Saskatchewan* 37 Oj
Weymont, *Quebec* 40 Kb
Weymouth, *England* 63 Fk
Weymouth, *Nova Scotia* 32 Gj
Whakatane, *New Zealand* 55 Fd
Whakatane, *New Zealand* 55 Fb
Whales, B. of, *Antarctica* 104 Mb
Whalsay, *Shetlands* 62 Ja
Whangarei, *New Zealand* 55 Ea
Wharanui, *New Zealand* 55 Ed
Wharton, *Texas* 49 Jh
Wharton L., *N.W.T.* 38 Yc
Whataroa, *New Zealand* 55 Ce
Wheatland, *Wyoming* 46 Ed
Wheatland Res., *Wyoming* 46 Ee
Wheatley, *Ontario* 34 Hk
Wheaton, *Minnesota* 46 Jc
Wheeler Dam, *Alabama* 45 Dc
Wheeler L., *N.W.T.* 38 Qd
Wheeler Pk., *Nevada* 47 Ff
Wheeler R., *Sask.* 39 Ub
Wheeling, *W. Virginia* 40 Fe
Whetstone Buttes, *N. Dakota* 46 Fb
Whipple Pt., *Nova Scotia* 32 Fj
Whiskey Gap, *Alberta* 36 Dj
Whiskey Jack Landing, *Man.* 37 Td
Whitbourne, *Nfld.* 33 Tf
Whitby, *England* 63 Gf
Whitby, *Ontario* 35 Mj
Whitchurch-Stouffville, *Ontario* 35 Lj
White, R., *Y.T.* 38 Cd
White B., *Newfoundland* 33 Qc
White Bear, *Sask.* 36 Jh
Whitebear Pt., *N.W.T.* 38 Wa
White Bear Reservoir, *Nfld.* 33 Qf
Whitecap L., *Manitoba* 37 Wb
Whitecourt, *Alberta* 36 Bd
White Earth, *N. Dakota* 46 Fa
Whitefish, *Montana* 42 Db
Whitefish, *Ontario* 34 Jf
Whitefish B., *Michigan* 40 Db
Whitefish Falls, *Ontario* 34 Jf
Whitefish L., *Alberta* 36 Ed
Whitefish L., *N.W.T.* 38 Ud
Whitefish L., *Ontario* 37 Nb
White Fox, *Saskatchewan* 37 Ne
Whitefox R., *Sask.* 37 Ne
White Gull Cr., *Sask.* 37 Ne
Whitehall, *Michigan* 40 Cd
Whitehall, *New York* 40 Kd
Whitehaven, *England* 63 Ef
Whitehorse, *Y.T.* 38 Fe
White I., *N.W.T.* 31 Ld
White L., *Louisiana* 49 Lh
White L., *Ontario* 34 Ed
White L., *Ontario* 35 Og
White Lake, *Ontario* 35 Og
Whitemouth, *Manitoba* 36 Fa
Whitemouth L. & R., *Man.* 36 Fa
Whitemud, R., *Alberta* 39 Pg
White Nile, *Sudan* 97 Gb
White Oil Springs. *See* Naft
White Otter L., *Ontario* 36 La
White Pass, *B.C.* 38 Ff
White Plains, *New York* 44 Db
White R., *Arkansas* 49 Ld
White R., *B.C.* 36 Bh
White R., *Indiana* 45 Da
White R., *Ontario* 34 Ed
White R., *S. Dakota* 42 Fc
White R., *Utah/Colorado* 48 Cb
White River, *Ontario* 34 Ed
White River, *S. Dakota* 46 Gd
White River Junction, *Vt.* 43 Mc
White River Lake, *Texas* 48 Gf
White Rock, *B.C.* 39 Jm
White Russia. *See* Byelorussia
Whitesail Reach, *B.C.* 39 Kj
Whitesand, R., *Alberta* 38 Pf
Whitesand R., *Sask.* 37 Pg
Whites Brook, *N.B.* 32 Ef
White Sea. *See* Beloye More
Whiteshell Prov. Park, *Man.* 36 Fa
Whitestone L., *Manitoba* 37 Ub
Whitestone R., *Y.T.* 38 Db
White Sulphur Springs, *Montana* 46 Bb
Whiteswan Ls., *Sask.* 37 Md
White Volta, R., *Ghana* 98 Eg
Whitewater L., *Ontario* 34 Ab
Whitewood, *Sask.* 37 Ph
Whiting, *New Jersey* 40 Jf
Whitla, *Alberta* 36 Fj
Whitney, *Ontario* 35 Mg
Whitney, L., *Texas* 49 Jg
Whitney, Mt., *California* 47 Dg
Whittier, *California* 47 Dj
Wholdaia L., *N.W.T.* 38 Ve
Whycocomagh, *N.S.* 33 Lh
Wiarton, *Ontario* 34 Jh
Wichita, *Kansas* 49 Jd
Wichita Falls, *Texas* 42 Ge
Wichita Mts., *Oklahoma* 49 He
Wichita R., *Texas* 49 Hf
Wick, *Scotland* 62 Eb
Wickenden, L., *Quebec* 32 Kd
Wickham, *Quebec* 35 Sg
Wickliffe, *Missouri* 49 Nd
Wicklow, *Eire* 63 Ch
Wicklow Head, *Eire* 63 Ch
Wicklow Mts., *Eire* 63 Cg
Widdifield, *Ontario* 35 Lf
Wielbark, *Poland* 69 Jb
Wielczka, *Poland* 69 Jd
Wieleń, *Poland* 69 Gb
Wieluń, *Poland* 69 Hc
Wien, *Austria* 69 Gd
Wiener Neustadt, *Austria* 69 Ge
Wiesbaden, *West Germany* 68 Cc
Wiesen, *Switzerland* 65 Eb
Wigan, *England* 63 Fg
Wight, I. of, *England* 63 Gk
Wignes L., *N.W.T.* 38 Ve
Wigtown, *Scotland* 63 Ef
Wigtown B., *Scotland* 63 Ef
Wijhe, *Netherlands* 64 Eb
Wijk-bij-Duurstede, *Netherlands* 64 Dc
Wikwemikong, *Ontario* 34 Jg
Wil, *Switzerland* 65 Ea
Wilberforce, *Ontario* 35 Mg
Wilcannia, *N.S.W.* 57 Hf
Wilcox, *Saskatchewan* 37 Nh
Wild Bight, *Nfld.* 33 Rd
Wild Goose, *Ontario* 37 Ob
Wild Hay, *Alberta* 39 Pj
Wildhorn, *Switzerland* 65 Cb
Wildnest L., *Sask.* 37 Pd
Wildstrubel, *Switz.* 65 Cb
Wildwood, *Alberta* 36 Be
Wildwood, *Florida* 45 Ff
Wildwood, *New Jersey* 40 Jf
Wilgar, *Ontario* 34 Eb
Wilhelm, Mt., *Papua New Guinea* 59 Pj
Wilhelmsburg, *W. Germany* 68 Cb
Wilhelmshaven, *W. Ger.* 68 Cb
Wilkes Barre, *Pennsylvania* 44 Cb
Wilkesboro, *N. Carolina* 45 Gb
Wilkes Coast, *Antarctica* 104 Jc
Wilkes Ld., *Antarctica* 104 Hb
Wilkie, *Saskatchewan* 36 Jf
Wilkin's Str., *Antarctica* 104 Sb
Wilkolaz, *Poland* 69 Kc
Willamette R., *Oregon* 47 Bc
Willcox, *Arizona* 48 Cf
Willemsdorp, *Netherlands* 64 Cc
Willemstad, *Curaçao* 52 Da
Willemstad, *Netherlands* 64 Cc
Willesden Green, *Alberta* 36 Cf
Williambury, *W. Australia* 56 Bd
William Creek, *S. Australia* 57 Ge
William L., *Manitoba* 37 Se
William R., *Saskatchewan* 39 Tf
Williams, *Arizona* 48 Ae
Williamsburg, *Kentucky* 45 Eb
Williamsburg, *Virginia* 45 Jb
Williamsford, *Ontario* 34 Jh
Williams Lake, *B.C.* 39 Mj
Williamsport, *Indiana* 49 Ob
Williamsport, *Nfld.* 33 Qc
Williamsport, *Pennsylvania* 44 Bb
Williamston, *N. Carolina* 45 Jc
Williamsville, *Missouri* 45 Bb
Willimantic, *Connecticut* 44 Db
Willingdon, *Alberta* 36 Ee
Willingdon, Mt., *Alberta* 39 Pk
Willingham Hills, *N.W.T.* 38 Rc
Williston, *Cape Province* 95 Cf
Williston, *N. Dakota* 46 Fa
Williston Lake, *B.C.* 39 Lg
Willmar, *Minnesota* 46 Kc
Willmar, *Saskatchewan* 37 Pj
Willmore Wilderness Provincial Park, *Alberta* 39 Oj
Willow, R., *B.C.* 39 Mj
Willowbrook, *Sask.* 37 Pg
Willow Bunch, *Sask.* 37 Mj
Willow Cr., *Alberta* 36 Dh
Willow Creek, *Montana* 46 Bc
Willowlake, R., *N.W.T.* 38 Nd
Willowmore, *Cape Province* 95 Cf
Willow Run, airport, *Mich.* 34 Gk
Willows, *Saskatchewan* 37 Mj
Willow Springs, *Missouri* 49 Ld
Wills Mt., *Pennsylvania* 44 Ac
Wilmette, *Illinois* 40 Cd
Wilmington, *California* 47 Dj
Wilmington, *Delaware* 44 Cc
Wilmington, *N. Carolina* 45 Jc
Wilnis, *Netherlands* 64 Cb
Wilno, *Ontario* 35 Ng
Wilson, *N. Carolina* 45 Jc
Wilson, C., *N.W.T.* 31 Ld
Wiltshire, *England* 63 Fj
Wiluna, *W. Australia* 56 De
Wimapedi, L., *Manitoba* 37 Sc
Wimborne, *Alberta* 36 Dg
Winagami L., *Alberta* 36 Ac
Winagami Provincial Park, *Alberta* 36 Ac
Winburg, *Orange Free State* 95 De
Winchendon, *Massachusetts* 40 Kd
Winchester, *England* 63 Gj
Winchester, *Kentucky* 45 Ea
Winchester, *Ontario* 35 Pg
Winchester, *Tennessee* 45 Dc
Winchester, *Virginia* 44 Ac
Wind, R., *Y.T.* 38 Fc
Windarra, *W. Australia* 56 De
Wind Cave Nat. Park, *S. Dakota* 46 Fd
Windermere, *Ontario* 34 Ge
Windermere & L., *England* 63 Ff
Windhoek, *Namibia* 95 Bd
Windigo, *Quebec* 35 Re
Windom, *Minnesota* 46 Kd
Windorah, *Queensland* 57 He
Wind River Pk., *Wyo.* 42 Ec
Windsor, *Colorado* 48 Eb
Windsor, *Connecticut* 44 Db
Windsor, *England* 63 Gj
Windsor, *Missouri* 49 Lc
Windsor, *N. Carolina* 45 Jb
Windsor, *Newfoundland* 33 Re
Windsor, *Nova Scotia* 32 Hj
Windsor, *Ontario* 34 Hk
Windsor, *Quebec* 35 Tg
Windsor, *Vermont* 40 Kd
Windthorst, *Saskatchewan* 37 Ph
Windward Is., *West Indies* 51 Gd
Windward Pass, *West Indies* 51 Ec
Windy L., *Saskatchewan* 37 Pd
Windy Pt., *N.W.T.* 38 Qe
Winefred L. & R., *Alta.* 36 Gc
Winfield, *Alberta* 36 Cf
Winfield, *Kansas* 49 Jd
Winfield, *W. Virginia* 45 Ga
Wingene, *Belgium* 64 Bc
Wingham, *Ontario* 34 Jj
Winisk, *Ontario* 31 Lf
Winisk, R., *Ontario* 31 Lg
Winisk L., *Ontario* 31 Lg
Winkler, *Manitoba* 37 Uj
Winnebago, *Minnesota* 46 Kd
Winnebago L., *Wisconsin* 40 Bc
Winnemucca, *Nevada* 47 Ee
Winnemucca L., *Nevada* 47 De
Winner, *S. Dakota* 46 Hd
Winnett, *Montana* 46 Cb
Winnfield, *Louisiana* 49 Lg
Winniandy, *Alberta* 39 Oj
Winnifred, *Alberta* 36 Fj
Winning Pool, *W. Australia* 56 Bd
Winnipeg, *Manitoba* 37 Uj
Winnipeg, L., *Manitoba* 37 Uf
Winnipeg Beach, *Man.* 37 Uh
Winnipeg Intl., airport, *Man.* 36 Da
Winnipegosis, *Man.* 37 Sg
Winnipegosis, L., *Man.* 37 Rf
Winnipesaukee, L., *N.H.* 40 Ld
Winnsboro, *S. Carolina* 45 Gc
Winona, *Minnesota* 46 Mc
Winschoten, *Netherlands* 64 Ea
Winslow, *Arizona* 48 Be
Winsted, *Connecticut* 44 Db
Winston Salem, *N. Carolina* 45 Gb
Winter, *Saskatchewan* 36 Hf
Winter Harb., *N.W.T.* 30 Hc
Winterhaven, *California* 47 Fj
Winter Haven, *Florida* 45 Gf
Wintering L., *Manitoba* 37 Uc
Winterport, *Maine* 32 Cj
Winterset, *Iowa* 49 Kb
Winterswijk, *Netherlands* 64 Ec
Winterthur, *Switzerland* 65 Da
Winterton, *Nfld.* 33 Tf
Winton, *New Zealand* 55 Bg
Winton, *Queensland* 57 Hd
Wirt, *Minnesota* 46 Lb
Wisbech, *England* 63 Hh
Wisconsin, *U.S.A.* 43 Hc
Wisconsin R., *Wisconsin* 40 Bc
Wisconsin Rapids, *Wisc.* 40 Bc
Wise, *Virginia* 45 Fb
Wiseton, *Saskatchewan* 36 Kg
Wishart, *Saskatchewan* 37 Og
Wishek, *N. Dakota* 46 Hb
Wisla, *Poland* 69 Jc
Wismar, *East Germany* 68 Db
Wistaria, *B.C.* 39 Kj
Wister, L., *Oklahoma* 49 Ke
Witchai L., *Manitoba* 37 Vc
Witchekan L., *Sask.* 36 Ke
Witham R., *England* 63 Gg
Withlacoochee B., *Florida* 43 Kf
Witless Bay, *Nfld.* 33 Uf
Witry, *Belgium* 64 De
Witten, *West Germany* 68 Bc
Wittenberg, *East Germany* 68 Ec
Wittenberge, *East Germany* 68 Db
Wittenoom, *Western Aust.* 56 Cd
Wittingen, *West Germany* 68 Db
Wittstock, *East Germany* 68 Eb
Wivenhoe, *Manitoba* 37 Wb
Wloclawek, *Poland* 69 Hb
Woerden, *Netherlands* 64 Cb
Wognum, *Netherlands* 64 Db
Wohlen, *Switzerland* 65 Da
Woito, *Ontario* 35 Ng
Wokam, *Indonesia* 83 Km
Woking, *Alberta* 39 Oh
Wolbrom, *Poland* 69 Hc
Woleai, *Caroline Islands* 102 Dg
Wolf, R., *Y.T.* 38 Ge
Wolf Bay, *Quebec* 33 Mc
Wolfe, *Saskatchewan* 36 Jf
Wolfeboro, *New Hampshire* 40 Ld
Wolfe City, *Texas* 49 Jf
Wolfe Island, *Ontario* 35 Oh
Wolfenbüttel, *W. Germany* 68 Db
Wolfe's Cove, *Quebec* 35 Sc
Wolf L., *Alberta* 36 Gd
Wolf L., *Y.T.* 38 He
Wolf Point, *Montana* 46 Ea
Wolfsberg, *Austria* 68 Fe
Wolfville, *Nova Scotia* 32 Hh
Wolgast, *East Germany* 68 Ea
Wolhusen, *Switzerland* 65 Ca
Wollal, *W. Australia* 56 Dc
Wollaston, C., *N.W.T.* 38 Pa
Wollaston Foreland, *Greenland* 41 Mb
Wollaston Is., *Chile* 54 Cj
Wollaston L., *Sask.* 30 Jf
Wollaston Lake, *Sask.* 39 Wf
Wollaston Pen., *N.W.T.* 38 Pa
Wollongong, *N.S.W.* 57 Kf
Wolseley, *Manitoba* 37 Oh
Wolstenholme C., *Quebec* 31 Me
Wolvega, *Netherlands* 64 Eb
Wolverhampton, *England* 63 Fh
Wolverine, R., *N.W.T.* 38 Ha
Wolvertem, *Belgium* 64 Cd
Wolverton, *England* 63 Gh
Woman, R., *Ontario* 34 He
Woman River, *Ontario* 34 He
Wonowon, *B.C.* 30 Gf
Wŏnsan, *Korea* 82 Jc
Wonthaggi, *Victoria* 57 Jg
Woodbridge, *Ontario* 35 Lj
Wood Buffalo Nat. Park, *Alberta/N.W.T.* 38 Qf
Woodbury, *New Jersey* 44 Cc
Woodfibre, *B.C.* 39 Ml
Wood Islands, *P.E.I.* 32 Kh
Wood L., *Manitoba* 37 Ua
Wood L., *Saskatchewan* 37 Oc
Woodlands, *Manitoba* 37 Uh
Woodlark I., *Papua New Guinea* 57 Ka
Wood Mountain, *Sask.* 36 Lj
Wood Mt., *Sask.* 36 Lj
Wood Mt., *Y.T.* 38 Ce
Woodridge, *Manitoba* 36 Fa
Woodroffe, Mt., *S. Australia* 56 Fe
Woodrow, *Saskatchewan* 36 Lj
Woods, L., *N. Terr.* 56 Fc
Woods, L. of the, *Minnesota/Ontario* 36 Ha
Woods Hole, *Massachusetts* 44 Eb
Woodside, *Utah* 48 Bc
Woodside, *Victoria* 57 Jg
Woodstock, *Illinois* 40 Bd
Woodstock, *N.B.* 32 Eg
Woodstock, *Ontario* 34 Kj
Woodstock, *Vermont* 40 Kd
Woodstock, *Virginia* 44 Ac
Woodville, *New Zealand* 55 Ed
Woodville, *Ontario* 35 Mh
Woodward, *Oklahoma* 49 Hd
Woodwards Cove, *N.B.* 32 Fj
Woody Point, *Nfld.* 33 Pd
Woody R., *Manitoba* 37 Qf
Woolford Prov. Park, *Alta.* 36 Dj
Woomera, *S. Australia* 57 Gf
Woonsocket, *Rhode Island* 44 Eb
Woonsocket, *S. Dakota* 46 Hc
Wooramel, *W. Australia* 56 Be
Worcester, *Cape Province* 95 Bf
Worcester, *England* 63 Fh
Worcester, *Massachusetts* 40 Ld
Wordsworth, *Sask.* 37 Pj
Workington, *England* 63 Ef
Workum, *Netherlands* 64 Db
Worland, *Wyoming* 46 Cc
Worms, *West Germany* 68 Cd
Worthington, *Minnesota* 46 Kd
Worthington, *Ontario* 40 Fb
Wostok, *Alberta* 36 Ee
Wotho, *Marshall Islands* 102 Ff
Wotton, *Quebec* 35 Tg
Woudenberg, *Netherlands* 64 Db
Woudrichem, *Netherlands* 64 Cc
Wour, *Chad* 99 Jd
Wouw, *Netherlands* 64 Cc
Wowoni, *Indonesia* 83 Hl
Wrangel I. *See* Vrangelya Ostrov.
Wrangell, *Alaska* 43 Zm
Wrangell, Mt., *Alaska* 43 Yl
Wrath C., *Scotland* 62 Db
Wray, *Colorado* 48 Eb
Wren, *Oregon* 36 Be
Wrentham, *Alberta* 36 Ej
Wrexham, *Wales* 63 Fg
Wright, *Quebec* 35 Of
Wrightsville, *Georgia, U.S.A.* 45 Fd
Wrightsville Beach, *N. Carolina* 45 Jc
Wrigley, *N.W.T.* 38 Md
Writing-on-Stone Prov. Park, *Alberta* 36 Fj

Wroclaw, Poland 69 Gc
Wrong L., Manitoba 37 Vf
Wroxton, Saskatchewan 37 Qg
Wubin, W. Australia 56 Cf
Wuchang, China 82 Jb
Wuchang, China 85 Gg
Wuchuan, China 84 Eb
Wudi, China 84 Hd
Wugang, China 85 Ej
Wuhai, China 84 Cc
Wuhan, China 84 Gg
Wuhsien. See Suzhou
Wuhu, China 84 Jg
Wukari, Nigeria 99 Gg
Wular L., Kashmir 90 Dc
Wuntho, Burma 89 Jd
Wuppertal, West Germany 68 Bc
Wuqiang, China 84 Gc
Württemberg, W. Germany 68 Cd
Wurung, Queensland 57 Hc
Würzburg, West Germany 68 Cd
Wurzen, East Germany 68 Ec
Wusuli Jiang, U.S.S.R/China 82 Ka
Wuta, Inner Mongolia, China 84 Cc
Wutsin. See Changzhou
Wuwei, China 84 Ad
Wuxi, China 84 Kg
Wuxiang, China 84 Fd
Wuxing, China 84 Kg
Wuyi Shan, China 85 Hj
Wuyuan, China 84 Db
Wuzhi Shan, Hainan, China 82 Eg
Wuzhou, China 85 El
Wyandotte, Michigan 40 Ed
Wyandra, Queensland 57 Je
Wye R., England-Wales 63 Fh
Wyk, West Germany 68 Ca
Wymark, Saskatchewan 36 Kh
Wyndham, New Zealand 55 Bg
Wyndham, W. Australia 56 Ec
Wynne, Arkansas 49 Me
Wynniatt B., N.W.T. 30 Hc
Wynyard, Saskatchewan 37 Ng
Wyoming, Ontario 34 Hk
Wyoming, U.S.A. 42 Ec
Wyoming Pk., Wyoming 46 Bd
Wysokie Mazowieckie, Poland 69 Kb
Wyszkow, Poland 69 Jb
Wytheville, Virginia 45 Gb

X

95 Ee
Xánthi, Greece 76 Ed
Xanxere, Brazil 54 Fc
Xapuri, Brazil 52 Df
Xenia, Montana 46 Ba
Xeró. See Peristéra I.
Xiachuan Dao, China 85 Fm
Xiajiang, China 85 Dk
Xiamen, China 85 Jk
Xi'an, China 84 De
Xiangtan, China 85 Fj
Xiangyin, China 85 Fh
Xianyang, China 84 De
Xiapu, China 85 Jj
Xichang, China 82 De
Xieng Khouang, Laos 87 Cc
Xigazê, China 89 Gc
Xi Jiang, China 82 Ff
Xilókastron, Greece 77 De
Xinchang, China 85 Kh
Xinghe, China 84 Fb
Xinghua, China 84 Jf
Xingtai, China 84 Gd
Xingu, Brazil 52 De
Xingyi, China 85 Bk
Xingzi, China 85 Hh
Xinhe, China 84 Gd
Xinhua, China 85 Ej
Xining, China 82 Dc
Xinning, China 85 Ej
Xin Xian, China 82 Fc
Xinxiang, China 84 Fe
Xinyang, China 82 Fd
Xinyang, China 84 Gf
Xique Xique, Brazil 53 Jf
Xuancheng, China 84 Jg
Xuanhua, China 84 Gb
Xuchang, China 84 Fe
Xuzhou, China 84 He

Y

Ya'an, China 82 Dd
Yaate, Lebanon 94 Ec
Yablonovy Khrebet, U.S.S.R. 79 Lc

Yabrud, Syria 94 Ed
Yadong, China 89 Gc
Yadong, China 89 Gc
Yagvildino, U.S.S.R. 81 Nc
Yahk, British Columbia 39 Pl
Yakima, Washington 47 Cb
Yako, Upper Volta 98 Ef
Yakoma, Zaire 96 Ed
Yaku jima, Japan 86 Aj
Yakutsk, U.S.S.R. 79 Mb
Yale, Michigan 40 Ed
Yalgoo, W. Australia 56 Ce
Yalinga, Cent. Afr. Rep. 96 Ec
Yalong Jiang, China 82 Dd
Yalouke, Cent. Afr. Rep. 96 Dc
Yalta, U.S.S.R. 80 Jj
Yalu, China 82 Ha
Yalu Jiang, China 82 Hb
Yalutorovsk, U.S.S.R. 78 Fc
Yamagata, Japan 86 Ge
Yamaguchi, Japan 86 Bg
Yamal, Polnostrov, U.S.S.R. 78 Fa
Yamaska, Quebec 35 Sg
Yamba L., N.W.T. 38 Sc
Yambol, Bulgaria 76 Fc
Yamdena, Indonesia 83 Km
Yamethin, Burma 89 Jd
Yampol, Ukraine 80 Fg
Yampol, Ukraine 80 Eg
Yamsk, U.S.S.R. 79 Qc
Yamuna R., India 91 Aa
Yamzho Yumco, China 89 Hc
Yanam, India 89 Fe
Yan'an, China 84 Dd
Yanaoca, Peru 52 Cf
Yanbu 'al Baḥr, Arabia 92 Ce
Yancheng, China 84 Kf
Yandoon, Burma 89 Je
Yangchow. See Jiangdu
Yangchüan, China 84 Gd
Yanggao, China 84 Fb
Yangjiang, China 82 Ff
Yangku. See Taiyuan
Yangquan, China 84 Fd
Yangtze Kiang. See Chang Jiang
Yangyuan, China 84 Gb
Yangzhou, China 84 Jf
Yanji, China 82 Jb
Yankton, S. Dakota 46 Jd
Yannina. See Ioannina
Yantai, China 84 Kd
Yanyuan, China 82 De
Yanzhou, China 84 He
Yaouiba, Bolivia 52 Eh
Yaoundé, Cameroun 99 Hh
Yap, Pacific Ocean 102 Cg
Yapen I., Irian Jaya 83 Ll
Yaraka, Queensland 57 Hd
Yarda, Chad 99 Je
Yarensk, U.S.S.R. 78 Db
Yarim, Yemen 92 Dg
Yarmouth, Nova Scotia 32 Fk
Yaroslavl, U.S.S.R. 80 Lc
Yartsevo, U.S.S.R. 79 Jb
Yarumal, Colombia 52 Bb
Yarylgach, U.S.S.R. 80 Hj
Yasanyama, Zaire 96 Ed
Yasin, Kashmir 90 Cb
Yasothon, Thailand 83 Dg
Yass, New South Wales 57 Jf
Yatakala, Niger 98 Ff
Yates R., Alberta 38 Ff
Yathkyed L., N.W.T. 31 Ke
Yatsushiro, Japan 86 Bh
Yauca, Peru 52 Cg
Yauri, Peru 52 Cf
Yautepec, Mexico 50 Ed
Yawata. See Kitakyūshū
Yazd, Iran 93 Fc
Yazdan, Iran 93 Hc
Yazd-e-Khvast, Iran 93 Fc
Yazoo City, Mississippi 49 Mf
Ybbs, Austria 68 Fd
Ye, Burma 89 Je
Yecheng, China 90 Eb
Yecla, Spain 71 Ec
Yecora, Mexico 50 Cb
Yéfira, Greece 77 Dd
Yefremov, U.S.S.R. 80 Le
Yegros, Paraguay 54 Ec
Yehcheng. See Karghalik
Yelabuga, U.S.S.R. 81 Lc
Yelan, U.S.S.R. 81 Fe
Yelatma, U.S.S.R. 81 Ec
Yeldyak, U.S.S.R. 81 Nc
Yelizarovo, U.S.S.R. 78 Fb
Yellandu, India 88 Fe
Yell I., Scotland 62 Ja

Yellow Creek, Sask. 37 Mf
Yellow Grass, Sask. 37 Nj
Yellowhead Pass, Alberta 39 Oj
Yellowknife, N.W.T. 38 Qd
Yellow R. See Huang He
Yellow Sea. See Huang Hai
Yellowstone, L., Wyoming 42 Dc
Yellowstone Nat. Park, Wyoming 46 Bc
Yellowstone R., Montana 46 Eb
Yelverton B., N.W.T. 31 La
Yelwa, Nigeria 98 Ff
Yemanzhelinka, U.S.S.R. 81 Qc
Yemen, S.W. Asia 92 Df
Yemen, People's Dem. Rep. of. See S. Yemen
Yenakiyevo, Ukraine 80 Lg
Yen-Bai, Vietnam 87 Cb
Yenbo. See Yanbu 'al Bahr
Yenchih. See Mingshui
Yenchow. See Jiande
Yenchow. See Yanzhou
Yengisar, China 90 Ea
Yenisey, R., U.S.S.R. 78 Hb
Yeniseysk, U.S.S.R. 79 Jc
Yeniseyskiy Zaliv, U.S.S.R. 78 Ha
Yenping. See Nanping
Yeovil, England 63 Fk
Yeppoon, Queensland 57 Kd
Yeráki, Greece 77 Df
Yerbogachen, U.S.S.R. 79 Kb
Yerevan, Armenia 78 Dd
Yerofey Pavlovich, U.S.S.R. 79 Mc
Yeropol, U.S.S.R. 79 Rb
Yerupaia, Peru 52 Bf
Yeshbum, S. Yemen 92 Eg
Yessey, U.S.S.R. 79 Kb
Yeste, Spain 71 Dc
Yesud Ha Ma'ala, Israel 94 Dd
Ye-u, Burma 89 Jd
Yeu, I. d', France 72 Bc
Ye Xian, China 84 Jd
Yeysk, U.S.S.R. 78 Cd
Yhu, Paraguay 54 Ec
Yi, Uruguay 54 Ed
Yianisadhes, Crete 77 Fg
Yiannitsá, Greece 77 Dd
Yiáros. See Yioúra
Yibin, China 85 Bh
Yibna, Israel 94 Cf
Yichang, China 84 Eg
Yicheng, China 84 Fg
Yichun, China 85 Gj
Yidha, Greece 77 Dd
Yidu, China 84 Jd
Yinchuan, China 84 Cc
Yinchwan, China 84 Cc
Yingchisha. See Yengisar
Yingchow. See Fuyang
Yingde, China 85 Fk
Yingkou, China 84 Lb
Ying Xian, China 84 Fc
Yining, China 78 Hd
Yinjiang, China 85 Dh
Yin Shan, China 84 Cb
Yioúra, Greece 77 Ef
Yirga-Alam, Ethiopia 97 Hc
Yishan, China 85 Dk
Yithion, Greece 77 Df
Yi Xian, China 84 Gc
Yiyang, China 85 Hh
Yocalla, Bolivia 52 Dg
Yochow. See Yueyang
Yogan, Co., Chile 54 Ch
Yoho Nat. Park, B.C. 39 Pk
Yokkaichi, Japan 86 Eg
Yoko, Cameroun 99 Hg
Yokohama, Japan 86 Fg
Yokosuku, Japan 86 Ge
Yokote, Japan 86 Gf
Yola, Nigeria 99 Hg
Yonago, Japan 86 Cg
Yonezawa, Japan 86 Gf
Yongfu, China 85 Dk
Yongji, China 84 Ee
Yongnian, China 84 Gd
Yongshun, China 85 Dh
Yongxin, China 85 Gj
Yonker, Saskatchewan 36 Hf
Yonkers, New York 44 Db
Yonne, France 72 Ec
York, Alabama 46 Cd
York, England 63 Gg
York, Nebraska 49 Jb
York, Pennsylvania 44 Bc
York, W. Australia 56 Cf
York, C., Queensland 57 Hb
York C., Greenland 41 Qb
Yorke Pen., S. Australia 57 Gf
York Factory, Manitoba 31 Kf

York Pt., Newfoundland 33 Rb
York R., Quebec 32 Ge
York R., Virginia 45 Jb
Yorkshire Moors, England 63 Gf
Yorkshire Wolds, England 63 Gf
York Sound, W. Australia 56 Db
Yorkton, Saskatchewan 37 Pg
Yorktown, Virginia 45 Jb
Yoro, Honduras 51 Bd
Yosemite Nat. Park, Cal. 47 Dg
Yoshkar Ola, U.S.S.R. 81 Hb
Youghal, Eire 63 Bj
Youghiogheny River Res., Pa. 44 Ac
Youkadouma, Cameroon 99 Jh
Young, New South Wales 57 Jf
Young, Saskatchewan 37 Mg
Young I., Balleny Islands 104 Lc
Youngstown, Alberta 36 Fg
Youngstown, Ohio 40 Fe
Yount Pk., Wyoming 46 Bd
Youyang, China 85 Dh
Youyu, China 84 Fb
Yozgat, Turkey 92 Bb
Ypsilanti, Michigan 40 Ed
Yreka, California 47 Be
Yssingeaux, France 73 Fd
Ystad, Sweden 67 Ej
Ytterhogdal, Sweden 66 Fe
Yüanchow. See Ichun
Yüanchow. See Zhijiang
Yüanling, China 85 Eh
Yucamani, Mt., Peru 52 Cg
Yucatán, Mexico 50 Gc
Yucatán Chan., Mex./Cuba 51 Bb
Yuci, China 84 Fd
Yueyang, China 85 Fh
Yugoslavia, Central Europe 74 Fc
Yugovsk, U.S.S.R. 81 Nb
Yuhuan, China 85 Kh
Yukhnov, U.S.S.R. 80 Jd
Yukon, R., Alaska/Y.T. 30 De
Yukon Territory, Canada 30 Fe
Yüksekova, Turkey 92 Db
Yulin, China 84 Dc
Yulin, Hainan, China 85 Dn
Yuma, Arizona 42 De
Yuma, Colorado 48 Fb
Yumen, China 79 Je
Yungchow. See Lingling
Yungki. See Jilin
Yungkia. See Wenzhou
Yungning. See Nanning
Yungping. See Lulong
Yunxi, China 84 Ef
Yun Xian, China 84 Ef
Yurievets, U.S.S.R. 81 Fb
Yurimaguas, Peru 52 Be
Yurlovka, U.S.S.R. 81 Hd
Yurmysh, U.S.S.R. 81 Rb
Yuö Shan, Taiwan 85 Kl
Yushu, China 82 Cd
Yuta, Jordan 94 Df
Yuti, Bolivia 52 Eg
Yu Xian, China 84 Gc
Yverdon, Switzerland 65 Bb

Z

Zaachila, Mexico 50 Ed
Zaandam, Netherlands 64 Cb
Zabaykal'sk, U.S.S.R. 79 Ld
Zabid, Yemen 92 Dg
Zäbol, Iran 93 Hc
Zabrze, Poland 69 Hc
Zacapa, Guatemala 50 Ge
Zacapoaxtla, Mexico 50 Ed
Zacatecas, Mexico 50 Dc
Zadar, Yugoslavia 74 Ec
Zadonsk, U.S.S.R. 80 Le
Zafarwal, Pakistan 90 Dd
Zafra, Spain 70 Bc
Zagazig, Egypt 99 Mb
Zagreb, Yugoslavia 74 Ec
Zähedän, Iran 93 Hd
Zahle, Lebanon 94 Dd
Zahxi Co, China 89 Fb
Zaidiya, Yemen 92 Df
Zainsk, U.S.S.R. 81 Lc
Zaire, C. Africa 96 Ee
Zaire (Zaire/Congo 96 Ed
Zaječar, Yugoslavia 76 Dc
Zakho, Iraq 92 Db
Zakin, Afghanistan 93 Hc
Zákinthos, Greece 77 Cf
Zakroczym, Poland 69 Jb
Zákros, Crete 77 Fg
Zălău, Romania 69 Ke
Zalew Wiślany, Poland 69 Ha
Zalma, Missouri 45 Bb

Zaltbommel, Netherlands 64 Dc
Zama L., Alberta 39 Of
Zambeze (Zambezi), Mozambique 95 Ec
Zambezi, S.E. Africa 95 Cc
Zambezi, Zambia 96 Eg
Zambia, Central Africa 95 Db
Zamboanga, Philippines 83 Hj
Zamora, Ecuador 52 Bd
Zamora, Spain 70 Cb
Zamora de Hidalgo, Mexico 50 Dd
Zanda, China 88 Eb
Zandvoort, Netherlands 64 Cb
Zanesville, Ohio 40 Ef
Zangla, Kashmir 90 Ed
Zanjan, Iran 92 Eb
Zante. See Zákinthos
Zanthus, W. Australia 56 Df
Zanzibar, East Africa 97 Hf
Zaozhuang, China 84 He
Zapala, Argentina 54 Be
Zapata Pen., Cuba 51 Cb
Zaporozh'ye, Ukraine 80 Jh
Zara. See Zadar
Zara, Turkey 92 Cb
Zaragoza, Colombia 52 Cb
Zaragoza, Mexico 50 Ec
Zaragoza, Spain 71 Eb
Zaragozo, Mexico 50 Db
Zarand, Iran 93 Gc
Zarasai, Lithuania 67 Mj
Zarauz, Spain 71 Da
Zaraza, Venezuela 52 Db
Zaria, Nigeria 98 Gf
Zarki, Poland 69 Hc
Zarqa, Jordan 94 Ee
Zaruma, Ecuador 52 Bd
Zarzis, Tunisia 99 Hb
Žatec, Czechoslovakia 68 Ec
Zavitinsk, U.S.S.R. 79 Mc
Zawiercie, Poland 69 Hc
Zawilah, Libya 99 Jc
Zaysan, Kazakhstan 78 Hd
Zaysan, Oz., Kazakhstan 78 Hd
Zbaszyń, Poland 69 Fb
Zduńska Wola, Poland 69 Hc
Zealand. See Sjaelland
Zealandia, Saskatchewan 36 Kg
Zebak, Afghanistan 93 Kb
Zebdani, Syria 94 Ed
Zebid Qadhima, Arabia 92 Ce
Zeebrugge, Belgium 64 Bc
Zeeland, Netherlands 64 Bc
Zeerust, Transvaal 95 De
Zegharta, Lebanon 94 Dc
Zeila, Somalia 97 Jb
Zeist, Netherlands 64 Db
Zeitz, East Germany 68 Ec
Zele, Belgium 64 Cc
Zelenogradsk, Poland 69 Ja
Zelenogradsk, U.S.S.R. 67 Jj
Železná Ruda, Czech. 68 Ed
Zelma, Saskatchewan 37 Mg
Zelzate, Belgium 64 Bc
Zemio, Cent. African Rep. 99 Lg
Zemun, Yugoslavia 76 Cb
Zengcheng, China 85 Fl
Zenica, Yugoslavia 76 Ab
Zenon Park, Sask. 37 Oe
Zepce, Yugoslavia 76 Ab
Zermatt, Switzerland 65 Cb
Zernez, Switzerland 65 Fb
Zetland. See Shetland Is.
Zevenbergen, Netherlands 64 Cc
Zeya, U.S.S.R. 79 Mc
Zeyma, Arabia 92 De
Zgierz, Poland 69 Hc
Zgorzelec. See Görlitz
Zhangbei, China 84 Gb
Zhangjiakou, China 84 Gb
Zhangpu, China 85 Hk
Zhangye, China 82 Dc
Zhangzhou, China 85 Hk
Zhanjiang, China 85 Fl
Zhaoqing, China 85 Aj
Zhaotong, China 89 Fb
Zhari Namco, China 89 Fb
Zhdanov, Ukraine 80 Kh
Zhecheng, China 84 Ge
Zhejiang, China 85 Jh
Zhen'an, China 84 Df
Zhenba, China 84 Cf
Zhengding, China 84 Gc
Zhengzhou, China 84 Fe
Zhenhai, China 85 Kh
Zhenjiang, China 84 Jf
Zhenyuan, China 85 Dj
Zhigansk, U.S.S.R. 79 Mb
Zhijiang, China 85 Dj

Zhijin, China 85 Bj
Zhitomir, Ukraine 80 Ff
Zhmerinka, Ukraine 80 Fg
Zhongba, China 89 Fc
Zhongdian, China 82 Ce
Zhongning, China 84 Bd
Zhongshan, China 85 Ek
Zhong Xian, China 85 Dg
Zhongxiang, China 84 Fg
Zhoushan Dao, China 85 Lg
Zhuolu, China 84 Gb
Zhuo Xian, China 84 Gc
Zhuzhou, China 85 Fj
Ziarat, Pakistan 88 Cb
Zibo, China 84 Jd
Zidani Most, Yugoslavia 74 Eb
Zierikzee, Netherlands 64 Bc
Zigong, China 85 Bh
Zikhron Ya'aqoy, Israel 94 Ce
Zilaf, Syria 94 Fe
Zile, Turkey 92 Ca
Zilfi, Arabia 92 Dd
Žilina, Czechoslovakia 69 Hd
Zillah, Libya 99 Jc
Zima, U.S.S.R. 79 Kc
Zimapán, Mexico 50 Ec
Zimbabwe, S. Africa 95 Dc
Zindajan, Afghanistan 93 Hc
Zinder, Niger 99 Gf
Zingst, East Germany 68 Ea
Zinjibär, S. Yemen 92 Eg
Zion Nat. Park, Utah 47 Gg
Zipaquira, Colombia 52 Cb
Zira, India 90 De
Zirc, Hungary 69 Ge
Zitácuaro, Mexico 50 Dd
Zittau, East Germany 68 Fc
Ziya He, China 82 Gc
Ziya He, China 84 Hc
Ziyun, China 85 Ck
Zizers, Switzerland 65 Eb
Zlato'ust, U.S.S.R. 81 Pc
Zmeinogorsk, U.S.S.R. 78 Hc
Żnin, Poland 69 Gb
Znojmo, Czechoslovakia 69 Gd
Zofingen, Switzerland 65 Ca
Zöhab, Iran 92 Ec
Zoissa, Tanzania 97 Hf
Zolder, Belgium 64 Dc
Zollino, Italy 75 Ge
Zomba, Malawi 97 Hh
Zonguldak, Turkey 92 Ba
Zorita, Spain 70 Cc
Zoute, Het, Belgium 64 Bc
Zoutkamp, Netherlands 64 Ea
Zrenjanin, Yugoslavia 76 Cb
Zucker L., N.W.T. 38 Ud
Zuevka, U.S.S.R. 81 Kb
Zug, Switzerland 65 Da
Zuger See, Switzerland 65 Da
Zuid Beijerland, Netherlands 64 Cc
Zuider Zee. See IJsselmeer
Zuidland, Netherlands 64 Cc
Zuidwolde, Netherlands 64 Eb
Zújar, Emb. del, Spain 70 Cc
Zukur, Jab., Yemen 92 Dg
Zula, Ethiopia 97 Ha
Zumbo, Mozambique 95 Ec
Zumpango, Mexico 50 Ed
Zundert, Netherlands 64 Cc
Zungeru, Nigeria 98 Gg
Zunhua, China 84 Hb
Zuni Mts., New Mexico 48 Cc
Zunyi, China 85 Cj
Zuoquan, China 84 Fd
Zurich, Ontario 34 Jj
Zurich, Switzerland 65 Da
Zürich, Switz. 65 Da
Zürich See, Switzerland 65 Da
Zurzach, Switzerland 65 Da
Zutphen, Netherlands 64 Eb
Zuwärah, Libya 99 Hb
Zwai L., Ethiopia 97 Hc
Zwartsluis, Netherlands 64 Eb
Zweeloo, Netherlands 64 Eb
Zweibrücken, W. Germany 68 Bd
Zweisimmen, Switzerland 65 Cb
Zwickau, East Germany 68 Ec
Zwoleń, Poland 69 Jc
Zwolle, Netherlands 64 Eb
Zyrardów, Poland 69 Jb
Zyryanka, U.S.S.R. 79 Qb
Zyryanovsk, Kazakhstan 78 Hd
Zyyi, Cyprus 94 Bc

TABLE OF DISTANCES

(STATUTE MILES)

	Vienna	Tokyo	Sydney	Singapore	San Francisco	Rome	Rio de Janeiro	Peking	Paris	Ottawa	Oslo	New York	Nairobi	Moscow	Madrid	London	Lisbon	Lagos	Johannesburg	Istanbul	Hong Kong	Hamburg	Geneva	Delhi	Darwin	Colombo	Cologne	Chicago	Cape Town	Canberra	Calcutta	Cairo	Buenos Aires	Brasilia	Bombay	Beirut	Bahamas (Nassau)	Baghdad
Athens	793	5,906	9,522	5,627	6,791	648	6,035	4,737	1,306	4,820	1,625	4,921	2,838	1,402	1,466	1,501	1,772	2,544	4,434	345	5,310	1,268	1,068	3,110	7,676	4,103	1,212	5,446	4,976	9,452	3,925	693	7,274	5,937	3,211	716	5,737	1,199
Baghdad	1,764	5,196	8,324	4,431	7,460	1,824	6,939	3,914	2,394	5,837	2,386	5,985	2,442	1,599	2,660	2,554	2,970	3,208	4,245	1,004	5,879	2,186	2,192	1,960	5,550	2,917	2,225	6,418	4,967	8,252	2,767	796	8,143	6,942	2,012	513	6,880	
Bahamas (Nassau)	5,126	7,596	9,477	10,613	2,761	5,072	4,025	7,868	4,486	1,404	4,670	1,096	7,779	5,673	4,301	4,335	4,102	5,454	7,879	5,879	9,070	4,740	4,692	8,364	10,399	9,783	4,666	1,297	7,492	9,590	9,037	6,382	4,318	3,457	8,792	6,449		
Beirut	1,390	5,594	8,813	4,934	7,299	1,361	6,481	4,336	1,981	5,483	2,123	5,604	2,430	1,533	2,180	2,163	2,484	2,786	4,173	614	4,752	1,849	1,761	2,470	6,998	3,388	1,847	6,090	4,811	8,739	3,279	350	7,700	6,458	2,508			
Bombay	3,703	4,183	6,312	2,432	8,392	3,831	8,339	2,945	4,353	7,569	4,129	7,786	2,819	3,139	4,671	4,481	4,981	4,737	4,327	2,995	2,672	4,057	4,173	709	4,508	949	4,151	8,042	5,116	6,246	1,035	2,698	9,287					
Brasilia	5,928	10,996	8,777	9,970	6,072	5,523	569	10,531	5,421	4,571	6,157	4,242	5,852	6,945	4,820	5,456	4,531	3,832	5,876	6,269	11,187	5,888	5,448	8,845	10,484	8,855	5,678	4,738	4,281	8,730	9,563	6,158	1,466					
Buenos Aires	7,358	11,403	7,311	9,863	6,465	6,945	1,213	12,001	6,878	5,639	7,624	5,303	6,473	8,388	6,266	6,919	5,985	5,044	4,933	7,616	11,467	7,348	6,892	9,815	9,117	9,167		5,624	4,279	7,272	10,279	7,366						
Cairo	1,470	5,939	8,950	5,129	7,458	1,321	6,153	4,678	1,992	5,508	2,271	5,602	2,203	1,809	2,080	2,195	2,365	2,443	3,893	763	5,048	1,946	1,755	2,736	7,206	3,513	1,900	6,137	4,507	8,863	3,533							
Calcutta	4,245	3,187	5,679	1,801	7,816	4,482	9,372	2,018	4,876	7,619	4,456	7,918	3,840	3,449	5,318	4,962	5,637	5,734	5,263	3,647	1,642	4,504	4,747	816	3,756	1,232	4,646	7,966	6,026	5,640								
Canberra	9,885	4,933	148	3,863	7,572	10,093	8,339	5,594	10,515	10,007	9,937	10,090	7,407	9,013	10,915	10,569	11,221	9,503	6,703	9,237	4,596	10,107	10,385	6,440	1,952	5,350	10,276	9,379	6,685									
Cape Town	5,673	9,147	6,830	6,001	10,252	5,251	3,784	8,040	8,026	6,503	8,000	7,804	2,548	6,313	5,339	6,010	5,333	2,974	790	5,224	7,372	6,074	5,597	5,769	6,962	4,890	5,903	8,520										
Chicago	4,701	6,307	9,233	9,355	1,851	4,826	5,309	6,585	4,140	651	4,044	723	8,022	4,956	4,192	3,945	3,997	5,980	8,712	5,476	7,788	4,249	4,385	7,472	9,345	8,977	4,248											
Cologne	463	5,809	10,292	6,441	5,600	677	5,942	4,860	247	3,072	639	3,765	4,008	1,284	883	331	1,149	3,069	5,475	1,239	5,729	227	323	3,862	8,334	5,102												
Colombo	4,658	4,261	5,430	1,698	9,047	4,739	8,508	3,208	5,295	8,530	5,098	8,755	3,019	4,106	5,569	5,416	5,870	5,247	3,916		2,523	5,105	5,019	1,513	3,746													
Darwin	8,008	3,365	1,960	2,079	7,652	8,238	9,970	3,727	9,683	9,983	7,990		7,304	7,062	9,070	8,619	8,847	6,602	7,404		2,656	8,151	8,480	4,571														
Delhi	3,448	3,640	6,483	2,580	7,692	3,669	8,740	2,352	4,091	7,055	3,724	7,304	3,366	2,702	4,509	4,183	4,828	5,019	4,980	2,833	2,344	3,732	3,946															
Geneva	507	6,094	10,425	6,523	5,823	444	5,680	5,104	245	3,754	962	3,852	3,782	1,498	627	468	929	3,069	5,189	1,190	5,918	540																
Hamburg	476	5,584	10,114	6,306	5,523	826	6,160	4,645	459	3,652	433	3,801	4,100	1,096	1,107	463	1,366	3,273	5,619	1,236	5,536																	
Hong Kong	5,418	1,787	4,585	1,606	6,900	5,764	10,998	1,213	5,986	7,722	5,341	8,055	5,441	4,444	6,540	5,993	6,847	7,357	6,661	4,989																		
Istanbul	779	5,575	9,297	5,383	6,709	843	6,377	4,394	1,393	5,003	1,522	4,872	2,966	1,106	1,686	1,562	2,003	2,849	4,637																			
Johannesburg	5,181	8,414	6,851	5,378	10,552	4,799	4,433	7,259	5,414	8,132	6,028	7,972	1,809	5,698	5,034	5,638	5,093	2,811																				
Lagos	2,971	8,380	9,647	6,935	7,801	2,494	3,745	7,119	2,913	5,363	3,704	5,249	2,381	3,886	2,380	3,109	2,359																					
Lisbon	1,432	6,931	11,294	7,385	5,669	1,161	4,794	6,009	894	3,345	1,694	3,358	4,023	2,419	319	972																						
London	791	5,959	10,575	6,760	5,354	908	5,750	5,077	215	3,323	723	3,441	4,250	1,565	774																							
Madrid	1,122	6,699	10,980	7,068	5,800	844	5,062	5,729	641	3,541	1,474	3,580	3,848	2,126																								
Moscow	1,033	4,656	9,020	5,249	5,862	1,491	7,169	3,607	1,542	4,437	1,012	4,660	3,944																									
Nairobi	3,624	6,992	7,541	4,631	9,600	3,346	5,553	5,719	4,026	7,369	4,456	7,352																										
New York	4,227	6,747	9,949	9,534	2,580	4,281	4,804	6,842	3,621	328	3,668																											
Oslo	848	5,237	9,918	6,251	5,189	1,253	6,486	4,374	822	3,480																												
Ottawa	4,095	6,427	9,863	9,213	2,440	4,176	5,131	6,509	3,518																													
Paris	648	6,037	10,534	6,666	5,578	689	5,688	5,116																														
Peking	4,636	1,308	5,558	2,770	5,922	5,068	10,764																															
Rio de Janeiro	6,136	11,538	8,403	9,781	6,612	5,713																																
Rome	477	6,135	10,137	6,224	6,250																																	
San Francisco	5,997	5,148	7,424	8,445																																		
Singapore	6,027	3,296	3,915																																			
Sydney	9,923	4,858																																				
Tokyo	5,681																																					

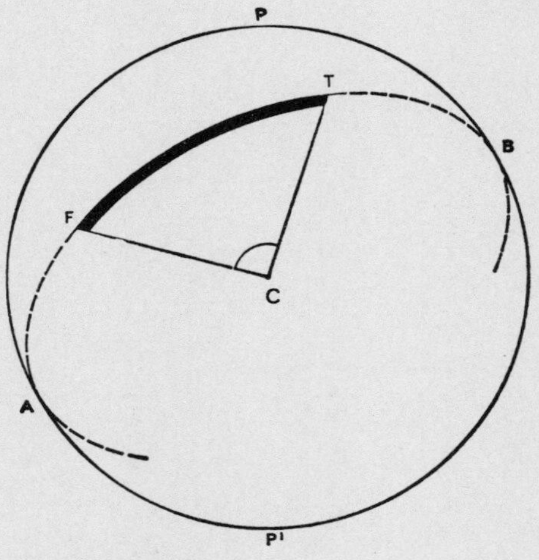

Miles	Kilometres
1	1·61
2	3·22
3	4·83
4	6·44
5	8·05
6	9·66
7	11·27
8	12·88
9	14·48
10	16·09
50	80·47
100	160·93
500	804·67
1,000	1609·34
5,000	8046·72
10,000	16093·44

P, P' = Poles
C = Centre of Earth
AB = Great Circle
FT = Two points on Great Circle AB. Thick line is the shortest distance between F and T

GREAT CIRCLE DISTANCES

Our Chart shows the shortest distance between any two places, calculated by the "great circle" method.

A great circle described on the surface of a globe is a circle which divides the globe into two exactly equal parts. If two points are marked on the globe and a great circle is described so as to pass through both points (and only one great circle can do so), then the length of the shorter of the two arcs of this great circle which lie between the two points is the shortest distance that can be measured between them. By using this method, the shortest distance between any two places on the Earth can be calculated.

On the various map projections in this Atlas, the great circle will appear in different shapes: it is important to appreciate the properties of the particular map in use if a great circle distance is to be measured from it.

A close degree of accuracy in obtaining a great circle distance can be achieved by the solution of a spherical trigonometry problem, the sides and angles of the triangle being made up from the relevant values from the sphere.

A great circle is the path of the rays detected by radio direction finders. All meridians are great circles.

WEATHER CHART

FARENHEIT / CENTIGRADE (side scale)

HOW HOT IS IT? — Average monthly temperatures — in degrees Fahrenheit at sea-level													HOW WET IS IT? — Average monthly rainfall — in inches												
JAN	FEB	MAR	APR	MAY	JUNE	JULY	AUG	SEP	OCT	NOV	DEC		JAN	FEB	MAR	APR	MAY	JUNE	JULY	AUG	SEP	OGT	NOV	DEC	Total for year
−18.0	−16.5	−8.5	8.5	31.0	49.0	56.5	50.0	38.0	20.0	−3.0	−16.0	Aklavik	.5	.5	.4	.5	.5	.8	1.4	1.4	.9	.9	.8	.4	9.0
83.5	82.0	76.5	67.5	59.5	54.0	53.0	58.0	65.0	73.0	78.5	82.0	Alice Springs	1.7	1.3	1.1	.4	.6	.5	.3	.3	.3	.7	1.2	1.5	9.9
48.0	49.0	53.0	59.5	68.5	76.0	81.0	81.0	74.5	67.0	58.0	51.5	Athens	2.2	1.6	1.4	.8	.8	.6	.2	.4	.6	1.7	2.8	2.8	15.9
49.5	53.0	59.5	71.0	82.0	89.0	93.0	93.0	87.0	76.5	64.0	53.0	Baghdad	.9	1.0	1.1	.5	.1	<.1	<.1	<.1	<.1	.1	.8	1.0	5.5
77.1	70.5	72.5	75.0	77.5	80.5	81.5	82.5	81.5	79.0	75.5	73.0	Bahamas (Nassau)	1.4	1.5	1.4	2.5	4.6	6.4	5.8	5.3	6.9	6.5	2.8	1.3	46.4
56.5	57.0	60.0	65.0	71.0	76.0	80.0	81.5	79.5	75.0	67.0	60.0	Beirut	7.5	6.2	3.7	2.2	.7	.1	<.1	<.1	.2	2.0	5.2	7.3	35.1
75.0	75.0	79.0	82.5	85.5	84.0	81.0	80.5	80.5	82.5	81.0	78.0	Bombay	.1	.1	.1	<.1	.7	19.1	24.3	13.4	10.4	2.5	.5	.1	71.2
74.0	73.0	69.5	62.5	55.5	49.0	49.5	51.5	55.0	59.5	66.0	71.5	Buenos Aires	3.1	2.8	4.3	3.5	3.0	2.4	2.2	2.4	3.1	3.4	3.3	3.9	37.4
56.0	58.5	63.5	70.0	77.0	81.5	83.0	83.0	79.0	75.5	68.0	59.0	Cairo	.2	.2	.2	.1	.1	<.1	0	0	<.1	<.1	.1	.2	1.1
67.5	71.5	81.0	86.0	86.5	85.5	84.0	83.5	84.0	81.5	74.0	67.0	Calcutta	.4	1.2	1.4	1.7	5.5	11.7	12.8	12.9	9.9	4.5	.8	.2	63.0
68.5	68.5	63.5	55.5	48.5	43.5	42.5	45.0	49.5	55.5	61.5	66.5	Canberra	1.9	1.7	2.2	1.6	1.8	2.1	1.8	2.2	1.6	2.2	1.9	2.0	23.0
69.0	69.5	67.5	62.5	58.0	55.5	54.0	55.0	57.0	61.0	64.0	67.0	Cape Town	.6	.3	.7	1.9	3.1	3.3	3.5	2.6	1.7	1.2	.7	.4	20.0
65.5	66.5	68.5	70.5	71.0	70.0	69.5	70.0	70.5	70.0	68.5	68.0	Caracas	.9	.4	.6	1.3	3.1	4.0	4.3	4.3	4.2	4.3	3.7	1.8	32.9
73.0	73.5	73.5	72.5	69.5	67.0	68.0	70.0	73.0	74.0	73.5	72.5	Catalão	11.8	10.2	8.8	3.8	1.1	.3	.5	.3	2.3	6.1	8.3	14.9	68.4
25.0	27.0	36.0	47.5	57.5	67.5	73.5	72.0	65.5	54.0	40.5	29.5	Chicago	2.0	2.0	2.6	2.8	3.4	3.5	3.3	3.2	3.1	2.6	2.4	2.0	32.9
61.5	61.0	58.0	53.5	48.0	43.5	42.5	44.0	48.5	53.0	56.5	60.0	Christchurch, N.Z.	2.2	1.7	1.9	1.9	2.6	2.6	2.7	1.9	1.8	1.7	1.9	2.2	25.1
36.0	38.0	43.0	49.5	57.5	62.5	65.5	64.5	59.0	51.0	43.0	38.0	Cologne	2.0	1.8	1.8	1.9	2.0	2.6	3.2	2.8	2.1	2.5	2.2	2.5	27.4
79.0	79.5	81.0	82.0	82.5	81.0	81.0	81.0	81.0	80.0	79.0	78.5	Colombo	3.5	3.5	5.8	9.1	14.6	8.8	5.3	4.3	6.3	13.7	12.4	5.8	93.1
83.5	83.5	84.0	84.0	82.0	78.5	77.0	79.5	82.5	85.0	86.0	85.0	Darwin	15.2	12.3	10.0	3.8	.6	.1	<.1	.1	.5	2.0	4.7	9.4	58.7
57.0	62.0	72.5	82.0	92.0	92.5	88.5	86.0	84.0	79.0	68.0	59.5	Delhi	.9	.7	.5	.3	.5	2.9	7.1	6.8	4.6	.4	.1	.4	25.2
61.0	60.5	61.0	62.5	64.5	67.5	70.5	71.5	71.5	69.5	66.0	62.5	Funchal, Madeira	2.5	2.9	3.1	1.3	.7	.2	<.1	<.1	1.0	3.0	3.5	3.3	21.5
34.0	36.5	43.0	49.5	57.0	64.0	67.5	66.5	60.5	51.0	42.0	35.5	Geneva	1.9	1.8	2.2	2.5	3.0	3.1	2.9	3.6	3.6	2.8	3.1	2.4	32.9
63.0	62.5	62.5	65.0	70.0	75.0	79.0	80.0	78.0	74.0	68.5	65.0	Hamilton, Bermuda	4.4	4.7	4.8	4.1	4.6	4.4	4.5	5.4	5.2	5.8	5.0	4.7	57.6
−5.5	−5.0	6.0	18.0	31.5	40.0	47.0	48.0	40.5	31.0	20.0	4.0	Hebron, Labrador	.9	.7	.9	1.1	1.6	2.1	2.7	2.7	3.3	1.6	1.1	.6	19.3
60.0	59.0	63.5	71.0	78.0	81.5	82.5	82.5	81.0	77.0	69.5	63.5	Hong Kong	1.3	1.8	2.9	5.4	11.5	15.5	15.0	14.2	10.1	4.5	1.7	1.2	85.1
40.5	42.0	45.5	53.0	60.5	68.5	73.0	73.5	68.0	60.5	53.5	46.0	Istanbul	3.7	2.3	2.6	1.9	1.4	1.3	1.7	1.5	2.3	3.8	4.1	4.9	31.5
48.0	49.0	55.5	61.5	69.0	72.5	75.0	75.5	73.5	70.0	61.5	52.0	Jerusalem	5.2	5.2	2.5	1.1	.1	<.1	0	0	<.1	.5	2.8	3.4	20.8
68.0	67.5	65.0	61.0	54.5	50.5	51.0	55.5	60.5	65.0	66.0	67.5	Johannesburg	4.5	4.3	3.5	1.5	1.0	.3	.3	.3	.9	2.2	4.2	4.9	27.9
81.0	83.0	83.5	83.0	81.5	79.5	78.5	77.5	78.5	79.5	81.5	81.5	Lagos	1.1	1.8	4.0	5.9	10.6	18.1	11.0	2.5	5.5	8.1	2.7	1.0	72.3
74.0	75.0	74.5	71.5	67.0	63.0	62.0	61.0	62.5	64.5	67.0	70.0	Lima	<.1	<.1	<.1	<.1	.2	.2	.3	.3	.3	.1	.1	<.1	1.6
75.5	75.5	74.5	72.5	66.5	61.0	61.0	66.0	74.5	80.5	79.0	76.5	Livingstone	5.7	6.0	4.3	1.0	.3	.1	0	<.1	.1	.9	2.9	5.2	26.5
39.5	40.0	44.0	48.0	54.0	60.0	64.0	63.0	59.0	51.0	44.0	40.5	London	2.0	1.5	1.4	1.8	1.8	1.6	2.0	2.2	1.8	2.3	2.5	2.0	22.9
55.5	56.5	57.5	60.0	62.5	66.0	70.5	71.0	69.5	65.0	61.5	51.0	Los Angeles	3.1	3.0	2.8	1.0	.4	.1	<.1	<.1	.2	.6	1.2	2.6	15.0
49.5	51.0	53.5	57.5	64.0	70.5	75.0	76.5	72.5	65.5	57.5	51.5	Majorca	1.4	1.6	1.5	1.3	1.3	1.0	.2	.8	2.5	2.8	2.8	2.2	19.4
54.0	56.0	61.0	64.0	66.0	65.5	63.0	63.5	63.5	60.0	57.0	54.5	Mexico City	.5	.2	.4	.8	2.1	4.7	6.7	6.0	5.1	2.0	.7	.3	29.5
67.5	68.0	71.0	73.5	77.5	80.0	82.0	82.0	81.0	77.5	72.0	69.0	Miami	2.8	2.1	2.5	3.2	6.8	7.0	6.1	6.3	8.0	9.2	2.8	2.0	58.8
81.0	81.5	82.5	81.0	78.5	77.5	76.0	76.0	77.0	79.0	80.0	80.5	Mombasa	1.0	.7	2.5	7.7	12.6	4.7	3.5	2.5	2.5	3.4	3.8	2.4	47.3
15.0	16.5	24.5	39.0	54.5	62.0	65.5	62.0	52.0	40.0	27.0	18.0	Moscow	1.5	1.4	1.1	1.9	2.2	2.9	3.0	2.9	1.9	2.7	1.7	1.6	24.8
65.5	67.0	67.0	66.5	64.0	61.5	60.0	61.0	63.5	65.5	65.0	64.5	Nairobi	1.5	2.5	4.9	8.3	6.2	1.8	.6	.9	1.2	2.1	4.3	3.4	37.7
54.5	57.5	63.0	69.0	75.5	81.0	83.0	83.0	79.5	71.5	62.5	56.0	New Orleans	4.6	4.2	4.7	4.8	4.5	5.5	6.6	5.8	4.8	3.5	3.8	4.6	57.4
30.5	31.0	37.5	49.5	60.5	68.5	74.0	73.0	69.5	59.0	44.0	35.0	New York	3.7	3.8	3.6	3.2	3.2	3.3	4.2	4.3	3.4	3.5	3.0	3.6	42.8
25.0	26.0	32.5	42.0	52.5	60.0	64.5	61.0	52.5	43.0	33.0	27.5	Oslo	1.7	1.3	1.4	1.6	1.8	2.4	2.9	3.8	2.5	2.9	2.3	2.3	26.9
12.0	12.5	25.5	41.0	55.0	65.0	69.5	66.0	58.0	45.5	32.5	16.5	Ottawa	2.9	2.2	2.8	2.7	2.5	3.5	3.4	2.6	3.2	2.9	3.0	2.6	34.3
37.0	39.0	44.0	50.5	57.0	62.5	65.5	65.0	59.5	51.5	43.5	38.0	Paris	1.5	1.3	1.5	1.7	2.0	2.1	2.1	2.0	2.0	2.2	2.0	1.9	22.3
74.0	74.0	71.0	66.5	61.0	57.0	55.5	56.0	58.5	61.5	66.5	71.0	Perth, W. Australia	.3	.4	.8	1.7	5.1	7.1	6.7	5.7	3.4	2.2	.8	.5	34.7
78.5	79.0	77.5	74.5	71.5	70.0	69.0	70.0	70.0	71.5	73.5	76.5	Rio de Janeiro	4.9	4.8	5.1	4.2	3.1	2.1	1.6	1.7	2.6	3.1	4.1	5.4	42.7
64.0	63.5	61.5	56.5	51.0	47.5	45.5	47.0	50.5	54.5	57.5	61.5	Rotorua	4.4	4.1	3.5	4.6	5.5	5.3	4.9	5.0	4.8	4.9	4.3	3.7	55.0
46.5	47.5	52.0	57.0	64.5	71.0	76.0	76.0	72.0	63.0	54.5	48.5	Rome	2.7	2.3	1.5	1.7	2.0	1.0	.6	.9	2.7	3.7	3.8	2.8	25.7
23.5	22.0	27.5	35.5	42.5	52.5	59.5	61.0	54.5	46.5	37.0	29.0	St. John's, Newfoundland	5.3	4.9	4.6	4.2	3.6	3.5	3.5	3.7	3.8	5.3	5.9	5.5	53.8
50.0	53.0	54.5	56.5	57.0	59.0	59.0	59.0	62.0	61.0	57.0	52.0	San Francisco	4.7	3.8	3.1	1.5	.7	.1	<.1	<.1	.3	1.0	2.5	4.4	22.1
34.5	37.0	40.5	48.5	58.5	67.0	72.0	71.5	64.0	54.5	44.5	39.0	Sevastopol	1.1	1.1	1.1	.9	.6	1.1	1.8	.6	1.1	1.5	1.2	1.1	12.2
79.5	80.5	81.5	81.5	82.0	81.5	81.5	81.0	81.0	80.5	80.5	80.5	Singapore	9.9	6.8	7.6	7.4	6.8	6.8	6.7	7.7	7.0	8.2	10.0	10.1	95.0
71.5	71.5	69.5	64.5	59.0	54.5	53.0	55.5	59.0	63.5	67.0	70.0	Sydney	3.5	4.0	5.0	5.3	5.0	4.6	4.6	3.0	2.9	2.8	2.9	2.9	46.5
53.5	54.5	56.5	58.0	63.5	68.0	72.0	73.5	70.5	65.5	58.5	54.5	Tangier	4.5	4.2	4.8	3.5	1.7	.6	<.1	<.1	.9	3.9	5.8	5.4	35.3
24.5	30.0	41.5	56.5	68.5	77.5	81.5	79.5	70.5	58.0	41.0	28.5	Tientsin	.2	.1	.4	.5	1.1	2.4	7.4	6.0	1.7	.6	.4	.2	21.0
38.0	39.5	45.0	54.5	62.5	69.5	76.5	79.0	72.5	62.0	51.5	42.5	Tokyo	1.9	2.9	4.2	5.3	5.8	6.5	5.6	6.0	9.2	8.2	3.8	2.2	61.6
64.0	64.0	62.0	59.5	56.5	54.0	53.5	54.0	55.0	57.5	60.5	62.5	Valparaíso, Chile	.1	<.1	.3	.6	4.1	5.9	3.9	2.9	1.3	.4	.2	.2	19.9
36.5	39.0	43.5	49.0	55.0	60.5	64.0	63.5	57.0	50.5	43.5	39.0	Vancouver	8.6	5.8	5.0	3.3	2.8	2.5	1.2	1.7	3.6	5.8	8.3	8.8	57.4
30.0	33.0	40.5	49.0	58.0	63.5	67.0	65.5	59.0	49.5	40.0	33.5	Vienna	1.5	1.4	1.8	2.0	2.8	2.7	3.0	2.7	2.0	2.0	1.9	1.8	25.6
−3.0	1.5	16.0	37.5	52.0	62.0	67.0	63.5	54.0	41.0	21.5	6.0	Winnipeg	.9	.9	1.2	1.4	2.3	3.1	3.1	2.5	2.3	1.5	1.1	.9	21.2

Inches	1	2	3	4	5	6	7	8	9	10	50	100
Millimetres	25.4	50.8	76.2	101.6	127.0	152.4	177.8	203.2	228.6	254.0	1270	2540

< = less than

THE READER'S DIGEST GREAT WORLD ATLAS

Published by

THE READER'S DIGEST ASSOCIATION (CANADA) LIMITED
215 Redfern Avenue, Montreal, Quebec H3Z 2V9

FOURTH EDITION

Fourth Edition Copyright © 1977 THE READER'S DIGEST ASSOCIATION (CANADA) LIMITED

ISBN 0-88850-018-1

Reprinted with amendments October 1981

Printed in Great Britain by

JOHN BARTHOLOMEW & SON LTD., EDINBURGH   HAZELL WATSON & VINEY LTD., AYLESBURY

BEN JOHNSON & CO. LTD., YORK

CANADIAN EDITION BOUND BY HARPELL'S PRESS COOPERATIVE, QUEBEC

Relief maps, pages 8-28, 114-115 © Geographical Projects Limited, London, 1961

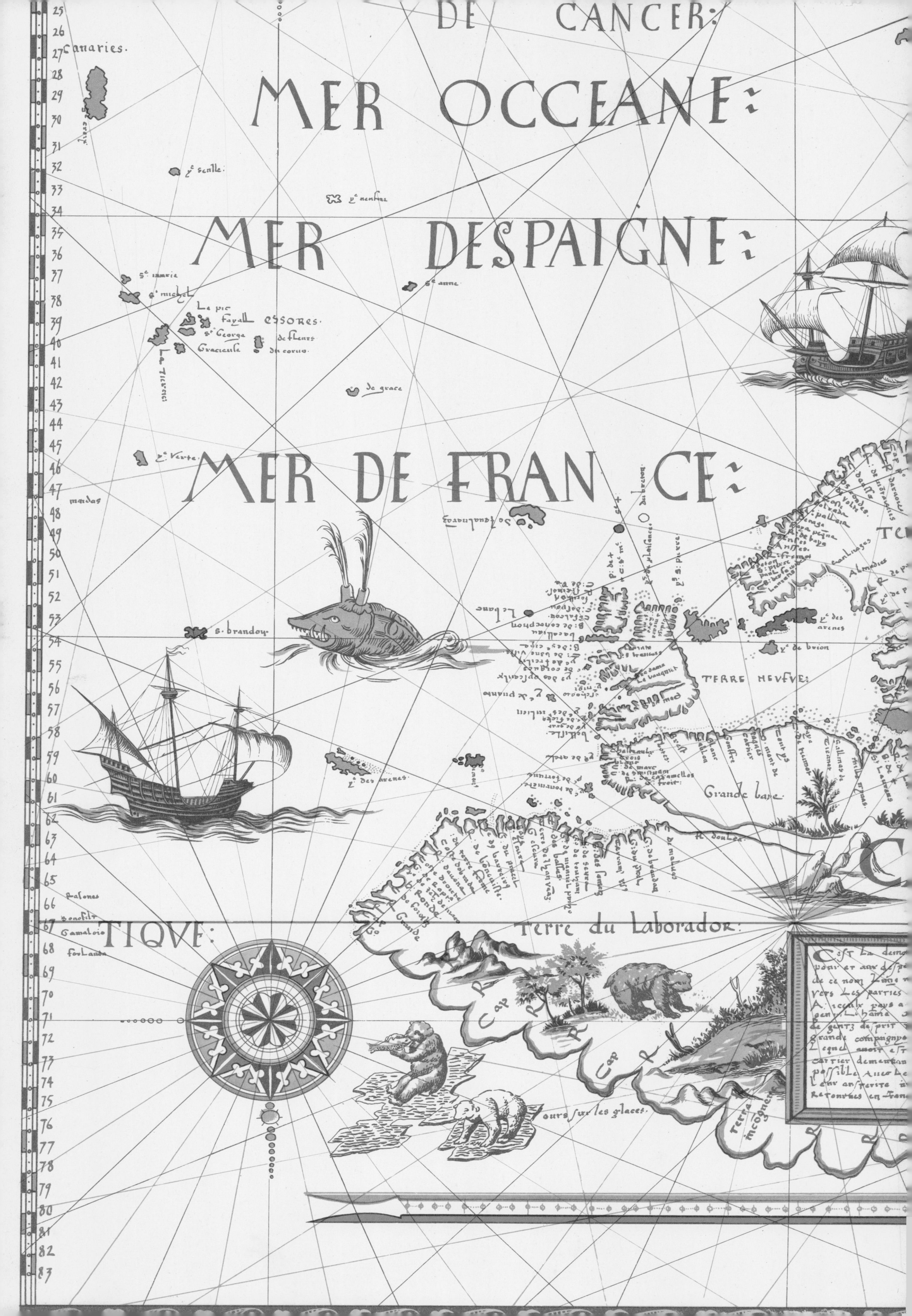
DE CANCER:
MER OCCEANE:
MER DESPAIGNE:
MER DE FRANCE:
TERRE NEUFUE:
Grande baie
TIQUE:
Terre du Laborador:
ours sur les glaces